Incompressible Flow

Contents

19   Axisymmetric and Three-Dimensional Ideal Flows   468

20   Boundary Layers   498

21   Flows at Low Reynolds Numbers   571

Preface

The third edition is a revised and slightly expanded version of the second edition. It is intended as an advanced textbook for the nomenclature, methods, and theory of fluid dynamics. The book also serves as a resource of equations and flow examples for research and development engineers and scientists. As in previous editions, the first half of the book deals with general flow of a Newtonian fluid, and the special characteristics of incompressible flows occupy the remainder.

My experience is that students first learn results. Given a fluid and geometry, what is flow li! ? More advanced students should know the conditions under which the results are valid and the place that the results occupy in fluid mechanics theory. Thus, a major theme of the book remains to show how the theory is organized.

I was not reluctant to add some new material, because instructors choose and skip topics as they desire. The new topics are in keeping with new areas of importance in research and applications, and make the book more comprehensive.

For those familiar with the earlier editions, I will outline the revisions. First, the strain vector, introduced in the second edition, is now given more emphasis and used to interpret vorticity stretching and turning. Another change is a derivation of the mechanical energy equation for a region with arbitrary motion. It illustrates how moving boundary work and flow work are convenient concepts but not basic physical ideas. Modern measurements of the pipe flow friction factor are also included. More detail on the mathematics of $E^2E^2\psi$ operator is presented in Chapter 12. Another addition is a presentation of the Jeffrey–Hamel solution for flow into or out of a plane wedge. This exact solution is covered in Chapter 14. It is of theoretical interest because it has nontrivial limit behavior at Re $\to$ 0 and Re $\to \infty$ that correspond to Stokes, ideal, and boundary layer flows. The boundary layer solution is also useful as an initial condition for boundary layers beginning at infinity.

Two examples of boundary layers beginning at infinity are now included. The first example is plane flow on a wall that is under a plane aperture. The pressure gradient of this problem is similar to flow through a converging–diverging nozzle. The second example is plane flow on the wall under a sluice gate. The ideal flow downstream has a free surface and approaches a uniform stream above a wall. This becomes an example of the concept of an effective origin of a similarity solution.

Four essentially new chapters have been written: They are Low Reynolds Number Flows, Lubrication Approximation, Surface Tension Effects, and Introduction to Micro Flows. The Low Reynolds Number Flows is a revised and expanded version of the coverage on low-Reynolds-number flow in the second edition. The lubrication approximation deserves a separate chapter because it applies to any long, geometrically thin, viscous channel flow. The Reynolds number must be bounded, but it does not need to be low. Chapter 23 on Surface Tension Effects deals with the static meniscus, constant tension flows, the moving contact line, a coating flow example, and some examples of

Marangoni flows. In the Introduction to Microflow Chapter 24, gases and liquids are treated separately and breakdown of the no-slip condition is discussed. No electrical or mixing effects are presented; they are left for special books on the subject.

The chapters on thermodynamics and vector calculus (Chapters 2 and 3) have been retained for those who use them occasionally. By modern standards the numerical programs are crude and unsophisticated. I retained them as a pedagogical exercise for students who will not become numerical analysts. Progress in computer capacity has made it possible to use very fine grids and obtain useful results with crude programs. Flow examples are spread through the book according to the important physics. In the index I have compiled the flow patterns according to the flow geometry and, if appropriate, the flow name.

RONALD L. PANTON

Austin, Texas
January 2005

Preface to the Second Edition

The goal of this edition remains the same: present the fundamentals of the subject with a balance between physics, mathematics, and applications. The level of the material provides serious students with sufficient knowledge to make a transition to advanced books, monographs, and the research literature in fluid dynamics.

The entire book has been reviewed. When the need was recognized, the presentation was changed for easier understanding, new material to aid comprehension added, and the latest viewpoints and research results were incorporated. Specific changes from the first edition are outlined below.

Chapter 2, on thermodynamics, has been distilled to essentials, and Chapter 8, on dimensional analysis, likewise has been tightened. Basic laws, the subject of Chapter 5, has two new examples of control region analyses (one steady and one unsteady) and a new section that contains the jump equations across an interface. For added emphasis, the mechanical energy equation is now given a separate section in Chapter 7. In keeping with the goal of placing the specific results in a general setting, the wave nature of fluid flow is illustrated in a new section on compressible waves. In this section, the solution for a piston oscillating in a long tube is presented. Other analytic solutions to several problems have been added. Flow in a ribbed channel illustrates complicated geometry, a rotating viscous coupling introduces a singular perturbation problem, while Burgers vortex, because of its physical importance, has been promoted from the homework problems to the text. Major reorganization of the chapter on vorticity, Chapter 13, includes grouping Helmholtz laws together, introducing the vortex reconnection phenomenon, and provides a separate section to discuss vortex breakdown.

To give the reader a glimpse at the engineering approach to designing airfoils, a section was added illustrating modeling with vortex elements. This is followed by an application section in which the behavior of actual airfoils is reviewed. In the area of boundary layers, revisions include the subjects of unsteady boundary layers and the eruption phenomenon, along with a more extensive discussion of critical points in streamlines.

The chapter on asymptotic expansions, Chapter 15, now gives more emphasis to overlap behavior, common parts, and the usefulness of composite expansions. Also, new model problems that display the singular characteristics of two- and three-dimensional Stokes flow are introduced. Some of this material aids the understanding of Chapter 21 on low Reynolds number flows, which also has been extensively reorganized and updated.

The discussion of transition has been repositioned into the chapter on stability, Chapter 22. Many new developments in this field—secondary instabilities; bypass mechanisms (a Morkovin diagram is now included); transient growth; and absolute, convective local, and global stability—are all introduced. A more coherent chapter on turbulence was attempted—Chapter 23. Turbulent channel flow is analyzed in detail, and the usefulness of composite expansions is exploited to organize experimental results. This accounts for the major effects of Reynolds number.

Since computational fluid dynamics is an area with its own books on methodology, the elementary methods of the first edition have not been supplemented. However, an indication of the power of the latest methods is shown by displaying new results of two problems. The first problem is high Reynolds number flow over a cylinder by a subgrid scale model, whereas the second problem is separation eruption on an impulsively started cylinder by a Langrangian Navier–Stokes calculation.

As in the first edition, all topics have been chosen to illustrate and describe, using continuum concepts, the elemental physical processes that one encounters in incompressible fluid flows.

RONALD L. PANTON

Austin, Texas
January 1995

Preface to the First Edition

This book is written as a textbook for students beginning a serious study of fluid dynamics, or for students in other fields who want to know the main ideas and results in this discipline. A reader who judges the scope of the book by its title will be somewhat surprised at the contents. The contents not only treat incompressible flows themselves, but also give the student an understanding of how incompressible flows are related to the general compressible case. For example, one cannot appreciate how energy interactions occur in incompressible flows without first understanding the most general interaction mechanisms. I subscribe to the philosophy that advanced students should study the structure of a subject as well as its techniques and results. The beginning chapters are devoted to building the concepts and physics for a general, compressible, viscous fluid flow. These chapters taken by themselves constitute the fundamentals that one might study in any course concerning fluid dynamics. Beginning with Chapter 6 our study is restricted to fluids that obey Newton's viscosity law. Only when we arrive at Chapter 10 do we find a detailed discussion of the assumptions that underlie the subject of incompressible flow. Thus, roughly half the book is fundamentals, and the rest is incompressible flow.

Applied mathematicians have contributed greatly to the study of fluid mechanics, and there is a tendency to make a text into a sampler of known mathematical solutions. A conscious effort was made in writing the book to strike an even balance among physics, mathematics, and practical engineering information. The student is assumed to have had calculus and differential equations; the text then takes on the task of introducing tensor analysis in index notation, as well as various special methods of solving differential equations that have been developed in fluid mechanics. This includes an introduction to several computer methods and the method of asymptotic expansions.

The book places heavy emphasis on dimensional analysis, both as a subject in itself and as an instrument in any analysis of flow problems. The advanced worker knows many shortcuts in this area, but the student needs to study the foundations and details in order to be convinced that these shortcuts are valid. Vorticity, vortex lines, and the dynamics of vorticity also receive an expanded treatment, which is designed to bring the serious student more information than is customary in a textbook. It is apparent that advanced workers in fluid mechanics must be able to interpret flow patterns in terms of vorticity as well as in the traditional terms of forces and energy.

The study of how changes in the Reynolds number influence flow patterns occupies a large part of the book. Separate chapters describe flows at low, moderate, and high Reynolds numbers. Because of their practical importance, the complementary subjects of inviscid flows and boundary-layer flows are treated extensively. Introductory chapters on stability and turbulence are also given. These last two subjects are so large as to constitute separate fields. Nevertheless, a beginning student should have an overview of the rudiments and principles.

The book is not meant to be read from front to back. The coverage is rather broad so that the instructor may select those chapters and sections that suit his or her goals. For example, I can imagine that many people, considering the level and background of their students, will skip Chapter 2 on thermodynamics or Chapter 3 on tensor index notation. I placed these chapters at the beginning, rather than in an appendix, with the thought that the student would be likely to review these subjects even if they were not formally assigned as a part of the course. Students who want more information about any chapter will find a supplemental reading list at the back of the book.

A chapter usually begins with an elementary approach suitable for the beginning student. Subsections that are marked by an asterisk contain more advanced material, which either gives a deeper insight or a broader viewpoint. These sections should be read only by the more advanced student who already has the fundamentals of the subject well in hand. Likewise, the problems at the end of each chapter are classified into three types: (A) problems that give computational practice and directly reinforce the text material, (B) problems that require a thoughtful and more creative application of the material, and finally (C) more difficult problems that extend the text or give new results not previously covered.

Several photographs illustrating fluid flow patterns have been included. Some illustrate a simplified flow pattern or single physical phenomenon. Others were chosen precisely because they show a very complicated flow that contrasts with the simplified analysis of the text. The intent is to emphasize the nonuniqueness and complexity possible in fluid motions. In most cases only the major point about a photograph is explained. The reader will find a complete discussion in the original references.

Writing this book has been a long project. I would like to express my appreciation for the encouragement that I have received during this time from my family, students, colleagues, former teachers, and several anonymous reviewers. The people associated with John Wiley & Sons should also be mentioned: At every stage their professional attitude has contributed to the quality of this book.

RONALD L. PANTON

Austin, Texas
January 1984

Incompressible Flow

1

Continuum Mechanics

The science of fluid dynamics describes the motions of liquids and gases and their interaction with solid bodies. There are many ways to further subdivide fluid dynamics into special subjects. The plan of this book is to make the division into compressible and incompressible flows. *Compressible flows* are those where changes in the fluid density are important. A major specialty concerned with compressible flows, *gas dynamics,* deals with high-speed flows where density changes are large and wave phenomena occur frequently. *Incompressible flows,* of either gases or liquids, are flows where density changes in the fluid are not an important part of the physics. The study of incompressible flow includes such subjects as hydraulics, hydrodynamics, aerodynamics, and boundary layer theory. It also contains background information for such special subjects as hydrology, lubrication theory, stratified flows, turbulence, rotating flows, and biological fluid mechanics. Incompressible flow not only occupies the central position in fluid dynamics but is also fundamental to the practical subjects of heat and mass transfer.

Figure 1.1 shows a ship's propeller being tested in a water tunnel. The propeller is rotating, and the water flow is from left to right. A prominent feature of this photograph is the line of vapor that leaves the tip of each blade and spirals downstream. The vapor is not itself important, but it marks a region of very low pressure in the core of a vortex that leaves the tip of each blade. This vortex would exist even if the pressure were not low enough to form water vapor. Behind the propeller one can note a convergence of the vapor lines into a smaller spiral, indicating that the flow behind the propeller is occupying a smaller area and thus must have increased velocity.

An airplane in level flight is shown in Fig. 1.2. A smoke device has been attached to the wingtip so that the core of the vortex formed there is made visible. The vortex trails nearly straight back behind the aircraft. From the sense of the vortex we may surmise that the wing is pushing air down on the inside while air rises outside the tip.

There are obviously some differences in these two situations. The wing moves in a straight path, whereas the ship's propeller blades are rotating. The propeller operates in water, a nearly incompressible liquid, whereas the wing operates in air, a very compressible gas. The densities of these two fluids differ by a factor of 800:1. Despite these obvious differences, these two flows are governed by the same laws, and their fluid dynamics are very similar. The purpose of the wing is to lift the airplane; the purpose of the propeller is to produce thrust on the boat. The density of the air as well as that of the water is nearly constant throughout the flow. Both flows have a vortex trailing

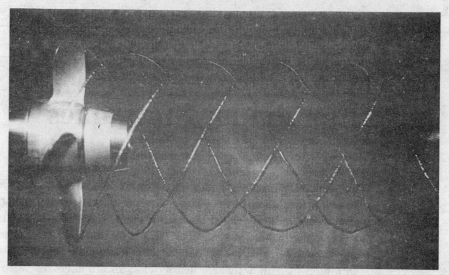

Figure 1.1 Water tunnel test of a ship's propeller. Cavitation vapor marks the tip vortex. Photograph taken at the Garfield Thomas Water Tunnel, Applied Research Laboratory, Pennsylvania State University; supplied with permission by B. R. Parkin.

away from the tip of the surface. This and many other qualitative aspects of these flows are the same. Both are incompressible flows.

In this book we shall learn many characteristics and details of incompressible flows. Equally important, we shall learn when a flow may be considered as incompressible and in exactly what ways the physics of a general flow simplifies for the incompressible case. This chapter is the first step in that direction.

Figure 1.2 Aircraft wingtip vortices. Smoke is introduced at the wingtip to mark the vortex cores. Photograph by W. L. Oberkampf.

1.1   CONTINUUM ASSUMPTION

Fluid mechanics, solid mechanics, electrodynamics, and thermodynamics are all examples of physical sciences in which the world is viewed as a continuum. The *continuum assumption* simply means that physical properties are imagined to be distributed throughout space. Every point in space has finite values for such properties as velocity, temperature, stress, and electric field strength. From one point to the next, the properties may change value, and there may even be surfaces where some properties jump discontinuously. For example, the interface between a solid and a fluid is imagined to be a surface where the density jumps from one value to another. On the other hand, the continuum assumption does not allow properties to become infinite or to be undefined at a single isolated point.

Sciences that postulate the existence of a continuum are essentially macroscopic sciences and deal, roughly speaking, with events that may be observed with the unaided eye. Events in the microscopic world of molecules, nuclei, and elementary particles are not governed by continuum laws, nor are they described in terms of continuum ideas. However, there is a connection between the two points of view. Continuum properties may be interpreted as averages of events involving a great number of microscopic particles. The construction of such an interpretation falls into the disciplines of statistical thermodynamics (statistical mechanics) and kinetic theory. From time to time we shall discuss some of the simpler microscopic models that are used for continuum events. This aids in a deeper understanding of continuum properties, but in no way does it make the ideas "truer." The fundamental assumptions of continuum mechanics stand by themselves without reference to the microscopic world.

The continuum concept developed slowly over the course of many years. Leonhard Euler (Swiss mathematician, 1707–1783) is generally credited with giving a firm foundation to the ideas. Previously, scientists had not distinguished clearly between the idea of a point mass and that of a continuum. In his major contributions, Sir Isaac Newton (1642–1727), actually used a primitive form of the point mass as an underlying assumption (he did at times, however, also employ a continuum approach). What we now call *Newton's mechanics* or *classical mechanics* refers to the motion of point masses. In the several centuries following Newton, problems concerning the vibration of strings, the stresses in beams, and the flow of fluids were attacked. In these problems it was necessary to generalize and distinguish point mass properties from continuum properties. The continuum assumption is on a higher level of abstraction and cannot be derived mathematically from the point mass concept. On the other hand, by integration and by introducing notions such as the center of mass and moments of inertia, we can derive laws governing a macroscopic point mass from the continuum laws. Hence, the continuum laws include, as a special case, the laws for a point mass.

1.2   FUNDAMENTAL CONCEPTS, DEFINITIONS, AND LAWS

It is hard to give a precise description of a *fundamental concept* such as mass, energy, or force. They are hazy ideas. We can describe their characteristics, state how they act, and express their relation to other ideas, but when it comes to saying what they are, we must resort to vague generalities. This is not really a disadvantage, because once we work with a fundamental concept for a while and become familiar with its role in physical processes, we have learned the essence of the idea. This is actually all that is required.

Definitions, on the contrary, are very precise. For example, pressure may be defined precisely after we have the ideas of force and area at hand. Once we have made a definition of a certain physical quantity, we may explore its characteristics and deduce its exact relation to other physical quantities. There is no question how pressure is related to force, but there is a certain haziness about what a force is.

The situation is analogous to the task of writing a dictionary. How can we write out the meaning of the first word? By the very nature of a dictionary we must use other words in defining the first word. The dilemma is that those words have not yet been defined. The second word is not much easier than the first. However, after the meanings of a few key words are established, the task becomes much simpler. Word definitions can then be formulated exactly, and subtle distinctions between ideas may be made. As we use the language and see a word in different contexts, we gain a greater appreciation of its essence. At this stage, the problem of which words were the very first to be defined is no longer important. The important thing is the role the word plays in our language and the subtle differences between it and similar words.

Stretching the analogy between a continuum and a dictionary a little bit further, we can draw a correspondence between the molecules of a continuum and the letters of a word. The idea conveyed by the word is essentially independent of our choice of the language and letters to form the word. In the same way, the continuum concepts are essentially independent of the microscopic particles. The microscopic particles are necessary but unimportant.

The mathematical rules by which we predict and explain phenomena in continuum mechanics are called *laws.* Some *restricted laws* apply only to special situations. The equation of state for a perfect gas and Hooke's law of elasticity are examples of this type of law. We shall distinguish laws that apply to all substances by calling them *basic laws.* There are many forms for the basic laws of continuum mechanics, but in the last analysis they may all be related to four laws: the three independent conservation principles for mass, momentum, and energy, plus a fundamental equation of thermodynamics. These suffice when the continuum contains a "simple substance" and gravitational, electrical, magnetic, and chemical effects are excluded. In fluid mechanics, however, we frequently want to include the gravity force. In such cases, a basic law for this force should be added to the list. Problems dealing with electrical, magnetic, and chemical effects would require correspondingly more basic laws.

Newton's second law is familiar to all students from their earliest course in physics:

$$F = Ma = M\frac{d^2x}{dt^2}$$

This law relates the ideas of force, mass, and acceleration. It should not be considered as a definition of force. It is our responsibility to identify and formulate all the different types of forces. In this law we usually consider distance, time, mass, and force to be fundamental concepts, and acceleration to be a defined quantity. Newton's law tells us that these quantities cannot take on independent values but must always maintain a certain relationship.

Which concepts are taken to be fundamental and which are defined is a matter of tradition and convenience. For example, we usually take length and time as fundamental and consider velocity to be defined by the time derivative of the position. On the other hand, we might take velocity and time as fundamental concepts and then consider distance to be defined by the integral

$$x = \int_0^t v \, dt$$

This would be unusual and awkward; however, it is conceptually as valid as defining velocity from the ideas of distance and time.

In this book we do not emphasize the philosophical aspects and the logical construction of continuum mechanics. This task belongs to a branch of mathematics called *rational mechanics*. Our efforts will fall short of its standards of rigor. Our purpose is to understand the physics and to quantify (if possible) practical situations in fluid mechanics. We do not intend to sacrifice accuracy, but we cannot afford the luxury of a highly philosophical approach.

1.3 SPACE AND TIME

The natural independent variables of continuum mechanics are three-dimensional space and time. We assume all the concepts and results of Euclidean geometry: length, area, parallel lines, and so on. Euclidean space is the setting for the progress of events as time proceeds independently. With these assumptions about the nature of time and space, we have ruled out relativistic effects and thereby limited the scope of our subject.

To measure space and other physical quantities, it is necessary to introduce a coordinate system. This brings up the question of how a quantity such as energy might depend on the coordinate system in which it is calculated. One of the major facts of physics is the existence of special coordinate systems called *inertial frames*. The laws of physics have exactly the same mathematical form when quantities are measured from any inertial coordinate system. The magnitude of the momentum or the magnitude of the energy will be different when measured in different coordinates; however, the physical laws deal only with changes in these quantities. Furthermore, the laws have a structure such that the same change will be observed from any inertial system. All inertial coordinate systems are related by *Galilean transformations*, in which one coordinate system is in uniform translational motion with respect to the other. Furthermore, any coordinate system that is in uniform translational motion with respect to an inertial system is also an inertial system. We sometimes say that a coordinate system that is fixed with respect to the "distant stars" is an *inertial coordinate system*. Of course, we cannot be too precise about this concept, or we run into relativity. The laboratory is not an inertial coordinate system because of Earth's rotation and acceleration. Nevertheless, many events occur in such a short time that Earth's rotation may be neglected and laboratory coordinates may be taken as an inertial system.

As mentioned above, all the facts of Euclidean geometry are assumed to apply to space, while time is a parameterlike independent variable that proceeds in a forward direction. At any instant in time we may define a *control volume,* or control region, as any closed region in space. It is our invention. The boundary is called a *control surface,* and we prescribe its motion in any manner we choose. The purpose of a control region is to focus our attention on physical events at the boundary and within the region. The ideas of control surface and control volume are generalizations of the *Euler cut* that were refined and promoted in the engineering literature by Prandtl. *Control surface* is a literal translational of the German *kontrollflache.* In German, "control" has the meaning of accounting; hence a "control surface" is a place where one must keep track of physical events (Vincenti, 1982).

It will be useful to define four types of regions that depend on how the surface of the region moves with time (Fig. 1.3). A *fixed region* (FR) is one where the control surface does not move at all but is fixed in space. We might imagine a fixed region as enclosing a compressor as shown in Fig. 1.3. The region surface cuts through the inlet and outlet pipes, and fluid flows across these surfaces into or out of the region. At another place the control surface must cut through the shaft that drives the compressor. Here we imagine that the control surface is stationary even though the material that composes the shaft is moving tangentially to the surface. When we use a fixed region, we must allow material to either cross the surface or slide along it.

The second type of region is called a *material region* (MR), because the surface moves with the local velocity of the material. Consider a bubble of gas that is rising through a liquid. As the bubble rises, it expands in size and the gas inside exhibits circulatory motion. A material region that just encloses the gas has a local velocity composed of three parts: the rising velocity of the bubble, the expansion velocity of the bubble, and the gas velocity at the interface due to the internal circulation (a sliding velocity tangent to the surface). If we omit the velocity of the internal circulation, the region will no longer strictly fit the definition of a material region. The surface will still always enclose the same material, but the surface will not have the local material velocity.

The third type of region is one where the surface velocity is the same at each location, but varies with time $w_i = W_i(t)$. For example, consider a region surrounding a

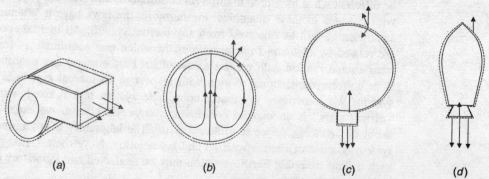

| (a) | (b) | (c) | (d) |

Figure 1.3 Control regions: (*a*) fixed region around a centrifugal blower; (*b*) material region around a rising bubble; (*c*) arbitrary region around a moving and collapsing balloon; (*d*) constant volume region around a rocket.

rocket. Material is ejected from the rocket nozzle and the region moves; however, the volume of region is constant. This is called a *volume region* (VR).

Any control region that does not fall into the first three categories is called an *arbitrary region* (AR). An example of an arbitrary region is given by a toy balloon that has been turned loose to move freely through the air. Choose the surface of the region to coincide with the balloon everywhere except at the mouth, where air is escaping. At this point the surface cuts across the plane of the exit and the air crosses the surface of the region. Such a region is very useful for an analysis; however, it must be classed as an arbitrary region.

In the examples above, the regions have been of finite size and have obviously been chosen in order to perform an engineering analysis. Control regions are also very useful for conceptual and theoretical purposes. When they are used for these purposes, one often considers a sequence of regions that become smaller and smaller. An example of this type of reasoning is presented in Section 1.4.

1.4 DENSITY, VELOCITY, AND INTERNAL ENERGY

Density is the mass per unit volume of a substance and is one of our fundamental concepts. We consider that the continuum has a density at every point in space. The following thought experiment is a popular way to illustrate the concept. Consider a specific point in space, and choose a fixed control region that encloses the point. Imagine that we freeze the molecules and then count the number of them within the region. With this information we form the ratio of the mass of the material to the volume of the region, that is, the average density of the control region. Let L be a measure of the size of the control region: L might be the distance across the central point to a certain position on the control surface. The experiment is then repeated with a smaller but geometrically similar control region. Each time the results are plotted as in Fig. 1.4. A logarithmic scale for L is used because L ranges over many orders of magnitude. When L is very large, say a mile, the measurement represents an average that might have little to do with the local fluid density. As L becomes small, the experiment produces a consistent number for M/V even as L ranges over several orders of magnitude. This number is the density at point P. Finally, the control region becomes so small that L approaches the distance between molecules. With only a few molecules within the volume, the ratio M/V jumps as the control region shrinks past a molecule. To continue the process produces even more scatter in M/V.

If we begin the process again with a different-shaped control region, we find a different curve for very large values of L, but as the length becomes a millimeter or so, the same plateau in M/V may occur. If so, it will be valid to take a continuum viewpoint and define a density at point P. Mathematically, the definition is expressed by

$$\rho = \lim_{L \to 0} \frac{\sum m_i}{V} \qquad (1.4.1)$$

where the summation occurs over all particles within the region. The limit process $L \to 0$ is understood to go toward zero but never to reach a molecular scale.

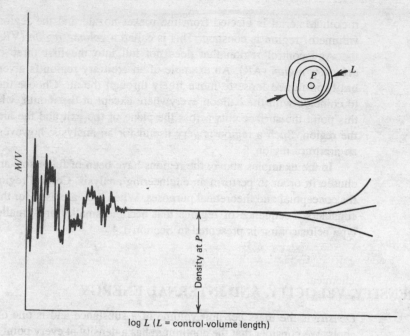

Figure 1.4   Thought experiment to define density.

In a flow where the number of molecules changes rapidly over a distance comparable to intermolecular distances, the continuum assumption will be suspect. To illustrate this, consider the problem of computing the internal structure of a shock wave. The thickness of a shock wave is only a few times the *mean free path* (the average distance a molecule travels before colliding with another molecule). Over this distance the density may increase by a factor of 2. Can the density profile be computed using continuum assumptions? This problem is a borderline case, and it turns out that the continuum calculation gives reasonable answers. In ordinary engineering situations, density gradients occur over distances on the order of centimeters, and the continuum assumption is unquestionably valid.

We can gain a better insight into the continuum assumption by reviewing some of the molecular properties of air. Air at atmospheric conditions contains 3×10^{19} molecules in 1 cm³. Numbers like this are hard to comprehend. How long would it take to count the molecules in 1 mm³ of air? Suppose that a superfast electronic counter can count at the rate of 1 million molecules per second. A simple calculation shows that for a cubic millimeter of air we would have to let the counter run for

$$3 \times 10^{10} \text{ s} = 8.3 \times 10^6 \text{ h} = 3.5 \times 10^5 \text{ days} = 1000 \text{ yr}$$

A cubic millimeter was chosen for this example because the time to count for a cubic centimeter would also be hard to comprehend.

A few other facts about air at standard conditions are worth noting. The mean free path is about 8×10^{-8} m ≈ 0.1 μm, and this is about 25 times the distance between molecules (3×10^{-9} m). In other words, a molecule passes about 25 molecules before it collides with another molecule. The number of molecules in a cube that is one mean free path on each side is 15,000, still a large number. It can be predicted by kinetic theory that the density of this volume will fluctuate in time by only 0.8% root mean square (rms). If we reduce the side of our volume to 0.1 mean free path, we now have only 15 molecules and the density fluctuation will be 25%. These numbers show that the mean free path also offers a convenient dividing line between the continuum and microscopic worlds. Another interesting fact about simple gases (as standard conditions) is that the distance between molecules is about 10 times the size of a simple molecule. (The nucleus of an atom is about 1/100,000 of the size of the atom.)

In liquids, the size required for the continuum hypothesis to be valid is somewhat smaller than for gases; however, the mean free path concept is not valid for liquids. The distances between molecules and the sizes of the molecules are roughly the same in liquids, so a smaller volume is required for a reasonable formulation of the density.

Velocity is another fundamental continuum concept that is based on the volume-limiting process. There are actually two ways to define fluid velocity: the molar-averaged velocity and the mass-averaged velocity. They may have different values if the fluid is a chemical mixture. The *mass-averaged velocity* is formed by the vector sum of all particle velocities with the mass used as a weighing factor:

$$\mathbf{v} = \lim_{L \to 0} \frac{\sum m_i \mathbf{v}_i}{\sum m_i} \tag{1.4.2}$$

The mass-averaged velocity is natural for problems of fluid flow where the momentum equation is important. The product $\rho \mathbf{v}$ gives the momentum per unit volume averaged over all particles. If the fluid is a chemical mixture, the average motion of one chemical species may not be in the direction of $\mathbf{v}$. We define the *molar-averaged velocity* of chemical species k by summing only over molecules of that species:

$$\mathbf{V}^{(k)} = \lim_{L \to 0} \frac{\sum \mathbf{v}_i^{(k)}}{n^{(k)}}$$

In this expression $n^{(k)}$ is the number of molecules of species k within the volume. The molar-averaged velocity of the entire mixture is the vector sum over all molecules divided by the total number of molecules:

$$\mathbf{V} = \lim_{L \to 0} \frac{\sum \mathbf{v}_i}{n}$$

Only if the fluid has a uniform chemical composition are the two velocities equal, $\mathbf{V} = \mathbf{v}$. In situations where there is mass diffusion or there are chemical reactions, it is sometimes more convenient to employ a molar-averaged velocity. Since we deal only with fluids of uniform composition in this book, the mass-averaged velocity will always be used.

The term *fluid particle* has at least two meanings in common usage. The first is a moving-point concept. Here we envision a point that moves with the local fluid velocity at each place in space. A line traced through the flow field by this method is called a *particle path*. We say that the point that traces the path is a fluid particle, or *material point*. For some purposes—for instance, to talk about the expansion of a fluid—it is necessary to consider a small chunk of the fluid. This second meaning for the term *fluid particle* is made precise by considering a small MR and allowing the size of the region to tend to zero. Which of the two meanings is intended is usually obvious from the context. Note that because of molecular diffusion, a fluid particle does not always consist of the same molecules. As a particle moves through the flow, it gains and loses molecules because of random molecular motions.

The third fundamental concept that we cover in this section is *internal energy*. The particle velocity defined above is the average velocity of the molecule, the velocity we observe from our macroscopic world. As far as the macroscopic world is concerned, the kinetic energy of this bulk motion is

$$\text{bulk-motion kinetic energy per unit mass} = \tfrac{1}{2}\mathbf{v} \cdot \mathbf{v} \tag{1.4.3}$$

However, this will not account completely for all the energy of the molecular translational motions. The true total kinetic energy sums the molecular velocities:

$$\text{total kinetic energy of translation} = \lim_{L \to 0} \frac{\sum m_i \tfrac{1}{2}\mathbf{v}_i \cdot \mathbf{v}_i}{\sum m_i} \tag{1.4.4}$$

The difference between Eqs. 1.4.4 and 1.4.3, the energy that is hidden from direct macroscopic observation, is the thermodynamic internal energy due to random translational motion. We can formulate an expression for this internal energy by introducing the random molecular velocities (denoted by a prime). To do this we subtract from each molecular velocity $\mathbf{v}_i$ the average fluid velocity $\mathbf{v}$:

$$\mathbf{v}_i' = \mathbf{v}_i - \mathbf{v}$$

In terms of $\mathbf{v}_i'$ the translational internal energy is expressed as

$$\text{internal energy from random translation velocities} = \frac{\sum m_i \tfrac{1}{2}\mathbf{v}_i' \cdot \mathbf{v}_i'}{\sum m_i} \tag{1.4.5}$$

Thus, the total molecular kinetic energy is split into two parts: a macroscopic part, which is observable as bulk motion, and a microscopic part, which is part of the internal energy. There are many other forms of microscopic energy that are hidden from our continuum world: molecular vibration, rotation, potential energies of molecular configurations, potentials of molecules close to each other, and so on. All of these forms of microscopic energy are accounted for in the thermodynamic internal energy.

The three properties discussed above—density, velocity, and internal energy—are basic and can be defined even when thermodynamic equilibrium does not exist.

1.5 INTERFACE BETWEEN PHASES

The interface between two phases offers some special difficulties in continuum mechanics. The most obvious problem is that the thickness of the interface is small compared to intermolecular distances. Consider for a moment a gas in contact with a liquid (Fig. 1.5). In the liquid the molecules are closely packed and exert strong attractive forces on each other. For a molecule that is deep within the liquid, these forces come from all

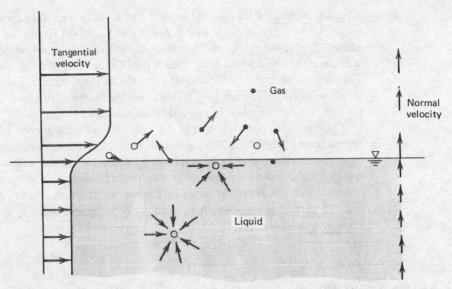

Figure 1.5 Liquid–gas interface. The tangential velocity is continuous, but the normal velocity may have a discontinuity.

directions. As we approach the surface the situation changes, because the neighboring liquid molecules are only on one side. The other side is occupied by a gas. Gas molecules are constantly bombarding the surface, becoming mingled with liquid, and sometimes being absorbed. If we idealize the interface as a surface with zero thickness, we must in general assign to it physical properties; it is a two-dimensional world. Each physical property then has a two-dimensional analogue in the interface; corresponding to density, for example, we have the mass per unit area (the absorbed mass). Energy per unit volume has a surface analogue in the energy per unit area. This includes not only the energy associated with the motions of interface molecules, but also the energy of the special configuration of molecules at the interface.

The two-dimensional interface world is much more complicated than our world. The geometry is non-Euclidean. Conservation laws are complicated because mass, momentum, and energy may change through interactions with the three-dimensional world. Deviations from theory are usual, because a few foreign molecules contaminating the surface can have a great influence. We shall not go into the thermodynamics and fluid mechanics of interfaces; the interested reader should consult Edwards et al. (1991).

Interfacial physics and chemistry are subjects in themselves. To make progress in our main interest, fluid mechanics, we shall have to assume a very simple model of the interface. In a great many practical applications, this model will suffice. We assume that an interface is a surface of zero thickness, which contains no mass, momentum, or energy. Across the interface the density is allowed to jump discontinuously. On the other hand, the temperature and tangential velocity are assumed to be continuous. This assumption is justified because molecules from both sides are constantly colliding and equilibrating within the surface layer. These ideas are illustrated in Fig. 1.5, where a gas flows over a liquid. Molecules leaving the surface and moving back into either fluid have the same tangential velocity. In other words, the velocity of fluid within the interface has only one value. This assumption, called the *no-slip condition*, is not an obvious fact. Indeed, it was once the subject of a long debate [see Goldstein (1965, p. 676) for a brief history]. The debate concerned surface tension and the fact that some liquids are attracted to certain solids whereas others are not. It turns out that wettability is not important and that the no-slip condition applies in general to all substances.

The velocity perpendicular to the interface is discontinuous whenever mass is transferred across the surface. This situation is illustrated by considering a vaporizing liquid. There is a continuous flow of vapor away from the surface with a mass flux $\rho v|_{\text{vap}}$. This must be balanced by an equal flux into the surface from the liquid side of $\rho v|_{\text{liq}}$. Since the two densities are quite different, the velocities must also be different. The discontinuity in normal velocity and the continuity of tangential velocity apply even if the surface itself is in motion.

1.6 CONCLUSIONS

In this first chapter we have attempted to define the scope and nature of fluid mechanics. The three fundamental continuum concepts of density, velocity, and energy were introduced. We shall introduce many more concepts as they are needed in later chapters. In all of our work we shall limit ourselves to exclude magnetic, electrical, and chemical effects. The fluids in the problems that we study will always be assumed to be homogeneous, simple, compressible substances. Even with all of these restrictions, there will be plenty of material to cover.

Perhaps the most fundamental restriction in our subject is the continuum assumption. The characteristic size of the flow must be a continuum scale length. There is a famous physical phenomenon called *Brownian motion,* which illustrates this restriction very nicely. The botanist Robert Brown, while observing life-forms in a water droplet by means of a microscope, noticed that some pollen particles in the water had a jittery motion. The motion was actually a random vibration where the velocity was abruptly changing direction at a high frequency. It gave the particles a fuzzy appearance. The pollen particles were a few micrometers in size, maybe 100 times the intermolecular spacing in water. Later, the reason for this random meandering of the particles was correctly ascribed to unequal and fluctuating molecular forces. The particle was not large enough that molecular bombardment on one side was always exactly counterbalanced on the other side.

Calculations of the motion were finally made by Einstein and Smoluchowski. They used an ad hoc mixture of molecular and continuum ideas. The random driving force was taken from molecular concepts, and a continuum viscous retarding force was assumed. Situations of this type, in the gray area between continuum mechanics and kinetic theory, have grown into what is now called *colloidal science.* It marks a boundary of continuum fluid mechanics where body sizes become comparable with molecular sizes (see Fig. 1.6).

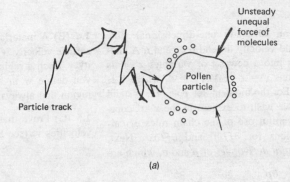

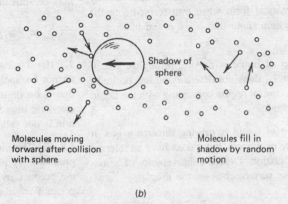

Figure 1.6   Failures of the continuum assumption: (*a*) body size compares with molecular dimensions (very small particle in a liquid); (*b*) body size compares with distance between molecules (sphere moving through a rarefied gas).

Another boundary for the continuum assumption occurs for finite-size bodies in gas flow. As the density is reduced and vacuum conditions approached, either at high altitudes or in vacuum systems, the distance between molecules may become several centimeters. Now the body size may be comparable to the mean free path. Consider a sphere shooting through a rarefied gas. Molecules that collide with the front of the sphere are sent forward several sphere diameters before they interact with other molecules and influence the gas motion. Behind the sphere there is a partial vacuum swept out by its motion. Several diameters back, the random molecular velocities fill this region in once more. This flow field is much different than the one we would find if the mean free path were very small compared to the diameter. The extension of fluid mechanics into this region is called *rarefied-gas dynamics*.

These illustrations show two ways in which the continuum assumption may fail: The characteristic length in the flow (the body diameter) may be so small that it compares with the molecular dimensions, or the mean free path of the fluid may be comparable with the characteristic length of the body.

PROBLEMS

1.1 (B) Consider an unsteady one-dimensional flow where the density and velocity depend on x and t. A Galilean transformation into a new set of variables x', t' is given by the equations $x = x' + Vt'$, $t = t'$, where V is a constant velocity. For the moment, let $f = f(x, t)$ stand for a function that we wish to express in the x'–t' coordinate system. By careful use of the chain rules of calculus, find expressions for $\partial f/\partial t'$ and $\partial f/\partial x'$. Next, consider the *substantial derivatives* of ρ and v, which are

$$\frac{\partial \rho'}{\partial t'} + v' \frac{\partial \rho'}{\partial x'}, \qquad \frac{\partial v'}{\partial t'} + v' \frac{\partial v'}{\partial x'}$$

Show that the substantial derivatives above have exactly the same mathematical form when transformed into the x–t coordinate system (note that $\rho' = \rho$ and $v' = v - V$).

1.2 (A) A droplet of liquid is moving through a gas. It evaporates uniformly, does not deform, and has no internal circulation. A control region coinciding with the liquid is what type of region?

1.3 (A) A droplet of liquid is moving through a gas. It does not evaporate or deform, but it does have an internal (and surface) circulation. Describe the velocity of a material region whose surface encloses the droplet.

1.4 (B) A material region was defined as one where the surface velocity $\mathbf{w}$ is everywhere equal to the fluid velocity $\mathbf{v}$. Such a region always contains the same fluid. Can you define $\mathbf{w}$ in a less restrictive way and still have a region that always contains the same material?

1.5 (C) Prove that the average of the random molecular velocities $\mathbf{v}_i'$ (see Eqs. 1.4.2 and 1.4.5) is zero, that is,

$$\lim_{L \to 0} \sum m_i \mathbf{v}_i' = 0$$

1.6 (B) Using Problem 1.5, prove that the total kinetic energy (per unit mass) of translational molecular motion may be split into two parts as follows:

$$\sum m_i \frac{1}{2} \mathbf{v}_i \cdot \mathbf{v}_i = \sum m_i \frac{1}{2} \mathbf{v}_i' \cdot \mathbf{v}_i' + \frac{1}{2} \mathbf{v} \cdot \mathbf{v} \sum m_i$$

1.7 (C) We have found that the continuum assumption cannot be applied to events with a characteristic length that is on the order of molecular scales. Is there a characteristic time interval for which the continuum assumption is not valid?

1.8 (B) The momentum $\mathbf{p}_j$ of a molecule is equal to the product $m_i \mathbf{v}_i$. From the definitions of ρ and $\mathbf{v}$, show that the product $\rho \mathbf{v}$ is the total momentum of all molecules per unit volume.

2

Thermodynamics

Engineering thermodynamics has two distinct aspects. The first is the analysis of work and energy transfers to a system (a material region). This aspect is taken up in Chapter 5. The second aspect, studied in this chapter, deals with thermodynamic properties and the relations between them. We study the thermodynamics of a simple compressible substance.

2.1 SYSTEMS, PROPERTIES, AND PROCESSES

A *simple system* is a special kind of control region. The matter contained within the region is homogeneous, isotropic, chemically inert, and not moving. The system is not subject to gravitational, electric, magnetic, or interfacial effects. It may receive work only through the normal pressure force. Thus, shear forces are taken to be zero. Special properties are given to the walls of the system whereby we allow interchanges of material, heat, or volume between the system and its adjacent surroundings. The walls may be either real or imaginary; that is, they may be actual solid surfaces containing a fluid or they may be imaginary surfaces that cut through the fluid at any location.

Certain properties of the system called *thermodynamic properties* (internal energy, entropy, temperature, etc.) are related to each other, and a change in one property may cause changes in the others. When we speak of the *state* of a system, we mean that all the thermodynamic properties have definite, unique values. A *process* is any mechanism by which the state of a system is changed. Some processes that we imagine may be very difficult to achieve experimentally; however, this has no bearing on our results. Most of the time we imagine a *reversible process*, which by definition consists of a sequence of equilibrium thermodynamic states.

Thermodynamic properties of a system may be classed into two categories: extensive and intensive. To define these terms, consider a system with uniform properties. Since we get to choose the system boundaries, we can redraw the boundary so that the size of a new system is a fraction λ of the old system; that is, $V_2 = \lambda V_1$. Any property of the system, X, that is reduced in proportion to the size of the system is called an *extensive property*. Extensive properties obey the relation

$$X_2 = \lambda X_1 \tag{2.1.1}$$

15

Energy, mole number, and the volume itself are example of extensive properties. Any property y that is unchanged is called an *intensive property*. Intensive properties obey the relation

$$y_2 = y_1 \tag{2.1.2}$$

Pressure and temperature are examples of intensive properties.

Another way to define *extensive* and *intensive* is to consider X as a function of V:

$$X = f(V)$$

Now we let $V \rightarrow \lambda V$ and $X \rightarrow \lambda^n X$, where n is an undetermined power. The preceding equation now reads

$$\lambda^n X = f(\lambda V)$$

and may be written as

$$\lambda^n f(V) = f(\lambda V) \tag{2.1.3}$$

If $n = 1$, the property is extensive, and in mathematical terminology f is said to be a *homogeneous function of degree one*. If $n = 0$, the property is intensive, and f is a *homogeneous function of degree zero*. We shall follow the standard practice of using capital letters for extensive properties and lowercase letters for intensive properties (with the exception of temperature).

2.2 INDEPENDENT VARIABLES

It is a fact of experience that fixing three independent properties will determine the thermodynamic state of a simple system containing a single chemical species. Some caution must be exercised, because just any choice of three variables may not give an independent set. For example, p, T, and ρ are not independent, but p, T, and V are independent. If one is interested only in the intensive state of the system, only two independent intensive properties need be chosen. Of the several choices of independent variables that may be made, two choices are preferred; E, V, and N (internal energy, volume, and number of moles of substance) or S, V, and N (entropy, volume, and mole number).

Although mathematically these variables are independent, it may be necessary to imagine complicated, perhaps unrealizable, experimental procedures to produce independence. For example, if the volume is varied, some heat must be transferred to maintain the original energy. If material is added to the system, it also adds energy that would have to be removed by heat transfer to retain the original energy level.

The amount of matter in a system can be measured by any of several equivalent variables. Systems containing a single chemical species are readily specified by N, the number of moles. When a system consists of a mixture of chemically inert species, we must in principle allow for changes in composition. Then an additional independent variable will be required for each species present. A mixture such as air, where the composition is uniform and does not change during a process, can be modeled as a pure substance. This modeling is done by using an average molecular weight and average values of other thermodynamic properties.

2.3 TEMPERATURE AND ENTROPY

Many of the concepts in thermodynamics—for example, mass, pressure, energy, and volume—are familiar from mechanics. The two completely new concepts in thermodynamics are temperature and entropy.

We are all aware that when two bodies of different temperatures are brought into contact, they exchange internal energy on the microscopic level by heat transfer. During this energy exchange we can detect no macroscopic motions or forces. This is the essential character of heat transfer. Heat transfer is called *conduction* if it occurs locally by the interaction of the molecules, and *radiation* if the energy is transferred by electromagnetic fields.

Let us consider the molecular mechanism of conduction in a solid or liquid. The molecules are closely packed, and they behave somewhat like oscillators, which vibrate about a mean position. The restoring force of the oscillator is the molecular repulsion force of the neighboring molecules. A large part of the internal energy of a liquid or solid is attributed to these random oscillatory motions. Now if one part of the substance has more energetic oscillators than another part, there is a tendency for the energy to redistribute itself so that all oscillators have the same energy. This is the microscopic energy transport process of heat conduction. Temperature is the macroscopic property that measures the possibility of heat transfer. The temperature of a solid or liquid is proportional to the amount of energy oscillating motions of the molecules.

Next we consider the microscopic interpretation of temperature substances in the gas phase. Gases have kinetic energy in translational molecular velocities. Consider two nearby positions in the gas, where the average kinetic energy of the molecules is slightly different. A molecule leaving the high-energy region enters the low-energy region, where it collides, and after a time it becomes indistinguishable from other molecules in the low-energy region. The result of this process is that the kinetic energy of the low region is increased. Similarly, some molecules from the low region, because of their random motion, find themselves migrating into the high-energy region. These molecules collide with high-energy molecules and cause a net reduction in the kinetic energy of the high-energy region. Again we have a microscopic process for transporting internal energy. The temperature of the gas is a measure of the translational kinetic energy of the molecules. For a perfect gas the precise formula is

$$\tfrac{3}{2}kT = \tfrac{1}{2}m\,\overline{U^2}$$

In this formula k is Boltzmann's constant, m the molecular mass, and U^2 the mean-squared random translational velocity of the molecules.

We can summarize as follows: There are microscopic mechanisms whereby internal energy, which is hidden at the molecular level, can be transported. The transport mechanism involves motions that equilibrate high- and low-energy particles. The tendency to transport energy in this way depends on the energy level itself, and temperature is defined to be proportional to the energy in the transferring mode. Internal energy, on the other hand, is the total energy in all microscopic modes of motion (translation, rotational, vibrational, potential, etc.).

So far, the microscopic interpretations of continuum properties have all been familiar terms from geometry and mechanics—concepts that we feel comfortable with. Entropy, our next subject, does not have such satisfying interpretations. On the other hand, it is a fundamental concept, so we cannot expect to say what it is but only describe what it does. Here are a few "what it does" statements. *Entropy* is something that is constant in a reversible process where there is no heat transfer. Entropy measures irreversibility in that irreversible effects always cause the entropy to increase. For a reversible process, the change in entropy S is the heat Q divided by the temperature T: $dS = dQ/T$. Entropy is the dependent variable of the fundamental thermodynamic equation of a substance. All of these statements tell us about the continuum nature of entropy. As with the previous properties, we might inquire into its microscopic foundation.

The microscopic interpretation of entropy is not very simple. We can give a brief idea, but a course in statistical mechanics is really required to appreciate the necessary concepts. The Austrian physicist Boltzmann related the entropy and the *thermodynamic probability* $\mathcal{W}$ by the famous equation

$$S = k \ln \mathcal{W}$$

To explain thermodynamic probability, consider a system in a fixed thermodynamic state. The system has certain values of the energy E and volume V, and a certain number of particles, N. Microscopically, there are many different arrangements (specific particle positions and velocities) of the N particles that will possess the same total energy. The thermodynamic probability is the number of different microscopic arrangements that will produce the given macroscopic thermodynamic state. The logarithmic scale between probability and entropy is required because thermodynamic probabilities are multiplicative in cases where entropies are additive. Thus, if two systems are considered as a composite system, the entropy is the sum $S = S_1 + S_2$, and the thermodynamic probability is the product $\mathcal{W} = \mathcal{W}_1 \mathcal{W}_2$. The logarithm is the only mathematical function between S and $\mathcal{W}$ that will give this characteristic.

2.4   FUNDAMENTAL EQUATIONS OF THERMODYNAMICS

Choosing values of E, V, and N fixes the thermodynamic state and determines the values of all the other thermodynamic properties. In particular, there is a relation for the entropy,

$$S = S(E, V, N) \tag{2.4.1}$$

The major point to make is that $S = S(E, V, N)$ contains all the thermodynamic information about a substance. In this sense it is a *fundamental equation* for the material in the system. If this single function is known, all thermodynamic properties may be found.

The fundamental differential equation of thermodynamics is

$$T \, dS = dE + p \, dV + \mu \, dN \tag{2.4.2}$$

All simple substances are governed by this equation (here μ is the chemical potential). It plays the central role in thermodynamics in the same way that Newton's laws play a central role in mechanics. It is possible to change our viewpoint and consider E as the dependent variable and use S, V, and $\bar{N}$ as the independent variables. Now the fundamental equation is

$$E = E(S, V, N) \tag{2.4.3}$$

and we reorganize Eq. 2.4.2 into

$$dE = T\,dS - p\,dV - \mu\,dN \qquad (2.4.4)$$

The differential calculus relation for Eq. 2.4.3 is

$$dE = \left.\frac{\partial E}{\partial S}\right|_{V,N} dS + \left.\frac{\partial E}{\partial V}\right|_{S,N} dV + \left.\frac{\partial E}{\partial N}\right|_{S,V} dN \qquad (2.4.5)$$

By comparing Eqs. 2.4.4 and 2.4.5, we can show that there are three *equations of state* for a substance, which may be found from Eq. 2.4.2 by differentiation:

$$T = T(S, V, N) = \left.\frac{\partial E}{\partial S}\right|_{V,N} \qquad (2.4.6)$$

$$-p = p(S, V, N) = \left.\frac{\partial E}{\partial V}\right|_{S,N} \qquad (2.4.7)$$

$$-\mu = \mu(S, V, N) = \left.\frac{\partial E}{\partial N}\right|_{S,V} \qquad (2.4.8)$$

2.5 EULER'S EQUATION FOR HOMOGENEOUS FUNCTIONS

The fact that extensive variables increase directly with the size of the system while all intensive properties remain the same leads to a special relation called *Euler's equation*. Suppose that two systems are in the same intensive thermodynamic state but one is λ times larger than the other. From Eqs. 2.1.3 and 2.4.3 we have

$$E(\lambda S, \lambda V, \lambda N) = \lambda E(S, V, N) \qquad (2.5.1)$$

Differentiation with respect to the parameter λ gives

$$\frac{\partial E(\lambda S, \lambda V, \lambda N)}{\partial(\lambda S)} \frac{\partial(\lambda S)}{\partial\lambda} + \frac{\partial E(\lambda S, \lambda V, \lambda N)}{\partial(\lambda V)} \frac{\partial(\lambda V)}{\partial\lambda} + \frac{\partial E(\lambda S, \lambda V, \lambda N)}{\partial(\lambda N)} \frac{\partial(\lambda N)}{\partial\lambda}$$

$$= E(S, V, N)$$

Note that

$$\frac{\partial E(\lambda S, \lambda V, \lambda N)}{\partial(\lambda S)} = \frac{\partial E(S, V, N)}{\partial S}$$

Of course, similar statements are true for the other derivatives. These relations, together with substitution of Eqs. 2.4.6 to 2.4.8, produce Euler's equation:

$$E = TS - pV - \mu N \qquad (2.5.2)$$

A knowledge of the three equations of state $T(S, V, N)$, $p(S, V, N)$, and $\mu(S, V, N)$ is equivalent to knowledge of the fundamental equation, since they could be substituted into Eq. 2.5.2 to produce $E(S, V, N)$.

2.6 GIBBS–DUHEM EQUATION

The Gibbs–Duhem equation shows that only two equations of state are actually independent (to within a constant). Differentiate Euler's equation, Eq. 2.5.2, to arrive at

$$dE = T \, dS + S \, dT - p \, dV - V \, dp - \mu \, dN - N \, d\mu$$

Subtracting Eq. 2.4.4 yields the *Gibbs–Duhem equation:*

$$0 = S \, dT - V \, dp - N \, d\mu \tag{2.6.1}$$

Assume that two equations of state are known, say $T(S, V, N)$ and $p(S, V, N)$. Substitution of these equations into Eq. 2.6.1 and integration would yield $\mu(S, V, N)$. The conclusion is that two equations of state give all the thermodynamic information about a substance.

2.7 INTENSIVE FORMS OF BASIC EQUATIONS

So far we have dealt with systems, and the thermodynamic properties have been considered to be properties of the system. When the size of the system increased, all extensive properties increased. This simple dependence allows us to place the theory on a completely intensive basis. There are several choices; a unit volume, a unit mole, and a unit mass are all used. We will use lowercase letters to indicate a unit mass and a $\sim$ to indicate a unit mole basis:

$$\tilde{x} = \frac{X}{N} \qquad x = \frac{X}{MN} \tag{2.7.1}$$

where M is the mass of 1 mol of substance (the molecular mass).

To place the fundamental differential equation in intensive form, solve Eq. 2.5.2 for μ and substitute into Eq. 2.4.4. Dividing by N and rearranging will lead to

$$d\left(\frac{E}{N}\right) = T \, d\left(\frac{S}{N}\right) - p\left(\frac{V}{N}\right) \tag{2.7.2a}$$

or

$$d\tilde{e} = T \, d\tilde{s} - p \, d\tilde{v} \tag{2.7.2b}$$

Hence, one can propose the fundamental equation as

$$\tilde{e} = \tilde{e}(\tilde{s}, \tilde{v}) \tag{2.7.3}$$

The intensive state of the system is determined by two intensive independent variables. If Eq. 2.7.2 is divided by M, the form based on a unit mass is obtained. Equations of state on an intensive basis are

$$T = T(S, V, N = 1) = T(\tilde{s}, \tilde{v}) = \left.\frac{\partial \tilde{e}}{\partial \tilde{s}}\right|_{\tilde{v}} \tag{2.7.4}$$

$$p = p(S, V, N = 1) = p(\tilde{s}, \tilde{v}) = \left.\frac{\partial \tilde{e}}{\partial \tilde{v}}\right|_{\tilde{s}} \tag{2.7.5}$$

In fluid mechanics it is customary to use the density instead of the specific volume: $\rho = v^{-1}$.

2.8   DIMENSIONS OF TEMPERATURE AND ENTROPY

The two concepts that are unique to the subject of thermodynamics are temperature and entropy. Energy, pressure, volume, mass, and so on, are familiar from mechanics, and for these items the primary dimensions used in mechanics can be carried over to thermodynamics. From the fundamental differential equation we see that the product of T and $\tilde{s}$ must have dimensions of energy per mole and that is all that is required. In light of statistical mechanics, and the microscopic interpretations of temperature and entropy, one would choose energy per mole for the temperature dimension and make the entropy dimensionless. Historically, this has not been done and an arbitrary temperature unit has been introduced. This inconsistent set of units requires that a dimensional constant R_0 (= energy per mole degree temperature) be added to the equations and gives entropy the same dimensions as those of R_0:

$$d\tilde{e} = R_0 T\, d\left(\frac{\tilde{s}}{R_0}\right) - p\, d\tilde{v} \qquad (2.8.1)$$

Thus, R_0 [$R_0 = 8.314$ kJ/(kg mol $\cdot$ K) $= 1545$ lb$_f \cdot$ ft/(lb$_m$ mol $\cdot$ °R)] has the same conceptual origin as the dimensional constant g_c [$g_c = 9.807$ kg$_m \cdot$ m/(kg$_f \cdot$ s^2) $= 32.17$ lb$_m \cdot$ ft/(lb$_f \cdot$ sec^2)], which must be introduced into mechanics when an inconsistent set of primary dimensions (force, mass, length, or time) are employed.

2.9   WORKING EQUATIONS

Many different choices of dependent and independent variables may be made in thermodynamics, each being advantageous for a particular type of problem. In fluid mechanics we use a unit mass basis and are concerned mainly with the temperature, pressure, and density. It is common to specify thermodynamic information by two equations of state of the form

$$p = p(\rho, T), \qquad e = e(\rho, T)$$

From a theoretical standpoint these equations are connected to the previous equations of state in the following way. The first is found by eliminating s between Eqs. 2.7.3 and 2.7.4 and solving for e. The second is found by eliminating s between Eqs. 2.7.4 and 2.7.5.

Frequently, a critical issue concerns how easy or difficult it is to change the density of a fluid. To assess this sensitivity, the $p = p(\rho, T)$ equation is expressed in a differential form:

$$\frac{d\rho}{\rho} = \alpha\, dp - \beta\, dT$$

Here α is the *isothermal compressibility coefficient* defined by

$$\alpha(p, T) \equiv \frac{1}{\rho}\left.\frac{\partial \rho}{\partial p}\right|_T \qquad (2.9.1)$$

and β is the *bulk expansion coefficient* defined by

$$\beta(p, T) \equiv -\frac{1}{\rho}\frac{\partial \rho}{\partial T}\bigg|_{p} \tag{2.9.2}$$

Sometimes β is called the *thermal expansion coefficient*.

A differential form of the energy equation of state is also very useful. Using calculus manipulations that are to be found in any thermodynamics text, one can arrive at

$$de = c_v(\rho, T)\, dT + \rho^{-2}\left(p - T\frac{\partial p}{\partial T}\bigg|_{\rho}\right) d\rho \tag{2.9.3}$$

In this equation $c_v \equiv (\partial e/\partial T)_\rho$ is the specific heat at constant volume. The name comes from the fact that the heat added to a material region (system) being held at constant volume is equal to $c_v(T_2 - T_1)$.

For subtle reasons that are not apparent, it is often useful to employ the *enthalpy*, which is related to the internal energy by

$$h \equiv e + \frac{p}{\rho} \tag{2.9.4}$$

The important differential relation for the enthalpy is

$$dh = c_p(p, T)\, dT + \rho^{-2}\left(\rho - T\frac{\partial \rho}{\partial T}\bigg|_{p}\right) dp$$

$$= c_p(p, T)\, dT + \rho^{-1}[1 + T\beta(p, T)]\, dp \tag{2.9.5}$$

The coefficient c_p is the specific heat at constant pressure. Note that the second term in both Eqs. 2.9.3 and 2.9.5 depends only on the $p = p(\rho, T)$ equation of state.

2.10   IDEAL GAS

All gases behave as ideal gases when the pressure is low compared to the critical pressure. The first equation of state for an ideal gas is

$$p\frac{V}{N} = p\tilde{v} = R_0 T$$

or, dividing by the molecular mass M,

$$pv = \frac{p}{\rho} = \frac{R_0}{M} T = RT \tag{2.10.1}$$

where $R_0/M \equiv R$ is the specific gas constant.

The validity of the perfect gas law is most easily assessed using the compressibility function. The *compressibility factor* is defined as

$$Z \equiv \frac{p}{\rho RT} = Z(P_r, T_r) \tag{2.10.2}$$

where P_r and T_r are the *reduced pressure* and *reduced temperature*, the values nondimensionalized by the temperature and pressure at the critical point p_c, T_c:

$$P_r \equiv \frac{p}{p_c}, \qquad T_r \equiv \frac{T}{T_c} \tag{2.10.3}$$

Figure 2.1 is a plot of $Z(P_r, T_r)$ constructed from experimental data on 26 different gases with simple molecules. These gases all fit the chart within 2.5%. (If the molecular structure of a gas is very complex, the Z function has the same character with a slightly different shape.) From this chart one can see that the perfect gas law ($Z = 1$) is valid not only at low pressures, but also for higher pressures as long as the temperature is high.

When $pv = RT$ is used to evaluate Eqs. 2.9.3 and 2.9.5, the terms in brackets are zero, indicating that e, h, c_v, and c_p are functions of temperature alone. The second equation of state for an ideal gas is

$$e - e_0 = \int_{T_0}^{T} c_v(T)\ dT \tag{2.10.4}$$

Furthermore, substituting $pv = RT$ into Eq. 2.9.4 and differentiating yields

$$c_p\ dT = (c_v + R)\ dT$$

Hence, $c_p - c_v = R$. From this relation we find that the ratio of specific heats is

$$\gamma \equiv \frac{c_p}{c_v} = 1 + \frac{R}{c_v} \tag{2.10.5}$$

Gamma is a nondimensional parameter that characterizes classes of ideal gases.

The assumption that the specific heats are constant is always reasonable for a modest temperature range. From Eq. 2.10.4 we interpret c_v as a proportionality constant between internal energy and temperature. In gases composed of monatomic molecules, the only form of internal energy is the kinetic energy of random translational motion. Since this is the same motion of which the temperature is a measure, we expect a constant value of c_v. Kinetic theory, in fact, predicts that $c_v/R = \frac{3}{2}$ ($\gamma = \frac{5}{3}$). In more complex molecules, internal energy also resides in molecular rotation and possibly in vibrations between atoms. A rule of physics, the *equipartition of energy*, says roughly that energy will be equally distributed between all available distinct modes of motion. A key word in the rule is "available." Some modes have their first quantum energy level so high that they are not excited at ordinary temperatures.

For instance, a diatomic molecule has three translational modes but only two rotational modes; rotation about the axis connecting the atoms is not "available" at room temperature. A diatomic molecule has a value of $c_v/R_0 = \frac{5}{2}$ ($\gamma = \frac{7}{5}$); more energy is needed to raise the temperature. At extremely high temperatures a vibration mode begins to appear. This mode is not yet fully excited when disassociation of the atoms begins to occur.

Gas molecules with many atoms have a complex structure with many possible vibration modes for energy storage. For these molecules, γ is correspondingly lower, approaching 1 as a lower limit.

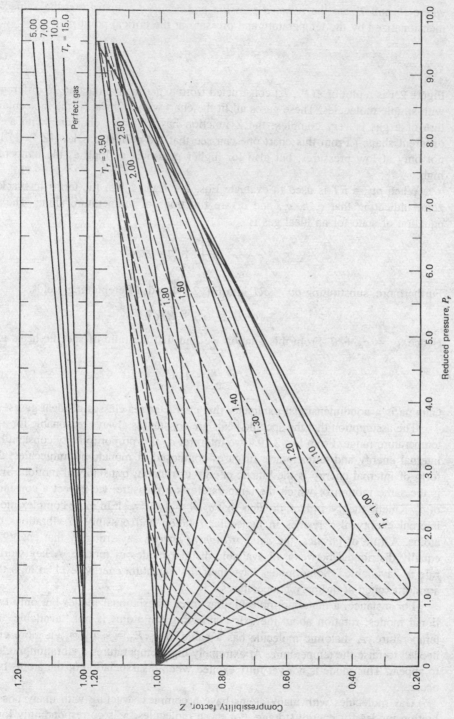

Figure 2.1 Compressibility chart. $Z \equiv p/\rho RT$. Dashed lines are lines of constant density. In the ideal gas limit, $\rho \to 0$ and $Z = 1$ results. Adapted with permission from Obert (1960).

2.11   INCOMPRESSIBLE SUBSTANCE

Whether a substance is incompressible or not should be considered in the context of the physical process of interest. For example, water in a heated pan is set in motion because of density gradients. Sound waves travel through steel because of compressibility. Nevertheless, we can use the thermodynamic term *incompressible substance* to indicate a substance where the density is essentially constant (α and β are both zero) and the thermodynamic state is independent of ρ. The fundamental equation 2.7.3 is now $\tilde{e} = \tilde{e}(\tilde{s})$ and the equation of state 2.7.4 is $T = T(\tilde{s})$. Eliminating $\tilde{s}$ gives $\tilde{e} = \tilde{e}(T)$ and the corresponding relation

$$e - e_0 = \int_{T_0}^{T} c_v(T)\, dT \qquad (2.11.1)$$

This is, incidentally, the same form as for a perfect gas.

The second equation of state for the pressure no longer exists; that is, Eq. 2.7.5 is undefined because $\tilde{e}$ is no longer a function of $\tilde{v}$. To be more precise, we cannot define a "thermodynamic" pressure. There is, of course, a pressure in an incompressible fluid (normal stress in a solid); however, it does not influence the thermodynamic state. Here the pressure is simply the force per unit area, and we say that it is only a *mechanical pressure* variable. This leads to conceptual difficulties in some previously defined variables that involve pressure. For instance, the enthalpy $h = e + p/\rho$ is no longer a purely thermodynamic variable.

A change in enthalpy has a thermodynamic part and a mechanical part:

$$\Delta h = \Delta e + \frac{1}{\rho} \Delta p$$

$$= c_v\, \Delta T + \frac{1}{\rho} \Delta p$$

As a practical matter the mechanical part is usually much smaller than the thermodynamic part. A conclusion that follows immediately is that an incompressible substance has only one specific heat:

$$c_p \equiv \left. \frac{\partial h}{\partial T} \right|_p = \frac{\partial}{\partial T}\left(e + \frac{p}{\rho} \right) = \frac{de}{dT} = c_v \qquad (2.11.2)$$

The ratio of specific heats, $\gamma = c_p/c_v$, is thus unity.

2.12   CONCLUSIONS

Thermodynamics as we have developed it deals with systems containing a uniform fluid at rest. We need to apply thermodynamics to a moving continuum where each point in space has different properties.

Recall that the size of a system can effectively be eliminated by making use of intensive variables. Since we may choose a control volume in any manner whatsoever, we may consider any point in the continuum and define the internal energy and density exactly as we did in Chapter 1. These two independent quantities, together with the equations of state of the substance, determine all the intensive thermodynamic properties at that point. Hence, we have no difficulty in putting thermodynamics on a local basis.

The extension of these ideas to a moving continuum is very simple, but it requires an additional assumption. The assumption is that the bulk motion of the fluid does not affect the thermodynamic state. From the microscopic view this assumption means that if we subtract from each molecule the average velocity of all the molecules, we will still have the same pattern of random molecular motion that would exist without the bulk motion velocity. In other words, the bulk motion does not affect the statistical averages of the molecular properties. The thermodynamic properties, in effect, are determined by an observer floating with the local fluid velocity.

PROBLEMS

2.1 (A) Which of the following are simple thermodynamic systems? (1) A cavity that contains a liquid where the top surface is a moving belt; (2) a container with a liquid in one-half in equilibrium with its vapor in the other half; (3) a steel rod being pulled in a tensile test machine.

2.2 (A) Is the ratio of two extensive properties a thermodynamic property? Is the ratio S/E intensive or extensive?

2.3 (A) Find the three equations of state for a system with the fundamental equation given below. Substitute the state equations into Euler's equation.

$$S = R_0 N \left(\frac{E}{E_0}\right)^{1/2} \frac{V}{V_0} \left(\frac{N}{N_0}\right)^{-3/2}$$

2.4 (A) If the entropy S is considered as the dependent variable in the fundamental differential equation, what are the proper definitions for T, p, and μ?

2.5 (B) A Mollier chart is a plot of $h(p, s)$ in the form of h as a function of s for lines of constant pressure. A chart for a certain substance has two lines given by the following equations:

At 30 psia: $h = 1050s - 650$ Btu/lb$_m$

At 35 psia: $h = 1050s - 630$ Btu/lb$_m$

At the point $s = 1.8$ Btu/lb$_m \cdot$ °R and $p = 30$, find the temperature, density, and internal energy.

2.6 (B) The fundamental differential equation of thermostatics may be rearranged so that different variables are used as dependent and independent. Suppose that the Gibbs function $G \equiv H - TS$ is to be taken as the dependent variable. What independent variables must be used if the result is to be a fundamental equation and contain all the thermodynamic information about the system?

2.7 (A) Find α and β for a perfect gas.

2.8 (A) Find a differential equation for the entropy $s(\rho, T)$ that could be integrated for known functions $p - \rho - T$ and c_v $(T, \rho = $ const$)$. (*Hint:* Use Eq. 2.7.2 ÷ M to begin.)

2.9 (A) Derive the entropy equation for a perfect gas with a constant specific heat using the result of Problem 2.8. The result is

$$ds = c_v \frac{dT}{T} - \frac{1}{\rho^2} \left.\frac{\partial p}{\partial T}\right|_\rho d\rho$$

3

Vector Calculus and
Index Notation

Mathematics is the language we use to quantify physical ideas. The development of mathematics and the development of science have taken place simultaneously and with a great deal of interaction. In some instances scientific needs have inspired mathematical progress; in others, originally abstract mathematical results have found later applications to science. Nevertheless, the best pedagogical viewpoint is to separate the subjects and distinguish clearly between physical and mathematical assumptions.

The purpose of this chapter is to introduce vector and tensor calculus. There are two ways in which we can approach the subject. One approach uses *symbolic* or *Gibbs's notation,* and the other uses *index* or *Cartesian notation.* When Gibbs's notation is employed, we are essentially looking at vector calculus as a separate mathematical subject. Scalars, vectors, and tensors are viewed as different types of things. That is, a vector is a single entity with special mathematical properties. The plus sign between two vectors has a different meaning than a plus sign between two scalars. We must make new definitions for vector and tensor addition, multiplication, integration, and so on. To study vector calculus in the Gibbs notation requires us to define many new operations and investigate which are allowed and which are disallowed.

There is a certain economy of effort in using Gibbs's notation, and many experienced workers prefer to use it. These workers, of course, know what is legal and what is illegal. Another advantage of the notation is a philosophical one. The symbols make no specific reference to a coordinate system. Gibbs's notation is sufficient for an abstract result, but for detailed problems we must write out a component equation in order to find a specific result.

The other approach to vector analysis uses *index notation.* This notation always deals with scalar variables. Whenever we write an equation we use the scalar component of a vector or the scalar component of a tensor. In this way we don't have to worry about legal and illegal operations. All our previous knowledge of algebra and calculus is immediately applicable. It is true that we will need a few new symbols and rules, but they will be essentially shorthand conventions. Index notation is frequently thought of as being restricted to a Cartesian coordinate system. This interpretation is the most straightforward, but index notation is not restricted to Cartesian systems. One can use index notation for any orthogonal coordinate system. (Another type of index notation with subscripts and superscripts applies to nonorthogonal systems as well.) Since most vector calculus results are tabulated in the common coordinate systems, we can usually find them (see Appendix B) and can use them without delving into their derivation.

Workers in fluid mechanics must have a knowledge of both symbolic and index notations. The two notations are used with equal frequency in the literature. Our plan will be to learn how to convert expressions from one notation into the other. In this way we can perform all algebra and calculus operations in index notation, and then as the final step convert the equation to Gibbs's notation. Similarly, when we encounter an equation in symbolic notation, we shall be able to write out its equivalent in index notation. By this means we do not have to learn all the special rules for vector products and differential operations. As more experience is gained, the reader may choose for himself/herself the notation that he/she prefers to use. The last two-thirds of the book has been written assuming that the reader has a working knowledge of both symbolic tensor notation and index notation.

3.1 INDEX NOTATION RULES

The measurement or description of certain types of physical quantities, such as position, velocity, or stress, requires that a coordinate system be introduced. The value of the x-direction velocity depends on how we set up the x-direction coordinate. The key to classifying quantities as scalars, vectors, or tensors is how their components change if the coordinate axes are rotated to point in new directions.

A scalar such as density or temperature is unchanged by such a rotation. It has the same value in either coordinate system. This is the defining characteristic of a scalar. To characterize vectors and tensors, we first investigate how the coordinates of a point in space change if we rotate the coordinate axes. In doing this exercise we introduce the rules of index notation.

Consider a right-handed Cartesian coordinate system where the point P has coordinates x_1, x_2, x_3. Each of these coordinates is a scalar number for which we use the generic name x_i and let $i = 1, 2,$ or 3, as needed. The typical coordinate of point P is x_i. A sketch of the situation is given in Fig. 3.1. If the coordinate system is rotated to new directions, the coordinates of P will change to a new set of numbers that we denote by a prime, x_j'. The exact amount of the rotations is given by the angles from the first set of coordinates to the second or primed coordinates. Let c_{ij}' be the cosine of the angle from the x_i-axis to the x_j'-axis,

$$c_{ij}' \equiv \cos(x_i, x_j')$$
$$c_{ij}' = \cos(x_i, x_j') = \cos(x_j', x_i) = c_{ji}' \tag{3.1.1}$$

The second expression follows from the fact that the angle from x_i to x_j' is the same as the angle from x_j' to x_i; that is, the angle is not directed.

From geometry one can find that the new values of the coordinates are related to the old values by the three equations

$$x_j' = c_{ij}' x_i \qquad \text{for} \quad j = 1', 2', \text{ or } 3' \tag{3.1.2}$$

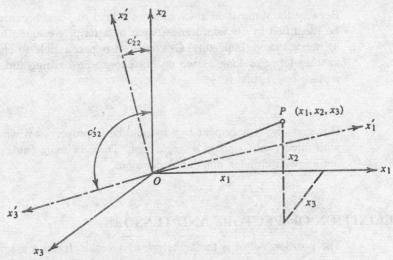

Figure 3.1   Rotation of coordinate axes.

This is an index notation equation that we will now explain. The j index is a *free index* and means that we can write Eq. 3.1.2 three times, substituting 1, 2, and 3 for j. The three scalar equations are

$$x_1' = c_{i1}' x_i$$
$$x_2' = c_{i2}' x_i \qquad (3.1.3)$$
$$x_3' = c_{i3}' x_i$$

The rule is that a free index occurs once and only once in each and every term in an equation. The index i in Eq. 3.1.2 is not a free index because it occurs twice. In the equation $a_k = b_i c_{ik} + d_{ijk} e_{ij}$, the free index is k. One is allowed to change the free index to another letter if it is changed in every term and does not repeat an already existing index. For example, replacing $k \Rightarrow n$ in the preceding expression, $a_n = b_i c_{in} + d_{ijn} e_{ij}$, gives an equivalent relation. Setting $k \Rightarrow i$ would be unacceptable because i would then appear more than once in some terms. Since real space always has three independent coordinates, we will always allow the free index to take on the values 1, 2, or 3, and writing this statement as in Eq. 3.1.2 will be omitted.

In Cartesian notation the second type of index occurs twice in a term. When an index occurs twice it is called a *dummy* or *summation index*. Consider the first equation in Eq. 3.1.2, where i occurs twice. The complete expression is actually

$$x_1' = c_{i1}' x_i = \sum_{i=1}^{3} c_{i1}' x_i$$
$$= c_{11}' x_1 + c_{21}' x_2 + c_{31}' x_3 \qquad (3.1.4)$$

Because the summation always ranges from 1 to 3 and because the summation index can be identified by its appearance twice in a term, we agree to omit the Σ symbol and associated range indicators. Of course, it is permissible to change the dummy index to another letter as long as we do not choose an existing index. In Eq. 3.1.2 we could replace $i \Rightarrow k$, that is,

$$x'_j = c'_{kj} x_k \tag{3.1.5}$$

However, the replacement $i \Rightarrow j$ would be improper, as it would produce an expression with three j subscripts in a single term. Three or more subscripts of the same letter are not allowed in index notation expressions.

3.2 DEFINITION OF VECTORS AND TENSORS

The position vector is the archetype of a vector. It has a magnitude and a direction that may be measured with respect to a chosen coordinate system. An alternative description of the position vector is to give its three components. Thus, a vector is something that has three scalar components. This is, of course, an incomplete description. Not every set of three scalars is a vector. The essential extra property of a vector is found if we rotate the coordinate axes used to measure the components. A mathematical definition of a vector is as follows: Three scalar quantities v_i $(i = 1, 2, 3)$ are the scalar components of a *vector* **v** if they transform according to

$$v'_j = c'_{ij} v_i \tag{3.2.1}$$

under a rotation of coordinate axes.

A special symbol for a vector in symbolic or Gibbs's notation is required. Boldface type, an arrow, an underline, or an overbar are common means of denoting vectors. The symbol v_j used in our notation does not, strictly speaking, represent the vector itself, but only a typical scalar component of the vector. This is important to remember when questions arise about proper mathematical operations. Most of the time, however, we shall not call v_j "a typical scalar component of the vector" but simply refer to it as "the vector v sub j." This terminology is mathematically imprecise, but on the other hand is brief and suggestive.

A tensor is defined by a generalization of the vector definition above. A (rank 2) tensor is defined as a collection of nine scalar components that change under a rotation of axes according to the formula

$$T''_{ij} = c'_{ki} c'_{\ell j} T_{k\ell} \tag{3.2.2}$$

A double sum on the dummy indexes k and ℓ is indicated on the right-hand side, while the free indexes i and j imply nine equations of this type as the indexes range over the values 1, 2, and 3 independently. Symbolic notation requires a special symbol to separate tensors from vectors and scalars. The notation is not uniform; we choose to use boldface sans serif type (**T**).

By following the pattern established in Eqs. 3.2.1 and 3.2.2, one can define tensors of rank 3 and higher.

To conclude this section, note that the inverse relation for Eq. 3.2.1 is found by interchanging the roles of the primed and unprimed coordinates. It is

$$v_j = c'_{ij} v'_i \qquad (3.2.3)$$

or equivalently,

$$v_i = c'_{ji} v'_j \qquad (3.2.4)$$

Equation 3.2.4 is obtained by changing indexes: $j \rightarrow i$ and $i' \rightarrow j'$.

3.3   SPECIAL SYMBOLS AND ISOTROPIC TENSORS

There are two special tensors that are used to assist in mathematical operations or statements. The first is the *Kronecker delta*, which is also known as the *substitution tensor* or *identity tensor*. It is defined as

$$\delta_{ij} \equiv \begin{cases} 1 & \text{if } i = j \\ 0 & \text{if } i \neq j \end{cases} \qquad (3.3.1)$$

This tensor is isotropic because the components are always the same no matter how the coordinates are rotated. In index notation the role of δ_{ij} is to change an index from one letter to another; it substitutes either i for j or in other cases j for i. For example, the expression $\delta_{ij} v_j$ is equal to v_i.

The second useful tensor is a third order isotropic tensor called the *alternating unit tensor*. This tensor is defined to be 1, 0, or -1, according to

$$\varepsilon_{ijk} = \begin{cases} 1 & \text{if } ijk = 123, 231, \text{ or } 312 \\ 0 & \text{if any two indexes are alike} \\ -1 & \text{if } ijk = 321, 213, \text{ or } 132 \end{cases} \qquad (3.3.2)$$

The appearance of ε_{ijk} in an index notation equation is equivalent to a cross in symbolic notation. By the definition of Eq. 3.3.2, the indexes may be rearranged according to the following rules: Moving an index from front to back or from back to front is permitted:

$$\varepsilon_{ijk} = \varepsilon_{jki} = \varepsilon_{kij} \qquad (3.3.3)$$

Interchanging two adjacent indexes causes a change in sign:

$$\varepsilon_{ijk} = -\varepsilon_{jik}$$
$$\varepsilon_{ijk} = -\varepsilon_{ikj} \qquad (3.3.4)$$

It also follows directly from the definitions that the equation

$$\varepsilon_{ijk} \varepsilon_{i\ell m} = \delta_{j\ell} \delta_{km} - \delta_{jm} \delta_{k\ell} \qquad (3.3.5)$$

is valid. An easy way to remember Eq. 3.3.5 is to write down the four δ values with a minus sign between them. The two free indexes of the first ε are distributed to the first position in each δ, keeping the same order:

$$\varepsilon_{ijk} \varepsilon_{i - -} = \delta_{j-} \delta_{k-} - \delta_{j-} \delta_{k-}$$

The second positions on each δ are filled by the free indexes of the second ε, using the same order in the first group and reversing the order for the second group.

As a matter of interest, δ_{ij} and ε_{ijk} are the only isotropic tensors for their respective ranks. The only fourth-order isotropic tensor is related to the previous tensors by the equation

$$I_{ijk\ell} = a\delta_{ij}\delta_{k\ell} + b(\delta_{ik}\delta_{j\ell} + \delta_{i\ell}\delta_{jk}) + c(\delta_{ik}\delta_{j\ell} - \delta_{i\ell}\delta_{jk})$$

To prove the assertions above is beyond the scope of our discussion.

3.4 DIRECTION COSINES AND THE LAW OF CONSINES

For a given fixed-coordinate system, one can represent any direction α by the direction cosines of that direction; that is, $c_{1\alpha} = \cos(x_1, \alpha)$, $c_{2\alpha} = \cos(x_2, \alpha)$, and $c_{3\alpha} = \cos(x_3, \alpha)$, as shown in Fig. 3.2. These cosines are, in fact, equal to the values of components of a unit vector α_i, which points in that direction. The Pythagorean theorem shows that

$$c_{1\alpha}^2 + c_{2\alpha}^2 + c_{3\alpha}^2 = \cos^2(x_1, \alpha) + \cos^2(x_2, \alpha) + \cos^2(x_3, \alpha) = 1 \qquad (3.4.1)$$

This is one of the laws of cosines.

All the laws for direction cosines can be derived by using Eq. 3.1.2, the defining relation for a vector. First consider that the inverse relation for Eq. 3.1.2 is found by noting that the role of the primed and unprimed coordinates may be interchanged. Considering the first set of coordinates as primed and the second as unprimed, Eq. 3.1.2 gives

$$x_j = c'_{ij}x'_i \qquad (3.4.2)$$

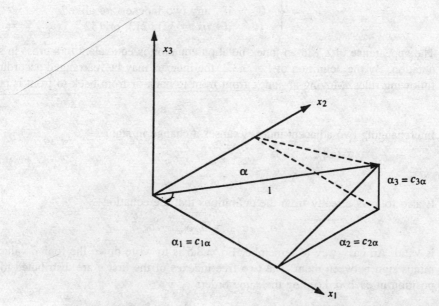

Figure 3.2 Relations between a unit vector α, its components, and the direction cosines.

Observe that the cosine is the same whether we measure the angle from the primed axes to the unprimed axes, or vice versa; $c'_{ij} = c'_{ji}$. (This is not the same as taking the transpose. The transpose of c'_{ij} is c'_{ji}.) This allows one to change Eq. 3.4.2 into

$$x_j = c'_{ji} x'_i \qquad (3.4.3)$$

Hence, either Eq. 3.4.2 or 3.4.3 can be considered as the inverse relation for Eq. 3.1.2.

If we substitute the inverse into the original expression, we will essentially obtain an identity. Substitute Eq. 3.4.3 into Eq. 3.1.2 (with $j \rightarrow k$, $i \rightarrow j$) to find

$$x'_k = c'_{jk} c'_{ji} x'_i \qquad (3.4.4)$$

To investigate this equation further, the $k = 1$ component is written

$$x'_1 = c'_{j1} c'_{ji} x'_i$$
$$= c'_{j1} c'_{j1} x'_1 + c'_{j1} c'_{j2} x'_2 + c'_{j1} c'_{j3} x'_3 \qquad (3.4.5)$$

Note that x'_1, x'_2, and x'_3 are independent; for example, assuming a fixed rotation, we may let the point in space change so that x'_1 changes while x'_2 and x'_3 remain the same. Since x'_1, x'_2, and x'_3 are independent, the coefficients in Eq. 3.4.5 must be

$$c'_{j1} c'_{j1} = 1 \qquad c'_{j1} c'_{j2} = 0 \qquad c'_{j1} c'_{j3} = 0 \qquad (3.4.6)$$

In general, when k is equal to i in Eq. 3.4.5, the cosine term is 1, and when k is not the same as i, the cosine term is zero. The *Kronecker delta* was defined (Eq. 3.3.1) to select out terms in exactly this manner. Equations 3.4.6 are called the *laws of cosines*. They are expressed in index notation as

$$c'_{jk} c'_{ji} = \delta_{ki} \qquad (3.4.7)$$

A second form of the expression is found by using Eq. 3.1.1:

$$c'_{kj} c'_{ij} = \delta_{ki}$$

(Note that the role of the primed and unprimed coordinates can be interchanged in these equations. This gives $\delta_{ki} = c'_{kj} c'_{ij}$.)

One further point is to be made by substituting Eq. 3.4.7 into Eq. 3.4.4. This yields

$$x'_k = \delta_{ki} x'_i \qquad (3.4.8)$$

The name *substitution tensor* comes from the fact that whenever δ_{ki} occurs in a term, it selects out only those components with $k = i$; hence, we can substitute k for i in that term and eliminate the delta. Thus, Eq. 3.4.8 is really the identity $x'_k = x'_k$.

3.5 ALGEBRA WITH VECTORS

Index notation allows us to use the standard algebra of scalars, since we do not employ the vector itself but only a typical scalar component. For example, if a is a scalar, the ith component of $a\mathbf{v}$ is av_i. Multiplication of Eq. 3.2.1 by a proves that this combination is indeed a vector:

$$(av'_j) = c'_{ij}(av_i) \tag{3.5.1}$$

The addition of two vectors is defined as the addition of the separate components. In index notation we write

$$w_i = u_i + v_i \tag{3.5.2}$$

If u_i is ($u_1 = 3$, $u_2 = 4$, $u_3 = 5$) and v_i is ($v_1 = 1$, $v_2 = 2$, $v_3 = 3$), then $w_1 = 3 + 1 = 4$, $w_2 = 4 + 2 = 6$, and $w_3 = 5 + 3 = 8$. The equivalent vector addition in symbolic notation is

$$\mathbf{w} = \mathbf{u} + \mathbf{v} \tag{3.5.3}$$

The plus sign in symbolic notation does not have the same meaning as the plus sign in ordinary algebra. It is a special process for vector entities.

We turn next to the scalar or inner product of two vectors. The scalar product b is defined as the sum $u_i v_i$. In symbolic notation it is denoted as the dot product $\mathbf{u} \cdot \mathbf{v}$. We have

$$b = u_i v_i = u_1 v_1 + u_2 v_2 + u_3 v_3 \tag{3.5.4}$$

Substitution of Eq. 3.2.4 into Eq. 3.5.4 shows how b is affected by rotating the axes:

$$b = u_i v_i = c'_{ji} u'_j c'_{ki} v'_k$$

$$= c'_{ji} c'_{ki} u'_j v'_k$$

$$= \delta'_{jk} u'_j v'_k$$

$$= u'_j v'_j$$

The product $u_i v_i$ is a scalar because its value does not change when the axes are rotated.

A geometric interpretation of the dot product is very useful. To make this interpretation, we consider a primed and an unprimed coordinate system. We choose the unprimed coordinate system so that $u_1 = u$ and $u_2 = u_3 = 0$. The primed system is chosen so that $v'_1 = v$ and $v'_2 = v'_3 = 0$. The inner product is then formed with Eq. 3.2.3 substituted for v_i. This is

$$b = u_i v_i = u_i c'_{ki} v'_k$$

$$= u_1 c'_{11} v'_1$$

$$= uv \cos(x_1, x'_1)$$

$$= uv \cos(\alpha, \beta) \tag{3.5.5}$$

where u and v are the magnitudes, and α and β are the directions of u_i and v_i, respectively. Equation 3.5.5 is the familiar formula for the dot product as the product of the magnitudes of the vectors and the cosine of the angle between the vectors.

An often-used consequence of Eq. 3.5.5 is if two nonzero vectors are perpendicular, their inner product is zero. Another important result is that the inner product of a vector with itself is the square of the magnitude:

$$v_i v_i = v^2 \tag{3.5.6}$$

It is tempting to write $v_i v_i$ as v_i^2, but the single i does not indicate that the summation rule should be applied.

An especially important interpretation of the scalar product happens when one of the vectors is a unit vector. Let a unit vector $\boldsymbol{\alpha}$ have a magnitude of 1 and an arbitrary direction α. Equation 3.5.5 shows that $\boldsymbol{\alpha} \cdot \mathbf{v}$ is

$$\alpha_i v_i = v \cos(\alpha, \beta) \tag{3.5.7}$$

This is the component v_i in the direction α. Hence, if we wish to project v_i in any direction, we form the scalar product v_i and the unit vector in that direction.

3.6 SYMMETRIC AND ANTISYMMETRIC TENSORS

Frequently, the components of a tensor are displayed as a matrix. The customary arrangement is

$$\begin{bmatrix} T_{11} & T_{12} & T_{13} \\ T_{21} & T_{22} & T_{23} \\ T_{31} & T_{32} & T_{33} \end{bmatrix}$$

The *transpose* of a tensor is the tensor obtained by interchanging two indexes; the transpose of T_{ij} is T_{ji}. To be specific, if we let the symbol $(T')_{ij}$ be the ij-component of the transpose of the tensor T_{ij}, then $(T')_{ij} = T_{ji}$; for example, $(T')_{12} = T_{21}$. In the matrix representation the transpose interchanges the components about the diagonal:

$$T_{ij} = \begin{bmatrix} T_{11} & T_{12} & T_{13} \\ T_{21} & T_{22} & T_{23} \\ T_{31} & T_{32} & T_{33} \end{bmatrix} \qquad T_{ji} = \begin{bmatrix} T_{11} & T_{21} & T_{31} \\ T_{12} & T_{22} & T_{32} \\ T_{13} & T_{23} & T_{33} \end{bmatrix} \tag{3.6.1}$$

The symbolic notation for the transpose is $\mathbf{T}^t$. A tensor is said to be *symmetric* if it is equal to its transpose. The tensor Q_{ij} is symmetric if

$$Q_{ij} = Q_{ji} \tag{3.6.2}$$

A tensor R_{ij} is called *antisymmetric* if it is equal to the negative of its transpose,

$$R_{ij} = -R_{ji} \tag{3.6.3}$$

The first tensor below is symmetric, while the second is antisymmetric:

$$Q_{ij} = \begin{bmatrix} 3 & 4 & 1 \\ 4 & 5 & -2 \\ 1 & -2 & 2 \end{bmatrix} \qquad R_{ij} = \begin{bmatrix} 0 & 3 & 1 \\ -3 & 0 & -5 \\ -1 & 5 & 0 \end{bmatrix}$$

A symmetric tensor has only six independent entries, since Eq. 3.6.2 relates the off-diagonal elements. An antisymmetric tensor has only three independent entries. The off-diagonal elements are related by Eq. 3.6.3, and the diagonal elements can satisfy this equation only if they are zero.

An arbitrary tensor T_{ij} may be decomposed into the sum of a symmetric tensor and an antisymmetric tensor. To show this, we start with T_{ij} and add and subtract one-half its transpose:

$$T_{ij} = \tfrac{1}{2}T_{ij} + \tfrac{1}{2}T_{ji} + \tfrac{1}{2}T_{ij} - \tfrac{1}{2}T_{ji} \tag{3.6.4}$$

Bracketing around the indexes is used to denote the symmetric and antisymmetric parts:

$$T_{(ij)} \equiv \tfrac{1}{2}(T_{ij} + T_{ji}) \tag{3.6.5}$$

$$T_{[ij]} \equiv \tfrac{1}{2}(T_{ij} - T_{ji}) \tag{3.6.6}$$

With these definitions we express Eq. 3.6.4 as

$$T_{ij} = T_{(ij)} + T_{[ij]} \tag{3.6.7}$$

We illustrate Eq. 3.6.7 with a specific example,

$$
\begin{bmatrix} 1 & 2 & 3 \\ 4 & 0 & 5 \\ 2 & 1 & 3 \end{bmatrix}
=
\begin{bmatrix}
1 & \dfrac{2+4}{2} & \dfrac{3+2}{2} \\[2mm]
\dfrac{4+2}{2} & 0 & \dfrac{5+1}{2} \\[2mm]
\dfrac{2+3}{2} & \dfrac{1+5}{2} & 3
\end{bmatrix}
+
\begin{bmatrix}
0 & \dfrac{2-4}{2} & \dfrac{3-2}{2} \\[2mm]
\dfrac{4-2}{2} & 0 & \dfrac{5-1}{2} \\[2mm]
\dfrac{2-3}{2} & \dfrac{1-5}{2} & 0
\end{bmatrix}
$$

$$
=
\begin{bmatrix} 1 & 3 & \tfrac{5}{2} \\ 3 & 0 & 3 \\ \tfrac{5}{2} & 3 & 3 \end{bmatrix}
+
\begin{bmatrix} 0 & -1 & \tfrac{1}{2} \\ 1 & 0 & 2 \\ -\tfrac{1}{2} & -2 & 0 \end{bmatrix}
$$

One can readily show that $T_{(ij)} = T_{(ji)}$; therefore, it is symmetric; and that $T_{[ij]} = -T_{[ji]}$; therefore, it is antisymmetric. Hence, Eq. 3.6.7 is the decomposition of an arbitrary tensor into symmetric and antisymmetric tensors. The *symmetric part* is $T_{(ij)}$ and the *antisymmetric part* is $T_{[ij]}$.

We define the *inner product of two tensors* as the double summation

$$a = T_{ij}S_{ji} \tag{3.6.8}$$

Symbolically, this is **T:S** [note that another product, $T_{ij}S_{ij}$, is possible and is denoted by **T:(S)'**]. There is a very important and useful fact about products of the form $T_{ij}S_{ji}$. If one of these tensors is symmetric and the other is antisymmetric, this product is zero. Simply writing out the terms and using the definitions 3.6.2 and 3.6.3 will establish this fact.

The dual vector d_i of a tensor T_{jk} is defined by the inner product

$$d_i = \varepsilon_{ijk}T_{jk} \tag{3.6.9}$$

(It may be proved that this product is indeed a vector.) Breaking T_{jk} into symmetric and antisymmetric parts gives

$$d_i = \varepsilon_{ijk}T_{(jk)} + \varepsilon_{ijk}T_{[jk]} \tag{3.6.10}$$

Now ε_{ijk}, by its definition, is antisymmetric with respect to any two indexes. Therefore, the first term is zero because it is the inner product of a symmetric and an antisymmetric tensor. Equation 3.6.10 becomes a statement that the dual vector depends only on the antisymmetric part of a tensor:

$$d_i = \varepsilon_{ijk} T_{[jk]} \qquad (3.6.11)$$

The inverse of Eq. 3.6.9 is found by multiplying both sides by ε_{ilm}, that is,

$$\varepsilon_{ilm} d_i = \varepsilon_{ilm} \varepsilon_{ijk} T_{jk}$$

Employing Eq. 3.3.5 gives

$$\varepsilon_{ilm} d_i = (\delta_{lj}\delta_{mk} - \delta_{lk}\delta_{mj})T_{jk}$$

$$= T_{lm} - T_{ml}$$

$$= 2T_{[lm]}$$

or

$$T_{[lm]} = \tfrac{1}{2}\varepsilon_{ilm} d_i \qquad (3.6.12)$$

The three independent components of an antisymmetric tensor are equivalent, in the information they give, to the three components of the dual vector. With this result, the decomposition Eq. 3.6.7 can also be expressed as

$$T_{ij} = T_{(ij)} + \tfrac{1}{2}\varepsilon_{ijk} d_k \qquad (3.6.13)$$

An arbitrary tensor may be expressed by its symmetric part plus its dual vector.

3.7 ALGEBRA WITH TENSORS

Considering tensors, vectors, and scalars together produces a great many different ways to multiply the components together. We have already covered the tensor multiplications that result in scalars: $S_{ij}T_{ji}$ and $S_{ij}T_{ij}$. The summation conventions make the meaning of these operations apparent. Many other types are possible. For example, $S_{ij}T_{jk} = R_{ik}$ (**S** · **T** = **R**) is the *tensor product* of two tensors. A *vector product* of a tensor and a vector is defined as

$$u_j = v_i T_{ij} = T_{ij} v_i \qquad (3.7.1)$$

The symbolic notation for this expression is **v** · **T**, where, in contrast to the index notation above, the order of symbols is important. The symbolic formula **T** · **v** stands for a different vector which in index notation is given by

$$w_i = T_{ij} v_j = v_j T_{ij} \qquad (3.7.2)$$

The *dyadic* or tensor product T_{ij} of two vectors u_i and v_i is defined to be

$$T_{ij} = u_i v_j = v_j u_i \qquad (3.7.3)$$

$$\mathbf{T} = \mathbf{uv}$$

Again the order **uv** is important in symbolic notation but is immaterial in index notation. The opposite order **vu** in symbolic notation is the transpose of Eq. 3.7.3. The index notation for **vu** is described as follows. Let

$$\mathbf{Q} = (\mathbf{T})^t = \underaccent{\sim}{\mathbf{vu}}$$

Then

$$\underaccent{\sim}{\mathbf{T}} = \underline{\mathbf{u}}\ \underline{\mathbf{V}}$$

$$Q_{ij} = T_{ji} = u_j v_i = v_i u_j \tag{3.7.4}$$

Hence, $u_j v_i$ is the transpose of $u_i v_j$.

If we have a tensor expression for T_{ij} and wish to write out the T_{11} component, we simply substitute $i = 1$ and $j = 1$. As an example, consider the following equation (no physical interpretation is implied):

$$T_{ij} = v_k w_i S_{kj} + a\delta_{ij} + \varepsilon_{ijk}\omega_k \tag{3.7.5}$$

The component T_{11} is

$$\begin{aligned}
T_{11} &= v_k w_1 S_{k1} + a\delta_{11} + \varepsilon_{11k}\omega_k \\
&= v_k w_1 S_{k1} + a \\
&= v_1 w_1 S_{11} + v_2 w_1 S_{21} + v_3 w_1 S_{31} + a
\end{aligned}$$

(handwritten: $i=1, j=1$; $\delta_{11}=1$; $\varepsilon_{11k}=0$)

In simplifying this expression we made use of the properties of δ_{ij} and ε_{ijk}. A second example is given by finding the T_{12} component of Eq. 3.7.5. It is

$$\begin{aligned}
T_{12} &= v_k w_1 S_{k2} + a\delta_{12} + \varepsilon_{12k}\omega_k \\
&= v_1 w_1 S_{12} + v_2 w_1 S_{22} + v_3 w_1 S_{32} + \omega_3
\end{aligned}$$

(handwritten: $\delta_{12}=0$; $k=1, \varepsilon_{121}=0$; $k=2$; $k=3, \varepsilon_{123}=1$)

In a similar manner we can find any component of Eq. 3.7.5.

The process called *contraction* on i and j selects out the diagonal components of T_{ij} and adds them together. In index notation, contraction is accomplished by changing i and j to the same symbol. In the example (Eq. 3.7.5), contraction of T_{ij} produces

$$\begin{aligned}
T_{ii} &= T_{11} + T_{22} + T_{33} \\
&= v_k w_i S_{ki} + a\delta_{jj} + \varepsilon_{iik}\omega_k \\
&= v_k w_i S_{ki} + 3a
\end{aligned}$$

In symbolic notation T_{ii} is denoted by tr(**T**) and is known as the *trace* of T. Notice that the contraction of δ_{ij} is 3 and the contraction of ε_{ijk} on any two indexes is 0.

3.8 VECTOR CROSS-PRODUCT

The *vector product* of two vectors ($\mathbf{u} \times \mathbf{v}$ in symbolic notation) is defined as

$$w_i = \varepsilon_{ijk} u_j v_k \tag{3.8.1}$$

The components are found by expanding the summations:

$$w_1 = \varepsilon_{123} u_2 v_3 + \varepsilon_{132} u_3 v_2 = u_2 v_3 - u_3 v_2$$

$$w_2 = \varepsilon_{231} u_3 v_1 + \varepsilon_{213} u_1 v_3 = u_3 v_1 - u_1 v_3$$

$$w_3 = \varepsilon_{312} u_1 v_2 + \varepsilon_{321} u_2 v_1 = u_1 v_2 - u_2 v_1$$

In symbolic notation the order of writing $\mathbf{u}$ and $\mathbf{v}$ is important, since $\mathbf{u} \times \mathbf{v} = -\mathbf{v} \times \mathbf{u}$. In Eq. 3.8.1 we are dealing with scalar components and the expression

$$w_i = v_k \varepsilon_{ijk} u_j \qquad (3.8.2)$$

is equally valid. An important point about the notation is that the first index on ε_{ijk} must be the component of the vector $\mathbf{w}$, the second index must be the same as that of the first vector of the product $\mathbf{u} \times \mathbf{v}$, and the last index must be associated with the last vector of the product $\mathbf{u} \times \mathbf{v}$ (of course, ε_{ijk} may be replaced by any of its equivalent forms as given in Eq. 3.3.4). As an aid in translating between notations, it is usually best to keep the order of $\mathbf{u}$ and $\mathbf{v}$ the same as that used in symbolic notation.

The cross-product produces a vector that is perpendicular to the plane of the two vectors and directed in the sense of right-handed rotation of the first vector onto the second. We may prove that $\mathbf{w} = \mathbf{u} \times \mathbf{v}$ is perpendicular to $\mathbf{v}$ by showing that the dot product $\mathbf{v} \cdot \mathbf{w}$ is zero. The product is

$$v_i w_i = v_i \varepsilon_{ijk} u_j v_k = \varepsilon_{ijk} v_i v_k u_j = 0 \qquad (3.8.3)$$

The dyadic $v_i v_k$ is symmetric and ε_{ijk} is antisymmetric; therefore, the product must be zero. A similar argument shows that $\mathbf{u} \cdot \mathbf{w}$ is zero and proves that $\mathbf{w}$ is perpendicular to the plane formed by $\mathbf{u}$ and $\mathbf{v}$. The same type of argument shows immediately that the cross-product of a vector with itself, $\mathbf{u} \times \mathbf{u}$, must always be zero.

The magnitude of the vector product is equal to the product of the magnitude of the vectors and the sine of the angle between the vectors:

$$w = uv \sin(\alpha, \beta) \qquad (3.8.4)$$

The proof is left as an exercise.

There are several complicated formulas in symbolic notation where various combinations of vector and scalar products occur. For example,

$$(\mathbf{a} \times \mathbf{b}) \cdot (\mathbf{c} \times \mathbf{d}) - (\mathbf{a} \cdot \mathbf{c})(\mathbf{b} \cdot \mathbf{d}) \qquad (\mathbf{a} \cdot \mathbf{d})(\mathbf{b} \cdot \mathbf{c}) \qquad (3.8.5)$$

We illustrate the use of Cartesian algebra by proving this equation. First, we write out the left-hand side (LHS) in index notation and collect terms:

$$\text{LHS} = \varepsilon_{ijk} a_j b_k \varepsilon_{ipq} c_p d_q = \varepsilon_{ijk} \varepsilon_{ipq} a_j b_k c_p d_q$$

Using Eq. 3.3.5 yields

$$\text{LHS} = (\delta_{jp} \delta_{kq} - \delta_{jq} \delta_{kp}) a_j b_k c_p d_q$$

$$= \delta_{jp} a_j c_p \delta_{kq} b_k d_q - \delta_{jq} a_j d_q \delta_{kp} b_k c_p$$

The properties of the substitution tensor $\boldsymbol{\delta}$ allows us to set $p = j$ and $q = k$ in the first term and $q = j$ and $p = k$ in the second term. This produces

$$\text{LHS} = a_j c_j b_k d_k - a_j d_j b_k c_k$$

This is the index notation form of the right-hand side of Eq. 3.8.5. Hence, we have completed the proof.

*3.9   ALTERNATIVE DEFINITIONS OF VECTORS AND TENSORS[1]

An alternative definition of a vector is as follows: A *vector* associates a scalar with any chosen direction in space by an expression that is linear in the direction cosines of the chosen direction. If we choose any direction α in space, a vector is something that associates a scalar with this direction (the component of v in the direction α) by a relation containing the direction cosines of α to the first power. The linear equation can be found from our previous definition. Let the direction α coincide with the x_1'-axis of a new coordinate system. Equation 3.2.1 for this axis reads

$$v_1' = c_{i1}' v_i = c_{11}' v_1 + c_{21}' v_2 + c_{31}' v_3 \tag{3.9.1}$$

or, denoting v_1' by $v^{(\alpha)}$,

$$v^{(\alpha)} = \cos(x_1, \alpha) v_1 + \cos(x_2, \alpha) v_2 + \cos(x_3, \alpha) v_3 \tag{3.9.2}$$

This is the alternative defining equation for a vector. The maximum value of $v^{(\alpha)}$ is the magnitude of **v**, and the direction that gives the maximum value is called the direction of the vector. Note that if α assumes the direction of a coordinate axis, then $v^{(\alpha)}$ is the number v_1, v_2, or v_3, as the case may be.

As with a vector, there is a useful alternative definition of tensor: A *tensor* is something that associates a vector with any chosen direction in space by an expression that is linear in the direction cosines of the chosen direction. To show the equivalence of this definition with Eq. 3.2.2, we let the chosen direction α be the $i' = 1'$ direction and write out Eq. 3.2.2 for $i' = 1'$:

$$T_{1j}'' = c_{k1}' c_{\ell j}' T_{k\ell} \tag{3.9.3}$$

Expanding the sum on k produces

$$T_{1j}'' = c_{11}' c_{\ell j}' T_{1\ell} + c_{21}' c_{\ell j}' T_{2\ell} + c_{31}' c_{\ell j}' T_{3\ell} \tag{3.9.4}$$

The equation is clarified somewhat by using superscripts to show the direction with which a particular vector is associated; that is, we let

$$T_j'^{(\alpha)} \equiv T_{1j}'' \qquad T_\ell^{(1)} \equiv T_{1\ell} \qquad T_\ell^{(2)} \equiv T_{2\ell} \qquad T_\ell^{(3)} \equiv T_{3\ell} \tag{3.9.5}$$

Inserting these definitions into Eq. 3.9.4 and multiplying by c_{ij}' yields

$$c_{ij}' T_j'^{(\alpha)} = c_{11}' c_{ij}' c_{\ell j}' T_\ell^{(1)} + c_{21}' c_{ij}' c_{\ell j}' T_\ell^{(2)} + c_{31}' c_{ij}' c_{\ell j}' T_\ell^{(3)} \tag{3.9.6}$$

The left-hand side is the vector associated with the α direction, whose components are measured in the primed coordinate system and transformed to the unprimed system. By recalling the formula 3.4.7 for the product of two cosines, Eq. 3.9.6 may be written as

---

[1] The asterisk before a section heading indicates material that may be skipped without loss of continuity.

$$T_i^{(\alpha)} = c_{11}'\delta_{i\ell}T_\ell^{(1)} + c_{12}'\delta_{i\ell}T_\ell^{(2)} + c_{13}'\delta_{i\ell}T_\ell^{(3)} \tag{3.9.7}$$

Changing subscripts to eliminate the substitution tensor gives

$$T_i^{(\alpha)} = c_{11}'T_i^{(1)} + c_{12}'T_i^{(2)} + c_{13}'T_i^{(3)} \tag{3.9.8}$$

This is the desired definition: A tensor associates a vector $T_i^{(\alpha)}$ with any direction in space by an equation that is linear in the direction cosines of the α direction. Note that $T_i^{(1)}$ is the vector *associated* with the x_1-direction. It does not usually lie along the x_1-direction.

Formula 3.9.8 may be written in a slightly different form by using the unit vector α_i, which you will recall is aligned with the x_1'-axis. From Fig. 3.2 we know that the components of α_i are the direction cosines. Hence,

$$T_i^{(\alpha)} = \alpha_1 T_i^{(1)} + \alpha_2 T_i^{(2)} + \alpha_3 T_i^{(3)} \tag{3.9.9}$$

Now we revert to the previous notation using Eq. 3.9.5:

$$T_i^{(\alpha)} = \alpha_j T_{ji} \tag{3.9.10}$$

The vector associated with the α-direction is the product of the unit vector in that direction with the tensor.

*3.10   PRINCIPAL AXES AND VALUES

The components of a second-order tensor change as we rotate the coordinate axes in which they are expressed (Eq. 3.2.2). This change is related to the fact that the vector $T_i^{(a)}$ associated with the direction α changes as α changes (Eq. 3.9.9). For a symmetric second-order tensor, there are three special directions, called *principal directions,* for which the vector $T_i^{(\alpha)}$ points exactly in the direction of the unit vector α_i. Thus, $T_i^{(\alpha)}$ can be given as a scalar λ, the *principal value,* times α_i,

$$T_j^{(\alpha)} = \alpha_i T_{ij} = \lambda \alpha_j \tag{3.10.1}$$

We rewrite the second equation of Eq. 3.10.1 in the form

$$\alpha_i(T_{ij} - \lambda\delta_{ij}) = 0 \tag{3.10.2}$$

Expanding this linear system for α_i yields

$$\alpha_1(T_{11} - \lambda) + \alpha_2 T_{21} + \alpha_3 T_{31} = 0$$
$$\alpha_1 T_{12} + \alpha_2(T_{22} - \lambda) + \alpha_3 T_{32} = 0 \tag{3.10.3}$$
$$\alpha_1 T_{13} + \alpha_2 T_{23} + \alpha_3(T_{33} - \lambda) = 0$$

These equations allow us to find the principal values and principal directions.

First note that by Kramer's rule a solution of Eq. 3.10.3 exists if, and only if, the determinant of the coefficients is zero. The determinant is a cubic equation (characteristic equation) for λ of the form

$$\lambda^3 - I^{(1)}\lambda^2 - I^{(2)}\lambda - I^{(3)} = 0 \tag{3.10.4}$$

Here the coefficients are given by

$$I^{(1)} = T_{ii} \qquad\qquad \text{or} \quad = \text{tr}(\mathbf{T})$$

$$I^{(2)} = \tfrac{1}{2}(T_{ij}T_{ji} - T_{ii}T_{jj}) \quad \text{or} \quad = \tfrac{1}{2}[\text{tr}(\mathbf{T}^2) - \text{tr}(\mathbf{T})^2] \qquad (3.10.5)$$

$$I^{(3)} = \tfrac{1}{6}\varepsilon_{ijk}\varepsilon_{pqr}T_{jq}T_{jq}T_{kr} \quad \text{or} \quad = \text{Det}[\mathbf{T}]$$

and are called the *basic invariants* of the tensor T_{ij}. Solution of Eq. 3.10.4 gives three answers: $\lambda^{(1)}$, $\lambda^{(2)}$, and $\lambda^{(3)}$. Each λ put into Eq. 3.10.3 gives a solution, together with the condition $\alpha_i\alpha_i = 1$, for a direction $\alpha_i^{(1)}$, $\alpha_i^{(2)}$, and $\alpha_i^{(3)}$, as the case may be. The λ values are always real numbers if T_{ij} is symmetric.

If the λ values are distinct, the vectors for the principal directions are orthogonal and form the principal axes of the tensor. Let $\lambda^{(1)}$ and $\lambda^{(2)}$ be distinct. From Eq. 3.10.2 they obey the equations

$$\alpha_i^{(1)}[T_{ij} - \lambda^{(1)}\delta_{ij}] = 0$$

$$\alpha_j^{(2)}[T_{ji} - \lambda^{(2)}\delta_{ji}] = 0$$

Multiplying the first equation by $\alpha_j^{(2)}$, the second by $\alpha_i^{(1)}$, subtracting, noting that $T_{ij} = T_{ji}$, and replacing indexes yields

$$0 = [\lambda^{(1)} - \lambda^{(2)}]\alpha_j^{(1)}\alpha_j^{(2)} \qquad (3.10.6)$$

Since by assumption $\lambda^{(1)} \neq \lambda^{(2)}$, the vectors $\alpha_j^{(1)}$ and $\alpha_j^{(2)}$ must be orthogonal.

If the tensor is expressed in the coordinates of the principal directions, it has a diagonal form with the principal values

$$\begin{vmatrix} \lambda^{(1)} & 0 & 0 \\ 0 & \lambda^{(2)} & 0 \\ 0 & 0 & \lambda^{(3)} \end{vmatrix}$$

If two of the principal values are alike, say $\lambda^{(2)} = \lambda^{(3)}$, only one principal direction is unique, $\alpha_i^{(1)}$. The other two principal directions lie in a plane perpendicular to $\alpha_i^{(1)}$ and may be chosen arbitrarily to form an orthogonal set. If all three principal values are equal, $\lambda^{(1)} = \lambda^{(2)} = \lambda^{(3)} = \lambda$, the tensor is isotropic, $T_{ij} = \lambda\delta_{ij}$, and the principal axes are completely arbitrary.

3.11   DERIVATIVE OPERATIONS ON VECTOR FIELDS

We next consider the calculus operation in index notation. Let a scalar ϕ, a vector component v_i, or a tensor component T_{ij} be a function of position x_i in space. The notation $\phi(x_i)$ means $\phi(x_1, x_2, x_3)$, and the notation $v_i(x_i)$ stands for the three functions $v_1(x_1, x_2, x_3)$, $v_2(x_1, x_2, x_3)$, and $v_3(x_1, x_2, x_3)$. When x_i is enclosed in parentheses to indicate a function, the index notation rules do not apply to the independent variable: $\phi(x_i)$ is obviously not a vector, and $v_i(x_i)$ is a vector and not a dot product. We say that $\phi(x_i)$ is a *scalar field* and that $v_i(x_i)$ is a *vector field*.

There are several derivative operations that may be formed with tensor functions. To begin, let the differential in space be represented by dx_i or equivalently, by a unit vector α_i times ds. That is,

$$dx_i = \alpha_i \, ds \tag{3.11.1}$$

Using the summation convention, the calculus expression for the dependent differential is

$$d\phi = \frac{\partial \phi}{\partial x_i} \, dx_i = \alpha_i \frac{\partial \phi}{\partial x_i} \, ds \tag{3.11.2}$$

For convenience we simplify the partial derivation symbol as follows:

$$\frac{\partial(\ )}{\partial x_i} = \partial_i(\ ) \tag{3.11.3}$$

Then Eq. 3.11.2 is written

$$d\phi = \partial_i \phi \, dx_i \tag{3.11.4}$$

As an example, let us consider the function $\phi = 3x_1 x_2 + 4 \exp(x_3)$. The derivatives $\partial_1 \phi = 3x_2$, $\partial_2 \phi = 3x_1$, $\partial_3 \phi = 4 \exp(x_3)$ can be thought of as a vector field with components $3x_2$, $3x_1$, $4 \exp(x_3)$. Equation 3.11.4 says that $d\phi$ is the inner product of $\partial_i \phi$ with the vector dx_i:

$$d\phi = 3x_2 \, dx_1 + 3x_1 \, dx_2 + 4 \exp(x_1) \, dx_3$$

The vector $\partial_i \phi$ exists at every point in space. It points in the direction for which $d\phi$ is a maximum and the magnitude is the amount $d\phi/ds$ for that direction. Symbolic notation uses the symbol ∇ for differentiation (i.e., component i; $[\nabla]_i = \partial_i$), and the equivalent form of Eq. 3.11.4 is

$$d\phi = \nabla \phi \cdot d\mathbf{x} = \boldsymbol{\alpha} \cdot \nabla \phi \, ds \tag{3.11.5}$$

It is easy to demonstrate that the three quantities $\partial_i \phi$ constitute a vector. We rewrite Eq. 3.11.5 in index notation and use the fact that the components of α_i are the direction cosines for the unit vectors:

$$\frac{d\phi}{ds} = \partial_1 \phi \cos(x_1, \alpha) + \partial_2 \phi \cos(x_2, \alpha) + \partial_3 \phi \cos(x_3, \alpha)$$

Since this has the form of Eq. 3.9.2, $\partial_i \phi$ must be a vector.

Formulas for vector and tensor functions are found by letting ϕ be the typical scalar component v_i or T_{ij}. The equations are

$$dv_i = \partial_j v_i \, dx_j \quad \text{or} \quad d\mathbf{v} = \boldsymbol{\alpha} \cdot \nabla \mathbf{v} \, ds$$

$$= d\mathbf{x} \cdot \nabla \mathbf{v}$$

$$= d\mathbf{x} \cdot \operatorname{grad} \mathbf{v} \tag{3.11.6}$$

$$dT_{ij} = \partial_k T_{ij} \, dx_k \quad \text{or} \quad d\mathbf{T} = \boldsymbol{\alpha} \cdot \nabla \mathbf{T} \, ds$$

$$= d\mathbf{x} \cdot \nabla \mathbf{T}$$

$$= d\mathbf{x} \cdot \operatorname{grad} \mathbf{T} \tag{3.11.7}$$

The partial derivatives in the expressions above are called *gradients,* and alternative symbolic notations are grad ϕ, grad **v**, and grad **T**. Notice that the gradient always raises the rank of a tensor by 1: The gradient of a scalar is a vector, the gradient of a vector is a tensor, and the gradient of a tensor is a third-rank tensor. Let $v_1 = 4x_1 x_2^2$, $v_2 = 3x_2 x_3$, and $v_3 = x_1 \exp(x_2)$. The nine partial derivatives that may be formed constitute the components of a tensor function,

$$\partial_i v_j = \begin{bmatrix} \partial_1 v_1 & \partial_1 v_2 & \partial_1 v_3 \\ \partial_2 v_1 & \partial_2 v_2 & \partial_2 v_3 \\ \partial_3 v_1 & \partial_3 v_2 & \partial_3 v_3 \end{bmatrix} = \begin{bmatrix} 4x_2^2 & 0 & \exp(x_2) \\ 8x_1 x_2 & 3x_3 & x_1 \exp(x_2) \\ 0 & 3x_2 & 0 \end{bmatrix}$$

If the contraction process is performed on a gradient, the result is called a *divergence.* Expressions for the divergence of a vector are

$$\begin{array}{cc} \partial_i v_i = \partial_1 v_1 + \partial_2 v_2 + \partial_3 v_3 \\ \nabla \cdot \mathbf{v} \qquad \text{div } \mathbf{v} \end{array} \tag{3.11.8}$$

and those for a tensor are

$$\partial_i T_{ij} \qquad \nabla \cdot \mathbf{T} \qquad \text{div } \mathbf{T} \tag{3.11.9}$$

Of course, there is no divergence defined for a scalar function. Notice that $\nabla \cdot \mathbf{v}$ is a scalar and $\nabla \cdot \mathbf{T}$ is a vector. The divergence decreases the rank by 1.

In addition to the derivatives discussed above, we can select terms from $\partial_i v_j$ and form a vector function called the *curl* (actually, the dual vector of the tensor $\partial_i v_j$). The notations are

$$s_i = \varepsilon_{ijk} \partial_j v_k \qquad \mathbf{s} = \nabla \times \mathbf{v} \qquad \mathbf{s} = \text{curl } \mathbf{v} \tag{3.11.10}$$

By using the properties of the tensor ε_{ijk}, we find that the components of Eq. 3.11.10 are

$$s_1 = \varepsilon_{123} \partial_2 v_3 + \varepsilon_{132} \partial_3 v_2 = \partial_2 v_3 - \partial_3 v_2$$

$$s_2 = \varepsilon_{231} \partial_3 v_1 + \varepsilon_{213} \partial_1 v_3 = \partial_3 v_1 - \partial_1 v_3$$

$$s_3 = \varepsilon_{312} \partial_1 v_2 + \varepsilon_{321} \partial_2 v_1 = \partial_1 v_2 - \partial_2 v_1$$

The curl is not necessarily perpendicular to the vector v_i (an exception of great importance is plane or axisymmetric flow where v_i is the velocity).

Second derivatives occur frequently in physical expressions. For example, the divergence of the gradient of a scalar function is

$$\partial_i \partial_i \phi \qquad \nabla \cdot (\nabla \phi) = \nabla^2 \phi \qquad \text{div(grad } \phi) \tag{3.11.11}$$

This particular expression is also called the *Laplacian* of ϕ:

$$\partial_i \partial_i \phi = \partial_1 \partial_1 \phi + \partial_2 \partial_2 \phi + \partial_3 \partial_3 \phi = \nabla^2 \phi \tag{3.11.12}$$

The Laplacian and all other derivative operations are tabulated in several coordinate systems in Appendix B.

We can also treat a vector function the same way. The divergence of a vector gradient is

$$\underline{\partial_i \partial_i v_j \qquad \nabla \cdot (\nabla \mathbf{v}) \qquad \text{div(grad } \mathbf{v})} \qquad (3.11.13)$$

The result of these differential operations is a vector. It is common to use the ∇^2 symbol with this derivative operation also, that is,

$$\nabla \cdot (\nabla \mathbf{v}) = \nabla^2 \mathbf{v} \qquad (3.11.14)$$

The symbol $\nabla^2 \mathbf{v}$ causes no problems in rectangular coordinates, as $\nabla^2 \mathbf{v}$ has three components of the type $(\nabla^2 \mathbf{v})_1 = \nabla^2 v_1$, where the right-hand side is the Laplacian of v_1. The difficulty comes in nonrectangular coordinate systems. Confusion can arise because

$$(\nabla^2 \mathbf{v})_{\text{component } i} \neq \nabla^2 (\mathbf{v}_{\text{component } i})$$

For examples, check the tables in Appendix B. As long as one is aware that the components of the Laplacian of a vector are not equal to the Laplacians of its components (except in rectangular coordinates), there should be no problem with using $\nabla \cdot (\nabla \mathbf{v}) \Rightarrow \nabla^2 \mathbf{v}$.

3.12   INTEGRAL FORMULAS OF GAUSS AND STOKES

The fundamental theorem of integral calculus is the formula relating the integral and the derivative of the integrand. For the integrand $f = d\phi/dx$,

$$\int_{x=a}^{x=b} f \, dx = \int_{x=a}^{x=b} \frac{d\phi}{dx} \, dx = \phi(b) - \phi(a) \qquad (3.12.1)$$

The equivalent theorem for a volume integral is called *Gauss's theorem*. We write Gauss's theorem for an arbitrary tensor function $T_{jk} \cdots (x_i)$:

$$\int_R \partial_i (T_{jk} \cdots) \, dV = \int_S n_i T_{jk} \cdots dS \qquad (3.12.2)$$

$T_{jk} \cdots$ may be scalar, vector, or tensor function of any rank. In Eq. 3.12.1 ϕ is evaluated at the endpoints of the line. The analogy with Eq. 3.12.2 is that $T_{jk} \cdots$ is evaluated on the surface S bounding the region R. When T_{jk} is evaluated in the surface integral, it must be multiplied by the local outward unit normal n_i depicted in Fig. 3.3 (the symbol n_i is reserved for a unit vector pointing outward from an area element dS). It is also important to note that in the volume integral of Eq. 3.12.2, the ∂_i must operate on the entire function. An integrand of the form $w_i \partial_i v_j$ is not of the proper type for Eq. 3.12.2 to apply. As an example, we take $T_{jk} \cdots$ as a scalar function ϕ. Then we have

$$\int_R \partial_i \phi \, dV = \int_S n_i \phi \, dS \qquad (3.12.3)$$

As another example, let $T_{jk} \cdots$ be a vector function v_i; then

$$\int_R \partial_i v_i \, dV = \int_S n_i v_i \, dS \qquad (3.12.4)$$

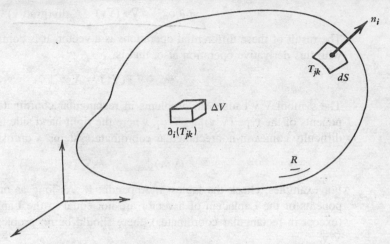

Figure 3.3   Gauss's theorem.

Recall that our index notation rules are in effect, so Eq. 3.12.3 stands for three equations ($i = 1, 2,$ or 3), whereas Eq. 3.12.4 is one equation where each integrand contains three terms.

A useful fact can be derived from Eq. 3.12.3 by letting ϕ be the constant value 1. Since $\partial_i 1 = 0$, Eq. 3.12.3 becomes a proof that the integral of any component of the outward normal around a closed surface is zero. That is,

$$0 = \int_S n_i \, dS \tag{3.12.5}$$

From this equation we can also deduce the geometric interpretation of $n_i \, dS$. Consider Fig. 3.4, where dS is the area of the right-hand surface that is oriented in the direction n_i. The projection of dS onto the x_1-plane is $dS]_1$ with an outward normal $(-1, 0, 0)$. The element dS, its projection $dS]_1$, and their connecting sidewall surface enclose a

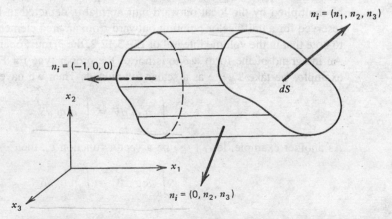

Figure 3.4   Projection of an element dS onto a coordinate plane.

volume; hence, we may apply Eq. 3.12.5 with $i = 1$. The $i = 1$ component of Eq. 3.12.5 does not contain a contribution from the sidewalls, because $n_1 = 0$ there. Thus,

$$0 = \int_S n_1 \, dS = -1 \, dS]_1 + n_1 \, dS$$

$$n_1 \, dS = dS]_1 \quad \text{or} \quad \cos(\alpha, x_1) \, dS = dS]_1 \tag{3.12.6}$$

The conclusion is that $n_1 \, dS$ gives us the projection of a surface onto a plane normal to the x_1-direction.

Next, we discuss another special integral formula called *Stokes's theorem*. Consider the surface in Fig. 3.5, and choose one side to be the outside. The curve bounding the surface is L, and a unit tangent t_i on L is directed according to the right-hand-screw convention (as we proceed along L in the direction of t_i, the interior is on the left). Finally, we let $\nabla \times \mathbf{v}$ be evaluated on dS and then take its component along the outward normal. Stokes's theorem says that

$$\int \mathbf{n} \cdot \nabla \times \mathbf{v} \, dS = \oint \mathbf{t} \cdot \mathbf{v} \, ds$$

or in index notation,

$$\int n_i \varepsilon_{ijk} \partial_j v_k \, dS = \oint t_i v_i \, ds \tag{3.12.7}$$

When v_i is the velocity, the line integral is the *circulation*, Γ. The quantity $\nabla \times \mathbf{v}$ is the *vorticity*, discussed in Chapter 4.

3.13 LEIBNITZ'S THEOREM

Integrals that involve a parameter often occur in fluid mechanics. In most cases, time plays the role of a parameter and the integrals are of the form

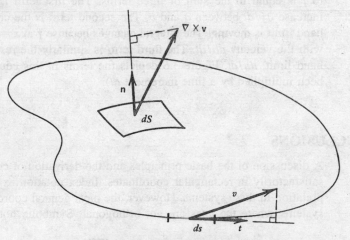

Figure 3.5 Stokes's theorem.

$$I_{ij\ldots}(t) = \int_{R(t)} T_{ij\ldots}(x_i, t)\, dV \qquad (3.13.1)$$

Here $T_{ij\ldots}$ stands for any scalar, vector, or tensor function of interest. Not only does time change the integrand, but the region of integration $R(t)$ may be moving. We let **w** be the velocity of the surface of R. In addition to translating, the surface may be expanding or contracting. The velocity w_i is any prescribed function of position on the surface. The theorem of Leibnitz allows us to find dI/dt in a convenient manner. The theorem is

$$\frac{d}{dt} \int_{R(t)} T_{ij\ldots}(x_i, t)\, dV = \int_R \frac{\partial T_{ij\ldots}}{\partial t}\, dV + \int_S n_k w_k T_{ij\ldots}\, dS \qquad (3.13.2)$$

A short notation for the derivative with respect to time will be $\partial_0 T_{ij}$. Equation 3.13.2 states that we may move the derivative with respect to time inside the integral if we add a surface integral to compensate for the motion of the boundary. The surface integral tells how fast T_{ij} is coming into R because of the surface velocity w_i. If the boundary does not move, $w_i = 0$ and the theorem merely says that it is permissible to interchange the order of differentiation and integration.

As a specific example, take T_{ij} as the constant scalar function 1 ($T_{ij} = 1$). The integral on the left of Eq. 3.13.2 is the volume of the region. Since $\partial_0 1 = 0$, Eq. 3.13.2 becomes

$$\frac{dV_R}{dt} = \frac{d}{dt} \int_R dV = \int_S n_k w_k\, dS \qquad (3.13.3)$$

The rate of change of the volume of a region is the integral of the normal component of the surface velocity over the region.

The one-dimensional version of Leibnitz's theorem is also very useful:

$$\frac{d}{dt} \int_{x=a(t)}^{x=b(t)} f(x, t)\, dx = \int_a^b \frac{\partial f}{\partial t}\, dx + \frac{db}{dt} f(x = b, t) - \frac{da}{dt} f(x = a, t) \qquad (3.13.4)$$

In this form the left-hand side is an integral where the integrand and the limits of integration are a function of the parameter t. The rate of change of this integral with respect to t is equal to the sum of three terms. The first term is the contribution due to the increase $\partial f/dt$ between a and b. The second term is the contribution because the right-hand limit is moving. The integral changes because f at $x = b$ is brought into the integral with the velocity db/dt. The third term is similarly the result of the motion of the left-hand limit, da/dt. Figure 3.6 depicts the terms in this equation (after the equation has been multiplied by a time increment dt).

3.14 CONCLUSIONS

A discussion of the basic principles and the derivation of conservation laws can be done satisfactorily in rectangular coordinates. Index notation expressions have a direct interpretation in these systems. However, the most general coordinate systems are curvilinear systems where the axes are not orthogonal. Symbolic notation such as $\nabla \cdot \mathbf{T}$ is more

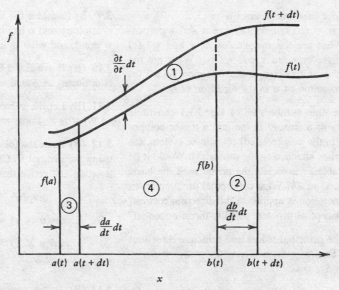

Figure 3.6 Leibnitz's theorem in one dimension.

general in the sense that it has meaning in a nonorthogonal systems, whereas in the present sense $\partial_i T_{ij}$ does not.

Algebra operations such as $v \cdot T$ or $v \times w$ are identical in orthogonal coordinates and rectangular coordinates. That is, we may erect at any point in the field a local rectangular coordinate system, whose axes coincide with those of the orthogonal system, so that the local tensor components can be identified with rectangular components.

Derivative operations involve the values of components not only at the local point, but at neighboring positions also. The distance vector in an orthogonal system includes scale factors, and the coordinate directions are constantly changing. The two expressions below offer an example of a component of ∇v in rectangular and spherical coordinates:

$$\nabla v|_{xy} = \frac{\partial v_y}{\partial x}, \qquad \nabla v|_{\theta r} = \frac{1}{r}\frac{\partial v_r}{\partial \theta} - \frac{v_\theta}{r}$$

Differential expression in cylindrical and spherical coordinate systems are used so frequently and are so complicated that they are tabulated in Appendix B.

PROBLEMS

3.1 (A) Point P is at $x_1 = 5$, $x_2 = 4$, $x_3 = 0$. What will be the coordinate of P in a coordinate system that is rotated $20°$ counterclockwise (x_1-axis toward x_2-axis) about the x_3-axis?

3.2 (A) Which of the following expressions are allowed in index notation (a, b, c, d, and e are arbitrary quantities)?

$$a = b_i c_{ij} d_j \qquad\qquad a_i = b_i + c_{ij} d_{ji} e_i$$

$$a = b_i c_i + d_j \qquad\qquad a_\ell = \varepsilon_{ijk} b_j c_k$$

$$a_i = \delta_{ij} b_i + c_i \qquad\qquad a_{ij} = b_{ji}$$

$$a_k = b_i c_{ki} \qquad\qquad a_{ij} = b_i c_j + e_{jk}$$

$$a_k = b_k c + d_i e_{ik} \qquad\qquad a_{k\ell} = b_i c_{ki} d_\ell + e_{ki}$$

3.3 (A) Consider the three vectors $\mathbf{u} = (3, 2, -7)$, $\mathbf{v} = (4, 1, 2)$, and $\mathbf{w} = (6, 4, -5)$. (a) Are $\mathbf{u}$ and $\mathbf{v}$ perpendicular? (b) What are the magnitudes of $\mathbf{v}$ and $\mathbf{w}$? (c) What is the angle between $\mathbf{v}$ and $\mathbf{w}$? (d) What are the components of a unit vector in the direction of $\mathbf{w}$? (e) What is the projection of $\mathbf{u}$ in the direction of $\mathbf{w}$?

3.4 (C) Do the nine numbers c_{ij}' of Eq. 3.1.1 constitute the components of a tensor? In the text a tensor component measured in the new (rotated) coordinate system was denoted by primes attached to the subscripts. Would it be equally acceptable to associate the prime with the basic symbol, that is, $\mathbf{v}_i'$ or T_{ij}'? What conceptual problem arises if this type of notation is applied to the direction cosines? Why is this conceptual problem actually inconsequential?

3.5 (C) Find the principal values and principal directions for the tensor $\mathbf{S}$: $S_{11} = S_{22} = S_{33} = S_{13} = S_{31} = S_{23} = S_{32} = 0$, $S_{12} = S_{21} = a$.

3.6 (B) Prove that the following equations are true by using index notation:

$$(\mathbf{a} \times \mathbf{b}) \cdot \mathbf{c} = \mathbf{a} \cdot (\mathbf{b} \times \mathbf{c}) = (\mathbf{c} \times \mathbf{a}) \cdot \mathbf{b}$$

$$\mathbf{t} \times (\mathbf{u} \times \mathbf{v}) = \mathbf{u}(\mathbf{t} \cdot \mathbf{v}) - \mathbf{v}(\mathbf{t} \cdot \mathbf{u})$$

$$\mathbf{u} \times \mathbf{v} = -\mathbf{v} \times \mathbf{u}$$

3.7 (A) consider the tensor T_{ij} defined below. Compute $T_{(ij)}$ and $T_{[ij]}$, find the dual vector for this tensor, and verify Eqs. 3.6.7 and 3.6.13:

$$T_{ij} = \begin{bmatrix} 6 & 3 & 1 \\ 4 & 0 & 5 \\ 1 & 3 & 2 \end{bmatrix}$$

3.8 Prove that the product $S_{ij}T_{ji}$ is zero if S_{ij} is symmetric and T_{ji} is antisymmetric.

3.9 (B) Consider the vector $\mathbf{w} = \mathbf{n} \times (\mathbf{v} \times \mathbf{n})$, where $\mathbf{v}$ is arbitrary and $\mathbf{n}$ is a unit vector. In which direction does $\mathbf{w}$ point, and what is its magnitude?

3.10 (B) Prove Eq. 3.8.4 by using primed and unprimed coordinates as was done in the proof of Eq. 3.5.5.

3.11 (B) Let the vector b_j be given by the function $b_j = x_j$. What is a simple relation for the vector gradient $\partial_i b_j$?

3.12 (B) Write the following formulas in Gibbs's notation using the symbol ∇. Convert the expressions to Cartesian notation and prove that the equations are correct.

$$\operatorname{div}(\phi\mathbf{v}) = \phi \operatorname{div} \mathbf{v} + \mathbf{v} \cdot \operatorname{grad} \phi$$

$$\operatorname{div}(\mathbf{u} \times \mathbf{v}) = \mathbf{v} \cdot \operatorname{curl} \mathbf{u} - \mathbf{u} \cdot \operatorname{curl} \mathbf{v}$$

$$\operatorname{curl}(\mathbf{u} \times \mathbf{v}) = \mathbf{v} \cdot \operatorname{grad} \mathbf{u} - \mathbf{u} \cdot \operatorname{grad} \mathbf{v}$$
$$+ \mathbf{u} \operatorname{div} \mathbf{v} - \mathbf{v} \operatorname{div} \mathbf{u}$$

3.13 (B) Is the operator $\partial_i \partial_j(\ )$ symmetric or antisymmetric? Prove the following: curl grad $\phi = 0$; div curl $\mathbf{v} = 0$.

3.14 (C) Derive the one-dimensional Leibnitz formula 3.13.4 by considering a suitable function and region in the three-dimensional formula 3.13.2.

3.15 (C) Verify that $v_j \partial_j v_i = \partial_i(\frac{1}{2}v^2) - \varepsilon_{ijk} v_j \omega_k$, where $\omega_k = \varepsilon_{klm}\partial_\ell v_m$ is the vorticity.

3.16 (A) Show that $\varepsilon_{ijk}\varepsilon_{ij\ell} = 2\delta_{k\ell}$.

3.17 (C) Prove that $\nabla\mathbf{v}:\nabla\mathbf{v} = \mathbf{S}:\mathbf{S} - \frac{1}{2}\omega^2$, where S is the strain rate (Eq. 4.4.2) and ω is the vorticity (Eq. 4.4.4).

3.18 (B) Prove that $-\nabla \times \omega = \nabla^2\mathbf{v}$ for an incompressible flow rate $\nabla \cdot \mathbf{v} = 0$ and ω is the vorticity (Eq. 4.4.4).

4

Kinematics of Local Fluid Motion

The characteristic that distinguishes between solids and fluids is how they respond to shear stresses. A solid responds with an angular strain; two lines originally at right angles are distorted to another angle. The strain continues until the displacement is sufficient to generate internal forces that balance the imposed shear force. Hooke's law of elastic solids states that the stress is proportional to the deformation. Fluids, on the other hand, cannot withstand an imposed shear force. They continue to deform as long as the stress is applied. Thus, in a fluid, we must relate the shear stress not to finite deformations but to rates of deformation. One of the reasons for studying kinematics is to find the exact mathematical expression for the rate of deformation. This is really part of the larger problem of breaking the motion of two neighboring fluid particles into elementary parts.

We will examine fluid movements in a small neighborhood and classify them into the elementary motions of translation, solid-body rotation, and deformations. Deformation can be further classified into two types: extension and shear. All of these motions are continual in a fluid and are dealt with on a rate basis. The translational rate is, of course, just the local particle velocity. The rotation rate and deformation rate are major concepts to be formulated and interpreted in this chapter.

Prior to discussing elementary motions, we devote Sections 4.1 to 4.3 to a review of the two different methods of describing fluid flows. These methods differ essentially in the choice of independent variables. The dependent quantities are the same for both descriptions. Once a viewpoint for describing flows and the kinematics of local motion is established, we shall be in a position to take up the dynamic equations in Chapter 5.

4.1 LAGRANGIAN VIEWPOINT

The *Lagrangian viewpoint* of fluid mechanics is a natural extension of particle mechanics. We focus attention on material particles as they move through the flow. Each particle in the flow is labeled, or identified, by its original position x_i^0. The temperature in Lagrangian variables is given by

$$T = T_L(x_i^0, \hat{t}) \tag{4.1.1}$$

The independent variables in the Lagrangian viewpoint are the initial position x_i^0 and the time $\hat{t}$. Let us use r_i for the position of a material point, or fluid particle. Initially, the fluid particle is at the position x_i^0, and the particle path through space is given by a

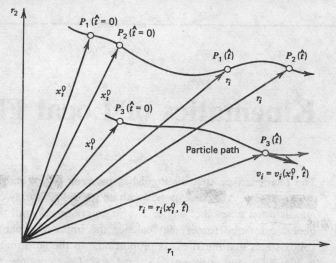

Figure 4.1 Lagrangian coordinates. The particle path is given by the history of the position vector $r_i = \tilde{r}_i(x_i^0, \hat{t})$.

function $\tilde{r}_i$. Note that r_i is the particle position dependent variable and $\tilde{r}_i$ is the particle path function:

$$r_i = \tilde{r}_i(x_i^0, \hat{t}) \qquad (4.1.2)$$

These functions give the paths of the particles with time $\hat{t}$ as a parameter.

The *velocity* and *acceleration* of a particle are defined by

$$v_i = \frac{\partial \tilde{r}_i}{\partial \hat{t}} \quad \text{and} \quad a_i = \frac{\partial^2 \tilde{r}_i}{\partial \hat{t}^2} \qquad (4.1.3)$$

In the Lagrangian description these quantities are functions of the particle identification tag x_i^0 and the time $\hat{t}$ as shown in Fig. 4.1. In steady flow, p_1 and p_2 follow the same path.

We illustrate these ideas with a problem known as the *ideal stagnation-point flow*. Assume that a two-dimensional blunt body is placed in a steady stream flowing from the top to the bottom of the page. When the flow goes around the body there must be a streamline (a formal definition of streamline will be given shortly) that divides the flow so that part of it proceeds to the right of the body and the remainder flows to the left. This streamline is called the *stagnation streamline*. There is a small neighborhood where the stagnation streamline intersects the body, and in this region the surface may be treated as flat. In certain cases we may neglect viscosity and allow the fluid to slip along the wall (a correction for viscosity is discussed later in the book). Figure 4.2 shows the resulting flow pattern. It is known that the particle positions for this problem are given

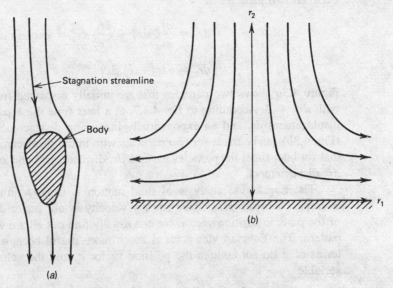

Figure 4.2   Stagnation-point flow pattern.

by the equations

$$r_1 = x_1^0 \exp(c\hat{t})$$

$$r_2 = x_2^0 \exp(-c\hat{t})$$ (4.1.4)

$$r_3 = x_3^0$$

The constant c is determined by the size and shape of the body and the free-stream velocity. The corresponding velocities are

$$v_1 = \frac{\partial \tilde{r}_1}{\partial \hat{t}} = cx_1^0 \exp(c\hat{t})$$

$$v_2 = \frac{\partial \tilde{r}_2}{\partial \hat{t}} = -cx_2^0 \exp(-c\hat{t})$$ (4.1.5)

$$v_3 = \frac{\partial \tilde{r}_3}{\partial \hat{t}} = 0$$

In this case it is easy to eliminate $\hat{t}$ from the particle path equations. Multiplying the first two equations of Eq. 4.1.4 yields the equation for a hyperbola,

$$r_2 = \frac{x_1^0 x_2^0}{r_1}$$

$$r_3 = x_3^0$$ (4.1.6)

Returning now to the particle path functions (Eq. 4.1.4), we compute the distance between two particles as

$$dr_1 = \frac{\partial \tilde{r}_1}{\partial x_1^0} dx_1^0 + \frac{\partial \tilde{r}_1}{\partial x_2^0} dx_2^0 = \exp(c\hat{t}) \, dx_1^0$$

$$dr_2 = \exp(-c\hat{t}) \, dx_2^0$$

(4.1.7)

Figure 4.3a shows two particles that are initially displaced from each other by dx_1^0 and with $dx_2^0 = 0$. According to Eq. 4.1.7, at a later time these particles will still have zero displacement dr_2 and an exponentially increasing displacement dr_1. A similar analysis (Fig. 4.3b) can be made for two particles with initial displacement $dx_1^0 = 0$, dx_2^0. It shows that for later times the particles have no dr_1 displacement and an exponentially decreasing dr_2 displacement.

The Lagrangian analysis of fluid motion is usually quite difficult and is seldom attempted. Furthermore, if we employ velocity as our major dependent quantity instead of the particle position vector, we can usually find out all we want to know about a flow pattern. The Eulerian viewpoint is much more useful because physical laws written in terms of it do not contain the position vector r_i, and the velocity appears as the major variable.

4.2 EULERIAN VIEWPOINT

The *Eulerian viewpoint* has us watch a fixed point in space x_i as time t proceeds. All flow properties, such as r_i and v_i, are considered as functions of x_i and t. The temperature of the fluid is given by $T = T_E(x_i, t)$. At a fixed time, $T_E(x_i, t)$ tells how the temperature changes in space; at a fixed point, $T_E(x_i, t)$ gives the local temperature history. The particle

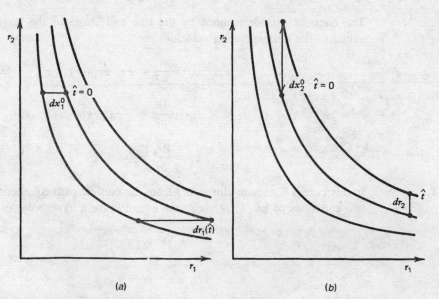

Figure 4.3   Relative motion of two particles in the stagnation flow: (a) particles initially separated by dx_1^0; (b) particles initially separated by dx_2^0.

position vector in Eulerian variables is simply

$$r_i = r_i(x_i, t) = x_i \tag{4.2.1}$$

The position vector in Eulerian variables has as components the local coordinates of the particle.

Substituting $r_i = x_i$ into Eq. 4.1.2 and noting the obvious equivalence between the time variables, we have the transformation between Lagrangian and Eulerian variables as

$$x_i = \tilde{r}_i(x_i^0, \hat{t})$$

$$t = \hat{t} \tag{4.2.2}$$

These relations connect the Eulerian variables x_i, t and the Lagrangian variables x_i^0, $\hat{t}$.

Particle path equations in Lagrangian variables are obtained by substituting $\hat{t} = t$ in Eq. 4.2.2 and relegating x_i^0 to the role of an initial condition:

$$x_i = \tilde{r}_i(x_i^0, t) \tag{4.2.3}$$

We retain $\tilde{r}_i$ as the function symbol in Eq. 4.2.3 to denote that this relation is a particle path function. (To be precise, recall that we used r_i with two meanings in Eq. 4.1.2: On the left-hand side it is the position vector, a dependent variable, while on the right-hand side it is the particle path function $\tilde{r}_i$.)

Streamlines in a flow are defined as lines that at any instant are tangent to the velocity vectors. If dx_i is a differential along a streamline, the tangency condition is expressed by the three equations

$$\frac{dx_1}{v_1} = \frac{dx_2}{v_2} = \frac{dx_3}{v_3} \tag{4.2.4}$$

The form of Eq. 4.2.4 in vector calculus is

$$\varepsilon_{ijk} v_j \, dx_k = 0 \quad \text{or} \quad \mathbf{v} \times d\mathbf{x} = 0 \tag{4.2.5}$$

The cross-product of two nonzero vectors is zero only if they are parallel. A unique direction for the streamline is determined at all points in space where the velocity is not zero. If the velocity becomes zero at a point (or along a line), it is possible for two or more streamlines to exist at that point. This is what happens at the stagnation point, where the streamline splits and moves around the body on each side. The term *stagnation point* comes from the fact that the velocity at this point must be zero.

Again consider the ideal stagnation-point flow. The Eulerian–Lagrangian transformation is given by

$$x_1 = x_1^0 \exp(c\hat{t})$$

$$x_2 = x_2^0 \exp(-c\hat{t})$$

$$t = \hat{t} \tag{4.2.6}$$

The term *velocity field* refers to the Eulerian function $v_i(x_i, t)$. **The velocity field is found** by substituting Eq. 4.2.6 into Eq. 4.1.5. The result is

$$v_1 = cx_1$$
$$v_2 = -cx_2$$

(4.2.7)

A flow where the Eulerian velocity field is independent of time is called a *steady flow*. Streamlines are obtained by substituting Eq. 4.2.7 into Eq. 4.2.4:

$$\frac{dx_2}{dx_1} = \frac{v_2}{v_1} = -\frac{x_2}{x_1}$$

(4.2.8)

Integration produces

$$x_2 = \frac{A}{x_1}$$

(4.2.9)

where A is an arbitrary constant. This hyperbola is the same equation as particle path equation 4.1.6. It is a general result that path lines and streamlines are identical in a steady flow. This finding is, of course, not true in an unsteady flow.

Another aspect of steady flow is that it depends on the coordinate system. A flow may be steady in one coordinate system and unsteady in another. A body moving with a uniform velocity through a stationary fluid produces an unsteady flow with respect to a stationary coordinate system: The flow around a boat is unsteady to an observer on the shore. However, the same flow is steady when observed from a coordinate system attached to the body: An observer on the boat itself finds that the flow is steady.

4.3   SUBSTANTIAL DERIVATIVE

When we adopt the Eulerian viewpoint, our attention is focused on specific points in space at various times. We lose the ability to easily track the history of a particle. In many instances we are required to express the time rate of change of a particle property in the Eulerian variables (x_i, t). The *substantial* (or material) *derivative* is an expression that allows us to formulate, in Eulerian variables, a time derivative evaluated as we follow a material particle.

Let F be a property of the flow under consideration. The parameter F may be expressed in Lagrangian variables by the function $F_L(x_i^0, \hat{t})$, or in Eulerian variables by the function $F_E(x, t)$; that is,

$$F = F_L(x_i^0, \hat{t})$$
$$F = F_E(x_i, t)$$

(4.3.1)

Equating these functions makes sense only if we substitute in transformation equation 4.2.2:

$$F = F_L(x_i^0, \hat{t}) = F_E(x_i = \tilde{r}_i(x_i^0, \hat{t}), t = \hat{t})$$

(4.3.2)

Now the rate of change of F as we follow a particle is found from the chain rules of calculus,

$$\frac{\partial F_L}{\partial \hat{t}} = \frac{\partial F_E}{\partial x_i} \frac{\partial \tilde{r}_i}{\partial \hat{t}} + \frac{\partial F_E}{\partial t} \frac{\partial t}{\partial \hat{t}} \tag{4.3.3}$$

But since $v_i = \partial \tilde{r}_i / \partial \hat{t}$, we have

$$\frac{\partial F_L}{\partial \hat{t}} = \frac{\partial F_E}{\partial t} + v_i \frac{\partial F_E}{\partial x_i} \tag{4.3.4}$$

We might now substitute Eq. 4.2.2 into the right-hand side of Eq. 4.3.4 so that $\partial F_L / \partial \hat{t}$ would appear as a function of x_i^0 and $\hat{t}$. Actually, what we are interested in is the physical interpretation of Eq. 4.3.4. We keep the right-hand side in Eulerian variables and note that this particular combination has the physical interpretation of the time derivative following a particle. This substantial derivative occurs so frequently in fluid mechanics that Stokes gave it a special symbol:

$$\frac{\partial (\ )}{\partial \hat{t}} = \frac{D(\ )}{Dt} \equiv \frac{\partial (\ )}{\partial t} + v_i \, \partial_i (\ ) \tag{4.3.5}$$

or in symbolic notation,

$$\frac{D(\ )}{Dt} \equiv \frac{\partial (\ )}{\partial t} + (\mathbf{v} \cdot \nabla)(\ )$$

The first term on the right-hand side is called the *local rate of change* because it vanishes unless F is changing with time at a fixed local point. The second term is called the *convective change* in F. It vanishes unless there are spatial gradients in F, that is, F has a different value in the neighborhood. This different value is convected (or advected) into the point by the flow velocity v_i.

We illustrate the substantial derivative with a short example. Let us take F to be the position vector r_j. Equation 4.2.1 says that in Eulerian variables $r_j = x_j$; hence,

$$\frac{Dr_j}{Dt} = \frac{\partial r_j}{\partial t} + v_i \, \partial_i r_j$$

$$= 0 + v_i \, \partial_i x_j$$

$$= v_i \, \delta_{ij}$$

$$= v_j \tag{4.3.6}$$

This equation is consistent with our previous definition of velocity and is the Eulerian counterpart to Eq. 4.1.3.

4.4 DECOMPOSITION OF MOTION

We are now ready to begin decomposition of the local fluid motion into elementary parts. We consider a primary material point called P and a neighboring point called P' as

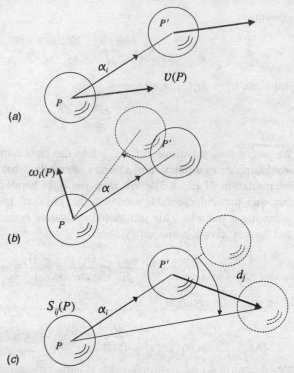

Figure 4.4 Relative motion of two material points: (a) translation; (b) solid-like rotation; (c) extensional and angular strain.

shown in Fig. 4.4. The vector position of P' relative to P is $dx_i = dr_i$, which can also be represented by a unit vector α_i and a distance ds. After an infinitesimal time, P and P' will have moved to new positions. The particle P will move according to the local velocity v_i, while P' will move with the velocity $v_i + dv_i$. Particle P is considered as the main particle, and after its translation velocity is subtracted, the motion of P' is then described as if we were observing it from the main particle. The statements made below are valid only locally in the limit as the distance between P and P' becomes small.

The motion of P and P' may be decomposed into three distinct components: a translation, a solid-body–like rotation, and a deformation. The translational motion is simply the velocity of P itself. All the other motions taken together are dv_i, the velocity of P' with respect to P. The velocity increment is given by the calculus expression

$$dv_j = \partial_i v_j \, dr_i$$

Recall from Eq. 3.6.7 that the velocity gradient may be decomposed into symmetric and antisymmetric parts. Thus,

$$dv_j = \partial_{(i} v_{j)} \, dr_i + \partial_{[i} v_{j]} \, dr_i \qquad (4.4.1)$$

It turns out that the symmetric part indicates the straining motions of P' with respect to P (strain and deformation are equivalent terms).

We denote it by

$$dv_j^{(s)} \equiv S_{ij} \, dr_i$$

where

$$S_{ij} \equiv \partial_{(i} v_{j)} \tag{4.4.2}$$

The antisymmetric part of Eq. 4.4.1 turns out to be associated with the solid-like rotational motion of P' around P. Thus, we let

$$dv_j^{(r)} = \partial_{[i} v_{j]} \, dr_i \tag{4.4.3}$$

This decomposition is determined uniquely for every point in the flow.

The motion of P' about P that is like a solid-body rotation must have the form of the rotation equation $\mathbf{V} = \mathbf{\Omega} \times \mathbf{R}$. To arrive at this form, recall that the antisymmetric part of a tensor may be replaced by its dual vector (Eqs. 3.6.9 and 3.6.12). Let ω_i be the dual vector defined by

$$\omega_i = \varepsilon_{ijk} \, \partial_j v_k, \qquad \boldsymbol{\omega} = \nabla \times \mathbf{v} \tag{4.4.4}$$

Since $\partial_{[i} v_{j]} = \frac{1}{2} \varepsilon_{ijk} \omega_k$, the rotational component of the motion is given by writing Eq. 4.4.3 as

$$dv_j^{(r)} = \tfrac{1}{2} \varepsilon_{ijk} \omega_k \, dr_i = \varepsilon_{jki} (\tfrac{1}{2} \omega_k) \, dr_i \tag{4.4.5}$$

Equation 4.4.5 has the rotation form $\mathbf{V} = \mathbf{\Omega} \times \mathbf{R}$. The vector $\boldsymbol{\omega}$ corresponding to an angular velocity in Eq. 4.4.5 is called the *vorticity*. Each point in the flow has a vorticity. The physical interpretation of Eq. 4.4.5 is that vorticity is twice the angular velocity of the solid-body rotation of P' about P.

Let us compute the vorticity of the stagnation-point flow. The velocity components for that flow are

$$v_1 = c x_1, \qquad v_2 = -c x_2, \qquad v_3 = 0$$

The vorticity is

$$\omega_1 = \varepsilon_{1jk} \, \partial_j v_k = \varepsilon_{123} \, \partial_2 v_3 + \varepsilon_{132} \, \partial_3 v_2 = 0$$

$$\omega_2 = \varepsilon_{2jk} \, \partial_j v_k = \varepsilon_{231} \, \partial_3 v_1 + \varepsilon_{213} \, \partial_1 v_3 = 0$$

$$\omega_3 = \varepsilon_{3jk} \, \partial_j v_k = \varepsilon_{312} \, \partial_1 v_2 + \varepsilon_{321} \, \partial_2 v_1 = 0$$

The particles in this flow do not have any solid-body rotation. Flows with $\omega_i = 0$ are called *irrotational*.

As a second example, consider viscous flow through a slot of width $2h$. The velocity is given by

$$v_1 = v_0 \left[1 - \left(\frac{x_2}{h} \right)^2 \right], \qquad v_2 = 0$$

In this flow the only nonzero component of the vorticity is perpendicular to the plane of the flow. It is

$$\omega_3 = \varepsilon_{321}\,\partial_2 v_1 + \varepsilon_{312}\,\partial_1 v_2 = \frac{2v_0}{h}\frac{x_2}{h}$$

The vorticity is a maximum at either wall and is zero on the centerline.

From these examples it is obvious that vorticity is not directly connected with curvature of the streamlines. In the first example the streamlines were curved but the vorticity was zero, whereas in the second example the streamlines were straight and the vorticity was finite.

Vorticity plays an important role in fluid mechanics. We shall return to the study of vorticity in Chapter 13. While we are on the subject, however, there is one important distinction to be made. The words *vorticity* and *vortex* are used with very different meanings in fluid mechanics. *Vorticity* is a local property of the flow field, whereas the word *vortex* is used to describe any type of swirling flow pattern. As a matter of fact, the vorticity is zero in an ideal vortex.

Next, we take up the straining motions. Straining or deformation is important because it is related to the stresses in the fluid. The total straining velocity is given by Eq. 4.4.2. It is directly proportional to the symmetric part of the velocity gradient tensor, $S_{ij} = \partial_{(i}v_{j)}$, which is called the *strain rate tensor* or the *rate-of-deformation tensor* (other common notations are $\partial_{(i}v_{j)} = S_{ij} = \varepsilon_{ij} = \dot{\gamma}_{ij}$ or def **v**). Our next major task is to find the physical interpretation for each component of the strain rate tensor.

It is useful to replace dr_i in Eq. 4.4.2 by the unit vector α_i times the scalar distance ds and to introduce a *strain vector, d_i*:

$$\frac{dv_j^{(s)}}{ds} = \alpha_i S_{ij} = d_j \qquad\qquad (4.4.6)$$

where $\mathbf{d} \equiv \boldsymbol{\alpha} \cdot \mathbf{S}$. For a point P' in the direction α_i from P, the vector d_i is the strain rate of P' with respect to P. It indicates the direction and velocity with which P' moves away from P. Hence, the strain vector does not necessarily point in the direction of α_i. The component along α_i is the extension strain (*es*), $dv_j^{(es)}$, and the component perpendicular to α_i is the shear strain (*ss*), $dv_j^{(ss)}$.

The extension strain has a magnitude $\boldsymbol{\alpha} \cdot \mathbf{d}$ and direction α; hence,

$$\frac{dv_j^{(es)}}{ds} = \alpha_j \alpha_i d_i \qquad\qquad (4.4.7)$$

We can gain an insight into the physical meaning of the strain rate components S_{ij} if we consider some special cases. Consider two particles P and P' that are separated only in the x_1-direction; that is, $\alpha_1 = 1$, $\alpha_2 = 0$, $\alpha_3 = 0$. Evaluating Eq. 4.4.7 for these two particles yields

$$dv_1^{(es)} = d_1\,ds = S_{11}\,ds$$

From this we interpret S_{11} as the extension rate between two particles separated in the x_1-direction (per unit separation distance). A similar argument shows that S_{22} is the extension rate for two particles originally separated by one unit in the x_2-direction. In general, we may state that the diagonal entries of the strain rate tensor are equal to the extension rates for particles separated in the coordinate directions.

The component of strain perpendicular to $\boldsymbol{\alpha}$, the shear strain, is found from the cross-product

$$\frac{d\mathbf{v}^{(ss)}}{ds} = (\boldsymbol{\alpha} \times \mathbf{d}) \times \boldsymbol{\alpha} \qquad (4.4.8)$$

(an alternative expression is $d\mathbf{v}^{(ss)} = d\mathbf{v}^{(s)} - d\mathbf{v}^{(es)}$). Consider the specific case where P and P' are separated in the x_1-direction; $\alpha_i = (1, 0, 0)$. For this case Eq. 4.4.8 reduces to

$$\frac{dv_1^{(ss)}}{ds} = 0$$

$$\frac{dv_2^{(ss)}}{ds} = d_2 = S_{12}$$

$$\frac{dv_3^{(ss)}}{ds} = d_3 = S_{13}$$

A physical interpretation of the off-diagonal component S_{12} is that it gives the shearing velocity in the x_2-direction of a particle P', which is originally separated from P only in the x_1-direction (per unit separation distance). Similarly, S_{13} indicates the shearing velocity in the x_3-direction of the same particles. In general, an off-diagonal element S_{ij} is proportional to the shearing velocity in the j-direction for a particle P' that is separated in the i-direction from a particle P. (We do not use the term *shear strain rate* for $dv_i^{(ss)}$, as that term is reserved for the rate of closure of the angle between two perpendicular lines.)

4.5   ELEMENTARY MOTIONS IN A LINEAR SHEAR FLOW

We consider a linear shear flow with an arbitrary constant c:

$$v_1 = cx_2 \qquad (4.5.1)$$

This example has elementary motions that are typical of any fluid flow. We shall compute all the different motions considering a variety of points, as illustrated in Fig. 4.5. First display the strain rate tensor and the vorticity. From Eq. 4.5.1 we find that

$$S_{11} = S_{22} = 0$$

$$S_{12} = S_{21} = \tfrac{1}{2}[\partial_1 v_2 + \partial_2 v_1] = \frac{c}{2}$$

$$d_j = \alpha_i S_{ij} = \alpha_1 S_{1j} + \alpha_2 S_{2j} \qquad (4.5.2)$$

$$d_1 = \alpha_2 S_{21} = \alpha_2 \frac{c}{2}$$

$$d_2 = \alpha_1 S_{12} = \alpha_1 \frac{c}{2}$$

The vorticity is

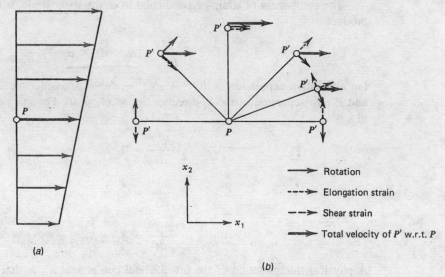

Figure 4.5 Kinematics of shear flow: (a) velocity profile; (b) particle motion for several choices of the particle position.

$$\omega_3 = -\partial_2 v_1 = -c \tag{4.5.3}$$

The vorticity of this flow has only one nonzero component.

Now we are in a position to calculate the elementary motions of P' with respect to P. The velocity due to solid-body rotation is found from Eq. 4.4.5. The two components of the rotation velocity are

$$dv_j^{(r)} = \varepsilon_{j3i}(\tfrac{1}{2}\omega_3)\alpha_i \, ds$$

$$dv_1^{(r)} = \frac{c}{2}\,\alpha_2 \, ds \tag{4.5.4}$$

$$dv_2^{(r)} = -\frac{c}{2}\,\alpha_1 \, ds$$

Figure 4.5 shows a central point P and several choices for the second point P'. We have taken the distance between the points, ds, to be unity. The rotational velocity $dv_i^{(r)}$ has the same magnitude for all choices of P'.

Next, compute the straining (deforming) motions. They are given by Eq. 4.4.6; for this flow the components are

$$dv_1^{(s)} = d_1 \, ds = \frac{c}{2}\,\alpha_2 \, ds$$

$$ \tag{4.5.5}$$

$$dv_2^{(s)} = d_2 \, ds = \frac{c}{2}\,\alpha_1 \, ds$$

These components are not plotted because we want to subdivide the straining motion further into elongation and shearing components. The elongation velocities are found from Eq. 4.4.7; for our linear shear flow this equation reduces to

$$dv_j^{(es)} = \alpha_j \alpha_1 \alpha_2 c \, ds \tag{4.5.6}$$

The components of this equation are obtained by inserting $j = 1$ and $j = 2$. The elongational velocities are given in the figure by short-dashed arrows. In this particular example the elongation strain rate is a maximum for $\alpha_1 = \alpha_2 = \pm 1/\sqrt{2}$ and a minimum for $\alpha_1 = -\alpha_2 = \pm 1/\sqrt{2}$.

Shearing motions of P' with respect to P can be found by subtracting the elongational from the total deformation rate:

$$dv_k^{(ss)} = dv_k^{(s)} - dv_k^{(es)}$$

The components are computed from Eqs. 4.5.5 and 4.5.6. The results are

$$dv_1^{(ss)} = (\tfrac{1}{2} - \alpha_1^2)\alpha_2 c \, ds$$
$$dv_2^{(ss)} = (\tfrac{1}{2} - \alpha_2^2)\alpha_1 c \, ds \tag{4.5.7}$$

These equations reveal that the maximum shearing deformation occurs on the coordinate axis $\alpha_1 = 0$ or $\alpha_2 = 0$. We can also see that the shearing deformation will be zero when both $\alpha_1 = \pm 1/\sqrt{2}$ and $\alpha_2 = \pm 1/\sqrt{2}$. This occurs at points that form a set of axes (the principal axes) rotated 45° from the coordinate axes.

In Fig. 4.5 the shearing strains are shown as a long-dashed arrow, while the total velocity of P' with respect to P is given by a heavy-line arrow. The point at 22.5° is the only point pictured that has all the different types of elementary motions.

The principal axes can be computed using the method of Section 3.10. For a strain rate tensor with $S_{12} = S_{21} = c/2$ and all other entries being zero, we evaluate Eq. 3.10.5 to find that the basic invariants are $I^{(1)} = I^{(3)} = 0$, and $I^{(2)} = c^2/4$. The characteristic equation, Eq. 3.10.4, is

$$\lambda^3 - \frac{c^2}{4}\lambda = 0$$

The solution for the principal values are $\lambda^{(1)} = c/2$, $\lambda^{(2)} = -c/2$, and $\lambda^{(3)} = 0$. Inserting $\lambda = \lambda^{(1)} = c/2$ into Eq. 3.10.3 yields the linear system for $\alpha_i^{(1)}$:

$$-\frac{c}{2}\alpha_1^{(1)} + \frac{c}{2}\alpha_2^{(1)} = 0$$

$$\frac{c}{2}\alpha_1^{(1)} - \frac{c}{2}\alpha_2^{(1)} = 0$$

Hence, the solution is $\alpha_1^{(1)} = \alpha_2^{(1)}$ and the condition $|\alpha_i^{(1)}| = 1$ sets the values at $\alpha_1^{(1)} = \alpha_2^{(1)} = 1/\sqrt{2}$. Similar algebra gives $\alpha_1^{(2)} = -1/\sqrt{2}$, $\alpha_2^{(2)} = 1/\sqrt{2}$. These results are in accord with the directions of maximum and minimum elongation strain together with zero shear strain found from Eqs. 4.5.6 and 4.5.7.

*4.6 PROOF OF VORTICITY CHARACTERISTICS

The *vorticity vector* at every point in the flow was defined by

$$\boldsymbol{\omega} = \nabla \times \mathbf{v} \tag{4.6.1}$$

We shall prove that ω_i is twice the angular velocity of the solid-body rotation motion of P' with respect to P.

Let the material line from P to P' be dr_j and note that the velocity of the motion of P' with respect to P is

$$\frac{\partial(dr_j)}{\partial \hat{t}} = \frac{\partial}{\partial \hat{t}}\left(\frac{\partial \tilde{r}_j}{\partial x_i^0}\right) dx_i^0 = \frac{\partial}{\partial x_i^0}\left(\frac{\partial \tilde{r}_j}{\partial \hat{t}}\right) dx_i^0 = \frac{\partial v_j}{\partial x_i^0} dx_i^0 = dv_j \tag{4.6.2}$$

We may reexpress this by using the substantial derivative (Eq. 4.3.5) and expanding the dv_j in Eulerian variables as follows:

$$\frac{D(dr_j)}{Dt} = dv_j = \partial_i v_j \, dr_i = (S_{ij} + \tfrac{1}{2}\, \varepsilon_{ijk}\omega_k)\, dr_i \tag{4.6.3}$$

Referring to Eq. 4.6.3, we argue that if the components of S_{ij} are zero, the motion of P' is like a solid-body rotation about P. The axis of rotation is along ω_i, and the angular velocity is $\omega_i/2$.

Next, we take up the converse problem: If the motion in the neighborhood of P is a solid-body rotation, does the second term in Eq. 4.6.3 give this motion? We can prove this is true if we can show that a solid-body rotation implies that $S_{ij} = 0$.

Consider another point P'' (Fig. 4.6) in the neighborhood of P and a distance $\delta r_j = \beta_j \delta s$ away. We shall use d for increments associated with P' and δ for those associated

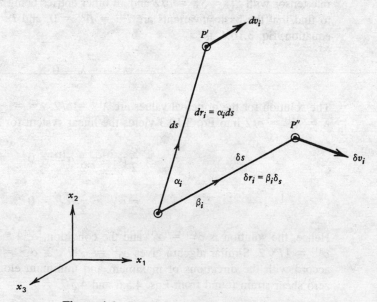

Figure 4.6 Relative motion of P' and P'' about P.

with P''. Form the inner product

$$dr_i \, \delta r_i = ds \, \delta s \cos \theta \qquad (4.6.4)$$

If the motion is a solid-body rotation, neither ds, δs, nor θ will change with time. Hence, a solid-body rotation implies that

$$\frac{D(dr_i \, \delta r_i)}{Dt} = 0 \qquad (4.6.5)$$

To explore the consequences of Eq. 4.6.5, we expand the left-hand side as

$$\frac{D(dr_i \, \delta r_i)}{Dt} = \delta r_i \frac{D(dr_i)}{Dt} + dr_i \frac{D(\delta r_i)}{Dt}$$

$$= \delta r_i \, dv_i + dr_i \, \delta v_i$$

Inserting $\delta v_i = \partial_j v_i \, dr_j$ and a similar equation for δv_i produces

$$\frac{D(dr_i \, \delta r_i)}{Dt} = \partial_j v_i \, dr_j \, \delta r_i + \partial_j v_i \, \delta r_j \, dr_i$$

$$= (\partial_j v_i + \partial_i v_j) \, dr_j \, \delta r_i$$

$$\frac{D(dr_i \, \delta r_i)}{Dt} = 2 S_{ji} \alpha_j \beta_i \, ds \, \delta s \qquad (4.6.6)$$

For a solid-body rotation the left-hand side is zero; hence S_{ji} must be zero, and the velocity in Eq. 4.6.3 consists entirely of the vorticity component. Therefore, we have proved that solid-body rotation and nonzero vorticity are equivalent.

*4.7 RATE-OF-STRAIN CHARACTERISTICS

All of the deformation (straining) motions are the result of the symmetric strain rate tensor S_{ij}. Consider again the three material points P, P', and P'' and the inner product $dr_i \, \delta r_i$. The time rate of change of this product is

$$\frac{D(dr_i \, \delta r_i)}{Dt} = \frac{D}{Dt} (ds \, \delta s \cos \theta)$$

$$= -ds \, \delta s \sin \theta \frac{D\theta}{Dt} + \cos \theta \left[ds \frac{D(\delta s)}{Dt} + \delta s \frac{D(ds)}{Dt} \right] \qquad (4.7.1)$$

We shall equate Eqs. 4.7.1 and 4.6.6 and investigate several special cases.

First take P' and P'' to be the same point. This means that $\alpha_i = \beta_i$, $ds = \delta s$, and $\theta = 0$. Equations 4.7.1 and 4.6.6 yield the relation

$$\frac{1}{ds} \frac{D(ds)}{Dt} = \alpha_i \alpha_j S_{ji} = \alpha_i d_i \qquad (4.7.2)$$

The left-hand side of Eq. 4.7.2 is called the *extensional strain rate*. It gives the extension between P and P' for an arbitrary choice of direction α_i.

Shearing (or angular) deformation is discussed next. Consider another special choice such that PP' and PP'' form a right angle, $\theta = \pi/2$. Equations 4.7.1 and 4.6.6 now reduce to

$$\left.\frac{D\theta}{Dt}\right|_{\theta=\pi/2} = -2\alpha_i\beta_j S_{ij} \tag{4.7.3}$$

This formula gives the shearing deformation rate between any two material lines that are originally at right angles (see Fig. 4.7b). In analogy with solid mechanics, this is called the *shear strain rate*. If we specialize to lines originally directed along the x_1- and x_2-directions [$\alpha_i = (1, 0, 0)$, $\beta_i = (0, 1, 0)$], we obtain

$$\left.\frac{D\theta}{Dt}\right|_{x_1-x_2} = -2S_{12} \tag{4.7.4}$$

The shearing strain rate between material lines along the x_1- and x_2-directions is measured by the S_{12} off-diagonal component of the strain rate tensor. Note that the shearing deformation does not depend on which axis is chosen first. This finding is reflected in the fact that S_{ij} is symmetric. Extensions of these arguments show that the off-diagonal elements of the strain rate tensor have a physical interpretation as the shearing strain rates between lines coinciding with coordinate directions.

4.8   RATE OF EXPANSION

As a material particle (i.e., a small piece of fluid) moves through the fluid, its size and shape may change. It is important to know when the volume of a fluid particle is changing. For instance, if a particle is expanding or connecting, it is doing work on the re-

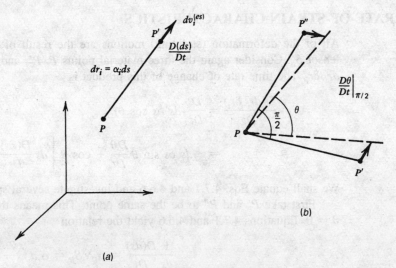

Figure 4.7   Deformation rates: (a) extension strain rate; (b) shear strain rate.

maining fluid, or vice versa. The volume of a material region (MR) is given by the integral

$$V_{\text{MR}} = \int_{R(t)} 1 \, dV \tag{4.8.1}$$

The surface velocity of the region R is equal to the local fluid velocity. Differentiating Eq. 4.8.1 with respect to time and applying Leibnitz's theorem (Eq. 3.13.2) with $w_i = v_i$, we find that

$$\frac{DV_{\text{MR}}}{Dt} = \frac{d}{dt} \int_R 1 \cdot dV = \int \partial_0 \cdot 1 \, dV + \int n_i w_i \cdot 1 \, dS = \int_S n_i v_i \, dS \tag{4.8.2}$$

Next, the surface integral is converted into a volume integral by Gauss's theorem (Eq. 3.12.4),

$$\frac{DV_{\text{MR}}}{Dt} = \int_R \partial_i v_i \, dV \tag{4.8.3}$$

Now the mean value theorem for integrals is used to arrive at

$$\frac{DV_{\text{MR}}}{Dt} = (\partial_i v_i)^* V_{\text{MR}} \tag{4.8.4}$$

The asterisk indicates that the integrand is evaluated at the appropriate point. This point must be within R. When we divide by V_{MR} and allow the volume to approach zero about a specific point, the term $(\partial_i v_i)^*$ will be evaluated at the point in question. Hence,

$$\lim_{V_{\text{MR}} \to 0} \frac{1}{V_{\text{MR}}} \frac{DV_{\text{MR}}}{Dt} = \partial_i v_i = \nabla \cdot \mathbf{v} \tag{4.8.5}$$

Equation 4.8.5 gives us a physical interpretation for $\nabla \cdot \mathbf{v}$ as the *rate of expansion* of a material region (or, if you like, a fluid particle). The rate of expansion is also known as the *dilation rate*.

We might also note that the sum $\partial_i v_i = \partial_1 v_1 + \partial_2 v_2 + \partial_3 v_3$ is equal to the trace of the strain rate tensor S_{ij}, that is, the sum of the extension rates in the three coordinate directions. The major subject of this book is incompressible flow, where the rate of expansion is nearly zero ($\nabla \cdot \mathbf{v} = 0$). This condition requires that the sum of the extension rates in the deformation tensor be zero. If extension is occurring along one coordinate axis, a compensatory contraction must occur along another axis.

*4.9 STREAMLINE COORDINATES

The streamlines of a flow may be used as the basis of a local orthogonal coordinate system. If the flow is smooth enough, the coordinate system can even be global. In general, however, the streamlines will contain knots or other complicated patterns that restrict the coordinates to a local definition. In this section we discuss the coordinate definitions and give the velocity and vorticity components in streamline coordinates.

Let r_i be the position vector to any point on a certain streamline as shown in Fig. 4.8. From some arbitrary origin, s will denote the distance along the streamline. We can consider $r_i(s)$ as describing the streamline completely. The unit vector tangent to the streamline is

$$t_i \equiv \frac{dr_i}{ds} \tag{4.9.1}$$

Since t_i has unit magnitude, it can change only in direction. This change must be perpendicular to t_i itself. Therefore, the principal normal direction is defined by

$$n_i \equiv R(s) \frac{dt_i}{ds} \tag{4.9.2}$$

where $R(s)$ is a scale factor to ensure that n_i is of unit length. The parameter $R(s)$ is called the *radius of curvature* ($k = 1/R$ is the curvature). A local orthogonal coordinate system is completed by defining the binormal direction to be perpendicular to t_i and n_i:

$$\mathbf{b} \equiv \mathbf{t} \times \mathbf{n} \tag{4.9.3}$$

The vectors t_i, n_i, and b_i are unit vectors in an orthogonal streamline coordinate system.

The velocity v_i is in the t_i direction and is given simply by $v_t = v$, $v_n = 0$, $v_b = 0$. In a local region near the streamline we may consider v as a function of $\mathbf{t}$, $\mathbf{n}$, and $\mathbf{b}$. The derivative $\partial v / \partial t$ is the change of v along the streamline, while $\partial v / \partial b$ are changes in the normal and binormal directions, respectively.

It is also possible to express the vorticity in the streamline coordinates (see Truesdell, 1954). The components are

$$\omega_t = (\mathbf{t} \cdot \nabla \times \mathbf{t}) \, v \tag{4.9.4}$$

$$\omega_n = \frac{\partial v}{\partial b} \tag{4.9.5}$$

$$\omega_b = \frac{v}{R} - \frac{\partial v}{\partial n} \tag{4.9.6}$$

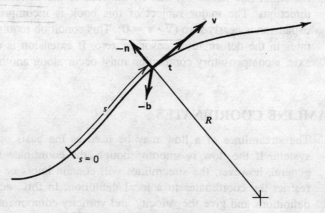

Figure 4.8 Streamline coordinates.

When ω_t is zero, the velocity and the vorticity are perpendicular to each other. This component depends on a geometric property of the streamlines, $\mathbf{t} \cdot \nabla \times \mathbf{t}$, multiplying the magnitude of the velocity. The normal vorticity component ω_n is directly related to the velocity gradient in the binormal direction. The last component ω_b has contributions from the streamline curvature R and from the local velocity gradient $\partial v / \partial n$.

The component ω_b is the only nonzero component in two-dimensional flows. It is typically the largest component in any flow. The two terms in Eq. 4.9.6 express a streamline curvature effect v/R and a local velocity gradient effect $-\partial v / \partial n$. Vorticity can exist because of either effect. For example, a solid-body rotation is given by $v = R\Omega$. This results in $\partial v / \partial n = -\Omega$, and hence $\omega_b = 2\Omega$. This corresponds to the interpretation of ω as twice the solid-body rotation. Another example is furnished by a solid wall with arbitrary curvature. Consider a two-dimensional plane flow. The velocity on the wall must be zero; hence $\omega_t = 0$, $\omega_n = 0$ (b_i is tangent to the wall), and

$$\omega_b = -\left. \frac{\partial v}{\partial n} \right|_{\text{wall}} \tag{4.9.7}$$

Wall vorticity and wall streamlines are discussed further in Section 13.2.

4.10   CONCLUSIONS

The motion in a small neighborhood of fluid has been investigated by considering the motion of two particles separated by a small amount. Instantaneously, the relative motion of these material particles is determined by the velocity gradient tensor $\partial_i v_j$ in an Eulerian description of the flow field. Further separation of the motion was made by decomposing $\partial_i v_j$ into its symmetric and antisymmetric parts. The symmetric part $\partial_{(i} v_{j)} = S_{ij}$ is termed the strain rate tensor because it produces deformation motions consisting of extension and shearing strains (the sum of the extensional strains in the coordinate directions $S_{ii} = \nabla \cdot \mathbf{v}$ indicates the volumetric expansion rate). The antisymmetric part $\partial_{[i} v_{j]}$ causes a solid-bodylike rotational motion. The three independent entries of $\partial_{[i} v_{j]}$ may be expressed in the form of a vorticity vector ω_i ($\boldsymbol{\omega} \equiv \nabla \times \mathbf{v}$). Thus, vorticity becomes another local property of the flow field in the same way that linear momentum v_i, kinetic energy $\frac{1}{2} v_i v_i$, and angular momentum $\mathbf{r} \times \mathbf{v}$ are local flow properties. Frequently, in the remainder of the book, we shall interpret flows in terms of vorticity and the physical events that establish certain vorticity patterns.

PROBLEMS

4.1 (A) The surface temperature of a lake changes from one location to another as $T(x_1, x_2)$. If you attach a thermometer to a boat and take a path through the lake given by $x_i = b_i(\hat{t})$, find an expression for the rate of change of the thermometer temperature in terms of the lake temperature.

4.2 (A) In a table of vector differential operators, look up the expressions for $\nabla \times \mathbf{v}$ in a cylindrical coordinate system.

(a) Compute the vorticity for the flow in a round tube where the velocity profile is

$$v_z = v_0\left[1 - \left(\frac{r}{R}\right)^2\right]$$

(b) Compute the vorticity for an ideal vortex where the velocity is

$$v_\theta = \frac{\Gamma}{2\pi r}, \qquad \Gamma \text{ constant}$$

(c) Compute the vorticity in the vortex flow given by

$$v_\theta = \frac{\Gamma}{2\pi r}\left[1 - \exp\left(-\frac{r^2}{4\nu t}\right)\right]$$

Sketch all velocity and vorticity profiles.

4.3 (B) Consider the viscous flow in a slot where the velocity profile is

$$v_1 = v_0\left[1 - \left(\frac{x_2}{h}\right)^2\right], \qquad v_2 = v_3 = 0$$

Here v_0 is the maximum velocity and h is the half-height. Let the primary point P be at $x_2 = h/2$. Let the secondary point P' be at various locations; angles of 0, 30°, 45°, and 90° to the x_1-axis and a distance ds away from P. Make a sketch with P, P', and vectors (roughly to scale) for the following quantities:

$$\frac{d(v_1^{(r)}/v_0)}{d(s/h)}, \quad \frac{d(v_1^{(es)}/v_0)}{d(s/h)}, \quad \frac{d(v_1^{(ss)}/v_0)}{d(s/h)}$$

4.4 (B) How long will it take a particle traveling on an ideal stagnation streamline to reach the stagnation point?

4.5 (A) Consider a two-dimensional flow with velocity components $v_1 = cx_1$, $v_2 = -cx_2$. Find expressions for the vorticity and the strain rate tensor.

4.6 (A) Consider a point at $x_2 = h/2$ in Problem 4.3. Find the rate of closure of the angle between two material lines in the x_1- and x_2-directions. Find the rate of closure of the angles between an x_1-line and lines at 45° from it.

4.7 (B) Compute the circulation Γ (Eq. 3.12.7) around a circuit including the origin for the velocity profiles of Problem 4.2(b) and (c).

4.8 (A) Find the rate of expansion for the stagnation-point flow: $v_1 = cx_1$, $v_2 = -cx_2$.

4.9 (A) Consider the two-dimensional flow given in cylindrical coordinates by $v_r = Q/2\pi r$, $v_z = v_\theta = 0$. Compute the components of the strain rate tensor for this flow.

4.10 (B) Show that an alternative expression for $dv_j^{(ss)}$ is $d\mathbf{v}^{(ss)} = -\boldsymbol{\alpha} \times (\boldsymbol{\alpha} \times d\mathbf{v}^{(s)})$. Prove that this is equivalent to $d\mathbf{v}^{(ss)} = d\mathbf{v}^{(s)} - d\mathbf{v}^{(es)}$.

4.11 (B) Compute the components of the strain rate tensor and vorticity vector for the Burgers vortex. The velocity components in cylindrical coordinates are (a, ν, Γ are constants)

$$V_r = -ar$$

$$V_z = 2az$$

$$V_\theta = \frac{\Gamma}{2\pi r}\left[1 - \exp\left(-\frac{r^2}{2\nu/a}\right)\right]$$

Note Appendix Tables B.1 and C.2.

5

Basic Laws

The laws we formulate in this chapter are of such a fundamental nature that they cannot be proven in the mathematical sense. They are the starting point. These laws are also basic in the sense that they apply to all substances, solids as well as fluids. The truth of the basic laws has been established by a sort of scientific evolution. Of all the propositions that have been put forward, these laws have survived the test of time. Results predicted from them correspond to our experience.

Through the years the laws and the concepts involved in the laws have undergone subtle changes. As different viewpoints in physics have developed, the concepts have been generalized, adapted, and reinterpreted. Fluid mechanics today is a mature subject where the basic concepts and laws are well developed. This does not mean that we completely understand the multitude of phenomena that occur in fluid mechanics. Even though the basic equations have been written, it often happens that their solution can be obtained, if at all, only by employing simplifying assumptions.

A derivation of a basic law is really the mathematical formulation of the relationships between several physical concepts. As we formulate the laws, we want to pay particular attention to the nature of such concepts as surface force, work, and heat flux. The final form of the laws will be differential equations that are valid at every point in the continuum.

There are three major independent dynamical laws in continuum mechanics: the continuity equation, momentum equation, and energy equation. These laws are formulated in the first part of this chapter. There are several additional laws that may be derived from the momentum equation. The first of these governs kinetic energy, the second angular momentum, and the third vorticity. The first two are treated in this chapter; the law governing vorticity is introduced in Chapter 13. The last law we study in this chapter is the second law of thermodynamics. In the final sections we give the integral or global forms of the laws and jump conditions that apply across discontinuities.

5.1 CONTINUITY EQUATION

The equation derived in this section has been called the *continuity equation* to emphasize that the continuum assumptions (the assumption that density and velocity may be defined at every point in space) are prerequisites. The continuum assumption is, of course, a foundation for all the basic laws. The physical principle underlying the equation is the conservation of mass. It may be stated in terms of a material region as follows: *The time rate of change of the mass of a material region is zero.* The mass of the material region (MR) is computed by integrating the density over the region. Thus, in mathematical terms we have

$$\frac{dM_{MR}}{dt} = \frac{d}{dt} \int_{MR} \rho \, dV = 0 \tag{5.1.1}$$

The bounding surface of the material region is moving with the local fluid velocity v_i (Fig. 5.1). We use Leibnitz's theorem (Eq. 3.13.2) with $w_i = v_i$ to move the time differentiation inside the integral:

$$\int_{MR} \partial_0 \rho \, dV + \int_{MR} n_i v_i \rho \, dS = 0 \tag{5.1.2}$$

Next, the theorem of Gauss changes the surface integral into a volume integral:

$$\int_{MR} [\partial_0 \rho + \partial_i (\rho v_i)] \, dV = 0 \tag{5.1.3}$$

(Note that this equation applies at every instant, and thus the restriction to a material region is no longer necessary. We could, in principle, choose a different region for each instant in time. The material region has already played out its role in that the surface velocity in Eq. 5.1.2 is the fluid velocity v_i.) Since the specific choice of the integration region is arbitrary, the only way Eq. 5.1.3 can be true is if the integrand is zero. It cannot happen that the integrand is positive in one part of the region and negative in another so that they always cancel out. If there were a part of space where the integrand was positive (say), we could immediately choose that place as the region of integration and violate Eq. 5.1.3. Thus, the integrand is identically zero everywhere and is the differential form of the continuity equation:

$$\partial_0 \rho + \partial_i (\rho v_i) = 0 \tag{5.1.4}$$

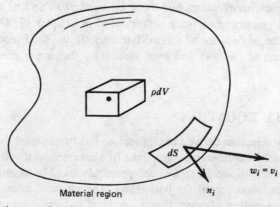

ρdV

dS

$w_i = v_i$

n_i

Material region

Figure 5.1 Continuity equation for a material region. Surface velocity is equal to fluid velocity.

or in symbolic notation,

$$\frac{\partial \rho}{\partial t} + \nabla \cdot (\rho \mathbf{v}) = 0$$

The special form of Eq. 5.1.4 for incompressible flow is $\nabla \cdot \mathbf{v} = 0$.

To get a better physical understanding of the terms in the continuity equation, let us evaluate the equation at point P in the center of a fixed differential volume element $\Delta x \, \Delta y \, \Delta z$. If we multiply Eq. 5.1.4 by $\Delta x \, \Delta y \, \Delta z$, the first term will be (for this example we employ x, y, z instead of 1, 2, 3)

$$\frac{\partial}{\partial t} (\rho \, \Delta x \, \Delta y \, \Delta z) \qquad (5.1.5)$$

The physical interpretation of ρ is the mass per unit volume, and $\Delta x \, \Delta y \, \Delta z$ is the volume of the fixed element. So their product is the mass of the fixed element. We then interpret the original term $\partial_0 \rho$ as the rate of change of mass per unit volume at a fixed point in space (Fig. 5.2).

The next term in Eq. 5.1.4 is actually three terms. Writing them out produces

$$\partial_i(\rho v_i) = \partial_x(\rho v_x) + \partial_y(\rho v_y) + \partial_z(\rho v_z)$$

We take the first term as typical, multiply it by $\Delta x \, \Delta y \, \Delta z$, and group the symbols as follows:

$$\frac{\partial}{\partial x} (\rho v_x \, \Delta y \, \Delta z) \, \Delta x \qquad (5.1.6)$$

The product $v_x \, \Delta y \, \Delta z$ is the volume flow rate across a $\Delta y \, \Delta z$ surface. Multiplying by ρ gives the mass flow rate $\rho v_x \, \Delta y \, \Delta z$. The net mass flow rate out of the element through the two surfaces $\Delta y \, \Delta z$ is given by $\partial_x(\rho v_x \, \Delta y \, \Delta z) \, \Delta x$. This is readily seen by computing the mass flow rate at each surface and subtracting. Consider the mass flow through the

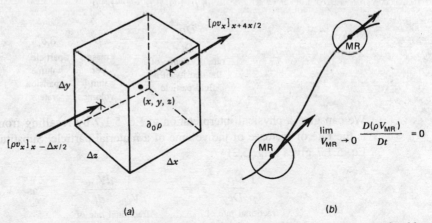

(a)   (b)

Figure 5.2 Interpretation of the differential continuity equation: (a) for an element fixed in space; (b) for a fluid particle.

surfaces at $x + \Delta x/2$ and $x - \Delta x/2$. The net difference is

$$\rho v_x|_{x+\Delta x/2}\, \Delta y\, \Delta z - \rho v_x|_{x-\Delta x/2}\, \Delta y\, \Delta z$$

Expand these terms in a Taylor series about x, and keep only the terms that will not drop out if we divide by $\Delta x\, \Delta y\, \Delta z$ and go to the limit $\Delta x \to 0$:

$$\left\{ \left[\rho v_x + \frac{\partial}{\partial x}(\rho v_x)\left(x + \frac{\Delta x}{2} - x\right) + \cdots \right] \right.$$
$$\left. - \left[\rho v_x + \frac{\partial}{\partial x}(\rho v_x)\left(x - \frac{\Delta x}{2} - x\right) + \cdots \right] \right\} \Delta y\, \Delta z$$

or

$$\underline{\frac{\partial}{\partial x}(\rho v_x)\, \Delta x\, \Delta y\, \Delta z}$$

Thus, Eq. 5.1.6 has the physical interpretation as the net x-direction mass flow rate out of the element. The other two terms, $\partial_y(\rho v_y)$ and $\partial_z(\rho v_z)$, are the net mass flow rates out of the element in the y- and z-directions, respectively. All these terms are called *convective terms* and represent the net rate of mass efflux out of the element. From the point of view of a fixed point in space, the continuity equation 5.1.4 is a balance between the rate of accumulation of mass and the net outflow:

$$\underset{\substack{\text{rate of accumulation}\\ \text{of mass per unit}\\ \text{volume at } P}}{\partial_0 \rho} + \underset{\substack{\text{net flow of}\\ \text{mass out of } P\\ \text{per unit volume}}}{\partial_i(\rho v_i)} = 0 \qquad (5.1.4)$$

The continuity equation may also be viewed from the standpoint of a material particle moving through the flow. Differentiate the second term in Eq. 5.1.4 and identify the substantial derivative (Eq. 4.3.5):

$$\partial_0 \rho + v_i \partial_i \rho = -\rho \partial_i v_i$$

$$\underset{\substack{\text{rate of change of}\\ \text{the density of a}\\ \text{fluid particle}}}{\frac{D\rho}{Dt}} = - \underset{\substack{\text{mass}\\ \text{per}\\ \text{unit}\\ \text{volume}}}{\rho} \underset{\substack{\text{particle}\\ \text{volume}\\ \text{expansion}\\ \text{rate}}}{\partial_i v_i} \qquad (5.1.7)$$

We can give a physical interpretation to Eq. 5.1.7 by recalling from Eq. 4.8.5 that $\nabla \cdot \mathbf{v}$ is the rate of increase of the volume of a material particle. Substitution of Eq. 4.8.5 into Eq. 5.1.7 gives (Fig. 5.2)

$$\underset{\substack{\text{fractional rate of}\\ \text{change of the density}\\ \text{of a material particle}}}{\frac{1}{\rho}\frac{D\rho}{Dt}} = - \underset{\substack{\text{fractional rate of}\\ \text{change of the volume}\\ \text{of a material particle}}}{\frac{1}{V_{MR}}\frac{dV_{MR}}{dt}} \qquad \text{as} \quad V_{MR} \to 0 \qquad (5.1.8)$$

The change in density of a particle is due entirely to changes in its volume. Equation 5.1.8 implies that the mass of a material particle ρV_{MR} is a constant.

5.2 MOMENTUM EQUATION

The momentum equation for a continuum is the analogue of Newton's second law for a point mass. It is not possible to derive the momentum equation from Newton's second law because the concepts of point mass and of continuum are distinctly different. The momentum principle is: *The time rate of change of the linear momentum of a material region is equal to the sum of the forces on the region.* Two types of forces may be imagined: body forces, which act on the bulk of the material in the region, and surface forces, which act at the boundary surface. We let F_i stand for a body force per unit mass and R_i stand for a surface force per unit area. The net force on the region consists of the two integrals (see Fig. 5.3),

$$\text{net force on material region} = \int_{\mathrm{MR}} \rho F_i \, dV + \int_{\mathrm{MR}} R_i \, dS$$

Next we must compute the momentum within the region. We usually think of the velocity v_i as the rate of change of position, but v_i can also play the role of the i-direction momentum per unit mass. The product ρv_i is the i-direction momentum per unit volume. Therefore, $\rho v_i \, dV$ is the i-direction momentum within the element dV. The rate of change of momentum of the region is computed as

$$\text{rate of change of momentum of a material region} = \frac{d}{dt} \int_{\mathrm{MR}} \rho v_i \, dV$$

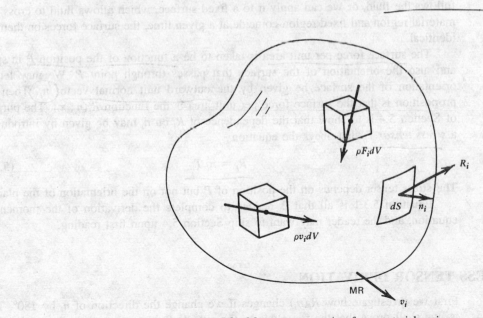

Figure 5.3 Momentum equation for a material region.

The momentum principle is then given by

$$\frac{d}{dt} \int_{MR} \rho v_i \, dV = \int_{MR} \rho F_i \, dV + \int_{MR} R_i \, dS \qquad (5.2.1)$$

The left-hand side can be changed by using Leibnitz's and Gauss's theorems as we did for the continuity equation. The result is

$$\int [\partial_0(\rho v_i) + \partial_j(\rho v_j v_i)] \, dV = \int \rho F_i \, dV + \int R_i \, dS \qquad (5.2.2)$$

This is not the final form of the equation; however, it is as far as we can proceed without knowing some details about the surface force R_i.

5.3 SURFACE FORCES

When we construct an imaginary closed surface, it divides the fluid into its inside and outside portions. The direct action of the outside fluid on the inside fluid is replaced by the concept of a surface force. Essentially, we imagine the outside fluid has vanished and been replaced by forces to produce the actual effect on the inside fluid. Surface forces are really momentum and force effects at the microscopic level. Although we speak of fluids, the results are applicable to solids as well.

The surface force concept is instantaneous. We construct the imaginary surface and evaluate the force at an instant in time. The bulk motion of the fluid or solid plays no direct role in this process. Neither does the prescription of the surface motion as a function of time. We can apply the surface force concept to a material surface, which follows the fluid, or we can apply it to a fixed surface, which allows fluid to cross. If a material region and fixed region coincide at a given time, the surface forces on them are identical.

The surface force per unit area is taken to be a function of the position P in space and also the orientation of the surface that passes through point P. We may let the orientation of the surface be given by the outward unit normal vector n_i. Then our proposition is that the surface force per unit area is the function $R_i(n_i; x_i)$. The purpose of Section 5.4 is to show that the dependence of R_i on n_i may be given by introducing a *stress tensor* T_{ij} that obeys the equation

$$R_j = n_i T_{ij} \qquad (5.3.1)$$

The stress tensor depends on the position of P but not on the orientation of the plane.

Equation 5.3.1 is all that is needed to complete the derivation of the momentum equation, and the reader may want to skip Section 5.4 upon first reading.

*5.4 STRESS TENSOR DERIVATION

First we investigate how $R_i(n_i)$ changes if we change the direction of n_i by 180°. That is, we shall prove that the force due to the outside fluid on the inside is exactly equal and opposite to the force due to the inside fluid on the outside. Consider a small volume centered at point P (Fig. 5.4). The two ends are parallel with area ΔS and located a distance $\Delta\ell$ apart. The normal vector for side 1 is n_i^{I} and that for side 2 is $n_i^{\mathrm{II}} = -n_i^{\mathrm{I}}$. The perimeter of ΔS is denoted by s, and the normal vector at any point on the side is n_i^{III}. We write the momentum equation 5.2.2 for this region using the mean value theorem for the integrals,

$$[\partial_0(\rho v_i) + \partial_j(\rho v_j v_i)]^* \, \Delta S \, \Delta\ell = (\rho F_i)^* \, \Delta S \, \Delta\ell + R_i^*(n_i^{\mathrm{I}}) \, \Delta S$$

$$+ R_i^*(n_i^{\mathrm{II}}) \, \Delta S + R_i^*(n_i^{\mathrm{III}})s \, \Delta\ell \qquad (5.4.1)$$

Here $R_i^*(n_i^{\mathrm{I}})$ stands for the stress on the surface with normal n_i^{I}. The asterisks indicate a mean value somewhere within the region of integration. As the region is shrunk to zero thickness ($\Delta\ell \rightarrow 0$), the body force and inertia terms drop out, leaving the surface forces in exact balance, that is,

$$0 = R_i^*(n_i^{\mathrm{I}}) \, \Delta S + R_i^*(n_i^{\mathrm{II}}) \, \Delta S \qquad (5.4.2)$$

Now letting $\Delta S \rightarrow 0$ requires that the mean values on both faces take on the value of R_i at point P. Letting $n_i = n_i^{\mathrm{I}} = -n_i^{\mathrm{II}}$ yields

$$R_i(n_i) = -R_i(-n_i) \qquad (5.4.3)$$

This proves that the force due to the inside fluid on the outside fluid is equal and opposite to the force due to the outside fluid on the inside fluid.

We proceed to see how the stress on a plane of arbitrary direction is related to the stress on planes in the coordinate direction. Figure 5.4*b* shows a tetrahedron with three surfaces ΔS_1, ΔS_2, and ΔS_3 parallel with the coordinate planes. The triangular face ΔS has the unit normal vector n_i and the unit normals in the coordinate directions are a_i, b_i, and c_i. Let ΔL be some typical dimension of the tetrahedron. We will let $\Delta L \rightarrow 0$ while keeping the same direction n_i for the triangular face. The volume of the tetrahedron is

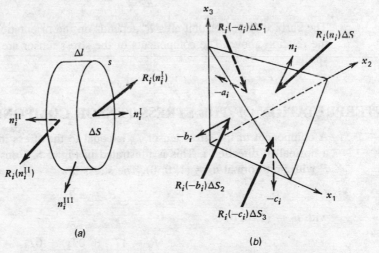

(a)

(b)

Figure 5.4   Surface forces: (*a*) on opposite sides of a surface; (*b*) on the faces of a tetrahedron.

proportional to $(\Delta L)^3$, and all the surfaces are proportional to $(\Delta L)^2$. If we write the momentum equation 5.2.2 for the region and again estimate the integrands by mean values, the equation will take the form

$$(\text{inertia terms})*(\Delta L)^3 = (\text{body force term})*(\Delta L)^3 + (\text{surface force terms})*(\Delta L)^2 \quad (5.4.4)$$

Dividing by $(\Delta L)^2$ and letting $\Delta L \to 0$ shows that the surface forces are in exact balance:

$$0 = (\text{surface force terms})* \qquad (5.4.5)$$

Writing out the surface forces explicitly produces the equation

$$0 = R_i^*(n_i)\,\Delta S + R_i^*(-a_i)\,\Delta S_1 + R_i^*(-b_i)\,\Delta S_2 + R_i^*(-c_i)\,\Delta S_3 \qquad (5.4.6)$$

The next step is to relate the side areas to the top area ΔS. In Chapter 3 (Eq. 3.12.6) we proved that the i-component of the unit normal vector times the area equals the projection of the area on an i-plane. Applying this to the tetrahedron gives

$$n_1\,\Delta S = \Delta S_1$$

$$n_2\,\Delta S = \Delta S_2 \qquad (5.4.7)$$

$$n_3\,\Delta S = \Delta S_3$$

Substituting Eq. 5.4.7 into Eq. 5.4.6, using the fact that $R_i(n_i) = -R_i(-n_i)$, and letting $\Delta S \to 0$ yields

$$R_i(n_i) = n_1 R_i(a_i) + n_2 R_i(b_i) + n_3 R_i(c_i) \qquad (5.4.8)$$

This equation has exactly the same form as Eq. 3.9.9, which defines a tensor. We can see this if we change the notation by letting the stresses associated with the x_i-plane be $R_i(a_i) = T_{1i}$, $R_i(b_i) = T_{2i}$, and $R_i(c_i) = T_{3i}$. Equation 5.4.8 can now be written as

$$R_i(n_i) = n_1 T_{1i} + n_2 T_{2i} + n_3 T_{3i}$$

$$R_i = n_j T_{ji} \qquad (5.4.9)$$

The surface force per unit area R_i depends on the orientation of the plane through P by the relation above. The components of the stress tensor are functions of the position in space.

5.5   INTERPRETATION OF THE STRESS TENSOR COMPONENTS

A component of the stress tensor T_{ij} is equal to the stress in direction j on a plane with a normal in direction i. This is illustrated in Fig. 5.5. Consider an x_2–x_3 plane through P with unit normal $n_i = (1, 0, 0)$. The stress law

$$R_j = n_i T_{ij} \qquad (5.3.1)$$

with $n_i = (1, 0, 0)$ is

$$R_j = 1 T_{1j} + 0 T_{2j} + 0 T_{3j}$$

and stress components become

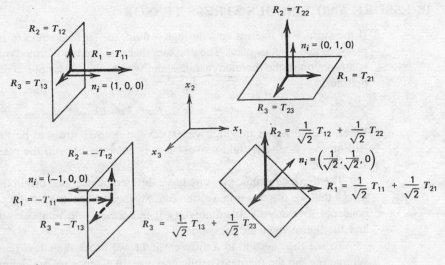

Figure 5.5   Surface forces related to components of the stress tensor for different orientations of the surface.

$$R_1 = T_{11} \qquad R_2 = T_{12} \qquad R_3 = T_{13} \qquad (5.5.1)$$

Similarly, for a plane with normal $n_i = (0, 1, 0)$ the stress components are

$$R_1 = T_{21} \qquad R_2 = T_{22} \qquad R_3 = T_{23} \qquad (5.5.2)$$

The components of T_{ij} are sometimes loosely called "stresses," but they are not actually the stresses. However, under certain conditions they are equal to the stresses. The stress R_i is related to the stress tensor T_{ij} by $R_j = n_i T_{ij}$. For example, consider again an x_2–x_3 plane, but this time take the normal to the left, $n_i = (-1, 0, 0)$. This reverses the designations of the inside and outside of the plane. Now from $R_j = n_i T_{ij}$ we have

$$R_1 = -T_{11} \qquad R_2 = -T_{12} \qquad R_3 = -T_{13} \qquad (5.5.3)$$

For this plane the stresses are equal to the negative of the stress tensor components.

One final example will close this section. Let us find the stress on a plane with normal $(1/\sqrt{2}, 1/\sqrt{2}, 0)$. Evaluating the components of $R_j = n_i T_{ij}$, we find that

$$
\begin{aligned}
n_i &= \left(\tfrac{1}{\sqrt{2}}, \tfrac{1}{\sqrt{2}}, 0\right) \\
R_j &= \left(\tfrac{1}{\sqrt{2}}, \tfrac{1}{\sqrt{2}}, 0\right) T_{ij}
\end{aligned}
$$

$$R_1 = \frac{1}{\sqrt{2}} T_{11} + \frac{1}{\sqrt{2}} T_{21}$$

$$R_2 = \frac{1}{\sqrt{2}} T_{12} + \frac{1}{\sqrt{2}} T_{22} \qquad (5.5.4)$$

$$R_3 = \frac{1}{\sqrt{2}} T_{13} + \frac{1}{\sqrt{2}} T_{23}$$

These components are shown in Fig. 5.5.

5.6   PRESSURE AND VISCOUS STRESS TENSOR

If the surface of interest cuts through a fluid, the surface stress R_i is further divided into pressure and viscous parts. The pressure that was used in thermodynamical equation 2.4.2 is a function of the thermodynamic state. We use the subscript t to denote thermodynamic pressure:

$$p_t = f(e, \rho) \qquad (5.6.1)$$

When a fluid is not moving, we expect the normal stress to be the pressure. Will this still be true when the fluid moves? If it is not true, how do the pressure and the normal stress differ?

The thermodynamic pressure has a different conceptual origin than that of the surface forces that we discussed in Section 5.5. Surface forces in $R_i = n_j T_{ji}$ are mechanical force concepts. Because of this ambiguity it is necessary to relate the normal surface stress and the thermodynamic pressure.

To see the question in a different light, we break the stress tensor into two parts by subtracting out the thermodynamic pressure. In essence we are defining the *viscous stress tensor* τ_{ij} by the equation

$$T_{ij} = -p_t \delta_{ij} + \tau_{ij} \qquad (5.6.2)$$

When a substance is not moving, we know that the normal stress is the same as the thermodynamic pressure. This requirement implies that the viscous stress τ_{ij} must vanish when there is no motion.

In general, the normal stress is the sum of the pressure and a normal viscous stress. For planes with normals in the coordinate directions the normal stresses are

$$\begin{cases} R_1 = T_{11} = -p_t + \tau_{11} \\ R_2 = T_{22} = -p_t + \tau_{22} \\ R_3 = T_{33} = -p_t + \tau_{33} \end{cases} \qquad (5.6.3)$$

Normal viscous stresses are frequently small compared to the pressure, so it is common to neglect τ_{11} in comparison with p_t in many engineering calculations (when the Reynolds number is large). However, there is an easily imagined experiment that illustrates a situation where the normal viscous stress is important. When we pour a very viscous liquid such as honey from a jar, the Reynolds number is small and the column of fluid obviously does not accelerate as fast as the local acceleration of gravity. A falling ball accelerates much more rapidly than the honey falling from the jar. The force that retards the honey column is an imbalance in the normal viscous force. If one were to cut the column instantaneously, the two parts would separate because the normal viscous tension stress would no longer retard the lower part.

Unlike the pressure, the normal stress can have different values for different directions of the vector n_i. We can average the normal surface force and call this average the mechanical pressure p_m. This average gives

$$p_m \equiv -\tfrac{1}{3}(T_{11} + T_{22} + T_{33}) = -\tfrac{1}{3} T_{ii} \qquad (5.6.4)$$

An incompressible fluid (a thermodynamic term) does not have a thermodynamic pressure, but it does have a mechanical pressure. When we are dealing with an incompressible fluid, the pressure variable is always interpreted as the mechanical pressure.

For a compressible fluid, what is the difference between the mechanical pressure and the thermodynamic pressure? As a first approximation, people proposed that the difference between the pressures is a linear function of the rate of expansion (Eq. 4.8.5). If the rate of expansion is zero, the fluid is behaving as if it were incompressible. So in this sense the assumption is consistent. Mathematically, the assumption is

$$p_m - p_t = \kappa \nabla \cdot \mathbf{v} = -\frac{\kappa}{\rho}\frac{D\rho}{Dt} \tag{5.6.5}$$

The coefficient κ is called the *bulk viscosity*. The second relation is obtained by using continuity equation 5.1.7. For common fluids it is nearly always assumed that κ is zero; thus, $p_m = p_t$, and there is no need to distinguish between mechanical and thermodynamic pressure. This is called *Stokes's assumption*.

Stokes's assumption implies that the average normal viscous stress is zero. To show this, we take the trace of Eq. 5.6.2 and divide by 3:

$$\tfrac{1}{3}T_{ii} = -p_t + \tfrac{1}{3}\tau_{ii} = 0$$

By Stokes's assumption,

$$p_t = p_m = -\tfrac{1}{3}T_{ii}$$

Combining the relations above, we find the desired result:

$$0 = \tau_{ii} = \tau_{11} + \tau_{22} + \tau_{33}$$

This is an equivalent statement of Stokes's assumption. We discus this assumption further in Chapter 6.

5.7 DIFFERENTIAL MOMENTUM EQUATION

The derivation of the differential momentum equation, which was started in Section 5.2, can now be completed. Substitution of the surface stress equation 5.3.1 into Eq. 5.2.2 and application of Gauss's theorem to the surface force yields

$$\int [\partial_0(\rho v_i) + \partial_j(\rho v_j v_i) - \rho F_i - \partial_j T_{ji}]\, dV = 0 \tag{5.7.1}$$

Since the region of integration is arbitrary, the integrand must be zero everywhere. Hence,

$$\partial_0(\rho v_i) + \partial_j(\rho v_j v_i) = \rho F_i + \partial_j T_{ji} \tag{5.7.2}$$

We can now introduce the pressure and viscous stress tensor by substituting Eq. 5.6.2 into Eq. 5.7.2. The result is

$$\partial_0(\rho v_i) + \partial_j(\rho v_j v_i) = \rho F_i - \partial_i p + \partial_j \tau_{ji}$$

In symbolic notation the equation is

$$\frac{\partial}{\partial t}(\rho \mathbf{v}) + \nabla \cdot (\rho \mathbf{v}\mathbf{v}) = -\nabla p + \nabla \cdot \tau + \rho \mathbf{F} \qquad (5.7.3)$$

This equation and the continuity equation are two of the most important equations of fluid mechanics.

To get a better idea of the physical role of each symbol in the momentum equation, we again consider an elementary cube $\Delta x\, \Delta y\, \Delta z$ located at the fixed point P (Fig. 5.6). We shall rederive the momentum equation by counting up the forces and momentum fluxes for this cube. This type of derivation is frequently shown in elementary books. It is not as general as the derivation given above, but it has the advantage of displaying the physical meaning of the terms from the point of view of a fixed position in space.

First, consider that the i-direction momentum within $\Delta x\, \Delta y\, \Delta z$ is given by

$$(\rho v_i)^*\, \Delta x\, \Delta y\, \Delta z$$

where the asterisk indicates an average value that exists somewhere within the region. In this term, ρv_i has the physical interpretation of the i-direction momentum per unit volume. The rate of change of i-momentum within the fixed region of space $\Delta x\, \Delta y\, \Delta z$ is

$$\Delta x\, \Delta y\, \Delta z\, \partial_0 (\rho v_i)^* \qquad (5.7.4)$$

We see that if Eq. 5.7.4 is divided by $\Delta x\, \Delta y\, \Delta z$ and then the element is shrunk to zero size, the average value must occur at point P. This results in the first term of Eq. 5.7.2; $\partial_0(\rho v_i)$ is the rate of increase of i-momentum per unit volume at point P.

Next, we consider the fact that i-momentum is carried into and out of the fixed region by fluid flow across the surfaces. Across face I of Fig. 5.6 there is a mass flow of $\rho v_x\, \Delta y\, \Delta z$, carrying with it the i-momentum v_i per unit mass. Hence, across this face the i-momentum going into the region is

$$(\rho v_x v_i)_{\mathrm{I}}^*\, \Delta y\, \Delta z \qquad (5.7.5)$$

If $i = x$, the flow carries x-momentum across the face; if $i = y$ (that is, $\rho v_x v_y$), the flow ρv_x carries y-momentum. On face II, which is on the opposite side of the cube, a flow ρv_x carries i-momentum out of the region. Instead of evaluating this on face II, we expand $\rho v_x v_i$ using a Taylor series from face I to face II; that is,

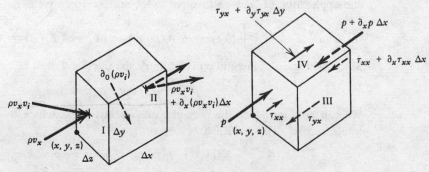

Figure 5.6   Interpretation of the differential momentum equation for a fixed element.

$$(\rho v_x v_i)^*_{\mathrm{II}} \, \Delta y \, \Delta z = (\rho v_x v_i)^*_{\mathrm{I}} \, \Delta y \, \Delta z + \frac{\partial}{\partial x} (\rho v_x v_i)^* \, \Delta x \, \Delta y \, \Delta z + O[\Delta x^2 \, \Delta y \, \Delta z] \quad (5.7.6)$$

The net i-momentum crossing the surface of the fixed region by fluid flow across faces I and II is found when Eq. 5.7.6 is subtracted from Eq. 5.7.5. the result is

$$-\frac{\partial}{\partial x} (\rho v_x v_i)^* \, \Delta x \, \Delta y \, \Delta z + O(\Delta x^2 \, \Delta y \, \Delta z)$$

Thus, the term $-\partial_x(\rho v_x v_i)$ is the net convection of i-momentum into a fixed unit volume at P by x-direction flow.

Fluid also flows across the Δx–Δz faces with a flow rate ρv_y. This leads to a net convection of i-momentum:

$$-\frac{\partial}{\partial y} (\rho v_y v_i)^* \, \Delta x \, \Delta y \, \Delta z + O[\Delta y^2 \, \Delta x \, \Delta z]$$

Similarly, across the two Δx–Δy surfaces, the net i-momentum gain by flow in the z-direction is

$$-\frac{\partial}{\partial z} (\rho v_z v_i)^* \, \Delta z \, \Delta y \, \Delta x + O[\Delta z^2 \, \Delta x \, \Delta y]$$

When the three terms above are divided by $\Delta x \, \Delta y \, \Delta z$ and the limit $\Delta x, \Delta y, \Delta z \to 0$ is taken, the higher-order terms go to zero, leaving

$$-\partial_j(\rho v_j v_i) \quad \text{or} \quad \nabla \cdot (\rho \mathbf{v}\mathbf{v}) \qquad (5.7.7)$$

as the net rate of increase of i-momentum because of fluid flow into a fixed unit volume.

Next we turn our attention to the forces. Forces that act on the cube are the body and surface forces. The body force is

$$(\rho F_i)^* \, \Delta x \, \Delta y \, \Delta z \qquad (5.7.8)$$

where F_i represents the force per unit mass. This is the most convenient terminology, since the weight of an object, $W_i = Mg_i$, is given on a unit-mass basis by $F_i = g_i$.

Surface forces on the element consist of pressure and viscous forces; that is, $R_i = -n_i p + n_k \tau_{ki}$. On face I the pressure force is $p_{\mathrm{I}}^* \, \Delta y \, \Delta z$. Counteracting this force is a force on face II,

$$-p_{\mathrm{II}}^* \, \Delta y \, \Delta z = -\left(p_{\mathrm{I}}^* + \frac{\partial p^*}{\partial x} \Delta x \right) \Delta y \, \Delta z + O[\Delta x^2 \, \Delta y \, \Delta z] \qquad (5.7.9)$$

The net unbalanced force $(p_{\mathrm{I}}^* - p_{\mathrm{II}}^*) \, \Delta y \, \Delta z$ is

$$-\frac{\partial p_{\mathrm{I}}^*}{\partial x} \Delta x \, \Delta y \, \Delta z + O[\Delta x^2 \, \Delta y \, \Delta z] \qquad (5.7.10)$$

Division by $\Delta x \, \Delta y \, \Delta z$ and letting $\Delta x, \Delta y, \Delta z \to 0$ produces $-\partial p / \partial x$. This is the x-direction pressure force on the unit element. Repeating the reasoning for pairs of faces in the Δy- and Δz-directions leads to a net i-direction pressure force equal to the gradient.

$$-\partial_i p \quad \text{or} \quad -\nabla p \tag{5.7.11}$$

The normal viscous force τ_{xx} acts on faces I and II in exactly the same way that the pressure does. Hence, corresponding to Eq. 5.7.10, we have a net x-direction force of

$$\frac{\partial \tau_{xx}}{\partial x} \Delta x \, \Delta y \, \Delta z + O[\Delta x^2 \, \Delta y \, \Delta z] \tag{5.7.12}$$

The sign is positive for a tension force.

Also acting in the x-direction are shear forces on the side surfaces. On face III the force is $-\tau_{yx}^* \, \Delta x \, \Delta z$. The companion force on face IV is

$$\tau_{yx}|_{\text{IV}} \, \Delta x \, \Delta z = \tau_{yx}^*|_{\text{III}} \, \Delta x \, \Delta z + \frac{\partial \tau_{yx}^*}{\partial y} \Delta y \, \Delta x \, \Delta z + \cdots$$

The net x-direction shear force for faces III and IV is

$$\frac{\partial \tau_{yx}^*}{\partial y} \Delta x \, \Delta y \, \Delta z + O[\Delta y^2 \, \Delta z \, \Delta x]$$

The remaining two faces, V and VI, produce the x-direction force

$$\frac{\partial \tau_{zx}^*}{\partial z} \Delta z \, \Delta x \, \Delta y + O[\Delta z^2 \, \Delta x \, \Delta y]$$

The total x-direction viscous forces for the element, after the limit has been taken, add up to $\partial_j(\tau_{jx})$. Similar expressions exist for the y- and z-direction viscous forces. In general, the i-direction viscous forces per unit volume at point P are

$$\partial_j \tau_{ji} \quad \text{or} \quad \nabla \cdot \tau \tag{5.7.13}$$

We put all of the preceding effects together to form the momentum equation,

$$\underset{\substack{\text{rate of} \\ i\text{-momentum} \\ \text{increase at} \\ \text{fixed point } P}}{\partial_0(\rho v_i)} + \underset{\substack{\text{net rate} \\ i\text{-momentum} \\ \text{is carried into } P \\ \text{by fluid flow } \rho v_j}}{\partial_j(\rho v_j v_i)} = \underset{\substack{i \\ \text{body} \\ \text{force} \\ \text{at } P}}{\rho F_i} - \underset{\substack{\text{net } i \\ \text{pressure} \\ \text{force} \\ \text{at } P}}{\partial_i p} + \underset{\substack{\text{net } i \\ \text{viscous} \\ \text{force} \\ \text{at } P}}{\partial_j \tau_{ji}} \tag{5.7.14}$$

All terms are on a unit-volume basis because we divided by $\Delta x \, \Delta y \, \Delta z$.

We may also interpret the momentum equation from the viewpoint of a material particle moving in the flow. In fact, this is a general procedure that can be applied to any conservation law. Consider the left-hand side in Eq. 5.7.14 and replace v_i with an arbitrary function $Q_{\ell m \ldots}$. The terms can be rearranged as follows:

$$\partial_0(\rho Q_{\ell m \ldots}) + \partial_j(\rho v_j Q_{\ell m \ldots})$$

$$= Q_{\ell m \ldots}[\partial_0 \rho + \partial_j(\rho v_j)] + \rho \, \partial_0 Q_{\ell m \ldots} + \rho v_j \, \partial_j Q_{\ell m \ldots}$$

$$= \rho \frac{D Q_{\ell m \ldots}}{Dt} \tag{5.7.15}$$

The term in brackets is zero by the continuity equation, and the last two terms are by definition the substantial derivative. Thus, the final form for the particle viewpoint is

$$\rho \frac{Dv_i}{Dt} = \rho \, \partial_0 v_i + \rho v_j \, \partial_j v_i = -\partial_i p + \partial_j \tau_{ji} + \rho F_i$$

(5.7.16)

$$\rho \left[\frac{\partial \mathbf{v}}{\partial t} + (\mathbf{v} \cdot \nabla)\mathbf{v} \right] = -\nabla p + \nabla \cdot \tau + \rho \mathbf{F}$$

This equation states that the mass per unit volume (ρ) times the acceleration of a material particle (Dv_i/Dt) is equal to the net force acting on the particle. This is *Newton's law* for a continuum particle. Note that the forces are the same whether we interpret the inertia terms from the viewpoint of a fixed point in space (Eq. 5.7.14) or from the viewpoint of a moving material particle (Eq. 5.7.16). Forces act instantaneously without regard to the past or future position of the volume or surface used for their evaluation. They have no memory or ability to anticipate the motion of the surface. Our choice for the surface motion can play no essential role in force concepts.

In Newton's mechanics, particles are of finite size with a fixed mass M. Their momentum is governed by the equation

$$M \frac{dv_i}{dt} = \sum \mathscr{F}_i$$

(5.7.17)

Sometimes students are introduced to this equation as stating that the rate of change of momentum is equal to the net forces:

$$\frac{d}{dt}(Mv_i) = \sum \mathscr{F}_i$$

(5.7.18)

Equation 5.7.18 is correct, since the mass is a constant. The reason that Eq. 5.7.18 is used is that it leads one more naturally to treat momentum as a fundamental property on the microscopic scale. Also, when relativity is considered, it is easier to modify Eq. 5.7.18 to the proper form. What is not proper on the continuum scale is to say that Eq. 5.7.18 is the more basic form and that Eq. 5.7.17 results as a special case for finite particles of constant mass. In Section 5.15, where global forms of the equations are applied to several problems, we study the motion of a uniformly evaporating drop. The results of that problem show that Eq. 5.7.17 governs the motion of the droplet even when the mass is changing. Thus, Eq. 5.7.18 does not describe continuum particles with variable mass.

*5.8   MOMENT OF MOMENTUM, ANGULAR MOMENTUM, AND SYMMETRY OF T_{ij}

On the microscopic scale the angular momentum equation is an independent law. In continuum mechanics we shall find that the linear momentum equation may be used to derive a moment of momentum equation that is the same as the angular momentum equation. Thus they are not independent. There is one "if" in this statement. If the angular momentum of the microscopic particles is randomly oriented, the vector sum for a large number of particles will be zero. On the other hand, if we imagine that the microscopic particles have their axes of rotation aligned in a special direction, the summation will give a net angular momentum on the continuum level. If this were the case, we would need to postulate a surface couple in addition to the surface force. Fortunately, in common fluids the microscopic angular momentum is randomly oriented and the couple does not exist. When this is true, the stress tensor T_{ij} is symmetric.

First consider the moment of momentum equation. Forming the cross product of the momentum equation, Eq. 5.7.2, with the distance vector from the origin $\mathbf{r}$ derives this equation. The algebra requires that one recognize the position vector $r_i = x_i$ is independent of time and that $\partial_i r_j = \delta_{ij}$.

$$\frac{\partial(\rho \varepsilon_{ijk} r_j v_k)}{\partial t} + \partial_p [\rho v_p (\varepsilon_{ijk} r_j v_k)] = \varepsilon_{ijk} r_j \partial_p T_{pk} + \rho \varepsilon_{ijk} r_j \mathbf{F}_k \qquad (5.8.1)$$

The angular momentum of the bulk motion, $\mathbf{r} \times \mathbf{v}$, is changed by torques of surface and body forces. Any origin is permitted for $\mathbf{r}$. The integral form of this equation is useful in the analysis of rotating machines.

If molecules comprising the continuum are spinning in a preferred direction, the sum of their angular momentum would not be zero. Let the net internal angular momentum per unit mass be $\tilde{\mathbf{a}}$. Moreover, angular momentum crossing an imaginary surface by molecular transport (diffusion) would produce a surface couple $n_j \Omega_{ji}$. We can also propose that an external physical process ρG_i would impart angular momentum directly to the individual particles. Conservation of total angular momentum, $\mathbf{r} \times \mathbf{v} + \tilde{\mathbf{a}}$, leads to the equation

$$\frac{\partial(\rho \varepsilon_{ijk} r_j v_k + \rho \tilde{a}_i)}{\partial t} + \partial_p [\rho v_p (\varepsilon_{ijk} r_j v_k + \tilde{a}_i)]$$

$$= \rho \varepsilon_{ijk} r_j F_k + \partial_p (\varepsilon_{ijk} r_j T_{pk}) + \rho G_i + \partial_j \Omega_{jk} \qquad (5.8.2)$$

Conservation of total angular momentum is a distinct physical law from linear momentum.

Subtracting the moment of momentum equation, Eq. 5.8.1, from Eq. 5.8.2 yields a relation governing internal angular momentum.

$$\frac{\partial(\rho \tilde{a}_i)}{\partial t} + \partial_p(\rho v_p \tilde{a}_i) = \varepsilon_{ijk} T_{jk} + \rho G_i + \partial_j \Omega_{jk} \qquad (5.8.3)$$

It is usually assumed that the molecular angular momentum is randomly distributed so that $\tilde{\mathbf{a}} = 0$ and furthermore $\mathbf{G}$ and $\mathbf{\Omega}$ are zero. Then $\varepsilon_{ijk} T_{jk} = 0$ and T_{ij} must be symmetric. Symmetry of $\mathbf{T}$ will be assumed from here on.

5.9   ENERGY EQUATION

The first law of thermodynamics states that the increase in energy of a material region is the result of work and heat transfers to the region. We discuss each of these concepts separately before combining them as required by the first law.

The energy of a material region contains contributions from all motions of the matter contained in it. The internal energy consists of microscopic motions such as random translation motion, molecular vibrations, molecular rotation, and any other microscopic energy modes. The sum of all these energies is the absolute thermodynamic internal energy e. The second form of energy is the kinetic energy of the bulk motion. For a unit mass this is $\frac{1}{2}v_iv_i = \frac{1}{2}v^2$. With these two forms of energy the total energy of the material region is (Fig. 5.7)

$$\text{total energy of material element } dV = \rho(e + \tfrac{1}{2}v^2)\,dV \tag{5.9.1}$$

A third type of energy is sometimes associated with the material. This is the potential energy that arises from a body force field. A conservative force field will allow a representation by a potential. Gravity may be represented by $F_i = g\partial_i Z$, where $Z(x_i)$ is the height above a reference plane. We have a choice of either considering that the potential energy $Z(x_i)$ is associated with the gravity field or of computing the work done by the force. We shall take the latter route.

Work is the energy change when a force causes material to move. Before we formulate this concept for a continuum, let us review how work is formulated in classical particle mechanics. If we take Newton's law for a solid particle, $M\,dv_i/dt = \mathscr{F}_i$, and multiply both sides by v_i, we arrive at

$$M\frac{d}{dt}\left(\frac{1}{2}v_iv_i\right) = v_i\mathscr{F}_i$$

The work rate is the projection of the force along the instantaneous direction of the velocity. Only this component of the force increases the kinetic energy of the particle. The component of force perpendicular to v_i causes the trajectory to curve, but it does not increase the kinetic energy. Hence, it does no work.

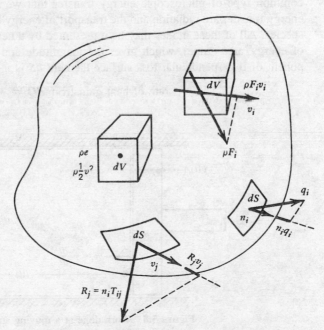

Figure 5.7   Energy equation for a material region.

The rate of work in a continuum is simply the component of the force in the direction of motion times the velocity of the matter. For the gravity force this is

$$\text{work rate of } \rho F_i \text{ on element } dV = \rho v_i F_i \, dV \qquad (5.9.2)$$

Similarly, the surface force (both pressure and viscous) at dS produces

$$\text{work rate of } R_i \text{ at element } dS = v_i R_i \, dS = n_j T_{ji} v_i \, dS \qquad (5.9.3)$$

Note that the past or future motion of the surface dS has nothing to do with the work. The important thing is the velocity of the material, not the velocity of the surface.

As an example, let us compute the work done by a piston moving into a cylinder as shown in Fig. 5.8. The position of the piston is $\ell(t)$, and the area is A. The piston force on the region is $p(t)A$. The matter at the sidewalls does not move, so the work is done only at the piston face. At the piston face, the fluid velocity is the same as the piston velocity. The work rate is then

$$\dot{W} = A p(t) \frac{d\ell}{dt}$$

From time 1 to time 2 the work is the formula familiar to thermodynamics

$$_1W_2 = \int_{t_1}^{t_2} \dot{W} \, dt = \int_{t_1}^{t_2} pA \frac{d\ell}{dt} \, dt = \int_{\ell_1}^{\ell_2} pA \, d\ell = \int_{V_1}^{V_2} p \, dV$$

We are now obligated to consider p as a function of V.

Heat transfer is the second way in which energy is transferred into a region. The heat flux is the sum of all microscopic modes of energy transfer. Conduction is the most common type of microscopic energy transfer that we shall encounter. Other modes of energy transfer are radiation and the transport of energy by diffusion of different chemical species. All of these modes may be represented by a heat flux vector $\mathbf{q}$ (with dimensions of energy/area $\cdot$ time), which gives the magnitude and direction of the flux. The component of $\mathbf{q}$ perpendicular to a surface element dS is $n_i q_i$; thus,

$$\text{rate of heat gain from } dQ = -n_i q_i \, dS \qquad (5.9.4)$$

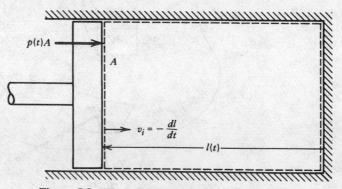

Figure 5.8 Work done at a moving solid boundary.

It is a matter of convention to define **q** as positive for a heat flux from the inside of the surface to the outside.

We are now ready to formulate the energy equation. *The rate of change of energy within a material region is equal to the rate that energy is received by heat and work transfers.* The mathematical statement is

$$\frac{d}{dt} \int_{MR} \rho \left(e + \frac{1}{2} v^2 \right) dV = -\int_{MR} n_i q_i \, dS + \int_{MR} n_i T_{ij} v_j \, dS + \int_{MR} \rho F_i v_i \, dV \quad (5.9.5)$$

At this point the mathematical processes are familiar. Using Leibnitz's and Gauss's theorems on the left-hand side and converting the surface integrals on the right-hand side with Gauss's theorem, we get an equation containing only volume integrals. The integrand of this equation is the energy equation. It is

$$\partial_0[\rho(e + \tfrac{1}{2}v^2)] + \partial_i[\rho v_i(e + \tfrac{1}{2}v^2)] = -\partial_i q_i + \partial_i(T_{ij}v_j) + \rho v_i F_i \quad (5.9.6)$$

In symbolic notation the energy equation is

$$\frac{\partial}{\partial t}\left[\rho\left(e + \frac{1}{2}v^2\right)\right] + \nabla \cdot \left[\rho\mathbf{v}\left(e + \frac{1}{2}v^2\right)\right] = -\nabla \cdot \mathbf{q} + \nabla \cdot (\mathbf{T} \cdot \mathbf{v}) + \rho\mathbf{v} \cdot \mathbf{F}$$

| rate of increase of energy per unit volume | convection of energy into a point by flow | net heat flow | work of surface forces | work of body forces |

$$(5.9.7)$$

This is the differential equation governing the total energy at any point in the continuum. The energy equation is not generally used in this form, but is split into two equations: the mechanical energy equation and the thermal energy equation. We discuss these equations in Section 5.10.

5.10 MECHANICAL AND THERMAL ENERGY EQUATIONS

The equation that governs kinetic energy is not an independent law but is derived from the momentum equation. The dot product of v_i with the momentum equation (and some algebraic manipulation) will yield the mechanical (kinetic) energy equation. It has the form

$$\partial_0\left(\rho \frac{1}{2}v^2\right) + \partial_i\left(\rho v_i \frac{1}{2}v^2\right) = -v_i\partial_i p + v_i\partial_j\tau_{ji} + \rho v_i F_i$$

$$\frac{\partial}{\partial t}\left(\rho \frac{1}{2}v^2\right) + \nabla \cdot \left(\rho\mathbf{v}\frac{1}{2}v^2\right) = -\mathbf{v} \cdot \nabla p + \mathbf{v} \cdot (\nabla \cdot \boldsymbol{\tau}) + \rho\mathbf{v} \cdot \mathbf{F}$$

$$(5.10.1)$$

Note that all of the work of the body force goes to accelerate the fluid and increase its kinetic energy.

The thermal energy equation is obtained by subtracting the mechanical energy equation from the total energy equation (Eq. 5.9.7). The result is

$$\partial_0(\rho e) + \partial_i(\rho v_i e) = -p\partial_i v_i + \tau_{ji}\partial_j v_i - \partial_i q_i \tag{5.10.2}$$

When this equation is written in symbolic notation (it is customary to employ the fact that τ_{ij} is symmetric so that $\tau_{ji}\partial_j v_i = \tau_{ij}\partial_j v_i = \boldsymbol{\tau}{:}\nabla\mathbf{v}$)

$$\rho\frac{De}{Dt} = \frac{\partial}{\partial t}(\rho e) + \nabla\cdot(\rho v e) = -p\nabla\cdot\mathbf{v} + \boldsymbol{\tau}{:}\nabla\mathbf{v} - \nabla\cdot\mathbf{q} \tag{5.10.3}$$

Note that all of the heat flux goes to increase the internal energy.

As with the continuity and momentum equations (see Eq. 5.7.15), the mechanical and thermal energy equations can be put into forms containing the substantial derivative.

The surface work terms in Eqs. 5.9, 5.10.1, and 5.10.2 are very interesting. The total work of surface forces may be split into two parts: pressure work and viscous work. Then these terms may be split again as diagrammed below:

$$
\partial_i(T_{ij}v_j)
\begin{cases}
\begin{array}{ccccc}
 & & ① & & ② \\
-\partial_j(pv_j) = & & -p\partial_j v_j & - & v_j\,\partial_j p \\
\text{pressure} & & \text{force} & & \text{velocity} \\
\text{work} & & \text{times} & & \text{times} \\
 & & \text{deformation} & & \text{force imbalance} \\
 & & \text{increases} & & \text{increases} \\
 & & \text{internal} & & \text{kinetic} \\
 & & \text{energy} & & \text{energy} \\
 & & & & \\
 & & ③ & & ④ \\
\partial_i(\tau_{ij}v_j) = & & \tau_{ij}\,\partial_i v_j & + & v_j\,\partial_i\tau_{ij} \\
\text{viscous} & & & & \\
\text{work} & & & &
\end{array}
\end{cases}
$$

(with $\partial_i(T_{ij}v_j)$ labeled "work of surface forces")

Terms 2 and 4 are the velocity times gradients of forces. The gradients indicate an imbalance in the forces that directly accelerates the fluid and increases its kinetic energy. Thus, these terms appear in the mechanical energy equation. Terms 1 and 3 are forces multiplied by fluid deformations. They occur in the thermal energy equation. Recall that $\partial_i v_i$ has the physical interpretation of the volumetric rate of expansion or contraction. Thus, term 1 is the heating or cooling of the fluid by compression or expansion, depending on the sign of $\partial_i v_i$. This is a reversible process. Term 3 is called *viscous dissipation*. It is responsible for heat generation in bearings and aerodynamic heating of spacecraft as they reenter Earth's atmosphere. Since τ_{ij} is symmetric, the product $\tau_{ij}\partial_i v_j$ is equal to $\tau_{ij}\partial_{(i}v_{j)}$ (see Eq. 3.6.8). This helps the physical understanding, as we recognize $\partial_{(i}v_{j)} = S_{ij}$ as the strain rate tensor. Thus, one may write $\boldsymbol{\tau}{:}\nabla\mathbf{v} = \boldsymbol{\tau}{:}\mathbf{S}$. Viscous dissipation is always positive and produces internal energy. This is an irreversible process, as we shall see when we study the entropy equation. In summary, surface forces have two effects: forces times deformations change the internal energy, while the velocity times an unbalanced force accelerates the fluid to change its kinetic energy.

Sometimes the work term in the kinetic energy equation is replaced by $v_j\partial_i\tau_{ij} = \partial_i(\tau_{ij}v_j) - \tau_{ij}\partial_i v_j$. This might be done for mathematical reasons. The difficulty with this form is that one is tempted to imagine a two-step process where all of the shear work accelerates the fluid, then subsequently kinetic energy of motion is changed into thermal energy by viscous dissipation. In actuality, only the unbalanced forces $\partial_i\tau_{ij}$ accelerate the fluid.

5.11 ENERGY EQUATION WITH TEMPERATURE AS THE DEPENDENT VARIABLE

In the most useful form of the thermal energy equation, temperature replaces internal energy as the major variable. Consider the definition of enthalpy, $h = e + \rho^{-1}p$. The differential is

$$de = dh - \rho^{-1}\,dp + \rho^{-2}p\,d\rho$$

Inserting Eq. 2.9.5 and regarding the variables as functions of space and time gives us

$$\frac{De}{Dt} = c_p\frac{DT}{Dt} - \rho^{-1}\beta T\frac{Dp}{Dt} + \rho^{-2}\,p\,\frac{D\rho}{Dt}$$

Using the continuity equation 5.1.7 to change the last term and combining with Eq. 5.10.3 yields the final result (using $\boldsymbol{\tau}{:}\nabla\mathbf{v} = \boldsymbol{\tau}{:}\mathbf{S}$):

$$\rho c_p\frac{DT}{Dt} = -\nabla\cdot\mathbf{q} + \boldsymbol{\tau}{:}\mathbf{S} + \beta T\frac{Dp}{Dt} \tag{5.11.1}$$

Thermodynamic equation-of-state information enters this equation through $c_p(p, T)$ and $\beta(p, T)$. The specific heat has not been assumed to be constant.

*5.12 SECOND LAW OF THERMODYNAMICS

The fundamental differential equation of thermodynamics (Eq. 2.7.2) and the energy equation can be combined to form an equation governing entropy. The thermodynamic equation is written in substantial derivative form,

$$T\frac{Ds}{Dt} = \frac{De}{Dt} - \frac{p}{\rho^2}\frac{D\rho}{Dt} \tag{5.12.1}$$

The last term is changed by using the continuity equation 5.1.7:

$$\rho T\frac{Ds}{Dt} = \rho\frac{De}{Dt} + p\nabla\cdot\mathbf{v} \tag{5.12.2}$$

Substituting thermal energy equation 5.10.3 into Eq. 5.12.2 yields

$$\rho\frac{Ds}{Dt} = -\frac{1}{T}\nabla\cdot\mathbf{q} + \frac{1}{T}\boldsymbol{\tau}{:}\mathbf{S} \tag{5.12.3}$$

To facilitate the physical interpretation we rewrite Eq. 5.12.3 using the identity $\nabla\cdot(\mathbf{q}/T) = (1/T)\,\nabla\cdot\mathbf{q} - (1/T^2)\mathbf{q}\cdot\nabla T$:

$$\rho\frac{Ds}{Dt} = -\nabla\cdot\frac{\mathbf{q}}{T} - \frac{1}{T^2}\,\mathbf{q}\cdot\nabla T + \frac{1}{T}\boldsymbol{\tau}{:}\mathbf{S} \tag{5.12.4}$$

The first term on the right-hand side is the entropy change of a material particl   a reversible effect of heat transfer. The sign of this term changes with the sign of th   at flux. The second and third terms are always positive. They represent irreversible increases in entropy because of heat transfer and viscous dissipation. The third irreversible process (in a nonreacting fluid) is due to diffusion. It does not appear, because have not allowed the fluid to be a chemical mixture of varying composition. The entropy equation shows that the flow of a fluid without viscosity and heat conduction must be isentropic.

The second law of thermodynamics is obtained by neglecting the second two irreversible terms, which are always positive, and changing the equal sign:

$$\rho \frac{Ds}{Dt} \geq - \nabla \cdot \frac{\mathbf{q}}{T} \qquad (5.12.5)$$

The integral form of the entropy equation is derived by the procedure that is given in the next section. The result is

$$\frac{d}{dt} \int_{AR} \rho s \, dV = - \int_{AR} \rho n_i (v_i - w_i) s \, dS - \int_{AR} \frac{\rho \, n_i q_i}{T} \, dS$$

$$- \int_{AR} \frac{1}{T^2} q_i \partial_i T \, dV + \int_{AR} \frac{1}{T} \tau_{ij} S_{ji} \, dV \qquad (5.12.6)$$

The effects of the volume integrals are irreversible.

5.13   INTEGRAL FORM OF THE CONTINUITY EQUATION

Frequently, we are interested in applying the basic laws to a finite region. Such equations are called *global equations* or simply *integral forms* of the equations. We have already postulated the integral forms for the special case of a material region. Here we extend the continuity law so that it applies to a region with arbitrary motion. The motion of the region is specified by w_i, the arbitrarily chosen velocity of its surface.

The starting point of the derivation is Leibnitz's rule for differentiating an integral over an arbitrary region (AR) that has limits that depend on time (Eq. 3.13.2):

$$\frac{d}{dt} \int_{AR} f \, dV = \int_{AR} \frac{\partial f}{\partial t} \, dV + \int_{AR} n_i w_i f \, dS$$

Let us choose $f = \rho$ and substitute the continuity equation 5.1.4 for $\partial_0 \rho$ in the volume integral on the right-hand side. This yields

$$\frac{d}{dt} \int_{AR} \rho \, dV = - \int_{AR} \partial_i (\rho v_i) \, dV + \int_{AR} n_i w_i \rho \, dS \qquad (5.13.1)$$

Application of Gauss's theorem and collecting terms gives the mass conservation law for a region with arbitrary motion:

$$\frac{d}{dt} \int_{AR} \rho \, dV = - \int_{AR} \rho (v_i - w_i) n_i \, dS \qquad (5.13.2)$$

The rate of change of mass within the region is equal to the integral of the mass flow relative to the moving boundary. The special cases of a material region or a fixed region are obtained by choosing $w_i = v_i$ or $w_i = 0$, respectively.

As an example, consider the container of cross-sectional area A_0 being filled with water from a pipe as shown in Fig. 5.9. The inflow pipe has an area A_1 and the average

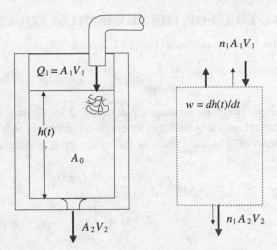

Figure 5.9   A cylinder with an orifice in the bottom being filled with a liquid.

inflow velocity is V_1. An orifice at the bottom of the tank, area A_2, allows water to exit at a velocity V_2. At any time the height of fluid in the container is $h(t)$, which is the object of the analysis. Let the arbitrary region be the water within the container so that the mass of water is $M = \rho A_0 h$ and the velocity of the region at 1 is $w = dh/dt$. Global mass balance equation 5.13.2 for this region is

$$\frac{d}{dt}(\rho A_0 h) = + \rho \left(V_1 - \frac{dh}{dt} \right) A_1 - \rho A_2 V_2 \qquad (5.13.3)$$

Simplifying the expression gives

$$\frac{d}{dt}(h) = \frac{V_1 A_1 - V_2(t) A_2}{A_0 - A_1} \qquad (5.13.4)$$

To find $h(t)$, we need detailed information about how $V_2(t)$ is related to $h(t)$.

The exact history of the continuity principle is not known. Although early Romans tried to tax users according to the amount of water the users received, they did not really understand the continuity law and the relationship between velocity, area, and flow rate. The first known accurate quantitative statements of the continuity principle are those of Leonardo da Vinci (see Rouse and Ince, 1957; Truesdell, 1968). Da Vinci was a keen observer of fluid motions and made many statements that showed his understanding of continuity. For example, he wrote: "By so much as you will increase the river in breadth, by so much you will diminish the speed of its course." He may even have been aware of the unsteady effects: "If the water is not added to or taken away from the river, it will pass with equal quantities in every degree of its length . . . ." Subsequent to da Vinci, the principle was probably rediscovered by many others.

5.14 INTEGRAL FORM OF THE MOMENTUM EQUATION

The Leibnitz theorem (Eq. 3.13.2) with $T_{ij\ldots} = \rho v_i$ is (for a region with arbitrary motion)

$$\frac{d}{dt} \int_{AR} \rho v_i \, dV = \int_{AR} \partial_0(\rho v_i) \, dV + \int_{AR} n_j w_j \rho v_i \, dS$$

We solve the momentum equation 5.7.2 for $\partial_0(\rho v_i)$, substitute in the equation above, and convert as many volume integrals as possible into surface integrals by using Gauss's theorem. The final result is the momentum principle for a region with arbitrary motion:

$$\frac{d}{dt} \int_{AR} \rho v_i \, dV = - \int [\rho n_j(v_j - w_j)v_i] \, dS + \int \rho F_i \, dV$$

$$+ \int_{\substack{\text{fluid} \\ \text{surfaces}}} (n_j \tau_{ji} - n_i p) \, dS + \int_{\substack{\text{solid} \\ \text{surfaces}}} n_j T_{ji} \, dS \qquad (5.14.1)$$

The rate of change of momentum within the region is equal to the rate that momentum is convected across the surface by the relative mass flow plus the sum of the forces. The surface force terms have been written in two parts. The part where fluid exists at the surface has been split into pressure and viscous forces, while the total stress concept is retained for regions where a solid exists at the surface.

It is interesting that the motion of the region does not affect the forces, nor does it influence the momentum instantaneously within the region. The motion of the surface has its only effect (other than the integration limit, of course) in the convection of matter in or out of the region; $\rho n_i(v_i - w_i)$. Moreover, any motion along the surface that we might assign to the surface velocity w_i (i.e., a sliding motion perpendicular to n_i) is irrelevant. Only the normal component $n_i w_i$ appears in the equation. The special cases of a material region ($w_i = v_i$) and a fixed region ($w_i = 0$) are readily found from Eq. 5.14.1.

For the first example we consider the steady flow of water in the reducing elbow shown in Fig. 5.10. We wish to find the forces in the bolts that are required to hold the flange in place. Let us apply the x component of Eq. 5.14.1 to a region that cuts across the flanges as shown. This region is chosen because all along the surface we either know the conditions or want to know something. In this example we want to know the force in the bolts; hence, the control region should be chosen to cut through the bolts.

The storage term on the left of Eq. 5.14.1 is zero because of the steady flow. On the right-hand side, the convection term $\rho n_j v_j v_x \, dS$ represents x momentum of the flow crossing the surface; flow rate $\rho n_j v_j \, dS$ times momentum per unit mass v_x. The sign of the first part, $\rho n_j v_j = \rho |n|\|v| \cos \theta$, depends only on the angle θ between n_j and v_j, therefore being positive for outflow. At point 1, $n_j v_j = -V_1$ and at point 2, $n_j v_j = V_2$. On the other hand, the sign of v_x depends on our choice of the positive x-direction. At point 1, $v_x = V_1$ and at point 2, $v_x = -\sin \alpha V_2$.

Next consider the forces. First note that if a constant atmospheric pressure was imagined to act entirely around the surface, it would have no net effect [$p_{\text{atm}} \int n_i \, dS = 0$]. Hence, we assume that atmospheric pressure is subtracted from all surface pressures, and thus we may use gauge pressures in our evaluation. At point 1 the pressure acts in the x-direction, while at point 2 $- \int n_x p \, dS = p_{2g} \sin \alpha A_2$. One can regard $n_x(p \, dS)$ as the x-component of force $p \, dS$ or $p(n_x \, dS)$ as the pressure times the projected area n_x

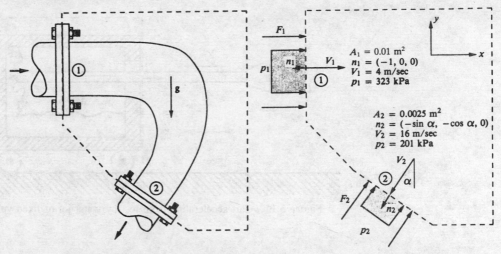

Figure 5.10   Momentum analysis of water flow through a reducing elbow.

dS. Where the surface of the analysis region cuts through the bolts there is a stress that produces the x-direction force $n_i T_{ix} dS$. Actually, the bolts are overtightened to compress the flange so we are really finding only the net force. Assume that the bolts transfer only normal forces F_1 and F_2; then the x-component is $F_x = F_1 + F_2 \sin \alpha$ (in any event there is a net force with a component F_x). The complete x momentum equation reads (note that p_g is the gauge pressure at section 1.)

$$0 = -\rho(-V_1)V_1 A_1 - \rho V_2(-V_2 \sin \alpha)A_2 + \rho_{1g}A_1 + p_{2g} (\sin \alpha) A_2 + F_x$$

$$-F_x = 999 \times 4^2 \times 0.01 + 999 \times 16^2 \times 0.707 \times 0.0025 + (323 - 101) \times 10^3$$

$$\times 0.01 + (201 - 101) \times 10^3 \times 0.707 \times 0.0025$$

$$-F_x = 3009 \text{ N} \tag{5.14.2}$$

If the weight of the elbow were given, one could find the vertical component of F_2, and hence F_1 could be found.

For the second example, consider a water jet shooting horizontally (no gravity) into a cart that captures all the incoming liquid as shown in Fig. 5.11. Initially, the cart is stationary and the mass is M_0. We wish to find the cart velocity $W(t)$ and mass $M(t)$ for given jet velocity V_{jet} and area A_{jet}. Choose a control region that surrounds and moves with the cart. The continuity equation 5.13.2 becomes

$$\frac{dM}{dt} = \rho(V_{jet} - W)A_{jet} \tag{5.14.3}$$

In the momentum equation we neglect any aerodynamic drag along with friction of the wheels. Furthermore, we assume, although the water is sloshing around in the cart, that the average velocity of all material within the cart is W.

Hence, the momentum equation 5.14.1 is

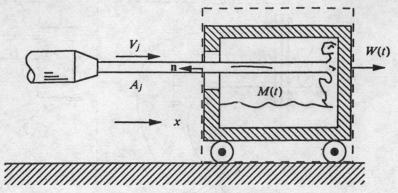

Figure 5.11   Cart accelerating from rest by water jet of fixed velocity.

$$\frac{d(MW)}{dt} = \rho(V_{\text{jet}} - W)V_{\text{jet}}A_{\text{jet}} \tag{5.14.4}$$

This can be simplified by employing Eq. 5.14.3 to get

$$M\frac{d(W)}{dt} = \rho(V_{\text{jet}} - W)^2 A_{\text{jet}}$$

Since V_{jet} is a constant, the form above suggests that it would be useful to introduce a variable that indicates the defect of the cart velocity from the ultimate speed V_{jet}. Let

$$\hat{W} \equiv V_{\text{jet}} - W \tag{5.14.5}$$

One can now simplify and again use Eq. 5.14.3 to arrive at

$$M\frac{d(\hat{W})}{dt} = -\hat{W}\frac{d(M)}{dt}$$

Time may be eliminated and the equation integrated to

$$\hat{W} = V_{\text{jet}}\frac{M_0}{M} \tag{5.14.6}$$

Inserting this into Eq. 5.14.3 yields the final result:

$$\frac{\hat{W}}{V_{\text{jet}}} = \frac{M_0}{M} = \left(1 + 2\,\frac{\rho A_{\text{jet}}V_{\text{jet}}}{M_0}\,t\right)^{-1/2} \tag{5.14.7}$$

If aerodynamic drag and wheel friction are accounted for, a computer solution is needed.

   This analysis can also be done using special equations for a *volume region,* which are given in Problem 5.19.

*5.15 MOMENTUM EQUATION FOR A DEFORMABLE PARTICLE OF VARIABLE MASS

An arbitrary control region is shown in Fig. 5.12. We let r_i stand for the position vector and define the mass M, the center of mass R_i, the velocity of the center of mass $\dot{R}_i$, and the momentum P_i of the region by integrals over the region:

$$M = \int \rho \, dV, \qquad R_i = \frac{1}{M} \int \rho r_i \, dV$$

$$\dot{R}_i = \frac{dR_i}{dt}, \qquad P_i = \int \rho v_i \, dV \qquad (5.15.1)$$

Later we shall need the continuity equation 5.13.2 for the region. It is

$$\frac{dM}{dt} = -\int \rho n_j (v_j - w_j) \, dS \qquad (5.15.2)$$

Another preliminary step is to find a relation between the momentum P_i of the region and the mass times the velocity of the center of mass, MR_j. Consider Leibnitz's theorem applied to the definition of MR_i,

$$\frac{d}{dt}(MR_i) = \frac{d}{dt} \int \rho r_i \, dV = \int \partial_0(\rho r_i) \, dV + \int n_j w_j \rho r_i \, dS \qquad (5.15.3)$$

Now by using the product rule for differentiation, we have the identity (note that $\partial_j r_i = \partial_j x_i = \delta_{ji}$)

$$\partial_j(r_i \rho v_j) = r_i \, \partial_j(\rho v_j) + \rho v_j \, \partial_j r_i$$

$$= r_i \, \partial_j(\rho v_j) + \rho v_i$$

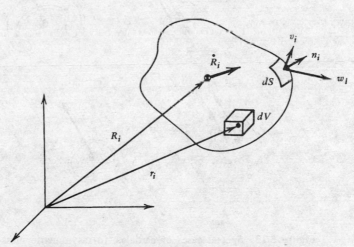

Figure 5.12 Finite deformable particle of variable mass.

Moreover, since the position vector $r_i = x_i$ is independent of time, $\partial_0(\rho r_i) = r_i \partial_0 \rho$. By the continuity equation this becomes $\partial_0(\rho r_i) = -r_i \partial_j(\rho v_j)$. Combining this with the result above shows that

$$\partial_0(\rho r_i) = -\partial_j(r_i \rho v_j) + \rho v_i$$

Substituting the expression above into Eq. 5.15.3 produces

$$M\frac{dR_i}{dt} + R_i\frac{dM}{dt} = \int [-\partial_j(r_i\rho v_j) + \rho v_i]\, dV + \int n_j w_j \rho r_i\, dS$$

The first volume integral is converted to a surface integral, and the continuity equation 5.15.2 is used to obtain the desired relation [· indicates $d(\ )/dt$]:

$$M\dot{R}_i = P_i - \int \rho(r_i - R_i)n_j(v_j - w_j)\, dS \qquad (5.15.4)$$

The mass times the velocity of the center of mass of a region is not necessarily equal to the momentum of the region if the region gains or loses mass.

The effect of the integral term in Eq. 5.15.4 is depicted in Fig. 5.13a. Consider a region that surrounds a liquid every particle of which is moving with a constant velocity $v_i = V_i$. The momentum is $P_i = MV_i$. At the back of the region small particles of liquid are being stripped away and leave the control region. Consequently, the center of mass of the region must move forward; thus, $R_i > V_i$, and $M\dot{R}_i > MV_i = P_i$. The integral term in Eq. 5.15.4 accounts for the fact that the center of mass of the region may move due to an asymmetric loss of mass from the region.

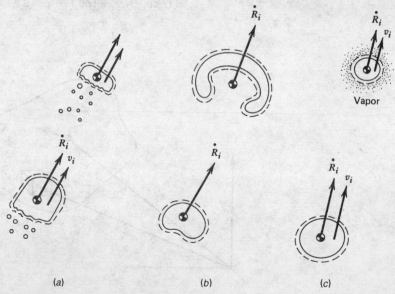

Figure 5.13 Special cases of particles: (a) asymmetric mass loss; (b) deforming particle; (c) vaporizing particle.

The momentum equation will be considered next. Introducing the definition of P_i into Eq. 5.14.1 gives

$$\frac{dP_i}{dt} = -\int \rho n_j (v_j - w_j) v_i \, dS + F_i^{(p)} + F_i^{(\nu)} + F_i^{(b)} \tag{5.15.5}$$

For convenience the following forces have been defined:

$$F_i^{(p)} = -\int n_i p \, dS, \qquad F_i^{(\nu)} = \int n_j \tau_{ji} \, dS, \qquad F_i^{(b)} = \int \rho F_i \, dV$$

In Eq. 5.15.5 the momentum P_i is eliminated in favor of R_i by substituting Eq. 5.15.4. The continuity equation 5.15.2 is employed to yield the final form,

$$M\ddot{R}_i = F_i^{(p)} + F_i^{(\nu)} + F_i^{(b)} - \int \rho n_j (v_j - w_j)(v_i - \dot{R}_i) \, dS$$

$$+ \frac{d}{dt} \int \rho n_j (v_j - w_j)(r_i - R_i) \, dS \tag{5.15.6}$$

This is the momentum equation for a finite-size deformable particle of variable mass.

The first integral accounts for momentum $v_i - \dot{R}_i$ that leaves the region with the mass flux $\rho n_j (v_j - w_j) \, dS$. Physically, this is a jet or rocket effect. The second integral accounts for the movement of the center of mass due to an asymmetric mass loss.

Several special cases will help interpret the momentum equation. In Fig. 5.13b a droplet of liquid moving in a gas is envisioned. Allow the droplet to deform but not to vaporize. Since there is no mass leaving the region, Eq. 5.15.6 is

$$M\ddot{R}_i = F_i^{(p)} + F_i^{(\nu)} + F_i^{(b)} \tag{5.15.7}$$

The mass times the acceleration of the center of mass equals the forces. Also, from Eq. 5.15.5 we see that $M\dot{R}_i = P_i$. If the droplet breaks into several parts, the control volume following the various parts, Eq. 5.15.7 is still true. The center of mass of the parts obeys Eq. 5.15.7.

Next, we consider a droplet that has an unusual shape and is also vaporizing. Furthermore, we assume that the liquid velocity at the surface is exactly equal to the velocity of the center of mass (Fig. 5.13b). For this example the first integral in Eq. 5.15.5 vanishes, but we are left with the second integral, which describes the movement of the center of mass because of shape changes.

Finally, we consider a spherical droplet (Fig. 5.13c) with the assumption that the vaporization is uniform and the fluid velocity is again uniform; hence, $v_i = \dot{R}_i$. In Eq. 5.15.6 the second integral becomes [let the uniform vaporization velocity be $\dot{m}/A = \rho n_j (v_j - w_j)$]

$$\frac{d}{dt} \left[\frac{\dot{m}}{A} \int (r_i - R_i) \, dS \right]$$

For every surface element of dS and a positive value of $r_i - R_i$ there is a symmetrically positioned element with a negative value. Therefore, the integral over the surface is zero. The final equation for a vaporizing droplet is exactly the same as Eq. 5.15.7 for a non-vaporizing droplet:

$$M \frac{d^2 R_i}{dt^2} = F_i^{(p)} + F_i^{(\nu)} + F_i^{(b)} \tag{5.15.8}$$

If vaporization is not uniform, the droplet is propelled by the jet effect and the full Eq. 5.15.6 must be used.

The proper form of the momentum equation for a deforming particle (control region) of variable mass is a relatively recent advance (see, e.g., Thorpe, 1962). It was clarified only after problems of rockets and space vehicles became important.

*5.16   ENERGY EQUATION IN INTEGRAL FORM

Any local differential law may be cast into an integral form for an arbitrary region. The procedure is to take f as the quantity of interest in Leibnitz's theorem, substitute the differential law for $\partial_0 f$, and convert all volume integrals of the form $\partial_i(\ ) \, dV$ into surface integrals.

The energy equation is derived in a similar fashion. Let $Z(x_i)$ be the distance above a horizontal reference plane in a gravity field with acceleration g. If we incorporate the potential $Z(x_i)$ for the gravity force, $F_i = -\partial_i(gZ)$, and let $e_t \equiv e + \frac{1}{2}v^2 + gZ$, the equation is

$$\frac{d}{dt} \int_{AR} \rho e_t \, dV + \int \mathbf{n} \cdot (\mathbf{v} - \mathbf{w}) \rho e_t \, dS$$

$$= -\int \mathbf{n} \cdot \mathbf{q} \, dS + \int_{\text{fluid}} \mathbf{n} \cdot \tau \cdot \mathbf{v} \, dS - \int_{\text{fluid}} \mathbf{n} \cdot \mathbf{v} p \, dS + \int_{\text{solid}} \mathbf{n} \cdot \mathbf{T} \cdot \mathbf{v} \, dS \tag{5.16.1}$$

The work of surface forces has been split into fluid and solid parts. Work of a rotating or translating shaft would appear as $\mathbf{n} \cdot \mathbf{T} \cdot \mathbf{v}$.

In engineering thermodynamics the work of the pressure forces is usually represented by two effects: flow work and moving boundary work. Note that the identity $\mathbf{v} = (\mathbf{v} - \mathbf{w}) + \mathbf{w}$ allows one to replace the pressure work term in Eq. 5.16.1 with

$$\int_{\text{fluid}} \mathbf{n} \cdot \mathbf{v} p \, dS = \int_{\text{fluid}} \mathbf{n} \cdot (\mathbf{v} - \mathbf{w}) \rho \frac{p}{\rho} \, dS + \int_{\text{fluid}} \mathbf{n} \cdot \mathbf{w} p \, dS$$

The first integral is the flow work imagined to push the fluid into the region, and the second term is the work performed by the moving boundary. This is an arbitrary decomposition based on historical developments.

The kinetic energy equation 5.10.1 can also be cast into an integral form. In doing so, it is customary to use the identities

$$v_i \partial_i p = \partial_i (v_i p) - p \partial_i v_i \quad \text{and} \quad v_i \partial_j \tau_{ji} = \partial_j (\tau_{ji} v_i) - \tau_{ji} \partial_j v_i$$

Thus we are replacing the pressure work that accelerates the fluid with the total work minus the compression work. Also, the accelerating shear work is replaced by the total shear work minus the viscous dissipation. The final equation reads

$$\frac{d}{dt} \int_{AR} \rho \, \frac{1}{2} \, v^2 \, dV = - \int_{AR} \rho n_i (v_i - w_i) \frac{1}{2} v^2 \, dS + \int_{AR} \rho F_i v_i \, dV$$

$$- \int_{AR} (n_i v_i p - n_i \tau_{ij} v_j) \, dS + \int_{AR} (p \partial_i v_i - \tau_{ij} \partial_i v_j) \, dV \quad (5.16.2)$$

The volume integral with $p \partial_i v_i$ is zero in incompressible flow, since $\partial_i v_i = 0$. Also in incompressible flow the body force term can be replaced by a potential (see Eq. 7.2.2). We defer giving examples until Sections 7.2 and 19.9 to 19.12.

5.17   JUMP EQUATIONS AT INTERFACES

Fluid–solid and fluid–fluid interface were discussed qualitatively in Section 1.5. The major interfaces characteristics are a jump in the density and continuity of the tangential velocity (no-slip). Let us imagine that material properties change smoothly through the interface as depicted in Fig. 5.14. This viewpoint is needed because the Leibnitz theorem as expressed in Eq. 3.10.2 requires continuous functions. The control region follows the interface with a velocity **w** (in the normal direction), and we denote the normal vectors as $\mathbf{n} = \mathbf{n}_{II} = -\mathbf{n}_I$. The global continuity equation 5.13.2 is

$$\frac{d}{dt} \int \rho \, dV = - \int_{II} \mathbf{n} \cdot (\mathbf{v} - \mathbf{w}) \rho \, dS + \int_I \mathbf{n} \cdot (\mathbf{v} - \mathbf{w}) \, \rho \, dS$$

As a final step we will let the thickness of the region approach zero and assume that the mass within the interface is zero:

$$0 = - \int \left\{ [\mathbf{n} \cdot (\mathbf{v} - \mathbf{w})\rho]_{II} - [\mathbf{n} \cdot (\mathbf{v} - \mathbf{w})\rho]_I \right\} \, dS \quad (5.17.1)$$

Hence, at any point on the interface,

$$[(v_n - w)\rho]_{II} = [(v_n - w)\rho]_I \quad (5.17.2)$$

A jump in the normal velocity is necessary because of the density jump.

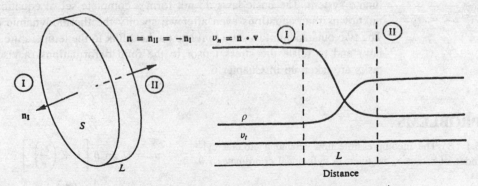

Figure 5.14   Analysis of a jump discontinuity in flow properties.

Repeating the arguments above for the momentum equation, Eq. 5.14.1, and assuming that no sources of momentum exist within the interface produces

$$0 = -\int \left\{ [(v_n - w)\rho\mathbf{v} + \mathbf{n}p - \mathbf{n} \cdot \boldsymbol{\tau}]_{\text{II}} - [(v_n - w)\rho\mathbf{v} + \mathbf{n}p - \mathbf{n} \cdot \boldsymbol{\tau}]_{\text{I}} \right\} dS \quad (5.17.3)$$

First consider the component of this equation that is tangent to the interface. The no-slip condition means that $v_{t\,\text{II}} = v_{t\text{I}}$, so the velocity terms cancel because of Eq. 5.17.2. The pressure force $-\mathbf{n}p$ has no component in the tangential direction, hence the result

$$[(\mathbf{n} \cdot \boldsymbol{\tau})_t]_{\text{I}} = [(\mathbf{n} \cdot \boldsymbol{\tau})_t]_{\text{II}} \quad (5.17.4)$$

The shear stress is continuous across the interface.

The normal component of the momentum equation yields

$$[(v_n - w)\rho v_n + p - \tau_{nn}]_{\text{II}} = [(v_n - w)\rho v_n + p - \tau_{nn}]_{\text{I}} \quad (5.17.5)$$

Here the normal viscous stress is denoted as $\tau_{nn} = (\mathbf{n} \cdot \boldsymbol{\tau})_n$. The surface tension concept (see Eq. 1.5.1) has not been included in Eq. 5.17.5.

The total energy equation, with $e_t = e + \frac{1}{2}v^2 + gZ$, for an interface in arbitrary motion with no internal sources of energy is similarly found employing Eq. 5.16.1. It is

$$[(v_n - w)\rho e_t - \mathbf{n} \cdot \boldsymbol{\tau} \cdot \mathbf{v} + v_n p + q_n]_{\text{II}} = [(v_n - w)\rho e_t - \mathbf{n} \cdot \boldsymbol{\tau} \cdot \mathbf{v} + v_n p + q_n]_{\text{I}}$$

The special case of no flow across the interface yields equal heat fluxes. Surfaces where the density is discontinuous characterize not only interfaces with phase changes, but also shock and combustion waves.

5.18   CONCLUSIONS

The basic laws we have formulated govern all continuum processes of all substances. They are given as both local differential equations and as global equations for a finite size control volume with arbitrary motion. The derivations that employ an arbitrarily shaped region, found in this text, are considered to be more general than the usual derivations, found in elementary texts, employing a box element in a rectangular coordinate system. The basic laws do not form a complete set of equations; there are more unknowns than equations even after we specify the thermodynamic equations of state. The two outstanding tasks are to relate the heat flux to the temperature field (a conduction law) and to relate the stress tensor to the fluid deformations (a viscosity law). These tasks are taken up in Chapter 6.

PROBLEMS

5.1 (B) The incompressible flow around a circular cylinder of radius r_0 is given in cylindrical coordinates r, θ as

$$v_r = -U \cos \theta \left[1 - \left(\frac{r_0}{r} \right)^2 \right]$$

$$v_\theta = U \sin \theta \left[1 + \left(\frac{r_0}{r} \right)^2 \right]$$

$$p = \frac{1}{2}\rho U^2 \left[2 \left(\frac{r_0}{r} \right)^2 (1 - 2 \sin^2 \theta) - \left(\frac{r_0}{r} \right)^4 \right]$$

In a rectangular system x, y, the velocity $v_x = v_r \cos \theta - v_\theta \sin \theta$. Consider the following fixed surfaces one unit in length: S_I with $r = R_0$ as $-\pi/2 \le \theta \le \pi/2$, S_{II} with $\theta = \pi/2$ as $r_0 \le r \le R_0$, S_{III} with $r = r_0$ as $-\pi/2 \le \theta \le \pi/2$, and S_{IV} with $\theta = -\pi/2$ as $r_0 \le r \le R_0$. These surfaces form a fixed region. Compute the following quantities and explain their physical significance: (a) $\int_{FR} \rho v_x \, dV$; (b) $\int_{S_I} \rho n_i v_i \, dS$; (c) $-\int_{S_{II}} n_x p \, dS$; (d) $\int_{S_{II}} \rho n_i v_i v_x \, dS$; (e) $-\int_{S_{III}} n_x p \, dS$; (f) $-\int_{S_{III}} n_r p r \, d\theta$.

5.2 (B) Look up the continuity equation in cylindrical and spherical coordinates. Write out the equations for the special case that the density is constant. Consider a flow that is purely radial [i.e., the only velocity is $v_r(r)$] and find the velocity as a function of r for each case. Sketch a graph of the velocity.

5.3 (A) The velocity profile in a two-dimensional flow is $v_x = v_0[1 - (y/h)^2]$. The stress tensor T_{ij} is $T_{xx} = T_{yy} = T_{zz} = -5$ and $T_{xy} = T_{yx} = -2\mu v_0(y/h^2)$. All other components are zero. Find the stress normal and tangential to a plane located at $y/h = \frac{1}{2}$ with its normal at a $30°$ angle to flow direction.

5.4 (B) Prove that for any continuous fluid property f,

$$\frac{d}{dt} \int_{MR} \rho f \, dV = \int \rho \frac{Df}{Dt} \, dV$$

A physical law states that the rate of change of ρf for a material region comes about by a volume effect Q per unit volume and a surface effect $n_i P_i$ per unit area. Show that the law has the differential form

$$\rho \frac{Df}{Dt} = Q + \nabla \cdot \mathbf{P}$$

Generalize this result for f as a second-order tensor component.

5.5 (B) Prove the Reynolds transport theorem,

$$\frac{d}{dt} \int_{MR} \rho f \, dV = \frac{d}{dt} \int_{FR} \rho f \, dV + \int_{FR} \rho n_i v_i f \, dS$$

5.6 (B) Consider a still fluid where the density is variable and $T_{ij} = -\delta_{ij} p$. Write the momentum equation with a gravity field $F_i = -g \, \partial_i Z(x_i)$. Derive the relation $\nabla \rho \times \nabla Z = 0$. If the fluid is at rest, the density gradient must lie in the Z-direction.

5.7 (B) Verify that mechanical energy equation 5.10.1 is a combination of the momentum equation and the continuity equation, and therefore is not a separate physical law.

5.8 (B) Introduce into Eq. 5.9.6 the gravity force $F_i = -g \, \partial_i Z$, where $Z(x_i)$ is the height above a reference plane. Show that the equation may be rewritten as

$$\partial_0(\rho e_t) + \partial_i(\rho v_i e_t) = -\partial_i q_i + \partial_i(T_{ij} v_j)$$

where

$$e_t \equiv e + \tfrac{1}{2}v^2 + gZ$$

5.9 (B) A piston of area A is in a cylinder of length L. Air occupies the volume, and a liquid fuel coats the hot surface of the piston. The fuel evaporates at a rate $\dot{m}$ and the piston moves with velocity $V_p(t)$. Formulate an expression for the rate of work at the gas–liquid boundary. The pressure in the cylinder $p(t)$ is uniform.

5.10 (A) Derive the global form of energy equations 5.16.1 and 5.16.2.

5.11 (A) A water jet into air leaves a nozzle horizontally with velocity V_j and diameter D. A solid cone pointing toward the jet has a half-angle α, and base $d > D$ has its axis aligned with the jet direction. What force is required to hold the cone stationary in the water jet?

5.12 (B) A very viscous liquid in laminar flow comes downward out of a long, round tube into air. After the fluid exits the tube, viscous forces smooth the parabolic exit velocity profile to a uniform value. This happens in a short distance from the exit, so that gravity forces are negligible. Apply the momentum equation to find the area of the jet when the uniform flow is first established.

5.13 (A) A very long tube 3 cm in diameter carries water at an average velocity of 5 m/s. A short nozzle attached to the end accelerates the flow with a 5:1 area reduction. Find the force between the pipe and the nozzle when the exit pressure is atmospheric (100 kPa) and the pipe pressure is 325 kPa.

5.14 (A) Do Problem 5.13 when the nozzle turns the flow by $120°$.

5.15 (C) A cart with frictionless wheels holds a water tank, motor, pump, and nozzle. The cart is on horizontal ground and initially still. At time zero the cart has a mass M_0 and the pump is started to produce a jet of water with area A_j, velocity U_{jet} at $30°$ to the horizontal. Find and solve the equations governing the mass and velocity of the cart as a function of time.

5.16 (B) If the force holding the cone in Problem 5.11 is suddenly removed and the cone is allowed to move, what are the equations that govern the acceleration of the cone if its mass is M_0? Organize the equations so that they display the smallest number of parameters or coefficients. Solve for the trajectory of the cone assuming typical values of parameters.

5.17 (C) Consider that the cone in Problem 5.16 has the tip truncated, forming a hole of diameter $d_0 = d/4$. Let the cone be hollow so that the part of the water intercepted by the hole enters the cone and remains inside. Reformulate the equations for this case. Neglect deflection of the water jet by gravity.

5.18 (A) Show that the volume of an arbitrary region is given by

$$\frac{dV_{AR}}{dt} = \int n_i w_i \, dS$$

5.19 (B) Consider an arbitrary region where the surface velocity $w_i = W_i(t)$ is constant in space but is a function of time, the volume that encloses a rocket, for example. Since the region volume is constant this is called a *volume region* VR. Denote the velocity relative to the moving region as $u_i = v_i - W_i$. Cast the integral continuity and momentum equations into forms where the velocity relative to the region appears together with the acceleration of the moving region dW_i/dt. The result is

$$\frac{d}{dt} \int_{VR} \rho \, dV + \int_{VR} \rho n_j u_j \, dS = 0$$

$$\frac{d}{dt} \int_{VR} (\rho u_i) \, dV + \frac{dW_i}{dt} \int_{VR} \rho \, dV$$

$$= -\int_{VR} \rho n_k u_k u_i \, dS + \int_{VR \text{ solid}} n_k T_{ki} \, dS$$

$$+ \int_{VR \text{ fluid}} n_k \tau_{ki} \, dS - \int_{VR \text{ fluid}} n_i p \, dSW$$

$$+ \int_{VR \text{ fluid}} \rho F_i \, dV$$

5.20 (B) The container in the example of Section 5.12 is wide and the incoming flow mixes with the water in the container. If the flow out of the orifice is quasisteady and inviscid, what is the velocity? Find the height as a function of time from an initial height h_0.

5.21 (A) A motor boat is speeding at velocity W_0 when the motor is turned off and a scoop is lowered into a still lake. The scoop captures flow with a cross section A. If the initial mass of the boat is M_0 and the wave and friction drag are negligible, what is the velocity of the boat as a function of time? Do this problem using the results of Problem 5.19.

5.22 (A) A cylindrical container of cross section A_0 has an open top and contains an initial mass M_0. Rain is falling vertically at velocity v_d with droplets of mass m_d of density n_d drops per unit volume. What force is required to hold the container?

5.23 (C) The container in Problem 5.22 is on a plane at angle θ to the horizontal. At time zero the container is released and it slides without friction (because the plane is wet) down the plane. Find the velocity and position histories of the cylinder.

5.24 (A) Redo the cart problem of Section 5.14 using the results of Problem 5.19.

6

Newtonian Fluids and the Navier–Stokes Equations

In this chapter we study the equations that relate the stress to the deformation and those that relate the heat flux to the temperature. Such relations are called *constitutive equations*. A given constitutive formula may be good for a large group of fluids, but one general formula cannot describe all fluids. The simplest relations are linear equations: The stress is proportional to the rate of strain (Newton's viscosity law), or the heat flux is proportional to the temperature gradient (Fourier's law). At ordinary pressures and temperatures all gases obey these relations, as do many simple liquids. Liquids made up of complex molecules, liquid mixtures, and slurries of fine particles in a liquid (including blood) do not obey linear relations and are said to be *non-Newtonian*.

The idea of a linear relation between stress and rate of strain was first put forward by Newton, and for this reason the viscosity laws bears his name. Much later, George S. Stokes (English mathematician, 1819–1903) and C. L. M. H. Navier (French engineer, 1785–1836) produced the exact equations that govern the flow of Newtonian fluids. These equations, or the appropriately generalized ones for compressible flow, are called the *Navier–Stokes equations*.

6.1 NEWTON'S VISCOSITY LAW

In Chapter 5 we proposed a surface stress R_j to describe the net intermolecular forces and microscopic momentum transport from one side of an imaginary surface to the other. The problem was decomposed into two effects by introducing a stress tensor T_{ij} such that $R_j = n_i T_{ij}$. Flow effects are contained in T_{ij}, and surface orientation effects are contained in n_i. From point to point, the local flow situation changes and causes the stress tensor to vary. We now formulate an expression for T_{ij} by assuming that it is a function $T_{ij}(\rho, e, \partial_k v_\ell)$ of the local thermodynamic state and the local velocity gradients. We cannot include the velocity by itself in this expression, because then a Galilean transformation would change the stress. This would certainly not conform to physical reality. The simplest form for $T_{ij}(\rho, e, \partial_k v_\ell)$ is a linear function of the velocity gradients with coefficients that depend on the thermodynamic state,

$$T_{ij} = A_{ij} + B_{ijk\ell}\, \partial_k v_\ell \tag{6.1.1}$$

The linearity assumption prohibits terms involving $\partial_k v_j\, \partial_j v_\ell$, the square of the velocity gradient.

There are two geometric properties that further restrict Eq. 6.1.1. The first is that most fluids are isotropic, having no preferred directions. Second, because we assumed that no moment acts on the surface (Section 5.8), the stress tensor is symmetric. If these restrictions are imposed, it may be shown (Prager, 1961; Jeffreys, 1963; Aris, 1962; Batchelor, 1967; Yih, 1969) that Eq. 6.1.1 must have the mathematical form

$$T_{ij} = A_1 \delta_{ij} + A_2 \, \partial_k v_k \delta_{ij} + A_3 \, \partial_{(i} v_{j)} \tag{6.1.2}$$

The coefficients A_1, A_2, A_3 are in principle thermodynamic functions. We can fix A_1 by arguing that when there is no motion, the equation must reduce to give the thermodynamic pressure; therefore, $A_1 = -p$. The common symbols for A_2 and A_3 are λ and 2μ. They are called the *second* and *first viscosity coefficients,* respectively. With this notation Eq. 6.1.2 becomes

$$T_{ij} = -p \delta_{ij} + \lambda \, \partial_k v_k \delta_{ij} + 2\mu \, \partial_{(i} v_{j)} \tag{6.1.3}$$

To continue, recall the definition of the mechanical pressure as the average normal stress,

$$-p_m \equiv \tfrac{1}{3} T_{ii} \tag{6.1.4}$$

The difference between the thermodynamic pressure [given by the equation of state $p(\rho, e)$ when the local values of ρ, e are inserted] and the mechanical pressure is computed from Eq. 6.1.3 by contracting on i and dividing by 3. The result may be rearranged to give

$$p - p_m = \left(\lambda + \frac{2}{3} \mu \right) \partial_k v_k = -\left(\lambda + \frac{2}{3} \mu \right) \frac{1}{\rho} \frac{D\rho}{Dt} \tag{6.1.5}$$

The last equality is obtained using the continuity equation.

Recall that an incompressible fluid has only a mechanical pressure. Equation 6.1.5 shows that the viscosity law will be consistent for an incompressible fluid ($D\rho/Dt = -\rho\partial_i v_i = 0$), as the right-hand size is zero and the symbol p will take on the meaning of the mechanical pressure. Furthermore, $p = p_m$ for the incompressible flow of any fluid. To discuss λ we must turn our attention to compressible flows. The question is, should there be any difference between the thermodynamic and mechanical pressures if the fluid is undergoing an expansion or compression? The assumption that the two pressures are equal is known as *Stokes's assumption,* and it means that

$$\lambda = -\tfrac{2}{3}\mu \tag{6.1.6}$$

This assumption is supported by kinetic theory when the fluid is a monatomic gas. Stokes's assumption is reasonably accurate for all engineering situations for both gases and simple liquids, at least for those liquids that are Newtonian in the first place. Thus, deviations from it are not important in practice. Stokes's assumption is commonly taken as just another characteristic of Newtonian fluids.

If a compression or expansion of a fluid is very rapid, such as a shock or sound wave, and the molecules have internal degrees of freedom, such as vibration or rotation, thermodynamic equilibrium is not maintained. At equilibrium the internal energy should be distributed equally to all internal modes of motion. However, after a rapid change of state the energy appears first in the translation mode and only after several additional molecular collisions is energy distributed to the rotation and later on, after more collisions, to the vibration modes. Thus, the mechanical pressure, which is associated with only the translation mode, is not the equilibrium thermodynamic value. That is, the local values of ρ and e, which are well defined even in thermodynamic nonequilibrium, substituted into the equilibrium state equation $p = p(\rho, e)$ do not give the mean value of the normal stresses. In certain situations (when the relaxation time is long compared to the flow time) the coefficient κ can be used to model these nonequilibrium effects. The absorption of sound waves is such a process. Absorption in noble gases follows Stokes's assumption in agreement with kinetic theory. Sound absorption in air has a nonzero κ but its value depends strongly on the water vapor content (which greatly modifies the relaxation times). With regard to water, impurities in even trace amounts, primarily magnesium sulfate and boric acid, affect the relaxation process in water. Even so, acoustic absorption in pure water has a bulk viscosity coefficient $\kappa \sim 3\mu$. A more general approach to relaxation process modeling uses a non-Newtonian viscosity law (Ash et al., 1994).

The final form of the stress relation Eq. 6.1.3 is written as

$$T_{ij} = -p\delta_{ij} - \tfrac{2}{3}\mu\ \partial_k v_k\ \delta_{ij} + 2\mu S_{ij} \tag{6.1.7}$$

The last two terms are the *deviatoric stress tensor,* defined by

$$\boldsymbol{\tau} = -\tfrac{2}{3}\mu\boldsymbol{\delta}\ \nabla \cdot v + 2\mu\mathbf{S} \tag{6.1.8}$$

This is, in essence, Newton's viscosity law. We also loosely refer to τ_{ij} as the *shear stress tensor,* although it also contains normal viscous components that add or subtract from the pressure. A very common term for τ_{ij} is the *viscous stress tensor.*

The first term in Eq. 6.1.8 contributes only to the normal stresses. A typical normal viscous stress is

$$\tau_{11} = 2\mu \left(\underset{\substack{\text{average} \\ \text{rate of} \\ \text{extension}}}{-\tfrac{1}{3}\ \partial_k v_k} + \underset{\substack{x_1\text{-direction} \\ \text{rate of} \\ \text{extension}}}{\partial_1 v_1} \right) \tag{6.1.9}$$

In this viscous stress, the extensional deformation $\partial_1 v_1$ is compared with the average extension rate for all three directions. If the extension rate is exactly equal to the average extension rate, the normal viscous stress τ_{11} is zero. Only extension rates greater or less than the average produce a normal viscous stress. Note that as a consequence of Stokes's assumption, the average normal viscous stress is always zero.

Now we turn our attention to the shearing stresses. A typical off-diagonal stress is

$$\tau_{21} = 2\mu\ \partial_{(2} v_{1)} = \mu(\partial_2 v_1 + \partial_1 v_2) \tag{6.1.10}$$

The strain rate tensor is the only contributor to the shear stresses. Recall that the off-diagonal elements of the strain rate tensor are the angular or shearing strains. Thus, Eq. 6.1.10 is a statement that the shear stress is proportional to the shearing strain rate.

We should remind ourselves of the theoretical status of Newton's viscosity law. It is not a fundamental law, merely a reasonable approximation for the behavior of many fluids. As applied to gases, it has some theoretical support because the kinetic theory of dilute monatomic gases produces Newton's viscosity law. The law is valid for simple liquids, but it fails for complex liquids. In any case, the important point is that if a fluid is Newtonian, it must have certain characteristics. Newton's viscosity law implies that a fluid has the following properties:

1. Stress is a linear function of strain rate.

2. The coefficients in the expression for the stress are functions of the thermodynamic state.

3. When the fluid is stationary, the stress is the thermodynamic pressure.

4. The fluid is isotropic.

5. The stress tensor is symmetric.

6. The mechanical and thermodynamic pressures are equal. The average normal viscous stress is zero. Stokes's assumption applies: $\lambda = -\frac{2}{3}\mu$.

Fluids that fail to be Newtonian usually do not satisfy the first property. The stress has nonlinear and sometimes time-dependent (elastic) relationships to the strain rate. Data of viscosity of liquids may be found in Viswanath and Natarajan (1989). For gas viscosities, consult Bird et al. (1960).

6.2   MOLECULAR MODEL OF VISCOUS EFFECTS

The molecules of an ideal gas are so far apart that the intermolecular forces are extremely small. Molecules spend most of their time in free flight between brief collisions in which their direction and speed are abruptly changed. If we imagine a plane separating the gas into two regions, the molecules do not attract or repel each other across this plane (contrary to the situation in liquids). The primary source of shear stress is the microscopic transport of momentum by random molecular options. Molecules migrating across the plane carry with them the momentum of the bulk velocity from their region of origin. A simple kinetic theory model of this mechanism gives a good insight into the process and at the same time produces an equation for the viscosity. We now take up a discussion of this model.

Recall shear stress equation 6.1.10,

$$\tau_{21} = \mu(\partial_2 v_1 + \partial_1 v_2)$$

We specialize this equation by considering a flow $v_1(x_2)$ as shown in Fig. 6.1. An x_2-plane, one unit square in area, separates the fluid into inside and outside parts. It is located at an arbitrary position x_2. The shear stress on the plane is

$$\tau_{21} = \mu \frac{dv_1}{dx_2} \tag{6.2.1}$$

To derive this equation, we must use four facts from kinetic theory. First, molecules that cross the plane begin their free flight, on the average, a distance $\frac{2}{3}$ of a mean free path (ℓ) away from the plane. Second, the mean free path is related to the molecular diameter d and the number density n by

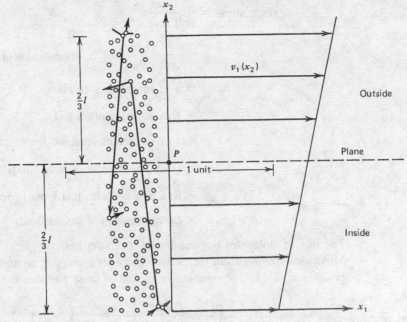

Figure 6.1 Molecular model of the viscosity of a gas.

$$\ell = \frac{1}{\sqrt{2}\pi d^2 n} \qquad (6.2.2)$$

The mean-free-path length is not a precisely defined concept because there are complicating factors. For example, molecules are moving relative to each other and they have a distribution of speeds. If one accounts for the relative velocities, the formula Eq. 6.2.2 is changed by a factor of 3/4 on the right-hand side. If one assumes the molecules have a Maxwellian distribution of velocities, the factor is 0.707. Third, the flux of molecules across the plane from one side to the other is

$$\text{rate that molecules cross a unit area} = \tfrac{1}{4}n\bar{v} \qquad (6.2.3)$$

where $\bar{v}$ is the average random molecular speed (without regard for direction). Fourth, and finally, the average molecular speed is related to the temperature by

$$\bar{v} = \sqrt{\frac{8kT}{\pi m}} \qquad (6.2.4)$$

where k is Boltzmann's constant and m is the molecular mass.

We formulate the shear stress by postulating that the force is equal to the rate momentum crosses the plane,

$$\text{shear stress} = \frac{x_1 \text{ force}}{\text{unit area}}$$

$$= \frac{\text{rate of change}}{\text{unit area}} \text{ of } (x_1\text{-momentum of inside fluid})$$

$$\tau_{21} = \text{flux of momentum received}$$

$$- \text{ flux of momentum lost}$$

$$\tau_{21} = \text{flux of molecules received from outside}$$

$$\times (x_1\text{-momentum of outside fluid})$$

$$- \text{ flux of molecules lost from inside}$$

$$\times (x_1\text{-momentum of inside fluid})$$

The flux of molecules is given by Eq. 6.2.3 for both outgoing and incoming molecules. Molecules arriving from the outside carry an average x_1 momentum associated with the position $x_2 + \frac{2}{3}\ell$. The momentum of one of these particles is

$$mv_1\big|_{x_2+2\ell/3} = m\left[v_1 + \frac{dv_1}{dx_2}\left(\frac{2}{3}\ell\right) + \cdots\right]_{x_2} \tag{6.2.5}$$

Molecules leaving the inside fluid cause a momentum loss of

$$mv_1\big|_{x_2-2\ell/3} = m\left[v_1 + \frac{dv_1}{dx_2}\left(-\frac{2}{3}\ell\right) + \cdots\right]_{x_2}.$$

The shear stress is then computed as the difference of the expressions above multiplied by molecular flux equation 6.2.3. The stress is

$$\tau_{21} = \frac{1}{4}\, n\bar{v}m\, \frac{4}{3}\ell\, \frac{dv_1}{dx_2} \tag{6.2.6}$$

This equation has the same form as Eq. 6.2.1, and we can identify the viscosity as

$$\mu = \tfrac{1}{3}n\bar{v}m\ell \tag{6.2.7}$$

Substituting Eqs. 6.2.2 and 6.2.4 gives a formula to predict the viscosity in terms of the molecular properties and the temperature:

$$\mu = \frac{2}{3d^2}\sqrt{\frac{mkT}{\pi^3}} \tag{6.2.8}$$

The gas viscosity increases for heavier molecules and decreases for larger molecules. In agreement with experiments, there is no effect of pressure. The viscosity increases as the square root of the absolute temperature according to this simple theory. Actually, the temperature effect is somewhat stronger. A more sophisticated kinetic theory model, which includes the intermolecular forces, gives a much better prediction of the temperature dependence. Detailed procedures for calculating the viscosity of gases are contained in Bird et al. (1960).

The viscosity of liquids is a much more difficult task to model on the molecular level. The molecules are closely packed, and the intermolecular forces are very important. Experiments again show that there is little influence of the pressure upon the viscosity. The temperature influence in liquids is opposite to that of gases: Increasing temperature causes a decrease in viscosity.

Since liquids are much like solids in that the molecules are closely packed, it will aid our thinking to view the stress–strain mechanism in solid materials. In a solid the stresses are directly proportional to the deformation as described by Hooke's law. We can more easily imagine the molecular situation if we consider a crystal with a definite lattice structure. If we imagine a plane slicing through the crystal, the sum of the intermolecular forces across this plane must balance the imposed shear. As a shear force is applied, the atoms move—that is, the average position of a vibrating atom changes—and the lattice is distorted. Because of the new directions and distances between atoms, the intermolecular forces are now different. The sum of forces on the plane now has a tangential component, which is the shear stress.

Note that during the deformation process, work is done on the crystal by the shear stress. Once the deformation stops, there is no longer work because there is no motion. When the stress is withdrawn, energy is retrieved as the crystal does work on the agent that supplies the force. In the strained state, the crystal has an extra internal energy associated with the deformed configuration. This is essentially a spring effect, as the energy is recovered reversibly when the deforming force is removed.

Liquids have intermolecular distances in the same range as solids; however, the molecules are not fixed in one position, and the configuration changes constantly. When a shear stress is applied to a liquid, the deformation continues as long as the force is applied. A velocity gradient must occur simultaneously with the shear stress, so there is a relative movement between molecules. The straining between molecules causes them to separate and brings them into new force fields of other molecules. The analogy with a deformed solid is that, on average, the configuration of molecules in a fluid subject to shear is such that there is a net intermolecular shear stress across our imaginary plane. (In kinetic theory this is sometimes referred to as a momentum transfer by "collisions" occurring at the plane. Closely packed molecules are always within the force field of their neighbors, and hence are always in a collision state.) The configuration of molecules in a liquid at rest is such that only a net normal force is transmitted across the plane. When a velocity gradient occurs, the net force is no longer normal but has a tangential component.

Because the process of forming new configurations and breaking up old configurations is ongoing, it requires a continuing input of work. In contrast to the solid, a liquid cannot store energy in a strained configuration. All the work done by a constant shear force is irreversible and eventually becomes random thermal motion of the molecules. This is, of course, the process of viscous dissipation, which was introduced in Section 5.10.

The shear force arises from two molecular mechanisms. The first is the net force field of the closely packed molecules of a liquid. A velocity gradient in the liquid gives rise to a "strained" molecular configuration, which in turn rotates the net force vector so that a shear stress exists. The second mechanism is momentum transport by random motion at the microscopic level, due to the mobility of fluid molecules. This kinetic contribution to the viscosity of liquids is small compared to the average strained configuration contribution discussed previously.

Even though the microscopic mechanisms in liquids and gases are quite different, the same continuum viscosity law governs both situations. The major effect is found in the viscosity coefficient itself: It has opposite temperature dependencies for liquids and for gases.

6.3   NON-NEWTONIAN LIQUIDS

Many industrially important chemicals and products do not obey Newton's viscosity law. A good example of non-Newtonian behavior is the class of materials called *high polymers*. These materials may consist of from 100 to over 10,000 monomer units chained together. The resulting molecular weight can be over 1 million. Thus, they are sometimes referred to as *macromolecules*. Although they form a chain in terms of chemical bonding, the monomers coil up in a random fashion to produce a ball-like molecule that is up to 100 times the diameter of a simple molecule such as oxygen. Of course, this molecule does not have a force field that extends out three or four molecular diameters as simple molecules do. In fact, a macromolecule is a somewhat spongy thing and changes its shape, especially when subjected to a shearing strain. Furthermore, a high-polymer material should not be viewed as a group of uniformly large giants. The method of producing the chemicals results in a size variation of several orders of magnitude. The molecular weight quoted is actually the average of a statistical distribution of molecular weights. For all the foregoing reasons, these substances show unusual viscous behavior. Even a very dilute solution of macromolecules in ordinarily Newtonian liquids such as water produces some non-Newtonian effects.

Another class of non-Newtonian liquids consists of mixtures, slurries, and suspensions. The particles in these fluids range from below the continuum length scale to several orders of magnitude above it. Examples of these fluids are clay suspended in water, toothpaste, blood, paper pulp suspended in water, oil-well drilling fluid, and so on. A mixture with continuum size particles is actually a *two-phase-flow problem*. There is no well-defined particle size above which mixtures should cease to be considered as uniform fluids and be treated as a two-phase systems.

Fluids may be non-Newtonian in several ways. The most common departures from Newtonian behavior are (1) the stress is a nonlinear function of the strain, (2) additional normal viscous stresses are produced by shearing, and (3) the fluid is elastic as well as viscous. Some fluids show only one of these effects, and others all of them.

Figure 6.2 is a sketch of stress versus rate of strain for a simple sharing motion. Newtonian fluids produce a straight line on this graph, and the slope is the viscosity. A fluid is said to be *shear thinning* if the apparent viscosity decreases with increasing strain rate. This behavior is characteristic of polymers. The most extreme case is a substance that has infinite viscosity, acting like a solid, until a certain level of stress is exceeded. Then the material becomes fluid with a Newtonian characteristic. A model of this behavior, called the *Binghman plastic,* gives the shear stress as

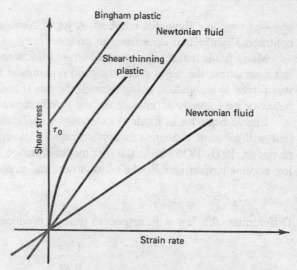

Figure 6.2 Shear stress as a function of strain rate for fluids with various viscous characteristics.

$$\tau = \pm\tau_0 + \mu\,\frac{dv}{dy} \quad \text{if} \quad |\tau| > \tau_0 \tag{6.3.1}$$

When a Bingham plastic flows in a tube, there is a core of fluid in the middle that moves as a solid plug. In this region the shear is less than τ_0, while next to the wall the stress is larger than τ_0 and the material flows as a fluid. Very concentrated slurries, those with a high volume of particle material, display this characteristic.

Fluids that exhibit a normal stress upon shearing give rise to many unusual and interesting flow phenomena. In most normal stress fluids a shear flow also results in a viscous tension stress along the streamline. Such fluids display the *Weisenberg effect:* They climb a rotating cylinder immersed in a container of the fluid. In ordinary Newtonian fluids the free surface is depressed near the rotating shaft. A higher pressure is required on the outside to balance the centrifugal force associated with the circular streamlines. A hydrostatic pressure gradient is established within the fluid when the free surface sinks near the rotating cylinder. On the other hand, a fluid that produces a normal stress upon shearing climbs the cylinder, because the extra viscous tension along the streamlines tends to pull them toward the center, and this effect is more than enough to cancel the centrifugal force. A pressure gradient from inside to outside is also needed to keep the streamlines in equilibrium. The liquid climbs the center rod to supply this pressure gradient.

Another normal-stress effect of commercial importance is called *die swell*. In the process of extruding plastics or of manufacturing threads, the fluid is forced through a die in a continuous manner. Outside the die, in the free air, the fluid may expand to a larger diameter than the die. While it is in the die, the normal tension stress is developed along the streamlines. As the fluid emerges from the die, only atmospheric pressure is imposed and the wall shear is released. The material contracts along streamlines, and hence swells. A Newtonian fluid does not show this behavior (except—for another reason—at very low Reynolds number). A jet of Newtonian fluid with straight streamlines contracts slightly as it exits from an orifice.

Many fluids that produce normal-stress effects are also viscoelastic. Since the transmit time across the die is short, the fluid remembers its state in the reservoir. Because it was forced to elongate in going through the die, it contracts once it leaves the die. Elastic behavior may greatly accentuate the die-swell phenomenon.

Elastic behavior in fluids is extremely complicated. Most of us have seen materials that will rebound if a stress is applied rapidly enough. James Clerk Maxwell (Scottish physicist, 1831–1879) made the first model equation for these substances by the following argument. Consider Hooke's law, where the stress is proportional to the strain Θ,

$$\tau = \eta\Theta \qquad (6.3.2)$$

Differentiate this law with respect to time to produce

$$\frac{1}{\eta}\frac{\partial\tau}{\partial t} = \frac{\partial\Theta}{\delta t} \qquad (6.3.3)$$

We now have the equation in the same dimensions as a viscosity law, and we identify the strain rate (in a simple shear flow) as $\partial\Theta/\partial t \approx \partial u/\partial y$. Maxwell's viscoelastic equation is a sum of both types of behavior; that is, the rate of deformation is proportional to the stress for fluidlike behavior plus the rate of change of stress as the elastic contribution:

$$\tau + \frac{\mu}{\eta}\frac{\partial\tau}{\partial t} = \mu\frac{\partial u}{\partial y} \qquad (6.3.4)$$

This is a linear viscoelastic law. It is the basis for generalizations of many types.

Unfortunately, most viscoelastic fluids, including the high polymers, are nonlinear. A nonlinear law is in fact obtained if we correct a logical error we made in deriving Eq. 6.3.4. We should have considered Hooke's law to apply as we follow a material particle. To do this, the differentiation with respect to time should be replaced with the substantial derivative in Eq. 6.3.3 and the corresponding term of Eq. 6.3.4. This will result in a nonlinear expression because the convective term in the substantial derivative is nonlinear. A more sophisticated and mathematically more complex model is produced by replacing the substantial derivative with a derivative that not only follows the particle velocity, but also rotates with the solid-body rotation. It is not our purpose to delve into the details of shear thinning, viscoelastic constitutive equations; the interested reader may consult Bird et al. (1977).

The last topic we wish to discuss in this section is *Thom's phenomenon*, which is also called the *drag-reduction phenomenon*. It illustrates how even a very dilute mixture of macromolecules in water can have a dramatic effect on fluid flows. Solutions with only a few hundred parts per million concentration of polymers still maintain a Newtonian viscosity characteristic of the bulk fluid. In high-velocity flows these solutions become turbulent just as the pure fluid would. The startling difference is that the turbulence has a different structure. High-frequency turbulence components are suppressed by the addition of the polymer, and in particular, the character of the viscous sublayer is changed markedly. The net result is a smaller velocity gradient next to the wall, and hence a smaller shear stress. In boundary layer flows this leads to a drag reduction and in pipe flows a smaller pressure drop for the same flow rate. There are several possible practical applications of this effect. One application that has been prohibited is in sailboat racing. It is illegal to coat the bottom of a sailboat with a polymer that would dissolve during the race.

*6.4   NO-SLIP CONDITION

The flow conditions at a contact surface between a solid and a fluid are important, as they enter into the mathematical formulation of flow problems. There are actually two conditions: one on the normal velocity and one on the tangential velocity. We consider a body surrounded by a flowing fluid or a channel that confines a fluid flowing through it. A kinematic condition we impose is that the particle paths cannot go into the solid. Mathematically, the requirement is that the fluid velocity perpendicular to the wall vanish. If n_i is a local unit normal to the surface, the condition is expressed as

$$n_i v_i|_{\text{wall}} = 0 \tag{6.4.1}$$

If the solid is moving with a local velocity V_i, the equivalent condition is

$$n_i(V_i - v_i)|_{\text{wall}} = 0 \tag{6.4.2}$$

In the case of steady flow the particle paths and streamlines are equivalent, and hence condition 6.4.1 may be interpreted as a statement that the solid walls are loci of streamlines.

The kinematic restriction makes no statement about the velocity component that is tangent to the wall. Viscosity is responsible for the tangential condition, whose proper form was discussed throughout the nineteenth century. Today we accept the no-slip condition as an experimental fact. The condition is

$$v_i|_{\text{wall}} = V_i \tag{6.4.3}$$

(Equation 6.4.3 includes the previous normal condition 6.4.2 as well as the no-slip tangential condition.)

Goldstein (1965) reviews the history of the no-slip condition. The condition itself is quite old; Daniel Bernoulli thought that it was necessary to account for the discrepancies between measured results and results calculated for (ideal) flows where viscosity was ignored. When one considers the various effects of surface tension, it is natural to suspect that the velocity of the fluid next to a wall might be influenced by the same things that influence surface tension: the chemical nature of the fluid or solid, the curvature of the surface, and so on. Coulomb provided some early evidence that this was not so. He experimented with a flat metal disk oscillating in water like a clock pendulum. Placing grease or grease together with powdered stone on the disk did not change the fluid resistance to the motion.

During the development period for this condition there were three alternative viewpoints. The first was that there was no slip at all, irrespective of the material and in accordance with the views of Bernoulli and Coulomb. The second was that a layer of stagnant fluid existed near the wall. Various things were supposed to determine the thickness of the layer: wall curvature, temperature, wall material, and fluid composition; it was supposed to be zero if the fluid did not wet the wall. At the outer edge of the stagnant layer the fluid was allowed to slip. The third viewpoint, due to Navier, was that the slip velocity v_0 should be proportional to the stress (proportionality constant a):

$$av_0\big|_{\text{wall}} = \mu \left.\frac{\partial v_1}{\partial x_2}\right|_{\text{wall}} \tag{6.4.4}$$

Navier proposed that an adjustment of the constant μ/a could reproduce the same effects as the assumption of a slipping stagnant layer. As it turns out, Eq. 6.4.4 is close to the truth, but the coefficient μ/a is always so small that v_0 is effectively zero. Thus, what was originally proposed to modify and explain the second viewpoint turns out to be a fairly accurate model that in practical cases reduces to the first viewpoint—the no-slip condition.

We can obtain a better idea of why a little slip seems to be required by doing a crude kinetic theory calculation. Consider a gas bounded by a solid wall as shown in Fig. 6.3. In the neighborhood of the wall, the velocity may be approximated by a slip value v_0 and a uniform gradient. Now we want to redo our previous molecular calculation of Section 6.2 for the special case that the x_2 plane is at the interface between the gas and the solid. The momentum carried from the fluid to the wall is again given by Eq. 6.2.5:

$$mv_1\big|_{x_2+2\ell/3} = mv_0 + m\frac{2}{3}\ell \left.\frac{dv_1}{dx_2}\right|_0 + \cdots$$

The thing that is different about a wall is that the returning gas molecules have interacted or collided with a dense collection of solid molecules that have no bulk velocity. The returning molecules are put into two categories. The coefficient σ is the percent of returning molecules that are diffuse and have, on average, no x-momentum (the wall is stationary). In the second category $(1 - \sigma)$ is the percentage of returning molecules that

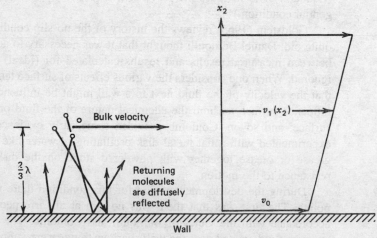

Figure 6.3   Kinetic model of slip flow at a solid wall.

have specular reflection and therefore have the x-momentum of their place of origin, that is, $v_0 + \frac{2}{3}\ell(dv_1/dx_2)$. Thus, an expression for the wall stress is

$$\tau_{21} = \text{net flux of momentum}$$

$$= \frac{1}{4} n\bar{v}m\left(v_0 + \frac{2}{3}\ell\frac{dv_1}{dx_2}\right) - (1 - \sigma)\frac{1}{4}n\bar{v}m\left(v_0 + \frac{2}{3}\ell\frac{dv_1}{dx_2}\right) \qquad (6.4.5)$$

Another expression for the wall stress is to assume that the molecules near the wall are in a state nearly like those in the bulk fluid and that Eq. 6.2.6 is roughly valid:

$$\tau_{21} = \frac{1}{4}n\bar{v}m\frac{4}{3}\ell\frac{dv_1}{dx_2} \qquad (6.2.6)$$

Equation expressions 6.4.5 and 6.2.6 relate the slip velocity and the gradient:

$$\sigma v_0 = (2 - \sigma)\frac{2}{3}\ell\frac{dv}{dx_2} \qquad (6.4.6)$$

The factor $\frac{2}{3}\ell$ is the place of origin of the incoming molecules and $\frac{2}{3}$ is usually ignored because of uncertainty in this estimate. Note that $\sigma = 0$ indicates perfect reflection, the wall does not retard the molecules, and there is no wall stress.

To interpret Eq. 6.4.6, let U and L be a characteristic velocity scale and a characteristic length scale of the continuum flow. Then $d(v_1/U)/d(x_2/L)$ is of order 1, and we can use Eq. 6.4.6 to find out how the slip velocity v_0 compares to U:

$$\frac{v_0}{U} = \frac{(2 - \sigma)}{\sigma}\text{Kn}\frac{d(v_1/U)}{d(x_2/L)} \qquad (6.4.7)$$

The slip velocity becomes zero as the Knudsen number ($\text{Kn} = \ell/L$, mean free path compared to the continuum length L) becomes small. For practical purposes there is no slip at the wall. Computer simulations of molecular dynamics (Koplik et al., 1989) also support the form of Eq. 6.4.7.

The conditions on the temperature at the interface between a solid and a fluid are analogous to those on the tangential velocity. Kinetic theory predicts a temperature jump that is again on the order of ℓ/L, that is, zero for most practical purposes.

Our faith in the no-slip condition is backed up by experiments. Detailed measurements on many flows show agreement with predictions where the no-slip condition has been assumed as part of the analysis. One notable exception is a moving contact line where the interface between two fluids is moving over a solid wall. Dussan and Davis (1974) discuss the singular nature of events at the contact line.

6.5 FOURIER'S HEAT CONDUCTION LAW

The formulation of a heat conduction law is a simpler task than that of the viscosity law. Following the same line of reasoning as for viscosity, we propose that the heat flux is a function of the thermodynamic state and the temperature gradient,

$$q_i = f(\rho, e, \partial_j T) \tag{6.5.1}$$

The most general relation that is linear in the temperature gradient is

$$q_i = A_i + B_{ij}\, \partial_j T \tag{6.5.2}$$

The coefficients A_i and B_{ij} are, in principle, functions of the thermodynamic state. Now we require that the heat flux vanish when the temperature gradient vanishes; therefore, A_i is zero. This leaves only B_{ij} as a tensor conductivity, and Eq. 6.5.1 reduces to

$$q_i = B_{ij}\, \partial_j T \tag{6.5.3}$$

This equation is frequently used to describe conduction in anisotropic solids, which exhibit a preferred direction for heat conduction. If the material is isotropic, we an assume that $B_{ij} = -k\delta_{ij}$, where k is the thermal conductivity (since δ_{ij} is the only isotropic second-order tensor). The final equation becomes

$$q_i = -k\, \partial_i T \tag{6.5.4}$$

The minus sign is dictated by the fact that heat flux is defined to be positive when energy is received.

The molecular interpretation of heat conduction was discussed in a qualitative way in Chapter 2. Here we add to that discussion a sketch of the kinetic theory of conduction in gases. The development is similar to that for viscosity. Referring again to Fig. 6.1, we are now seeking to compute the internal energy that crosses the plane. The flux of molecules across the plane is the same as before, $\frac{1}{4}n\bar{v}$. These molecules originate at $x_2 \pm \frac{2}{3}\ell$, on the average, and they carry with them the internal energy of that location. In Fig. 6.1 we assume that there is a temperature gradient $T(x)$. The energy of each particle is evaluated at $x_2 + \frac{2}{3}\ell$ for particles coming from above:

$$\text{energy of a particle above the plane} = mc_v[T]_{x_2 + 2\ell/3}$$

$$= mc_v\left[T + \frac{\partial T}{\partial x_2}\left(\frac{2}{3}\ell\right) + \cdots\right]_{x_2} \tag{6.5.5}$$

and at $x_2 - \frac{2}{3}\ell$ for particles coming from below:

$$\text{energy of a particle below the plane} = mc_v\left[T + \frac{\partial T}{\partial x_2}\left(-\frac{2}{3}\ell\right) + \cdots\right]_{x_2} \tag{6.5.6}$$

The net transport of internal energy by molecular mechanisms is the heat flux

$$-q = \frac{1}{4}\, n\bar{v}mc_v\, \frac{4}{3}\, \ell\, \frac{\partial T}{\partial x_2} \tag{6.5.7}$$

Comparing Eq. 6.5.7 with conduction law 6.5.4 shows that the conductivity is

$$k = \tfrac{1}{3}n\bar{v}mlc_v \tag{6.5.8}$$

Substituting Eqs. 6.2.2 and 6.2.4 gives a formula for the thermal conduct

$$k = \frac{2c_v}{3d^2} \sqrt{\frac{mkT}{\pi^3}} = c_v\mu \qquad (6.5.9)$$

This equation is independent of pressure, a fact verified by experiments, and has a square-root temperature variation. Experiments show that the true temperature variation is somewhat stronger, just as was the case for viscosity. A more refined calculation, where account is taken of the intermolecular forces, gives a stronger temperature dependence that is more in line with experiments. Notice that any energy carried across the plane in internal molecular modes is accounted for in c_v, which we leave as constant in the equation.

The ratio of viscosity to thermal conductivity is an important quantity, as it compares the rate of diffusion of momentum with that of energy. This ratio is called the *Prandtl* (Pr) *number*,

$$\text{Pr} \equiv \frac{\mu c_p}{k} = \frac{\mu c_v}{k} \frac{c_p}{c_v} \qquad (6.5.10)$$

Equation 6.5.9 shows that the Prandtl number should be constant at the value $\text{Pr} = c_p/c_v = \gamma$. The prediction of a constant Pr is correct, but the value is about a factor of 2 too high. The more sophisticated kinetic theory gives $\text{Pr} = \frac{2}{3}c_p/c_v$, which is roughly correct.

6.6 NAVIER–STOKES EQUATIONS

The continuity equation, the momentum equations with Newton's viscosity law, and an energy equation with Fourier's conduction law are commonly referred to as the Navier–Stokes equations. Alternatively, in incompressible flow, we also use the term to apply to the same equations where the density, viscosity, and thermal conductivity are constant.

The Navier–Stokes equations are easily found by substituting Eqs. 6.1.8 and 6.5.4 into Eqs. 5.7.6 and 5.11.1. Appendix C contains these equations in rectangular, cylindrical, and spherical coordinates.

$$\frac{\partial \rho}{\partial t} + \mathbf{v} \cdot \nabla \rho = -\rho \nabla \cdot \mathbf{v} \qquad (6.6.1)$$

$$\rho\left(\frac{\partial \mathbf{v}}{\partial t} + \mathbf{v} \cdot \nabla \mathbf{v}\right) = -\nabla p + \rho \mathbf{g} - \frac{2}{3}\nabla(\mu \nabla \cdot \mathbf{v}) + 2\nabla \cdot (\mu \mathbf{S}) \qquad (6.6.2)$$

$$\rho c_p\left(\frac{\partial T}{\partial t} + \mathbf{v} \cdot \nabla T\right) = \nabla \cdot (k\nabla T) - \frac{2}{3}\mu(\nabla \cdot \mathbf{v})^2 + 2\mu \mathbf{S}{:}\mathbf{S} + \beta T \frac{Dp}{Dt} \qquad (6.6.3)$$

The Navier–Stokes equations are completed by specifying thermodynamic state equations $p = p(\rho, T)$, $c_p = c_p(\rho, T)$, and $\beta = (1/\rho)\,\partial\rho/\partial T]_p = \beta(\rho, T)$ and transport relations $\mu = \mu(\rho, T)$ and $k = k(\rho, T)$.

6.7 CONCLUSIONS

A fluid-flow problem for a general fluid is governed by several equations. First, there are the basic relations for continuity, three momentum equations and an energy relation. Second, there are the constitutive equations for the surface stresses and the heat flux. These equations are not basic, but they do apply to groups of substances. Various transport coefficients are introduced in the constitutive relations. They are quasithermodynamic properties that depend on the composition of the fluid and its thermodynamic state. Third, the thermodynamics of the fluid must be specified through two equations of state $p(\rho, T)$ and $e(\rho, T)$. All of these equations are required to give a well-posed problem for a general flow situation.

PROBLEMS

6.1 (A) Stokes's flow (low-Reynolds-number incompressible flow) over a sphere has velocity components

$$v_r = U \cos \theta \left[1 + \frac{1}{2} \left(\frac{r_0}{r} \right)^3 - \frac{3}{2} \left(\frac{r_0}{r} \right) \right]$$

$$v_\theta = U \sin \theta \left[-1 + \frac{1}{4} \left(\frac{r_0}{r} \right)^3 + \frac{3}{4} \left(\frac{r_0}{r} \right) \right]$$

Compute all components of the viscous stress tensor in r, θ, φ coordinates.

6.2 (A) In Problem 6.1, find the maximum τ_{rr} and compare it with the dynamic pressure $\frac{1}{2}\rho U^2$ by forming their ratio.

6.3 (B) An ideal "inviscid" flow over a cylinder has the velocity components given in Problem 5.1. Compute all components of the viscous stress tensor. Compute $\nabla \cdot \tau$. Why is this flow called *inviscid*?

6.4 (B) Prove that a Newtonian fluid constant viscosity in incompressible flow obeys the relation $\nabla \cdot \tau = \mu \nabla^2 v$.

6.5 (C) Evaluate the Navier–Stokes equations for the velocity profiles of the Hill's spherical vortex given in Section 13.6. Integrate to find the pressure.

6.6 (A) Two long trains carrying coal are traveling in the same direction side by side on separate tracks. One train is moving at 40 ft/sec and the other at 50 ft/sec. In each coal car a man is shoveling coal and pitching it across to the neighboring train. The rate of coal transfer is 4 tons/min for each 100 ft of train length. This rate is the same for both trains. Find the extra force on each train per unit length caused by this mechanism.

6.7 (B) For a Newtonian fluid, show that the viscous dissipation is given by

$$\tau : \nabla v = -\frac{2}{3}\mu(\nabla \cdot v)^2 + 2\mu S{:}S$$

6.8 (A) Evaluate the surface tension equation 1.5.1 for Newtonian fluids where fluid A is a spherical drop in liquid B.

7

Some Incompressible
Flow Patterns

In previous chapters we dealt with the basic physics and the general ideas that apply to flow fields. What makes one flow situation different from another is the boundary conditions. Boundary conditions include the location and motion of walls, imposed pressure differences, prescribed velocities, assumptions of symmetry, and so on. The formulation of boundary conditions follows a few rules, for example, the no-slip condition, but in general we must use physical intuition and make reasonable assumptions. One purpose of this chapter is to present some examples of simple flows and the arguments used in their analysis.

In this chapter we assume that all the flows are incompressible. Later in the book we make a detailed analysis of what it means for a flow to be incompressible. For our present purposes we can simply assume that an incompressible flow has a constant density, viscosity, specific heat capacity, and thermal conductivity. With these assumptions the velocity field can be found using the continuity and momentum equations without regard for the energy equation and equations of state. Thus, the mechanical and thermal aspects of the flow can be separated.

7.1 PRESSURE-DRIVEN FLOW IN A SLOT

Consider two reservoirs with surfaces that are at two different elevations (Fig. 7.1). A tube connects the reservoirs so that water may flow between them. We assume that the reservoirs are so large that the flow into or out of the reservoir causes only a very slow rise or fall in the surface elevation. For purposes of the analysis, the fluid in the reservoirs is at a constant height. Since the hydrostatic pressures near each end of the horizontal tube are different, we expect a flow to develop and attain a quasisteady state.

The entrance to the tube is well rounded, and the fluid enters smoothly from the reservoir, having an almost constant velocity across the tube. The acceleration of the fluid from nearly zero velocity in the reservoir to the average value is accomplished by pressure forces, the pressure p_1 at the tube entrance being somewhat smaller than the hydrostatic pressure p_0 at the same level in the reservoir. Since friction is not important in the entrance region, the exact value of the pressure can be computed using Bernoulli's equation, applied along the central streamline (readers who are not familiar with this equation will find it in Section 7.2):

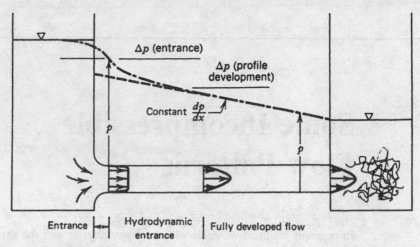

Figure 7.1   Pressure-driven flow in a slot (Poiseuille flow).

$$p_0 - p_1 = \tfrac{1}{2}\rho V_1^2$$

Although the bulk of the flow satisfies the no-friction assumption, flow very close to the wall must be retarded by friction. In fact, the no-slip condition requires zero velocity on the wall itself. Thus, the entrance profile has a thin portion near the wall where the velocity drops from V_1 to zero because of viscosity.

While the subject is at hand, we might note another aspect of the flat entrance profile that is inaccurate. It turns out that no matter how carefully the entrance is shaped, the profile is not completely flat but contains a slightly lower velocity than V_1 on the centerline and bulges of higher velocity farther out. This effect may be explained as follows. As the flow enters the tube, the streamlines are curved. To force the particles to follow a curved path, a normal pressure force must exist. The pressure on the outside of the streamline, toward the centerline, is higher than the pressure on the inside of the streamlines. Through Bernoulli's equation we know that a low pressure implies a high velocity, and vice versa. Even though the wall becomes flat, there is still some curvature of the interior streamlines at this point. The streamlines will be very nearly parallel only after we go downstream in the flat wall section for about one or two slot widths. This effect is very slight for a well-rounded entrance and can be ignored for most engineering applications.

The entrance profile, nearly flat with steep drop-offs next to the wall, undergoes further change as the flow proceeds down the tube. The viscous shear stress is at first confined to particles near the wall, but gradually it affects particles farther and farther from the wall. Each cross section of the tube must have the same mass flow rate, so when particles are slowed down near the wall, particles in the center must be accelerated. Pressure forces are responsible for accelerating the center particles, so the pressure must continue to decrease in the flow direction. Finally, when a balance between the pressure forces and the shear forces is attained, the profile no longer changes as we go to new positions down the tube; the profile is *fully developed*. The region where the flow profile is developing is called the *entrance region* or, more precisely, the hydrodynamic entrance region. The hydrodynamic entrance is usually long: 50- to 100-tube widths is not uncommon in engineering situations. The entrance region becomes short only when the flow is very slow (in the sense that the Reynolds number is small).

In the fully developed region it is possible to quantify the analysis with very little effort. To make things even simpler, we assume that the tube is a two-dimensional slot of height h. Taking an x–y coordinate system on the bottom wall in Fig. 7.2, we assume that nothing changes with z and that v_z is zero. We also assume that v_x is not a function of x, since the profile is fully developed. When these assumptions are inserted into the continuity equation (Table C.1)

$$\frac{\partial v_x}{\partial x} + \frac{\partial v_y}{\partial y} + \frac{\partial v_z}{\partial z} = 0$$

it reduces to

$$\frac{\partial v_y}{\partial y} = 0 \tag{7.1.1}$$

Upon partial integration we find that $v_y = v_y(x \text{ only})$. The no-slip condition at the walls requires that $v_y = 0$ for all x; hence v_y must be zero everywhere. This is a general truth when v_x is a function of y alone.

Turning now to the y-direction momentum equation (Table C.5), we have

$$\rho v_x \frac{\partial v_y}{\partial x} + \rho v_y \frac{\partial v_y}{\partial_y} = -\frac{\partial p}{\partial y} - \rho g + \mu \frac{\partial^2 v_y}{\partial x^2} + \mu \frac{\partial^2 v_y}{\partial y^2}$$

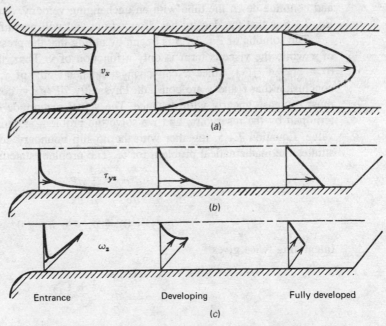

Figure 7.2   Profiles of (a) velocity; (b) shear stress; (c) vorticity.

Since v_y is zero, this simplifies to

$$\frac{\partial p}{\partial y} = -\rho g \qquad (7.1.2)$$

Pressure changes in the y-direction are the result of hydrostatic effects. Partial integration yields

$$p = -\rho g y + P(x) \qquad (7.1.3)$$

The function $P(x)$ is the pressure along the bottom wall where $y = 0$. In anticipation of the x-momentum equation, we note that the pressure gradient in the x-direction is at most a function of x. This result is found from Eq. 7.1.3 since

$$\frac{\partial p}{\partial x} = \frac{dP}{dx} \qquad (7.1.4)$$

We employ this fact as we write the x-direction momentum equation,

$$\rho v_x \frac{\partial v_x}{\partial x} + \rho v_y \frac{\partial v_x}{\partial y} = -\frac{dP}{dx} + \mu \frac{\partial^2 v_x}{\partial x^2} + \mu \frac{\partial^2 v_x}{\partial y^2}$$

Simplifying produces

$$0 = -\frac{dP}{dx} + \mu \frac{\partial^2 v_x}{\partial y^2} \qquad (7.1.5)$$

This relation states that at every point in the flow, the net pressure force is exactly balanced by the net shear stress. As a result of this balance, particles are not accelerated and continue down the tube with an unchanging velocity. Another thing to notice about Eq. 7.1.5 is that the density has dropped out and will not influence the velocity profile.

The solution of Eq. 7.1.5 is begun by noting that the pressure term is only a function of x while the viscous term is only a function of y. Thus, the equation is of the form $0 = g(x) + f(y)$. Since x can change independently of y, we arrive at the familiar conclusion that f and g are constant. Physically, $dP/dx = $ const means that the pressure must decrease linearly with distance. The actual magnitude of the pressure drop is determined by the reservoirs, and we solve the problem assuming that dP/dx is a known value. Equation 7.1.5, together with the no-slip boundary conditions at the walls, constitutes the mathematical problem for v_x. The problem statement is

$$\frac{d^2 v_x}{dy^2} = \frac{1}{\mu} \frac{dP}{dx} = \text{const} \qquad (7.1.6)$$

$$v_x(y = 0) = v_x(y = h) = 0 \qquad (7.1.7)$$

Integrating twice gives

$$v_x = \frac{1}{2\mu} \frac{dP}{dx} y^2 + C_1 y + C_2$$

Applying the boundary conditions determines the velocity profile as a parabola in y,

$$v_x = -\frac{h^2}{2\mu}\frac{dP}{dx}\left[\left(\frac{y}{h}\right) - \left(\frac{y}{h}\right)^2\right] \tag{7.1.8}$$

When the pressure gradient is negative, the flow is in the positive direction.

The velocity profile is a key result in any fluid-flow analysis because many other flow properties are found from it by simple relations. We begin by computing the flow rate across a section that is one unit deep in the z-direction:

$$Q = \int_{A_x} n_i v_i \, dA = \int_0^h v_x \, dy$$

$$= -\frac{h^3}{12\mu}\frac{dP}{dx} = \frac{h^3}{12\mu}\frac{\Delta P}{L} \tag{7.1.9}$$

In the relation above, the (positive) pressure difference between two points (at the same elevation) a distance L apart has replaced the pressure gradient.

The flow rate equation corresponding to Eq. 7.1.9 for round tubes was first given independently by G. Hagen (1839) (German engineer, 1797–1884) and J. Poiseuille (1840) (French physician, 1799–1869). They formulated the equation after careful experiments done with water in tubes of a variety of sizes and lengths. A good discussion of these researchers is given by Prandtl and Tietjens (1934); a copy of the data from this source is also given by Schlichting (1950). At the time of the experiments, the entrance length effect was not completely understood, and when short tubes were used, it caused a deviation from Eq. 7.1.9. Poiseuille could not explain this deviation, but Hagen came very close when he attributed it to an extra pressure drop required to accelerate the fluid. It is interesting that Poiseuille's motive for performing the experiments was to learn more about human blood flow.

Equation 7.1.9 is the basis for two types of measuring devices. The first is an apparatus to measure viscosity. Typically, a reservoir is used to impose pressure on a vertical capillary tube, which is open to the atmosphere. The time that it takes a given quantity of fluid to flow through the apparatus is a direct indication of the viscosity (in fact, viscosities are sometimes quoted in terms of *Saybolt seconds* or *Redwood seconds* instead of in dimensionally correct units). These devices offer an inexpensive and accurate method of measuring viscosities.

The second apparatus is for measuring flow rates. Any parallel, laminar flow has a flow rate equation that is linear in the pressure drop. Hence, if one is sure the flow through a tube, or a bank of tubes, is laminar and fully developed, the pressure drop is directly proportional to the flow. Unfortunately, most industrially important flows are so fast that they are turbulent and the linear relation is not valid.

Another form of Eq. 7.1.9 contains the average velocity (defined by the relation $Q = v_{ave}h$),

$$v_{ave} = \frac{h^2}{12\mu}\frac{\Delta P}{L} \tag{7.1.10}$$

The maximum velocity is found from Eq. 7.1.8 by evaluating at $y/h = \frac{1}{2}$:

$$v_{max} = \frac{h^2}{8\mu} \frac{\Delta P}{L} \tag{7.1.11}$$

Comparing these expressions shows that

$$v_{ave} = \tfrac{2}{3} v_{max} \tag{7.1.12}$$

If flow in a circular tube is investigated, one finds that the average velocity is only one-half the maximum velocity.

A more convenient form for the velocity profile is found by substituting Eq. 7.1.11 into Eq. 7.1.8:

$$\frac{v_x}{v_{max}} = 4\left[\frac{y}{h} - \left(\frac{y}{h}\right)^2\right] \tag{7.1.13}$$

From this we compute the shear stress,

$$\tau_{yx} = \mu \frac{dv_x}{dy} \tag{7.1.14}$$

$$\frac{\tau_{yx}}{\mu v_{max}/h} = 4\left[1 - 2\left(\frac{y}{h}\right)\right]$$

In all parallel-flow problems there is a proportionality between vorticity and shear stress:

$$\omega_z = -\frac{dv_x}{dy} = -\frac{\tau_{yx}}{\mu} \tag{7.1.15}$$

Figure 7.2 gives the profiles of velocity, shear stress, and vorticity at several sections along the tube. Note that the core of the entrance profile has no vorticity or shear stress.

The picture we have drawn of the flow through a tube corresponds to reality if the Reynolds number of the flow is moderate. At Reynolds numbers ($Re = v_{ave}h/\nu$) above 1400 to 1600, the flow is turbulent. Depending on the external disturbances, the critical Re can actually be from 1000 to 8000. When the flow becomes turbulent, our assumption of steady flow is invalid. This brings up a point that is well to remember about any analysis of fluid flow phenomena. A solution to the Navier–Stokes equations for a given geometry may not be unique.

7.2 MECHANICAL ENERGY, HEAD LOSS, AND BERNOULLI EQUATIONS

Mechanical energy equation 5.10.1 is

$$\partial_0(\rho\tfrac{1}{2}v^2) + \partial_i(\rho v_i \tfrac{1}{2}v^2) = \rho v_i F_i + v_j \, \partial_i T_{ij} \tag{7.2.1}$$

Let $Z(x_i)$ be the distance above a horizontal reference plane in a gravity field with acceleration g. If we express the gravity force by its potential, $F_i = -\partial_i(gZ(x_i))$, the work of gravity is $\rho v_i F_i = -\rho v_i \, \partial_i(gZ)$. Next, consider the continuity equation multiplied by

$-gZ$ and note that gZ is independent of time:

$$-\partial_0(\rho gZ) - gZ\,\partial_i(\rho v_i) = 0 \tag{7.2.2}$$

Adding this to the gravity work term produces

$$\rho v_i F_i = -\rho v_i\,\partial_i(gZ) - \partial_0(\rho gZ) - gZ\,\partial_i(\rho v_i)$$

$$= -\partial_i(\rho v_i gZ) - \partial_0(\rho gZ) \tag{7.2.3}$$

Next, note that the surface work term can be written as

$$v_j\,\partial_i T_{ij} = \partial_i(T_{ij}v_j) - T_{ij}\,\partial_i v_j \tag{7.2.4}$$

Combining the above gives the following form for the mechanical energy equation:

$$\partial_0[\rho(\tfrac{1}{2}v^2 + gZ)] + \partial_i[\rho v_i(\tfrac{1}{2}v^2 + gZ)] = \partial_i(v_j T_{ij}) - T_{ij}\,\partial_i v_j \tag{7.2.5}$$

Now let us continue to derive a global mechanical energy equation for an arbitrary region that moves with a surface velocity w_i. The surface velocity is any specified function of space and time. The total of the kinetic and potential energies within this region is treated by Leibnitz's theorem:

$$\frac{d}{dt}\int_{AR}\rho\left(\frac{1}{2}v^2 + gZ\right)dV = \int_{AR}\partial_0\left[\rho\left(\frac{1}{2}v^2 + gZ\right)\right]dV + \int_{AR}n_i w_i \rho\left(\frac{1}{2}v^2 + gZ\right)dS \tag{7.2.6}$$

Next, substitute Eq. 7.2.5 into the volume integral on the right-hand side, and whenever possible use the Gauss theorem to convert volume integrals into surface integrals:

$$\frac{d}{dt}\int_{AR}\rho\left(\frac{1}{2}v^2 + gZ\right)dV = -\int_{AR}\rho n_i(v_i - w_i)\left(\frac{1}{2}v^2 + gZ\right)dS + \int_{\substack{\text{fluid}\\\text{surfaces}}}n_i T_{ij}v_j\,dS$$

$$+ \int_{\substack{\text{solid}\\\text{surfaces}}}n_i T_{ij}v_j\,dS + \int_{AR}T_{ij}\,\partial_i v_j\,dV \tag{7.2.7}$$

The surface force integrals have been split into areas where the control region cuts through solid material and regions cutting fluid areas. The stress in the solid $n_i T_{ij}$ is multiplied by the velocity of the material in the direction of the stress to obtain the shaft work:

$$\dot{W}_{\text{shaft}} = \int_{\substack{\text{solid}\\\text{surfaces}}}n_i T_{ij}v_j\,dS \tag{7.2.8}$$

Work of a rotating or translating shaft is described by this term. In fluid regions the stress tensor is decomposed into pressure and viscous parts, $T_{ij} = -p\delta_{ij} + \tau_{ij}$. At the same time insert a term called *boundary pressure work* and compensate by subtracting its definition:

$$\dot{W}_{\text{boundary}} = -\int_{\substack{\text{fluid}\\\text{surfaces}}}n_i w_i p\,dS \tag{7.2.9}$$

For a fixed region this is zero.

$$\frac{d}{dt} \int_{AR} \rho \left(\frac{1}{2} v^2 + gZ \right) dV = - \int_{AR} \rho n_i (v_i - w_i) \left(\frac{1}{2} v^2 + gZ \right) dS + \dot{W}_{\text{shaft}}$$

$$- \int_{\substack{\text{fluid} \\ \text{surfaces}}} n_i v_i p \, dS + \int_{\substack{\text{fluid} \\ \text{surfaces}}} n_i \tau_{ij} v_j \, dS$$

$$+ \int_{\substack{\text{fluid} \\ \text{surfaces}}} n_i w_i p \, dS + \dot{W}_{\text{boundary}}$$

$$+ \int_{AR} \tau_{ij} \, \partial_i v_j \, dV + \int_{AR} p \, \partial_i v_i \, dV \qquad (7.2.10)$$

The reason for introducing the boundary work idea is to allow the pressure work to be organized into a flow work concept. *Flow work* is the pressure times the velocity relative to the surface, or, in effect, the mass flow into the region times p/ρ:

$$\text{flow work} = - \int_{AR} \rho n_i (v_i - w_i) \frac{p}{\rho} \, dS \qquad (7.2.11)$$

The final general form for the compressible flow in an arbitrary region is

$$\frac{d}{dt} \int_{AR} \rho \left(\frac{1}{2} v^2 + gZ \right) dV = - \int_{AR} \rho n_i (v_i - w_i) \left(\frac{1}{2} v^2 + gZ + \frac{p}{\rho} \right) dS + \dot{W}_{\text{shaft}}$$

$$+ \int_{\substack{\text{fluid} \\ \text{surfaces}}} n_i \tau_{ij} v_j \, dS + \dot{W}_{\text{boundary}} + \int_{AR} \tau_{ij} \, \partial_i v_j \, dV$$

$$+ \int_{AR} p \, \partial_i v_i \, dV \qquad (7.2.12)$$

The volume integrals that remain are the compression work and the viscous dissipation (note that $\tau_{ij} \, \partial_i v_j = \tau : \mathbf{S} = 2\mu \mathbf{S} : \mathbf{S}$). Flow work and boundary pressure work are not primitive concepts but are very common and useful in engineering applications.

Consider an application of the mechanical energy equation where the flow is incompressible. The last term, compression work, in Eq. 7.2.12 is zero. Further, consider a fixed region where there is one inlet flow and one outlet flow that are steady. Call the average velocity V, so that the mass flow rate is $\dot{m} = \rho A V$. The flow on the interior is at least periodic. A propeller or impeller may be turning inside, but there is on the average no increase in $\rho(\frac{1}{2} v^2 + gZ)$ inside the volume. Another assumption is that the Reynolds number is high, so that the viscous forces at the fluid surfaces are small compared to the pressure forces. Finally, introduce the term *head loss* to account for the viscous dissipation within the entire region:

$$\dot{m} g h_l = \int_{FR} \tau : \mathbf{S} \, dV \qquad (7.2.13)$$

One further simplification is to employ a kinetic energy coefficient α, defined by

$$\alpha \dot{m} \frac{1}{2} V^2 = \int_A \rho n_i v_i \frac{1}{2} v^2 \, dS \tag{7.2.14}$$

Denote the inlet stream as 1 and the outlet as 2; then a very useful and well-known form of the mechanical energy equation is obtained:

$$\left(\alpha \frac{1}{2} V^2 + gZ + \frac{p}{\rho} \right)_1 - \left(\alpha \frac{1}{2} V^2 + gZ + \frac{p}{\rho} \right)_2 = \frac{\dot{W}_{\text{shaft}}}{\dot{m}} + gh_l \tag{7.2.15}$$

For turbulent flow the nearly flat profiles mean that $\alpha = 1$ is an acceptable assumption.

Reconsider the horizontal pipe flow problem of Section 7.1. What if the same pipe was inclined at some angle such that $Z_1 \neq Z_2$? Let the velocity be the same for both situations. The energy equation is

$$\left(\frac{p}{\rho} + gZ \right)_1 - \left(\frac{p}{\rho} + gZ \right)_2 = gh_{l1-2} \tag{7.2.16}$$

Since the velocity, the velocity profiles, and the stress profiles are identical for the two situations, the viscous dissipation and head loss are the same. Thus, the previous analysis can be adapted to an inclined pipe by replacing

$$\frac{p}{\rho} \to \frac{p}{\rho} + gZ$$

In turbulent flows the head loss is determined from experiments. Head loss data for pipes, valves, contractions, expansions, and so on, are tabulated in engineering reference books such as Blevins (1984) and Idelchik (1994).

Applying Eq. 7.2.15 to a steady-flow streamtube without any friction effects, that is, $h_{\ell 1-2} = 0$, results in the Bernoulli equation:

$$\frac{1}{2} v^2 + \frac{p}{\rho} + gZ = \text{const} \tag{7.2.17}$$

This equation applies along any streamline where the flow is steady, incompressible, and inviscid. In common fluids, such as water and air, the viscous stresses are roughly 1 to 2% of the pressure, and the inviscid assumption may often be used employing Eq. 7.2.17 as a reasonable estimate of the pressure.

The head loss, as defined in Eq. 7.2.13, is very general and quite useful in the analysis of flow system problems. Each component of the flow system has its head loss. A nondimensional head-loss coefficient is formed by taking the kinetic energy per unit mass of the entering (or exiting) fluid as a reference:

$$K \equiv \frac{gh_\ell}{\frac{1}{2}v_{\text{ref}}^2} \quad \text{or} \quad gh_\ell = K\frac{1}{2}v_{\text{ref}}^2 \tag{7.2.18}$$

Notice that K may be much greater than 1. For example, a valve that is slightly open has a high-speed jet through the small open area. The energy of this jet is completely dissipated and constitutes the head loss. This energy may be 100 times the kinetic energy of the flow into the valve body, which is the reference kinetic energy.

The head loss for straight tubes with a fully developed profile increases linearly with the length of the tube. This fact leads to the introduction of the *friction factor* f so that

$$K = \frac{L}{D} f \qquad (7.2.19)$$

The physical interpretation of f is the fraction of reference kinetic energy that is dissipated in a length of tube equal to the diameter D.

Theory for laminar flow in round tubes indicates that the friction factor decreases as $64/\text{Re}$. Turbulent flow, on the other hand, demands an experimental measurement. Figure 7.3 shows modern measurements on smooth tubes. Any elementary fluid mechanics book will display the older measurements and include the effects of wall roughness. The University of Oregon group (Swanson et al., 2002) used various gases (He, O_2, CO_2, SF_6) at low Reynolds numbers and liquid helium at their higher values. The Princeton experiments (Zagarola and Smits, 1998; and McKeon et al., 2004) used compressed air at up to 220 atm. These facilities and fluids are quite different but produce agreement in an overlap range from $\text{Re} = 3 \times 10^4$ to 1×10^6. McKeon et al. (2004) note that the viscous sublayer is so thin at the highest four Reynolds number points that wall roughness effects may begin.

We mentioned previously that the hydrodynamic entrance region of the tube in Section 7.1 suffers an extra pressure drop. The reason is found if we apply the kinetic energy equations between the entrance, where the velocity is uniform at v_{ave}, and a downstream station where the parabolic profile exists. The term for convection of kinetic energy in Eq. 7.2.14 contains the velocity cubed, and since the parabolic profile has a maximum equal to $\frac{3}{2}$ times the average, there is significantly more kinetic energy in the fully de-

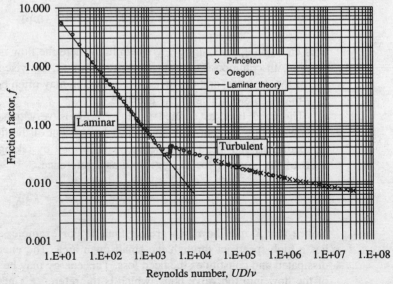

Figure 7.3 Experimental measurements of pipe friction from University of Oregon, courtesy of R. J. Donnelly, and from Princeton, courtesy of A. J. Smits. Details are given in Zagarola and Smits (1998), Swanson et al. (2002), and McKeon et al. (2004).

veloped profile than in the entrance profile. This increase in energy requires an extra pressure drop to accelerate the flow. The viscous dissipation in the entrance region is concentrated near the wall, but if the entrance is smooth, it is not significantly higher than the fully developed value. As a matter of fact, in a round tube the convection of kinetic energy by the fully developed profile is twice the convection of kinetic energy by the entrance profile.

We turn now to a discussion of the events at the exit of the tube into the second reservoir. A sharp exit as shown in Fig. 7.4 will always cause flow separation and a jet of fluid will issue into the reservoir. It is common to assume that the streamlines at the exit plane are still exactly parallel to the walls. If this is so, the y-momentum equation again simplifies to Eq. 7.1.2, the hydrostatic pressure equation. Our picture of the jet exit is then one where the pressure at the exit plane is the hydrostatic pressure that normally occurs in the reservoir in the absence of motion.

A jet issuing into a reservoir is a very unstable flow where small perturbations grow very rapidly. Turbulence quickly develops in this region, at first being confined to the edge between the reservoir fluid and the jet fluid. This is a region of high shear. As we proceed farther away from the exit, the turbulence grows and eventually the jet is completely turbulent. At the same time the turbulence grows; it entrains fluid from the reservoir, which in turn induces a slight flow of reservoir fluid toward the jet. Once the jet becomes completely turbulent, the centerline velocity begins to decay, accompanied by a spreading of the jet. The decay continues until all the directed kinetic energy of the jet is transformed into the random kinetic energy of turbulent eddies.

The ultimate fate of turbulent eddies is to be destroyed by the action of viscosity. Viscous dissipation finally claims all the turbulent energy and transforms it into random

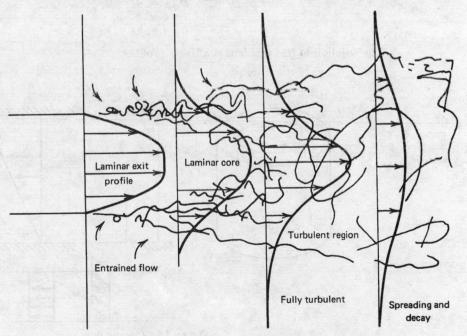

Figure 7.4 Decay of a jet exiting into a reservoir.

molecular motion. With a sensitive thermometer we would find a slight increase in the fluid temperature.

7.3   PLANE COUETTE FLOW

The simple shear flow named after M. F. A. Couette (1858--1943) is often used to introduce the concept of viscosity. We imagine two concentric circular cylinders with the gap between them filled with fluid (Fig. 7.5). One of the cylinders, say the inner one, is rotated while the other is stationary. We can make the analysis simpler if we consider that the gap width is very small compared to the inner radius. This allows us to model the flow as the flow in a plane, two-dimensional slot with one moving wall and one stationary wall.

The analysis to find the velocity profile is very similar to that for Poiseuille flow in Section 7.1. We assume a unidirectional flow $v_x(y)$ that is independent of x. In the x-direction momentum equation we make the additional assumption that there is no pressure gradient in the x-direction. This yields

$$0 = \mu \frac{d^2 v_x}{dy^2} \tag{7.3.1}$$

which means that the shear stress on each side of a particle is exactly balanced: The shear stress is a constant across the gap. Notice that the viscosity can be divided out of Eq. 7.3.1, implying that neither viscosity nor density affects the profile. The boundary conditions for the problem represent the no-slip condition applied to each wall,

$$v_x(y = 0) = 0$$
$$v_x(y = h) = V_0 \tag{7.3.2}$$

The solution to this problem is a linear profile,

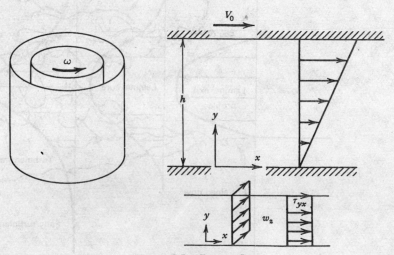

Figure 7.5   Couette flow.

$$v_x = \frac{V_0 y}{h} \tag{7.3.3}$$

Calculating the shear stress from this profile gives a constant value, as we anticipated above:

$$\tau_{yx} = \mu \frac{dv_x}{dy} = \mu \frac{V_0}{h} \tag{7.3.4}$$

The vorticity is also a constant:

$$\omega_z = -\frac{dv_x}{dy} = -\frac{V_0}{h} \tag{7.3.5}$$

These quantities are plotted in Fig. 7.5. The corresponding analysis for flow between concentric cylinders is also easily accomplished.

The assumption we made that v_x is only a function of y is not always true. Another stable laminar flow pattern exists where the flow breaks up into a series of cells like doughnuts stacked on top of each other. Each cell has a shear profile plus a spiral vortex with its core in the center of the doughnut. The vortex in one cell rotates in one direction and neighboring vortices on either side rotate in the opposite direction. G. I. Taylor (English physicist, 1886–1970) did the experiments and theory for this flow and the pattern is called a *Taylor–Couette flow*. Taylor vortices occur when the *Taylor number*, Ta $\equiv (V_0 h / \nu) \cdot (h / R_i) > 1700$. Actually the Taylor–Couette pattern is not always stable and many more complex patterns, discussed in Section 25.13, have been found.

7.4   PRESSURE-DRIVEN FLOW IN A SLOT WITH A MOVING WALL

In the problems we analyzed in Sections 7.1 and 7.3, the velocity was governed by linear differential equations and linear boundary conditions. In this section we study a composite flow. Let the Poiseuille flow velocity be $v_x^{(1)}$ and the Couette flow velocity be $v_x^{(2)}$; then the algebraic sum represents the flow in a slot with a moving wall and an imposed pressure gradient, both acting simultaneously:

$$v_x = v_x^{(1)} + v_x^{(2)}$$

$$v_x = -\frac{h^2}{2\mu} \frac{dP}{dx} \left[\frac{y}{h} - \left(\frac{y}{h} \right)^2 \right] + V_0 \frac{y}{h}$$

or in a slightly different form,

$$\frac{v_x}{V_0} = (1 + \mathbb{P}) \frac{y}{h} - \mathbb{P} \left(\frac{y}{h} \right)^2$$

In this equation $\mathbb{P}$ is a nondimensional parameter that indicates the relative effects of the pressure gradient and the wall motion. The parameter $\mathbb{P}$ is given by

$$\mathbb{P} \equiv -\frac{1}{2}\frac{h^2}{V_0\mu}\frac{dP}{dx} = 4\frac{v_{max}^{(1)}}{V_0}$$

Velocity profiles are shown in Fig. 7.6. We shall find that these velocity profiles are good local approximations to the flow in slider bearings.

7.5 DOUBLE FALLING FILM ON A WALL

The double falling film is a problem designed to illustrate the boundary conditions between two immiscible liquids and the boundary condition between gases and liquids. Consider the flow situation depicted in Fig. 7.7, where a smooth plane is inclined at an angle θ to the vertical. Two immiscible liquid films flow down the plane under the influence of gravity. The actual thickness of each film is controlled by the method by which the flow is established. We do not concern ourselves with how the flow is established or how long it takes to reach a steady profile independent of x. These problems are avoided by assuming that the film thicknesses h_a and h_b have known values.

We take a rectangular coordinate system aligned with the flow and having the x-axis on the plate. As with all problems in this chapter, we assume that there is only one nonzero velocity component, which is a function of y alone. This assumption was shown previously to satisfy the continuity equation identically. The y-direction momentum equation is once again the hydrostatic balance

$$0 = -\frac{\partial p}{\partial y} - \rho g \sin\theta \qquad (7.5.1)$$

Here ρ is either ρ_a or ρ_b, as needed. A partial integration of this equation gives

$$p = -\rho g y \sin\theta + f(x) \qquad (7.5.2)$$

The arbitrary function $f(x)$ is evaluated using the fact that atmospheric pressure p_0 exists

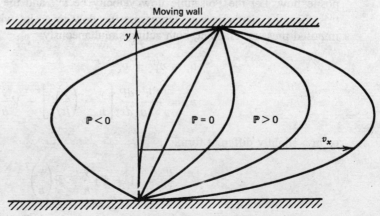

Figure 7.6 Velocity profiles for combined Couette–Poiseuille flow. The pressure-gradient parameter is $\mathbb{P}$.

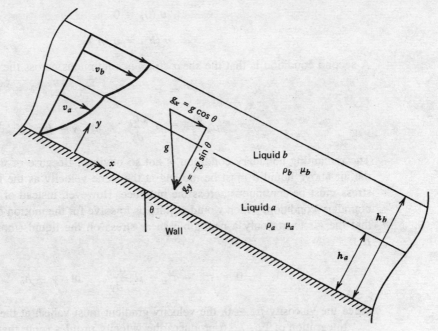

Figure 7.7 Films of two immiscible fluids falling down an inclined wall.

on the top of liquid b; hence,

$$p = \rho_b g(h_b - y) \sin \theta + p_0, \qquad h_a \leq y \leq h_b \qquad (7.5.3)$$

The pressure at the interface we denote as $p(h_a) = p_1$. Thus,

$$p_1 = \rho_b g(h_b - h_a) \sin \theta + p_0 \qquad (7.5.4)$$

Finally, the pressure in liquid a is found from Eq. 7.5.2 and the condition above:

$$p = \rho_a g(h_a - y) \sin \theta + p_1, \qquad 0 \leq y \leq h_a \qquad (7.5.5)$$

The pressure on the plate surface is in general slightly higher than ambient. If the plate is horizontal ($\theta = \pi/2$), the entire weight of the fluid is imposed, while if the plate is vertical, there is no pressure change through the liquid and the plate is at atmospheric pressure.

The flow is driven by the component of gravity along the plate. In this direction the momentum equation simplifies to

$$0 = \mu \frac{d^2 v_x}{dy^2} + \rho g \cos \theta \qquad (7.5.6)$$

We drop the subscript x in the equations that follow. This should cause no confusion, since there is only one velocity component. It will also allow us to use v_a and v_b as symbols for the velocity in liquids a and b, respectively.

Next we turn to the boundary conditions. The no-slip condition applies at the wall and also at the interface; hence,

$$v_a(0) = 0 \tag{7.5.7}$$

$$v_a(h_a) = v_b(h_a) \tag{7.5.8}$$

A second condition is that the shear stress is continuous across the interface:

$$\tau_{yx}^a = \tau_{yx}^b \tag{7.5.9}$$

$$\mu_a \frac{dv_a}{dy} = \mu_b \frac{dv_b}{dy} \quad \text{at} \quad y = h_a$$

The remaining boundary condition is not so obvious. Because of the no-slip condition, the air above liquid b must be moving at the same velocity as the liquid, and the shear stress must be continuous across the interface. However, instead of applying the correct boundary condition, which would require us to solve for the motion of the air, we assume that the air exerts only a negligible shear stress on the liquid (more precisely $\mu_b \gg \mu_a$):

$$0 \approx \tau_{yx}^{\text{air}} = \tau_{yx}^b = \mu_b \frac{dv_b}{dy} \quad \text{at} \quad y = h_b \tag{7.5.10}$$

Since the viscosity $\mu_b \neq 0$, the velocity gradient must vanish at the interface.

Integration of Eq. 7.5.6 produces the velocity profiles (note that $\mu/\rho = \nu$):

$$v_a = -\frac{g}{2\nu_a} y^2 \cos\theta + C_1 y + C_2 \tag{7.5.11}$$

$$v_b = -\frac{g}{2\nu_b} y^2 \cos\theta + C_3 y + C_4 \tag{7.5.12}$$

Applying the no-slip condition, Eq. 7.5.7 gives $C_2 = 0$, while at $y = h_b$ the vanishing shear Eq. 7.5.10 shows that

$$C_3 = \frac{g}{\nu_b} h_b \cos\theta = \frac{h_b \nu_a}{h_a \nu_b} \frac{g}{\nu_a} h_a \cos\theta \tag{7.5.13}$$

The interface stress condition 7.5.9 and interface velocity condition yield

$$C_1 = \frac{gh_a}{\nu_a} \cos\theta \left[\frac{\rho_b}{\rho_a} \left(\frac{h_b}{h_a} - 1 \right) + 1 \right] \tag{7.5.14}$$

$$C_4 = \frac{gh_a^2 \cos\theta}{\nu_a} \left[\frac{1}{2} + \frac{1}{2}\frac{\nu_a}{\nu_b} - \frac{\rho_b}{\rho_a} + \left(\frac{\rho_b}{\rho_a} - \frac{\nu_a}{\nu_b} \right) \frac{h_b}{h_a} \right] \tag{7.5.15}$$

The velocity profiles are

$$v_a = \frac{gh_a^2 \cos\theta}{\nu_a} \left\{ \left[1 + \frac{\rho_b}{\rho_a} \left(\frac{h_b}{h_a} - 1 \right) \right] \frac{y}{h_a} - \frac{1}{2}\left(\frac{y}{h_a} \right)^2 \right\}$$

$$v_b = \frac{gh_a^2 \cos\theta}{\nu_a} \left[\frac{1}{2} + \frac{1}{2}\frac{\nu_a}{\nu_b} - \frac{\rho_b}{\rho_a} + \left(\frac{\rho_b}{\rho_a} - \frac{\nu_a}{\nu_b} \right) \frac{h_b}{h_a} + \frac{\nu_a h_b}{\nu_b h_a} \frac{y}{h_a} - \frac{1}{2}\frac{\nu_a}{\nu_b}\left(\frac{y}{h_a} \right)^2 \right]$$

An example of these velocity profiles is given in Fig. 7.7 for the case of a less viscous fluid on top of a more viscous fluid. We also note that the case of a single falling film is retrieved from the v_a equation by setting $h_b/h_a = 1$.

7.6   OUTER SOLUTION FOR ROTARY VISCOUS COUPLING

Here we seek to find the flow that would exist in a thin gap between the end wall of a cylinder and a pistonlike device that is rotated with speed Ω. Figure 7.8 shows the situation and defines a cylindrical coordinate system. The cylinder could be attached to a second shaft that rotates at a different speed so that $\Omega = \Omega_1 - \Omega_2$. Assume that the flow is completely circumferential; $v_z = 0$, $v_r = 0$, and $v_\theta = v_\theta(r, z)$. The boundary conditions of no-slip require that

$$v_\theta(r, z = 0) = 0$$

$$v_\theta(r, z = h) = r\Omega \qquad (7.6.1)$$

$$v_\theta(r = R, z) = 0$$

Note that there is a discontinuity in the boundary conditions at $r = R$, $z = H$, where the piston meets the cylinder wall. To be more specific would require more details of the exact geometry of the piston corner and the side wall. The flow in this region is not our main interest.

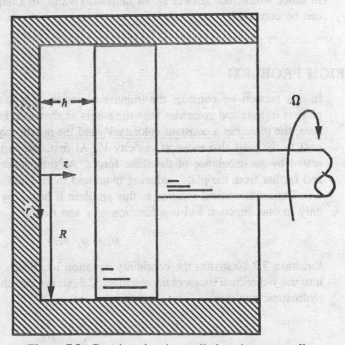

Figure 7.8   Rotating plate in a cylinder: viscous coupling.

When the assumption $v_\theta = v_\theta(r, z)$ is used to simplify the θ-direction momentum equation (Table C.5), we find that

$$0 = \frac{\partial}{\partial r}\left[\frac{1}{r}\frac{\partial}{\partial r}(rv_\theta)\right] + \frac{\partial^2 v_\theta}{\partial z^2} \tag{7.6.2}$$

When the gap is thin, that is, $h/R \to 0$, the change in v_θ across the z-direction gap, $0 - r\Omega$ in a distance h, are much larger than the changes in the r-direction, $0 - R\Omega$ in a distance R. Locally, at any r location the flow will be much like the Couette flow of Section 7.3. Therefore, we ignore the term in Eq. 7.6.2 with r variation and try to satisfy the simplified equation

$$0 = \frac{\partial^2 v_\theta}{\partial z^2}$$

Solving this equation (allowing the boundary condition to vary with r) produces

$$v_\theta = r\Omega \frac{z}{h} \tag{7.6.3}$$

The main idea is to seek to satisfy the dominant term(s) in the problem and neglect the others. This answer just happens to satisfy the complete equation 7.6.1.

There is a difficulty with the solution 7.6.3 in that it does not satisfy the third boundary condition of Eq. 7.6.1; the no-slip condition at the sidewall $v_\theta(r = R, z) = 0$. Along this wall the answer is "singular" because it does not give the proper behavior. In other words, our answer is not uniformly valid. In Chapter 11 we consider how this can be corrected.

7.7 RAYLEIGH PROBLEM

In this section we consider the impulsive motion of a flat plate in its own plane. The plate is infinite and coincides with the x-axis as shown in Fig. 7.9. For times greater than zero, the plate has a constant velocity V_0 and the no-slip condition requires that the fluid next to the wall also move at velocity V_0. At first, the particles near the wall are accelerated by an imbalance of the shear forces. As time proceeds, this effect is felt farther and farther from the plate, inducing more and more fluid to move along with the plate.

The mathematical solution to this problem is begun by assuming that the velocity is only in one direction and is a function of y and t only:

$$v_x = v_x(y, t) \tag{7.7.1}$$

Equation 7.7.1 satisfies the continuity equation identically. Substituting this assumption into the y-direction momentum equation, C.5, shows that the pressure is governed by the hydrostatic equation

$$0 = -\frac{\partial p}{\partial y} - \rho g \tag{7.7.2}$$

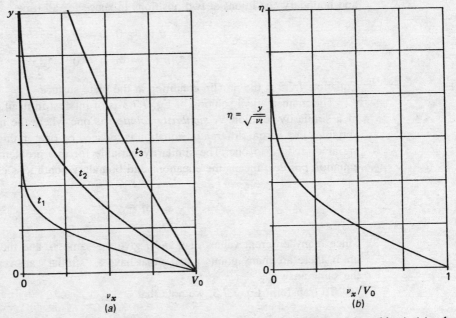

Figure 7.9 Impulsive motion of a flat plate in its own plane (the Rayleigh problem): (a) velocity profile of various times; (b) velocity profile in similarity variables.

Integration gives

$$p = -\rho g y + p_0$$

where we take the pressure to be uniform on the plate at a value p_0. Although Eq. 7.7.2 shows an infinite negative pressure at $y \rightarrow \infty$, we realize that the finite extent of any apparatus would prohibit this result. The important point is that p is not a function of x.

The flow is governed by the x-momentum equation, which simplifies to

$$\rho \frac{\partial v_x}{\partial t} = \mu \frac{\partial^2 v_x}{\partial y^2} \tag{7.7.3}$$

Acceleration of a fluid particle is the result of an imbalance in the shear forces acting on the particle. We also note that ρ and μ do not enter the problem independently but only in the combination μ/ρ, which is by definition the kinematic viscosity:

$$\nu \equiv \frac{\mu}{\rho} \qquad \left[\frac{L^2}{T} \right]$$

We will find that ν is a much more important parameter in fluid mechanics than the absolute viscosity μ (except in low-Reynolds-number flows).

Mathematically, Eq. 7.7.3 is also called the *heat* or *diffusion equation*. It is a parabolic differential equation. The proper conditions to prescribe for parabolic equations are an initial condition for all space,

$$v_x(y, t = 0) = 0 \tag{7.7.4}$$

and boundary conditions at two positions in space for all time,

$$v_x(y = 0, t) = V_0 \tag{7.7.5}$$

$$v_x(y \to \infty, t) = 0 \tag{7.7.6}$$

Equation 7.7.5 is the no-slip condition at the plate surface.

The mathematical solution of Eq. 7.7.3 is of interest in itself, since it is an example of a similarity solution. A *similarity solution* is one where the number of independent variables in a partial differential equation is reduced by one; in this case two independent variables reduce to one. The similarity variable for this problem (a partial differential equation *problem* means the equations and boundary conditions considered together) is

$$\eta = \frac{y}{2\sqrt{\nu t}} \tag{7.7.7}$$

Since many different values of y and t give the same η, and the answer depends only on η, there are many points y and t that have a "similar" answer (in this case, exactly the same answer).

To transform Eq. 7.7.3, we note that

$$\frac{\partial(\ )}{\partial t} = \frac{d(\ )}{d\eta} \frac{\partial \eta}{\partial t} = -\frac{yt^{-3/2}}{4\sqrt{\nu}} \frac{d(\ )}{d\eta} = -\frac{1}{2} \frac{\eta}{t} \frac{d(\ )}{d\eta}$$

$$\frac{\partial(\ )}{\partial y} = \frac{d(\ )}{d\eta} \frac{\partial \eta}{\partial y} = \frac{1}{2\sqrt{\nu t}} \frac{d(\ )}{d\eta}$$

$$\frac{\partial^2(\ )}{\partial y^2} = \frac{\partial}{\partial y} \left[\frac{d(\ )}{d\eta} \frac{\partial \eta}{\partial y} \right] = \frac{\partial}{\partial y} \left[\frac{1}{2\sqrt{\nu t}} \frac{d(\ )}{d\eta} \right] = \frac{1}{2\sqrt{\nu t}} \frac{\partial}{\partial y} \left[\frac{d(\ )}{d\eta} \right]$$

$$= \frac{1}{2\sqrt{\nu t}} \frac{d}{d\eta} \left[\frac{d(\ )}{d\eta} \right] \frac{\partial \eta}{\partial y} = \frac{1}{4\nu t} \frac{d^2(\ )}{d\eta^2}$$

For the dependent variable we introduce the symbol f and note that f is assumed to be a function of η alone:

$$\frac{v_x}{V_0} \equiv f(\eta) \tag{7.7.8}$$

Substituting the relations above into Eq. 7.7.3 produces an ordinary differential equation as promised:

$$f'' + 2\eta f' = 0 \tag{7.7.9}$$

If the choice of a trial similarity variable does not produce an ordinary differential equation, the trial is unsuccessful.

Even if a similarity variable is found for a particular differential equation, it may not work. To be applicable, the similarity variable must make the boundary conditions on the original problem transform so that the new problem makes sense. The boundary conditions for the present problem transform as follows:

$$v_x(y, t = 0) = 0 \Rightarrow f(\eta \to \infty) = 0$$

$$v_x(y = 0, t) = V_0 \Rightarrow f(\eta = 0) = 1 \qquad (7.7.10)$$

$$v_x(y \to \infty, t) = 0 \Rightarrow f(\eta \to \infty) = 0$$

When the original problem, consisting of a partial differential equation and three boundary conditions, changes into one consisting of a second-order ordinary differential equation, we can allow only two boundary conditions. Accordingly, our similarity variable is successful, since it has collapsed two boundary conditions of Eq. 7.7.10 to the same thing. The three original conditions become only two conditions in the transformed variables.

Equation 7.7.9 may be integrated once, considering f' as the dependent variable. This yields

$$f' = C_1 \exp(-\eta^2) \qquad (7.7.11)$$

Integrating again,

$$f = C_1 \int_0^\eta \exp(-\xi^2) \, d\xi + C_2$$

The integral above looks simple but is in fact not an elementary function. It is a "higher" function called the *error function*. The error function is defined as

$$\text{erf}(\eta) \equiv \frac{2}{\sqrt{\pi}} \int_0^\eta \exp(-\xi^2) \, d\xi \qquad (7.7.12)$$

One can see from the definition that $\text{erf}(0) = 0$, and the factor in front of the integral has been chosen so that $\text{erf}(\infty) = 1$. The final answer, which satisfies the boundary conditions, is

$$f(\eta) = 1 - \text{erf}(\eta) \qquad (7.7.13)$$

$$\frac{v_x}{V_0} = 1 - \text{erf}\left(\frac{y}{2\sqrt{\nu t}}\right)$$

This answer is graphed in Fig. 7.9. Before discussing it we also compute the shear stress and the vorticity,

$$\omega_z = -\frac{\partial v_x}{\partial y} = -\frac{V_0}{2\sqrt{\nu t}} \frac{df}{d\eta} = \frac{V_0}{\sqrt{\pi \nu t}} \exp(-\eta^2) \qquad (7.7.14a)$$

and

$$\tau_{yx} = \mu \frac{\partial v_x}{\partial y} = -\mu \omega_z \qquad (7.7.14b)$$

(Note that the shear stress is a function of the similarity variable only if it is scaled by the square root of the time; that is, $\tau_{yx} \sqrt{\pi \nu t}/\mu V_0$ is a nondimensional shear stress that is a function of η alone.) We are most interested in the shear stress on the plate itself. It is

$$\tau_{yx}(0) = -\frac{\mu V_0}{\sqrt{\pi \nu t}} \tag{7.7.15}$$

The stress is infinite at the initial instant and decreases as $1/\sqrt{t}$.

The velocity profile shows that the influence of the plate extends to infinity immediately after the plate starts moving. At large distances the error function vanishes exponentially [actually, erf $\eta \sim \eta^{-1} \exp(-\eta^2)$ as $\eta \to \infty$], but there is still a minute viscous influence throughout the flow. We can rationalize the influence at infinity by considering the molecular model of gas viscosity. Molecules that collide with the plate absorb some extra momentum before returning to the fluid. Although for the most part the molecules collide with other molecules several times before getting very far from the plate; in principle, there is the possibility of molecules traveling to infinity without a collision.

Let us consider the place where the velocity has dropped to 1% of the plate value ($v_x/V_0 = 0.01$). Figure 7.9b shows that η is about 1.8 at this position, which we denote by $y = \delta$. Then

$$\eta\left(\frac{v_x}{V_0} = 0.01\right) = 1.8 = \frac{\delta}{2\sqrt{\nu t}}$$

and

$$\delta = 3.6\sqrt{\nu t} \tag{7.7.16}$$

The diffusion of viscous effects is a basic phenomenon in fluid mechanics and we frequently need to estimate how far diffusion has progressed. The quantity δ, called the *viscous diffusion distance,* is useful for this purpose. The major effects of viscosity are contained between the wall and $y = \delta$. Notice that diffusion slows down as time goes on, that it depends on the kinematic (not the absolute) viscosity, and that is independent of the plate velocity. In terms of viscous diffusion, air is more viscous than water by a factor of about 10. We amplify this remark by computing the diffusion length after 1 min for air,

$$\delta = 10.8 \text{ cm} \qquad (\nu = 0.150 \text{ cm}^2/\text{s})$$

and for water,

$$\delta = 2.8 \text{ cm} \qquad (\nu = 0.010 \text{ cm}^2/\text{s})$$

In general, viscous diffusion is a slow process; in most flow fields a particle travels a great distance in a minute. (Only $\frac{1}{3}$ s is required for a particle to go from the nose of a Boeing 747 to the tail when the flight speed is 500 mph.)

The mathematical solution to this problem was first given by Stokes (1851, Note B). We now call it the Rayleigh problem because Rayleigh (1911) used the results in a creative way to derive a skin friction law. The problem concerned the skin friction for laminar flow over a flat plate of length L moving at velocity V_0. Lanchester (1907) had given a skin friction law in his book *Aerodynamics,* but Rayleigh sought a physical derivation. He argued that we should watch the plate move through a stationary fluid and imagine that we are looking at one point in space as the plate moves by. When the leading edge of the plate passes our vantage point, it is similar to the initial instant of the infinite plate motion. Farther back along the plate, the shear stress decreases because the particles have been in "contact" with the plate for a longer time. Rayleigh proposed that the flow at any position on the finite plate is the same as that on an impulsively started infinite plate after a time t equal to the time since the leading edge passed the vantage point. The key to Rayleigh's argument was the idea of replacing t by x/V_0, where x is the distance from the leading edge. If we make this substitution in Eq. 7.7.15, the local shear stress on the finite plate becomes

$$\tau = \frac{\mu V_0}{\sqrt{\pi \nu}} \sqrt{\frac{V_0}{x}} \qquad (7.7.17)$$

The total drag force is found by integrating over the length of the plate. The resulting formula is not very accurate, but it has the proper trends with all the parameters. Perhaps more important than the drag formula itself was the argument Rayleigh used to obtain it. The same argument is frequently employed to estimate the proper trends for phenomena involving viscous diffusion. For many purposes it does not matter if the magnitude is exactly right.

In closing we note that the Rayleigh problem also applies to the flow above a stationary plate when the fluid is started impulsively with a uniform velocity. The two answers are related by a Galilean transformation.

7.8 CONCLUSIONS

This chapter has illustrated the analytical approach to fluid-flow problems. An essential ingredient at the outset of any analysis is an assumption about how the flow varies in space and time. Unless such assumptions are made, the Navier–Stokes equations are too complicated to solve.

We have no guarantee that our solution will occur in reality, nor can we expect a unique answer. The Navier–Stokes equations are known to produce several solutions for exactly the same boundary conditions.

The most important example in this chapter is probably Rayleigh's flat plate problem. The impulsive motion of a plate in an infinite fluid is the simplest example of viscous diffusion. The resulting estimate for the depth of penetration of viscous diffusion as a function of time is often taken as a basis for thinking about diffusion in more complicated problems. A second aspect of this problem is the way Rayleigh used it to find a drag formula for a wing moving through a still fluid. The steady flow in a wing-fixed coordinate system is a transient flow in a ground-fixed system. The initial value problem for the unsteady flow has the same character as the steady flow when one identifies x and Ut (though this analogy is only approximate). A third important aspect of this problem is that it introduces the idea of similarity. Since similarity reduces the number of independent variables, it very often occurs in field problems with two or more variables.

PROBLEMS

7.1 (B) Find the velocity profile for laminar flow in a round pipe with given fluid and pressure drop $\Delta P/L$.

7.2 (B) Using the answer from Problem 7.1, find the shear stress on the wall and the volume flow rate.

7.3 (B) A shaft of radius R is rotating at a speed Ω. The stress in the shaft is $T_{z\theta} = rT_0$. Find an expression for the work rate and torque.

7.4 (B) In the reducing elbow problem of Section 5.14, is the given pressure change from 1 to 2 too low, too high, or just about right?

7.5 (A) Consider the annulus formed between a rod of radius r_0 and a tube of radius r_1. Find the velocity profile for Couette flow where the inner rod is rotated with speed Ω. Neglect gravity. Do not assume that the gap is small compared to the radius.

7.6 (A) For the same geometry as in Problem 7.5, but $\Omega = 0$, find the velocity profile if the rod is pulled in the axial direction at a speed $v_z = V_0$. Neglect gravity and any pressure gradient.

7.7 (A) For the same geometry as in Problem 7.5, but $\Omega = 0$, find the velocity profile if a pressure gradient $\Delta p/L$ is applied in the direction of the rod axis. Neglect gravity.

7.8 (A) Show that the linear sum of velocity profiles in Problems 7.5 to 7.7 represents the flow in an annulus with an imposed pressure gradient and a rotating, translating rod.

7.9 (B) A vertical pipe of radius r_0 has a film of liquid flowing downward on the outside. Find the velocity profile for a given film thickness and find an expression for the flow rate Q.

7.10 (A) Let the pipe in Problem 7.9 turn with a speed Ω. Find the velocity profile for this situation.

7.11 (A) A horizontal channel of height H has two fluids of different viscosities and densities flowing because of a pressure gradient. Find the velocity profiles if the height of the interface is h_a.

7.12 (B) Consider that the rotating plate and cylinder (Section 7.6) are conical in shape with cone angle β ($\beta = \pi/2$ would produce the plate shown in Fig. 7.7). The constant z-direction gap is still small compared to the cone radius R. Find the velocity profile in the gap.

7.13 (B) Consider the partial differential equation $yT_x = \alpha T_{yy}$ with boundary conditions $T(x = 0, y) = 0$, $T(x, y = \infty) = 0$, $T(x, y = 0) = T_0$. Find constants C and a that produce a similarity variable $\eta = y/Cx^a$ for this problem.

7.14 (B) Consider the Rayleigh problem, but allow the plate velocity to be a function of time, $V_0(t)$. By differentiation show that the shear stress $\tau = \mu \, \partial u/\partial y$ obeys the same diffusion equation that the velocity does. Suppose that the plate is moved in such a way as to produce a constant surface shear stress. What are the velocity profile and the surface velocity for this motion?

7.15 (C) A large vertical pipe has water flowing upward on the inside. At the pipe end the water overflows and flows downward on the outside of the pipe as in Problem 7.9. Let the pipe radius be r_0, the liquid film thickness h, and the average steady velocity V. If L_e is the length from the end required for viscous forces to establish the fully developed profile, estimate to within a multiplicative constant L_e in terms of the appropriate variables.

7.16 (A) In the Rayleigh plate problem, the diffusion depth is $\delta(t)$. Find the outward velocity of the diffusion layer as a function of layer thickness and other parameters. Express it also as a function of time.

7.17 (B) In the Rayleigh plate problem, allow the plate to move in a time-dependent manner $v_x(y = 0, t) = V_0t^n$. Are similarity solutions of the form $v^* = v_x/A(t) = f(\eta)$, where $\eta = y/\delta(t)$, possible? What are the scaling functions $A(t)$ and $\delta(t)$? Are there any restrictions on the exponent n? Find a closed-form solution for $n = \frac{1}{2}$. What is the stress at the wall for this case ($n = 1$ also has a closed-form solution)?

7.18 (A) Oil used in a viscous coupling has a viscosity of 300,000 cS (100 cS/cm² · s). If the coupling has a 5-cm radius and 1-mm gap width, what difference in rotary speeds is needed to transmit a torque of 50 N · m? Is the same power produced by both the input and output shafts?

7.19 (B) Consider a differential equation for the form $y^nT_t = \alpha T_{yy}$, where n and α are constants. Assume the similarity solution $T = T(\eta)$ where $\eta = g(y, t)$. Show that $T_{yy} = g_{yy}T_\eta + (g_y)^2T_{\eta\eta}$. Find the ordinary differential equation. What form does it take for $\eta = y/(Ct^a)$? What type of boundary and initial conditions will yield a similarity solution?

8

Dimensional Analysis

Up to this point, our attention has been focused on describing physical concepts and formulating the laws that govern them. The existence of measurement methods—procedures to assign a number to a variable—was taken for granted. In this chapter we study the measurement and dimensional nature of physical variables. The major fact used in dimensional analysis is that no natural or fundamental units of measure exist for the physical variables. There are, of course, many universal constants in physics—the charge of an electron, Planck's constant, the gravitational constant between attracting masses, the speed of light, and so on. The point is that these constants are not relevant to all physical processes. The charge on an electron is not a fundamental unit to measure the current in an electric motor. The speed of light is not a fundamental unit to measure the speed of a water wave. Lacking any universally relevant measuring units in the physical world, we are obliged to construct our own scales. Our measuring scales are arbitrary inventions and as such can play no essential role in physical processes. If we change the size of the length unit, all variables involving length must increase or decrease in an appropriate way. By considering the dimensional aspect of a problem alone, one can simplify the problem and find important information. This can be done even if the problem is too complex to allow us to analyze it in detail.

8.1 MEASUREMENT AND DIMENSIONS

There are two major classes of quantities: things that are counted and things that are measured. A quantity that is counted—for instance, a number of molecules—is dimensionless. A quantity that is measured typically has a dimension associated with it.

The most elementary form of measurement is simply a comparison of the object we want to measure with a defined scale. A length of interest is compared with a meter scale, for example. The scale defines a unit, and the prescribed measuring method must include a procedure to extrapolate and interpolate. Sometimes even the simplest comparison requires an external device. A balance is a mechanism to compare two masses; a clock is a device that allows us to compare two times.

The key element of any measurement is the definition of the unit. We cannot begin to measure length, for example, without first defining a foot, a cubit, a light year, or some other length unit. All the length concepts that have been defined have a common property called the *length dimension*. We give the term *length dimension* a symbol, L, and we will show that L can be considered as a number.

Consider two measuring units of different sizes: a new unit (say, the foot) and an old unit (say, the yard). The size of a variable in the new unit is $\hat{\ell}$, the size in the old unit is ℓ, and L is the ratio of the new measuring unit to the old measuring unit. Hence,

$$\hat{\ell} \qquad = \qquad \ell \qquad \times \qquad L \qquad\qquad (8.1.1)$$

size of	size	ratio of
variable	variable	size of
in terms of	in terms of	new
new measuring	old measuring	unit to
scale	scale	old unit

L is a hypothetical scale-change ratio. Note that L has the same value no matter what third scale of units is used to measure the old and new units.

In a similar manner, a mass quantity would be written as

$$\hat{m}_{\text{new}} = m_{\text{old}} \times M$$

or a time quantity,

$$\hat{t}_{\text{new}} = t_{\text{old}} \times T$$

In general, the circumflex means a variable in new units, a lowercase letter means the size in old units, and the corresponding capital letter is the scale-change ratio.

Physical equations can be regarded as relations between the ℓ-type variables. When we substitute numbers into an equation, they are ℓ-type numbers. However, it is a fundamental assumption of dimensional analysis that physical equations must be valid in any system of measurement units we choose. Thus, the equations must also be valid if the new ($\hat{\ell}$-type) variables are substituted into them. We shall need these facts in proving the pi theorem.

In the early history of dimensional analysis, the word *dimension* and the symbols M, L, and so on (which, incidentally, were introduced by Maxwell in 1871), had a more abstract and vague meaning than we have defined. The term *dimension* was used to refer to some ultimate physical nature of a concept. As time went on, it was found that physical concepts do not have ultimate dimensions. For our purposes we take the restricted viewpoint that a dimension is a number as defined by Eq. 8.1.1 or a similar equation. We shall always use the word *dimension* to mean a scale-change ratio.

Not all variables need have their own measuring units. Velocity, defined as the rate of change of a length, has a magnitude that changes if we change either the length or the time unit. The size of a velocity $\hat{v}$ in new units is related to the size v in an old system of units by the equation $\hat{v}_{\text{new}} = V v_{\text{old}}$:

$$v = \frac{dx}{dt} = \frac{d(\hat{x}/L)}{d(\hat{t}/T)} = \frac{T}{L}\hat{v} \quad \text{or} \quad \hat{v}_{\text{new}} = \frac{L}{T} v_{\text{old}}$$

Consider another example; Newton's law implies that any force $\mathscr{F} = m\, dv/dt$ (measured in an M, L, T system) obeys the relation

$$\hat{\mathscr{F}}_{\text{new}} = \mathscr{F}_{\text{old}} M^1 L^1 T^{-2}$$

The dimensions that we choose as a basis to measure other quantities are called *primary dimensions*. A *secondary dimension* is expressible as a product of powers of the primary dimensions, such as $V = LT^{-1}$ or $F = MLT^{-2}$.

In a later section it is shown that for any physical quantity y in old units, the size of $\hat{y}$ in new units is given by the general expression.

$$\hat{y} = y \, M^a L^b T^c \qquad (8.1.2)$$

The meaning of the symbols is analogous with Eq. 8.1.1: M is the mass-scale ratio, L is the length-scale ratio, and T is the time-scale ratio. The exponents a, b, and c are always fractions, but theoretically they could be irrational numbers. (The fact that only fractions occur as exponents is a result of the structure of physics. In constructing physical theory we have not defined, at least not yet, a physical concept that is a combination of M, L, and T raised to an irrational power.) In writing Eq. 8.1.2, we have implied that M, L, and T are sufficient to express any other physical variable. A more general statement would be given by *Bridgman's equation,*

$$\hat{y} = y \, P_1^d P_2^e P_3^f \cdots \qquad (8.1.3)$$

The symbol P stands for a primary dimension. The difference between Eqs. 8.1.2 and 8.1.3 emphasizes that we must choose which dimensions are primary and that M, L, and T are not the only choices possible.

One of the key questions in dimensional analysis is the minimum number of primary dimensions that are required in Eq. 8.1.3. The answer is three. Three primary dimensions are sufficient to express the dimensions of all physical variables. This statement applies to mechanical, electrical, and thermodynamic variables all taken at the same time. As examples, consider the following quantities and their dimensions in the M, L, T system:

$$\text{temperature} = L^2/T^2$$

$$\text{electric charge (statcoulombs)} = M^{1/2}L^{3/2}/T$$

$$\text{thermal conductivity} = 1/LT$$

Here we interpret temperature as an energy per unit mass, and thus the perfect gas law is $T = p/\rho$. As a practical matter, however, all standard unit systems employ temperature as a primary dimension. Take note that the specification of three primary dimensions is only a sufficient number. It is possible and practical to take four or even five primary dimensions. When this is done, something must be inserted into the variable list to account for the redundancy. This topic is discussed in more detail in Section 8.5.

8.2   VARIABLES AND FUNCTIONS

Relationships between physical variables are expressed by mathematical functions. A mathematical *function,* as you know, relates one dependent variable to one or more independent variables. Physical equations also contain *constants,* which come from boundary conditions, appear in the governing laws, or arise from thermodynamic data. For example, consider the incompressible flow over a sphere (Fig. 8.1). Let the pressure p at any point **x** in the flow be the dependent variable. In mathematical notation,

$$p = f(\mathbf{x}, U, \rho, \mu, d, p_\infty) \qquad (8.2.1)$$

In this equation, U is the free-stream velocity, ρ the density, μ the viscosity, d the diameter, and p_∞ the free-stream pressure.

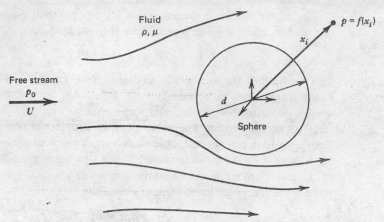

Figure 8.1 Flow over a sphere.

The object of dimensional analysis is to group several variables together to form a new variable that is nondimensional. In our present example, the ratio

$$\Pi = \frac{p}{\rho U^2} \tag{8.2.2}$$

is a nondimensional pressure. Since Buckingham's (American physicist, 1867–1940) statement of the *pi theorem,* it has been tradition to use Π (the mathematical symbol for product) as a symbol for a nondimensional variable. The exponents of the primary dimensions of a *nondimensional variable* are all zero; that is, Bridgman's equation for a nondimensional variable is simply

$$\hat{\Pi} = \Pi \; M^0 L^0 T^0$$
$$\hat{\Pi} = \Pi \tag{8.2.3}$$

The value of a nondimensional variable is completely independent of the measuring units. In this sense it is a universal or natural variable since it does not involve human-invented scales. The combination ρU^2 is regarded as a natural measuring scale for the pressure p. A natural scale may change from one problem to another; thus, ρU^2 is not always the natural scale for pressure.

Dividing Eq. 8.2.1 by ρU^2 yields

$$\Pi \equiv \frac{p}{\rho U^2} = \frac{1}{\rho U^2} \; f(\mathbf{x}, \, U, \, \rho, \, \mu, \, \check{d}, \, p_\infty) \tag{8.2.4}$$

The pi theorem, stated formally in Section 8.3, proves that it is possible to reorganize Eq. 8.2.4 and group variables together into a new function that contains only nondimensional variables:

$$\frac{p}{\rho U^2} = F\left(\frac{\mathbf{x}}{d}, \, \frac{\rho \, dU}{\mu}, \, \frac{p_\infty}{\rho U^2}\right) \tag{8.2.5}$$

This equation contains only four variables, compared to the seven required in the original dimensional form Eq. 8.2.1. This is one of the most useful aspects of dimensional analysis. When a function is expressed in nondimensional variables, the number of variables is less than when the same relation is expressed in dimensional variables.

The importance of reducing the number of variables is often illustrated by the following analogy. Consider how a function would be represented graphically. A function of two variables can be represented by a single line graphed on a single page. A function of three variables requires several lines, one for each value of the third variable, but it still fits on one page. Functions of four variables require a book of graphs, and five variables a shelf full. For six or seven variables one would need a library of books to contain the required information. Considered in this light, reducing the number of variables from seven to four is a great simplification. To do the experiments or to make the calculations for a single book of graphs is a reasonable task, but to fill the library shown in Fig. 8.2 is an undertaking to which you could dedicate a lifetime.

Everything that is measured must be included in the variable list, since the value of each quantity depends on the choice of measurement units. Distinctions between independent variables, boundary values, parameters, physical constants, universal constants, and dimensional constants are made according to the physical role that the variable plays in the function. In dimensional analysis these distinctions are unimportant, and all such items must be included in the list of variables. If a process involves the gravitational attraction force F_{12} between two masses M_1 and M_2 a distance r apart, the gravitational constant k ($F_{12} = kM_1M_2/r^2$) must be included in the variable list. The numerical value of k depends on the units of measurement chosen.

The pi theorem deals with functions that describe physical processes. Furthermore, the functions must be in a proper form where all variables are shown. Frequently, prac-

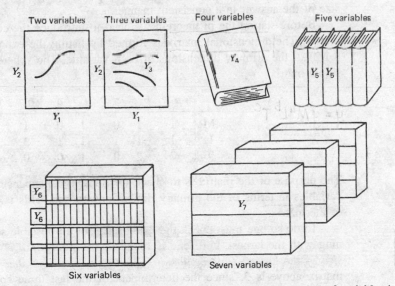

Figure 8.2 Records of information expand geometrically as the number of variables increases.

ticing engineers use equations where specific units are assumed. For example, the speed of sound in air is given by

$$a = 20.1\sqrt{T} \tag{8.2.6}$$

where a is in meters per second (m/s) and T is in kelvin (K). The fact that the value 20.1 is a dimensional constant is not noted explicitly. The proper form of this equation is

$$a = (\gamma g_c RT)^{1/2} \tag{8.2.7}$$

Unhappily, there are some equations in use today (for pipe friction and channel friction) that are dimensionally inconsistent. These equations are mere correlations of experimental data and must be used only for the fluids employed in the experiments.

A popular example of an improper physical function is the sum of the equations for the position and for the velocity of a falling body, $s = \frac{1}{2}gt^2$ and $v = gt$. This result gives

$$v = gt + s - \tfrac{1}{2}gt^2$$

which implies that $v = f(g, s, t)$. This is not true. We cannot substitute independent numbers for g, t, and s to retrieve values of v. A mathematician would not accept this as a function in the first place.

8.3 PI THEOREM AND ITS APPLICATION

The pi theorem tells how many nondimensional variables are required for a given set of dimensional variables. It is based on two assumptions: (1) all variables obey Bridgman's equation 8.1.3, and (2) proper functions expressing a physical result are valid irrespective of the scale units for the primary dimensions. Changing the size of the units changes the size of the answer in a consistent manner.

Before stating the pi theorem we need to introduce the concept of the dimensional matrix. The dimensional matrix is formed by listing the exponents (a, b, and c in Eq. 8.1.2) of the primary dimensions of each variable. The sphere problem has the dimensional matrix

$$\hat{y} = y M^a L^b T^c$$

	p	p_∞	x	μ	d	ρ	U
M	1	1	0	1	0	1	0
L	-1	-1	1	-1	1	-3	1
T	-2	-2	0	-1	0	0	-1

The purpose of the matrix is to check for linear independence of the dimensions of the variables in terms of the primary dimensions chosen. This is done by finding the rank of the matrix.

To do so one must check the determinant of all possible square submatrices, beginning with the largest, until one is found that is nonzero. *The rank of the matrix is the size of the largest square submatrix that has a nonzero determinant.* The rank of the matrix above is 3, since the determinant of the last three columns is nonzero. If the determinants of all possible 3×3 submatrices are zero, one proceeds to check all $2 \times$

2 submatrices until one with a nonzero determinant is found. The rank of the dimensional matrix tells how many fewer variables will occur when a function is expressed in nondimensional variables.

We now give a statement of the *pi theorem:* Assume that we are given a proper physical function with *n* variables,

$$x_1 = f(x_2, x_3, x_4, \ldots, x_n) \tag{8.3.1}$$

Furthermore, all the variables obey Bridgman's equation,

$$\hat{x}_i = x_i P_1^a P_2^b P_3^c \tag{8.3.2}$$

Here the *P* values are primary dimensions and *a*, *b*, and *c* are exponents. Under these assumptions it is possible to organize the original variables into nondimensional forms—that is, find some values for α's such that

$$\Pi = x_1^{\alpha_1} x_2^{\alpha_2} \cdots x_n^{\alpha_n} \tag{8.3.3}$$

Moreover, when the original function is expressed in nondimensional variables, it is simpler in that it contains only $m = n - r$ variables:

$$\Pi_1 = f(\Pi_2, \Pi_3, \ldots, \Pi_m) \tag{8.3.4}$$

where *r* is the rank of the dimensional matrix.

The name *pi theorem* comes from Buckingham's (1914) discussion of dimensional analysis. In this paper he explained the repeating-variable method of forming the Π groups and stated how many nondimensional variables would occur. Buckingham felt that the principle of dimensional homogeneity, which had been initiated by Fourier (1822), was the cornerstone of the method (Euler's writings also touch on the subject of measurement and dimensions). Buckingham's paper stimulated the subject, and his method was widely adopted. However, he was not the first to publish a pi theorem. Independently, the French engineer A. Vashy (1892) and the Russian physicist D. Riabouchinsky (1911) published statements that were equivalent to the pi theorem. Even earlier, Rayleigh (1879), although he did not give a pi theorem, formalized an indicial method, or power-product method, of finding nondimensional relationships. This method still finds favor among many workers.

The pi theorem was not proved adequately in the early papers, and some confusion remained. It concerned the number of pi variables required, $m = n - r$. The first statements of the theorem did not use the rank *r* of the dimensional matrix. Instead, they said the number of pi values was equal to the number of dimensional variables minus the number of "necessary" primary dimensions. The word *necessary* was vague, because a method for determining what was necessary was not provided. Bridgman (1922) pointed out that, for some problems, using the MLT system gives a different answer than using the FLT system. The variables of Bridgman's example could be expressed by two dimensions in one primary system, whereas three were required in the other. Van Driest (1946) gave the solution by pointing out that the number of pi variables will be different if the dimensions of the variables are not independent in terms of the primary dimensions chosen. By using the rank of the dimensional matrix in our statement of the pi theorem, we have tested automatically for independence.

There are several methods of finding a set of pi variables for a given problem. As one gains more and more experience, shortcuts are found, and finally a trial-and-error method becomes the quickest. We first explain a fairly formal method due to Buckingham (1914), which is commonly used in elementary texts.

The first step is to choose r repeating variables from the x variables, where r is the rank of the matrix. The repeating variables must be linearly independent, so the submatrix of their dimensional exponents must have a nonzero determinant. In our example, ρ, d, and U meet this condition and will be chosen as the repeating variables. The repeating variables will occur in all the pi variables. Therefore, if we want the dependent variable to occur in only one pi variable, it should not be chosen as a repeating variable.

Consider the r repeating variables plus one of the remaining x variables. Since there are only r independent dimensions, a nondimensional variable may be formed from these $r + 1$ variables. Taking the pressure p and the repeating variables ρ, d, and U, we form the first pi variable (using new units), that is, we construct $\hat{\Pi}_1$ as

$$\hat{\Pi}_1 = \hat{p}(\hat{\rho})^{\alpha}(\hat{d})^{\beta}(\hat{U})^{\gamma} \tag{8.3.5}$$

We seek values of the exponents α, β, and γ that make Eq. 8.3.5 nondimensional. Substituting Eq. 8.1.2 for each variable in Eq. 8.3.5 gives

$$\Pi_1 \, M^0 L^0 T^0 = p \, ML^{-1}T^{-2}\rho^{\alpha} \, (ML^{-3})^{\alpha} d^{\beta} \, (L)^{\beta} U^{\gamma} \, (LT^{-1})^{\gamma}$$

$$= p\rho^{\alpha}d^{\beta}U^{\gamma} \, M^{1+\alpha} L^{-1-3\alpha+\beta+\gamma} T^{-2-\gamma} \tag{8.3.6}$$

This equation must hold for all choices of the scale ratios M, L, T; therefore, the exponents of M, L, and T must be zero. Hence, Eq. 8.3.6 becomes

$$\Pi_1 = p\rho^{\alpha}d^{\beta}U^{\gamma} \tag{8.3.7}$$

Equating the exponents of M, L, and T in Eq. 8.3.6 to zero yields a set of equations that determines the values of α, β, and γ:

$$
\begin{aligned}
\text{M exponent:} &\quad 0 = 1 + \alpha &&\Rightarrow \alpha = -1 \\
\text{T exponent:} &\quad 0 = -2 - \gamma &&\Rightarrow \gamma = -2 \\
\text{L exponent:} &\quad 0 = -1 - 3\alpha + \beta + \gamma \\
&\quad 0 = -1 + 3 + \beta - 2 \Rightarrow \beta = 0
\end{aligned}
\tag{8.3.8}
$$

(Note that the solution of the nonhomogeneous system above is guaranteed if the determinant of the coefficients of α, β, γ is nonzero. This is the same determinant as that used to show that the rank of the dimensional matrix was 3.) Thus, we find that the first nondimensional variable is

$$\Pi_1 = \frac{p}{\rho U^2} \tag{8.3.9}$$

Taking each remaining x variable in turn, together with the r repeating variables, will produce the required $n - r$ nondimensional variables. They turn out to be

$$\Pi_2 = \frac{p_0}{\rho U^2}, \qquad \Pi_3 = \frac{x}{d}, \qquad \Pi_4 = \frac{\mu}{\rho \, dU} \qquad (8.3.10)$$

These are the variables that were listed in Eq. 8.2.5 as the nondimensional form of our result.

There is another method, which is somewhat simpler, called the *method of scales.* In this method we form units for the primary dimensions by using the repeating variables. This may be done by inspection in most instances. These units are "natural" measuring units for the specific problem. In the sphere problem the natural length unit is the diameter of the sphere. So we use the freedom to define a length unit to set

$$L = d \qquad (8.3.11)$$

A natural mass scale is formed from the sphere diameter and the fluid density. Let

$$M = \rho d^3 \qquad (8.3.12)$$

The time scale is formed using the fluid velocity and sphere diameter:

$$T = \frac{d}{U} \qquad (8.3.13)$$

In essence we are organizing the repeating variables into groups so that the pi groups can be formed by inspection. Now the first nonrepeating variable p has the dimensions

$$p \frac{M}{LT^2}$$

To cancel these dimensions we divide by the mass scale and multiply by the length scale and the time scale squared. Hence,

$$\Pi_1 = p \frac{d(d/U)^2}{\rho d^3} = \frac{p}{\rho U^2} \qquad (8.3.14)$$

The process is continued using each nonrepeating variable in turn. The scale method is recommended only when the rank of the matrix is equal to the number of primary dimensions.

8.4   PUMP OR BLOWER ANALYSIS: USE OF EXTRA ASSUMPTIONS

Let us consider the analysis of a pump designed for use with incompressible liquids. The analysis is also valid for fans and blowers that transport gases; however, we shall not prove it. A schematic of the pump and a typical test setup are shown in Fig. 8.3. Before we list the variables we must agree on the choice of primary dimensions. We choose three primary dimensions: M, L, and T.

The second task is to list the variables that enter the problem. An accurate list is essential to obtain the correct answer. Leaving out a variable leads to an erroneously simple result, while including an extraneous variable usually leads to an extra pi group (but sometimes to a problem where it is impossible to nondimensionalize the extra vari-

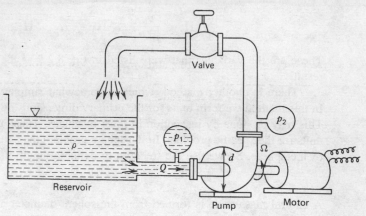

Figure 8.3   Test setup for pump performance.

able). As an aid in listing the variables, let us imagine how a pump test would be performed. We want to be particularly careful about considering all the things that might be changed to cause a different flow situation in the pump. The size of the machine is characterized by the single dimension d. This may be taken as the impeller diameter or any other convenient dimension. We assume that if the size of the machine changes, all of its dimensions change in proportion to d. A motor is coupled to the pump and turns the impeller at a constant speed. As test conditions change, it may be necessary to adjust the motor to maintain the constant speed. We assume that the motor is of such a type that this may be done. With these stipulations, the geometry of the pump and the motion of all internal parts are fixed by the variables d and Ω.

The pump draws liquid in from a reservoir at a pressure p_1 and discharges it at a pressure p_2. A valve of the outlet is used to simulate the piping resistance and change the back pressure. As the back pressure changes, the volume flow through the machine also changes. In essence a series of tests with different valve positions gives the pressure rise versus flow rate for the pump under fixed geometry and speed conditions. Changing the valve position will be considered as equivalent to controlling the flow rate Q as an independent variable and determining the pressure rise as the dependent variable. (Actually, we could consider the position of the valve as an independent variable and the pressure rise as the dependent variable. That would be one problem. Then considering the valve position as determining the flow rate would be a second problem. Eliminating the valve position between these two problems leaves variables that refer only to the pump. Either the pressure or the flow rate could be considered as the independent variable replacing the valve position.)

Since the fluid is incompressible, no thermodynamic processes occur, and the fluid is characterized by its density ρ. There are two extra pieces of information that can be part of the problem. First, incompressible flow theory tells us (or will tell us) that the level of pressure in a flow field is not important. That is, if the inlet pressure is raised a certain amount by increasing the level of fluid in the reservoir, the outlet pressure increases an equal amount. This fact is taken into account by considering $\Delta p = p_2 - p_1$ as a single variable and not p_2 and p_1 separately. The second extra assumption concerns friction. Does viscosity play an important role in determining the pressure in the pump? Again a knowledge of some of the general characteristics of fluid flows is useful. In most engineering situations pumps operate at high Reynolds numbers, viscous forces are much smaller than pressure forces, and unless the viscous forces act over a large area, they can usually be neglected in comparison with the pressure forces. We make the assumption that viscosity may be neglected and proceed to state the problem as

$$p_2 = f(Q, \rho, d, \Omega) + p_1 \qquad (8.4.1)$$

$$p_2 - p_1 \equiv \Delta p = f(Q, \rho, d, \Omega)$$

Now the pi theorem is applied to Eq. 8.4.1. The dimensional matrix is

	Δp	Q	ρ	d	Ω
M	1	0	1	0	0
L	-1	3	-3	1	0
T	-2	-1	0	0	-1

We choose ρ, d, and Ω as repeating variables. The last three columns have a nonzero determinant, so the rank is 3. This means that we expect $5 - 3 = 2$ nondimensional variables. Let d be the length scale, ρd^3 the mass scale, and Ω^{-1} the time scale; then the two nondimensional variables are found to be

$$\Pi_1 = \frac{\Delta p}{\rho d^2 \Omega^2} \qquad \Pi_2 = \frac{Q}{d^3 \Omega} \qquad (8.4.2)$$

The nondimensional form of Eq. 8.4.1 becomes

$$\frac{\Delta p}{\rho d^2 \Omega^2} = f_1 \left(\frac{Q}{d^3 \Omega} \right) \qquad (8.4.3)$$

Experiment measurements on a pump of a given size are shown in Fig. 8.4a in dimensional terms. (Pressure is measured in terms of the "head," that is, $\Delta p/\rho g$ for water.) Figure 8.4b shows the same data in nondimensional form. Note that we could have drawn the characteristic curved for the pump by testing it at only one speed. One of the great powers of dimensional analysis is illustrated by this problem. By varying only two quantities in a test, Δp and Q, we can actually find the dependence for three additional variables, d, ρ, and Ω. Even though we did not test other fluids or different-size pumps, the data can be used to predict what would happen if we used a smaller pump or changed the fluid from water to oil.

Another interesting facet of the test is that we can consider the tests at different speeds as an evaluation of the effect of viscosity. To see this, let us consider what would happen if viscosity were important to the flow. Dimensional analysis would yield the same answer as before except for the addition of a new variable, the Reynolds number based on the impeller tip velocity. The answer is

$$\frac{\Delta p}{\rho d^2 \Omega^2} = f \left(\frac{Q}{d^3 \Omega}, \text{Re} \right) \qquad (8.4.4)$$

where

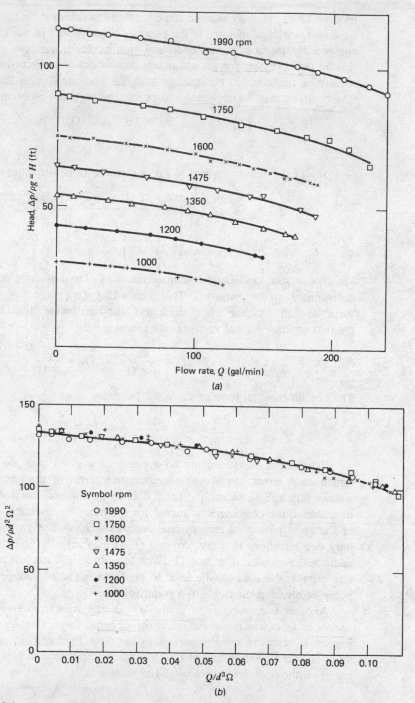

Figure 8.4 Pressure versus flow rate for a backward-bladed pump (test fluid water): (*a*) dimensional variables; (*b*) nondimensional variables. Data courtesy of Byron Short.

$$Re \equiv \frac{\Omega d^2 \rho}{\mu} \tag{8.4.5}$$

Now from Eq. 8.4.5 we see that changes in the speed change the Reynolds number, which is equivalent to changing the viscosity of the fluid. The fact that all the different speed curves fall roughly together when plotted in Fig. 8.4 verifies that viscosity is not important in this case.

Lest we give the false impression that pumps always behave according to Eq. 8.4.3, we should point out that cavitation may occur. At very low pressures, in the neighborhood of $\frac{1}{30}$ atm, water will boil and produce pockets of vapor. The lowest pressure in the system occurs on the moving blades, and when cavitation occurs there, the pump characteristics change. Dimensional analysis, including cavitation, would include the vapor pressure of the liquid and lead to another dimensional parameter. Pumps, hydrofoils, ship propellers, and nozzle flows are all cases where cavitation is possible. For a review article on cavitation, see Arndt (1981).

8.5 NUMBER OF PRIMARY DIMENSIONS

There have been several attitudes toward the question of how many primary dimensions are required. The question is not as simple as it might first seem. Let us be more precise and ask the question: If we have a complicated continuum problem involving mechanics, thermodynamics, and electrodynamics, what is the minimum number of dimensions required to express the dimensional variables? That is, how many P values are needed in Bridgman's equation,

$$\hat{x} = x \, P_1^{\alpha} P_2^{b} P_3^{c} \cdots \tag{8.5.1}$$

for any variable of interest? It is a fact of experience that all of our physical concepts may be expressed in terms of three primary dimensions [see Sedov (1959) for more discussion of this point].

During the first part of the twentieth century some physicists thought that five dimensions were required. They added temperature and an electrical unit to M, L, and T. It is not the usual practice to express thermodynamic or electrical concepts in terms of mass, length, and time; but it can be done (energy and force are ideas common to all subjects). Since the number of primary dimensions plays such an important role in the pi theorem, it is natural to inquire about how the pi theorem changes if we use more or less than three primary dimensions. We begin with the customary discussion of mechanics and Newton's second law.

Newton's second law equates the forces to the mass times the acceleration:

$$F = m \, \frac{dv}{dt} \tag{8.5.2}$$

If we take the viewpoint that mass, length, and time are primary dimensions, the dimensions of force are ML/T^2. A newton of force is just a shorter name for 1 kilogram meter per second squared ($1 \text{ kg} \cdot \text{m/s}^2$). There is an alternative viewpoint, where one assumes that there are four primary dimensions, F, M, L, and T. If this viewpoint is taken,

Newton's second law must be written to include a dimensional constant g_c:

$$F = \frac{m}{g_c} \frac{dv}{dt} \tag{8.5.3}$$

Because we overspecified the number of primary dimensions, we must introduce a compensating *dimensional unifier,* the mathematics. In the British engineering system, where we use the pound-force, pound-mass, foot, and second, the value of g_c is

$$g_c = 32.17 \frac{\text{lb}_\text{m} \cdot \text{ft}}{\text{lb}_\text{f} \cdot \text{sec}^2} \tag{8.5.4}$$

So the conclusion is that if we take the viewpoint that there are four primary dimensions, a dimensional unifier appears in the governing laws and in all the answers.

The solution to a problem governed by Newton's law, e.g., the position of the body as a function of time, will then contain the dimensional unifier g_c:

$$x = f(t, m, \ldots, g_c)$$

In dimensional analysis any quantity that changes magnitude when the size of the primary unit is changed must be considered a variable. If, for example, we defined the "double-foot" as a new length unit, g_c would be 16.1 $\text{lb}_\text{m} \cdot \text{dbft}/\text{lb}_\text{f} \cdot \text{sec}^2$. Thus, in a dimensional analysis with F, M, L, and T as a primary dimensions, the dimensional matrix would look like

	x_1	x_2	$\cdots$	g_c
M				1
L				1
T				-2
F				-1

The effect on the pi theorem is nil. The rank of the matrix has been increased by one and the number of dimensional variables has also be increased by one.

Consider another less obvious example. What if the problem involves an angle and we choose to measure the angle in degrees? The primitive definition of an angle is the length of an arc divided by the radius, a dimensionless quantity called the *radian.* However, if we insist on using the degree unit as a primary dimension, all formulas will contain a unifying dimensional constant, $2\pi/360$ (rad/deg). The dimensional matrix should be constructed as

	x_1	x_2	$\cdots$	$2\pi/360$
M				0
L				0
T				0
degree				-1

Whenever an additional primary dimension is added to the basic three, there must (in general) be a compensating dimensional unifier.

Although there is something special about the number of primary dimensions, there is nothing special about which dimensions are chosen for the primary role. For instance, we could use area instead of length. Then the dimensional exponent of a length would be one-half, and dimensional variables would be expressed as

$$\hat{x} = x \, M^a A^b T^c \tag{8.5.5}$$

As another example, consider using speed as a primary dimension instead of time. It would be related to the length and time dimensions by

$$S = LT^{-1} \tag{8.5.6}$$

Eliminating time from Eq. 8.1.2, which governs all variables, gives an equation of identical form but with different exponents:

$$\hat{x} = x \, M^a L^b T^c = x \, M^a L^{b+c} S^{-c}$$

$$= x \, M^a L^{b_1} S^{c_1} \tag{8.5.7}$$

The primary dimensions are now mass, length, and speed. Any transformation of the primary dimension is allowed as long as the form of Bridgman's equation is unchanged. That is, any product of the primary dimensions to any powers could be used as new primary dimensions. More complicated functions such as $\sin(L/T)$ or $\exp(M)$ are not acceptable.

Three primary dimensions are sufficient for any problem but are not always necessary. A problem in kinematics could be formulated using only L and T. If M were also included, all entries on the M row of the dimensional matrix would be zero and the rank would automatically be reduced from three to two. This is a somewhat trivial example but should be kept in mind.

At the outset of this section we spoke of different viewpoints on the question of the number of primary dimensions required for a general problem. Many writers take the viewpoint that the number of primary dimensions depends on the problem being solved and whether we write the governing laws with a dimensional unifier. The question is further complicated by the fact that some special problems do not actually require a dimensional unifier (e.g., heat transfer in incompressible flow). The structure of the equations that govern the subject may allow the dimensional unifier to be eliminated from the problem. When a dimensional unifier is not needed, it is because supplementary information about the physics has been introduced into the analysis. If we make a rule that supplementary information must be explicitly introduced into an analysis, three primary dimensions are sufficient, and the rank of the dimensional matrix will tell us if they are necessary.

*8.6   PROOF OF BRIDGMAN'S EQUATION

The equation $\hat{x} = x \, M^a L^b T^c$ is the cornerstone of dimensional analysis. It is not usually given a name. Bridgman (1922) seems to be the first to state it explicitly and offer proof, so we shall refer to it as *Bridgman's equation*.

To prove Bridgman's equation we adopt a different notation in this section. Subscripts will refer to different values of the same variable: y_1 is a specific value of y, and y_2 is another value of the same variable. Consider m as the mass variable. In accord with Eq. 8.1.1, we write

$$\hat{m} = m \, M \tag{8.6.1}$$

Next, we consider a variable y that depends in some way on mass. Force, pressure, power, and density are examples. If y also depends on length and time, we temporarily hold those variables constant. Assume that

$$y = f(m) \qquad (8.6.2)$$

For instance, y might be the density of a sphere with a certain volume. Our first step is to consider two spheres made of different substances, so that m_1 has one value and m_2 another. The numbers m_1 and m_2 are found using a certain mass unit. Bridgman reasoned that there must be something intrinsic about a physical concept, in this case the density, that is independent of the measuring units. He proposed that the ratio of the densities of the two spheres should be a constant independent of the scale unit. In mathematical terms,

$$\frac{y_1}{y_2} = \frac{f(m_1)}{f(m_2)} = C \qquad (8.6.3)$$

This is the major assumption: *The ratio of two definite values of any physical variable does not depend on the size of the measuring units of the primary dimensions.* As far as we know, all our physical concepts satisfy this assumption.

To proceed with the proof, we put Eq. 8.6.3 in the form

$$f(m_1) = Cf(m_2) \qquad (8.6.4)$$

Consider how a change in the unit ratio M will affect the problem. Since $\hat{m} = m\text{M}$, we hold $\hat{m}$ constant while m and M change. Differentiating Eq. 8.6.4 with respect to M yields

$$f'(m_1) \frac{dm_1}{d\text{M}} = Cf'(m_2) \frac{dm_2}{d\text{M}} \qquad (8.6.5)$$

while from $\hat{m} = m\,\text{M}$ we also have the constraining equations

$$0 = m_1 \, d\text{M} + \text{M} \, dm_1$$

$$0 = m_2 \, d\text{M} + \text{M} \, dm_2$$

Substituting these equations into Eq. 8.6.5 and using Eq. 8.6.3 to replace C yields

$$\frac{m_1 f'(m_1)}{f(m_1)} = \frac{m_2 f'(m_2)}{f(m_2)} = \text{const} = k \qquad (8.6.6)$$

This equation holds for all choices of m_1 and m_2 independently, and therefore each side is a constant.

Equation 8.6.6 is solved as follows (we can drop the subscript):

$$\frac{m}{f} \frac{df}{dm} = k$$

$$\ln \frac{f}{f_0} = k \ln \frac{m}{m_0} \qquad (8.6.7)$$

$$\frac{y}{y_0} = \frac{f}{f_0} = \left(\frac{m}{m_0} \right)^k$$

The reference values are fixed by setting y_0 equal to $\hat{y}$ when $m_0 = \hat{m}$.

Substituting this into Eq. 8.6.7 and noting that $\hat{m} = m\text{M}$, we have

$$\hat{y} = y\,\text{M}^k \tag{8.6.8}$$

The exponent of the mass dimension is unrestricted.

The proof is completed by noting that the process may be repeated for the second and third variables of a more general function $y = f(m, \ell, t)$. This final result is Bridgman's equation

$$\hat{y} = y\,\text{M}^{k_1}\text{L}^{k_2}\text{T}^{k_3} \tag{8.6.9}$$

This is the same form as Eq. 8.1.2.

*8.7   PROOF OF THE PI THEOREM

Consider a function that describes a physical process and contains n dimensional variables. Let x_1 be the dependent variable and write the function as

$$x_1 = f(x_2, x_3, \ldots, x_n) \tag{8.7.1}$$

Assume that all variables in Eq. 8.7.1 may be expressed in terms of three primary dimensions according to Bridgman's equation,

$$\hat{x}_i = x_i\,\text{M}^{a_i}\text{L}^{b_i}\text{T}^{c_i} \tag{8.7.2}$$

In addition to this equation, another major assumption is needed. We assume that the function 8.7.1 is valid for any measuring units we might choose. A function relating physical variables is valid for any choice of M, L, and T. In particular, if we choose to use the "new" units, Eq. 8.7.1 becomes

$$\hat{x}_1 = f(\hat{x}_2, \hat{x}_3, \ldots, \hat{x}_n) \tag{8.7.3}$$

Another way of looking at this is that Eq. 8.7.1 should be valid when M = 1, L = 1, and T = 1.

The mass–length–time symbols will be used in the proof; however, they have no special properties, and any primary dimensions would suffice. The fact that three primary dimensions are sufficient to express all physical variables is the result of the intrinsic structure of physics and is not subject to proof.

The dimensional matrix for the problem contains the dependent variable as the first entry. If necessary we renumber the variables so that the rank of the matrix formed by x_2, x_3, and x_4 is 3 (the determinant is nonzero). We are going to prove the theorem for the case that $r = 3$. The matrix is

	x_1	x_2	x_3	x_4	$\cdots$	x_n
M	a_1	a_2	a_3	a_4	$\cdots$	a_n
L	b_1	b_2	b_3	b_4	$\cdots$	b_n
T	c_1	c_2	c_3	c_4	$\cdots$	c_n

The three variables x_2, x_3, x_4 will become new primary dimensions or scales. We define the new scales by the relations

$$S_2 \equiv \frac{\hat{x}_2}{x_2} \qquad S_3 \equiv \frac{\hat{x}_3}{x_3} \qquad S_4 \equiv \frac{\hat{x}_4}{x_4} \qquad (8.7.4)$$

In terms of the M, L, T units, the new scales are (by Eq. 8.7.2)

$$S_2 = M^{a_2}L^{b_2}T^{c_2} \qquad S_3 = M^{a_3}L^{b_3}T^{c_3} \qquad S_4 = M^{a_4}L^{b_4}T^{c_4} \qquad (8.7.5)$$

To express a variable in the new S scales, we need relations for M, L, and T in terms of the S scales. To do this, consider products of S_2, S_3, S_4 raised to some as yet undetermined exponents. First, we find the powers that will produce a mass scale; that is, we solve the following equation for A_2, A_3, and A_4:

$$S_2^{A_2}S_3^{A_3}S_4^{A_4} = M^1L^0T^0$$

Substituting from Eq. 8.7.5, we have

$$M^1L^0T^0 = M^{a_2 A_2}L^{b_2 A_2}T^{c_2 A_2}M^{a_3 A_3}L^{b_3 A_3}T^{c_3 A_3}M^{a_4 A_4}L^{b_4 A_4}T^{c_4 A_4} \qquad (8.7.6)$$

Since M, L, and T are arbitrary, this equation is true only if the exponents sum to zero. This produces the system of linear equations for the unknowns A_2, A_3, A_4:

$$\text{Exponent of M:} \quad a_2 A_2 + a_3 A_3 + a_4 A_4 = 1$$

$$\text{Exponent of L:} \quad b_2 A_2 + b_3 A_3 + b_4 A_4 = 0 \qquad (8.7.7)$$

$$\text{Exponent of T:} \quad c_2 A_2 + c_3 A_3 + c_4 A_4 = 0$$

A unique solution of this nonhomogeneous system is guaranteed by Cramer's rule if the determinant of the coefficients is nonzero. This condition is satisfied, since the coefficients of system 8.7.7 are the same coefficients as appear in the dimensional matrix. We had arranged the variables so that this determinant was nonzero at the start.

Coefficients for the L and T dimensions are found by the same process. When this is completed we have the following relations between the new scales and the old M, L, T scales:

$$M = S_2^{A_2}S_3^{A_3}S_4^{A_4}$$

$$L = S_2^{B_2}S_3^{B_3}S_4^{B_4} \qquad (8.7.8)$$

$$T = S_2^{C_2}S_3^{C_3}S_4^{C_4}$$

The linear system of equations for the B parameters is the same as that for the A parameters except that the right-hand column of Eq. 8.7.7 is 0, 1, 0. Similarly, the system for the C parameters has the right-hand column 0, 0, 1.

All the dimensional variables in the problem may be expressed in terms of the new S dimensions by substituting Eq. 8.7.8 into Eq. 8.7.2:

$$\hat{x}_i = x_i (S_2^{A_2}S_3^{A_3}S_4^{A_4})^{a_i}(S_2^{B_2}S_3^{B_3}S_4^{B_4})^{b_i}(S_2^{C_2}S_3^{C_3}S_4^{C_4})^{c_i}$$

This is Bridgman's equation with primary scales S_2, S_3, S_4, that is,

$$\hat{x}_i = x_i \, S_2^{\alpha_i}S_3^{\beta_i}S_4^{\gamma_i} \qquad (8.7.9)$$

where the exponents are defined according to the relations

$$\alpha_i = a_i A_2 + b_i B_2 + c_i C_2$$

$$\beta_i = a_i A_3 + b_i B_3 + c_i C_3$$

$$\gamma_i = a_i A_4 + b_i B_4 + c_i C_4$$

Up to this point we have essentially done two things: we have chosen new scale units $S_2 = \hat{x}_2/x_2$, S_3, and S_4, and we have shown that Bridgman's equation can be written in terms of the new scales. The dimensional matrix would now look like this:

	x_1	x_2	x_3	x_4	x_5	$\cdots$	x_n
S_2	α_1	1	0	0	α_5	$\cdots$	α_n
S_3	β_1	0	1	0	β_5	$\cdots$	β_n
S_4	γ_1	0	0	1	γ_5	$\cdots$	γ_n

We have essentially diagonalized the entries for the repeating variables.

Now we are ready to show that physical functions are homogeneous and then use this fact to nondimensionalize the variables. Substituting Eq. 8.7.9 into Eq. 8.7.1 yields

$$\hat{x}_1 S_2^{-\alpha_1} S_3^{-\beta_1} S_4^{-\gamma_1} = f(\hat{x}_2 S_2^{-1}, \hat{x}_3 S_3^{-1}, \hat{x}_4 S_4^{-1}, \hat{x}_5 S_2^{-\alpha_5} S_3^{-\beta_5} S_4^{-\gamma_5}, \ldots, \hat{x}_n S_2^{-\alpha_n} S_3^{-\beta_n} S_4^{-\gamma_n}) \quad (8.7.10)$$

Substituting Eq. 8.7.3 for $\hat{x}_1$ in Eq. 8.7.10 produces

$$S_2^{-\alpha_1} S_3^{-\beta_1} S_4^{-\gamma_1} f(\hat{x}_2, \hat{x}_3, \ldots, \hat{x}_n) = f(\hat{x}_2 S_2^{-1}, \ldots, \hat{x}_n S_2^{-\alpha_n} S_3^{-\beta_n} S_4^{-\gamma_n}) \quad (8.7.11)$$

In mathematical terms a function is called *homogeneous of order k* if the substitution $\lambda x \rightarrow x$ produces λ^k times the original function,

$$\lambda^k f(x) = f(\lambda x) \quad (8.7.12)$$

The physical function 8.7.11 is homogeneous of degree α_1 in the x_2 variable, of degree β_1 in the x_3 variable, and of degree γ_1 in the x_4 variable. If we used different repeating variables and retraced the previous steps, we would find that the physical equation is homogeneous to some degree in all variables. Thus, all physical equations come from a special class of functions called *homogeneous functions*.

We could apply the term *dimensionally homogeneous* to the fact that physical equations are homogeneous functions of the variables chosen as repeating variables. However, various workers have their own special definitions of the phrase. Langhaar (1951) makes the assumption that physical equations are valid for all choices of M, L, and T as the proper definition. Often, the definition is that each additive term in an equation must have the same dimensions. This is really just a facet of the meaning we have given above.

There are just a few steps left to prove the pi theorem. Notice that the size of a unit in the new primary dimensions, S_2, S_3, and S_4, is arbitrary. Let us select

$$S_2 = \hat{x}_2, \qquad S_3 = \hat{x}_3, \qquad S_4 = \hat{x}_4 \quad (8.7.13)$$

This selection also means that $x_2 = x_3 = x_4 = 1$; that is, we are using the values of x_2,

x_3, and x_4 as scale units. Equation 8.7.10 now reads

$$\frac{\hat{x}_1}{\hat{x}_2^{\alpha_1}\hat{x}_3^{\beta_1}\hat{x}_4^{\gamma_1}} = f\left(1, 1, 1, \frac{\hat{x}_5}{\hat{x}_2^{\alpha_5}\hat{x}_3^{\beta_5}\hat{x}_4^{\gamma_5}}, \ldots, \frac{\hat{x}_n}{\hat{x}_2^{\alpha_n}\hat{x}_3^{\beta_n}\hat{x}_4^{\gamma_n}}\right) \tag{8.7.14}$$

The variables in this equation are all nondimensional. This is shown by considering Eq. 8.7.9 and substituting the scale definitions 8.7.4 to arrive at

$$\hat{x}_i = x_i\left(\frac{\hat{x}_2}{x_2}\right)^{\alpha_i}\left(\frac{\hat{x}_3}{x_3}\right)^{\beta_i}\left(\frac{\hat{x}_4}{x_4}\right)^{\gamma_i}$$

Rearranging yields

$$\frac{\hat{x}_i}{\hat{x}_2^{\alpha_i}\hat{x}_3^{\beta_i}\hat{x}_4^{\gamma_i}} = \frac{x_i}{\hat{x}_2^{\alpha_i}\hat{x}_3^{\beta_i}\hat{x}_4^{\gamma_i}} \tag{8.7.15}$$

The values of the pi variables are independent of the choice of the M, L, and T units, that is, $\hat{\Pi} = \Pi$. Therefore, the variables in Eq. 8.7.15 are nondimensional, and we change the symbols in Eq. 8.7.14 accordingly. The new function has $n - r$ nondimensional variables:

$$\Pi_1 = f(1, 1, 1, \Pi_5, \Pi_6, \ldots, \Pi_n) \tag{8.7.16}$$

It is no longer a homogeneous function in these variables and has a completely arbitrary mathematical form. This completes the proof of the pi theorem for the case $r = 3$. The reader wishing to know the modifications necessary for r less than three may consult Langhaar (1951), Brand (1957), or Sedov (1959). Some instructive examples are in Panton (2004).

8.8   DYNAMIC SIMILARITY

Two different physical problems are *dynamically similar* if the variables in one problem can be put in correspondence with the variables in the other. This is a very general statement, which even includes electrical–mechanical analogies. The simplest type of similarity occurs when two situations have different dimensional variables but the same nondimensional variables.

Consider a physical phenomenon governed by the equation

$$\Pi_1 = f(\Pi_2, \ldots, \Pi_k) \tag{8.8.1}$$

If two flows have the same values of the independent variables, the dependent variables should be the same. Calling one flow the model and the other the prototype, then

$$\Pi_{im} = \Pi_{ip}, \qquad i = 1, 2, \ldots, k \tag{8.8.2}$$

There is an implicit assumption that both situations are governed by the same unique function. However, there are many instances in fluid mechanics where a unique answer is not obtained. For example, the same flow rate through a converging–diverging nozzle can be obtained with two different flow patterns (and pressure ratios). One is completely subsonic, while the other contains supersonic flow and shock waves. Which flow pattern occurs depends on the past history of the imposed pressures. In general, failure of the uniqueness assumption is the exception rather than the rule.

For an example, assume that we have a pump 6 in. in diameter. At the design point the flow is 10 gal/min with a head rise of 15 ft of water. What would be the performance of a geometrically similar pump with diameter 12 in. operating with the same fluid and at the same speed? The pi variables at the design point would be equal:

$$\frac{Q_2}{d_2^3 \Omega_2} = \frac{Q_1}{d_1^3 \Omega_1}$$

$$Q_2 = Q_1 \left(\frac{d_2}{d_1}\right)^3 = 80 \text{ gal/min} = 10 \left(\frac{12}{6}\right)^3$$

$$\frac{\Delta p_2}{\rho_2 d_2^2 \Omega_2^2} = \frac{\Delta p_1}{\rho_1 d_1^2 \Omega_1^2}$$

$$\frac{\Delta p_2}{\rho g} = \frac{\Delta p_1}{\rho g} \left(\frac{d_2}{d_1}\right)^2 = 60 \text{ ft}$$

The electric motor turning at the same speed would require more power.

8.9 SIMILARITY WITH GEOMETRIC DISTORTION

The theory of the geometrically similar flow situations is easily handled by the pi theorem where the nondimensional variables of the two situations are equal. There are other types of similarity where the geometry differs between the two flows. In these situations we must look at the equations and boundary conditions governing the flow field. As an example of an analysis of this type, we discuss the theory of flow over thin two-dimensional airfoils as shown in Fig. 8.5.

The origin of the equations and boundary conditions that govern the flow will not be given. The reader unfamiliar with them will not lose much in the way of understanding, as the procedure is essentially mathematical. In subsonic compressible flow a perturbation velocity potential ϕ is the major dependent variable. It is a function of x and y coordinates and the Mach number M. All of these variables are nondimensionalized in such a way that the airfoil is one unit long and the free-stream velocity is 1. The convenient abbreviation $\beta \equiv (1 - M^2)^{1/2}$ is employed. The governing equation and boundary conditions are

$$\beta^2 \frac{\partial^2 \phi}{\partial x^2} + \frac{\partial^2 \phi}{\partial y^2} = 0 \tag{8.9.1}$$

At infinity the perturbation vanishes:

$$\frac{\partial \phi}{\partial x}\bigg|_\infty = \frac{\partial \phi}{\partial y}\bigg|_\infty = 0$$

and on the surface of the airfoil,

$$\frac{dy_s}{dx} = \frac{\partial \phi}{\partial y}\bigg|_s$$

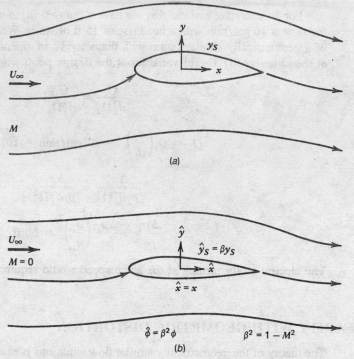

Figure 8.5 Dynamic similarity between (a) subsonic compressible flow and (b) an equivalent incompressible flow over a distorted model.

These equations are sufficient to solve for $\phi(x, y, \beta)$.

Now, suppose that the compressible flow variables are transformed as follows:

$$\tilde{x} = x, \qquad \tilde{y} = \beta y, \qquad \tilde{\phi} = \beta^2 \phi \qquad\qquad (8.9.2)$$

Substituting into the differential equation 8.9.1 yields

$$\beta^2 \frac{\partial^2(\tilde{\phi}/\beta^2)}{\partial \tilde{x}^2} + \frac{\partial^2(\tilde{\phi}/\beta^2)}{\partial \tilde{y}^2}\left(\frac{d\tilde{y}}{dy}\right)^2 = 0$$

$$\frac{\partial^2 \tilde{\phi}}{\partial \tilde{x}^2} + \frac{\partial^2 \tilde{\phi}}{\partial \tilde{y}^2} = 0 \qquad\qquad (8.9.3)$$

The boundary conditions far from the body are

$$\frac{\partial(\tilde{\phi}/\beta^2)}{\partial \tilde{x}} = 0, \qquad \frac{\partial \tilde{\phi}}{\partial \tilde{x}} = 0$$

$$\frac{\partial(\tilde{\phi}/\beta^2)}{\partial \tilde{y}}\frac{d\tilde{y}}{dy} = 0, \qquad \frac{\partial \tilde{\phi}}{\partial \tilde{y}} = 0$$

On the surface of the body the boundary condition is

$$\frac{d}{d\tilde{x}}\left(\frac{\tilde{y}}{\beta}\right) = \frac{\partial}{\partial\tilde{y}}\left(\frac{\tilde{\phi}}{\beta^2}\right)\frac{d\tilde{y}}{dy}$$

$$\frac{d\tilde{y}}{d\tilde{x}} = \frac{\partial\tilde{\phi}}{\partial\tilde{y}}$$

The solution to this problem, $\tilde{\phi}(\tilde{x}, \tilde{y})$, is identical to the solution for $M = 0$, that is, $\phi_0 = \phi(x, y; \beta = 1)$. Thus, the compressible flow over an airfoil at Mach number M is related to the incompressible flow over an airfoil with a stretched shape. The length of the airfoil is the same (since $\tilde{x} = x$), but the surface coordinates are related by $\tilde{y} = \beta y$. This is an example of similarity between distorted models. The original nondimensional problem $\phi(x, y; \beta)$ has a mathematical structure that allows a new, smaller set of variables $\tilde{\phi}(\tilde{x}, \tilde{y})$. This new function is the same between the actual flow and the equivalent incompressible flow.

The physical result of this problem is that subsonic compressible flow over thin objects is qualitatively the same as incompressible flow. The streamlines and forces undergo only slight modifications as the Mach number increases. The exact magnitude and nature of the modification as well as the completely different phenomena that occur in transonic and supersonic flow is the subject of compressible-flow theory.

Distorted models are frequently used in hydraulics to model dams, river systems, and other large-scale problems. As with the compressible-flow example above, the local differential equations must be used to establish similarity of distorted models.

One of the largest hydraulic models ever constructed is a model of the Mississippi River basin built by the U.S. Army Corps of Engineers. Figure 8.6 shows only a portion of the model. Horizontal directions on the model have the scale ratio $1:2000$ (model/ prototype). On the model this places Sioux City, Iowa, about $\frac{1}{2}$ mile from the mouth of the Mississippi River, an actual distance of about 1000 miles on the real river. Vertical distances on the model are scaled $1:100$, giving a distortion factor of $20:1$ (vertical/ horizontal). The actual elevation of Sioux City is 1100 ft, so the corresponding point on the model would be just 11 ft higher than the mouth of the river. Through a detailed analysis of the governing equations, one can determine that the time scales are such that 5.4 min on the model corresponds to one day on the river. With the time scale compressed in this way, it is possible to trace the history of hypothetical flood in a reasonably short experiment.

The model has had many uses. It has been used primarily to evaluate the effect that dams, levees, and reservoirs have on the river flow, especially on the management of flood conditions. Upon several occasions the model has been used to forecast the progress of flood-fighting efforts. With the highly developed and managed system that the Mississippi has today, disastrous floods are much less frequent than in years past. Another use for the model is for public relations. Groups of civic leaders are brought to the model to see how proposed flood control projects will benefit their regions.

The model has also been used to aid in developing a computer model of the river system. Ideally, fluid dynamic events on the hydraulic model, the computer model, and the real river should all agree. This means that some empirical coefficients in the computer model may actually be checked by running the hydraulic model at the conditions desired. In this way extreme flood conditions, which may never actually occur, can be verified.

Figure 8.6   Model of the Mississippi river. Courtesy of U.S. Army Corps of Engineers Waterways Experiment Station, Vicksburg, Mississippi. Reprinted with permission.

8.10   NONDIMENSIONAL FORMULATION OF PHYSICAL PROBLEMS

In many instances we know the equations that govern a problem and can write out the relevant laws and conditions. the fact that solutions of physical problems must be dimensionally homogeneous is only contained implicitly in the governing equations. It is often ignored as one finds the solution. This is a bad practice. If we recast the problem into nondimensional variables, we explicitly use the information that physical functions are dimensionally homogeneous. Boundary conditions and physical constants are used to nondimensionalize the dependent and independent variables. The nondimensional form of the problem will contain all the necessary variables. Inspection of these equations will reveal the nondimensional functions without using the pi theorem. Moreover, frequently there is information contained in the governing equations that reduces the number of nondimensional variables even more than the pi theorem would predict. The advantages of nondimensonalizing a problem are great; the problem has the fewest variables and the simplest mathematical structure when expressed in nondimensional variables.

Nondimensional variables may be thought of as variables whose scales or units of measurement come from the problem itself. In this sense they are natural scales. The standard units of measurement, such as the meter, the kilogram, and the second, have no special importance to any physical processes. The important scales (the S values of Eq. 8.7.4) come from the list of variables for the problem.

Let us consider for a moment the anatomy of a nondimensional variable ($y*$). A nondimensional variable consists of three parts: the dimensional variable y, a reference value y_0, and the sale or unit y_s:

$$y* = \frac{y - y_0}{y_s} \qquad (8.10.1)$$

The first question to answer in composing nondimensional variables is about the reference y_0. Is the absolute value of the variable important to the problem, or only its value compared to a reference? For example, in heat conduction only differences in temperature are important; therefore, we should look for a reference value at some point in the field. Once the reference has been decided upon, attention can be turned to the scale y_s. The scale is some combination of boundary conditions and/or dimensional constants that has the same dimensions as y. Its most important characteristics is that it measures the range that y takes on in the problem. If y takes on maximum and minimum values, we ask ourselves how large the difference in these values is. We do not need its exact value, only a quantity that estimates it.

Pressure is a good example. Consider a compressible flow where the pressure changes by expansion and compression. The absolute magnitude of the pressure is important In this case the work of the process depends on the absolute level, not just the difference between initial and final values. The reference should be zero, and the proper nondimensional pressure is

$$p* = \frac{p}{p_s} \qquad (8.10.2)$$

The scale p_s is some specified pressure in the problem (say, the initial pressure). Pressure in this case plays a thermodynamic role as well as providing a force.

On the other hand, for incompressible flow the level of the pressure is not important. In this case some specified pressure in the flow is used as a reference p_0. If the flow involves fluid inertia, the changes in pressure are the result of dynamic processes. Thermodynamic changes in pressure are absent. The unit of pressure is a characteristic kinetic energy (per unit mass) of the flow, the dynamic pressure

$$\tilde{p} = \frac{p - p_0}{\frac{1}{2}\rho V_0^2} \qquad (8.10.3)$$

If the flow involves strong viscous forces, the correct scale incorporates viscosity:

$$p** = \frac{p - p_0}{\mu U_0 / L}$$

Moreover, in lubrication flows a fourth type of pressure scale is appropriate.

Perhaps the best way to demonstrate how to nondimensionalize a problem is through examples. We first consider the plane Couette flow problem worked in Chapter 7. The problem is

$$\frac{d^2 u}{dy^2} = 0$$

$$\begin{aligned} y = 0, & \quad u = 0 \\ y = h, & \quad u = V_0 \end{aligned} \qquad (8.10.4)$$

The first place to look for scales is in the boundary conditions. We have already eliminated any reference value for y by choosing the coordinate system on the lower wall. The range of y is from 0 to h, so h is the obvious scale. Let the nondimensional y variable be

$$y^* = \frac{y - 0}{h - 0} = \frac{y}{h} \qquad (8.10.5)$$

By similar reasoning the velocity variable has a reference value 0 on the lower wall, and we expect the upper wall velocity V_0 to be the maximum:

$$u^* = \frac{u - 0}{V_0 - 0} = \frac{u}{V_0} \qquad (8.10.6)$$

In terms of the new variables, the boundary conditions are now pure numbers independent of measuring units:

$$y^* = 0, \qquad u^* = 0$$
$$y^* = 1, \qquad u^* = 1 \qquad (8.10.7)$$

The differential equation transforms by substituting for the dependent variable and transforming the independent variable:

$$\frac{d^2u}{dy^2} = \frac{d^2(u^*V_0)}{dy^2} = V_0 \frac{d^2u^*}{dy^{*2}} \left(\frac{dy^*}{dy} \right)^2 \qquad (8.10.8)$$

$$\frac{d^2u^*}{dy^{*2}} = 0$$

A lot of information can be found without solving the problem. Since there are no parameters to vary in Eqs. 8.10.7 and 8.10.8, we conclude that $u^* = f(y^*)$. The solution to Eq. 8.10.8 is actually $u^* = y^*$.

As a second example, consider the flow in a slot that is driven by a constant pressure gradient. The problem is

$$\mu \frac{d^2u}{dy^2} = \frac{dp}{dx}$$
$$y = 0, \qquad u = 0$$
$$y = h, \qquad u = 0 \qquad (8.10.9)$$

The y variable is nondimensionalized as before: $y^* = y/h$. The boundary conditions show that $u = 0$ at the walls, and we find no information about how large u will become. The maximum value of u is determined by a balance between the pressure force and the viscous force. This information is contained within the differential equation itself. A convenient procedure is to assume an unknown velocity scale u_s:

$$\tilde{u} = \frac{u - 0}{u_s} \qquad (8.10.10)$$

Substituting gives

$$\frac{\mu u_s}{h^2}\frac{d^2\tilde{u}}{dy^{*2}} = \frac{dp}{dx}$$

Now, the scale u_s is fixed so that the right-hand side is a pure number and the differential equation is free of parameters. Let u_s be chosen as

$$u_s = -\frac{h^2}{\mu}\frac{dp}{dx} \tag{8.10.11}$$

The problem in nondimensional variables becomes

$$\frac{d^2\tilde{u}}{dy^{*2}} = -1$$

$$y^* = 0, \quad \tilde{u} = 0 \tag{8.10.12}$$
$$y^* = 1, \quad \tilde{u} = 0$$

It is not important that the right-hand side is chosen to be 1. What is important is that the size of the velocity profile is measured by $(h^2/\mu)(-dp/dx)$. The minus sign compensates for the fact that dp/dx is negative for a positive velocity. Again we have a problem without any parameters, so we know that the answer has the functional form $\tilde{u} = f(y^*)$. For the record, the solution is $\tilde{u} = \frac{1}{2}(y^* - y^{*2})$.

Next, we consider a combination of the two preceding problems (Fig. 8.7). Couette flow with an imposed pressure gradient offers an example where two natural velocity scales appear in the same problem. In dimensional variables the problem is

$$\frac{d^2u}{dy^2} = \frac{1}{\mu}\frac{dp}{dx}$$

$$y = 0, \quad u = 0 \tag{8.10.13}$$
$$y = h, \quad u = V_0$$

If we choose to use the wall velocity V_0 as a scale, the problem transforms into

$$\frac{d^2u^*}{dy^{*2}} = \frac{h^2}{\mu V_0}\frac{dp}{dx} \equiv -\mathbb{P}$$

$$y^* = 0, \quad u^* = 0 \tag{8.10.14}$$
$$y^* = 1, \quad u^* = 1$$

The new parameter $\mathbb{P}$ defined above compares the pressure velocity scale with the wall velocity. The structure of the equations and boundary conditions indicates that the solution is of the form $u^* = f(y^*; \mathbb{P})$. From our work in Chapter 7 we know that the actual answer is

$$\frac{u}{V_0} = u^*(y^*; \mathbb{P}) = y^* + \frac{1}{2}\mathbb{P}(y^* - y^{*2}) \tag{8.10.15}$$

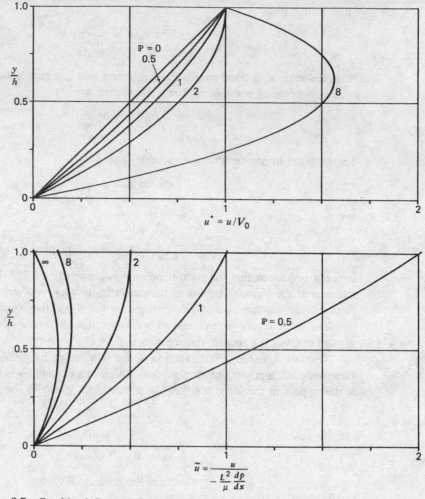

Figure 8.7 Combined Couette–Poiseuille flow in different nondimensional variables. The pressure gradient parameter is $\mathbb{P}$.

Now let us reconsider the problem, using u_s as the velocity scale. The problem is

$$\frac{d^2\tilde{u}}{dy^{*2}} = -1$$

$$y^* = 0, \qquad \tilde{u} = 0$$
$$y^* = 1, \qquad \tilde{u} = \mathbb{P}^{-1} \tag{8.10.16}$$

The parameter $\mathbb{P}$ now appears in the boundary conditions, and the differential equation is free of parameters. The solution is still of the form $u^* = f(y^*; \mathbb{P})$ as shown below:

$$\bar{u} = \frac{u}{-(L^2/\mu)(dp/dx)} = \frac{u^*}{\mathbb{P}} = \frac{1}{\mathbb{P}} y^* + \frac{1}{2}(y^* - y^{*2}) \qquad (8.10.17)$$

This result is the same equation as Eq. 8.10.15 except that the velocity variable has a different scale.

What if we have a solution and want to retrieve a special case by letting a parameter approach a certain value? For instance, $\mathbb{P} \rightarrow 0$ means that the pressure–velocity scale is small compared to the moving-wall scale. Allowing $\mathbb{P} \rightarrow 0$ in the form $\bar{u}(y^*; \mathbb{P}))$ gives an infinite answer. The velocity is not properly nondimensionalized for this limit. Allowing $\mathbb{P} \rightarrow 0$ in $u^*(y^*; \mathbb{P})$ produces the proper result:

$$u^* = y^* \qquad (8.10.18)$$

which is the velocity profile for Couette flow without a pressure gradient. On the other hand, for $\mathbb{P} \rightarrow \infty$, Eqs. 8.10.16 and 8.10.17 are the correct form.

If the two velocity scales are about the same size, the parameter $\mathbb{P}$ is a reasonable magnitude. In this case it makes no difference which scale is used for the velocity. If one scale is much larger than the other, the dominant scale should be used in forming the nondimensional variables. If a limiting process is to be applied to an answer (or, more likely, to the problem itself before the answer is obtained), the variables must be properly nondimensionalized for that limit process.

8.11   CONCLUSIONS

Dimensional analysis allows us to express mathematical or experimental results in their simplest form. The most complicated situations benefit the most from reducing the number of variables.

There are two fundamental ideas behind dimensional analysis. The first is that a measurement scale is not an intrinsic part of a physical quantity. The only intrinsic aspect is that the ratio of two different values is independent of the measurement system in which they are expressed. This fact led to Bridgman's equation. The second idea is that a law governing physical variables must be valid for all different measurement systems. Together, these ideas under the pi theorem.

Even sharper results than given by the pi theorem are obtained if we can bring into play extra information provided by laws that govern the physics or by assumptions about the functional form of the result. The latter assumptions are based on either physical or purely intuitive arguments.

Nondimensional variables may be thought of as variables that are measured by a scale unit arising from the physical event itself. Proper selection of natural scales produces variables of a modest numerical size. The first, and sometimes the most difficult step in organizing an analysis or in organizing experimental results is to find the proper scales for forming nondimensional variables.

PROBLEMS

8.1 (A) Rework the pump analysis using F, M, L, T as primary variables.

8.2 (A) Rework the pump analysis using M, S (speed), and T as primary variables.

8.3 (A) A list of variables for a problem has only one variable with the dimension of mass. In what two possible ways could the list be in error?

8.4 (A) Repeat the pump analysis except instead of ΔP as the dependent variable find the torque required to drive the motor. What is the power required?

8.5 (B) Could the relation 1 Pa $\equiv$ 1 N/m^2 be a unifying dimensional constant?

8.6 (A) The speed of a surface water (liquid) wave is thought to depend on the wave height, the wavelength, the depth of the water, and the acceleration of gravity. What would happen if density was also proposed to be an important parameter? Find a nondimensional form of the answer. $V = f(A, \lambda, h, g)$

8.7 (B) After making a list of variables for a problem, a worker states: "If I have left anything off of the list, that just means I need another pi variable." When is this statement true and when is it untrue?

8.8 (A) A windmill is designed to operate at 20 rpm in a 15-mph wind and produce 300 kW of power. The blades are 1.75 ft in diameter. A model 1.75 ft in diameter is to be tested at 90-mph wind velocity. What rotor speed should be used, and what power should be expected?

8.9 (A) A propeller is placed in a tank of chemicals to mix them together. The diameter is D, the rotation speed is N, and the power to turn the propeller is P. The fluid density is ρ and the viscosity is μ. Tests in water ($\rho = 1000$ kg/m^3, $\mu = 1.01 \times 10^{-3}$ Pa $\cdot$ s) show that a propeller $D = 225$ mm rotating at 23 rev/s requires a driving power of 159 N $\cdot$ m/s. Calculate the speed and torque required to drive a dynamically similar propeller, 675 mm in diameter in air ($\rho = 1.2$ kg/m^3, $\mu = 1.86 \times 10^{-5}$ Pa $\cdot$ s).

8.10 (B) Extend the derivation of Bridgman's equation to three variables; that is, consider $y = f(m, l, t)$.

8.11 (B) The pressure at the end of a round pipe p_2 is a function of the initial pressure p_1, the density ρ, the average velocity V, the viscosity μ, the size of the wall roughness ε (length), the length of the pipe L, and the diameter d. By making several physical assumptions, find the simplest nondimensional relation that governs the pressure in incompressible flow.

8.12 (C) Instant nondimensionalization of the Navier–Stokes equations is sometimes done in the following way.

Suppose that the problem has characteristic U_0, L, ρ_0 specified. Imagine that these values are used as the measuring scales, and then set them equal to unity. Any distance symbol x_i is measured in terms of L and is really x_i/L, v_i is really v_i/U_0, and ρ is really ρ/ρ_0. What is v in terms of the measuring scales U_0, L, ρ_0? What is p in terms of U_0, L, ρ_0? If the flow is incompressible, what does the momentum equation reduce to?

8.13 (C) The pressure p_2 downstream of a shock wave in a perfect gas (specified γ) depends on the thermodynamic state ahead of the shock, p_1, T_1, and the flow velocity v_1 (shock is stationary). Find the nondimensional relation for the pressure p_2 using M, L, T, and degree as primary dimensions. (Note that the dimensions of R can be deduced from $p/\rho = RT$.)

8.14 (B) Consider the momentum equation for incompressible flow with constant viscosity. and $g = 0$. The problem has a characteristic length L and velocity U.

$$\rho \left(u \frac{\partial u}{\partial x} + v \frac{\partial u}{\partial y} \right) = - \frac{\partial p}{\partial x} + \mu \left(\frac{\partial^2 u}{\partial x^2} + \frac{\partial^2 u}{\partial y^2} \right)$$

(A)   (B)   (C)

If terms (A) $\approx$ 0, what is the proper nondimensional pressure? If terms (C) $\approx$ 0, what is the proper nondimensional pressure?

8.15 (B) A viscous liquid jet is falling freely (pressure is atmospheric). The x-coordinate is pointing in the direction of gravity with the origin at the nozzle, where the initial velocity is U. Assume that the velocity is uniform at each location, $u = u(x)$. Simplify the x-momentum equation and find nondimensional variables for u and x. Do any parameters appear in the equation or boundary conditions?

8.16 (C) A dinosaur skeleton has been sinking through a pit of Newtonian tar for several years. The velocity is so slow that the density (inertia) of the fluid is not important. To calculate how long it will take for the skeleton to sink to the bottom of the tar pit, the drag force must be found. Tests to find the drag force on a model skeleton will be conducted. The tests will be run in a tank of glycerin by pulling the model through the tank at any desired velocity with a wire. A drag force on the wire will be measured. How many tests are needed? What velocities should be used? How is the actual drag force related to the measured drag force?

9

Compressible Flow

To reach our goal of understanding when a flow may be considered as incompressible, we need to know some of the characteristics of compressible flows. Our main purpose in this chapter is to study the flow of a fluid that has completely arbitrary thermodynamic equations.

We will study two problems. The Couette flow problem illustrates how a shear profile generates thermal energy by viscous dissipation. The temperature gradients from this process may then lead to density variations. It is important to know the parameters that affect this process. The second problem is a piston oscillating in a tube. We will study how the piston sends out pressure waves to initiate the fluid motion. The pressure (or expansion) waves compress the fluid and cause variations in density. This problem also introduces and defines the speed of sound, which is a thermodynamic property of the fluid.

From a practical standpoint, the Couette problem is a model of how heat is generated in a bearing. The same effect occurs on high-speed airplanes and rockets because there is a layer of shear flow next to the surface. It is sometimes noted that this problem is an exact solution to the Navier–Stokes equation—that is, a solution to the full equations without assuming any transport properties or thermodynamic functions are constant. Illingworth (1950) was the first to give this analysis in his paper on solutions of the (compressible) Navier–Stokes equations. (He also shows that compressible Poiseuille flow is impossible.)

The oscillating piston problem illustrates how compressible effects are to be transmitted in unsteady flow by waves. There are also similar physical wave events in steady supersonic flows. In these situations the wave nature is tied inherently to compressible effects.

9.1 COMPRESSIBLE COUETTE FLOW: ADIABATIC WALL

We consider only the plane flow case. The algebra is somewhat simpler and it contains the essential physics; there is no mathematical difficulty in solving the problem for the cylindrical case. Figure 9.1 gives a picture of the flow and defines the boundary conditions. Our first assumption is that none of the flow properties depend on x, z, or t. The major dependent variables are

$$v_x = v_x(y), \qquad v_y = v_y(y)$$

$$T = T(y), \qquad \rho = \rho(y)$$

(9.1.1)

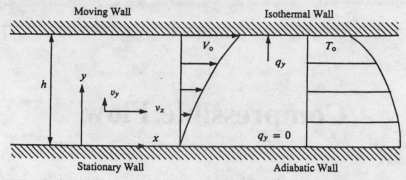

Figure 9.1 Compressible Couette flow for a fluid with known equation of state, viscosity law $\mu(T, p)$, and conductivity law $k(T, p)$.

Enforcing the no-slip boundary conditions leads to the following:

$$v_x(0) = 0, \qquad v_y(0) = 0$$
$$v_x(h) = V_0, \qquad v_y(h) = 0 \tag{9.1.2}$$

Since the energy equation is now involved in the problem, we also need boundary conditions on the heat transfer. Assume that the upper wall is isothermal and that the lower wall is adiabatic. This means that

$$T(h) = T_0 \qquad q_y(0) = 0 \tag{9.1.3}$$

We might, as an alternative, have assumed that the lower wall was also isothermal at a different temperature T_1. By choosing an adiabatic lower wall instead, we shall be able to pin down to what extent viscous dissipation influences the temperature profile. If we had allowed a constant temperature on the lower wall, there would be a characteristic temperature scale $(T_0 - T_1)$ for conduction across the gap; the temperature profile might have been dominated by conduction, so that we would have lost the effect of viscous dissipation.

The governing equations will be considered one by one as they are simplified for this problem. First, continuity equation 5.1.4 under the assumptions 9.1.1 reduces to

$$\frac{d}{dy}(\rho v_y) = 0 \tag{9.1.4}$$

This means that ρv_y must be a constant. Applying the boundary condition $v_y(0) = 0$ shows the constant to be zero. Therefore, we find that there is no y-direction motion.

In anticipation of the momentum equations, we calculate the viscous stresses (Eq. 6.1.8) employing the fact that $v_x(y)$ is the only velocity component ($v_y = 0$). They are

$$\tau_{xx} = \tau_{yy} = 0 \tag{9.1.5}$$

$$\tau_{yx} = \tau_{yx} = \mu \frac{dv_x}{dy} \tag{9.1.6}$$

Next we consider the y-direction momentum equation 5.7.14. It simplifies to

$$0 = \frac{dp}{dy} \tag{9.1.7}$$

implying that the pressure is a constant. This is an important result with respect to the thermodynamics of the fluid. A simple compressible substance has only two independent intensive properties, and we have just shown that one of them is constant. Since the pressure has only one value for the entire flow, we may consider all the transport properties as a function of the temperature only.

The x-direction momentum equation 6.6.2 reduces to a statement that the net shear on a particle is zero:

$$0 = \frac{d\tau_{yx}}{dy} \tag{9.1.8}$$

This integrates to

$$\tau_{yx} = \text{const} = \tau_0 = \mu \frac{dv_x}{dy} \tag{9.1.9}$$

where τ_0 denotes the constant shear stress. We shall come back to this equation later after a few other facts have been established from the energy equation.

The heat flux vector (Eq. 6.5.4) under the assumption $T = T(y)$ becomes

$$q_x = 0, \qquad q_y = -k \frac{dT}{dy} \tag{9.1.10}$$

Employing this information along with our previous assumptions, we find that energy equation 6.6.3 balances the net conduction away from a point with the energy generated at the point by viscous dissipation. In mathematical terms,

$$0 = -\frac{dq_y}{dy} + \tau_0 \frac{dv_x}{dy} \tag{9.1.11}$$

We can integrate this equation to give the relation

$$-q_y + \tau_0 v_x = C_1 \tag{9.1.12}$$

The parameter C_1 is determined to be zero by noting that both v_x and q_y are zero on the lower wall. Upon substituting Eqs. 9.1.9 and 9.1.10 into Eq. 9.1.12, we find that

$$k \frac{dT}{dy} + \mu v_x \frac{dv_x}{dy} = 0$$

or, written another way,

$$\frac{d}{dy} \left(\frac{1}{2} v_x^2 \right) = -\frac{k}{\mu} \frac{dT}{dy} \tag{9.1.13}$$

Now we are in a position to use the fact that the transport properties may be considered as a function of temperature alone (the pressure is constant). Without even stating the relations for $k(T)$ and $\mu(T)$ explicitly, we can write the integral of Eq. 9.1.13 from $y = h$ to an arbitrary point y (T' denotes a dummy integration variable):

$$\frac{1}{2} v_x^2 - \frac{1}{2} V_0^2 = - \int_{T_0}^{T} \frac{k(T')}{\mu(T')} \, dT' \qquad (9.1.14)$$

This form is somewhat unusual. We found v_x as a function of the temperature T. Since μ and k are always positive, the integral is an increasing function of T, and in principle we may find the inverse function $T(v_x)$.

To continue, let us one again consider Eq. 9.1.9:

$$\mu(T) \frac{dv_x}{dy} = \tau_0$$

Since T is a function of v_x, this may be written as

$$\mu(T(v_x)) \, dv_x = \tau_0 \, dy$$

Upon integration from $y = 0$, where $v_x = 0$, to an arbitrary y, v_x, we find the relation (v_x' denotes a dummy integration variable)

$$y = \frac{1}{\tau_0} \int_0^{v_x} \mu(T(v_x')) \, dv_x' \qquad (9.1.15)$$

This is the velocity profile in the inverse form $y = y(v_x)$. The temperature profile can be found in principle by inverting Eq. 9.1.15 and substituting into Eq. 9.1.14. We find the constant τ_0 in Eq. 9.1.15 by integrating Eq. 9.1.15 all the way across the wall, that is,

$$\tau_0 = \frac{1}{h} \int_0^{V_0} \mu(T(v_x')) \, dv_x' \qquad (9.1.16)$$

This concludes all the necessary relations. In principle, we have an exact solution. Equations 9.1.7 and 9.1.14 to 9.1.16 give us the velocity and two thermodynamic properties, p and T, at every point in the flow.

Note that the thermodynamic equations of state have not been specified, and indeed they do not appear in the solution. The energy equation of state (involving the heat capacity) is absent because there is no storage or convection of energy in the problem. The second equation of state is necessary only if we want to find the density from $\rho = \rho(p, T)$.

9.2 FLOW WITH POWER LAW TRANSPORT PROPERTIES

As a specific example, we compute the results when the viscosity and thermal conductivity are governed by power laws. Assume that

$$\mu = \mu_0 \left(\frac{T}{T_0}\right)^n \qquad k = k_0 \left(\frac{T}{T_0}\right)^n \qquad (9.2.1)$$

The exponent n is arbitrary at this stage. It is chosen to make Eq. 9.2.1 fit the experimental data for a given substance. The reference constants μ_0 and k_0 are the values at the upper wall, where the temperature is T_0. Substitution of Eq. 9.2.1 into Eq. 9.1.14 gives an equation where n drops out,

$$v_x^2 - V_0^2 = -2 \frac{k_0}{\mu_0} \int_{T_0}^{T} dT'$$

Performing the integration and rearranging yields the temperature–velocity relation,

$$T = T_0 + \frac{1}{2} \frac{\mu_0}{k_0} (V_0^2 - v_x^2) \tag{9.2.2}$$

Recall that at the upper wall the velocity is V_0 and the temperature is T_0. The velocity profile with constant shear τ_0, causes the temperature to increase through the action of viscous dissipation, by the amount $\mu_0 V_0^2 / 2k_0$ at the opposite wall. This is true irrespective of the value of h. The important conclusion of this chapter is that $\mu_0 V_0^2 / 2k_0$ is the scale for temperature increase by a shear profile next to an adiabatic wall.

The velocity profile will be found next. We take Eq. 9.1.15 and substitute Eq. 9.2.1 to get the integral

$$y = \frac{1}{\tau_0} \int_0^{v_x} \mu_0 \left[\frac{T(v_x')}{T_0} \right]^n dv_x'$$

$$= \frac{\mu_0}{\tau_0} \int_0^{v_x} \left[1 + \frac{1}{2} \frac{\mu_0}{k_0 T_0} (V_0^2 - v_x'^2) \right]^n dv_x' \tag{9.2.3}$$

To proceed further, we must specify n. We consider two cases: $n = 0$, which implies constant properties, and $n = 1$, which is more like the behavior of a perfect gas.

For $n = 0$, integration of Eq. 9.2.3 produces

$$y = \frac{\mu_0}{\tau_0} v_x$$

Upon evaluating τ_0 at $y = h$, we obtain the answer given in Chapter 7:

$$\frac{v_x}{V_0} = \frac{y}{h} \tag{9.2.4}$$

The corresponding temperature profile is obtained by substituting Eq. 9.2.4 into Eq. 9.2.2:

$$T = T_0 + \frac{1}{2} \frac{\mu_0 V_0^2}{k_0} \left[1 - \left(\frac{y}{h} \right)^2 \right] \tag{9.2.5}$$

For $n = 1$, the situation is only slightly more complicated. By performing algebra analogous to that above, we find that the velocity equation is

$$\frac{y}{h} = \frac{v_x}{V_0} \frac{1 + \mu_0 V_0^2 / (2k_0 T_0) \left[1 - \frac{1}{3} (v_x / V_0)^2 \right]}{1 + \mu_0 V_0^2 / (3k_0 T_0)} \tag{9.2.6}$$

In this equation we cannot solve explicitly for v_x. Because of this, the corresponding equation for the temperature cannot be stated as an explicit function of y but must remain in the form Eq. 9.2.2.

9.3 INVISCID COMPRESSIBLE WAVES: SPEED OF SOUND

In this section we consider an initially still fluid that is semi-infinite in the x-direction. After time zero, the wall at $x = 0$ is oscillated in the normal direction according to

$$x_p = A[1 - \cos \omega t]$$

$$u_p = A\omega \sin \omega t$$

(9.3.1)

The flow could be produced by a piston in a long, wide tube. When the piston moves in the normal direction rather than sliding in its own plane, it compresses the fluid. Pressure waves are sent from the piston into the fluid, where they induce a compression and also engender a velocity in the x-direction. We assume that the flow is a one-dimensional, unsteady flow depending on x and t. It is important that the piston motion begin smoothly, but it is not important that the motion is sinusoidal.

The initial quiescent state has thermodynamic properties ρ_0, T_0, s_0, c_{p0}, transport properties k_0, μ_0, and speed of sound a_0. The speed of sound a_0 is a result of the analysis. Events travel through the fluid with this speed. A nondimensional velocity formed with this scale is $U = u/a_0$. From the piston motion there is a time scale ω^{-1} and another velocity scale $A\omega$. In a general compressible flow the fluid velocities are of order a_0 and $U = u/a_0$ is the correct nondimensional variable. If the piston velocity is small compared to a_0, the flow is still compressible; however, it is a special case of *acoustics*. The ratio of scales u_0/a_0 is the piston Mach number. The length scale of the flow field is not determined by the piston amplitude but by the distance a sound wave travels in one time unit, a_0/ω. Nondimensional variables are as follows:

$$
\begin{array}{lll}
x^* = x/(a_0/\omega), & t^* = t\omega, & u^* = u/(A\omega) \\
\rho^* = \rho/\rho_0, & T^* = T/T_0, & V = U/a_0 \\
s^* = s/s_0, & k^* = k/k_0, & p^* = p/(\rho_0 a_0^2) \\
a^* = a/a_0, & & \mu^* = \mu/\mu_0
\end{array}
$$

(9.3.2)

Nondimensional parameters that arise include a Reynolds number, a Mach number, and a Prandtl number:

$$\text{Re} = \frac{A\omega a_0}{\omega \nu} = \frac{Aa_0}{\nu}, \qquad M = \frac{A\omega}{a_0}, \qquad \text{Pr} = \frac{\mu_0 c_{p0}}{k_0}$$

(9.3.3)

Note that the Reynolds number is based on the piston velocity and the length scale a_0/ω. For air the product $a_0/\nu = 2.5 \times 10^7$ m^{-1}. Thus, it does not take very much amplitude A to produce a large Reynolds number. The same is true for typical liquids; for water $a_0/\nu = 1.5 \times 10^9$ m^{-1}, and for glycerin $a_0/\nu = 2 \times 10^6$ m^{-1}. In light of these values it is reasonable to consider the limiting situation for high Reynolds numbers; terms preceded by $1/\text{Re}$ in the equations will be neglected. This limit will preserve the compressible fluid-flow nature in which we are interested.

First consider the entropy equation 5.12.3 for a Newtonian fluid:

$$\rho \frac{Ds}{Dt} = -\frac{1}{T}\nabla \cdot \mathbf{q} + \frac{1}{T}\boldsymbol{\tau}{:}\mathbf{S}$$

$$q_x = -k\frac{\partial T}{\partial x} \tag{9.3.4}$$

$$\boldsymbol{\tau}{:}\mathbf{S} = \frac{4}{3}\mu\left(\frac{\partial u}{\partial x}\right)^2$$

In nondimensional form we find that

$$\rho^*\left(\frac{\partial s^*}{\partial t^*} + U\frac{\partial s^*}{\partial x^*}\right) = \frac{c_{p0}}{s_0}\frac{M}{\text{Pr Re}}\frac{1}{T^*}\frac{\partial}{\partial x^*}\left(k^*\frac{\partial T^*}{\partial x^*}\right)$$

$$+ \frac{4}{3}\frac{\omega^2 A^2}{c_{p0}T_0}\frac{c_{p0}}{s_0}\frac{M}{\text{Re}}\frac{1}{T^*}\left(\frac{\partial u^*}{\partial x^*}\right)^2 \tag{9.3.5}$$

Next, specialize to the case of a high Reynolds number. For $\text{Re} \Rightarrow \infty$, Eq. 9.3.5 becomes a statement that the substantial derivative of s^* is zero.

$$\frac{\partial s^*}{\partial t^*} + U\frac{\partial s^*}{\partial x^*} = 0 \tag{9.3.6}$$

The entropy of a fluid particle does not change. Hence, $s^* = 1$ is the solution.

The thermodynamic equation of state for the pressure can be expressed in the form $p^* = p^*(\rho^*, s^* = 1)$. Since the entropy is constant, the pressure and all other thermodynamic properties may be considered as a function of a single variable, for example, the density. An incremental change in the pressure can be written as

$$\frac{dp^*}{d\rho^*} = \left.\frac{\partial p^*}{\partial \rho^*}\right|_{s^*} = a^{*2} \tag{9.3.7}$$

It will turn out that Eq. 9.3.7 is the definition of the speed of sound. We leave this to consider the dynamic equations.

The continuity equation is

$$\frac{\partial \rho}{\partial t} + \frac{\partial \rho u}{\partial x} = 0$$

$$\frac{\partial \rho^*}{\partial t^*} + \frac{\partial \rho^* U}{\partial x^*} = 0 \tag{9.3.8}$$

and the momentum equation is

$$\rho\left(\frac{\partial u}{\partial t} + u\frac{\partial u}{\partial x}\right) = -\frac{\partial p}{\partial x} + \frac{4}{3}\frac{\partial}{\partial x}\left(\mu\frac{\partial u}{\partial x}\right)$$

$$\rho^*\left(\frac{\partial U}{\partial t^*} + U\frac{\partial U}{\partial x^*}\right) = -\frac{\partial p^*}{\partial x^*} + \frac{4}{3}\frac{M}{\text{Re}}\frac{\partial}{\partial x^*}\left(\mu^*\frac{\partial U}{\partial x^*}\right)$$

The viscous term drops out for the limit of high Reynolds number, leaving

$$\frac{\partial U}{\partial t^*} + U \frac{\partial U}{\partial x^*} = -\frac{1}{\rho^*} \frac{\partial p^*}{\partial x^*} \tag{9.3.9}$$

Introduce a new notation for x and t:

$$T = t^*, \qquad X = x^*$$

Since temperature no longer enters the problem, there should be no confusion in denoting time by T.

Piston motion equation 9.3.1 in the variables X, T, $U_p = Mu_p^*$ is

$$X_p = M(1 - \cos T) \tag{9.3.10}$$

$$U_p = M \sin T$$

By using subscripts to denote differentiation, the continuity and momentum equations are

$$\rho_T^* + U\rho_X^* + \rho^* U_X = 0 \tag{9.3.11}$$

$$U_T + UU_X + \frac{1}{\rho^*} p_X^* = 0$$

It is convenient to define a new thermodynamic variable by [note that for $s^* = 1$, $a^* = a^*(\rho^*)$]

$$\lambda(\rho^*) \equiv \int_1^{\rho^*} a^*(\rho'^*) \frac{d\rho'^*}{\rho'^*} \tag{9.3.12}$$

Employing Eq. 3.13.4, we see that the derivatives are $\partial\lambda/\partial T = (a^*/\rho^*)\, \partial\rho^*/\partial T$ and $\partial\lambda/\partial X = (a^*/\rho^*)\, \partial\rho^*/\partial X$. Furthermore, from Eq. 9.3.7 we have $\partial p^*/\partial X = a^{*2}\, \partial\rho^*/\partial X$. Substituting these relations into Eq. 9.3.11 gives

$$\lambda_T + U\lambda_X + a^* U_X = 0 \tag{9.3.13}$$

$$U_T + UU_X + a^*\lambda_X = 0$$

Adding and subtracting Eq. 9.3.13 results in the first-order wave equations

$$\frac{\partial(U + \lambda)}{\partial T} + (U + a^*) \frac{\partial(U + \lambda)}{\partial X} = 0 \tag{9.3.14}$$

$$\frac{\partial(U - \lambda)}{\partial T} + (U - a^*) \frac{\partial(U - \lambda)}{\partial X} = 0$$

These relations have a form similar to the substantial derivative except that the "convection" velocity is $U + a^*$ in the first equation and $U - a^*$ in the second. Trajectories in the $X-T$ plane with slopes $U \pm a^*$ are called C^+ and C^- characteristics. From Eq. 9.3.14 we find that $U + \lambda \equiv 2R$ is a constant along any C^+ characteristic and along any C^- characteristic the quantity $U - \lambda \equiv -2S$ is constant. The trajectory of a C^+ characteristic, denoted by $X_+(T)$, has a slope

$$\frac{dX_+}{dT} = U + a^*, \qquad U + \lambda = 2R = \text{constant}$$

$$\text{(9.3.15)}$$

$$\frac{dX_-}{dT} = U - a^*, \qquad U - \lambda = -2S = \text{constant}$$

Physically, a forward-propagating signal moves at the local flow speed U plus the local *speed of sound* a^*. Of course, this is precisely the reason that we call a^*, defined mathematically by Eq. 9.3.7, the speed of sound.

Solving the relations 9.3.15 gives U, λ in terms of the constants R, S:

$$U = R - S$$

$$\text{(9.3.16)}$$

$$\lambda = R + S$$

In general, waves run in both directions and each characteristic curve can have different R and S values. A *simple wave* by definition runs in only one direction and either $S = 0$ or $R = 0$.

Consider Fig. 9.2, where the piston motion produces significant right running C^+ waves, a simple wave. The C^- characteristics that cross this wave originate in the undisturbed gas where $U = 0$, $\lambda(\rho^* = 1) = 0$. Hence, along these C^- lines $U + \lambda = 2S = 0$. Since the entire flow has C^- characteristics that originate in the undisturbed gas, S is zero for the entire flow. Along and C^+ characteristics the relations 9.3.16, with $S = 0$, show that

$$U = R = \lambda = \text{constant}$$

$$\text{(9.3.17)}$$

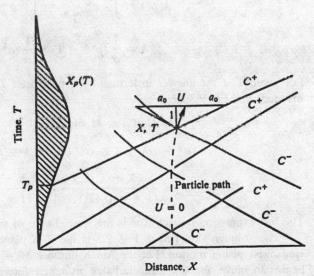

Figure 9.2 Trajectories of characteristics in a space–time diagram.

The velocity and thermodynamic state are the same all along any given C^+ line. In a simple wave the velocity and the thermodynamic state are directly related. Furthermore, the C^+ characteristics are straight lines with constant slope $U + a^*$.

Refer to Fig. 9.2 again. At any point X, T the C^+ characteristic comes from the piston, where we denote the time with the special symbol $T = T_p$. Consider T_p as a parameter in the solution. Along C^+ there is a constant fluid velocity $U = V_p(T_p)$ and a constant speed of sound $a^*(\lambda)$. The thermodynamic equation of state must be known in order to relate a^* and λ. However, when $a^*(\lambda)$ is known, it may be evaluated from $\lambda = U = U_p(T_p)$. A simple right running wave has the solution

$$U = U_p(T_p) \qquad \text{if} \quad T > X$$

$$U = 0 \qquad \text{if} \quad T < X \qquad (9.3.18)$$

$$a^* = a^*(\lambda = U_p(T_p))$$

where T_p, X, and T are related by the equation for a straight line in X–T space with a slope $1/(U + a^*)$:

$$T - T_p = \frac{X - X_p(T_p)}{U_p(T_p) + a^*[\lambda = U_p(T_p)]} \qquad (9.3.19)$$

These ideas can be made clearer if we consider a special equation of state. Assume that for some constant α the speed of sound is approximated by

$$a^* = \rho^{*\alpha} \qquad (9.3.20)$$

A perfect gas actually has $\alpha = (\gamma - 1)/2$ and Eq. 9.3.20 is exact. Water is well represented by a constant of about $\alpha = 3 - 4$. From Eq. 9.3.12,

$$\lambda(\rho^*) \equiv \int_1^{\rho^*} a^* \frac{d\rho^*}{\rho^*} = \int_1^{\rho^*} \rho^{*(\alpha-1)} \, dp^* \qquad (9.3.21)$$

$$\lambda = \frac{1}{\alpha}(\rho^{*\alpha} - 1) = \frac{1}{\alpha}(a^* - 1)$$

For given X, T the answer in terms of the parameter T_p is Eq. 9.3.18 (with Eq. 9.3.21 inserted) and Eq. 9.3.19:

$$U = U_p(T_p) = M \sin T_p$$

$$a^* = \alpha\lambda + 1 = \alpha U_p(T_p) + 1 = \alpha M \sin T_p + 1 \qquad (9.3.22)$$

$$T - T_p = \frac{X - X_p(T_p)}{(1 + \alpha)U_p(T_p) + 1} = \frac{X - M(1 - \cos T_p)}{(1 + \alpha)M \sin T_p + 1}$$

The last expression in each line is the special case of sinusoidal piston motion.

The solution sketched in Fig. 9.3 is the T–X plane for a gas with $\gamma = 1.4$ and a sinusoidal piston motion. Let the Mach number $M = U_{p,\text{max}}/a_0 = 0.1$. As the piston begins to move, the C^+ characteristics propagate forward, causing the undisturbed gas to move and compress—a pressure wave, if you like. Because both U and a^* increase, the dT/dX slopes of the C^+ characteristics decrease when the piston is in the time period

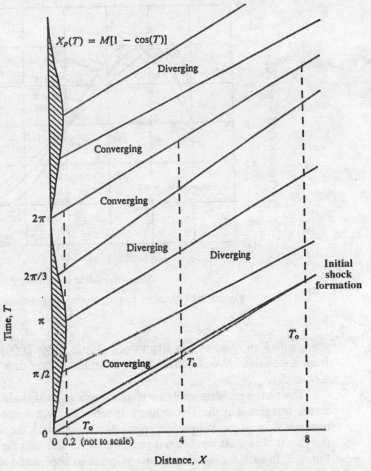

Figure 9.3 Time–distance wave diagram for $M = 0.1$.

$0 - \pi/2$. Thus, the characteristics tend to converge. For characteristics originating in the time period $\pi/2 - 3\pi/2$, the opposite is true; the characteristics diverge. The convergence–divergence of the wave can also be seen in Fig. 9.4, where the velocity at a specific X-location is plotted as a function of the time after the wave first arrives. At $X = 0.2$ the wave differs little from a sine wave. At $X = 4$ the compression portions (U increasing) are steepening and the expansion portions are spreading. The steepening process gives an almost infinite increase in pressure when we look at $X = 8$. A discontinuous jump in pressure, infinite slope, constitutes the formation of a shock wave. Shock waves have significant viscous and thermal effects and are not isentropic. After the formation of a shock the analysis must be modified to include places where the velocity and thermodynamic properties jump discontinuously. For stronger piston motion, that is, larger M, the shock forms closer to the piston. As one looks at larger X-positions, one would see the shock becoming stronger and stronger. Ultimately, all compression is incorporated into the shock and the expansion occupies the region between shocks. This is the final

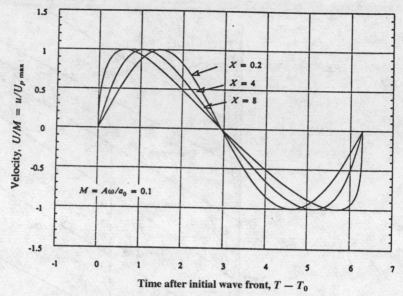

Figure 9.4   Velocity history at various positions, gas $\gamma = 1.4$.

state, called an *N-wave* [see Blackstock (1962, 1966, 2000) for details of the transition from a sine to an *N*-wave]. The *N*-wave can last a long time before viscous effects cause it to decay.

The piston problem contains physical processes that also occur in steady supersonic flows. Imagine that the *T*-coordinate is replaced by a space coordinate *Y*. A steady supersonic flow in the *Y*-direction encounters a wall with the shape $x_{\text{wall}} = A(1 - \cos \omega y)$ for $y > 0$. The wall would send pressure waves out into the flow in a pattern similar to Fig. 9.3. In fact, for small *A*, a case relevant to supersonic wing design, the answers are exactly the same. Supersonic thin airfoil theory is the same as acoustics in a moving reference frame. The sonic boom from a high-flying airplane is the *N*-wave propagating to the ground.

9.4   CONCLUSIONS

Compressible Couette flow shows us the way in which a shear flow influences the temperature profile through viscous dissipation. The temperature profile has a maximum increase in temperature equal to $(\mu_0/2k_0)V_0^2$. Note that this is true for the most general fluids, irrespective of *n*. It is instructive to cast Eq. 9.2.2 into a nondimensional form according to the philosophy of Section 8.10. We want a nondimensional variable of the form

$$T^* = \frac{T - T_{\text{ref}}}{T_{\text{scale}}}$$

Rearranging Eq. 9.2.2, we find the equation

$$\frac{T - T_0}{\mu_0 V_0^2 / k_0} = \frac{1}{2} \left[1 - \left(\frac{v_x}{V_0} \right)^2 \right]$$

(9.4.1)

$$T^* = \tfrac{1}{2}(1 - v^{*2})$$

We see clearly that T_0 is only a reference value. The natural temperature scale is $\mu_0 V_0^2 / k_0$. This is an estimate of the temperature rise that we can expect because of viscous dissipation from a velocity gradient of order V_0/h.

The oscillating piston problem shows how infinitesimal pressure waves, generated by wall motion in the normal direction, travel at a sound speed defined by the thermodynamic property $a = \partial p / \partial \rho)_s$. A variation of density is an essential part of such waves. It is the result of compression of the fluid. Compression waves collect together to form shock waves. All of these same processes occur in steady supersonic flows.

PROBLEMS

9.1 (A) Solve for the compressible flow in a slot with the stationary wall held at a constant temperature T_1 that is different from the upper wall temperature T_0. What specific form does the answer take for $n = 0$ in Eq. 9.2.1?

9.2 (A) A shaft 3 cm in diameter rotates at 30,000 rpm. A stationary collar around the shaft is 2 cm long and has a gap of 0.1 mm. Estimate the temperature of the shaft if the outer collar is at 340 K.

9.3 (B) Solve the Couette flow problem of Section 9.2 where the walls form an annulus with radii r_0 and r_1.

9.4 (B) Explain why the temperature of the adiabatic wall does not depend on the thickness of the shear layer.

9.5 (C)"Acoustics" is a flow with compressible effects and small amplitudes of motion; that is, $M \rightarrow 0$. Consider Eqs. 9.3.11 (rewritten with the substitution $U = Mu^*$), Eq. 9.3.7, and the state equation $p^* = (a^*)^\alpha$ (Eq. 9.3.20). The initial state is uniform and still. Assume expansions in powers of the independent parameter M of the form $F^* \sim F^{(0)} + MF^{(1)} + \cdots$ for ρ^*, u^*, p^*, and a^*. Show that $\rho^{(0)} = 1$, $p^{(0)} = 1$, $a^{(0)} = 1$. Derive the governing equations $\rho_T^{(1)} + u_X^{(0)} = 0$ and $u_T^{(0)} + \rho_X^{(1)} = 0$. Differentiate with respect to T and X in all possible combinations. Add and subtract to arrive at the acoustic wave equations $\rho_{TT}^{(1)} - \rho_{XX}^{(1)} = 0$ and $u_{TT}^{(0)} - u_{XX}^{(0)} = 0$.

9.6 (B) Retrieve the acoustics answer from Eq. 9.3.22 by inserting $U = Mu^*$ and taking the limit $M \Rightarrow 0$ with u^*, $a^{(1)} = (a^* - 1)/M$, X, and T of order one. What is $\rho^{(1)} = (\rho^* - 1)/M$?

10

Incompressible Flow

Incompressible flow is a principal subdivision of fluid mechanics. It includes within its boundaries a great many problems and phenomena that are found in engineering and nature. Flows of gases, as well as those of liquids, are frequently incompressible. Laypersons are usually surprised to learn that the pattern of the flow of air can be similar to that of water. From a thermodynamic standpoint, gases and liquids have quite different characteristics. As we know, liquids are often modeled as incompressible fluids. However, *incompressible fluid* is a thermodynamical term, whereas *incompressible flow* is a fluid mechanical term. We can have an incompressible flow of a compressible fluid.

The main criterion for incompressible flow is that the Mach number be low ($M \rightarrow 0$). This is a necessary condition. In addition, other conditions concerning heat transfer must be satisfied. There are several different situations of heat transfer under which incompressible flow can occur. In this chapter a detailed study of these situations will be made. As part of this study we derive the equations that govern incompressible flow. Then we shall be in a position to observe some of the general features and characteristics of incompressible flow.

10.1 CHARACTERIZATION

The term *incompressible flow* is applied to any situation where changes in the density of a particle are negligible. A mathematical definition is

$$\frac{1}{\rho} \frac{D\rho}{Dt} = 0$$

From the continuity equation we have

$$\frac{1}{\rho} \frac{D\rho}{Dt} = -\partial_i v_i = \lim_{V_{MR} \to 0} -\frac{1}{V_{MR}} \frac{DV_{MR}}{Dt}$$

This shows that equivalent definitions are that $\nabla \cdot \mathbf{v} = 0$ (the rate of expansion is zero) or $DV_{MR}/Dt = 0$ (the rate of change of the volume of a particle is zero). Notice that all particles do not have to have the same density. The only requirement is that the density of each particle remain unchanged. In some cases (e.g., the ocean, where salt content and temperature are functions of depth) the density of adjacent particles changes but any one particle has a constant density. These *stratified flows* exhibit such interesting and unusual phenomena that they constitute a separate branch of fluid mechanics. We shall not study any stratified flows in this book. It will always be assumed that the density of all particles is the same.

The density of the fluid is also governed by a thermodynamic equation of state. For a general fluid we may write this as

$$\rho = \rho(p, T) \tag{10.1.1}$$

$$\frac{1}{\rho}\frac{D\rho}{Dt} = \alpha \frac{Dp}{Dt} - \beta \frac{DT}{Dt}$$

where the isothermal compressibility is

$$\alpha(p, T) \equiv \frac{1}{\rho}\left.\frac{\partial \rho}{\partial p}\right|_T$$

and the bulk thermal expansion coefficient is

$$\beta(p, T) \equiv -\frac{1}{\rho}\left.\frac{\partial \rho}{\partial T}\right|_p$$

The functions α and β are thermodynamic variables that characterize the fluid. We want to study the most general type of fluid by leaving α and β unrestricted. When that is done, the right-hand side of Eq. 10.1.1 will be small only if the pressure and temperature changes are small enough. In turn, the magnitudes of these variables are governed by dynamic processes occurring in the flow field. The energy and momentum equations will play a major role in fixing the pressure and temperature. The advantage of writing the equation of state in the form Eq. 10.1.1 is that the flow-field effects are isolated in Dp/Dt and DT/Dt, while the thermodynamic character of the fluid is isolated in α and β.

With dimensional analysis fresh in our minds, we should feel a little uneasy about the statement that temperature and pressure changes are to be small. Certainly, we should not use dimensional variables that compare temperature and pressure with common units of measurement. We must nondimensionalize the pressure and temperature with scales that are determined by the dynamics of the flow. Since scales for nondimensionalizing variables are found in the boundary conditions and equations that govern the flow, we must be more specific about the problem statement.

10.2 INCOMPRESSIBLE FLOW AS LOW-MACH-NUMBER FLOW WITH ADIABATIC WALLS

Consider the two flow situations depicted in Fig. 10.1. The external flow in Fig. 10.1b has specified values of velocity v_0, density ρ_0, and temperature T_0 far away from the body. The type of fluid is given so that the thermodynamic functions $\alpha(p, T)$, $\beta(p, T)$, and $c_p(p, T)$ are also known in principle. Knowledge of the fluid also implies that equations for the transport coefficients $\mu(p, T)$ and $k(p, T)$ are available. We shall not need to specify the thermodynamic data in detail, but can perform the analysis for a general Newtonian fluid. In the case of an internal flow problem (Fig. 10.1a), a similar specification is given at a certain reference location.

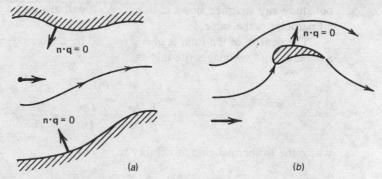

Figure 10.1 Incompressible flows with adiabatic walls: (*a*) internal flow; (*b*) external flow.

The body has a characteristic length L. It may also have other characteristic lengths, but they will not concern us, as they form geometric ratios with L when the problem is nondimensionalized. The no-slip condition on the solid surfaces requires that the velocity be zero. We also assume that the walls are adiabatic, so that no heat enters the flow through the walls. Later in this chapter we shall do the problem again assuming a fixed wall temperature.

A list of all equations that govern the problem is as follows:

Thermodynamics:

$$\frac{1}{\rho}\frac{D\rho}{Dt} = \alpha\frac{Dp}{Dt} - \beta\frac{DT}{Dt} \tag{10.2.1}$$

with

$$\alpha = \alpha(p, T), \qquad \beta = \beta(p, T), \qquad c_p = c_p(p, T)$$
$$\mu = \mu(p, T), \qquad k = k(p, T) \tag{10.2.2}$$

Continuity:

$$\frac{1}{\rho}\frac{D\rho}{Dt} = -\partial_i v_i \tag{10.2.3}$$

Momentum:

$$\rho\frac{Dv_i}{Dt} = -\partial_i p + \partial_j \tau_{ji} + \rho g_i \tag{10.2.4}$$

New viscous stress:

$$\partial_j \tau_{ji} = -\tfrac{2}{3}\partial_i(\mu\partial_j v_j) + 2\partial_j(\mu S_{ji}) \tag{10.2.5}$$

Energy:

$$\rho c_p \frac{DT}{Dt} = \partial_i(k\partial_i T) + \Phi + \beta T\frac{Dp}{Dt} \tag{10.2.6}$$

where the viscous dissipation function Φ is defined by (Problem 6.7)

$$\Phi \equiv \boldsymbol{\tau}:\mathbf{S} = -\tfrac{2}{3}\mu(\partial_i v_i)^2 + 2\mu S_{ij}S_{ji}$$

The boundary conditions at the reference position are

$$v_i = (v_0, 0, 0), \qquad T = T_0, \qquad \rho = \rho_0, \qquad p = p_0 \qquad (10.2.7)$$

and on the walls,

$$v_i = 0, \qquad n_i q_i = 0$$

A general fluid-flow problem for a given geometric arrangement would require the solution of Eqs. 10.2.1 to 10.2.7. The dependent variables are ρ, p, T, and v_i. Note that all the equations are coupled together. For instance, the momentum equation contains terms in density, pressure, and viscosity. These quantities depend on the local temperature. In turn, the temperature is governed by the energy equation, which contains the velocity in the convection terms. Even the most modern computers can deal effectively with these equations only for simple cases.

10.3   NONDIMENSIONAL PROBLEM STATEMENT

Not all the terms in Eqs. 10.2.1 to 10.2.7 have the same importance in determining the flow solution. To determine which terms are large and which are small, we must cast the equations into nondimensional variables. Many of the nondimensional variables are formed in a straightforward manner using the boundary values. In this way we define

$$x_i^* = \frac{x_i}{L}, \qquad t^* = \frac{tv_0}{L}$$

$$v_i^* = \frac{v_i}{v_0}, \qquad \rho^* = \frac{\rho}{\rho_0}$$

$$\alpha^* = \frac{\alpha}{\alpha_0}, \qquad \beta^* = \frac{\beta}{\beta_0} \qquad (10.3.1)$$

$$c_p^* = \frac{c_p}{c_{p0}}, \qquad \mu^* = \frac{\mu}{\mu_0}$$

$$k^* = \frac{k}{k_0}, \qquad F_i^* = \frac{g_i}{v_0^2/L} = \hat{\mathbf{g}} \cdot \mathrm{Fr}^{-2}$$

[The Froude (Fr) number is defined in Eq. 10.3.4. $\hat{\mathbf{g}}$ is a unit vector.] The temperature and pressure variables need some special consideration.

In incompressible flow, pressure will play the role of a force in the momentum equation. Since pressure occurs as a gradient in this equation, a reference level may be subtracted without any effect. That is, for any reference p_0,

$$\partial_i(p - p_0) = \partial_i p$$

The first step in finding the pressure scale is to substitute the definitions of Eq. 10.3.1 into the momentum equation. Then we argue that both the pressure and inertia terms would be needed in a general incompressible flow problem. Although there may be cases where one of the other terms is zero, there are certainly many incompressible flows where both terms are present. We use p_s temporarily to symbolize the proper scale, that is, let

$$p^* = \frac{p - p_0}{p_s}$$

Substituting into the momentum equation, we find that

$$\rho^* \frac{Dv_i^*}{Dt^*} = \frac{p_s}{\rho v_0^2} \frac{\partial p^*}{\partial x_i^*} + \text{viscous terms} + \text{body force}$$

This equation shows that the pressure term will be of the same order as the inertia terms if the nondimensional pressure is defined to be

$$p^* = \frac{p - p_0}{\rho_0 v_0^2} \tag{10.3.2}$$

When pressure changes in the flow are dominated by momentum effects, Eq. 10.3.2 is the proper nondimensional pressure variable.

Our experience with the Couette flow (Eq. 9.4.1) can help in formulating the nondimensional temperature. In the problems we have posed, one boundary value is a fixed temperature, which can serve as a reference, while the other boundary is adiabatic. If we consider the physical processes, we expect that heat (thermal energy) will be generated in the flow field by viscous dissipation. This heat will then be redistributed by conduction and carried to new places by convection. If we try the same nondimensional temperature that was used in Couette flow in the energy equation, we find that all three terms— convection, conduction, and dissipation—are of the same order. Thus, we define

$$T^* = \frac{T - T_0}{\mu_0 v_0^2 / k_0} = \frac{T - T_0}{\Pr v_0^2 / c_{p0}} \tag{10.3.3}$$

In the second form, the Prandtl number ($\Pr = \mu_0 c_{p0} / k_0$) has been introduced. This is a standard dimensionless ratio used in heat transfer. Some workers prefer to use v_0^2 / c_{p0} by itself as the temperature scale. The results will be the same in either case, because the Prandtl number is of moderate size. (If we were dealing with flows where the Prandtl number took on extreme values, 0 or ∞, we would need to be more careful.)

When the nondimensional variables defined above are substituted into the problem 10.2.1–10.2.7, several nondimensional groups occur. They are listed below:

$$\text{Re} = \frac{\rho_0 L v_0}{\mu_0}, \qquad \Pr = \frac{\mu_0 c_{p0}}{k_0}, \qquad \gamma_0 = \frac{c_{p0}}{c_{v0}}$$
$$\text{Fr}^2 = \frac{v_0^2}{gL}, \qquad M = \frac{v_0}{a_0}, \qquad A = \alpha_0 \rho_0 c_{p0} T_0, \qquad B = \beta_0 T_0 \tag{10.3.4}$$

Three parameters involve the flow velocity v_0 while the other four are thermodynamic parameters. In formulating these nondimensional parameters we have used the relation for the speed of sound derived in many thermodynamics books:

$$a_0^2 = \frac{\gamma_0}{\rho_0 \alpha_0} \tag{10.3.5}$$

The details of the substitution are simplified by noting that

$$M^2 = \frac{v_0^2}{a_0^2} = \frac{v_0^2 \rho_0 \alpha_0}{\gamma_0} \tag{10.3.6}$$

and that

$$\frac{v_0^2}{c_{p0} T_0} = \frac{M^2 \gamma_0}{A} \tag{10.3.7}$$

The final form of the mathematical problem statement in nondimensional variables is as follows:

Thermodynamics:

$$\frac{1}{\rho^*} \frac{D\rho^*}{Dt^*} = \gamma_0 M^2 \left(\alpha * \frac{Dp^*}{Dt^*} - \frac{\mathrm{Pr}\, B\beta^*}{A} \frac{DT^*}{Dt^*} \right) \tag{10.3.8}$$

Continuity:

$$\frac{1}{\rho^*} \frac{D\rho^*}{Dt^*} = -\partial_i^* v_i^* \tag{10.3.9}$$

Momentum:

$$\rho^* \frac{Dv_i^*}{Dt^*} = -\partial_i^* p^* + \partial_j^* \tau_{ji}^* + \hat{g}_i \rho^* \, \mathrm{Fr}^{-2} \tag{10.3.10}$$

Viscous stress:

$$\partial_j^* \tau_{ji}^* = \frac{1}{\mathrm{Re}} \left[-\frac{2}{3} \partial_i^* (\mu^* \partial_j^* v_j^*) + 2\partial_j^* (\mu^* S_{ij}^*) \right] \tag{10.3.11}$$

Energy:

$$\rho^* c_p^* \frac{DT^*}{Dt^*} = \frac{1}{\mathrm{Re}} \frac{1}{\mathrm{Pr}} [\partial_i^* (k^* \partial_i T^*) + \Phi^*] + \beta^* B \left(\frac{1}{\mathrm{Pr}} + \frac{\gamma_0 M^2}{A} T^* \right) \frac{Dp^*}{Dt^*} \tag{10.3.12}$$

where

$$\Phi^* = \frac{\Phi}{\mu_0 v_0^2 / L^2} \tag{10.3.13}$$

Boundary conditions at the reference position:

$$v_i^* = (1, 0, 0), \qquad T^* = 0, \qquad \rho^* = 1 \tag{10.3.14}$$

Boundary conditions at the walls:

$$v_i^* = 0, \qquad n_i q_i^* = 0 \qquad\qquad (10.3.15)$$

The thermodynamic functions α^*, β^*, μ^*, k^*, and c_p^* complete the problem. Assuming our guesses about the proper natural scales for the nondimensional variables are correct, each variable is of order 1. Furthermore, the nondimensionalizing process has introduced several parameters (M, γ_0, Pr, A, B, Fr, Re) into the equations. For any given flow problem these parameters have specific fixed values. If they are large or small, they magnify or diminish the effect of the terms in which they appear as coefficients.

At this stage we can see that incompressible flow will result when the right side of Eq. 10.3.8 becomes small, that is, in the limit $M^2 \to 0$. When $D\rho^*/Dt^* = 0$, the density of a particle is constant. This causes a domino effect in the remaining equations. In Eq. 10.3.9 the left side is zero, so that $\nabla^* \cdot \mathbf{v}^* = 0$. Terms containing $\nabla^* \cdot \mathbf{v}^*$ in the viscous stress and dissipation relations become small, as does the term preceded by M^2 in the energy equation. It also turns out that all the thermodynamic functions μ^*, k^*, c_p^*, α^*, and β^* are constant.

The thermodynamic functions depend on the absolute magnitudes of the temperature and pressure. Let us consider the viscosity as an example:

$$\mu = \mu(p, T)$$

We know that at the reference state T_0, p_0 the viscosity is μ_0. Consider the nondimensional viscosity function

$$\mu^* = \frac{\mu}{\mu_0} = \mu^*\left(\frac{T}{T_0}, \frac{p}{p_0}\right) \qquad\qquad (10.3.16)$$

This function may be expanded in a double Taylor series about $T/T_0 = 1$ and $p/p_0 = 1$:

$$\mu^* = 1 + \left.\frac{\partial \mu^*}{\partial(T/T_0)}\right|_{1,1} \frac{T - T_0}{T_0} + \left.\frac{\partial \mu^*}{\partial(p/p_0)}\right|_{1,1} \frac{p - p_0}{p_0} + \cdots \qquad (10.3.17)$$

However, $(T - T_0)/T_0$ is not the proper variable for the flow field. From the definition of T^* and Eq. 10.3.7 we have

$$\frac{T - T_0}{T_0} = \frac{\text{Pr}\,\gamma_0}{A} M^2 T^* \qquad\qquad (10.3.18)$$

and similarly, from the definition of p^* and Eq. 10.3.6,

$$\frac{p - p_0}{p_0} = \frac{\gamma_0 M^2 p^*}{p_0 \alpha_0} \qquad\qquad (10.3.19)$$

In this equation $p_0 \alpha_0$ is a new dimensionless constant. Substituting Eqs. 10.3.18 and 10.3.19 into Eq. 10.3.17 and allowing the Mach number to become small shows that

$$\mu^* = 1 \quad \text{or} \quad \mu = \mu_0 = \text{const} \qquad\qquad (10.3.20)$$

The same argument can be applied to all the other thermodynamic functions. The dynamic processes do not change the temperature or pressure enough to cause any appreciable change in the thermodynamic state. All the thermodynamic coefficients may be considered constants.

10.4   CHARACTERISTICS OF INCOMPRESSIBLE FLOW

The main criterion for incompressible flow is that the Mach number is low ($M \to 0$), that is, all velocities are small compared to the speed of sound. Recall that the speed of sound is given by Eq. 9.3.7:

$$a_0^2 = \left. \frac{\partial p}{\partial \rho} \right|_s \tag{10.4.1}$$

When a_0 appears in the incompressible flow derivation, its role is not to tell how fast waves travel, but to indicate how much density change accompanies a certain pressure change. Pressure changes in the flow are on the order of $\rho_0 v_0^2$. A flow decelerated from $v = v_0$ at one location in the flow to $v = 0$ at another will undergo a pressure change $\Delta p = \frac{1}{2}\rho_0 v_0^2$ (neglecting viscosity). With these considerations the Mach number is interpreted as follows:

$$M^2 = \frac{v_0^2}{a_0^2} = v_0^2 \left. \frac{\partial \rho}{\partial p} \right|_s = \frac{\rho_0 v_0^2}{\rho_0} \left. \frac{\partial \rho}{\partial p} \right|_s$$

$$\approx \Delta p \frac{1}{\rho_0} \frac{\Delta \rho}{\Delta p} = \frac{\Delta \rho}{\rho_0} \tag{10.4.2}$$

The parameter M^2 is a measure of the size of density changes compared to the fluid density. As $M^2 \to 0$, density changes become only a small fraction of the fluid density.

Although $M^2 \to 0$ is required for incompressible flow, it is not the only requirement. Some flows where $M^2 \to 0$ are low-speed compressible flows. In these cases density changes are caused by temperature changes. In the analysis above this did not happen because the wall was adiabatic. There was not enough heat generated by viscous dissipation to cause large temperature changes.

We now list the governing equations for incompressible flow derived in Section 10.3:

Thermodynamics:

$$\frac{D\rho^*}{Dt^*} = 0 \tag{10.4.3}$$

$$\rho^* = c_p^* = \alpha^* = \beta^* = \mu^* = k^* = 1$$

Continuity:

$$\partial_i^* v_i^* = 0 \tag{10.4.4}$$

Momentum (recall from Problem 6.4 that $2\partial_j S_{ji} = \partial_j \partial_j v_i$ if $\partial_i v_i = 0$):

$$\frac{Dv_i^*}{Dt^*} = -\partial_i^* p^* + \frac{1}{\text{Re}} \partial_j^* \partial_j^* v_i^* + \hat{g}_i \, \text{Fr}^{-2} \tag{10.4.5}$$

Energy:

$$\frac{DT^*}{Dt^*} = \frac{1}{\text{Re}} \frac{1}{\text{Pr}} (\partial_i^* \partial_i^* T^* + 2S_{ij}^* S_{ji}^*) + \frac{B}{\text{Pr}} \frac{Dp^*}{Dt^*} \tag{10.4.6}$$

Boundary conditions at the reference location:

$$v_i^* = (1, 0, 0), \quad T^* = 0, \quad \rho^* = 1, \quad p^* = 0 \tag{10.4.7}$$

Boundary conditions at the walls:

$$v_i^* = 0, \quad n_i q_i^* = 0 \tag{10.4.8}$$

Inspection of these equations reveals quite a lot about incompressible flow. First, the density and all thermodynamic coefficients are constants. A separate independent assumption that ρ, c_p, μ, and k are constant is not needed. It would be inconsistent to solve an incompressible flow problem and allow viscosity to be a function of temperature. We would not obtain any greater accuracy (the viscosity would only change slightly), and the mathematics would be considerably more complicated.

Because the density and transport properties are constant, the continuity and momentum equations are decoupled from the energy equation. This result is extremely important, as it means that we may solve for the three velocities and the pressure without regard for the energy equation or the temperature. The velocity field in incompressible flow is unaffected by heat transfer and thermal effects.

Since pressure is determined by the momentum equation, it plays the role of a mechanical force and not a thermodynamic variable. Moreover, pressure occurs only under a derivative and therefore, as we remarked previously, the level of the pressure is not important in incompressible flow. An incompressible flow solution will determine $p^* = (p - p_0)/\rho v_0^2$ without any need to specify p_0. If in a given flow the reference p_0 is increased, the level of all pressures in the flow increases, so that p^* has the same values. The velocities and streamlines do not change when the pressure is increased.

Another important fact about incompressible flow is that only two parameters, the Reynolds number and the Froude number, occur in Eq. 10.4.5. The appearance of the Froude number is important in flows where there is a free surface. Open-channel flows, water waves, and the flow of liquid jets or sheets are examples of free-surface flows. In confined flows (i.e., those flows where the fluid occupies the entire region between walls or the entire region on the outside of a body), the gravity force produces an equivalent hydrostatic effect, which may be separated out of the flow problem. This is discussed in detail in Section 10.5. Meanwhile, we note that in incompressible confined flows, the Froude number does not appear explicitly in the problem.

For a given geometry, the character of a confined velocity field depends on the single dimensionless number Re. Of course, other parameters, such as geometric ratios, velocity ratios, and so on, may enter the problem through boundary conditions, but the Reynolds number is the only constant in the governing equations. As it appears in Eq. 10.4.5, the Reynolds number indicates the size of the viscous force term relative to the other terms. Flow patterns change their character as the Reynolds number takes on different values. For this reason, subsequent chapters dealing with flow patterns are organized according to the Reynolds number. It is only a slight exaggeration to say that the study of incompressible flow is a study of the Reynolds number.

Mathematically speaking, the momentum equation is nonlinear in the velocity v^*. The substantial derivative

$$\frac{Dv_i^*}{Dt^*} = \partial_0 v_i^* + v_j^* \partial_j^* v_i^* \tag{10.4.9}$$

contains v_i^* twice in the second term. This nonlinear term prevents the use of many of the standard mathematical techniques. It is also the cause of many interesting and unusual phenomena that occur in fluid mechanics. The equations are elliptic, and in general we specify the velocity around the surface of a region to determine the velocity field on the inside of the region.

Once the velocity and pressure are found, they may be substituted into the energy equation, leaving temperature as the sole dependent variable. The substantial derivative is now linear in T:

$$\frac{DT^*}{Dt^*} = \partial_0 T^* + v_j^* \partial_j^* T^* \tag{10.4.10}$$

Also notice that the temperature always occurs under a derivative everywhere in Eq. 10.4.6. This means that in incompressible flow, only changes in temperature with respect to some reference are important. As with pressure, the level of the reference temperature does not affect the solution. If ρ, μ, c_p, and k had not become constants, the absolute temperature would enter the problem through these variables. The actual temperatures in the flow do not differ very much from T_0. This can be seen by recalling Eq. 10.3.18. When we reorganize the temperature variable T^* so that T is compared to the reference value T_0, we get

$$\frac{T - T_0}{T_0} = \frac{1}{\Lambda} \Pr \gamma_0 M^2 T^*$$

or

$$\frac{T}{T_0} = 1 + \frac{1}{A} \Pr \gamma_0 M^2 T^* \tag{10.4.11}$$

Since T^* is of order 1, the actual temperatures are nearly the same as T_0. The variable T^* may be thought of as a correction of order M^2 to a uniform temperature. The problem of solving the energy equation really belongs to the subject of convective heat transfer, and we do not pursue it after this chapter.

10.5 SPLITTING THE PRESSURE INTO KINETIC AND HYDROSTATIC PARTS

The body force due to gravity plays no role in determining the velocity field of many incompressible flows. This is true if the flow does not have a free surface where a boundary condition on pressure is specified. Essentially, we can split the pressure into two parts: a kinetic part associated with the flow pattern and a hydrostatic part that accounts for the gravity effect. The hydrostatic part has the same variation as in a static fluid, hence the name.

To develop these ideas consider the momentum equation

$$\frac{Dv_i}{Dt} = -\frac{1}{\rho} \partial_i p + g_i + \nu \partial_j \partial_j v_i$$

Denote the height above a horizontal reference plane by $Z(x_i)$, as shown in Fig. 10.2. Recall that the gravity force has a potential; $g_i = -g\partial_i Z$. Substituting this into the momentum equation along with a constant p_{ref} gives

$$\frac{Dv_i}{Dt} = -\frac{1}{\rho}\,\partial_i(p + \rho g Z - p_{ref}) + \nu\partial_j\partial_j v_i \qquad (10.5.1)$$

Next introduce the following definitions:

$$p_{hyd} = -\rho g Z + p_{ref}$$

$$p_{kin} = p - p_{hyd} = p + \rho g Z - p_{ref} \qquad (10.5.2)$$

$$p = p_{hyd} + p_{kin}$$

Since the hydrostatic (hyd) component of the pressure has a simple universal solution, we really need only find the kinetic (kin) portion of the pressure.

The momentum equation now has only the kinetic pressure as a variable and no gravity force appears.

$$\frac{Dv_i}{Dt} = -\frac{1}{\rho}\,\partial_i p_{kin} + \nu\partial_j\partial_j v_i \qquad (10.5.3)$$

Only the kinetic pressure occurs in the momentum equation. It determines the pressure force that results in the streamline pattern and the velocity field (if boundary conditions on the pressure are absent).

At $Z = 0$, $p_{hyd} = p_{ref}$ and $p_{kin} = p - p_{ref}$. Choosing some upstream point or other special place on $Z = 0$, one can set the reference so that $p_{kin} = 0$.

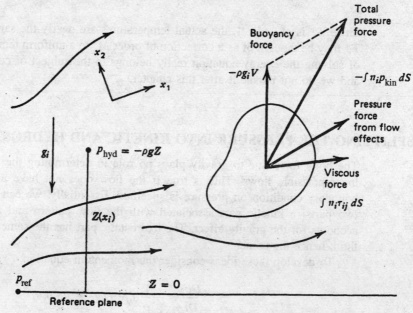

Figure 10.2 Separation of kinetic and hydrostatic effects.

It is common practice to strike the gravity force from the momentum equation and let the symbol p stand for the kinetic portion without any special notation or nomenclature. Physically, the flow pattern about a fish swimming at any depth and in any orientation is the same (as long as the fish is far enough below the surface that the surface is undisturbed).

As an illustration, consider the flow in a rectangular water tunnel with an object mounted in the test section. Far upstream of the object the water speed is uniform at U. Take $Z = 0$ along the bottom wall and at an upstream position, where the pressure is constant set $p = p_{ref}$ and $p_{kin} = 0$. At the far upstream position, as one crosses the tunnel, the pressures are

$$p = p_{ref} - \rho g Z$$

$$p_{hyd} = p_{ref} - \rho g Z \qquad (10.5.4)$$

$$p_{kin} = 0$$

The hydrostatic component of the pressure has been removed from the problem.

A frequent form for nondimensional pressure, called the pressure coefficient or the Euler number, uses the dynamic pressure as the scale:

$$C_{p\ total} = \frac{p + \rho g Z - p_{ref}}{\frac{1}{2}\rho v_0^2} - \frac{p_{kin} - p_{ref}}{\frac{1}{2}\rho v_0^2} - \frac{2gL}{v_0^2}\frac{Z}{L} = C_{p\ kin} - \frac{2}{Fr^2}\frac{Z}{L} \qquad (10.5.5)$$

In confined flows the Froude number is only a multiplying constant for the hydrostatic part of the pressure.

The total pressure force on a body is frequently of interest. The net pressure force (Fig. 10.2) is given by the integral

$$F_i^{(p)} = -\int n_i p \, dS \qquad (10.5.6)$$

We introduce the pressure splitting, Eq. 10.5.2, into the integral to give

$$F_i^{(p)} = -\int n_i p_{kin} \, dS - \int n_i p_{hyd} \, dS \qquad (10.5.7)$$

The second integral is the net force on the body due to hydrostatic pressure—the buoyancy force that the body would experience if the flow were absent. The buoyancy force may be computed by substituting Eq. 10.5.4 and using Gauss's theorem:

$$F_i^{(p)} = -\int n_i p_{kin} \, dS + \int n_i \rho g Z \, dS - \int n_i p_{ref} \, dS$$

$$= -\int n_i p_{kin} \, dS + \rho g \int \partial_i Z \, dV - p_{ref} \int n_i \, dS$$

Noting that $g \partial_i Z = -g_i$ and that $\int n_i \, dS = 0$, we obtain

$$\underset{\substack{\text{total}\\ \text{pressure}\\ \text{force}}}{F_i^{(p)}} = -\underset{\substack{\text{pressure}\\ \text{force due}\\ \text{to flow}}}{\int n_i p_{kin} \, dS} - \underset{\substack{\text{buoyancy}\\ \text{force}}}{\rho g_i V} \qquad (10.5.8)$$

This is the familiar result that the buoyancy force is equal to the weight of fluid the body displaces and is in the direction opposite to the gravity vector. Equation 10.5.8 says that the buoyancy force and the pressure force due to flow may be separated in an unambiguous way in incompressible flow.

*10.6   MATHEMATICAL ASPECTS OF THE LIMIT PROCESS $M^2 \to 0$

From a mathematical viewpoint the complete compressible Navier–Stokes problem stated in Sections 10.2 and 10.3 has six dependent variables v_i, ρ, p, and T. Consider v_i as a typical variable. It is a function of position and a number of nondimensional constants,

$$v_i^* = f(x_i^*; M, \text{Re}, \text{Fr}, \text{Pr}, \gamma_0, A, B, p_0\alpha_0) \qquad (10.6.1)$$

If we knew this complete answer, we could set $M = 0$ and obtain the incompressible result

$$v_{i\,\text{IC}}^* = f(x_i^*; 0, \text{Re}, \text{Fr}) \qquad (10.6.2)$$

The other parameters are not listed, because we found that they dropped out of the problem when $M^2 \to 0$.

Of course, the Mach number is never exactly zero for any flow. However, if Eq. 10.6.1 is not a strong function of M, the answer with $M = 0$ is a good approximation for flows with a small but nonzero M. As a general rule of experience, if $M < \frac{1}{3}$, Eq. 10.6.2 will give a fairly close result for external flows. We usually do not know how fast Eq. 10.6.1 actually changes with M, as that depends on the exact shape of the body or the flow passage [in pipelines $(p_1 - p_2)/p_1$ is a useful indication].

It is actually a much too complicated problem to find the complete answer to Eq. 10.6.1 and then set $M = 0$. The procedure we followed was to take the limit $M \to 0$ in the governing equations and hope that the resulting equations would produce Eq. 10.6.2 when they were solved. This amounts to an interchange of differentiation and a limiting process. On a typical term the process would be

$$\lim_{M \to 0} \partial_i^* v_j^* \stackrel{?}{=} \partial_i^*(\lim_{M \to 0} v_j^*) = \partial_i^* v_{j\,\text{IC}}^* \qquad (10.6.3)$$

Moving the limiting process inside the derivative cannot always be justified mathematically. In this case, and in most other cases in fluid mechanics, it works out correctly.

Another danger in letting $M \to 0$ in the governing equations is that the variables may not have been nondimensionalized properly. As $M \to 0$, all variables must be nondimensionalized so that they are of order 1, that is, they have finite values at $M = 0$. If a variable went to zero (or infinity) as $M \to 0$ and we did not know it, we would obtain the wrong equation (Fig. 10.3). In nondimensionalizing the variables, we are actually make guesses as to how they vary with M in the neighborhood of $M = 0$.

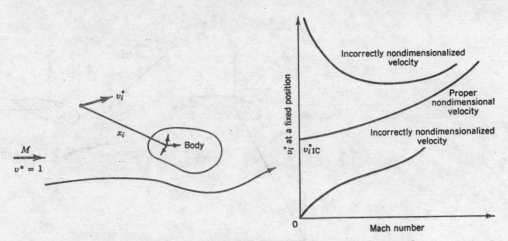

Figure 10.3 Different nondimensional forms in the limit $M \to 0$.

*10.7 INVARIANCE OF INCOMPRESSIBLE FLOW EQUATIONS UNDER UNSTEADY MOTION

The incompressible flow equations satisfy a special invariance that allows some unsteady flows to be analyzed from a moving coordinate system. As an example, suppose that a body is oscillating back and forth in a fluid. We could analyze this problem by using a coordinate system fixed in the body and by applying the usual incompressible flow equations. There would be no special terms needed to account for the acceleration of the coordinate system.

We begin the proof by letting x_i, t be an inertial reference frame. As shown in Fig. 10.4, the origin of the noninertial frame is moving with a velocity $V_i(t)$, which is completely arbitrary in both magnitude and direction. However, rotation of the $\hat{x}_i$ system is not allowed. We will prove that the same equations govern the flow in the moving system as in the inertial system. The coordinates and velocities are related by the transformations

$$\hat{x}_i = x_i - \int_0^t V_i(t')\, dt' - R_i(0)$$

$$\hat{t} = t \tag{10.7.1}$$

$$\hat{v}_i = v_i - V_i$$

The Galilean transformation is a special case when V_i is constant. From these equations the partial derivatives for $f(\hat{x}\,(x,\,t),\, \hat{t} = t)$ are computed as

$$\frac{\partial}{\partial x_i} = \frac{\partial}{\partial \hat{x}_i} \quad \text{and} \quad \frac{\partial}{\partial t} = \frac{\partial}{\partial \hat{t}} - V_i \frac{\partial}{\partial \hat{x}_i} \tag{10.7.2}$$

The continuity equation is unchanged by the transformation because

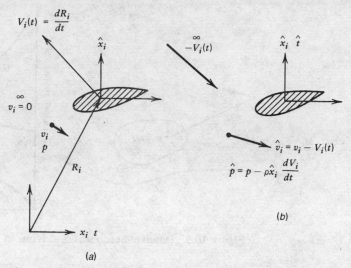

Figure 10.4 Unsteady translation: (*a*) body moving through an infinite fluid with translation $V_i(t)$; (*b*) equivalent flow in body-fixed coordinates.

$$\frac{\partial v_i}{\partial x_i} = \frac{\partial}{\partial \hat{x}_i}(\hat{v}_i + V_i) = \frac{\partial \hat{v}_i}{\partial \hat{x}_i} = 0 \tag{10.7.3}$$

The momentum equation in inertial coordinates is

$$\frac{\partial v_j}{\partial t} + v_i \frac{\partial v_j}{\partial x_i} = -\frac{1}{\rho}\frac{\partial p}{\partial x_j} + \nu \frac{\partial^2 v_j}{\partial x_i\,\partial x_i} \tag{10.7.4}$$

This is transformed into

$$\frac{\partial \hat{v}_j}{\partial \hat{t}} - V_i\frac{\partial \hat{v}_j}{\partial \hat{x}_i} + \frac{\partial V_j}{\partial \hat{t}} + \hat{v}_i\frac{\partial \hat{v}_j}{\partial \hat{x}_i} + V_i\frac{\partial \hat{v}_j}{\partial \hat{x}_i} = -\frac{1}{\rho}\frac{\partial p}{\partial \hat{x}_j} + \nu \frac{\partial^2 \hat{v}_j}{\partial \hat{x}_i\,\partial \hat{x}_i}$$

The two terms in V_i cancel. Now the unsteady-coordinate acceleration term can be rewritten as follows:

$$\frac{\partial V_j}{\partial \hat{t}} = \frac{dV_j}{dt} = \delta_{ij}\frac{dV_i}{dt} = \frac{\partial \hat{x}_i}{\partial \hat{x}_j}\frac{dV_i}{dt} = \frac{\partial}{\partial \hat{x}_j}\left(\hat{x}_i\frac{dV_i}{dt}\right) \tag{10.7.5}$$

In this form we may include this term with the pressure and define a new pseudopressure variable $\hat{p}$ according to

$$\hat{p} \equiv p + \rho \hat{x}_i \frac{dV_i}{dt} \tag{10.7.6}$$

The momentum equation now takes on the same form as in an inertial system, namely,

$$\hat{\partial}_0 \hat{v}_j = \hat{v}_i \hat{\partial}_i \hat{v}_j = -\frac{1}{\rho}\hat{\partial}_j \hat{p} + \nu \hat{\partial}_i \hat{\partial}_i \hat{v}_j \tag{10.7.7}$$

These equations are illustrated in Fig. 10.4, where a body is depicted moving through an infinite fluid without rotating. The fluid at infinity is at rest and a uniform pressure. The equivalent problem shown in (b) has a fixed body with the flow at infinity $V_i(t)$. The velocities in the two problems are related by Eq. 10.7.1 and the pressures by Eq. 10.7.6. The pressures in (b) consist of the pressure p due to the flow pattern of (a) and a pressure $\rho \hat{x}_i \, dV_i/dt$ required to accelerate the fluid. Since the fluid extends to infinity, the pressure at infinity will become infinite. It takes an infinite force to accelerate an infinite amount of fluid.

An alternative viewpoint is to retain the pressure equivalence between the two flows, that is, $p = \hat{p}$. Now the term $-dV_j/dt$ is added to the problem in $\hat{x}_i$ coordinates as an effective body force term. This may be viewed as an imaginary body force required to accelerate the stream at infinity.

*10.8   LOW-MACH-NUMBER FLOWS WITH CONSTANT-TEMPERATURE WALLS

We have seen how $M \to 0$ with adiabatic walls is an example of incompressible flow. In many instances there is significant heat transfer through the walls. In this case we can isolate the flow situation by imagining that the walls are held at some fixed temperature T_w that is different from T_0. If the wall actually has a temperature distribution along its surface, T_w is an estimate (such as the maximum) of the wall temperature. We may not be able to find the exact distribution of the wall temperature without solving a problem including the interior of the wall, but this is not important. As long as we can estimate T_w, we can assume that some external agent exists that will give the proper wall temperatures on the flow boundaries. This new problem is dominated by different physical processes than the adiabatic wall problem. We must redo the nondimensional scales for the temperature and reanalyze the results. When this is done, we shall find that the flow is a compressible flow as long as $(T_0 - T_w)/T_0$ is finite. The further special case of small temperature differences will turn out to be an imcompressible flow.

The problem now has a characteristic temperature scale $T_0 - T_w$, which is a driving force for the conduction of heat from the walls into the fluid. Since we expect that all temperatures will lie between these two values, the proper nondimensional temperature is

$$\hat{T} = \frac{T - T_0}{T_w - T_0} \qquad (10.8.1)$$

The temperature variable T^* for the adiabatic wall problem is related to $\hat{T}$ by the equation

$$T^* = \frac{T_w - T_0}{T_0} \frac{A}{\gamma_0 \, \mathrm{Pr} \, M^2} \hat{T} \qquad (10.8.2)$$

Since we expect no change in the nondimensional form of any other variables, we can substitute Eq. 10.8.2 into the adiabatic wall analysis (Eqs. 10.3.8 to 10.3.17) and again let the Mach number approach zero.

Temperature does not appear in the continuity and momentum equations, so the previous forms (Eqs. 10.3.9 and 10.3.10) remain unchanged. The equation of state is revised by substituting Eq. 10.8.2 into Eq. 10.3.8. This yields

$$\frac{1}{\rho^*}\frac{D\rho^*}{Dt^*} = \gamma_0 M^2 \alpha^* \frac{Dp^*}{Dt^*} - \beta^* B \frac{T_w - T_0}{T_0}\frac{D\hat{T}}{Dt^*} \tag{10.8.3}$$

When Eq. 10.8.2 is substituted into Eq. 10.3.12, the energy equation changes to

$$\rho^* c_p^* \frac{D\hat{T}}{Dt^*} = \frac{1}{\text{Pr Re}}\partial_i^*(k^*\partial_i^*\hat{T}) + \frac{\gamma_0 M^2}{A\,\text{Re}}\frac{T_0}{T_w - T_0}\Phi^*$$

$$+ \frac{\beta^* B \gamma_0 M^2}{A}\left(\frac{T_0}{T_w - T_0} + \hat{T}\right)\frac{Dp^*}{Dt^*} \tag{10.8.4}$$

A typical transport property is recast in terms of $\hat{T}$ by inserting Eqs. 10.8.1 and 10.3.19 into Eq. 10.3.17:

$$\mu^* = 1 + \frac{d(\mu/\mu_0)}{d(T/T_0)}\frac{T_w - T_0}{T_0}\hat{T} + \frac{d(\mu/\mu_0)}{d(p/p_0)}\frac{\gamma_0}{p_0\alpha_0}M^2 p^* + \cdots \tag{10.8.5}$$

The boundary conditions at the reference position are

$$v_i^* = (1, 0, 0), \qquad \hat{T} = 0, \qquad \rho^* = 1 \tag{10.8.6}$$

and on the walls

$$v_i^* = 0, \qquad \hat{T} = 1 \text{ (or a known function)}$$

The limit $M^2 \to 0$ gives a low-speed compressible flow where the thermodynamic state equation shows that the density changes only because of the large changes in temperature:

$$\frac{1}{\rho^*}\frac{D\rho^*}{Dt^*} = -\beta^* B \frac{T_w - T_0}{T_0}\frac{D\hat{T}}{Dt^*} \tag{10.8.7}$$

The energy equation for the flow shows that convection and conduction determine the temperature field:

$$\rho^* c_p^* \frac{D\hat{T}}{Dt^*} = \frac{1}{\text{Pr Re}}\partial_i^*(k^*\partial_i\hat{T}) \tag{10.8.8}$$

Transport properties and thermodynamic functions such as c_p^* are not constants but depend on temperature:

$$\mu^* = 1 + \frac{d(\mu/\mu_0)}{d(T/T_0)}\frac{T_w - T_0}{T_0}\hat{T} + \cdots \tag{10.8.9}$$

The continuity and momentum equations no longer simplify, but must be considered with their temperature dependence. The complete set of equations is coupled together through the transport properties and the density. They apply to flows where the walls supply significant heating to the fluid. Problems of natural or free convection are of this type. Further simplifications, the Boussinesq approximations, are discussed by Spiegel and Veronis (1960) and by Mihaljan (1962).

The low-speed compressible flow equations contain a new parameter $(T_w - T_0)/T_0$. This parameter compares the temperature changes in the flow, as measured by $T_w - T_0$, with the absolute temperature. In many flows of practical engineering interest this is a small number, which suggests that we consider the special cases where $(T_w - T_0)/T_0 \to$ 0. When this limiting process is applied to Eqs. 10.8.7 and 10.8.9, we again retrieve an incompressible flow with constant properties: low Mach number flow about a body with a small temperature difference. This flow is governed by the same equations as the adiabatic case except that the energy equation is a little different. Equation 10.8.8 has only convection and conduction terms, while for the adiabatic case, Eq. 10.4.6 also includes a viscous dissipation and a pressure term. Many heat transfer problems studied in textbooks fall int the category, where simplified energy equation 10.8.8 may be used. These flows have the same general characteristics of incompressible flow that were discussed in connection with the adiabatic wall case. A typical isothermal wall problem with a small temperature difference would have $T_w - T_0 \approx 50°R$ (30 K) and an absolute temperature of 500°R (300 K); thus, $(T_w - T_0)/T_0 \approx 0.1$.

The low-Mach-number flow over a body with a small temperature difference is a double limiting process. We found that incompressible flow results when

$$\lim_{\Delta T/T_0 \to 0} \ [\lim_{M \to 0} (\text{Navier–Stokes})]$$

Notice that Eq. 10.8.4 contains expressions like $M^2 T_0/\Delta T$, which go to zero in this limit. It is important to realize that if the order of limiting is interchanged, Eq. 10.8.8 does not result from Eq. 10.8.4. A true mathematical limit does not exist at the point $\Delta T/T_0 = 0$, $M^2 = 0$. Incompressible flow exists for any limit

$$\lim_{\substack{M \to 0 \\ \text{and} \\ \Delta T/T_0 = f(M)}} (\text{Navier–Stokes})$$

where

$$\frac{M^2}{\Delta T/T_0} = \frac{M^2}{f(M)} \to 0$$

Most engineering cases meet these conditions. We now discuss those cases that do not.

Let us consider what happens if the temperature difference is extremely small, say 5 or 10°C. For this we should do some careful thinking about the temperature scale for forming the nondimensional temperature. The temperature scale is our best guess as to how large temperature variations in the flow are going to be; it is an estimate of the maximum minus the minimum. If the profile is dominated by conduction from the walls, the proper temperature scale is

$$\Delta T_{\text{isothermal wall}} = T_w - T_0$$

However, there is always viscous dissipation generating heat within the fluid. This effect might also increase the temperature a few degrees. So for very small $T_w - T_0$ our guess might be invalid. Recall that the adiabatic wall temperature scale, Eq. 10.3.3, is

$$\Delta T_{\text{adiabatic wall}} = \frac{\text{Pr } v_0^2}{c_{p0}} = \frac{1}{A} \text{ Pr } \gamma_0 T_0 M^2$$

If we use air as an example ($\gamma_0/A = \gamma_0 - 1 = 0.4$) and we let $T = 500°R$ and $M = 0.3$, the resulting rise in temperature is $\Delta T_{\text{adiabatic}} = 13°R$ (7°C).

In order to decide which temperature scale to use, we can form the ratio

$$\frac{\Delta T_{\text{adiabatic}}}{\Delta T_{\text{isothermal}}} \approx \frac{\text{Pr } v_0^2}{c_{p0}(T_w - T_0)}$$

$$= \frac{M^2 \gamma_0 \text{ Pr}}{A} \frac{T_0}{T_w - T_0} \qquad (10.8.10)$$

If this variable is small, the isothermal analysis will be valid; if it is large, the adiabatic analysis will apply. It is, of course, possible that the two temperature scales are of the same order. In this case the temperature field is not dominated by either conduction or viscous dissipation. In principle, we could use either temperature scale for this situation. In such cases the adiabatic scale and energy equation 10.4.6 are appropriate as they stand. This equation contains conduction, pressure, work, and dissipation, as the problem demands. The parameter we defined in Eq. 10.8.10 is related to the Eckert number found in the heat transfer literature. When Pr is of order 1, the Eckert number essentially indicates the relative influence of conduction and viscous dissipation in the heat transfer process.

*10.9   ENERGY EQUATION PARADOX

The incompressible flow energy equation we derived in Section 10.8 balances the convection and conduction terms:

$$\rho c_p \frac{DT}{Dt} = k \nabla^2 T \qquad (10.9.1)$$

This equation is valid for a low-Mach-number flow (with a small imposed temperature difference). It was derived as a simplification of the complete thermal energy equation,

$$\rho c_p \frac{DT}{Dt} = k \nabla^2 T + \Phi + \beta T \frac{Dp}{Dt} \qquad (10.9.2)$$

Now as an alternative, we might have started the analysis with a different form of the energy equation in which c_v appears rather than c_p. The complete energy equation in terms of c_v is

$$\rho c_v \frac{DT}{Dt} = k \nabla^2 T + \Phi - T \left.\frac{\partial p}{\partial T}\right|_\rho \nabla \cdot \mathbf{v} \qquad (10.9.3)$$

If we take an off-hand look at this equation and try to guess which terms could be neglected in incompressible flow, we would strike out the last term because $\partial_i v_i \approx 0$ and the viscous dissipation term because we have seen in our previous work that it is negligible for small Mach numbers. That would leave Eq. 10.9.3 as a balance between convection terms and conduction terms, but with an important difference. Equation 10.9.1 has c_p as a coefficient, while the simplified version of Eq. 10.9.3 has c_v as a coefficient. This is the paradox. The correct equation 10.9.1 implies that convection of enthalpy is balanced by heat conduction, whereas the appearance of c_v in Eq. 10.9.3 implies that internal energy is convected.

We cannot resolve this paradox by explaining that for *incompressible fluids* the differences between c_v and c_p vanish. Although this is a true statement, it misses the point. The case under discussion is the incompressible flow of a *compressible fluid*. Gases are very compressible fluids, and c_p for them is distinctly different from c_v, no matter what the flow situation is.

To resolve the paradox and convince ourselves that the analysis in Section 10.8 that produces Eq. 10.9.1 is correct, we shall redo the analysis starting from Eq. 10.9.3. This will show that our off-hand guesses were wrong. When nondimensional variables are introduced into Eq. 10.9.3, we arrive at

$$\frac{\rho^* c_v^*}{\gamma_0} \frac{D\hat{T}}{Dt^*} = \frac{1}{Re\,Pr} \nabla^* \cdot (k^*\nabla^*\hat{T}) + \frac{T_0 M^2}{\Delta T\,A} \Phi^* - \left(\hat{T} + \frac{T_0}{\Delta T}\right) \frac{B\beta^*}{A\alpha^*} \nabla^* \cdot v^* \quad (10.9.4)$$

In computing the last term, the following thermodynamic identity has been used:

$$\left.\frac{\partial p}{\partial T}\right|_\rho = \frac{\beta}{\alpha} \quad (10.9.5)$$

The limit $M^2 \to 0$ applied to Eq. 10.9.4 removes the dissipation term, just as in Section 10.8. We are left with the equation

$$\frac{\rho^* c_v^*}{\gamma_0} \frac{D\hat{T}}{Dt^*} = \frac{1}{Re\,Pr} \nabla^* \cdot (k^*\nabla^*\hat{T}) - \left(\hat{T} + \frac{T_0}{\Delta T}\right) \frac{B\beta^*}{A\alpha^*} \nabla^* \cdot v^* \quad (10.9.6)$$

The second limit process, that for small temperature differences $\Delta T/T_0 \to 0$, cannot be applied to Eq. 10.9.6 without some rearranging. The difficulty is the term containing

$$\frac{T_0}{\Delta T} \nabla^* \cdot v^*$$

This is recognized as an indeterminate form $\infty \cdot 0$, since we know that $\partial_i^* v_i^*$ will become zero in the limit $\Delta T/T_0 \to 0$. The continuity equation 10.3.9 and the state equation 10.8.7 show that

$$-\nabla^* \cdot v^* = \frac{1}{\rho^*} \frac{D\rho^*}{Dt^*} = -\frac{\Delta T}{T_0} B\beta^* \frac{D\hat{T}}{Dt^*} \quad (10.9.7)$$

When Eq. 10.9.7 is substituted into Eq. 10.9.6, we find that the term with $\partial_i^* v_i^*$ is finite and may be taken to the right-hand side. We now have

$$\left[\frac{\rho^* c_v^*}{\gamma_0} + \frac{B^2\beta^{*2}}{A\alpha^*}\left(\frac{\Delta T}{T_0} + 1\right)\right] \frac{D\hat{T}}{Dt^*} = \frac{1}{Pr\,Re} \nabla^* \cdot (k^*\nabla^*\hat{T}) \quad (10.9.8)$$

It takes just a little more work to show that the coefficient in brackets is actually the proper c_p^* term. From thermodynamic theory we have the relation

$$c_p = c_v + \frac{T}{\rho} \frac{\beta^2}{\alpha} \quad (10.9.9)$$

The nondimensional form of this equation is

$$\rho^* c_p^* = \frac{\rho^* c_v^*}{\gamma_0} + \frac{B^2\beta^{*2}}{A\alpha^*}\left(1 + \hat{T}\frac{\Delta T}{T}\right) \quad (10.9.10)$$

Comparing Eq. 10.9.10 with the term in brackets in Eq. 10.9.8, we get the final form. Thus, the final form of Eq. 10.9.8 does indeed have $\rho^* c_p^*$ preceding the substantial derivative of the temperature. Our more detailed analysis shows that Eq. 10.9.3 does reduce to Eq. 10.9.1 for incompressible flow. The paradox is explained by noting that when the limit $\Delta T/T_0 \rightarrow 0$ is applied to Eq. 10.9.3, the convection and conduction terms are just as small as the term containing $\partial_i v_i$. Thus, all three terms are important. A slight rearrangement of the $\partial_i v_i$ term using the continuity and state equations allows that term to be combined with the c_v term to produce the correct term, where c_p is the coefficient of the substantial derivative.

We have illustrated the energy equation paradox for incompressible flow with constant-temperature boundaries. The same paradox arises in the case of incompressible flow where the boundaries are adiabatic. To resolve the paradox in this case, one must nondimensionalize Eq. 10.9.3 using the temperature variable T^* appropriate to the adiabatic wall problem. Some algebraic steps similar to those above lead to the proper form of the energy equation 10.3.12 where c_p^* is the coefficient.

10.10   CONCLUSIONS

Incompressible flows require low Mach numbers for adiabatic flow boundaries, and low Mach numbers plus small temperature differences for boundaries with prescribed temperatures. In either case the flows have effectively constant properties and the fluid-flow events are independent of the heat transfer events. This is, in itself, a considerable simplification.

Only two nondimensional parameters, the Froude and Reynolds numbers, occur in the incompressible flow equations. In free-surface flows the Froude number is important; however, in confined flows its effect can be isolated into a hydrostatic pressure of no dynamic significance. The Reynolds number, on the other hand, is always a significant quantity in incompressible flow. The flow behaves differently and is dominated by different mechanisms as the Reynolds number changes.

PROBLEMS

10.1 (A) What are the values of α, β, A, and B for air and water at standard conditions?

10.2 (A) For air, sketch a graph of $\mu(T)$ from 0 to 100°C. Replot μ/μ_0 as a function of T/T_0 for $T_0 = 30$°C. Consider air at 30°C flowing at $M = 0.3$. At a certain point in the flow $T^* = 1$. What is the value of μ/μ_0 at this point?

10.3 (A) Air at standard temperature and pressure is flowing at $M = 0.4$. Estimate the stagnation pressure. Estimate the density change between the free stream and the stagnation point if the flow is isentropic. What is the fractional change in density?

10.4 (B) A thin extensible plastic garden hose has a nozzle at the end to control the flow from zero to the maximum, which is determined by the hydrant pressure. Is the flow in the hose independent of the level of pressure p_0 at the entrance to the nozzle?

10.5 (B) An incompressible flow at moderate-to-high Reynolds number has a certain velocity U_0 in a region of size L. If water and air are both used in this situation, which fluid is the more viscous?

10.6 (A) A vehicle 50 cm in diameter is moving at a depth (to the center) of 4 m under the surface of a fresh-water lake. The speed is 9 m/s. Tests have shown that at the shoulders $C_{p\,\mathrm{kin}} = -2.3$ at this Reynolds number. If atmospheric pressure is 100 kPa, what are the pressures at the upper and lower shoulders of the vehicle (separated by 50 cm in depth)?

10.7 (B) the center of a cylinder of radius r_0 oscillates according to $X_0 = A \sin \Omega t$ in a fluid that is at rest at infinity. If this problem is to be solved using a coordinate system fixed to the cylinder, what are the proper boundary conditions on the pressure and velocity? Assume that the solution results in a surface pressure distribution $\hat{p}_s(\hat{\theta}) = F(\hat{\theta}) \cos \omega \hat{t}$. What are the true pressures on the surface?

10.8 (C) Consider the oscillating piston problem of Section 9.3. Incompressible flow employs the pressure variable $\hat{p} \equiv (p^* - 1)/M^2$. Insert this into the state equation 9.3.20 to show that $\rho^* = 1$ as $M \Rightarrow 0$. The distance scale in incompressible flow is a geometric length or the flow velocity times a time; $\hat{x} \equiv x/A = x^*/M$. Insert these assumptions into Eq. 9.3.10 to show that $u_x^* = 0$ and $u_{\hat{T}}^* = -\hat{p}_x$. Hence, for an oscillating piston in incompressible flow, the velocity is uniform in space as $u^* = v_p^* = \sin T$. What is the pressure?

10.9 (A) Fill in the mathematical steps in Section 10.8.

11

Some Solutions of the Navier–Stokes Equations

The problems we investigate in this chapter are simplified situations that allow explicit mathematical answers. They will be useful in learning how pressure and viscous forces produce different flow patterns. Consider the momentum equation for incompressible flow:

$$\partial_0 v_i + v_j \partial_j v_i = -\frac{1}{\rho}\,\partial_i p + \nu \partial_j \partial_j v_i$$

There are four terms in this equation: local acceleration, convective acceleration, pressure forces, and viscous forces. Since the density is constant, we can incorporate it into the nondimensional pressure and it will be eliminated from the problem. The viscosity, on the other hand, will normally occur as a parameter in the solution, usually in the form of a Reynolds number. With two exceptions, all of the problems in this chapter are so simple that only the viscous term and one other term are nonzero. With only two nonzero terms, one can always incorporate the viscosity into the definition of a nondimensional variable. Hence, ν no longer appears explicitly in the solution, and the velocity profile is independent of the Reynolds number. This is only a mathematical result. Experimentally, the solution may exist only in a certain range of Reynolds numbers, usually at low values, and a more complicated pattern or a turbulent flow is found for other Reynolds numbers.

On the mathematical side, this chapter offers examples of a variety of methods for solving partial differential equations. Separation of variables, splitting and transforming dependent variables, similarity solutions, and finally, a numerical technique for ordinary differential equations are illustrated. Whenever it is feasible, sufficient mathematical details are given so that the reader may supply the intermediate steps without undue effort. However, in a few instances the reader will be asked to accept a result or be prepared for a lengthy mathematical exercise.

Another mathematical problem concerns notation. When we get down to the details of solving the Navier–Stokes equations, it is inconvenient to use the index notation x_1, x_2, x_3, v_1, v_2, v_3, and so on. For a rectangular Cartesian coordinate system we shall change to the standard symbols x, y, z for the coordinates and u, v, w for the corresponding velocities. In cylindrical and spherical coordinates we shall use r, θ, z and r, θ, φ, respectively. The velocity components in these systems will be v_r, v_θ, v_z and v_r, v_θ, v_φ.

11.1   PRESSURE-DRIVEN FLOW IN TUBES OF VARIOUS CROSS SECTIONS: ELLIPTICAL TUBE

Consider the flow in a tube of arbitrary cross section, and assume that the velocity has only one component, which is along the tube axis. This assumption may not be correct. There may also be other solutions to the flow equations that contain other velocity components and secondary flows. The flow pattern we get experimentally may depend on the transient events by which the flow is established. Although there are not a lot of detailed measurements, it is generally thought that the axial solutions are valid at low Reynolds numbers—for example, in the flow through the passageways of porous materials.

Let us proceed with the solution by noting that if $v_z = w$ is the only velocity component, the momentum equations in directions perpendicular to the flow tell us that there is no pressure gradient in those directions. We may therefore conclude that the pressure is a function of z only. The z-direction momentum equation becomes

$$0 = -\frac{dp}{dz} + \mu \frac{\partial^2 w}{\partial x^2} + \mu \frac{\partial^2 w}{\partial y^2} \tag{11.1.1}$$

As in a circular pipe, the density drops out of the problem and we surmise that the velocity is determined solely by the pressure gradient and the absolute viscosity. Since dp/dz is a function of z alone and w is a function of x and y, the only way that Eq. 11.1.1 can be satisfied is if dp/dz is constant. Therefore, we take dp/dz as a prescribed number. At either end of the tube we must have some external agent that provides the pressure difference and drives the flow. The mathematical statement of the problem is completed by the no-slip condition

$$w(\text{wall}) = 0 \tag{11.1.2}$$

Equation 11.1.1 is a Poisson equation and is of elliptic type. This means that if we change the shape of the boundary in one region of the wall, it will affect the solution everywhere across the cross section.

Next, we undertake to nondimensionalize the variables. Let L be a characteristic dimension of the cross section. Nondimensional space variables are

$$x^* = \frac{y}{L}, \qquad y^* = \frac{z}{L} \tag{11.1.3}$$

There is no characteristic velocity in the problem, so we must form one from the constants in the differential equation. By trial and error we find that the differential equation will have a simple form if we define the nondimensional velocity as

$$w^* = \frac{w}{-(L^2/\mu)\,(dp/dz)} \tag{11.1.4}$$

(From another point of view one may find the characteristic velocity by asking: How can a quantity with dimensions L/T be formed from μ, L, and dp/dz?) In this type of problem the pressure force balances the net viscous force everywhere in the flow field (see Eq.

11.1.1), so it is appropriate that the ratio of dp/dz to the viscosity is a measure of the maximum velocity. The problem in nondimensional variables is

$$\nabla^2 w^* = \frac{\partial^2 w^*}{\partial x^{*2}} + \frac{\partial^2 w^*}{\partial y^{*2}} = -1 \tag{11.1.5}$$

Specifying the shape of the cross section completes the problem.

We continue the solution for a tube that has an elliptical cross section as shown in Fig. 11.1. Solutions for a wide variety of shapes are given by Berker (1963). The equation for the ellipse wall location is

$$\left(\frac{x}{a}\right)^2 + \left(\frac{y}{b}\right)^2 = 1 \quad \text{or} \quad x_w^{*2} + K y_w^{*2} = 1 \quad \text{where} \quad K = \left(\frac{a}{b}\right)^2 \tag{11.1.6}$$

In this equation the semiaxes are a in the x-direction and b in the y-direction. We have chosen a as the characteristic length previously denoted by L.

One approach to solving a Poisson equation is to introduce a new dependent variable so that it becomes a Laplace equation. Consider a new variable

$$W = w^* + C_1 x^{*2} + C_2 y^{*2} \tag{11.1.7}$$

Computing the Laplacian gives

$$\nabla^2 W = \nabla^2 w^* + 2C_1 + 2C_2 \tag{11.1.8}$$

Evidently, Eq. 11.1.5 will transform to $\nabla^2 W = 0$ if we require that

$$2C_1 + 2C_2 = 1 \tag{11.1.9}$$

The exact values of C_1 and C_2 are fixed by considering the boundary condition. On the wall $w^* = 0$ and Eq. 11.1.7 becomes

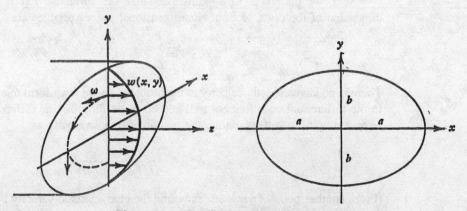

Figure 11.1   Parallel flow in an elliptical tube.

$$W(\text{wall}) = C_1 x_w^{*2} + C_2 y_w^{*2}$$

$$= C_1 \left(x_w^{*2} + \frac{C_2}{C_1} y_w^{*2} \right). \qquad (11.1.10)$$

Comparing this with Eq. 11.1.6, we see that we can arrange for $W(\text{wall})$ to be the constant C_1 if we set $C_2/C_1 = K$. Substituting this into Eq. 11.1.9 gives the constants as

$$C_1 = \frac{1}{(2(1 + K)}, \qquad C_2 = \frac{K}{2(1 + K)} \qquad (11.1.11)$$

The mathematical problem now is to solve $\nabla^2 W = 0$ for the boundary condition $W = C_1$ on the wall. One of the characteristics of the Laplace equation is that the maximum and minimum values of the solution must occur on the boundary of the domain. Thus, we need look no further; the only solution is $W = C_1$. Setting Eq. 11.1.7 equal to C_1 and using Eq. 11.1.11, we find that the velocity is given by

$$w^* = \frac{1}{2(1 + K)} (1 - x^{*2} - Ky^{*2}) \qquad (11.1.12)$$

The velocity has the same value at any point on an ellipse $(x^{*2} + Ky^{*2} = C)$ that has the same eccentricity as the tube wall.

The vorticity components are

$$\omega_z = \frac{1}{K + 1} x^*, \qquad \omega_y = - \frac{K}{K + 1} y^*$$

In addition, one can show that the vortex lines (lines connecting the vorticity vectors in a tangential manner) are also ellipses and that the vorticity has a constant magnitude on any ellipse:

$$|\omega| = \frac{1}{K + 1} (x^{*2} + Ky^{*2})^{1/2}$$

Notice that the vorticity does not depend on the Reynolds number; the only parameter that appears in the equation is a geometric parameter K. Integration of the velocity profile yields the volume flow rate

$$\frac{Q}{-(a^4/\mu)(dp/dz)} = \frac{\pi}{4} \frac{1}{K^{1/2}(K + 1)}$$

All tube flow problems have a flow rate–pressure drop relation of the form $Q = Ca^4 \mu^{-1} dp/dz$, where C depends on the shape of the cross section.

11.2 FLOW IN A RECTANGULAR TUBE

The velocity profile $w^*(x^*, y^*)$ for pressure-driven flow in a tube with a rectangular cross section can be solved by a series expansion. Figure 11.2 shows the cross section with sides $2L$ by $2a \cdot L$ and defines a coordinate system with the origin in the center. We

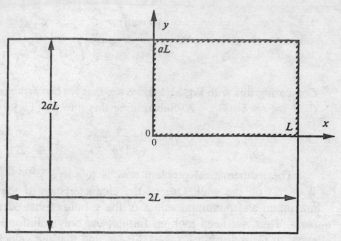

Figure 11.2   Coordinate system and analysis region for flow in a rectangular duct.

proceed as in Section 11.1 and use the nondimensional variables of Eqs. 11.1.3 and 11.1.4 to arrive at a Poisson equation 11.2.5; $\nabla^2 w^* = -1$. Next, introduce a new dependent variable $W = w^* - f$, where $\nabla^2 f = -1$. For this problem a suitable choice is $f = \frac{1}{2}(a^2 - y^2)$. The equation governing W is the Laplace equation; $\nabla^2 W = \nabla^2 w^* - \nabla^2 f = 0$ (solving partial differential equations is a trial-and-error process):

$$w^* = \tfrac{1}{2}(a^2 - y^{*2}) + W(x^*, y^*) \tag{11.2.1}$$

Assume that W is a separation-of-variables form:

$$W = Y(y^*)X(x^*) \tag{11.2.2}$$

Boundary conditions are applied to the upper quarter of the domain; $0 \le x^* \le 1$, $0 \le y^* \le a$ as follows:

$$
\begin{aligned}
y^* = a, & \qquad w^* = 0, & \qquad W = 0 = Y(a)X(x^*) \\
y^* = 0, & \qquad \partial w^*/\partial y^* = 0, & \qquad \partial W/\partial y^* = 0 = Y'(0)X(x^*) \\
x^* = 0, & \qquad \partial w^*/\partial x^* = 0, & \qquad \partial W/\partial x^* = 0 = Y(y^*)X'(0) \\
x^* = 1, & \qquad w^* = 0, & \qquad W = 0 = \tfrac{1}{2}(a^2 - y^{*2}) + Y(y^*)X(1)
\end{aligned}
\tag{11.2.3}
$$

We could as well apply the no-slip condition at $x^* = -1$ and $y^* = -a$, however, the symmetry conditions at $x^* = 0$ and $y^* = 0$ are equivalent and will be necessary in Section 11.3.

To proceed we evaluate the Laplace equation

$$0 = \nabla^2 W = \nabla^2[Y(y^*)X(x^*)] = Y''X + YX''$$

or

$$\frac{Y''}{Y} = -\frac{X''}{X} = \pm\,\alpha = \text{constant} \tag{11.2.4}$$

Because each side of Eq. 11.2.4 is a function of a different variable, they must be a constant that is designated as $\pm\alpha$. Choosing $-\alpha$ leads to solutions of $Y'' + \alpha Y = 0$ of the form $\sin \alpha y^*$ and $\cos \alpha y^*$. Corresponding solutions of $X'' - \alpha X = 0$ have the form $\exp(\alpha x^*)$ and $\exp(-\alpha x^*)$, or equivalently, $\sinh \alpha x^*$ and $\cosh \alpha x^*$. A solution where A, B, C, and D are constants is

$$W = (A \cos \alpha y^* + B \sin \alpha y^*)[C \exp(\alpha x^*) + D \exp(-\alpha x^*)]$$

The sine solutions will not fit the second boundary condition of Eq. 11.2.3 and therefore are discarded by setting $B = 0$.

Since the Laplace equation is linear, we may add any number of solutions with distinct values of α_n ($n = 1, 2, 3, \ldots, N$). Consider the following construction as a possible answer. [The constants $C = D = \exp(-\alpha_n)$ are chosen to fit the third equation in 11.2.3.]

$$w^* = \frac{1}{2}(a^2 - y^{*2}) + \sum_{n=1}^{N} A_n \cos \alpha_n y^* \{\exp[\alpha_n(x^* - 1)] + \exp[-\alpha_n(x^* + 1)]\}$$

$$\tag{11.2.5}$$

Let us check the boundary conditions of Eq. 11.2.3. The first BC is

$$y^* = a, \quad w^* = 0 = \sum_{n=1}^{N} A_n \cos \alpha_n a \{\exp[\alpha_n(x^* - 1)] + \exp[-\alpha_n(x^* + 1)]\}$$

The above will be true if $\cos \alpha_n a = 0$. Thus, α_n must be $\pi/2, 3\pi/2, 5\pi/2, \ldots$, or, in general,

$$\alpha_n = \frac{(2n - 1)\pi}{2a}, \quad n = 1, 2, 3, \ldots \tag{11.2.6}$$

The next boundary condition is

$$y^* = 0, \quad \frac{\partial w^*}{\partial y^*} = 0 = \sum_{n=1}^{N} A_n \sin(0)\{\exp[\alpha_n(x^* - 1)] + \exp[-\alpha_n(x^* + 1)]\}$$

The third boundary condition is also satisfied by the "fortunate" choice of constants inserted in the exponential functions of Eq. 11.2.5:

$$x^* = 0, \quad \frac{\partial w^*}{\partial x^*} = 0 = \sum_{n=1}^{N} A_n \cos \alpha_n y^* [\alpha_n \exp(-\alpha_n) - \alpha_n \exp(-\alpha_n)]$$

The final boundary condition will determine the constants A_n. At $x^* = 1$,

$$w^* = 0 = \frac{1}{2}(a^2 - y^{*2}) + \sum_{n=1}^{N} A_n \cos \alpha_n y^* [1 + \exp(-2\alpha_n)] \tag{11.2.7}$$

There are a couple of ways that Eq. 11.2.7 can be satisfied. Take $N = \infty$ and let the summation be a Fourier cosine expansion (a half-range expansion with extended period to have only odd terms in the cosine) of the function $-\frac{1}{2}(y^{*2} - a^2)$. The final answer is (see, e.g., Rosenhead, 1963, p. 136)

$$w^* = \frac{1}{2}(a^2 - y^{*2}) + \frac{2}{a} \sum_{n=1}^{N} \frac{(-1)^n}{\alpha_n^3} \cos \alpha_n y^*$$

$$\times \frac{\exp[\alpha_n(x^* - 1)] + \exp[-\alpha_n(x^* + 1)]}{1 + \exp(-2\alpha_n)} \tag{11.2.8}$$

Here the coefficients α_n are given by Eq. 11.2.6. Note that the exponential terms can also be written as $\cosh \alpha_n x^* / \cosh \alpha_n$. The convergence of this series is assured.

A second method to satisfy Eq. 11.2.7 is to choose N as a finite number and consider the N points (called *collocation points*)

$$y_i^* = \frac{(i - 1)a}{N}, \qquad i = 1, 2, 3, \ldots, N$$

At these N points Eq. 11.2.7 is satisfied exactly:

$$\frac{1}{2}(y_i^{*2} - a^2) = \sum_{n=1}^{N} A_n \cos \alpha_n y_i^*[1 + \exp(-2\alpha_n)], \qquad i = 1, 2, \ldots, N \tag{11.2.9}$$

The N equations 11.2.9 are a linear set that may be solved for the A_n values. If N is large, the electronic computer would be used. This method is introduced because it will be used in Section 11.3 in a more complicated problem.

11.3   CHANNEL WITH LONGITUDINAL RIBS

Figure 11.3 shows the cross section of a channel with symmetric ribs. Consider one section of this periodic geometry. The domain is divided into two rectangles; aL by cL and $(a - b)L$ by $(1 - c)L$. Applying the method of Section 11.2 to each rectangle gives velocity profiles:

$$w_I^* = \frac{1}{2}(a^2 - y^{*2}) + \sum_{n=1}^{N} A_n \cos \alpha_n y^*\{\exp[\alpha_n(x^* - c)]$$

$$+ \exp[-\alpha_n(x^* + c)]\} \tag{11.3.1}$$

$$w_{II}^* = \frac{1}{2}[(a - b)^2 - y^{*2}] + \sum_{m=1}^{M} B_m \cos \beta_m y^*\{\exp(\beta_m(x^* - 2 + c)]$$

$$+ \exp[-\beta_m(x^* - c)]\} \tag{11.3.2}$$

The number of terms N is arbitrary; however, M and N are related by

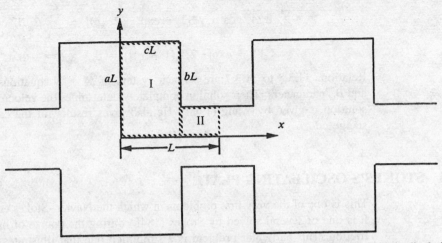

Figure 11.3 Coordinate system and analysis regions for flow in a duct with longitudinal ribs.

$$M = \text{Integer}\left[\frac{N(a - b)}{a}\right]$$

Separation constants α_n and β_m are fixed so that the cosine terms become zero to satisfy the no-slip condition on the upper wall of each domain:

$$\alpha_n = \frac{(2n - 1)\pi}{2a}, \qquad \beta_m = \frac{(2m - 1)\pi}{2(a - b)} \qquad (11.3.3)$$

Applying boundary conditions along $x^* = c$ determines the constants A_n and B_m. Select N equally spaced collocation points at $x^* = c$ and

$$y_i^* = \frac{(i - 1)a}{N}, \qquad i = 1, 2, 3, \ldots, N \qquad (11.3.4)$$

The first M of these points are on the common boundary of I and II, while the points from $M + 1$ to N are along the wall of domain I. Along the wall, $x^* = c$, $(a - b) \leq y^* \leq a$, $w^* = 0$ is required. Where the two domains meet, $x^* = c$, $0 \leq y^* \leq (a - b)$, we require that both the values and the normal slope match; $w_I^* = w_{II}^*$ and $\partial w_I^* / \partial x^* = \partial w_{II}^* / \partial x^*$. Enforcing these conditions gives us

$$\sum_{n=1}^{N} A_n \cos \alpha_n y_i^*[1 + \exp(-2\alpha_n c)] = \frac{1}{2}(y_i^{*2} - a^2), \qquad i = M + 1 \text{ to } N \quad (11.3.5)$$

$$\sum_{n=1}^{N} A_n \cos \alpha_n y_i^*[1 + \exp(-2\alpha_n c)] - \sum_{m=1}^{M} B_m \cos \beta_n y_i^*\{1 + \exp[-2\beta_m(1 - c)]\}$$

$$= \frac{1}{2}(b^2 - 2ab), \qquad i = 1 \text{ to } M$$

$$(11.3.6)$$

$$\sum_{n=1}^{N} \alpha_n A_n \cos \alpha_n y_i^*[1 - \exp(-2\alpha_n c)] - \sum_{m=1}^{M} \beta_m B_m \cos \beta_n y_i^*$$

$$\times \{1 - \exp[-2\beta_m(1 - c)]\} = 0, \qquad i = 1 \text{ to } M \tag{11.3.7}$$

Relations 11.3.5 to 11.3.7 are a linear system of $M + N$ equations for the unknown A_n and B_m parameters. Their solution completely determines the velocity profile. An example solution is given by Wang (1994). He also gives results for the case when the ribs are staggered.

11.4 STOKES'S OSCILLATING PLATE

This is one of the very first problems in which the Navier–Stokes equations were solved. It is one of several solved by Stokes (1845) during the course of his study of pendulum friction. This particular problem is a simplified one that illustrates the flow engendered by an oscillating boundary. A semi-infinite fluid is at rest initially and bounded below by a solid plane at $y = 0$. The problem is to find the motion of the fluid after the plate begins to oscillate in its own plane with a velocity given by

$$u_w = u_0 \sin \Omega t \tag{11.4.1}$$

If we assume that the fluid has a single velocity component $u(y, t)$, the x-direction momentum simplifies to

$$\frac{\partial u}{\partial t} - \nu \frac{\partial^2 u}{\partial y^2} = 0 \tag{11.4.2}$$

The boundary conditions are that the fluid is initially quiescent, the velocity is bounded at infinity, and the no-slip condition applies at the plate surface:

$$u(y, t = 0) = 0 \tag{11.4.3}$$

$$u(y \to \infty, t) < \infty \tag{11.4.4}$$

$$u(y = 0, t) = u_0 \sin \Omega t \tag{11.4.5}$$

The solution to this problem can be expressed as the sum of a transient and a steady-state solution. In this section we give the steady-state solution, and in Section 11.6 the transient solution. The steady-state solution is a repetitive oscillation found by ignoring the initial condition.

Examining the boundary conditions we find that u_0 is a velocity scale and Ω^{-1} is a time scale. Therefore, we define nondimensional variables as

$$U = \frac{u}{u_0}, \qquad T = \Omega t \tag{11.4.6}$$

These variables are substituted into the differential equation together with the assumption that $Y = y/\alpha$. We find that the problem will not contain any parameters if we choose α so that the nondimensional distance is

$$Y = \frac{y}{(\nu/\Omega)^{1/2}} \tag{11.4.7}$$

The problem statement in nondimensional variables is

$$\frac{\partial U}{\partial T} - \frac{\partial^2 U}{\partial Y^2} = 0 \tag{11.4.8}$$

$$U(Y, T = 0) = 0 \tag{11.4.9}$$

$$U(Y \rightarrow \infty, T) = 0 \tag{11.4.10}$$

$$U(Y = 0, T) = \sin T = \mathcal{Im} \exp(iT) \tag{11.4.11}$$

The last condition has been written as the imaginary part, $\mathcal{Im}$, of a complex function. It is advantageous to consider U as a complex variable and then, in accord with Eq. 11.4.11, take the imaginary part as our answer.

The steady-state solution is sought by ignoring the initial boundary condition 11.4.9 and stipulating that the time dependence is an oscillation. We assume a solution of the form

$$U = f(Y) \exp(iT) \tag{11.4.12}$$

When this form is substituted into the differential equation, we obtain

$$(f'' - if) \exp(iT) = 0 \tag{11.4.13}$$

Since $\exp(iT)$ is nonzero, we require that the factor in parentheses be zero. This furnishes a differential equation for f. A solution is assumed of the form

$$f = A \exp(aY)$$

where the constants may be complex. This assumption will produce a zero value of the parentheses in Eq. 11.4.13; that is, $f'' = if$, if

$$a = \pm\sqrt{i} = +\frac{1 + i}{\sqrt{2}} \tag{11.4.14}$$

We now have a solution to the differential equation:

$$U = A \exp\left[\frac{\pm(1 + i)Y}{\sqrt{2}} \right] \exp(iT) \tag{11.4.15}$$

The requirement that the answer be bounded at infinity dictates that the minus sign be chosen. The constant A is found by considering the boundary conditions. Setting $Y = 0$ in Eq. 11.4.15 and comparing with the wall condition 11.4.11, we find that $A = 1$. The imaginary part of Eq. 11.4.15 becomes

$$U = \mathcal{Im}\left\{ \exp\left[-\frac{(1 + i)Y}{\sqrt{2}} \right] \exp(iT) \right\}$$

or

$$U = \exp\left(-\frac{Y}{\sqrt{2}}\right) \sin\left(T - \frac{Y}{\sqrt{2}}\right) \qquad (11.4.16)$$

Figure 11.4 shows velocity profiles at various times.

The velocity profile is damped in the y-direction by the first exponential term in Eq. 11.4.16. Denote the position $y = \delta$ as the place where the amplitude has decreased to 1% of the wall value. This occurs at about $Y/\sqrt{2} = 4.5$. Converting to dimensional variables, we find that the thickness of this region is

$$\delta = 4.5\left(\frac{2\nu}{\Omega}\right)^{1/2} \qquad (11.4.17)$$

The depth to which viscosity makes itself felt is proportional to $\sqrt{\nu}$, just as it was in the Rayleigh problem of Chapter 7.

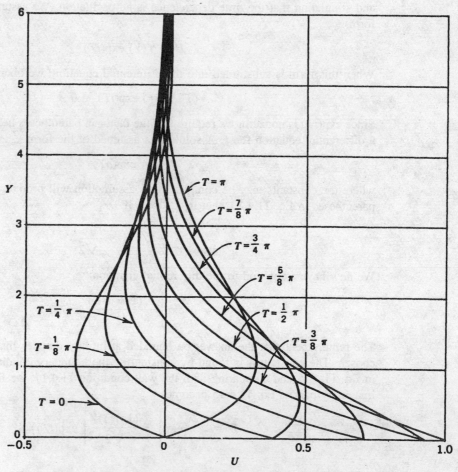

Figure 11.4 Stokes flow near an oscillating plate. The wall oscillates as $U_0 = \sin T$.

From the second term in Eq. 11.4.16, we have a wavelike behavior. A certain point on the wave is given when $T - Y/\sqrt{2}$ takes a specific value. In dimensional terms this point travels through space according to

$$y = C + \sqrt{2\nu\Omega}\, t \qquad (11.4.18)$$

The wave velocity is $(2\nu\Omega)^{1/2}$. The mathematical solution may be thought of as damped viscous waves traveling away from the wall. This interpretation is really tied up with the oscillating boundary condition. The physical process that is occurring is viscous diffusion. The Rayleigh problem does not have a physical wave velocity, although one can trace the depth of penetration of the diffusion effect as a function of time. Note in Fig. 11.4 how the effect of the wall motion is delayed. When the wall reverses its motion and generates a net shear in the opposite direction at $T = \pi/2$, a net accelerating force from viscosity still exists deeper in the fluid, say $Y = 2$. Only after some time delay does the net shear force within the fluid change sign and begin to decelerate the fluid.

11.5   WALL UNDER AN OSCILLATING FREE STREAM

Another interpretation of Stokes's problem can be made. We employ the fact, discussed in Section 10.7, that the equations governing incompressible flow are invariant under an "unsteady" Galilean transformation. This enables us to turn the problem of Section 11.4 around and say that the wall is stationary and the fluid far away is oscillating. An oscillating pressure gradient from external sources is needed to cause the free stream to oscillate.

The oscillating free-stream problem is analyzed as follows. The same nondimensional variables will be used that were defined in Section 11.4. To distinguish the present problem the velocity will have an overbar, $\overline{U}(Y, T)$. The momentum equation is

$$\frac{\partial \overline{U}}{\partial T} = -\frac{\overline{dP}}{dX} + \frac{\partial^2 \overline{U}}{\partial Y^2} \qquad (11.5.1)$$

The pressure ($\overline{P} = p/\rho u_0 \Omega L$, $X = x/L$) does not vary in the y-direction as may be deduced from the y-direction momentum equation. At $Y \to \infty$ the fluid is oscillating with a velocity

$$\overline{U}(Y \to \infty, T) = \sin T \qquad (11.5.2)$$

A pressure force $-dp/dx \propto \cos T$ would produce this motion. Because the wall is stationary,

$$\overline{U}(Y = 0, T) = 0 \qquad (11.5.3)$$

According to Section 10.7, we can choose a new $\hat{x}_i$-coordinate system that moves so that a particle in the free stream appears to be fixed ($\hat{x} = x - \cos T + 1$, $\hat{Y} = Y$). The velocity of the $\hat{x}_i$-coordinate system, V_i, is the same as the fluid velocity, Eq. 11.5.2, that is,

$$V_x = U_\infty = \sin T \qquad (11.5.4)$$

Any fluid velocity $\hat{U}$ measured in the new system is related to the actual fluid velocity and coordinate system velocity by Eq. 10.7.1:

$$\hat{U} = \overline{U} - V_x = \overline{U} - \sin T \tag{11.5.5}$$

Hence, the boundary conditions 11.5.2 and 11.5.3 become

$$\hat{U}(\hat{Y} \to \infty, T) = \sin T - \sin T = 0 \tag{11.5.6}$$
$$\hat{U}(\hat{Y} = 0, T) = -\sin T$$

Since we are assured by Section 10.7 that the governing equations in the new oscillating coordinates are unchanged in form, we may conclude that the new problem is simply Stokes's problem for a wall motion of $-\sin T$. The solution to the problem for $\hat{U}$ is the negative of Eq. 11.4.16, and the solution to the original problem is found by combining Eq. 11.4.16 and 11.5.5.

$$\overline{U} = -\sin\left(T - \frac{Y}{\sqrt{2}}\right) \exp\left(-\frac{Y}{\sqrt{2}}\right) + \sin T \tag{11.5.7}$$

This is the velocity profile for a uniform stream oscillating above a fixed wall. The first term is a viscous effect, and the second is the inviscid oscillation of the main stream.

At any distance from the wall, Eq. 11.5.7 is the sum of two sine waves with the same frequency. It is always possible to represent this as a single wave with a different amplitude and a phase lag. Thus an equivalent form for Eq. 11.5.7 is

$$\overline{U} = A \sin(T + \Theta) \tag{11.5.8}$$

where

$$A = \left[1 - 2 \exp\left(-\frac{Y}{\sqrt{2}}\right) \cos \frac{Y}{\sqrt{2}} + \exp\left(-\frac{2Y}{\sqrt{2}}\right)\right]^{1/2} \tag{11.5.9}$$

and

$$\Theta = \tan^{-1} \frac{\exp(-Y/\sqrt{2}) \sin(Y/\sqrt{2})}{1 - \exp(-Y/\sqrt{2}) \cos(Y/\sqrt{2})} \tag{11.5.10}$$

One unexpected result is that the maximum amplitude of the oscillation is not at $Y \to \infty$ but at an intermediate point near the wall.

Figure 11.5 gives velocity profiles for several times. The overshoot occurs at $Y \approx 3.2$, approximately one-half a viscous length away from the wall. To gain an insight into how the overshoot occurs, let us differentiate Eq. 11.5.5 to obtain

$$\frac{\partial \overline{U}}{\partial T} = \cos T - \cos\left(T - \frac{Y}{\sqrt{2}}\right) \exp\left(-\frac{Y}{\sqrt{2}}\right) \tag{11.5.11}$$

Written below is the differential equation that governs the flow.

$$\frac{\partial \overline{U}}{\partial T} = -\frac{d\overline{P}}{dX} + \frac{\partial^2 \overline{U}}{\partial Y^2} \tag{11.5.12}$$

Since the pressure gradient is $-\cos T$, the term in Eqs. 11.5.11 and 11.5.12 correspond in the same order that they have been written. A pressure gradient of $\cos T$ acts uniformly through the layer to drive the flow. At the wall $Y = 0$, the viscous force exactly coun-

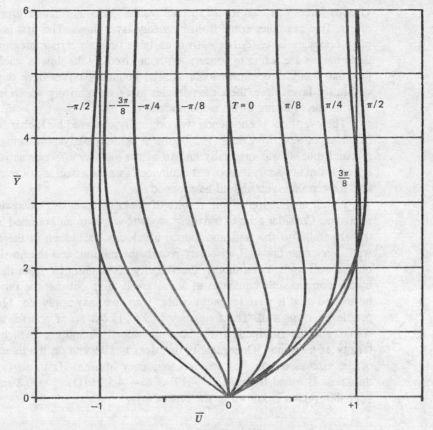

Figure 11.5 Oscillating stream above a wall. The free stream oscillates as $U_\infty = \sin T$.

teracts the pressure force so that no motion occurs. As we move away from the wall, the oscillating viscous stresses die out according to the exponential factor. It is the intermediate region where the behavior is most complicated. The term $\cos(T - Y/\sqrt{2})$ contains a phase lag of $Y/\sqrt{2}$ compared to the term in $\cos T$. At the wall the phase lag is zero and the terms cancel. At small distances Y, the term in $\cos(T - Y/\sqrt{2})$ peaks at later times, so the mismatch allows the fluid to accelerate. However, at certain distances from the wall the lag is so great that the viscous and pressure terms actually add together. The combined effect is to accelerate the fluid to higher velocities than those produced by the pressure force acting alone. We rationalize this by noting that the net viscous stress created at the wall diffuses into the flow and is attenuated at the same time. About half a cycle after the net viscous force was generated, viscous diffusion has carried it slightly from the wall, but it is still strong enough to aid the pressure force, which has now changed its direction. The combination of these forces accelerates the fluid to produce the overshoot.

Two general mechanisms occurring in incompressible flow are illustrated by this problem: Pressure forces are transmitted instantaneously through the fluid, while viscous forces are transmitted by viscous diffusion. The difference in time scales of pressure and viscous forces can lead to unexpected results. Viscous forces are not always a damping effect. Two examples come from boundary layer flows. The first is the fact that the flat plate boundary layer ($dp/dx = 0$) is unstable because certain pressure and viscous stress disturbances are acting in concert. Without viscosity the flow is stable. The second is the fact that many three-dimensional skewed boundary layers have the maximum velocity within the layer. Here, there are particles that have a history which includes pressure and viscous forces acting in the same direction.

The overshoot phenomenon was originally observed by Richardson and Tyler (1929) in turbulent pipe flow. Sexl (1930) gave a laminar analysis showing the same effect for a round tube. It was originally known as the *annular effect* or as *Richardson's annular effect*. From our analysis above it is obvious that the effect is not related to the geometry, and the term *annular* should be dropped.

As an application of the results of Stokes's analysis, we review a problem from acoustics. Consider a set of traveling acoustic waves in air bounded by a wall. The waves travel parallel to the wall and induce a velocity oscillation in the fluid away from the wall. Very near the wall, viscosity retards the motion, and the no-slip condition applies on the wall itself. Even though the velocity of the fluid far from the wall is determined by the compressible equations of acoustics, it turns out that the flow near the wall may be treated as if it were incompressible. Thus, we may apply Eq. 11.5.8 for the velocity profile near the wall. The frequency in Eq. 11.5.8 is, of course, the frequency of the sound, and the amplitude is the acoustic velocity amplitude, which depends on the intensity of the sound. One quantity that does not depend on the intensity is the thickness of the viscous region. For a sound frequency of 1000 Hz in air ($\nu = 0.15$ cm^2/s) the thickness is found from Eq. 11.4.17 as $\delta = 4.5(2\nu/\Omega)^{1/2} = 0.8$ mm. In acoustics this very thin region is known as the *Stokes layer*.

*11.6   TRANSIENT FOR A STOKES OSCILLATING PLATE

At the initiation of the plate motion and during the first cycle of the oscillation, the velocity profile in the fluid differs from that given by the steady-state solution 11.4.16. During this period the solution consists of the sum of a transient and a steady-state solution,

$$U = U_s + U_t \tag{11.6.1}$$

The solution U_s is given in Eq. 11.4.16. In this section we shall find U_t, the transient solution.

Mathematically, the problem for U_t is given by the diffusion equation,

$$\frac{\partial U_t}{\partial T} - \frac{\partial^2 U_t}{\partial Y^2} = 0 \tag{11.6.2}$$

The fluid is initially quiescent; hence the transient answer must exactly cancel the steady-state solution at $T = 0$. From Eq. 11.4.16 we have

$$U_t(Y, T = 0) = -U_S(Y, T = 0)$$

$$= \exp\left(-\frac{Y}{\sqrt{2}}\right) \sin \frac{Y}{\sqrt{2}} \qquad (11.6.3)$$

It turns out that the only way to solve this problem in closed form is to represent the initial condition in complex-variable form (Panton, 1968). Therefore, we write Eq. 11.6.3 as

$$U_t(Y, T = 0) = \mathscr{I}m\left\{\exp\left[-\frac{(1 - i)Y}{\sqrt{2}}\right]\right\} \qquad (11.6.4)$$

The other boundary conditions are

$$U_t(Y \to \infty, T) = 0 \qquad (11.6.5)$$

$$U_t(Y = 0, T) = 0 \qquad (11.6.6)$$

Equation 11.6.6 reflects the fact that the oscillating part of the boundary condition at the wall has already been satisfied by the steady-state solution.

There is a problem in heat conduction that is mathematically equivalent to our problem. Consider the unsteady heat conduction in a semi-infinite slab where an initial temperature profile (Eq. 11.6.4) decays while the surface temperature is held at zero (Eq. 11.6.6). The solution to this problem is discussed in many texts and can be expressed as an integral. In their classic text on heat conduction solutions, Carslaw and Jaeger (1947) give the solution as

$$U_t = (4\pi T)^{-1/2} \int_0^\infty f(\xi)\left\{\exp\left[-\frac{(Y - \xi)^2}{4T}\right] - \exp\left[-\frac{(Y + \xi)^2}{4T}\right]\right\} d\xi \qquad (11.6.7)$$

Here the function $f(\xi)$ is the initial temperature profile, and for our problem it is the initial velocity profile. Upon substituting Eq. 11.6.4 for $f(\xi)$, the integral Eq. 11.6.7 is found to be tractable and is given, for instance, by Abramowitz and Stegun (1964). The result is

$$U_t(Y, T) = \mathscr{I}m\left\{\frac{1}{2}\exp\left(-\frac{CY}{\sqrt{2}} - iT\right)\mathrm{erfc}\left[\left(\frac{1}{2}T\right)^{1/2}\left(C - \frac{Y}{T\sqrt{2}}\right)\right]\right.$$

$$\left. - \frac{1}{2}\exp\left(+\frac{CY}{\sqrt{2}} - iT\right)\mathrm{erfc}\left[\left(\frac{1}{2}T\right)^{1/2}\left(C + \frac{Y}{T\sqrt{2}}\right)\right]\right\} \qquad (11.6.8)$$

where $C = 1 - i$. The combined solution $U_s + U_t$ is given in Fig. 11.6. From the graphs we see that the transient is only significant during the first cycle of the oscillation.

There are several other types of plate motion that lead to exact results. For example, if the velocity increases as t^n, solutions may be found. All of these problems may be turned around and considered as a prescribed motion of an external stream over a fixed plate. They may also be added together to give a composite motion, because the problem is linear. Thus, an arbitrary motion might be expressed as a polynomial in time, and each t^n term would contribute an exact answer to the combined motion. Another approach to

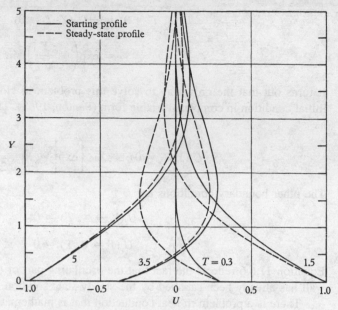

Figure 11.6 Starting transient for Stokes flow.

the problem of an arbitrary plate motion is to represent the motion as a Fourier sine series. Then the solutions of this section and Section 11.6 can be found for each term in the series

$$u(y = 0, t) = A \sin \Omega t + B \sin 2\Omega t + \cdots$$

This method can represent most motions with a small number of terms. Finally, we mention that an integral method (Duhamel's integral) is also available for direct numerical evaluations of the integral in Eq. 11.6.7.

11.7 FLOW IN A SLOT WITH A STEADY AND OSCILLATING PRESSURE GRADIENT

In Chapter 7 we found that flow in a slot with a constant-pressure gradient resulted in a parabolic velocity profile. Here we consider that an extra oscillatory component is added to the steady gradient. The pressure is then

$$-\frac{1}{\rho}\frac{\partial p}{\partial x} = -\frac{1}{\rho}\frac{dp}{dx}\bigg|_{0} + K \cos \Omega t \qquad (11.7.1)$$

The coordinate system is taken with x in the flow direction and with its origin in the center of a channel of width $2h$.

The first step in an analytical solution is to assume that u is a function of y and t but not a function of x. Then the continuity equation simplifies to $\partial v/\partial y = 0$, and hence v is a function of x alone. Since v is zero on the wall, it must be zero everywhere.

The x-direction momentum equation simplifies to

$$\frac{\partial u}{\partial t} = -\frac{1}{\rho}\frac{dp}{dx}\bigg|_0 + K \cos \Omega t + \nu \frac{\partial^2 u}{\partial y^2} \tag{11.7.2}$$

Upon this equation we impose boundary conditions of no slip at the wall and assume that the flow is symmetric about $y = 0$:

$$u(y = h, t) = 0, \qquad \frac{\partial u}{\partial y}(y = 0, t) = 0 \tag{11.7.3}$$

The initial condition is omitted, as we will seek only the steady-state result.

The equation and boundary conditions are linear in u; so the answer may be separated into a part with the constant pressure gradient u_1 (the solution is the parabola given in Chapter 7) and an oscillatory part u_2 that satisfies

$$\frac{\partial u_2}{\partial t} = K \cos \Omega t + \nu \frac{\partial^2 u_2}{\partial y^2} \tag{11.7.4}$$

Of course, u_2 obeys the same boundary conditions, Eq. 11.7.3. In future work we shall replace $\cos \Omega t$ by $\exp(i\Omega t)$ and take the real part of the answer to satisfy Eq. 11.7.4.

Turning our attention to finding nondimensional variables, we choose

$$T = \Omega t, \qquad Y = \frac{y}{h}$$

The proper scale for the velocity is not so obvious. Let us denote it by α and substitute $U_2 = u_2/\alpha$ into Eq. 11.7.4:

$$\frac{\Omega \alpha}{K}\frac{\partial U_2}{\partial T} = \exp(iT) + \frac{\nu \alpha}{h^2 K}\frac{\partial^2 U_2}{\partial Y^2} \tag{11.7.5}$$

There are two ways to define α so that a coefficient will disappear from Eq. 11.7.5: $\alpha = K/\Omega$ or $\alpha = h^2 K/\nu$. We choose the first form, which implies that the magnitude of the velocity depends on the amplitude and frequency of the oscillation. The problem now reads

$$\frac{\partial U_2}{\partial T} = \exp(iT) + \frac{1}{\lambda^2}\frac{\partial^2 U_2}{\partial Y^2}$$

$$U_2(Y = 1, T) = 0, \qquad \frac{\partial U_2}{\partial Y}(Y = 0, T) = 0 \tag{11.7.6}$$

where

$$U_2 = \frac{u_2}{K/\Omega}, \qquad \lambda = \frac{h}{\sqrt{\nu/\Omega}}$$

The parameter λ compares the slot height with the viscous diffusion length. We cannot eliminate λ from the problem; if we incorporated λ into a new distance variable ($\hat{Y} = \lambda Y$), we would have a differential equation free of parameters, but λ would appear explicitly in the boundary condition, for example, $U(\hat{Y} = \lambda, T) = 0$. It is usually better strategy to deal with a parameter in the equation than in the boundary condition. Furthermore, the variable Y was used in the $U_1(Y)$ solutions.

We seek a steady-state oscillatory solution to Eq. 11.7.6 by trying to find an answer in the form

$$U(Y, T) = \exp(iT)F(Y) \tag{11.7.7}$$

Substituting this into Eq. 11.7.6 produces the problem

$$iF = 1 + \lambda^{-2}F''$$
$$F(Y = 1) = 0, \qquad F'(Y = 0) = 0 \tag{11.7.8}$$

Next, the constant i is incorporated into a new dependent variable by the definition

$$\hat{F} = F + i \tag{11.7.9}$$

The problem now reads

$$\hat{F}'' = i\lambda^2\hat{F}$$
$$\hat{F}(Y = 1) = i, \qquad \hat{F}'(Y = 0) = 0 \tag{11.7.10}$$

Solutions of Eq. 11.7.10 are $\exp(\pm\lambda\sqrt{i}Y)$ or, equivalently, a linear combination of exponentials such as sinh or cosh. We find that the sinh answer will not fit the boundary conditions at $Y = 0$, so we try

$$\hat{F} = A \cosh(\pm\lambda\sqrt{i}Y) \tag{11.7.11}$$

where A is determined by the boundary condition at $Y = 1$:

$$A = \frac{i}{\cosh(\pm\lambda\sqrt{i})} \tag{11.7.12}$$

The answer is obtained by putting Eqs. 11.7.7, 11.7.11, and 11.7.12 together. When this is done, we find that the velocity is

$$U_2 = \mathscr{R}e\left(-i + i\frac{\cosh\sqrt{i}\lambda Y}{\cosh\sqrt{i}\lambda}\right)\exp(iT) \tag{11.7.13}$$

The real part, $\mathscr{R}e$, of this equation is the answer [note again that $\sqrt{i} = \pm(1 + i)/\sqrt{2}$]. We also notice that Y appears only as the combination $\hat{Y} = \lambda Y$, the very combination we chose to avoid at the beginning of the analysis.

The real part of Eq. 11.7.13 can be expressed in elementary functions; however, the algebra is lengthy. To write the answer completely, we introduce the notation

$$\Lambda \equiv \frac{\lambda}{\sqrt{2}} = \frac{h}{\sqrt{2\nu/\Omega}} \tag{11.7.14}$$

and

$$C(x) \equiv \cosh x \cos x$$

$$S(x) \equiv \sinh x \sin x$$

$$M(Y; \Lambda) \equiv C(\Lambda Y)C(\Lambda) + S(\Lambda Y)S(\Lambda) \qquad (11.7.15)$$

$$N(Y; \Lambda) \equiv C(\Lambda Y)S(\Lambda) - S(\Lambda Y)C(\Lambda)$$

$$J(\Lambda) \equiv C^2(\Lambda) + S^2(\Lambda)$$

The answer, the real part of Eq. 11.7.13, can now be written as

$$U_2 = \left[1 - \frac{M(Y; \Lambda)}{J(\Lambda)} \right] \sin T - \frac{N(Y; \Lambda) \cos T}{J(\Lambda)} \qquad (11.7.16)$$

These profiles must be superimposed on the parabolic profile U_1 from the steady flow component.

The parameter $\Lambda = h/\sqrt{2\nu/\Omega}$ compares the slot width with the viscous diffusion length. As Λ approaches zero, the viscous diffusion length becomes much larger than h. Other things being equal, we can imagine that this occurs when $\Omega \to 0$ (a low-frequency limit). Perhaps a better interpretation is to consider Λ^2 as the ratio of the time for viscous effects to diffuse across the slot $(h^2/2\nu)$ to the period of a pressure oscillation $(1/\Omega)$. Then $\Lambda^2 \to 0$ means that the viscous time is small compared to the oscillation period. In any event, the form of the velocity profile valid as $\Lambda \to 0$ is found from Eq. 11.7.16 by noting that $C(x) \sim 1$ and $S(x) \sim x^2$ as $x \to 0$. The result is

$$U_2 = -\Lambda^2(1 - Y^2) \cos T \qquad (11.7.17)$$

The same equation in dimensional variables is

$$\frac{u_2}{-Kh^2/\nu} = \frac{1}{2}\left[1 - \left(\frac{y}{h}\right)^2 \right] \cos \Omega t \qquad (11.7.18)$$

This is a quasi-steady-state result. The velocity profile is a parabola with the amplitude modified to correspond to the pressure gradient at that instant. Viscous diffusion is rapid enough to keep the profile in a quasi-steady-state. Since we know the exact answer (in Eq. 11.7.17), we are able to save the nontrivial part of the answer in the limit $\Lambda = \lambda/\sqrt{2} \Rightarrow 0$. Actually, the limit $\lim_{\Lambda \to 0} U(Y, T; \Lambda) = 0$. Recall that we had two choices for the nondimensional velocity. The second choice was $\hat{U}_2 = u_2/(h^2 K/\nu) = U_2/\lambda^2$. Thus, Eq. 11.7.17 is actually

$$\hat{U}_2 = \tfrac{1}{2}(1 - Y^2) \cos T \qquad (11.7.19)$$

From this we see that the correct answer will result if we use the nondimensional form $\hat{U}_2 (Y, T; \Lambda)$ for the limit $\Lambda \to 0$. This function is of order 1.

The opposite extreme, $\Lambda \to \infty$, means that the viscous diffusion depth is small compared to the slot width. This is the high-frequency limit. For large values of x the proper approximations to Eq. 11.7.15 are

$$C(x) \sim \tfrac{1}{2} \exp(x) \cos x$$

$$S(x) \sim \tfrac{1}{2} \exp(x) \sin x$$

(11.7.20)

With these relations and employing some trigonometric identities, one can show that Eq. 11.7.16 becomes

$$\lim_{\Lambda \to \infty} U_2(Y, T; \Lambda) = \sin T$$

(11.7.21)

This result, $U_2 = \sin T$, is valid in the core region but fails to be correct at the wall, where the no-slip boundary condition should be satisfied. It is called an *outer answer*.

Near the wall viscous effects are always important. However, in the limit $\Lambda \to \infty$ they are concentrated to a thin region. The thickness of this region is proportional to the viscous diffusion distance $\sqrt{\omega}/\Omega$. To keep variables of order 1, we need a new distance variable. First transfer the origin from the centerline to the wall using $\bar{y} = h - y$. Then form a nondimensional variable using the viscous diffusion distance as a scale:

$$\eta = \frac{\bar{y}}{\sqrt{2\nu/\Omega}} = \frac{h - y}{\sqrt{2\nu/\Omega}}$$

$$= \Lambda(1 - Y)$$

(11.7.22)

At the wall $\eta = 0$, and at the centerline $\eta = \Lambda$. To find the behavior near the wall, we substitute η for Y in Eq. 11.7.16 using Eq. 11.7.22. Then the limit $\Lambda \to \infty$ produces

$$U_2 = \sin T - \sin(T - \eta) \exp(-\eta)$$

(11.7.23)

This is called an *inner answer*.

The first term in Eq. 11.7.23 is the inviscid response to an oscillating pressure gradient. It satisfies Eq. 11.7.4 without the viscous term; that is, $\partial U / \partial T = \cos T$. As we move a few viscous lengths away from the wall, the second term drops out and the solution predicts that the flow will perform a simple oscillation, $U_2 = \sin T$, with no y dependence. The second term in Eq. 11.7.23 is the same answer that we found for Stokes's problem of an oscillating free stream over a solid wall. When the viscous length is small, the flow behaves as if the opposite wall were absent. The flow is an inviscid oscillation of the bulk of the fluid with a Stokes layer at each wall.

11.8   DECAY OF AN IDEAL LINE VORTEX (OSEEN VORTEX)

An *ideal vortex* is a flow with circular streamlines where the particle motion is irrotational. Incompressible and irrotational flows are called *ideal flows*. The velocity profile of an ideal vortex obeys the equation

$$v_\theta = \frac{\Gamma}{2\pi r}$$

(11.8.1)

Here the constant Γ is the circulation defined by integral equation 3.12.7; it indicates the strength of the vortex. As we shall see in later chapters, an irrotational flow has no net viscous forces. Thus, Eq. 11.8.1 represents an inviscid flow (see Fig. 11.7a). At the origin, Eq. 11.8.1 indicates that the velocity becomes infinite. Such behavior is prohibited be-

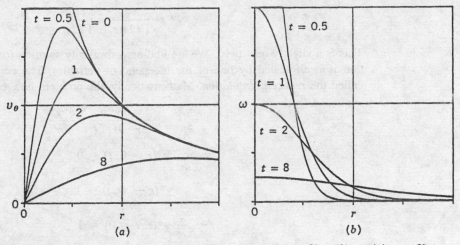

Figure 11.7   Viscous decay of an ideal vortex: (*a*) velocity profiles; (*b*) vorticity profiles at corresponding times. Scales are arbitrary.

cause continuity requires that the velocity be zero at the origin. To meet this requirement we must have a core region where the flow is rotational and viscous forces are important.

The mathematical problem that we shall solve in this section might be considered as an ideal vortex that at time zero is forced to obey the zero-velocity condition at the origin. The problem is much like the Rayleigh impulsive plate problem in that the effects of viscosity diffuse through the fluid. In the present case the streamlines are curved rather than straight as in the Rayleigh problem. Ultimately, viscous forces will destroy the vortex completely.

To begin the mathematical solution we assume that the velocity $v_\theta(r, t)$ is a function of r and t only. The continuity equation is satisfied by this assumption, and the θ-direction momentum equation simplifies to the following form:

$$\frac{\partial v_\theta}{\partial t} = -\nu \frac{1}{r^2} \frac{\partial (r v_\theta)}{\partial r} + \nu \frac{1}{r} \frac{\partial^2 (r v_\theta)}{\partial r^2} \tag{11.8.2}$$

Boundary conditions are

$$v_\theta(r = 0, t) = 0$$

$$v_\theta(r \to \infty, t) \sim \frac{\Gamma}{2\pi r} \tag{11.8.3}$$

$$v_\theta(r, t = 0) = \frac{\Gamma}{2\pi r}$$

We note that neither r nor t has a natural measuring scale in the boundary conditions. This leads us to suspect that a similarity solution might be appropriate.

Before we construct the similarity variable, let us nondimensionalize the dependent variable. The boundary conditions and differential equation will have an especially simple form if we use $1/r$ in the velocity scale:

$$\gamma^* \equiv \frac{v_\theta}{\Gamma/2\pi r} = \frac{r v_\theta}{\Gamma/2\pi} \tag{11.8.4}$$

This is a slightly new twist. We are finding a similarity solution for a dependent variable that is itself scaled by one of the independent variables. The combination $\gamma = r v_\theta$ is called the *reduced circulation*. Mathematically, the problem now consists of

$$\frac{\partial \gamma^*}{\partial t} = -\frac{\nu}{r}\frac{\partial \gamma^*}{\partial r} + \nu \frac{\partial^2 \gamma^*}{\partial r^2}$$

$$\gamma^*(r = 0, t) = 0$$

$$\gamma^*(r \to \infty, t) \sim 1 \tag{11.8.5}$$

$$\gamma^*(r, t = 0) = 1$$

At this point we have found a nondimensional dependent variable using information contained in the boundary conditions. We can find the similarity variable by using dimensional analysis (not all similarity variables may be found in this way). Assume a solution of the form $\gamma^* = \gamma^*(r, t, \nu)$. Dimensional analysis shows that two variables are required. Since one pi variable is γ^*, the other must be formed from r, t, and ν. Hence, with a little trial and error we find the similarity variable

$$\eta = \frac{r}{\sqrt{\nu t}} \tag{11.8.6}$$

The next task is to transform the problem into the variable η. Employing the notation

$$\gamma^* = f(\eta) \tag{11.8.7}$$

and applying the same mathematical procedures as in the Rayleigh problem, we find the transformed equation

$$f'' + \left(\frac{\eta}{2} - \frac{1}{\eta}\right) f' = 0 \tag{11.8.8}$$

This differential equation does not explicitly contain either r or t, so the similarity variable is valid as far as the differential equation is concerned. To be completely successful, the boundary conditions must also transform, and at the same time they must reduce from three to two in number. The boundary conditions in Eq. 11.8.5 transform into

$$\gamma^*(r = 0, t) = f(\eta = 0) = 0$$

$$\gamma^*(r \to \infty, t) = f(\eta \to \infty) \sim 1 \tag{11.8.9}$$

$$\gamma^*(r, t = 0) = f(\eta \to \infty) = 1$$

The equations constitute only two distinct boundary conditions, so Eqs. 11.8.8 and 11.8.9 form a compatible problem.

Straightforward integration of Eq. 11.8.8 gives the reduced circulation as

$$\gamma^* = f(\eta) = 1 - \exp\left(-\frac{\eta^2}{4}\right) \qquad (11.8.10)$$

Returning to dimensional variables, we find the velocity profile corresponding to this equation is

$$v_\theta = \frac{\Gamma}{2\pi r}\left(1 - \exp\left(-\frac{r^2}{4\nu t}\right)\right] \qquad (11.8.11)$$

or, in a slightly different form,

$$v_\theta = \frac{\Gamma}{2\pi\sqrt{\nu t}}\frac{1}{\eta}\left[1 - \exp\left(-\frac{\eta^2}{4}\right)\right] \qquad (11.8.12)$$

This solution is called an *Oseen vortex* (it is also called a *Lamb vortex*). Typical velocity profiles are plotted in Fig. 11.7 and (in similarity variables) in Fig. 11.8. Notice that v_θ is not a function of the similarity variable η, but either v_θ/r^{-1} or $v_\theta/t^{-1/2}$ is a function of η only.

The Oseen vortex profile is one member of a family of vortex profiles that satisfy the Navier–Stokes equations. For example, another profile discovered by G. I. Taylor is given by

$$v_\theta = \frac{H}{8\pi}\frac{r}{\nu t^2}\exp\left(-\frac{r^2}{4\nu t}\right)$$

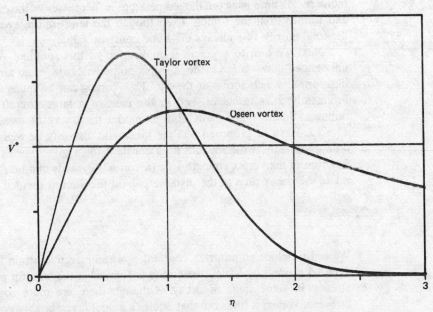

Figure 11.8   Profiles for Oseen and Taylor vortices in similarity variables. For the Oseen vortex, $V^* \propto v_\theta/t^{-1/2}$, while for the Taylor vortex, $V^* \propto v_\theta/t^{-3/2}$. In each case $\eta = r/\sqrt{\nu t}$.

The constant H in this relation is physically the amount of angular momentum in the vortex (the Oseen vortex contains an infinite amount of angular momentum). The similarity form of Taylor's vortex is also shown in Fig. 11.8.

The vorticity in the Oseen vortex is found from the relation

$$\omega_z = \frac{1}{r} \frac{\partial}{\partial r} (rv_\theta) = \frac{\Gamma}{4\pi\nu t} \exp\left(-\frac{\eta^2}{4}\right) \tag{11.8.13}$$

Sketches of the vorticity profiles at various times are shown in Fig. 11.7b. At any instant the distribution is a Gaussian bell curve. Where the vorticity is nonzero the flow is viscous, and where the vorticity is zero the flow remains like the original ideal vortex. The height of the curve falls off as t^{-1}, and the width increases by viscous diffusion as $(\nu t)^{1/2}$. The total vorticity in the flow may be computed either directly from Eq. 11.8.13 or by applying Stokes's theorem. The result shows that the total vorticity is a constant and equal to the circulation:

$$\int_0^\infty \omega_z 2\pi r \, dr = \Gamma \tag{11.8.14}$$

Equation 11.8.14 is an example of the interpretation of vorticity as the local circulation per unit area.

In terms of vorticity, this solution is analogous to a heat-conduction problem where a finite amount of energy Γ is concentrated in a line source at time zero. Subsequently, the heat is conducted radially away from the line. This causes the temperature ω_z to increase. As time goes on, the temperature ω_z decreases as the energy is dispersed farther and farther from the source. Even though the temperature eventually approaches zero, the total energy Γ is always the same constant value.

Next we turn to a practical application of this solution. Any lifting surface in an unbounded flow—a fan blade, a ship's propeller blade, or an airplane wing—has a trailing vortex, which forms at the tip. This vortex can be quite strong and concentrated. Frequently, it is turbulent, and in the case of a large aircraft it may last for several minutes. Squire (1965) was able to model the decay of these vortices by using Eq. 11.8.12. First, he proposed that the kinematic viscosity be replaced by an effective turbulent viscosity, which would be a constant for a given vortex but would change as a function of the vortex strength Γ/ν (a vortex Reynolds number). Second, he proposed to relate the decay time to the distance behind the aircraft divided by the aircraft speed:

$$t \to \frac{z - z_0}{V_\infty} \tag{11.8.15}$$

We must include an arbitrary constant z_0 as an effective origin for the ideal vortex. The detailed process by which the vortex is formed at the wingtip produces a vortex that is already in some stage of decay. Although there are more sophisticated models of a turbulent vortex, it turns out that Squire's model is reasonably good. The predicted decay of the maximum velocity ($\sim z^{-1/2}$) and growth of the core ($\sim z^{1/2}$) are fairly accurate when the proper effective origin z_0 is used in the model.

11.9   PLANE STAGNATION-POINT FLOW (HIEMENZ FLOW)

The next flow we discuss is a local flow solution—one that is good in only a small part of the entire flow field. Consider a two-dimensional body in an infinite stream as shown in Fig. 11.9a. In subsequent chapters we show that the flow in the neighborhood of the stagnation point has the same character irrespective of the shape of the body (as long as the flow is two-dimensional). A high Reynolds number is necessary for this to be true. The neighborhood where this solution is valid may not be very large, but it is nevertheless a finite size. You might imagine that you are at the stagnation point and begin shrinking in size. Soon the surface, as far as you are concerned, becomes flat. You cannot see the details of the flow as it approaches or what happens after it turns and goes away; however, in a small neighborhood near your vantage point, the flow is much like Fig. 11.9b.

To analyze the problem, we assume a flat wall with a two-dimensional flow $u(x, y)$, $v(x, y)$, which obeys the Navier–Stokes equations and the no-slip boundary conditions,

$$u(x, y = 0) = 0, \qquad v(x, y = 0) = 0 \tag{11.9.1}$$

Far away from the wall, the flow approaches as if it is slowing down linearly, that is,

$$v(x, y \rightarrow \infty) = -ay + b = -a\left(y - \frac{b}{a}\right) \tag{11.9.2}$$

Also far away from the wall and as we go along the wall in x, the external flow is accelerating as

$$u_e \equiv u(x, y \rightarrow \infty) = ax \tag{11.9.3}$$

The reason these boundary conditions are appropriate is not obvious. Equations 11.9.2 and 11.93 are actually the solution for an inviscid flow near a stagnation point (the

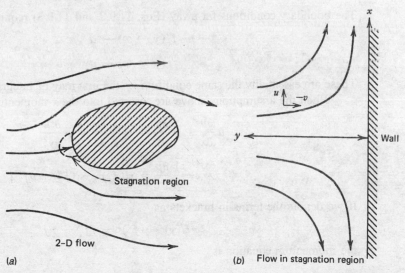

Figure 11.9   Local solution for stagnation-point flow (2-D = two-dimensional).

solution used in the example in Chapter 4). The only effect that viscosity has in the inviscid far field is to shift the apparent location of the wall by the amount b/a as shown by Eq. 11.9.2. The constant a in these equations is proportional to the free-stream velocity far away from the body divided by a characteristic dimension of the body:

$$a = \frac{\alpha U_\infty}{L} \tag{11.9.4}$$

The constant of proportionality α depends on the exact shape of the body.

It will turn out that the separation-of-variables assumption

$$u = xf'(y) \tag{11.9.5}$$

gives the proper form for the answer. The reason that the derivative of f is used in Eq. 11.9.5 instead of the completely equivalent form $u = xF(y)$ is that the continuity equation

$$\frac{\partial u}{\partial x} + \frac{\partial v}{\partial y} = 0 \tag{11.9.6}$$

$$f'(y) + \frac{\partial v}{\partial y} = 0$$

integrates to

$$v = -f(y) + C(x)$$

Since $v(x, 0) = 0$, the function of integration $C(x)$ turns out to be zero, and

$$v = -f(y) \tag{11.9.7}$$

Hence, Eqs. 11.9.5 and 11.9.7 will satisfy the continuity equation, and the two unknowns u and v are replaced by one unknown, $f(y)$. The no-slip condition is satisfied if

$$f'(y = 0) = 0 \quad \text{and} \quad f(y = 0) = 0 \tag{11.9.8}$$

The boundary conditions far away (Eqs. 11.9.2 and 11.9.3) require that

$$f'(y \to \infty) \to a \tag{11.9.9}$$

$$f(y \to \infty) \to ay - b$$

These are essentially the same condition, as the first may be integrated to give the second.

When the assumptions above are inserted into the x-momentum equation, we obtain

$$u\frac{\partial u}{\partial x} + v\frac{\partial u}{\partial y} = -\frac{1}{\rho}\frac{\partial p}{\partial x} + \nu\frac{\partial^2 u}{\partial y^2}$$

$$-\frac{1}{\rho}\frac{\partial p}{\partial x} = x[(f')^2 - ff'' - \nu f''']$$

If we denote the terms in brackets as

$$-H(y) \equiv (f')^2 - ff'' - \nu f''' \tag{11.9.10}$$

the momentum equation is

$$-\frac{1}{\rho}\frac{\partial p}{\partial x} = -xH(y)$$

Partial integration yields

$$\frac{1}{\rho} p = \frac{1}{2} x^2 H(y) + K(y) \tag{11.9.11}$$

The function $K(y)$ is the pressure along the stagnation streamline at $x = 0$. In anticipation of the y-momentum equation, we compute the derivative

$$-\frac{1}{\rho}\frac{\partial p}{\partial y} = -\frac{1}{2} x^2 H' - K'$$

Putting this, together with our previous assumptions, into the y-momentum equation yields

$$v\frac{\partial v}{\partial y} = -\frac{1}{\rho}\frac{\partial p}{\partial y} + v\frac{\partial^2 v}{\partial y^2} \tag{11.9.12}$$

$$ff' = -\tfrac{1}{2} x^2 H' - K' - vf''$$

This equation cannot be true for arbitrary x and y unless $H' = 0$. Hence, H is constant, and Eq. 11.9.10 is the differential equation that governs the problem. When Eq. 11.9.10 is evaluated as $y \to \infty$ with the assumption that $f''(\infty)$ and $f'''(\infty)$ are zero (a requirement that the flow smoothly approach the free-stream conditions), we find that

$$-H = a^2$$

The complete problem for $f(y)$ now reads

$$(f')^2 - ff'' - vf''' = a^2$$
$$f(0) = 0 \tag{11.9.13}$$
$$f'(0) = 0$$
$$f'(\infty) = a$$

We have waited until the last possible moment before nondimensionalizing. Since a has dimensions $1/T$, and v has dimensions L^2/T, a length scale is $\sqrt{v/a}$ and a velocity scale is $\sqrt{va}$ (for the v velocity; the u-velocity scale is ax in view of Eq. 11.9.3). Therefore, it is appropriate to define new variables as follows:

$$\eta = \frac{y}{\sqrt{v/a}}, \qquad F = \frac{f}{\sqrt{va}} = \frac{-v}{\sqrt{va}}, \qquad F' = \frac{f'}{a} = \frac{u}{ax} = \frac{u}{u_e} \tag{11.9.14}$$

When this choice of variables is substituted into Eq. 11.9.13, we obtain

$$(F')^2 - FF'' - F''' = 1$$
$$F(0) = 0 \tag{11.9.15}$$
$$F'(0) = 0$$
$$F'(\infty) = 1$$

The problem is now free of all parameters and therefore can be solved once and the solution used for all stagnation points. That is, the same solution may be applied for all different bodies and flow velocities as characterized by $a = \alpha U_\infty/L$ and for all different fluid viscosities as characterized by v.

The mathematical problem given as Eq. 11.9.15 is a third-order nonlinear ordinary differential equation. It does not have a closed-form solution. The boundary conditions are applied at two different points, $\eta = 0$ and $\eta \to \infty$. For this reason it is called a *two-point boundary value problem*.

One purpose of this section is to learn how problems of this type are solved using a standard computer program, which solves a system of coupled first-order differential equations. The first step in arranging the problem for the computer is to convert the third-order differential equation into three first-order differential equations. Consider the new dependent variables defined by

$$Y_1 = F, \qquad Y_2 = F', \qquad Y_3 \equiv F'' \tag{11.9.16}$$

The original differential equation 11.9.15 now becomes

$$Y_3' = Y_2^2 - Y_3 Y_1 - 1 \tag{11.9.17}$$

and from the definitions above, two other equations are

$$Y_2' = Y_3$$

$$Y_1' = Y_2$$

Thus, the third-order equation is replaced by the three ordinary equations given above. In general, this method can be used to replace an nth-order ordinary differential equation by n first-order differential equations of the form

$$Y_i' = f_i(x, Y_1, Y_2, \ldots, Y_n), \qquad i = 1, 2, \ldots, n$$

The functions f_i in this equation are unrestricted.

Boundary data for the computer equation must be given at an "initial" location (let $\eta = x$ be the computer independent variable). From Eq. 11.9.15 we find that our boundary conditions are

$$Y_1(0) = 0, \qquad Y_2(0) = 0, \qquad Y_2(\infty) = 1 \tag{11.9.18}$$

We have no known condition for $Y_3(0)$; instead, there is a known value for $Y_2(\infty)$. The most popular way around this difficulty is to assume a value for $Y_3(0)$, solve the problem, then compare the result for $Y_2(\infty)$ with that required by the original boundary condition. This is called a *shooting method* and is sometimes automated so that the computer makes a new guess for $Y_3(0)$ based on the last error in $Y_2(\infty)$.

A second question arises because the integration should extend over the infinite domain $X[0, \infty]$. We must pick a finite value of X and call it $X = \infty$. In general, this value depends on the answer, and we must either do an asymptotic analysis as $X \to \infty$ or watch the solution and make sure the answer has stabilized at the chosen "$X = \infty$" point.

Graphs of the results for u and v velocity profiles are given in Fig. 11.10. The v velocity is a function of y only, and the slope dv/dy is zero at the wall. (The latter fact is a general result; the velocity component normal to a wall and its derivatives are zero at a solid wall for any flow.) Far away from the wall, the v velocity increases linearly as required by Eq. 11.9.2. From the solution one can evaluate the constant b/a in Eq. 11.9.2. In nondimensional form Eq. 11.9.2 is

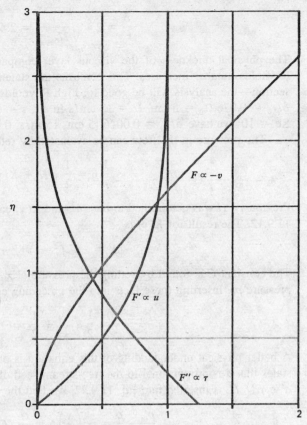

Figure 11.10   Hiemenz stagnation profile.

$$\lim_{\eta \to \infty} (\eta - F) = \frac{b/a}{\sqrt{\nu/a}} = 0.648 \qquad (11.9.19)$$

This equation is the effective displacement of the wall, b/a, in nondimensional form.

The horizontal velocity profile has the same shape at each location in x, while the magnitude of the profile increases in proportion to x; $u = axF' = u_e F'$. The distance from the wall at which u is 99% of the free-stream value is a constant; $u/u_e \gtrsim 0.99$ when $\eta \geq 2.4$. Denote this thickness by δ:

$$\frac{\delta}{\sqrt{\nu/a}} = \eta_{99} = 2.40$$

$$\delta = 2.40\sqrt{\nu/a} \qquad (11.9.20)$$

The shear stress and vorticity are confined within this region, which has a thickness proportional to $\sqrt{\nu}$.

As a concrete example let us consider the stagnation region on a circular cylinder. For a body of this shape, it is known from inviscid flow theory that the constant $a = 2U/r_0$, where U is the free-stream speed and r_0 the cylinder radius. Hence, the thickness of the stagnation region is

$$\frac{\delta}{r_0} = 2.4 \sqrt{\frac{\nu}{2U_\infty r_0}} = 2.4 \text{Re}^{-1.2} \tag{11.9.21}$$

The physical thickness of the viscous layer compared to the radius decreases as the Reynolds number increases. This confirms the statement made at the beginning of this section—the analysis will be good for high Reynolds numbers. For $\text{Re} = 1000$ we have $\delta/r_0 = 0.076$ ($r_0 = 5$ cm, $U = 15$ cm/s in air, $\nu = 0.15$ cm^2/s, $\delta = 0.38$ cm), and for $\text{Re} = 10^5$ we have $\delta/r_0 = 0.0076$ (5 cm, 15 m/s, 0.038 cm).

The pressure in the flow can be evaluated by returning to Eq. 11.9.11:

$$\frac{1}{\rho} p = \frac{1}{2} x^2 H + K(y)$$

Previously, H was determined to be $-a^2$, and $K(y)$ can be determined by integrating Eq. 11.9.12. The result for $K(y)$ is

$$K = -\tfrac{1}{2} f^2 - \nu f' + C$$

The constant C is found by setting the pressure at $x = 0$, $y = 0$ equal to the stagnation pressure p_0. Inserting these facts into the preceding equation gives

$$\frac{p_0 - p}{\rho} = \frac{1}{2} a^2 x^2 + \frac{1}{2} \nu a F^2 + \nu a F' \tag{11.9.22}$$

A better physical understanding of this equation is obtained if we recall that Eq. 11.9.4 states that a is proportional to the free-stream seed divided by a body dimension. When $a = \alpha U_\infty / L$ is inserted into Eq. 11.9.22, we find the nondimensional pressure as

$$\frac{p_0 - p}{\tfrac{1}{2} \rho U_\infty^2} = \alpha^2 \left(\frac{x}{L}\right)^2 + \frac{\alpha}{\text{Re}} (F^2 + 2F') \tag{11.9.23}$$

where

$$\text{Re} = \frac{U_\infty L}{\nu}$$

As long as we are close to the surface, F and F' are of order 1; hence, in this region the second term becomes negligible as the Reynolds number becomes large (the condition for the analysis to apply). This means that the pressure near the wall is nearly constant across the viscous-dominated region. Equation 11.9.23 is essentially the Bernoulli equation in the free stream, since Eqs. 11.9.3 and 11.9.4 show that $\alpha x/L = u(x, y \to \infty)/U_\infty$. The fact that the pressure is constant *across* the viscous layer is a general result, which we shall find is valid for all boundary layers.

This problem was first analyzed by Hiemenz (1911), and improved calculations have been done by many people over the course of years. A similar problem for the stagnation point on an axisymmetric blunt body can also be solved exactly (Homann, 1936). Howarth (1951) solved the general two-dimensional stagnation-point problem where flow comes toward the point in the y-direction and leaves in the x- and z-directions according to $u(x, y \to \infty, z) = a_1 x$ and $w(x, y \to \infty, z) = a_2 z$. These problems are taken up in Chapter 20.

11.10   BURGERS VORTEX

The viscous line vortex of Section 11.8 spreads out by viscous diffusion as time proceeds. This spreading can be counteracted and a steady flow obtained if we supply a radial inflow toward the center. Consider a steady swirling vortex $v_\theta(r)$ with its axis along the z-direction. To this flow we add a symmetric radial inflow (a is a strength constant):

$$v_r = -ar \tag{11.10.1}$$

Because v_r becomes unbounded as $r \to \infty$, we must consider this valid only as a local solution.

The flow toward the vortex must escape along the z-axis. To find the outflow, solve the continuity equation for $\partial v_z / \partial z$:

$$\frac{\partial v_z}{\partial z} = -\frac{1}{r}\frac{\partial(rv_r)}{\partial r} = -\frac{1}{r}\frac{\partial(ar^2)}{\partial r} = 2a$$

Integrating yields

$$v_z = 2az \tag{11.10.2}$$

The velocities $v_r = -ar$ and $v_z = 2az$ constitute an axisymmetric inviscid flow toward a stagnation point at the origin. The strain rates for this flow are $S_{rr} = S_{\theta\theta} = -a$ and $S_{zz} = 2a$. One can picture stretching the vortex along its axis at a rate given by the constant a, as depicted in Fig. 11.11.

Next, we simplify the θ-direction momentum equation (Appendix C) assuming $v_\theta(r$ only) and insert $v_r = -ar$:

$$-ar\frac{dv_\theta}{dr} - av_\theta = \nu\frac{d}{dr}\left[\frac{1}{r}\frac{d}{dr}(rv_\theta)\right] \tag{11.10.3}$$

The boundary conditions require no-slip at the origin and assume that the vortex behaves as an ideal vortex as $r \to \infty$:

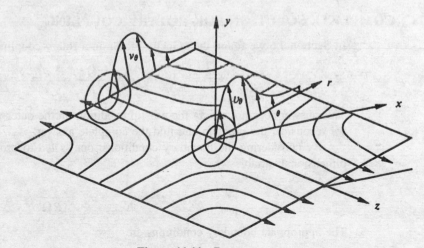

Figure 11.11   Burgers vortex.

$$v_\theta(0) = 0, \qquad v_\theta(r \to \infty) = \frac{\Gamma}{2\pi r} \tag{11.10.4}$$

Since the left side of Eq. 11.10.3 equals $-a\, d(rv_\theta)/dr$, we can introduce the reduced circulation as the dependent variable

$$\gamma^* \equiv f = \frac{2\pi r v_\theta}{\Gamma} \tag{11.10.5}$$

In terms of the reduced circulation, Eq. 11.10.3 becomes

$$-a\frac{df}{dr} = \nu\frac{d}{dr}\left(\frac{1}{r}\frac{df}{dr}\right) \tag{11.10.6}$$

Finally, the nondimensional radial variable $\eta \equiv r/\sqrt{\nu/2a}$ changes Eq. 11.10.6 into exactly the same form as Eq. 11.8.8 but with a different definition of η:

$$f'' + \left(\frac{1}{2}\eta - \frac{1}{\eta}\right)f' = 0 \tag{11.10.7}$$

Thus the solution is the same form as Eq. 11.8.10:

$$f = 1 - \exp\left(-\frac{\eta^2}{4}\right)$$

$$v_\theta = \frac{\Gamma}{2\pi r}\left[1 - \exp\left(-\frac{r^2}{2\nu/a}\right)\right] \tag{11.10.8}$$

The vorticity in the core of the vortex tries to diffuse outward but is restrained by the radial inflow $v_r = -ar$ to establish a steady state.

　　Another interesting vortex with axial flow in both directions is called a *Sullivan* (1959) *vortex* (see Problem 13.15). A strained spiral vortex is given by Lundgren (1982).

11.11　COMPLETE SOLUTION FOR ROTARY COUPLING

In Section 7.6 we found the velocity profile in a rotary coupling as

$$v_\theta = \frac{r\Omega z}{h} \tag{7.6.3}$$

This answer does not satisfy the no-slip condition on the outer wall, $v_\theta(R, z) = 0$. Here, we reconsider the problem and find the complete answer.

　　By considering the boundary conditions, one is led to propose the following nondimensional variables:

$$r^* = \frac{r}{R}, \qquad z^* = \frac{z}{h}, \qquad v_\theta^* = \frac{v_\theta}{R\Omega}, \qquad \varepsilon = \frac{h}{R} \tag{11.11.1}$$

The appropriate boundary conditions are

$$v_\theta^*(r^*, z^* = 0) = 0, \qquad v_\theta^*(r^*, z^* = 1) = r^*, \qquad v_\theta^*(r^* = 1, z^*) = 0 \quad (11.11.2)$$

Assuming that $v_\theta^*(r^*, z^*)$, nondimensional momentum equation 7.6.2 is

$$0 = \varepsilon^2 \frac{\partial}{\partial r^*} \left[\frac{1}{r^*} \frac{\partial}{\partial r^*} (r^* v_\theta^*) \right] + \frac{\partial^2 v_\theta^*}{\partial z^{*2}} \qquad (11.11.3)$$

Now we can see that the formal limit $\varepsilon \rightarrow 0$ leaves only the second term in Eq. 11.11.3, for which we previously found the solution

$$v_{\theta\,\text{outer}}^* = r^* z^* \qquad (11.11.4)$$

This is called the *outer solution*. At the sidewall, Eq. 11.11.4 gives $v_\theta^*(r^* = 1, z^*) = 1$ instead of the no-slip condition $v_\theta^*(r^* = 1, z^*) = 0$. Along the line $r^* = 1$, the solution is singular. We will now find the correct answer in this neighborhood.

To develop an *inner problem* (actually, a problem for flow near the sidewall), introduce a new radial coordinate so that the origin is at the wall where the answer is wrong:

$$y \equiv R - r \qquad (11.11.5)$$

Next, we must choose a scale for y. One expects that the size of the region where the sidewall influences the flow depends on h, not R; thus we use h as the scale:

$$\tilde{y} \equiv \frac{y}{h} = \frac{1 - r^*}{\varepsilon} \qquad (11.11.6)$$

Substituting our newly rescaled variable, $r^* = 1 - \varepsilon\tilde{y}$, into Eq. 11.11.3 and transforming the variable with $dr^*/d\tilde{y} = -\varepsilon$ yields

$$0 = \frac{\partial}{\partial \tilde{y}} \left\{ \frac{1}{(1 - \varepsilon\tilde{y})} \frac{\partial}{\partial \tilde{y}} [(1 - \varepsilon\tilde{y}) v_\theta^*] \right\} + \frac{\partial^2 v_\theta^*}{\partial z^{*2}} \qquad (11.11.7)$$

For small values of ε the equation for the flow near the sidewall is [using the same symbol for the functions $v_\theta^*(r^*, z^*)$ and $v_\theta^*(\tilde{y}, z^*)$]

$$0 = \frac{\partial^2 v_\theta^*}{\partial \tilde{y}^2} + \frac{\partial^2 v_\theta^*}{\partial z^{*2}} \qquad (11.11.8)$$

In the new variables the boundary conditions in the limit $\varepsilon \rightarrow 0$ ($\tilde{y}, z^*$ *fixed*) are

$$v_\theta^*(\tilde{y}, z^* = 0) = 0, \qquad v_\theta^*(\tilde{y}, z^* = 1) = 1 - \varepsilon\tilde{y} = 1, \qquad v_\theta^*(\tilde{y} = 0, z^*) = 0$$

$$(11.11.9)$$

The solution to Eqs. 11.11.8 and 11.11.9 is called the *inner solution*. Because the Laplace equation requires boundary conditions on a closed domain, the conditions 11.11.9 are not enough. We have no condition on $v_\theta^*(\tilde{y} \rightarrow \infty, z^*)$.

The missing boundary condition is supplied by a process called *matching*. In this problem one requires the answer $v_{\theta\,\text{outer}}^*(r^*, z^*)$ as $r^* \rightarrow 1$ to match the inner answer $v_\theta^*(\tilde{y}, z^*)$ as $\tilde{y} \rightarrow \infty$. Matching supplies the missing boundary condition. The matching condition is

$$v^*_{\theta \text{inner}}(\tilde{y} \to \infty, z^*) = v^*_{\theta \text{outer}}(r^* = 1, z^*) \tag{11.11.10}$$

Since we know the outer answer, $v^*_\theta = r^* z^*$, we can complete the boundary condition.

$$v^*_{\theta \text{inner}}(\tilde{y} \to \infty, z^*) = z^* \tag{11.11.11}$$

The *common part* is the part of the functions that match, that is $v^*_{\theta \text{ common part}} = z^*$.

The separation of variables technique applied to Eq. 11.11.8 produces the solution

$$v^*_{\theta \text{inner}}(\tilde{y}, z^*) = z^* - \frac{2}{\pi} \sum_n \frac{(-1)^{n+1}}{n} \exp(-n\pi\tilde{y}) \sin(n\pi z^*) \tag{11.11.12}$$

This answer is valid only in the neighborhood of the sidewall. It satisfies the sidewall boundary condition and merges smoothly into the previous outer solution as $r^* \to 1$. Neither the inner nor the outer solution is uniformly valid.

We can obtain a uniformly valid answer by constructing a *composite expansion*. Consider adding the two solutions together and subtracting the common part:

$$v^*_{\theta \text{composite}} = v^*_{\theta \text{inner}}(\tilde{y}, z^*) + v^*_{\theta \text{outer}}(r^*, z^*) - v^*_{\theta \text{common part}}(z^*) \tag{11.11.13}$$

with $\tilde{y} = (1 - r^*)/\varepsilon$. For positions near the sidewall the last two terms cancel and the first term is the correct answer. For positions in the outer region the first and last terms cancel and the middle term is the correct answer. In the overlap region all three terms equal the common part, which again is the correct answer. Substituting Eqs. 11.11.4, 11.11.10, and 11.11.12 into Eq. 11.11.13 yields

$$v^*_{\theta \text{composite}} = r^* z^* - \frac{2}{\pi} \sum_n \frac{(-1)^{n+1}}{n} \exp\left[-\frac{n\pi(1 - r^*)}{\varepsilon}\right] \sin n\pi z^* \tag{11.11.14}$$

This answer contains the parameter $\varepsilon = h/R$, which does not appear in either the inner or outer solution. It is a uniformly valid answer.

The rotary viscous coupling exemplifies a *singular perturbation* problem. For the special case of a thin gap ($\varepsilon \Rightarrow 0$), we have two answers. One answer is good away from the sidewall, and the other is good near the sidewall. These are called *matched asymptotic expansions* of the true answer. The true answer may be approximated by a composite expansion, in which the mixing of the two previous answers changes with the parameter ε.

11.12 VON KÁRMÁN VISCOUS PUMP

This problem concerns a very large flat disk rotated at speed Ω in a semi-infinite fluid as shown in Fig. 11.12a. Attention is focused on the flow on one side of the disk in the local region near the axis of rotation. At the surface of the disk, the no-slip condition requires that the fluid rotate with the same velocity as the disk. Viscous effects diffuse away from the disk and induce a rotation in nearby fluid in the same manner as Rayleigh's impulsive plate. However, there is no pressure gradient in the radial direction to balance the centrifugal force. Once particles have been accelerated by the plate, they are also flung out in a radial flow. Continuity demands that we replace the outward-moving fluid. This is accomplished by an axial flow toward the disk from the quiescent fluid far from

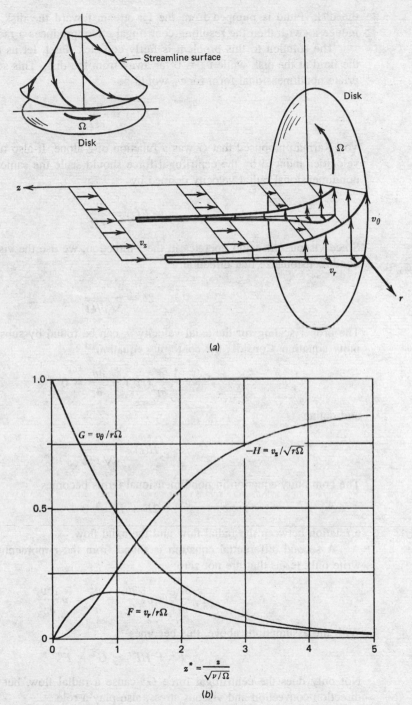

Figure 11.12   Von Kármán viscous pump: (a) physical setup; (b) velocity profiles.

the disk. Fluid is pumped from the far stream toward the disk, where viscous forces induce a swirl; then the resulting centrifugal effect produces a radial flow.

The solution to this problem is fairly complex. First, let us note that $v_\theta = r\Omega$ for the fluid at the disk while $v_\theta = 0$ far away from the disk. This suggests that the appropriate nondimensional form for v_θ would be

$$G(z) \equiv \frac{v_\theta}{r\Omega} \tag{11.12.1}$$

Von Kármán proposed that G was a function of z alone. It also turns out that the radial velocities induced by the centrifugal force should scale the same way. We let F be the nondimensional radial velocity defined by

$$F(z) \equiv \frac{v_r}{r\Omega} \tag{11.12.2}$$

Since viscous diffusion operates in the z-direction, we use the viscous length $\sqrt{\nu/\Omega}$ to nondimensionalize that direction:

$$z^* \equiv \frac{z}{\sqrt{\nu/\Omega}} \tag{11.12.3}$$

The proper scaling for the axial velocity v_z can be found by substituting into the continuity equation. Consider the continuity equation

$$\frac{1}{r}\frac{\partial}{\partial r}(r v_r) + \frac{\partial v_z}{\partial z} = 0$$

and define

$$H(z) \equiv \frac{v_z}{\sqrt{\nu\Omega}} \tag{11.12.4}$$

The continuity equation in nondimensional terms becomes

$$2F + H' = 0 \tag{11.12.5}$$

a relation between the radial flow and the axial flow.

A second differential equation is found from the r-momentum equation. Here we write only terms that are not zero:

$$v_r \frac{\partial v_r}{\partial r} + v_z \frac{\partial v_r}{\partial z} - \frac{v_\theta^2}{r} = \nu \frac{\partial^2 v_r}{\partial z^2}$$

With the assumptions above, this becomes

$$F^2 + HF' - G^2 = F'' \tag{11.12.6}$$

Not only does the centrifugal force G^2 cause a radial flow, but two minor effects, z-direction convection and viscous stress, also play a role.

The θ-momentum equation is similarly complicated. It is

$$v_r \frac{\partial v_\theta}{\partial r} + v_z \frac{\partial v_\theta}{\partial z} + \frac{v_r v_\theta}{r} = \nu \frac{\partial^2 v_\theta}{\partial z^2}$$

Transforming to nondimensional variables gives

$$FG + HG' + FG = G'' \tag{11.12.7}$$

The major effect in this equation is the convection HG' competing with the viscous diffusion G''.

After defining the nondimensional pressure,

$$P(z) \equiv \frac{p}{\rho \Omega \nu}$$

the last equation is obtained from the z-momentum equation. It is

$$v_z \frac{\partial v_z}{\partial z} = -\frac{1}{\rho} \frac{\partial p}{\partial z} + \nu \frac{\partial^2 v_z}{\partial z^2}$$

$$-HH' = -P' + H''$$

A better form is obtained if we eliminate H'' by using the continuity equation:

$$2HF - 2F' = P' \tag{11.12.8}$$

We now have three coupled ordinary differential equations, 11.12.5 to 11.12.7, for the unknowns F, G, and H, while, in principle, P need not be determined from Eq. 11.12.8 until the first three equations are solved.

Boundary conditions are imposed as follows:

At $z^* = 0$:
$$v_\theta = r\omega, \qquad G(0) = 1$$
$$v_r = 0, \qquad F(0) = 0$$
$$v_z = 0, \qquad H(0) = 0 \tag{11.12.9a}$$
$$p = 0, \qquad P(0) = 0$$

At $z^* \to \infty$:
$$v_r = 0, \qquad F(\infty) = 0$$
$$v_\theta = 0, \qquad G(\infty) = 0 \tag{11.12.9b}$$

This is another two-point boundary value problem and may be solved by computer computations. When Eqs. 11.12.5 to 11.12.8 are written as six first-order differential equations, we gain F' and G' as additional variables. Initial guesses $F'(0)$ and $G'(0)$ replace the boundary conditions at $z \to \infty$. Rogers and Lance (1960) found that the initial condition $F'(0) = 0.510233$ and $G'(0) = -0.514922$ give solutions that closely satisfy Eq. 11.12.9.

Graphs of the solutions are given in Fig. 11.12b. The swirling flow near the plate is confined to the region out to about $z^* = 5.5$. Once again we denote the thickness of the viscous region as δ. By using Eq. 11.12.3, we find that

$$\delta = 5.5 \sqrt{\frac{\nu}{\Omega}}$$

which might be interpreted as the characteristic length for the viscous diffusion that occurs in one revolution of the disk. The main counteracting effect is the flow of fluid toward the plate. From the solution we find that $H(\infty) = 0.886$; thus the disk produces a volume flow per unit area of

$$v_z(\infty) = 0.886\sqrt{\nu\Omega}$$

The more viscous fluid display a better pumping effect. The average distance the flow moves in the z-direction in one revolution is proportional to

$$L = \frac{v_z}{\Omega} \sim \frac{\sqrt{\nu\Omega}}{\Omega} \sim \sqrt{\frac{\nu}{\Omega}}$$

Because the flow balances viscous diffusion and convection, this length and δ have the same parametric dependence.

To get a feeling for the size of this effect, let us assume that a disk is spinning in air ($\nu = 0.15$ cm^2/s) at 1200 rpm (125 rad/s). The axial flow will be at a velocity

$$v_z(\infty) = 0.886\sqrt{0.15 \times 125} = 3.85 \text{ cm/s}$$

and the viscous region will be

$$\delta = 5.5\sqrt{\frac{0.15}{125}} = 0.19 \text{ cm}$$

At higher speed, the thickness δ becomes even smaller, while the axial flow velocity increases.

The radial flow occurs because there is no pressure gradient in the r-direction to force the particles into circular motion. An interesting variation of the problem is where the flow at infinity rotates as a solid body and the disk is stationary. This is like a vortex core interacting with a solid wall. In this case there must be a radial pressure gradient at infinity to maintain the solid-body-like rotation. Viscous forces near the wall slow the fluid down and destroy the balance between the pressure gradient and the centrifugal inertia force. In this region the pressure gradient accelerates the flow inward toward the center. Continuity then produces an outward flow along the z-axis. This flow is known as the *Bödewadt* (1940) *problem*. The solution has some of the characteristics of a tornado intersecting with the ground; however, tornadolike solutions in general can be very much more complicated.

Both of these problems are special cases of the general situation where the fluid at infinity and the disk may be assigned different rotation speeds. Another set of problems involves disks set finite distances apart.

11.13 CONCLUSIONS

Viscous diffusion has been the major theme of this chapter. Shear stresses generated at a wall take some time to diffuse into the interior. The important physical property of the controlling viscous diffusion is the kinematic viscosity $\nu(\text{L}^2/\text{T})$. The depth of penetration of viscous diffusion in a time t is given by $\sqrt{\nu t}$.

Pressure forces, on the other hand, are transmitted instantaneously in an incompressible flow because the effective speed of sound is infinite. For example, consider the problem where the fluid oscillates back and forth above a fixed wall. The pressure gradient along the wall is established instantaneously by some external agent. Viscous effects diffusing from the wall have a much slower time scale. We found an unexpected overshoot in the velocity profile because the pressure and viscous forces could combine at a certain distance from the wall. The disparity in time scales for transmitting pressure forces (instantaneous) and for transmitting viscous forces (diffusive) is responsible for many striking phenomena in fluid mechanics. We shall see these mechanisms again in later chapters.

The rotary viscous coupling problem illustrates an approximate solution to a singular perturbation problem. Perturbation methods, discussed more fully in Chapter 15, are applied not only to specific problems but also to theories of special classes of problems, for example, thin airfoil theory, low Reynolds number theory, and boundary layer theory.

PROBLEMS

11.1 (B) The cross section of a tube is an equilateral triangle with sides of length ℓ and a horizontal base. Flow in the tube is produced by an imposed pressure gradient dp/dz. Check that the velocity profile is given by

$$w(x, y) = \frac{1}{2\sqrt{3}\,\mu\ell}\left(-\frac{dp}{dz}\right)\left(y - \frac{\sqrt{3}}{2}\,\ell\right)(3x^2 - y^2)$$

where the coordinate origin is at the apex of the triangle with y bisecting the angle and positive downward, and x is horizontal. Check that the flow rate is

$$Q = \frac{\sqrt{3}}{320}\frac{\ell^4}{\mu}\left(-\frac{dp}{dz}\right)$$

11.2 (A) Waves in shallow water induce an oscillatory motion that extends to the bottom. The motion is parallel to the bottom and sinusoidal. Estimate the thickness of the viscous effect caused by the no-slip condition at the bottom when the wave period is 5 s.

11.3 (B) Solve for the velocity profile above a plate that oscillates in its own plane according to $u(0, t) = u_0 \sin \Omega t$. Choose the nondimensional y variable as $Y = y/\sqrt{2\nu/\Omega}$.

11.4 (B) Consider an infinite stream oscillating according to $u(t) = u_0 \sin \Omega t$. What pressure gradient would cause this oscillation? A solid wall is inserted into the flow so that it is parallel to the motion. What is the shear stress on the wall? What is the phase of the wall shear stress

with respect to the velocity $u(y \to \infty, t)$? What is the y location, as a function of time, where the particle acceleration is a maximum (of either sign)? How much of the acceleration is due to pressure and how much to viscosity?

11.5 (A) Flow in a slot of width $2h$ is driven by a pressure gradient $dp/dx|_0 + K \cos \Omega t$. How does the average flow rate for this situation compare with the flow rate produced by the steady gradient $dp/dx|_0$?

11.6 (A) Flow in a pipe has a steady component and an oscillatory component. Develop a criterion to determine when quasi-steady-state assumptions can be used to find the wall shear stress.

11.7 (A) Plot the complete velocity profiles for the flow in a slot with an oscillating pressure gradient. Assume that

$$\frac{-1}{\rho k}\frac{dp}{dx}\bigg|_0 = 2$$

Plot typical profiles of U/Λ^2 for the cases $\Lambda = 0.1, 1.0$, and 10.

11.8 (B) The function $\gamma^*(r, t, \nu)$ determined by Eq. 11.8.5 leads to the nondimensional form $\gamma^*(\eta)$, where $\eta = r/\sqrt{\nu t}$. What does dimensional analysis predict about the function $v_\theta(r, t, \Gamma, \nu)$? Why does the first form lead to a sharper result?

11.9 (B) Fluid is contained in a slot of width h. Find the velocity profile if the lower wall oscillates sinusoidally in its own plane while the upper wall is fixed.

11.10 Consider the problem of flow in a slot with an oscillating pressure gradient (Section 11.7). Place the differential equation and boundary conditions of the problem in variables appropriate to the high-frequency limit $\Lambda \Rightarrow \infty$. Use Y as the distance variable. Find the solution if $\Lambda \Rightarrow \infty$. Repeat the process for the distance variable η.

11.11 (B) Find the pressure field for an Oseen vortex. (*Hint:* Look for integrals that cancel.) What is the pressure at the origin?

11.12 (A) Find the exact relations for the maximum velocity and its position (the core radius) as functions of time for the Oseen vortex.

11.13 (A) Solve for the velocity profile in the stagnation-point flow. Tabulate $F(\eta)$, $F'(\eta)$ and $F''(\eta)$ for $\eta = 0.0$, $0.2, 0.4, \ldots , 3.0$. Use $\eta_\infty = 12$.

11.14 (B) Air flows around a cylinder of 5-cm radius at 15 cm/s (the Reynolds number is 1000), with the free-stream velocity perpendicular to the axis. Find the dimensional u and v components of the velocity at a point 0.15 cm away from the surface and 0.5 cm away from the symmetry plane on the upwind side of the cylinder. Find the shear stress on the wall at a point 0.5 cm away from the symmetry plane.

11.15 (B) Note that the derivative of Eq. 11.8.5 with respect to t produces the same equation for $\partial \gamma / \partial t$ as the original equation for γ. Differentiate Eq. 11.8.12 with respect to t and compare with Taylor's vortex equation. Reproduce another vortex velocity profile of your own.

11.16 (A) Integrate Eq. 11.8.8 once to find f', then again by parts to find Eq. 11.8.10.

11.17 (A) Show that the flow $v_r = -ar$, $v_z = 2az$, $v_\theta = 0$ satisfies the Navier–Stokes equations. Sketch the streamlines and compute the strain rate components.

11.18 (B) Compute the viscous dissipation occurring in Burgers vortex.

11.19 (C) Consider a long circular cylinder of radius R_0 in an unbounded viscous fluid. The cylinder is oscillated around its axis so that the surface velocity is $v_\theta \doteq R_0 \Omega \sin \omega t$. Set up the differential equations and boundary conditions to find the velocity profile. Nondimensionalize and identify the physical interpretation of any parameter. Consider the special case where viscous effects are confined to the neighborhood of the surface. Introduce a new space variable and cast the problem in a form that reduces to Stokes's oscillating flat plate in the proper limit.

11.20 (B) Consider the transient development of the velocity profile in the viscous coupling of Section 11.11. Assume the fluid is at rest at time zero, $v_\theta(r, z, t = 0) = 0$. For time $T > 0$ the piston in impulsively turned at speed, $v_\theta(r, z = h, t > 0) = r \Omega$. Include the time-dependent term in the momentum equation, Eq. 11.11.3. What is the proper nondimensional form for the time variable? *About* how long will it take for the transient to die out and the fully developed profile to be established?

12

Streamfunctions and the Velocity Potential

Two very useful ideas are introduced in this chapter: the streamfunction and the velocity potential. These quantities have physical interpretations, and, perhaps more important, they are frequently used as dependent variables in the solution of flow problems. In this role they replace the velocity components. The streamfunction and the velocity potential exist only for specific types of flows that meet certain kinematic restrictions.

A streamfunction exists when a flow has symmetry with respect to a coordinate system and also has zero rate of expansion everywhere; $\nabla \cdot \mathbf{v} = 0$. Since the remainder of this book deals with incompressible flows, this second criterion is always met.

The velocity potential, on the other hand, does not require any symmetry of the flow field, but it imposes a much stronger requirement on the particle motion, namely, that the vorticity is zero throughout the flow; $\omega = \nabla \times \mathbf{v} = 0$. In Chapter 13 we shall find that viscous forces may be neglected in irrotational flows. Because of this, the velocity potential is useful in inviscid flows.

12.1 STREAMLINES

Consider a three-dimensional flow where the space coordinates are x, y, and z and the corresponding velocity components are u, v, and w. Since at any instant a streamline is everywhere tangent to the velocity vector, the projected slopes of a streamline (stm) are given by

$$\frac{dy}{dx}\bigg|_{stm} = \frac{v}{u}, \qquad \frac{dy}{dz}\bigg|_{stm} = \frac{v}{w}, \qquad \frac{dx}{dz}\bigg|_{stm} = \frac{u}{w} \qquad (12.1.1)$$

A more compact form for these equations is

$$\frac{dx}{u} = \frac{dy}{v} = \frac{dz}{w} \quad \text{or} \quad \mathbf{v} \times \mathbf{t}\, ds = 0 \qquad (12.1.2)$$

For a given velocity field, the solutions of this set of equations are the streamline trajectories.

Several aspects of streamlines should be noted. First, when the velocity is zero, there is no unique direction for the streamline. If the streamline should happen to split or branch, it must do so at places where the velocity is zero. Such points are called *stagnation points*. As an example, consider the streaming flow around a blunt axisymmetric body. The streamline on the axis approaches the nose, and the velocity becomes zero. This streamline then splits into an infinite number of streamlines, which follow the surface of the body (Fig. 12.1). As another example, consider the trailing edge of an airfoil with a finite angle. The wall streamlines from the top and bottom surfaces come together at an angle, then leave the surface in a streamline that divides the upper flow from the lower flow. At this stagnation point (or, more properly, stagnation line) the velocity must be zero. Stagnation points are not limited to surfaces and may occur in the interior of the fluid as well. If the velocity is zero anywhere, it is possible for the streamline to split.

On a solid, stationary wall the no-slip condition requires that the velocity be zero. Nevertheless, we are able to define a wall streamline by the following limiting process. Consider a smooth wall and erect a local coordinate system at point P on the wall. The wall will lie in the x–z plane with y as the normal direction. A flat wall is assumed for simplicity; the argument is also valid for curved walls. The continuity equation at P is

$$\frac{\partial u}{\partial x} + \frac{\partial v}{\partial y} + \frac{\partial w}{\partial z} = 0 \tag{12.1.3}$$

Since u and w are zero all along the wall, $\partial u/\partial x = 0$ and $\partial w/\partial z = 0$. From Eq. 12.1.3 this implies that $\partial v/\partial y = 0$ on a solid wall. This fact is often useful in itself; we shall use it in a Taylor's expansion. Taylor's series for the velocity components as we leave the wall in the y direction are

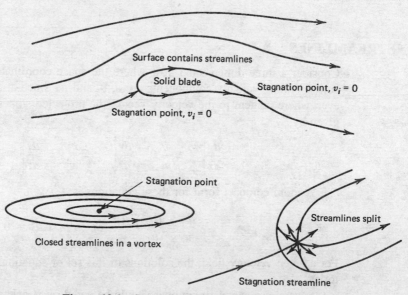

Figure 12.1   Streamline patterns with stagnation points.

$$u = 0 + \frac{\partial u}{\partial y}\Big|_0 y + \cdots$$

$$v = 0 + 0 + \frac{\partial^2 v}{\partial y^2}\Big|_0 \frac{y^2}{2} + \cdots \qquad (12.1.4)$$

$$w = 0 + \frac{\partial w}{\partial y}\Big|_0 y + \cdots$$

Now we are in a position to find the direction of the wall streamline:

$$\frac{dz}{dx}\Big|_{\text{stm}} = \tan\theta = \lim_{y\to 0} \frac{w}{u} = \frac{\partial w/\partial y|_0}{\partial u/\partial y|_0} \qquad (12.1.5)$$

where θ is the angle the wall streamline makes with the x-axis in the plane of the wall. We can also conclude that the streamline lies in the wall because the streamline angles in the y–x and y–z planes; that is, limits of v/u and v/w are both zero.

It is often said that in incompressible flow, streamlines cannot end within the fluid. They either come from and return to infinity, or they form closed loops. It is also possible, however, for them to emanate from surfaces, but only if they are stagnation streamlines. These results can be understood by considering a small streamtube (which does not contain a stagnation streamline in its interior). The streamtube consists of two ends, A_1 and A_2, and a side surface that contain streamlines (Fig. 12.2). Assuming that there are no sources within the streamtube, apply Gauss's theorem to the continuity equation:

$$0 = \int \partial_i v_i \, dV = \int n_i v_i \, dS$$

The velocity vector and the surface normal are always perpendicular on the side surface, $n_i v_i = 0$, while on the end surfaces they are nearly parallel.

$$0 = \int_{A_1} n_i v_i \, dS + \int_{A_2} n_i v_i \, dS$$

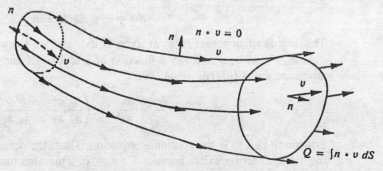

Figure 12.2 Streamtube at an instant in time.

From this equation one argues that streamtubes can never end within the fluid. If a finite integral exists for the surface A_1, then A_2 could vanish only if the velocity became infinite. An infinite velocity represents an unrealistic situation that violates the continuum assumption; therefore, A_2 is always finite. It is, of course, possible that streamtubes could form closed loops. The argument also applies to streamlines, as they can be considered as the limit of a streamtube of small area.

12.2   STREAMFUNCTION FOR PLANE FLOWS

Streamlines are everywhere tangent to the velocity vectors. An equation that would describe such lines in a plane, two-dimensional flow may be written in the form

$$\psi = \psi(x, y) \tag{12.2.1}$$

where ψ is called the *streamfunction*. When ψ is constant, Eq. 12.2.1 is a relation between x and y that describes a streamline. If ψ is given a new value, the relation $\psi(x, y) = \psi$ describes a different streamline.

The streamfunction is more useful than you might at first suspect. All the properties of the flow—the velocities, the pressure, and so on—may be related to it. The streamfunction is a single scalar unknown that can yield a complete description of the flow.

Let us start the mathematical development by noting that if ψ exists, it must obey the general differential relation

$$d\psi = \frac{\partial \psi}{\partial x} \, dx + \frac{\partial \psi}{\partial y} \, dy \tag{12.2.2}$$

Next, we propose the important definition that relates ψ and the velocities. At this stage the definitions are tentative; we must demonstrate later that they are appropriate and mathematically proper. Let

$$u = \frac{\partial \psi}{\partial y}, \qquad v = -\frac{\partial \psi}{\partial x} \tag{12.2.3}$$

[Note that an arbitrary constant (or function of time) may be added to ψ without affecting the velocities.] Substituting into Eq. 12.2.2 gives

$$d\psi = -v \, dx + u \, dy \tag{12.2.4}$$

This is a Pfaffian form ($dF = M \, dx + N \, dy$), and we know from mathematics that it is "exact"—that is, ψ is really a function of x and y—if and only if the following derivatives are equal ($\partial M / \partial y = \partial N / \partial x$):

$$-\frac{\partial v}{\partial y} = \frac{\partial u}{\partial x}, \qquad \left(\frac{\partial^2 \psi}{\partial y \, \partial x} = \frac{\partial^2 \psi}{\partial x \, \partial y} \right) \tag{12.2.5}$$

Equation (12.2.5) is the continuity equation. Thus, the definitions 12.2.3 are proper and the streamfunction exists because $\nabla \cdot \mathbf{v} = 0$. This also means that any streamfunction will automatically satisfy the continuity equation.

From Eq. 12.2.4 we can show that when ψ is constant, the resulting equation describes a streamline. If ψ is a constant, $d\psi$ is zero and Eq. 12.2.4 becomes

$$\frac{v}{u} = \frac{dy}{dx}\bigg|_{\psi=\text{const}} \qquad (12.2.6)$$

The velocity vector is tangent to the curve ψ = const, the definition of a streamline.

The second major characteristic of the streamfunction is that the numerical difference in ψ between two streamlines is equal to the volume flow rate between those streamlines. To prove this, consider two streamlines with values ψ_A and ψ_B, as shown in Fig. 12.3. Two points A and B are chosen and connected by any smooth path. The volume flow per unit width between the streamlines is

$$Q_{AB} = \int_{A-B} n_i v_i \, ds = \int_{A-B} (n_x u + n_y v) \, ds \qquad (12.2.7)$$

where n is normal to the integration element ds. By geometry we have the relations $n_x \, ds = dy$ and $n_y \, ds = -dx$. With these relations, Eq. 12.2.7 becomes

$$Q_{AB} = \int_{A-B} (u \, dy - v \, dx) = \int_{A-B} d\psi$$

$$= \psi_B - \psi_A \qquad (12.2.8)$$

The flow rate between streamlines is the difference in their streamfunction values. This equation is also unaffected by the addition of an arbitrary constant to ψ.

There are two other important relations involving the streamfunction. The first is a relation between ψ and the vorticity. In plane (two-dimensional) flow the vorticity has only one nonzero component:

$$\omega = \omega_z = \varepsilon_{zjk} \partial_j v_k = -\frac{\partial u}{\partial y} + \frac{\partial v}{\partial x} \qquad (12.2.9)$$

When Eq. 12.2.3 is introduced into Eq. 12.2.9, we find that

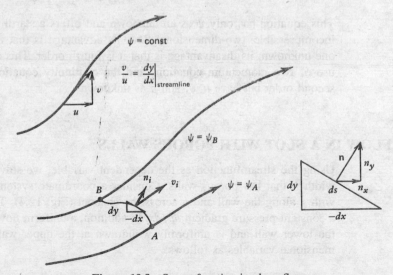

Figure 12.3   Streamfunction in plane flow.

$$-\omega_z = \frac{\partial^2 \psi}{\partial x^2} + \frac{\partial^2 \psi}{\partial y^2} = \nabla^2 \psi \qquad (12.2.10)$$

This equation takes on added importance in irrotational flows. Then ω is zero, and ψ satisfies the Laplace equation. In Chapter 14 we use this equation in a computation scheme where ψ and ω are the major dependent variables.

The major equation involving ψ is derived from the momentum equations. In plane, two-dimensional flow these are

$$\frac{\partial u}{\partial t} + u\frac{\partial u}{\partial x} + v\frac{\partial u}{\partial y} = -\frac{1}{\rho}\frac{\partial p}{\partial x} + \nu\frac{\partial^2 u}{\partial x^2} + \nu\frac{\partial^2 u}{\partial y^2} \qquad (12.2.11a)$$

$$\frac{\partial v}{\partial t} + u\frac{\partial v}{\partial x} + v\frac{\partial v}{\partial y} = -\frac{1}{\rho}\frac{\partial p}{\partial y} + \nu\frac{\partial^2 v}{\partial x^2} + \nu\frac{\partial^2 v}{\partial y^2} \qquad (12.2.11b)$$

The pressure is eliminated from these equations by the following process: Differentiate Eq. 12.2.11a with respect to y so that $\partial^2 p/\partial y\,\partial x$ occurs; similarly, differentiate Eq. 12.2.11b with respect to x so that $\partial^2 p/\partial x\,\partial y$ occurs; subtract the two equations to cause these terms to cancel. By using Eq. 12.2.9 to identify the vorticity, we then have

$$\frac{\partial \omega}{\partial t} + u\frac{\partial \omega}{\partial x} + v\frac{\partial \omega}{\partial y} = \nu\nabla^2\omega \qquad (12.2.12)$$

Finally, Eqs. 12.2.3 and 12.2.10 are used to eliminate the velocities and the vorticity. The equation then becomes

$$\frac{\partial}{\partial t}\nabla^2\psi + \frac{\partial \psi}{\partial y}\frac{\partial}{\partial x}\nabla^2\psi - \frac{\partial \psi}{\partial x}\frac{\partial}{\partial y}\nabla^2\psi = \nu\nabla^4\psi \qquad (12.2.13)$$

where (subscripts denote differentiation)

$$\nabla^4\psi \equiv \psi_{xxxx} + 2\psi_{xxyy} + \psi_{yyyy}$$

This equation has only ψ as an unknown and offers a starting point for solution of any incompressible, two-dimensional flow. Its advantage is that it is a single equation with one unknown; its disadvantage is that it is fourth order. This contrasts with our previous use of two momentum equations and the continuity equation. These equations are of second order but have u, v, and p as unknowns.

12.3   FLOW IN A SLOT WITH POROUS WALLS

Using the streamfunction as the dependent variable, we solve for the flow in a slot of width h that has porous walls. Consider a coordinate system origin on the lower wall with x along the wall and y across the channel (Fig. 12.4). The main flow is driven by a constant-pressure gradient dp/dx. In addition, a uniform flow of velocity v_0 issues from the lower wall and is uniformly withdrawn at the upper wall. To begin, define nondimensional variables as follows:

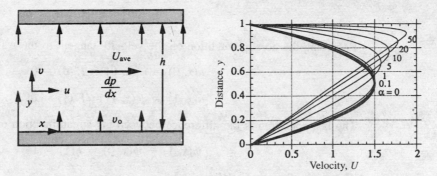

Figure 12.4   Flow in a channel with porous walls.

$$x^* = \frac{x}{h}, \qquad y^* = \frac{y}{h}, \qquad u^* = \frac{u}{U_{\text{ave}}}, \qquad v^* = \frac{v}{U_{\text{ave}}}$$

$$\psi^* = \frac{\psi}{U_{\text{ave}}h} = \frac{\psi}{Q}, \qquad v_0^* = \frac{v_0}{U_{\text{ave}}}, \qquad \text{Re} = \frac{U_{\text{ave}}h}{\nu}, \qquad \alpha = v_0^*\text{Re} = \frac{v_0 h}{\nu} \tag{12.3.1}$$

In defining these variables we implicitly assume that U_{ave}, or equivalently, $Q = U_{\text{ave}}h$, is given. After introducing all nondimensional variables, we drop the * notation for the remainder of this section.

The flow is assumed to be fully developed, that is,

$$u(y \text{ only}) = \frac{\partial \psi}{\partial y}, \qquad v(y \text{ only}) = -\frac{\partial \psi}{\partial x}$$

Let us integrate Eq. 12.1.2 from $(x, y) = (0, 0)$ along the bottom wall to $(x, 0)$ and then into the flow to (x, y):

$$\psi(x, y) - \psi(0, 0) = \int_{x=0;y=0}^{x;y=0} -v_0 \, dx + \int_{x;y=0}^{x;y} u \, dy \tag{12.3.2}$$

Since ψ is only defined up to an arbitrary constant, we may arbitrarily chose the value for one streamline. Set the streamline through $(0, 0)$ to zero; $\psi(0, 0) = 0$. To continue, note that v_0 is constant in the first integral of Eq. 12.3.2 and that the second integral is a function of only y. Hence,

$$\psi(x, y) = -v_0 x + F(y) \tag{12.3.3}$$

Relation 12.3.3 shows that $v = -\partial\psi/\partial x = v_0$ is constant throughout the entire flow.

The appropriate boundary conditions are given below using subscripts to indicate partial differentiation. Specifying $\psi = 0$ on the streamline through the origin requires that

$$\psi(0, 0) = F(0) = 0 \tag{12.3.4a}$$

The v velocity at both walls, v_0, has already been satisfied by Eq. 12.3.3:

$$v = -\psi_x = v_0 \tag{12.3.4b}$$

Enforcing the no-slip condition on the velocity tangent to the walls gives

$$u(x, 0) = \psi_y(x, 0) = F'(0) = 0 \tag{12.3.4c}$$

$$u(x, 1) = \psi_y(x, 1) = F'(1) = 0 \tag{12.3.4d}$$

The last condition is the difference between the streamfunction on both walls:

$$\psi(x, 1) - \psi(x, 0) = F(1) = 1 \tag{12.3.4e}$$

This is the flow-rate relation 12.2.8.

Substituting Eq. 12.3.3 into the differential equation that governs the streamfunction (Eq. 12.2.13) produces

$$\alpha F''' = F^{(iv)} \tag{12.3.5}$$

Here a convenient notation is $\alpha = v_0^* \, \mathrm{Re} = v_0 h / \nu$. Alpha compares the vertical velocity v_0 to the velocity of viscous diffusion at a distance measured by h. Solving Eq. 12.3.5 and applying boundary conditions 12.3.4 yields

$$u = F' = \frac{C_1}{\alpha^2} \{\exp(\alpha y) - 1 + [1 - \exp(\alpha)]y\} \tag{12.3.6}$$

$$F = \frac{C_1}{\alpha^3} [\exp(\alpha y) - 1] + \frac{C_1}{\alpha^2} \left\{ \frac{1}{2} [1 - \exp(\alpha)]y^2 - y \right\} \tag{12.3.7}$$

where

$$C_1 = \frac{2\alpha^3}{(2 - \alpha)\,[\exp(\alpha) - 1] - 2\alpha} \tag{12.3.8}$$

Velocity profiles for various values of the blowing parameter are shown in Fig. 12.4. Profiles for negative α are mirror images of those for positive α because of geometric symmetry. As the transverse blowing or sucking velocity becomes large compared to the velocity of viscous diffusion across h, the effects of viscosity are confined to the opposite wall, where a steep gradient exists. Since $U_{ave} = Q/h$ was used to nondimensionalize the problem, all of the curves have the same area or flow rate.

The pressure gradient that drives the main flow does not explicitly occur in the problem when the streamfunction is employed. One may specify dp/dx or Q, but not both. To find dp/dx, we must consider the momentum equation. For this flow Eq. 12.2.11a is a balance between convection of momentum by the vertical velocity, viscous shear, and the pressure force:

$$\alpha \frac{du}{dy} - \frac{d^2u}{dy^2} = -\frac{dp}{dx} \tag{12.3.9}$$

In this relation, pressure has been nondimensionalized by $\mu U_{ave}/h$ (see Eq. 8.10.14). Evaluating Eq. 12.3.9 by using Eq. 12.3.6 yields

$$-\frac{dp}{dx} = \frac{C_1(\alpha)}{\alpha}[1 - \exp(\alpha)] \qquad (12.3.10)$$

Inserting Eq. 12.3.8 gives the final form. It shows the change in driving pressure gradient for flows with the same flow rate and different blowing parameters α.

*12.4 STREAMLINES AND STREAMSURFACES FOR A THREE-DIMENSIONAL FLOW

In this section we take a more general approach to the problem of describing streamlines. There are several ways to describe a line that is embedded in space. The method most useful for our purposes is to regard the line as the intersection of two independent surfaces f and g (Fig. 12.5):

$$f = f(x, y, z) \qquad (12.4.1)$$
$$g = g(x, y, z)$$

As f and g take on different values, we are describing different streamlines. These surfaces will be called *streamsurfaces* and are regarded as solutions to Eq. 12.1.1. For any velocity field, mathematicians tell us that it is possible to find two such sets of independent surfaces f and g as long as $\mathbf{v}$ is not zero. This is a local result. We can find the surfaces for any point in the flow, but we cannot necessarily find one set that will work for the entire flow. Most flows are simple enough that this is not a problem. Another aspect of Eq. 12.4.1 is that the surfaces are not unique. Any surface h described by a function of f and g,

$$h = h(f, g) \qquad (12.4.2)$$

is also a streamsurface. We could replace either f or g in Eq. 12.4.1 with the new function h. Since the walls or solid surfaces containing a flow must also contain a set of streamlines, this result means that it is always possible to make one set of surfaces in Eq. 12.4.1 have a member that coincides with the walls bounding the flow.

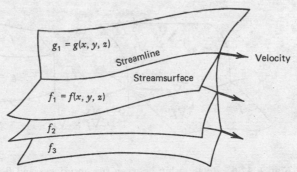

Figure 12.5 Streamsurfaces f_1 and g_1 intersect to define a streamline.

At this point we digress for a moment to discuss some properties of surfaces. It is necessary to have this background material to understand the development of the streamfunction. The equation

$$f = f(x, y, z) \tag{12.4.3}$$

describes a surface in space for each value of f. The equation is a numbering system for each surface as well as an equation to determine the shape of the surface. For instance, any other function constructed from f produces the same set of surfaces, but assigns a different number to each; that is, $F = F(f)$ gives the same surfaces as f.

As an illustration, consider the planes described by $f = x - y$. Now $f = 2$ is a certain plane from this set. However, the equation $F = (x - y)/3$ gives the same plane when $F = \frac{2}{3}$, or the equation $F = \exp(x - y)^2$ gives the same plane when $F = e^4$. Thus, the shape of the surfaces, which is the only property important for the intersection of two surfaces, and the numbering system for the surfaces are somewhat independent.

Another property of a surface is its normal vector. At each point of the surface there is a normal vector given by ∇f. Although the direction of this gradient is always normal, its magnitude depends on the numbering system chosen for the surfaces. When we state that two sets of surfaces are independent, as in Eq. 12.4.1, we are requiring that their normals not be parallel. Thus, f and g are independent if $\nabla f \times \nabla g \neq 0$.

Now we can return to the central question: How are the functions f and g related to the velocity? Since ∇f and ∇g are perpendicular to the streamsurfaces, they are also perpendicular to the velocity. Hence, the product $\nabla f \times \nabla g$ will be in the direction of the velocity as shown in Fig. 12.6a. The velocity itself can be obtained if we adjust the magnitude by a function h:

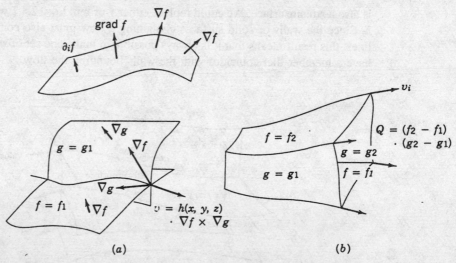

(a) (b)

Figure 12.6 Relationship between streamsurfaces and flow properties: (a) $\mathbf{v} = h\nabla f \times \nabla g$; ($b$) $Q = (f_2 - f_1)(g_2 - g_1)$.

$$\mathbf{v} = h(x, y, z)\nabla f \times \nabla g \tag{12.4.4}$$

Up to this point the discussion has been very general and applied to any vector field. Actually, Eq. 12.4.4 does not represent much progress, as the three components of the vector $\mathbf{v}$ are replaced by three functions f, g, and h on the right-hand side.

The continuity equation in incompressible flow states that the rate of expansion is always zero: $\nabla \cdot \mathbf{v} = 0$ ($\mathbf{v}$ is a solenoidal vector field). From this it is possible to prove that one may choose f and g in Eq. 12.4.4 in such a way as to make $h = 1$. In practice the streamfunction is identified with $f \to \psi$:

$$\mathbf{v} = \nabla f \times \nabla g \quad \text{if} \quad \nabla \cdot \mathbf{v} = 0$$

$$= \nabla \psi \times \nabla g \tag{12.4.5}$$

Equation 12.4.5 is the important relation between the streamsurfaces and the velocity. It corresponds to the relations 12.2.3 for plane flows. The surfaces ψ and g are not uniquely determined, and several choices are possible.

The streamsurfaces ψ and g are also related to the flow rate. Consider the streamtube formed by the surfaces ψ_1, ψ_2, g_1, and g_2 as shown in Fig. 12.6b. We simply state the flow rate equation without proof (see Yih, 1969):

$$Q = (\psi_2 - \psi_1)(g_2 - g_1) \tag{12.4.6}$$

Note that this relation and Eq. 12.4.5 remain unchanged if one adds an arbitrary constant to either ψ or g.

To illustrate how these equations work, we return to the plane flow case in rectangular coordinates. There the proper choices are $g = z$ and $f = \psi$. Then Eq. 12.4.5 becomes (subscripts take on values x, y, z)

$$v_i = \varepsilon_{ijk} \partial_j \psi \, \partial_k(z) = \varepsilon_{ijk} \partial_j \psi \, \delta_{kz}$$

$$v_i = \varepsilon_{ijz} \partial_j \psi$$

$$v_x = \varepsilon_{xjz} \partial_j \psi = \frac{\partial \psi}{\partial y}$$

$$v_y = \varepsilon_{yjz} \partial_j \psi = -\frac{\partial \psi}{\partial x}$$

The flow rate is computed for a unit depth in the z-direction:

$$Q = (\psi_2 - \psi_1)(z_2 - z_1) = \psi_2 - \psi_1 \tag{12.4.7}$$

These formulas correspond to the relations given in Section 12.3.

The incompressible continuity equation $\nabla \cdot \mathbf{v} = 0$ allows a general flow with three independent velocity components to be represented in terms of two streamsurfaces. When, in addition, a flow possesses a symmetry such that only two velocity components are nonzero, it is possible to choose g as a set of coordinate planes and thus reduce the problem to one of finding the remaining streamsurfaces $f = \psi$. Flow of primary interest are plane flows in either rectangular or cylindrical coordinates and axisymmetric flows in either cylindrical or spherical coordinates. Equations for these flows are given in Appendix D.

12.5 VECTOR POTENTIAL AND THE E² OPERATOR

There is another method of formulating the streamfunction, which is complementary in that it gives us more information and allows us to connect the streamfunction with the vorticity. Once this is done, we may find the general equation governing the streamfunction simply by substituting into the dynamic equation governing vorticity (Chapter 13).

Consider a vector function **B** defined by the relation

$$\mathbf{B} \equiv f\nabla g = \psi\nabla g \tag{12.5.1}$$

which gives ψ in terms of **B**. We compute the curl of **B**:

$$\nabla \times \mathbf{B} = \nabla \times (\psi\nabla g)$$
$$= \nabla\psi \times \nabla g + \psi\nabla \times \nabla g$$

Since the last term is always zero for any scalar function g, we find that Eq. 12.4.5 is equivalent to

$$\mathbf{v} = \nabla \times \mathbf{B} \quad \text{if} \quad \nabla \cdot \mathbf{v} = 0 \tag{12.5.2}$$

The vector $\mathbf{B} \equiv \psi\nabla g$ is called the *vector potential* (not to be confused with the velocity potential). Equation 12.5.1 does not define **B** uniquely. We may also specify that **B** be chosen so that $\nabla \cdot \mathbf{B} = 0$ (**B** is solenoidal as well as **v**). This is also true in our application of ψ and g to flows that are symmetric with respect to an orthogonal coordinate system. ($\nabla \cdot \mathbf{B} = \psi\nabla^2 g + \nabla\psi \cdot \nabla g$: for all coordinate systems in Appendix D, g is taken as a coordinate plane and the numbering system is chosen so that $\nabla^2 g = 0$. Moreover, the symmetry of the flow and the orthogonality of the coordinates imply that $\nabla\psi$ is perpendicular to ∇g.)

The first important relation is found by computing the vorticity and using a vector identity,

$$-\omega = -\nabla \times \mathbf{v} = -\nabla \times (\nabla \times \mathbf{B})$$
$$= \nabla^2\mathbf{B} - \nabla(\nabla \cdot \mathbf{B}) \tag{12.5.3}$$

or since $\nabla \cdot \mathbf{B} = 0$,

$$-\omega = \nabla^2\mathbf{B} \tag{12.5.4}$$

This is the general formula that corresponds to Eq. 12.2.10. You will find the proper simplified form of this equation in each of the streamfunction tables. [Recall that $\nabla^2\mathbf{B}$ stands for the vector $\nabla \cdot \nabla\mathbf{B}$. This is important because in some coordinate systems and for certain components, it is not true that $(\nabla^2\mathbf{B})_{\text{component}} = \nabla^2(\mathbf{B}_{\text{component}})$.]

The streamfunction satisfies the continuity equation by virtue of the way in which it is constructed. For an equation to govern ψ, we must look to the momentum equations. Actually, the equation we need is the vorticity transport equation. It is derived by taking $\nabla \times$ the momentum equation. This is done in Chapter 13. The equation is

$$\frac{\partial \omega}{\partial t} + \mathbf{v} \cdot \nabla \omega = \omega \cdot \nabla \mathbf{v} + \nu \nabla^2 \omega \tag{12.5.5}$$

Substitution of $-\omega = \nabla^2 \mathbf{B}$, $\mathbf{v} = \nabla \times \mathbf{B}$, and $\mathbf{B} = \psi \nabla g$ produces a single fourth-order equation for ψ. The only restriction is that the flow must be incompressible and that it must have symmetry with respect to an orthogonal coordinate system. In all symmetric flows the vector $\mathbf{B}$ has only one nonzero component, the vorticity has only one nonzero component, and the vorticity is perpendicular to the velocity. This makes plane and axisymmetric flows somewhat special since Eqs. 12.5.4 and 12.5.5 have only one non-trivial component. These equations form the basis for many numerical solution methods where the vorticity and streamfunction are the major unknowns.

Next we consider the viscous term $\nabla^2 \omega$ and its relation to the streamfunction for an arbitrary orthogonal coordinate system. The coordinates will be q_1, q_2, q_3, the unit vectors $\mathbf{i}_1, \mathbf{i}_2, \mathbf{i}_3$, and the metric coefficients h_1, h_2, h_3. An incremental distance vector $d\mathbf{R}$ is

$$d\mathbf{R} = \mathbf{i}_1 \frac{dq_1}{h_1} + \mathbf{i}_2 \frac{dq_2}{h_2} + \mathbf{i}_3 \frac{dq_3}{h_3} \tag{12.5.6}$$

A compendium of properties and tensor calculus relations for 40 coordinate systems is provided in Moon and Spencer (1971). Happel and Brenner (1983) give a summary with many geometric details for the 11 most common systems. Two types of systems are of most interest. In both types, q_1 and q_2 are any orthogonal coordinate system in a plane. The first type is cylindrical systems where the $q_3 = z$ are parallel planes. The second type is systems of rotation where $q_3 = \theta$ is the asmuthal angle of rotation of the q_1–q_2 plane. The flows have symmetry with respect to the q_3 coordinate, that is, the physical velocity components are $v_1 (q_1, q_2)$, $v_2 (q_1, q_2)$, and $v_3 = 0$, and the streamfunction is $\psi(q_1, q_2)$. For both systems we take the $g = q_3$ in Eq. 12.5.1.

First, some general formulas from vector analysis will be listed. The general formula for the gradient of a scalar function $s(q_1, q_2, q_3)$ is

$$\nabla s = \mathbf{i}_1 h_1 \frac{\partial s}{\partial q_1} + \mathbf{i}_2 h_2 \frac{\partial s}{\partial q_2} + \mathbf{i}_3 h_3 \frac{\partial s}{\partial q_3} \tag{12.5.7}$$

For the present purposes it is only necessary to consider an arbitrary vector u with a single component, which is a function of q_1 and q_2,

$$\mathbf{u} = \mathbf{i}_3 u_3(q_1, q_2) \tag{12.5.8}$$

For such a vector,

$$\nabla \times \mathbf{u} = \mathbf{i}_1 h_2 h_3 \frac{\partial}{\partial q_2} \left(\frac{u_3}{h_3} \right) - \mathbf{i}_2 h_3 h_1 \frac{\partial}{\partial q_1} \left(\frac{u_3}{h_3} \right) \tag{12.5.9}$$

Also,

$$\nabla \times \nabla \times \mathbf{u} = \mathbf{i}_3 h_1 h_2 \left\{ -\frac{\partial}{\partial q_1} \left[\frac{h_3 h_1}{h_2} \frac{\partial}{\partial q_1} \left(\frac{u_3}{h_3} \right) \right] - \frac{\partial}{\partial q_2} \left[\frac{h_2 h_3}{h_1} \frac{\partial}{\partial q_2} \left(\frac{u_3}{h_3} \right) \right] \right\} \tag{12.5.10}$$

This formula is useful because of the identity $\nabla^2 \mathbf{u} = \nabla(\nabla \cdot \mathbf{u}) - \nabla \times \nabla \times \mathbf{u}$ with $\nabla \cdot \mathbf{u} = 0$ in many cases.

Recall that the vector potential is $\mathbf{B} = \psi \nabla g$. Using $s = g = q_3$ for either cylindrical systems or systems of rotation, from Eq. 12.5.7 we find that $\nabla g = \mathbf{i}_3 h_3$. Thus, Eq. 12.5.1 for the vector potential is

$$\mathbf{B} = \mathbf{i}_3 h_3 \psi \qquad (12.5.11)$$

In cylindrical systems $g = q_3 = z$ and $h_3 = 1$, while in systems of rotation $q_3 = \theta$ and $h_3 = h_3 (q_1, q_2)$. The velocity is related to the streamfunction by Eq. 12.5.2. Inserting Eq. 12.5.10 into Eq. 12.5.8 yields

$$\mathbf{v} = \nabla \times \mathbf{B} = \mathbf{i}_1 h_2 h_3 \frac{\partial \psi}{\partial q_2} - \mathbf{i}_2 h_1 h_3 \frac{\partial \psi}{\partial q_1} \qquad (12.5.12)$$

Next, consider the vorticity relation, Eq. 12.5.3. Replacing $\mathbf{u}$ by $\mathbf{B}$ in Eq. 12.5.10 and introducing Eq. 12.5.11 produces

$$\omega = \nabla \times (\nabla \times \mathbf{B})$$

$$= -\mathbf{i}_3 h_1 h_2 \left[\frac{\partial}{\partial q_1} \left(\frac{h_1 h_3}{h_2} \frac{\partial \psi}{\partial q_1} \right) + \frac{\partial}{\partial q_2} \left(\frac{h_2 h_3}{h_1} \frac{\partial \psi}{\partial q_2} \right) \right] \qquad (12.5.13)$$

Note that, like the vector potential $\mathbf{B}$, the vorticity is perpendicular to the plane of the velocities.

Equation 12.5.13 motivates the definition of the E^2 operator. Let

$$h_3 \cdot E^2(\ ) \equiv h_1 h_2 \left\{ \frac{\partial}{\partial q_1} \left[\frac{h_1 h_3}{h_2} \frac{\partial (\ )}{\partial q_1} \right] + \frac{\partial}{\partial q_2} \left[\frac{h_2 h_3}{h_1} \frac{\partial (\ )}{\partial q_2} \right] \right\} \qquad (12.5.14)$$

With this definition Eq. 12.5.13 becomes

$$\omega = -\mathbf{i}_3 h_3 E^2 \psi \qquad (12.5.15)$$

Hence, the streamfunction is related to the vorticity through the E^2 operator.

Another quantity of interest is the viscous term in the momentum equation. Using $\mathbf{u} \rightarrow \omega$ in Eqs. 12.5.8 and 12.5.9 gives the formula

$$\nabla \cdot \tau = \mu \nabla^2 \mathbf{v} = \mu \nabla \cdot \mathbf{v} - \mu \nabla \times \omega = -\mu \nabla \times \omega$$

$$= -\mu \nabla \times (-\mathbf{i}_3 h_3 E^2 \psi)$$

$$= \mu \left[\mathbf{i}_1 h_2 h_3 \frac{\partial}{\partial q_2} (E^2 \psi) - \mathbf{i}_2 h_3 h_1 \frac{\partial}{\partial q_1} (E^2 \psi) \right] \qquad (12.5.16)$$

This is useful to compute the pressure field in Stokes flow where $\nabla p = \nabla \cdot \tau$.

Finally, the viscous term in the vorticity equation can be computed using Eq. 12.5.10 as the pattern with $\mathbf{B}$ replaced with ω.

$$\nabla^2 \omega = -\nabla \times (\nabla \times \omega) = \mathbf{i}_3 h_3 E^2 \left[-E^2 (\psi) \right]$$

$$= -\mathbf{i}_3 h_3 E^2 E^2 (\psi) \qquad (12.5.17)$$

This form is very useful in low-Reynolds-number flow, where $\nabla^2 \omega = -\nabla \times \nabla \times \omega = 0$.

An important example is the spherical coordinate system r, θ, φ, with metric coefficients

$$h_1 = 1, \qquad h_2 = \frac{1}{r}, \qquad h_3 = \frac{1}{r \sin\theta} \tag{12.5.18}$$

For this system

$$\mathrm{E}^2(\ ) = \frac{\partial^2}{\partial r^2}(\ ) + \frac{\sin\theta}{r^2}\frac{\partial}{\partial\theta}\left[\frac{1}{\sin\theta}\frac{\partial(\ )}{\partial\theta}\right] \tag{12.5.19}$$

The $\mathrm{E}^2(\ )$ operator is similar but distinct from the Laplacian operator $\nabla^2(\ ) = \nabla \cdot \nabla(\ )$. However, they are identical in the special case of a conjugate cylindrical system. A conjugate cylindrical system is one where $q_3 = g = z$, $q_1 = \xi$, $q_2 = \eta$, and in addition, the rectangular coordinates $x + iy$ are an analytic function of $\zeta = \xi + i\eta$. For such a system the metric coefficients are $h_3 = 1$ and $h_1 = h_2 = h(\xi, \eta)$. The equation governing the streamfunction is

$$0 = \nabla^2\nabla^2\psi = \mathrm{E}^2\mathrm{E}^2\psi = \left(\frac{\partial^2}{\partial\xi^2} + \frac{\partial^2}{\partial\eta^2}\right)\left[h^2\left(\frac{\partial^2\psi}{\partial\xi^2} + \frac{\partial^2\psi}{\partial\eta^2}\right)\right] \tag{12.5.20}$$

Thus, ψ is a biharmonic function.

As an example of a conjugate cylindrical system, which will be used later, consider the bipolar cylindrical system (Happel and Brenner, Milne–Thompson). The coordinates are $(q_1 = \xi, q_2 = \eta, q_3 = z)$ with a scale parameter $c > 0$. The transformation is

$$x + iy = ic \cot(\xi + i\eta)$$

$$x = \frac{c \sinh\eta}{\cosh\eta - \cos\xi}, \qquad y = \frac{c \sin\xi}{\cosh\eta - \cos\xi} \tag{12.5.21}$$

$$h_1 = h_2 = h - \frac{\cosh\eta - \cos\xi}{c}, \qquad h_3 = 1$$

The definition and choice of domain of the variables is not uniform in the literature. However, the choice $0 \leq \xi \leq 2\pi$ and $-\infty \leq \eta \leq +\infty$ will place $\eta > 0$ in the right half-plane. Curves where η = constant are circles given by

$$(x - c \coth\eta)^2 + y^2 = c^2 \operatorname{csch}^2\eta \tag{12.5.22}$$

The center of the circles, say $\eta = \eta_0$, are at $x_0 = c \cot\eta_0$, $y_0 = 0$, and the radius is $c\,|\operatorname{csch}\eta_0|$. Circles with negative constant η are in the left half-plane as shown in Fig. 12.7. For $\eta = -\infty$, the circle is a dot located at $(-c, 0)$, $\eta = 0$ is a y-axis with center at $\pm\infty$. Positive η places the circle in the right half-plane, and as $\eta \to \infty$ the circle is a dot located at $(c, 0)$.

The curves where ξ = constant follow the equation

$$x^2 + (y^2 - c \cot\xi)^2 = c^2 \csc^2\xi \tag{12.5.23}$$

These are circular arcs (not complete circles) with centers on the y-axis at $(x = 0, y = c \cot\xi)$. Each arc terminates on the x-axis at the limit points $(x = \pm c, y = 0)$. When

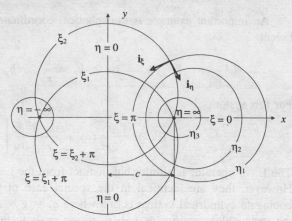

Figure 12.7 Bipolar cylindrical coordinates given by $x + iy = ic \cot(\xi + i\eta)$.

$\xi \to 0$ (or $\xi \to 2\pi$), the arc becomes the x-axis with $x > c$ and $x < c$. Arcs with $0 < \xi < \pi$ are in the upper half-plane beginning and ending at $x = \pm c$, $y = 0$. The arc $\xi = \pi$ is the x-axis between the limit points. For example, the arc with $\xi = \pi/4$ is in the upper half-plane beginning and ending at $x = \pm c$, $y = 0$. The part of this circle that continues into the lower half-plane has ξ increased by π, that is, the arc with $\xi = \pi/4 + \pi = 5\pi/4$.

12.6 VELOCITY POTENTIAL AND THE UNSTEADY BERNOULLI EQUATION

Most students are familiar with the fact that a conservative force field may be represented by a potential. The gravity force is the best-known example. The weight force per unit mass is given by

$$F_i = - g\partial_i Z$$

where g is the acceleration of gravity and $Z(x_i)$ is the vertical distance above a reference plan. Under special circumstances the velocity field itself may be represented by a *velocity potential*. The potential and the velocity are related by

$$v_i = \partial_i \phi \qquad (12.6.1)$$

where ϕ may have an arbitrary constant added without a change in v_i. This equation replaces three unknwon velocity components by a single unknown scalar function ϕ. In the light of this simplification one can guess that the conditions under which Eq. 12.6.1 exists are very restrictive. It turns out that the necessary and sufficient condition for a velocity potential to exist is that the flow is irrotational,

$$\boldsymbol{\omega} = \nabla \times \mathbf{v} = 0 \qquad (12.6.2)$$

A flow field that lacks vorticity is a very special situation where the particles have never experienced a net viscous force; it is an inviscid flow. (The terms *potential flow* and *inviscid flow* are almost synonymous and are frequently used interchangeably.) The great advantage of the velocity potential is that it may be used in three-dimensional flows; no special symmetry is required. The great disadvantage is that it works only for inviscid flows.

The velocity potential is frequently used in compressible flow and acoustics. However, our interest is its application to incompressible flows. The major equation that governs ϕ for incompressible flows is found by substituting Eq. 12.6.1 into the continuity equation. The result is

$$0 = \partial_i v_i = \partial_i \partial_i \phi = \nabla^2 \phi \qquad (12.6.3)$$

The velocity potential satisfies the Laplace equation. Solutions to the Laplace equation are termed *harmonic functions*. There is a vast amount of mathematical information about this equation, which goes under the name *potential theory*. More will be said about the characteristics of potential flows in a later chapter. At this point it is sufficient to note that two kinematic conditions, zero vorticity and zero expansion, have led to an equation for a single unknown that will determine the velocity field.

If the velocity is determined from purely kinematic considerations, what role does the momentum equation play? The momentum equation 5.7.16 can be written using Problems 3.15 and 6.4 together with the identity $\nabla^2 \mathbf{v} = -\nabla \times \boldsymbol{\omega}$ (from Problem 3.18) as

$$\frac{\partial \mathbf{v}}{\partial t} + \nabla \left(\frac{1}{2} v^2 + \frac{p}{\rho} + gZ \right) = \mathbf{v} \times \boldsymbol{\omega} - \nu \nabla \times \boldsymbol{\omega} \qquad (12.6.4)$$

The terms on the right must be zero because the vorticity is zero. The unsteady term is changed by inserting Eq. 12.6.1:

$$\frac{\partial \mathbf{v}}{\partial t} = \frac{\partial}{\partial t} (\nabla \phi) = \nabla \left(\frac{\partial \phi}{\partial t} \right)$$

Hence Eq. 12.6.4 may be written

$$\nabla \left(\frac{\partial \phi}{\partial t} + \frac{1}{2} v^2 + \frac{p}{\rho} + gZ \right) = 0$$

This integrates to the unsteady Bernoulli equation for irrotational flow,

$$\frac{\partial \phi}{\partial t} + \frac{1}{2} v^2 + \frac{p}{\rho} + gZ = C(t) \qquad (12.6.5)$$

The "constant" C is a function of time, which must be determined from boundary information. Assuming that the velocities have been determined as discussed above, the Bernoulli equation tells us what pressure forces are required to produce those motions.

12.7   FLOW CAUSED BY A SPHERE WITH VARIABLE RADIUS

We discuss an example of the application of the velocity potential and Bernoulli equation. Consider a sphere embedded in an infinite fluid. The sphere surface undergoes a prescribed expansion or contraction $R(t)$ as depicted in Fig. 12.8. This problem, and varia-

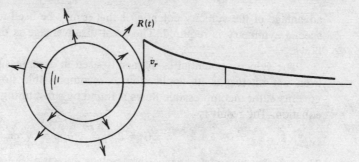

Figure 12.8   Expansion of a sphere in an infinite fluid.

tions of it, are relevant to boiling, to cavitation [one of the first applications to cavitation was by Rayleigh (1917)], and to acoustics. We assume that the radial expansion or contraction of the sphere produces a purely radial flow through the action of pressure forces. Pressure forces cannot impart any rotational motion to the particles. Rotation can only be started by unbalanced shear stresses (these facts are proved in Chapter 13). In such a motion the velocity is related to the potential by

$$v_r = \frac{\partial \phi}{\partial r} \tag{12.7.1}$$

In spherical coordinates, the governing equation 12.6.3 for $\phi(r, t)$ is

$$\nabla^2 \phi = \frac{1}{r^2} \frac{\partial}{\partial r} \left(r^2 \frac{\partial \phi}{\partial r} \right) = 0 \tag{12.7.2}$$

Boundary conditions are that the fluid is stationary at infinity and that it follows the sphere motion at $r = R(t)$:

$$v_r = \frac{\partial \phi}{\partial r} (r \rightarrow \infty, t) = 0 \tag{12.7.3}$$

$$v_r = \frac{\partial \phi}{\partial r} (r = R, t) = \dot{R}(t) \tag{12.7.4}$$

From Eqs. 12.7.2 and 12.7.4 we find that

$$r^2 \frac{\partial \phi}{\partial r} = C_1(t) = r^2 v_r = R^2 \dot{R} \tag{12.7.5}$$

In light of 12.7.1, this is really an equation for the fluid velocity; that is,

$$v_r = \left(\frac{R}{r} \right)^2 \dot{R} \tag{12.7.6}$$

The velocity decays as r^{-2}. A second integration of Eq. 12.7.5 yields

$$\phi = \int_\infty^r \frac{\partial \phi}{\partial r}\, dr + \phi_\infty = -\frac{R^2 \dot{R}}{r} + \phi_\infty \qquad (12.7.7)$$

where ϕ_∞ may be taken as zero to fix the arbitrary constant.

Next, we imagine that the pressure far away from the bubble has a constant value (i.e., the pressure minus the hydrostatic contribution is a constant). With the results above, Bernoulli's equation 12.6.5 becomes

$$-\frac{1}{r}[R^2\ddot{R} + 2R(\dot{R})^2] + \frac{1}{2}\left(\frac{R^2\dot{R}}{r^2}\right)^2 + \frac{p}{\rho} = \frac{p_\infty}{\rho} \qquad (12.7.8)$$

The pressure approaches the pressure at infinity as r^{-1}. A quantity of importance is the pressure at the bubble surface:

$$\frac{p(R) - p(\infty)}{\rho} = R\ddot{R} + \frac{3}{2}\dot{R}^2 \qquad (12.7.9)$$

Rayleigh used this result to find the time it takes for a cavitation bubble to collapse (see Knap et al., 1970). For this problem it is assumed that the bubble is somehow formed at time zero without any internal pressure. With this restriction, Eq. 12.7.9 can be integrated to find the time of collapse.

As an example, consider a sphere that undergoes a prescribed sinusoidal oscillation. One-half of the flow might model a hemispherical loudspeaker in a plane wall. The surface has a motion with a nondimensional amplitude ε:

$$R = R_0(1 - \varepsilon \sin \omega t)$$

Substituting into Eq. 12.7.9 and evaluating gives the pressure on the surface of the sphere needed to produce the motion

$$\frac{p(R) - p(\infty)}{\rho R_0^2 \omega^2} = -\varepsilon \sin \omega t + \frac{2}{3}\varepsilon^2\left(1 - \frac{5}{2}\sin^2 \omega t\right)$$

Although the velocity of the sphere is a sinusoid, the pressure is asymmetric and shows a small, $\frac{2}{3}\varepsilon^2$, constant increase above $p(\infty)$.

12.8 CONCLUSIONS

The streamfunction and velocity potential offer us alternative variables to use in describing fluid flows. Through their mathematical relationships with the velocity, $\mathbf{v} = \nabla\psi \times \nabla g = \nabla \times \mathbf{B}$ and $\mathbf{v} = \nabla\phi$, they can give a complete description of the flow. However, only in the case of flows with symmetry is the streamfunction useful. We need the symmetry so that g surfaces may be taken as coordinate surfaces and are therefore known. The velocity potential, on the other hand, is a natural choice for flows without vorticity.

In fact, the terms *potential flow* and *irrotational flow* are used interchangeably because $\omega = 0$ is a necessary and sufficient condition for ϕ to exist.

PROBLEMS

12.1 (A) Find the streamfunction for the ideal flow toward a plane stagnation point. The velocity components are $u = ax$ and $v = -ay$. Plot several streamlines using equal increments in ψ.

12.2 (B) Find the streamfunction for a stream oscillating above a fixed plate. The velocity is given by Eq. 11.5.7.

12.3 (A) Find the streamfunction for the asymptotic suction profile $u = u_0[1 - \exp(-yV_0/v)]$, which occurs when a streaming motion u_0 goes over a porous plate with a sucking velocity V_0. Sketch several streamlines with equal increments in ψ.

12.4 (B) Consider a uniform stream from left to right with a speed U. Find the streamfunction for this flow in all four coordinate systems of Appendix D.

12.5 (B) An infinitely small point source of fluid exists at the origin. The flow away from the source is purely radial and is irrotational. Find the streamfunction and velocity potential in spherical coordinates for this flow.

12.6 (A) Formulate and solve the differential equation boundary conditions for the combined Couette–Poiseuille flow in a slot. Find the pressure drop–flow rate expression.

12.7 (A) Find the velocity potential for a uniform stream. Solve the problem for each of the coordinate systems of Appendix D.

12.8 (B) The Hiemenz stagnation-point flow has velocity components $u = xf'(y)$ and $v = -f(y)$. How is f related to the two-dimensional stream function ψ? What equation governs ψ for this flow? Express this equation in terms of f, and compare it with Eq. 11.9.13.

12.9 (B) Demonstrate that the solution for a channel with porous walls where the lower wall also slides with velocity U_0 is

$$F = \frac{C_1}{\alpha^3}[\exp(\alpha y) - 1]$$

$$+ \frac{C_1}{\alpha^2}\left\{\frac{1}{2}[1 - \exp(\alpha)]y^2 - y\right\} + U_0\left(y - \frac{1}{2}y^2\right)$$

where

$$C_1 = \frac{\alpha^3(2 - U_0)}{(2 - \alpha)[\exp(\alpha) - 1] - 2\alpha}$$

Plot $F'(y)$ profiles for $U_0 = 0.5$ and $\alpha = \pm 0, 5, 10,$ and 50.

12.10 (B) Show that the limit $\alpha \rightarrow 0$ of Eqs. 12.3.6 to 12.3.8 produces the answer for Poiseuille flow. Note that for small a, $\exp(a) = 1 + a + a^2/2 + a^3/3! + \cdots$.

12.11 (B) Prove that the nondimensional pressure gradient for Problem 12.9 is

$$G(\alpha, U_0) \equiv -\frac{dp}{dx} = \frac{C_1}{\alpha}[1 - \exp(\alpha)] - \alpha U_0$$

where $C_1(\alpha, U_0)$ is given in Problem 12.9. Is it proper to call $G(\alpha, U_0)$ the pressure gradient per unit flow rate? Show that $G(0, U_0) = -12 + 6U_0$ (note Problem 12.10). Plot $G(\alpha, U_0)/G(0, 0)$ for $U_0 = 0, \pm 0.5,$ and -50, $\alpha < 50$. Note minimum values and interpret.

12.12 (C) Consider an axisymmetric flow v_r, v_z in cylindrical coordinate. Would the addition of a swirl of the form $v_\theta(r, z)$ change the continuity equation? Regard the relations between v_r and ψ and v_z and ψ in Table D.3 as definitions of ψ. Does the relation between ω_θ and ψ given in Table D.3 still hold? What are the expressions for the other vorticity components ω_r and ω_z?

12.13 (B) The streamfunction for flow over a circular cylinder is $\psi = Ur \sin \theta(1 - r_0^2/r^2)$. Find the pressure distribution on the surface.

12.14 (B) Find the pressure distribution on the surface of Hill's spherical vortex. The streamfunction is given in Eq. 13.6.2.

12.15 (C) Prove the flow rate equation $Q = (f_2 - f_1)(g_2 - g_1)$.

Vorticity Dynamics

The momentum equations for incompressible flow focus our attention on the velocity and pressure as the major items of interest. Interactions that occur in a flow field are explained in terms of inertia, pressure forces, gravity forces, and viscous forces. These basic concepts are the elements at our disposal in interpreting fluid dynamic events. In this chapter we broaden our outlook. In many instances it is advantageous to interpret the events in a flow in terms of the vorticity and the dynamic events that are interacting to give a certain vorticity distribution.

The existence of vorticity generally indicates that viscous effects are important. This occurs because fluid particles can only be set into rotation by an unbalanced shear stress. Vorticity dynamics, roughly speaking, offers a method to separate a flow into viscous and inviscid effects. It is especially valuable in cases where there is only a weak inter-action between viscous and inviscid effects.

13.1 VORTICITY

In Chapter 4 we defined vorticity as

$$\boldsymbol{\omega} = \nabla \times \mathbf{v} \tag{13.1.1}$$

Vorticity has several physical interpretations. The most common is that vorticity measures the solid-bodylike rotation of a material point P' that neighbors the primary material point P. Since the motion is like a solid-body rotation, the rotation velocity increment of P' with respect to P is

$$d\mathbf{v}^{(r)} = \tfrac{1}{2}\boldsymbol{\omega} \times d\mathbf{r} \tag{13.1.2}$$

where $\boldsymbol{\omega}$ is the vorticity at P and $d\mathbf{r}$ is the distance increment from P and P'.

Several other slightly different interpretations may be attached to vorticity. For instance, we know that at each point one may find a set of orthogonal principal axes. Particles on these axes have no shearing deformation, and their instantaneous motion is translation, expansion, and rotation. Therefore, a second interpretation is that vorticity is a measure of the instantaneous rotation rate of the principal axes.

Our next interpretation is a more vivid physical picture. Imagine that a small spherical piece of fluid about P is instantaneously frozen. The frozen ball would then translate and rotate as a result of the previous motion of its particles. If we give the frozen sphere the same angular momentum about P that the unfrozen particles had, the rotation will occur at a speed $\omega/2$ and the <u>angular momentum</u> will be given by the product of the vorticity and the moment of inertia of a sphere,

$$L = \tfrac{1}{2}I\omega \tag{13.1.3}$$

The calculation that leads to this result is valid only for a sphere; the same statement cannot be made for a frozen ellipsoidal particle. Another slight difficulty with the frozen-ball concept occurs if we try to apply it at a solid wall. The <u>no-slip condition at the wall</u> means that the particles are not translating; however, they are <u>undergoing a rotation</u>. To compute the rotation of the particle P on the wall we must look at the particle P' a small distance away within the fluid. Note that the velocity derivatives are discontinuous at the wall, so we must compute the vorticity of the fluid particles by using derivatives only on the fluid side. If we wanted to use the frozen-ball idea at the wall, we would need to imagine that the fluid is extended into the wall in such a way that the velocity derivatives are continuous. We might imagine that the wall consists of an array of marbles, which are rotating but remain at the same location on the wall.

The final interpretation is in a somewhat different vein. It connects vorticity and circulation. Circulation, you will recall, was defined (Eq. 3.12.7) as the line integral around a closed circuit,

$$\Gamma = \oint_C t_i v_i \, ds \tag{13.1.4}$$

From Stoke's theorem we have the equivalent expression

$$\Gamma = \int_A n_i \omega_i \, dS \tag{13.1.5}$$

where A is any surface having C as its boundary. In this form we interpret the integrand as the circulation per unit area:

$$n_i \omega_i = \frac{d\Gamma}{dS} \tag{13.1.6}$$

The vorticity is the circulation per unit area for an elemental surface perpendicular to the vorticity vector.

13.2 KINEMATIC RESULTS CONCERNING VORTICITY

Many of the ideas we have associated with the velocity field may be adapted to apply also to the vorticity field. For example, a vortex line is defined as a line that is everywhere tangent to the vorticity vectors. In general, vortex lines are distributed throughout the flow. Sometimes regions of the flow are idealized to have zero vorticity and hence have no vortex lines. For example, in the high-Reynolds-number flow over a wing, the vortex lines are concentrated near the surface and in the wake behind the wing. The flow away from these regions is idealized as irrotational. On the other hand, in the flow in a pipe the vortex lines are rings that exist throughout the fluid.

On a solid, stationary wall the no-slip condition requires that the velocity be zero. Nevertheless, we were able to define a wall streamline by a limiting process (Eq. 12.1.5). Consider a smooth wall, and erect a local coordinate system at a point P on the wall. The wall will lie in the x–z plane with y as the normal direction. A flat wall is assumed for simplicity; the argument is also valid for curved walls.

The vorticity components at the point P on the wall are calculated as follows:

$$\omega_x = \frac{\partial w}{\partial y} - \frac{\partial v}{\partial z} = \frac{\partial w}{\partial y}\bigg|_0$$

$$\omega_y = \frac{\partial u}{\partial z} + \frac{\partial w}{\partial x} = 0 \qquad (13.2.1)$$

$$\omega_z = \frac{\partial v}{\partial x} - \frac{\partial u}{\partial y} = -\frac{\partial u}{\partial y}\bigg|_0$$

The vorticity component perpendicular to the wall is zero, so we know that the vorticity vector lies in the wall. An additional fact of importance is that wall vortex lines are always perpendicular to the wall streamlines. This is found by direct calculation of the slope together with the previous result (Eq. 12.1.5) for streamlines.

$$\frac{dz}{dx}\bigg|_{\text{vortex line}} = \frac{\omega_z}{\omega_x} = \frac{-\partial u/\partial y|_0}{\partial w/\partial y|_0} = \frac{-1}{dz/dx|_{\text{streamline}}} \qquad (13.2.2)$$

Away from the wall, vortex lines and streamlines are not necessarily perpendicular. The primary exceptions are two-dimensional and axisymmetric flows where $\mathbf{v}$ and $\boldsymbol{\omega}$ are perpendicular. In a general three-dimensional flow, the vorticity and velocity vectors are not perpendicular except when the wall is approached.

Everywhere on the surface of a body, the streamlines and vortex lines are orthogonal. When the vorticity is nonzero, a unique direction for the vortex line is assured. If a vortex line leaves the surface, it can only do so at a point (or line) where the vorticity is zero. Just as in the case of streamlines, it is necessary to have $\boldsymbol{\omega} = 0$ at any place where a vortex line splits and goes in several directions. Because of its very definition as the curl of the velocity, we know that the "rate of expansion" for vorticity must be zero. That is, the vector identity $\nabla \cdot \nabla \times \mathbf{v} = 0$ takes the form $\nabla \cdot \boldsymbol{\omega} = 0$ when the vorticity is identified.

The fact that vorticity is a solenoidal vector ($\nabla \cdot \boldsymbol{\omega} = 0$) means that vortex lines and vortex tubes obey the same rules that streamlines and streamtubes obey as a consequence of the fact that $\nabla \cdot \mathbf{v} = 0$; namely, vortex tubes cannot end within the fluid; they must either form closed loops, extend to infinity, or intersect a wall at a place where the vorticity is zero. Another statement that results from the solenoidal condition is derived by considering the integral of $\nabla \cdot \boldsymbol{\omega} = 0$ over any volume and applying Gauss's theorem:

$$0 = \int \partial_i \omega_i \, dV = \int n_i \omega_i \, dS \qquad (13.2.3)$$

This equation may be applied to a vortex tube with end caps A_1 and A_2. On the surface of the vortex tube $n_i \omega_i = 0$, so the only contributions come from the end caps. Equation 13.2.3 implies that the integral over any cross section of a vortex tube is constant:

$$-\int_{A_1} n_i \omega_i \, dS = \int_{A_2} n_i \omega_i \, dS = \Gamma \tag{13.2.4}$$

The integral of $n_i \omega_i$ across a vortex tube is called the *strength* of the vortex tube. Equation 13.2.4 says that the strength of a vortex tube must be constant, and from Eq. 13.1.5 it is equal to the circulation of any circuit around the vortex tube. There is an analogy between Γ and the flow rate Q of a streamtube.

It is well to note that all the results of this section apply to the flow at an instant. In steady flow it is perhaps natural to consider vortex lines and vortex tubes fixed in space. In other words, an identity is given to a vortex tube that goes through the same points in space. We often talk the same way about streamtubes in a steady flow. A streamtube through the same points in space is thought to retain its identity as time goes on. The identity comes from the fact that a fluid particle can be given a Lagrangian identification, a specific x_i^0 in Eq. 4.1.2, and all particles passing a certain Eulerian position will trace the same streamline or particle path. Because ω is generally not in the same direction as $\mathbf{v}$, a vortex line through a Eulerian position in a steady flow does not connect particles of the same identity at later times. Sometimes (in inviscid flow) it is advantageous as well as permissible to imagine that vortex lines in a steady flow are not stationary, but move along with the fluid velocity. More discussion concerning this will be given later. The major point of the present discussion is that Eq. 13.2.4 applies at any instant to any vortex tube. At the next instant in time the definition of the vortex tube can change in any manner we choose.

Earlier in the book, we remarked that the term *vortex* generally refers to a flow in which the fluid swirls. A collection or concentration of vortex lines is not necessarily a vortex. Several rigorous mathematical definitions of a vortex have been offered. The reader should consult the work of Jeong and Hussain (1995) for a definition and discussion of previous alternative definitions.

13.3   VORTICITY EQUATION

The dynamic equation that governs vorticity is derived from the momentum equation. We start with the momentum equation for incompressible flow,

$$\partial_0 v_i + v_j \partial_j v_i = -\frac{1}{\rho} \partial_i p + \nu \partial_j \partial_j v_i \tag{13.3.1}$$

Into this equation we substitute the vector identity (Problem 3.15)

$$v_j \partial_j v_i = \partial_i (\tfrac{1}{2} v_j v_j) + \varepsilon_{ijk} \omega_j v_k \tag{13.3.2}$$

The resulting equation is differentiated with ∂_q and multiplied by ε_{pqi} to yield

$$\partial_0 (\varepsilon_{pqi} \partial_q v_i) + \varepsilon_{pqi} \partial_q \partial_i (\tfrac{1}{2} v_j v_j) + \varepsilon_{pqi} \partial_q (\varepsilon_{ijk} \omega_j v_k) = -\frac{1}{\rho} \varepsilon_{pqi} \partial_q \partial_i p + \nu \varepsilon_{pqi} \partial_j \partial_j \partial_q v_i$$

$$\tag{13.3.3}$$

Consider this equation term by term. The first term can be identified as the time derivative of the vorticity. The second term is zero because ε_{pqi} is antisymmetric and $\partial_q \partial_i$ is symmetric; the same can be said for the pressure term on the right-hand side. Moreover, note that the last term contains the vorticity. The term we skipped is expanded to yield (the last line below is obtained by noting that $\partial_k v_k$ and $\partial_j \omega_j$ are always zero)

$$\varepsilon_{pqi}\varepsilon_{ijk}\partial_q(\omega_j v_k) = \partial_k(\omega_p v_k) - \partial_j(\omega_j v_p) \tag{13.3.4}$$

$$= v_k\partial_k\omega_p - \omega_j\partial_j v_p$$

Collecting these results yields the final vorticity transport equation:

$$\partial_0\omega_i + v_j\partial_j\omega_i = \omega_j\partial_j v_i + \nu\partial_j\partial_j\omega_i$$

or in symbolic notation,

$$\underset{\substack{\text{rate of change of}\\\text{particle vorticity}}}{\frac{D\boldsymbol\omega}{Dt}} = \underset{\substack{\text{rate of deforming}\\\text{vortex lines}}}{\boldsymbol\omega \cdot \nabla\mathbf{v}} + \underset{\substack{\text{net rate of viscous}\\\text{diffusion of }\boldsymbol\omega}}{\nu\nabla^2\boldsymbol\omega} \tag{13.3.5}$$

This equation is almost as important to fluid mechanics as the momentum equation itself.

One of the most interesting things about the vorticity equation 13.3.5 is not what appears, but what does not appear: namely, the pressure. The usefulness of vorticity in interpreting fluid-flow problems is that vorticity tracks only the effect of viscous forces; pressure and gravity forces do not change the vorticity directly. The physical reason behind this has to do with the fact that vorticity is an indicator of solid-body rotation. Pressure forces and gravity forces act through the center of mass of a particle and cannot produce a rotation. On the other hand, shear stresses act tangentially at the surface of a particle and, if they are unbalanced, will generate vorticity.

The intimate connection between unbalanced shear stresses, or viscous action, and vorticity is made even clearer by noting that the viscous term in the momentum equation can be written as (Problems 3.18 and 6.4)

$$\nabla \cdot \boldsymbol\tau = \mu\nabla^2\mathbf{v} = -\mu\nabla \times \boldsymbol\omega \tag{13.3.6}$$

An unbalanced shear stress can exist only when the vorticity is nonzero. As a general rule the existence of vorticity means that a particle is, or at least in its past history was, subjected to net viscous forces.

As an aside, one should note that Eq. 13.3.5 is not the proper vorticity equation for a stratified flow of an incompressible fluid. The density gradient in these flows implies that the center of mass of a particle does not coincide with its geometric center. Since pressure forces act through the geometric center, they can now generate rotational motion. This is one of the distinctive characteristics of stratified flows. Internal vorticity generation processes occur in the oceans and the atmosphere when density differences are significant.

13.4   VORTICITY DIFFUSION

This section deals with the physical meaning and interpretation of $\nu\nabla^2\boldsymbol\omega$, the last term in the vorticity equation of Eq. 13.3.5. It shows that vorticity can diffuse through a flow by viscous action in the same way that momentum diffuses. There is also an analogy with heat transport. Recall that the thermal energy equation, after simplification for incompressible flow with constant temperature boundaries, is

$$\rho c_p \frac{DT}{Dt} = k\nabla^2 T \tag{13.4.1}$$

Comparing this equation with Eq. 13.3.5, we see that there is an analogy between vorticity and temperature in plane two-dimensional flows. These flows have only one vorticity component ω_z, and since $\boldsymbol{\omega} \cdot \nabla \mathbf{v}$ is always zero, the equation governing ω_z is of the same form as Eq. 13.4.1. The fact that vorticity takes on negative values is immaterial, as the temperature could include an arbitrary reference level without changing the governing equation. All of the problems in Chapters 7 and 11 obey this analogy except for von Kármán's problem and pressure-driven flow in tubes of arbitrary cross section, which are not plane flows.

In most of the steady-state problems—pressure-driven flow in a slot, Couette flow, and the falling film—the vorticity obeys the simplified equation

$$0 = \frac{\partial^2 \omega}{\partial y^2}$$

The vorticity is distributed so that the vorticity "flux," in analogy with the heat flux q, is constant:

$$\frac{\partial \omega}{\partial y} = \text{const}$$

The unsteady problems—Rayleigh's problem, Stokes's problem, the oscillating pressure gradient in a slot, and the vortex decay problems—are classical diffusion problems. They all obey a vorticity equation of the form

$$\frac{\partial \omega}{\partial t} = \nu \frac{\partial^2 \omega}{\partial y^2} \tag{13.4.2}$$

The rate of change of vorticity at a point is equal to the net diffusion flux into the point. Note especially that the viscous diffusion of momentum and of vorticity have the same diffusivity constant ν.

We learned from these problems that the depth of penetration of viscous diffusion obeyed a relation of the form

$$\delta \propto \sqrt{\nu t} \tag{13.4.3}$$

The viscous diffusion length is independent of the size of the vorticity pulse that occurs at the boundary. For example, in Rayleigh's problem the magnitude of the impulsive velocity given to the plate does not affect the diffusion length.

The velocity of viscous diffusion (the velocity of the edge of the viscous layer) depends on the distance from the source. That is,

$$\frac{d\delta}{dt} \sim \sqrt{\frac{\nu}{t}} \sim \frac{\nu}{\delta} \tag{13.4.4}$$

This is the velocity with which the viscous layer diffuses away from the plate.

The plane stagnation-point problem of Chapter 11 shows a balance between viscous diffusion and convection. In this flow, convection occurs by both u and v flow velocities. The proper equation is

$$u\frac{\partial \omega}{\partial x} + v\frac{\partial \omega}{\partial y} = \nu\frac{\partial^2 \omega}{\partial y^2}$$

Diffusion of vorticity in the y-direction is counteracted by the downward convection from the negative v velocity and the outward convection by the u velocity. A constant thickness of the vortical region $\delta \approx \sqrt{\nu/a}$ results. Again the viscous thickness is proportional to $\sqrt{\nu}$.

Another way to find this relation is to equate the magnitude of the flow toward the wall ($v = -ay$) and the diffusion velocity

$$|v| = \frac{d\delta}{dt} \quad \text{or} \quad a\delta = \frac{\nu}{\delta}$$

The location δ is where these velocities balance. The Burgers vortex has the same characteristics except in cylindrical geometry.

13.5   VORTICITY INTENSIFICATION BY STRAINING VORTEX LINES

Next, look at the first term on the right-hand side of Eq. 13.3.5; namely, $\boldsymbol{\omega} \cdot \nabla\mathbf{v}$. This term represents the generation or destruction of vorticity by two processes: stretching or turning the vortex lines. To back up this interpretation let us consider a material line with two points dr_j apart. The motion of dr_j with time was computed in Eq. 4.6.3 as

$$\frac{\partial(dr_j)}{\partial\hat{t}} = dr_i\partial_i v_j \tag{13.5.1}$$

This equation has exactly the same form as Eq. 13.3.5 when the viscous term in the latter equation is ignored. The vorticity vector ω_j plays a role analogous to the material line vector dr_j. Stretching a vortex line produces vorticity in the same way that stretching a material line produces length. Such a process is, of course, reversible: The contraction of a vortex line decreases the vorticity. There is also another effect in the term $\boldsymbol{\omega} \cdot \nabla\mathbf{v}$: that of turning by angular strain. The vector nature of ω_i (and dr_i) means that turning a vortex line creates vorticity in one direction at the expense of vorticity in another direction.

This is more clearly seen by noting that in the term $\boldsymbol{\omega} \cdot \nabla\mathbf{v}$, the velocity gradient may be replaced by the rate-of-strain tensor, that is,

$$\omega_i\partial_i v_j = \omega_i\partial_{(i}v_{j)} = \omega_i S_{ij} = |\omega|\, d_j^{(\omega)} \tag{13.5.2}$$

Here $d_j^{(\omega)}$ is the strain vector (Eq. 4.4.6) for the vorticity direction $\omega_i/|\omega| = n_i$. (Proof of this equation follows by substituting Eq. 3.5.13 for the velocity gradient: $\omega_i\partial_i v_j = \omega_i[\partial_{(i}v_{j)} + \frac{1}{2}\varepsilon_{kij}\omega_k]$. The last term is zero because $\omega_i\omega_k$ is symmetric and ε_{kij} is antisymmetric.) To illustrate further, write out the vorticity equation 13.3.5, and insert Eq. 13.5.2. The term $|\omega|d_j^{(\omega)}$ is the magnitude of the vorticity times the strain rate between two particles on the vortex line, that is, the strain vector $d_j^{(\omega)}$. The strain vector has a component along the vortex line (extension of the line) and perpendicular to the line (vortex line turning). The decomposition into these components is a complicated expression:

$$\frac{D\boldsymbol{\omega}}{Dt} = |\boldsymbol{\omega}|\ \mathbf{d}^{(\omega)} = |\boldsymbol{\omega}|\ [\alpha \cdot (\alpha \cdot \mathbf{d}^{(\omega)}) + \alpha \times (\mathbf{d}^{(\omega)} \times \alpha)] \qquad (13.5.3)$$

The first term on the right-hand side is vorticity generated by stretching the vortex line while the second term is vorticity generated by turning the vortex line with angular deformations.

In making the interpretation that the $\boldsymbol{\omega} \cdot \nabla \mathbf{v}$ term represents vortex line turning and stretching, we have tacitly assumed that the vortex line at any instant is a material line moving with the fluid velocity. This is, in fact, true is inviscid flows, where the viscous diffusion is zero. For this case the analogy between the motion of a material line governed by Eq. 13.5.1 and that of a vortex line governed by Eq. 13.3.5 is exact. In viscous flows, where the diffusion term is nonzero, we must qualify our interpretation because vortex lines cannot be given an identity and treated as moving with the fluid. Under these circumstances we can say that $\boldsymbol{\omega} \cdot \nabla \mathbf{v}$ generates vorticity *as if* the vortex line were moving as a material line.

As noted earlier, the stretching and turning mechanism is absent in all plane flow. In such flows the vorticity vector is perpendicular to the velocity vector, so the vortex lines are perpendicular to the plane of the flow. Since everything is uniform in the vortex line direction, the lines have a constant length and do not turn. Other flows where $\boldsymbol{\omega} \cdot \nabla \mathbf{v}$ is always zero include the unidirectional flows of the first example of Chapter 11. In these flows the vortex lines form closed loops perpendicular to the straight streamlines. They do not turn or expand.

13.6   HILL'S SPHERICAL VORTEX

There is an interesting example of a flow in which the stretching of vortex lines plays a dominant role. Hill's (1894) spherical vortex is a model of the internal flow in a gas bubble moving in a liquid, or a droplet of an immiscible liquid moving through another liquid. Because of the motion outside the bubble, an internal circulation is set up. Figure 13.1 gives a diagram of the geometry and sets a cylindrical coordinate system moving with the bubble so that the internal flow is steady. The vortex lines for this flow are circular loops around the z-axis. As the flow carries vortex lines to positions of larger radius, the loops increase in length, $2\pi r$, in direct proportion to the radius. Due to the vortex line stretching effect, the vorticity is therefore proportional to the radius:

$$\omega_\theta = Cr = \frac{5U}{R}\frac{2\pi r}{2\pi R} \qquad (13.6.1)$$

The constant C has been given the value $5U/2R$ for reasons that will surface later (it turns out that Hill's vortex solution satisfies the complete Navier–Stokes equations, including the viscous terms).

Let us examine the vorticity equation 13.3.5 as it applies to Hill's vortex. Only the θ component has nonzero vorticity. The terms in Eq. 13.3.5 are as follows:

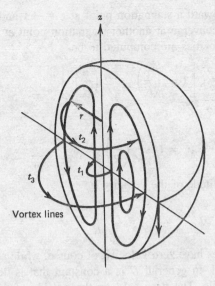

Figure 13.1 Hill's spherical vortex. Vortex lines are complete circles. Those shown are for the same fluid particles at three different times. Kidney-shaped lines are streamlines. Left one-half of the sphere is cut away for clarity.

Convection:
$$\frac{D\omega_\theta}{Dt} = v_r \frac{\partial \omega_\theta}{\partial r} = C v_r$$

Stretching:
$$\boldsymbol{\omega} \cdot \nabla \mathbf{v}|_\theta = \omega_\theta \frac{v_r}{r} = C v_r$$

Diffusion:
$$\nu \nabla^2 \omega|_\theta = \nu \frac{\partial}{\partial r}\left[\frac{1}{r}\frac{\partial}{\partial r}(r\omega_\theta)\right] = 0$$

Thus, the vorticity balance is between convection and stretching without any net viscous diffusion.

Although this is a completely viscous problem, there is no net diffusion of vorticity. In this case we can imagine that the vortex lines are material lines that move with the fluid. The increase in vorticity is wholly the result of generation by vortex line stretching. The fact that v_r does not have to be specified emphasizes that any movement of the circular vortex lines is allowed as long as the vorticity is proportional to the circumference of the loop.

Let us digress for a moment to give the complete details of Hill's solution. The streamfunction for this flow is given by

$$\psi = \frac{UR^2}{2}\left(\frac{r}{R}\right)^2\left[1 - \left(\frac{z}{R}\right)^2 - \left(\frac{r}{R}\right)^2\right] \tag{13.6.2}$$

Thus ψ is zero on the axis of the bubble ($r = 0$) and over the spherical surface given by

$$\left(\frac{r}{R}\right)^2 + \left(\frac{z}{R}\right)^2 = 1$$

The flow goes along the axis toward a stagnation point at $z = +1$ and then around the outer portion of the bubble to converge at another stagnation point at $z = 1$. From the formulas of Chapter 12, the velocities are computed to be

$$v_z = U\left[1 - \left(\frac{z}{R}\right)^2 - 2\left(\frac{r}{R}\right)^2\right]$$

and

$$v_r = U \cdot \frac{r}{R}\left(\frac{z}{R}\right)$$

At the bubble surface, the magnitude of the velocity is

$$(v_r^2 + v_z^2)^{1/2} = U \cdot \frac{r}{R}$$

The stagnation points at the poles have zero velocity, of course, while at the equator, the maximum velocity U is attained. In general, U is a constant that is determined by the flow on the outside of the bubble. The flow field on the outside of the bubble can be found for the two special cases of low and high Reynolds numbers (Sections 19.8 and 21.8).

13.7 PRODUCTION OF VORTICITY AT A STATIONARY WALL

A fixed solid wall is the source of the vorticity that enters the flow above it. The first fact of importance is the direct connection between the viscous shear stress on the wall and the vorticity. We restrict the discussion to Newtonian fluids. At a solid wall a Newtonian fluid has no normal viscous force; the viscous stress vector lies in the wall and has the same direction as the wall streamline.

To relate the vorticity and the wall shear stress, consider a flat wall with a coordinate system at a point P with x–z along the wall and y normal to the wall (see Fig. 13.2).

The results of Section 12.1 showed that on the wall many velocity derivatives are zero:

$$\frac{\partial u}{\partial x} = 0, \qquad \frac{\partial w}{\partial z} = 0, \qquad \frac{\partial v}{\partial y} = 0 \qquad (13.7.1)$$

First, consider the simplest case by choosing the streamline to lie along the x-axis ($\theta = 0$ in Eq. 12.1.5). Then $w = 0$ and

$$\left.\frac{\partial w}{\partial y}\right|_0 = 0 \qquad (13.7.2)$$

A computation of the viscous stress on the wall, inserting Eqs. 13.7.1 and 13.7.2, yields

$$\mathbf{F}_{j \text{ viscous}} = n_i \tau_{ij} \qquad (13.7.3)$$

$$\mathbf{F}_{x \text{ viscous}} = n_y \tau_{yx} = \mu \frac{\partial u}{\partial y}$$

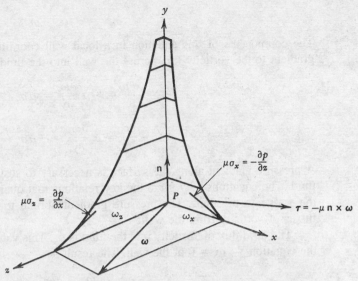

Figure 13.2   Vorticity and vorticity flux at a solid wall.

Now, from Eq. 13.2.1 note that $\omega_z = -\partial u/\partial y$ ($\omega_x = \omega_y - 0$). Hence, Eq. 13.7.3 becomes

$$F_{x \text{ viscous}} = -\mu \omega_z \tag{13.7.4}$$

The wall vorticity is directly proportional to the wall shear stress.

A direct calculation in an arbitrary coordinate system will shown that Eq. 13.7.4 is a special case of the general expression

$$F_{\text{viscous}} = \mathbf{n} \cdot \boldsymbol{\tau} = -\mu \mathbf{n} \times \boldsymbol{\omega} \tag{13.7.5}$$

The wall shear and the vorticity are directly related, with the viscosity as the proportionality constant. In terms of the temperature analogy we can think of the wall shear stress as the *vorticity temperature*. When the wall shear is high, the vorticity is large.

Just as the temperature of a wall does not indicate how much energy is leaving the wall, the wall vorticity does not indicate how much vorticity flux is entering the flow. Recall that the heat flux equation says that the heat flux across a plane with orientation n_i is given by $n_i q_i$, where q_i is the heat flux vector. By analogy, we define the vorticity flux σ_i as the inner product with the *vorticity flux tensor*, that is,

$$\sigma_i \equiv -n_j \partial_j \omega_i \tag{13.7.6}$$

(Note the analogy with the stress and the stress tensor.) The vector σ_i is the flux of i vorticity across a plane with normal n_j. [This viewpoint is due to Lighthill (1963).]

We can find out about σ_i at the wall from the momentum equation. Consider the momentum equation in the form (Eq. 12.5.4)

$$\partial_0 v_i + \partial_i \left(\frac{1}{2} v^2 + \frac{p}{\rho} \right) = -\varepsilon_{ijk} \omega_j v_k - \nu \varepsilon_{ijk} \partial_j \omega_k \tag{13.7.7}$$

Evaluating this equation at the wall where $v_i = 0$ yields

$$\partial_i p = -\mu \varepsilon_{ijk} \partial_j \omega_k \qquad (13.7.8)$$

The components of this equation in a local wall coordinate system relate the pressure gradient to the vorticity flux across the wall into the fluid. The components are

$$\frac{\partial p}{\partial x} = -\mu \frac{\partial \omega_z}{\partial y} = \mu \sigma_z$$

$$\frac{\partial p}{\partial z} = \mu \frac{\partial \omega_x}{\partial y} = -\mu \sigma_x \qquad (13.7.9)$$

A pressure gradient along the surface is necessary to sustain a flux of vorticity into the fluid. The equations 13.7.9 are the key relations that quantify the flux of vorticity from the wall into the fluid. The pressure gradient normal to the wall, $\partial p / \partial y$, is related to fluxes of vorticity from the wall.

The third flux of vorticity into the fluid is σ_y. This value may be found by evaluating the equation $\nabla \cdot \boldsymbol{\omega} = 0$ at the wall. The result is

$$\sigma_y = -\frac{\partial \omega_y}{\partial y} = \frac{\partial \omega_x}{\partial x} + \frac{\partial \omega_z}{\partial z} \qquad (13.7.10)$$

Although ω_y is zero at the wall, there may be a flux of ω_y vorticity out of the wall. This flux depends on the distribution of ω_x and ω_z on the wall itself.

Up to this point a major theme has been that pressure does not influence vorticity. More precisely, it does not do so directly. The pressure gradient–vorticity flux relation in Eq. 13.7.9 gives a coupling whereby pressure forces associated with inviscid motions can introduce vorticity into the fluid. It was indicated previously that the major mechanism for generating vorticity was the torque produced by an unbalanced shear stress. A little analysis will convince us that this is also true at the wall. For particles at the wall the momentum equation reduces to

$$0 = -\frac{1}{\rho} \partial_i p + \partial_j \tau_{ji} \qquad (13.7.11)$$

Since particles at the wall are restrained from gaining linear momentum, any pressure gradient must be exactly canceled by the unbalanced shear. Hence, in this special situation, the vorticity-producing stresses can be replaced by the pressure gradient. Fluid particles at a wall cannot have a linear translational velocity, but they do indeed have a "rotational" velocity.

13.8 PRODUCTION OF VORTICITY AT A TRANSLATING WALL

Consider a body that has an arbitrary translation velocity $V_i(t)$ as depicted in Fig. 13.3. We focus attention on a local neighborhood of the wall where the moving $\hat{x}_i$ coordinate system is located. The wall in this coordinate system is stationary. The flow, as observed from the translating coordinate system, is governed by the usual incompressible equations (see Section 10.7) except for the pressure. In the moving frame the equations contain a pseudo-pressure $\hat{p}$. If we perform the analysis of Section 13.7 in the frame moving with

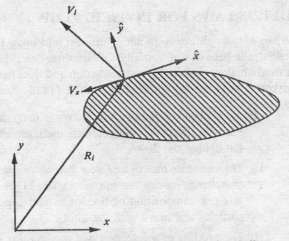

Figure 13.3 Vorticity flux at a moving wall.

the wall (note that the analysis of Section 13.7 is valid for an unsteady flow above a stationary wall) the flux of vorticity into the fluid is

$$\frac{\partial \hat{p}}{\partial r} = -\mu \frac{\partial \omega_z}{\partial y} = \mu \sigma_z \qquad (13.7.9)$$

However, the pseudopressure is $\hat{p} = p + \rho x_i (dV_i/dt) = p + \rho x (dV_x/dt) + \rho y (dV_y/dt)$ (Eq. 10.7.6). Evaluating Eq. 13.7.9 gives

$$\mu \sigma_z = \frac{\partial p}{\partial x} + \rho \frac{dV_x}{dt} \qquad (13.8.1)$$

The flux of z-vorticity into the fluid is given by the actual pressure gradient plus the acceleration of the wall in the x-direction. In a similar manner one finds that

$$-\mu \sigma_y = \frac{\partial p}{\partial y} + \rho \frac{dV_y}{dt} \qquad (13.8.2)$$

The flux of vorticity from a wall depends on the sliding acceleration of the wall. The pressure gradient in the normal direction and the normal wall acceleration do not produce a flux of vorticity into the fluid. However, this motion may set up a true pressure gradient along the wall, which does contribute.

An expanding sphere generates an irrotational potential flow (Chapter 12) because the wall motion is always in the normal direction. A plane wall, such as a piston or loudspeaker, moving only in the normal direction, would also generate a potential motion. On the other hand, a sliding wall such as the Rayleigh flat plate generates vorticity because of the wall motion in its own plane. The actual dp/dx in the fluid is zero, but the contribution of $\rho \, dV_x/dt$ is important. Vorticity flux generation occurs only during the acceleration phase. Once a steady velocity is attained, the vorticity flux becomes zero. An impulsive motion can be regarded as a finite amount of vorticity that is dumped into the flow at the initial instant.

13.9 HELMHOLTZ'S LAWS FOR INVISCID FLOW

When viscous diffusion is not significant and body forces can be represented by a potential, the behavior of vorticity follows three laws due to Helmholtz. In many instances a fluid obtains vorticity by viscous action and then the subsequent motion is inviscid; the viscous forces are negligible. Helmholtz's (1858; translated by Tait, 1867) laws are:

I. *No element of fluid, which was not originally in rotation, is made to rotate.* Particles originally without vorticity in an inviscid flow remain without vorticity throughout the flow.

II. *The elements that at any time belong to one vortex line, however they may be translated, remain on one vortex line.* One may envision that vortex lines or tubes, a composition of lines with end caps, always constitute the same fluid particles and move with the fluid.

III. *The product of the section and the angular velocity of an infinitely thin vortex filament is constant throughout its whole length and retains the same value during all displacements of the filament. Hence, vortex filaments must be closed curves or must have their ends in the bounding surface of the fluid.* This essentially means that Γ = constant of Eq. 13.2.4 applies for all time to a material vortex tube moving with the fluid.

Consider the vorticity equation 13.3.5 for a situation where the viscous term is negligible. In Lagrangian independent variables it is

$$\frac{d\omega}{d\hat{t}} = \boldsymbol{\omega} \cdot \nabla \mathbf{v} \qquad (13.9.1)$$

Assume that a fluid particle initially has no vorticity, $\omega = 0$. One solution of Eq. 13.9.1 is $\omega = 0$ for all subsequent times. If $\nabla \mathbf{v}$ is continuous and we consider it as known, the theory of ordinary differential equations shows that Eq. 13.9.1 has a unique solution and this solution must be $\omega = 0$. This is the mathematical statement of law I.

Equation 13.9.1 has the same form as the relation for the motion of a material line element, Eq. 4.6.3:

$$\frac{d(\delta \mathbf{r})}{d\hat{t}} = \delta \mathbf{r} \cdot \nabla \mathbf{v} \qquad (13.9.2)$$

At time zero choose a point P and select $\delta \mathbf{r}$ (the vector to a neighboring particle P') to lie in the same direction as ω. The magnitudes are related $\delta \mathbf{r} = \varepsilon \omega$ for some number ε. Multiplying Eq. 13.9.1 by ε and subtracting from Eq. 13.9.2 gives Whitham (1963)

$$\frac{d(\delta \mathbf{r} - \varepsilon \omega)}{d\hat{t}} = (\delta \mathbf{r} - \varepsilon \omega) \cdot \nabla \mathbf{v} \qquad (13.9.3)$$

Since $\delta \mathbf{r} - \varepsilon \omega = 0$ initially, one solution for all time is

$$\delta \mathbf{r} = \varepsilon \omega \qquad (13.9.4)$$

Again, applying the uniqueness theorem (for continuous $\nabla\mathbf{v}$) means that this is the only solution. The vorticity vector of a material particle is a constant fraction of the material line differential. As a particle moves through the flow, the vorticity vector always points to the same neighbor. If the distance to the neighbor increases there is a proportional increase in ω. It is therefore permissible to imagine that vortex lines follow the flow and connect the same material particles as they move along as stated in law II.

The third law states that the strength of a material vortex tube is constant as it moves through the flow. One may prove this as follows: Construct a vortex tube at some instant. With the aid of law II we can visualize that the tube follows the same material particles as time proceeds. The analysis of Section 13.3 is applied to this material vortex tube to show that Eq. 13.2.4 holds for all time.

13.10 KELVIN'S THEOREM

Kelvin's theorem concerns the change in circulation of a set of material particles. Consider the circulation around a certain loop, and follow the material particles as they move. The symbol Γ_{ml} will emphasize that as time proceeds the same material loop is to be used in the calculation. It will be an aid in the mathematics if we consider distances along the material curve to be a function of a parameter m. As m goes from m_1 to m_2 we proceed around the curve and return to the starting point. From the definition of circulation we have

$$\Gamma_{\text{ml}} = \oint_C t_i v_i \, ds = \oint_C v_i \, dr_i = \int_{m_1}^{m_2} v_i \frac{\partial r_i}{\partial m} \, dm$$

where ml = material line.

The quantities v_i and r_i are formulated in Lagrangian variables: $v_i(r_0, \hat{t})$ and $r_i(r_0, \hat{t})$ [or, with m as a parameter specifying the curve, $r_i(r_0(m), \hat{t})$]. The time rate of change of the circulation is computed as follows:

$$\frac{d\Gamma_{\text{ml}}}{d\hat{t}} = \frac{d}{d\hat{t}} \int_{m_1}^{m_2} v_i \frac{\partial r_i}{\partial m} \, dm$$

$$= \int_{m_1}^{m_2} \frac{\partial v_i}{\partial \hat{t}} \frac{\partial r_i}{\partial m} \, dm + \int_{m_1}^{m_2} v_i \frac{\partial}{\partial \hat{t}} \left(\frac{\partial r_i}{\partial m} \right) dm$$

The second integral turns out to be zero (see Eq. 4.1.3), since

$$\int v_i \frac{\partial (dr_i)}{\partial \hat{t}} = \int v_i \, dv_i = \int d\left(\frac{1}{2} v_i v_i \right) = 0$$

The beginning and end points of the circuit are identical and have the same velocity. We are left with

$$\frac{d\Gamma_{\text{ml}}}{d\hat{t}} = \oint \frac{\partial v_i}{\partial \hat{t}} \, dr_i$$

Converting the expression to Eulerian variables gives

$$\frac{D\Gamma_{ml}}{Dt} = \oint \frac{Dv_i}{Dt}\, dx_i$$

Further simplification can be found if we substitute the momentum equation for incompressible flow. This produces

$$\frac{D\Gamma_{ml}}{Dt} = \oint \left[-\partial_i \left(\frac{p}{\rho}\right) + \nu\partial_j\partial_j v_i \right] dx_i$$

Noting that the pressure term integrates to zero yields Kelvin's theorem,

$$\frac{D\Gamma_{ml}}{Dt} = \oint \nu\partial_j\partial_j v_i\, dx_i \tag{13.10.1}$$

The circulation around a material loop of particles changes only if the net viscous force on those particles gives a nonzero integral. For the special case of inviscid flow, the right side is zero and the circulation of a material loop never changes.

13.11 INVISCID MOTION OF POINT VORTICES

The idea of inviscid motion of vortex lines might at first seem paradoxical, since vorticity must be generated by unbalanced viscous forces. However, there are many instances when the net viscous force produces vorticity in a transient process and the subsequent flow occurs as an inviscid flow carrying vorticity. A smoke ring is such an example. After the ring is generated, the vorticity is confined to a thin ring, but the fluid motion occurs in a much larger region. Even a region that is permeated with vorticity (so to speak) may behave in an inviscid manner in certain instances. Since viscous diffusion is such a slow process, events on a time scale much shorter than the diffusion time may be considered as inviscid. For such events vortex lines are material lines and move with the flow.

Let us consider a specific example. Assume that two potential line vortices of opposite rotation are a distance $2h$ apart. We view the line vortex as a collection of vortex lines, or a vortex tube, which has been shrunk to zero area. There must actually be a core of finite size, but it is not important for the present problem. The flow everywhere outside the core is irrotational and therefore inviscid. By Helmholtz's laws, vortex lines may be regarded as material lines, and hence they move with the local fluid velocity. A single vortex by itself has no tendency to move, but two counterrotating vortices propel each other through the fluid. The problem for the velocity field is linear. The velocity at any point is the vector sum of the velocity from vortex A and that from vortex B. The velocity field due to vortex A has a magnitude v_A given by (Eq. 11.8.1)

$$v_A(\mathbf{r}) = \frac{\Gamma}{2\pi|\mathbf{r} - \mathbf{r}_A|}, \qquad \mathbf{r} \neq \mathbf{r}_A \tag{13.11.1}$$

The direction of v_A is perpendicular to $\mathbf{r} - \mathbf{r}_A$. This equation is valid everywhere except at the core position $\mathbf{r} = \mathbf{r}_A$, where the viscous forces are important and $v_A(r_A) = 0$. Vortex B has a negative circulation, while vortex A, with a positive circulation, is a distance $2h$ away. We regard vortex B as a material line and require that it move with the local fluid velocity. The velocity of vortex B is the motion induced at B by the velocity field of vortex A:

$$v_A(\mathbf{r} = \mathbf{r}_B) = V_B = \frac{\Gamma}{4\pi h} \tag{13.11.2}$$

Similarly, the core of vortex A is propelled at the same speed by the flow set up by vortex B. Figure 13.4 shows the fluid motion set up by the vortices.

Thus, one can observe that the vortices set up by the stroke of a canoe paddle are not stationary but propel themselves through the water in a direction opposite the motion of the boat. The same mechanism is responsible for the motion of a smoke ring. When a pair of self-propelled vortices approach a solid wall, a very interesting series of events happen. The inviscid events are easily described by replacing the wall with a mirror-image set of vortices. The symmetry of the arrangement makes the x-axis a streamline, which as far as inviscid flow is concerned can be taken as a wall. As the vortex pair approaches the wall, the image vortices become important, and the velocity induced by them pushes the vortices along the wall. The closer to the wall the vortex comes, the faster the image vortex will propel it along. One can show by calculation that the trajectories of the vortices form a curve known as the *cross curve*.

This argument can be extended to apply to a ring vortex encountering a wall. Now, as the vortex nears the wall and begins to move outward, it must stretch. Stretching results in a proportional increase in the vorticity. For example, one can observe the increase in rotation of a smoke ring as it nears a wall. An extensive discussion of the dynamics at concentrated regions of vorticity is Saffman (1992). Another example is the

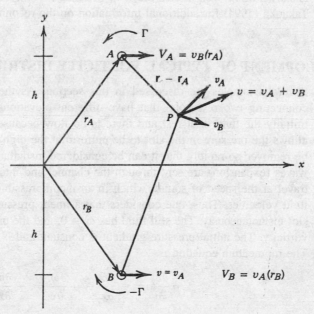

Figure 13.4 Motion of a pair of line vortices by self-induction.

motion of two concentric vortex rings of opposite rotation investigated by Weidman and Riley (1993).

13.12 RECONNECTION OF VORTEX LINES

Vortex lines can undergo interesting topological histories that include splicing together and splitting apart. The experimental evidence is most clearly presented by the interaction of vortices in an otherwise inviscid flow. Rouse in his 1964 film directed two vortex rings toward each other with a small angle of intersection (Fig. 13.5). The two vortices fuse together and the junction then splits apart to form into one elliptic ring vortex that oscillates in shape. For the vortex lines of two rings to become a single vortex, the lines must fuse together; that is, they intersect in a "stagnation" point of vorticity. Subsequently, the vorticity lines split and separate to make a single ring. This vortex line cutting and connecting process must involve viscosity to some extent, however, the event takes place on a very rapid time scale and the involvement of viscosity may be minor. The time between frames in Fig. 13.5 is $\frac{1}{24}$ s.

A similar event can occur with two line vortices of opposite rotation that come together as seen in Fig. 22.17 (see also Van Dyke, 1982). Here the vortices come from the tips of an airplane wing. They fuse together at several places and form ring vortices that dissipate.

If the angle between the colliding rings is larger, the rings merge, splice together, and then split apart into two new rings. The new rings move in a plane perpendicular to the original plane, and each ring contains core fluid from both of the original rings. This is shown in the well-known thesis of Schatzle (1987). The reader is referred to Kida and Takaoka (1994) for additional information on the reconnection phenomenon.

13.13 DEVELOPMENT OF TYPICAL VORTICITY DISTRIBUTIONS

Several examples are discussed in this section. As the first example, consider a slot connecting two reservoirs that have different elevations, as in Fig. 7.1. Consider that initially the fluid is at rest and there is no flow because a cover at the exit of the slot allows the pressure in the slot to be uniform at the high value (Fig. 13.6). Let the cover be removed so rapidly that it can be considered instantaneous. As this happens, pressure waves (expansion) are sent through the channel and into the left reservoir. These waves travel at the speed of sound, which in an incompressible flow is very fast compared to fluid velocities. Thus, one considers that a linear pressure gradient is established in the slot instantaneously. The still fluid has $\omega = 0$, and the pressure forces do not impart any vorticity. The initial pressure gradient is constant and is required to accelerate the fluid. The momentum equation is

$$\rho \, \frac{\partial v_x}{\partial t} = -\frac{\partial p}{\partial x} - \mu \, \frac{\partial \omega_z}{\partial y} = -\frac{\partial p}{\partial x} - \mu \sigma_z \qquad (13.13.1)$$

Here the viscous force has been expressed as a flux of vorticity (Eqs. 13.3.6 and 13.7.3). Although the initial vorticity is zero, there is a vorticity flux at each wall:

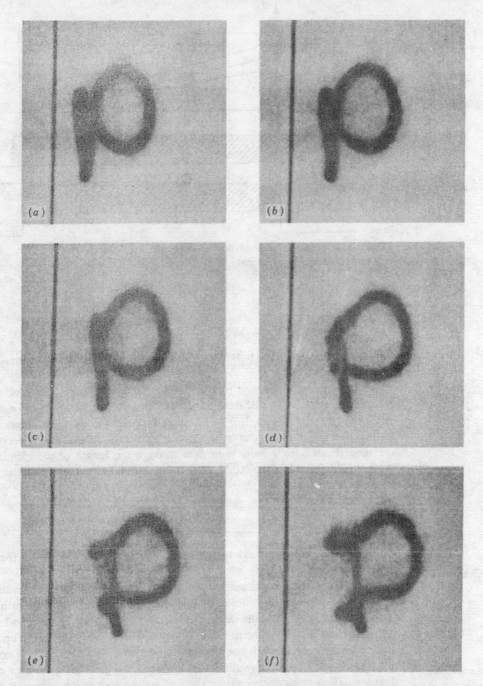

Figure 13.5   Collision of two vortex rings. Rings are moving left to right with a small approach angle. From the film *Characteristics of Laminar and Turbulent Flow,* by H. Rouse, 1964, University of Iowa Audiovisual Center.

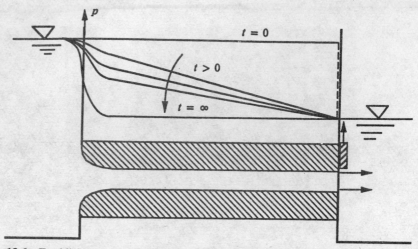

Figure 13.6 Establishment of flow through a channel for the case $t_{vis} \gg t_{flo}$; Re $\rightarrow \infty$. Vorticity is limited to a thin layer near the walls.

$$-\frac{\partial p}{\partial x} = \mu \sigma_z \big|_0 \qquad (13.13.2)$$

The final state and how it is established depends on the competition of pressure and viscous effects.

There are two important time scales to consider. The viscous time scale is the time it takes for vorticity to diffuse halfway across a slot of width h. By using the Rayleigh analogy, $t_{vis} = (h/7.2)^2/\nu$. If $h = 10$ cm and the fluid is air, t_{vis} is about 30 s. For a more viscous fluid such as vegetable oil ($\nu = 1.1$ cm^2/s), $t_{vis} = 2$ s. The second time scale is the time it takes for a particle to flow through the length of the channel. We estimate $t_{flo} = L/U$, where L is the length of the channel and U is the average velocity. The ratio of the time scales is

$$\frac{t_{vis}}{t_{flo}} \sim \frac{h^2}{\nu}\frac{U}{L} = \frac{h}{L}\,\text{Re} \qquad (13.13.3)$$

One could also couch the discussion in terms of a viscous length (for the time L/U) and the channel height.

As the first case consider that the flow time is short compared to the viscous time; that is, Re $\rightarrow \infty$ with h/L finite. In this situation the vorticity flux term in Eq. 13.13.1 is zero except near the walls. Most particles go through the channel so fast that vorticity diffusion does not affect them. Particles begin with no vorticity in the upstream reservoir and go completely through the channel in irrotation flow. Vorticity is confined to small neighborhoods near each wall. After the pressure gradient generates new vorticity it diffuses only a small distance from the wall before convection sweeps it downstream and out the reservoir exit.

As particles are accelerated from the reservoir into the entrance the pressure is reduce. After the initial instant the pressure gradient in the channel, and hence the acceleration, is reduced progressively to the steady values as shown in Fig. 7.1. Ultimately, in the steady state, the pressure gradient in the channel is zero and all the pressure drop is used to accelerate the fluid from the reservoir to the mouth of the tube. The final flow velocity is found from the Bernoulli equation; $U^2 = 2(p_1 - p_2)/\rho$.

For the next case consider that t_{vis} and t_{flo} are the same order of magnitude. Events after the removal of the cover are much the same as the first case except that in the steady state the vortical regions are thicker and grow to merge at the center as the flow exits the pipe. The entire channel is the hydrodynamic entrance region as discussed in Section 7.1. Now a nonlinear pressure drop exists throughout the channel as the centerline flow is continually accelerated. The centerline velocity is $U_{\mathrm{cl}} = 2Ap/\rho$ and $U_{\mathrm{ave}} = U_{\mathrm{cl}}/2$.

If t_{vis} is reduced further compared to t_{flo}, the length of the hydrodynamic entrance decreases and the remaining portion of pipe is a fully developed Poiseuille flow with the appropriate linear pressure gradient.

The case when t_{vis} is much smaller than t_{flo} requires that diffusion effects traverse the channel while the particles move only a short distance down the tube. In this case, Eq. 13.13.1, including the viscous term, governs the acceleration. The hydrodynamic entrance region vanishes and the fully developed parabolic profile is established essentially at the entrance. The entire pressure drop between the reservoirs, except for a small entrance loss, is used to overcome the viscous forces. The average velocity in this instance is found from Eq. 7.1.9; $U = h^2(p_1 - p_2)/12\mu L$. A pressure gradient down the channel means that a vorticity flux continues to enter the flow according to Eq. 13.7.9. For a plane slot the fully developed vorticity profile is linear. The vorticity flux is thus constant. Vorticity flux from one wall passes through the fluid and exits through the opposite wall. In terms of the heat equation analogy a linear temperature gradient has a constant heat flux. Another point of view is that a flux of positive vorticity enters from one wall and a flux of negative vorticity enters from the other. They diffuse together and annihilate each other. Each term in the vorticity equation is identically zero; this, of course, includes the net vorticity flux.

Steady flow in a round tube is slightly different. A parabolic velocity profile in cylindrical coordinates leads to a conical increase in vorticity from the centerline, $\omega_\theta = 2rv_{\mathrm{max}}/R^2$. This in turn implies a constant flux of vorticity through the fluid. Again, all terms in the vorticity transport equation are identically zero. In particular, the net vorticity diffusion term is zero. At first it might seem paradoxical that the net vorticity diffusion is zero, while the tube has a constant vorticity flux from the wall. It is, of course, impossible for a tube to have a constant heat flux from the wall and a steady temperature profile. However, this problem does not have plane geometry, and it does not obey the analogy between temperature and vorticity. The net diffusion term for vorticity in tube flow is

$$\nabla^2 \boldsymbol{\omega} = \nabla^2 \boldsymbol{\omega}|_\theta = \frac{\partial}{\partial r}\left[\frac{1}{r}\frac{\partial}{\partial r}(r\omega_\theta)\right] = 0$$

The corresponding term in the heat equation is different:

$$\nabla^2 T = \frac{1}{r}\frac{\partial}{\partial r}\left(r\frac{\partial T}{\partial r}\right) = 0$$

The vorticity ω_θ cannot be made analogous to the temperature, because $(\nabla^2\boldsymbol{\omega})_\theta \neq \nabla^2\omega_\theta$.

The second qualitative example is the external flow over an airfoil. Assume that the flow is strictly two-dimensional, resulting in a vorticity vector that is always perpendicular to the velocity, as shown in Fig. 13.7. Furthermore, the Reynolds number is assumed large. This means that the vorticity diffusion is primarily normal to the wall. A local coordinate system with $y = 0$ on the surface of the airfoil and x in the flow direction is assumed. The origin is placed at the stagnation point so that the positive x-axis is on the upper surface. The curvature of this coordinate system is not important since our arguments are only qualitative in nature.

The stagnation point is a point of zero shear, and hence by Eq. 13.7.5, zero vorticity. As the flow accelerates away from the stagnation point on the upper surface, the shear stress becomes positive, and the vorticity, again through Eq. 13.7.5, becomes negative. In this region the pressure drops, and we have a flux of negative vorticity from the wall,

$$\mu \sigma_z = -\mu \frac{\partial \omega_z}{\partial y} = \frac{\partial p}{\partial x} < 0$$

The surface acts as a source to generate negative vorticity in the flow. Somewhere near the front of the airfoil the pressure reaches a minimum, followed by a gentle increase as the flow proceeds toward the trailing edge. In this region $\partial p / \partial x$ is positive, meaning that the wall acts as a sink to absorb some of the negative vorticity from the flow. The wall flux is positive (negative vorticity diffusing toward the wall). Notice that the maximum vorticity now occurs within the flow, as the sign of $\partial \omega_z / \partial y$ is negative at the wall. This process continues until the trailing edge is reached.

On the bottom side of the airfoil similar processes occur, except that the x-coordinate is now decreasing in the flow direction and the signs of the events switch. The pressure gradient accelerating the flow generates positive vorticity, while the subsequent decelerating pressure gradient creates a sink for positive vorticity. When the trailing edge is reached, the upper and lower streams must merge. At this point there is a discontinuity in the vorticity. This discontinuity is quickly washed out as the flow goes downstream. The negative vorticity from the upper surface and the positive vorticity from the lower surface merge into the wake. These regions diffuse together to destroy the wake. It is

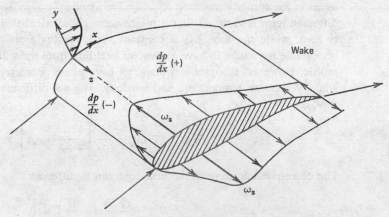

Figure 13.7 Vorticity distribution over an airfoil. Section cut through chord allows vorticity on lower surface to be shown.

usually permissible in practical cases to assume that the vorticity has not diffused very far from the surface by the time the flow reaches the trailing edge. A calculation of the net vorticity across the wake shows it to be zero:

$$\text{average } \omega_z \text{ at trailing edge} = \int_{\delta_L}^{\delta_U} \omega_z \, dy = \int_{\delta_L}^{\delta_U} \frac{\partial u}{\partial y} \, dy = (u)_{\delta_L}^{\delta_U} = 0 \quad (13.13.4)$$

(In this calculation we neglect a small contribution to the vorticity from $\partial v/\partial x$. This contribution is very small for high Reynolds numbers, and in any event it dies out as the wake profile decays.)

Another interesting fact is that the net flux of vorticity from the surface of the airfoil is zero. This is proved by integrating the vorticity flux over the surface from the lower-side trailing edge x_L to the upper-side trailing edge x_U:

$$\text{total flux of } \omega_z \text{ from airfoil} = \int_{\text{TE lower}}^{\text{TE upper}} \sigma_z \, dx = -\int_{\text{TE lower}}^{\text{TE upper}} \frac{\partial \omega_z}{\partial y} \, dx$$

$$= \frac{1}{\mu} \int_{x_l}^{x_U} \frac{dp}{dx} \, dx = \frac{1}{\mu} (p)_{x_l}^{x_U} = 0 \quad (13.13.5)$$

The last step above makes use of the fact that for a thin wake the pressure of the merging streams is the same. The sources and sinks of vorticity over the surface of the airfoil must cancel each other out.

Although the airfoil no longer puts out a net vorticity flux, there is a net vorticity within the flow. If we integrate the vorticity in the region outside the airfoil out to a radius R and then let $R \to \infty$, we find that

$$\int \omega_z \, dA = \oint_R t_i v_i \, ds = \Gamma \quad (13.13.6)$$

a finite number equal to the circulation. The net nonzero vorticity is inserted into the flow during the transient process by which the flow is established. In the transient process the flow does not leave the trailing edge smoothly, and the *starting vortex* is formed. Figure 13.8 depicts a starting vortex formed by impulsively moving the airfoil. The starting vortex contains the same net amount of vorticity as the airfoil but with the

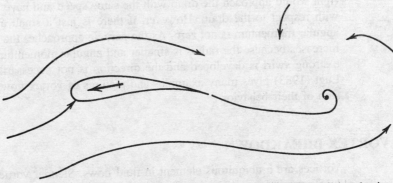

Figure 13.8 Vortex generated during the starting transient when an airfoil just begins to move.

opposite sign. A circulation loop going around the airfoil and including the starting vortex has $\Gamma = 0$.

Let us consider, from the standpoint of vorticity, another of the basic problems of fluid mechanics, the semi-infinite flat plate in a uniform stream. Again consider the high-Reynolds-number case, where diffusion only occurs normal to the plate. The flat plate does not have a pressure gradient along its surface, and therefore there is no flux of vorticity from the wall. Very far away from the plate the free stream is irrotational. Consider a control volume containing the plate and with two stations a short distance apart on faces 1 and 2. The global vorticity equation for this region is

$$0 = -\int_{\text{face } 1} u\omega_z \, dy + \int_{\text{face } 2} u\omega_z \, dy$$

The convection of vorticity across each section is the same. Where does this vorticity originate? Its source is in the neighborhood of the leading edge. We might think of the leading edge as having the same effect as an airfoil whose nose radius is allowed to approach zero. Even when the flat plate is sharp, there are pressure gradients near the leading edge, which are the source of the vorticity. In the limit, the upper surface has a negative line source of vorticity at the leading edge. The lower surface has a corresponding positive line source. If we revert to the temperature analogy, the flat plate constitutes a line sink of energy on the upper leading edge and a line source on the underside. In other words, the leading edge is a doublet with its axis in the vertical direction. The plate itself is an adiabatic wall. Vorticity conducted from the doublet at the front is carried downstream by the fluid flow.

Another commonly observed situation is the *bathtub vortex* one sees at an intake pipe drawing fluid from a reservoir or the outlet tube draining a tank. It is often speculated that the rotation of Earth imparts an initial vorticity to the fluid when it is still in the reservoir. As the tank is emptied the vorticity is stretched and intensified to give the intense swirl at the drain pipe. Earth's rotation would give a different rotation in the northern and southern hemispheres if this is the dominant effect. It is true that one can, with great care, arrange a tank draining process where the initial vorticity of Earth is important. Shapiro (1962) did such experiments in the northern hemisphere, and Trefethen et al. (1965) verified the opposite effect by conducting experiments in Sydney, Australia. In the common situation initial motions and boundary layers are dominant and the direction of rotation is not the same for all situations. Consider an oblong tank with a drain. If the flow toward the drain were absolutely symmetric, particles on the left and right would approach the drain with the same speed and have no net angular momentum with respect to the drain. However, if there is just a small amount of eccentricity, the angular momentum is not zero. As the particle approaches the drain, the angular velocity increases because the radius is smaller and angular momentum is conserved. Ultimately, a strong swirl is developed and the direction is not necessarily that of Earth's rotation. Lugt (1983) gives many examples and pictures of vortex flows and a qualitative discussion of their behavior.

13.14 VORTEX BREAKDOWN

Vortices are a ubiquitous element in fluid flows. Slender vortices were displayed in Fig. 1.1, a marine propeller tip; Fig. 1.2, an airplane wing tip, and one will find vortices formed on a delta wing in Fig. 19.12. We will also observe that vortices are major structural elements of turbulence. Slender vortices undergo an interesting transition process called *vortex breakdown.*

Two experimental test apparatuses to study vortex breakdown are shown in Fig. 13.9. The first is simply a cylindrical tank that has a lid that can be rotated about the axis of the cylinder. A flow toward the lid is engendered by the von Kármán pump effect of Section 11.12. In contact with the rotating lid, the fluid gains a swirling velocity and simultaneously is pushed outward by centrifugal forces. As the outflow approaches the fixed sidewalls it must turn downward along the sides, then at the bottom wall toward the center, where the flows from all sides meet, and turn upward moving along the cylinder axis toward the lid. A slender vortex is formed along the axis and under certain conditions breaks down, as illustrated in Fig. 13.10.

The second type of experiment is a continuous flow device. A purely radial flow toward the axis is created. At some radius a cascade of vanes imparts a swirling motion to the flow. The swirl intensified by conservation of angular momentum (see the analysis in Section 19.2) as the axis is approached. A tube contains the flow after it turns to the axial direction, and a slight divergence of the tube walls creates a mild adverse pressure gradient that stabilized the vortex breakdown to one position. Photographs from Sarpkaya (1971) are shown in Fig. 13.11. A third type of experiment, not shown, is a cylindrical can with a small outlet tube at one end and a tangential entry slot along the outer circumference.

Vortex breakdown is currently defined [Leibovich (1984) and Visbal (1995) review the subject] as a flow where there is a stagnation point on the axis followed by a region of reverse flow. The first helix configuration of Fig. 13.11a is now called a *disturbance* rather than a breakdown. Two major types of breakdown are the bubble type, typical of high swirl conditions, and spiral type, typical of low swirl conditions. In the bubble type, dye approaching from the axis enters the bubble from the rear, circulates around (sometimes with two cells), and then leaves through the rear. In the spiral type the recirculation region does not receive dye and the filament abruptly veers off in a spiral that rotates.

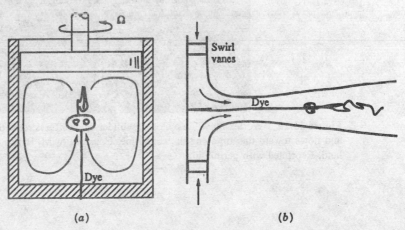

Figure 13.9   Two types of vortex breakdown experiments: (*a*) cylindrical tank with a rotating lid; (*b*) axisymmetric apparatus with radial inflow across a row of several vanes.

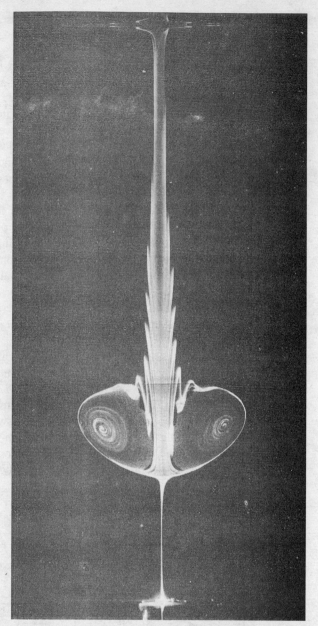

Figure 13.10 "Vortex burst" in a closed cylinder whose top is rotated. Dye seeps in at the bottom and flows toward the top along the centerline. Courtesy of M. P. Escudier, BBC, Baden, Switzerland. Reprinted with permission.

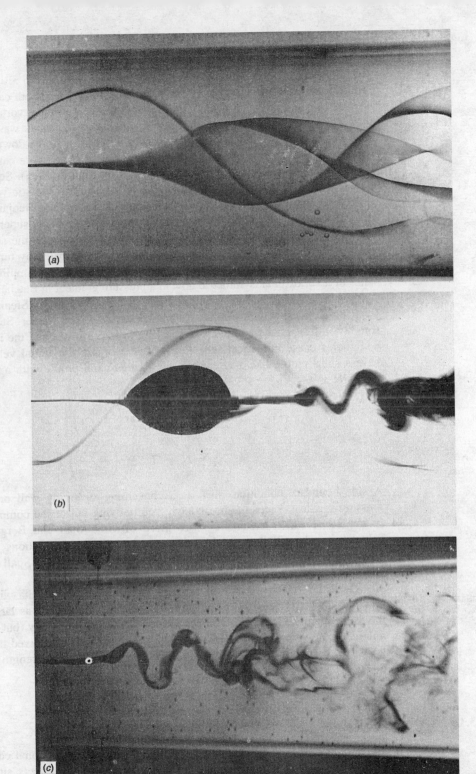

Figure 13.11 Typical types of vortex breakdown: (*a*) double helix; (*b*) axisymmetric; (*c*) spiral. Courtesy of T. Sarpkaya, Naval Postgraduate School. Reprinted with permission.

Visbal (1995), has concluded that the unsteady spiral breakdown also lacks a stagnation point on the axis. Turbulence develops farther downstream in both cases. Both types are essentially nonsteady and asymmetric flows. Several aspects of vortex breakdown have analogues in the hydraulic jump of open channel flow and shock waves of compressible flow. For example, the location of breakdown is sensitive to the downstream conditions.

Just like free surfaces and compressible fluids, a vortex core can support waves of long wavelength as shown in an early analysis by Squire (1965). Squire's criterion for vortex breakdown is that a swirl parameter based on characteristic velocities $Sq = V_\theta / V_z$ (also known as a *Rossby number*) takes on certain values. Benjamin introduced the idea of conjugate states; the upstream and downstream flows are supercritical (faster than the wave speed) and subcritical (slower than the wave speed), the same as in a shock wave or a hydraulic jump (indeed, excess energy is dissipated by turbulence in the hydraulic jump and in vortex breakdown). The reader will find a simplified analysis of the states of a vortex in axisymmetric flow in a pressure gradient in Batchelor (1967) (Section 7.5), while a review and extension of these theories is given by Stuart (1987).

Complete calculations of vortex breakdown using the Navier–Stokes equations are somewhat difficult. Essentially, one is trying to trap a wave, and the inflow and outflow boundaries cause numerical reflections. Most workers use initial velocity profiles that have a swirl profile like a viscous vortex and an axial profile with a Gaussian bump at the core:

$$v_\theta = \frac{K}{r}\left[1 - \exp\left(-\frac{ar^2}{2\nu}\right)\right]$$

$$v_z = U_\infty + U_0 \exp\left(-\frac{ar^2}{2\nu}\right)$$

A side boundary condition, such as a converging–diverging wall or a slight adverse pressure gradient, keeps the breakdown from moving out of the computational domain. Examples of earlier calculations are those of Grabowski and Berger (1976). These calculations showed that steady axisymmetric breakdown solutions can be obtained. Unsteady nonaxisymmetric calculations were accomplished by Spall et al. (1990) for bubble-type breakdowns.

The axial velocity profile in experimental tests and over delta wings typically has an excess of axial velocity in the core. This excess, U_0, can be as large as three times the free-stream velocity, U_∞. Vortices formed at wingtips typically (but not always) have a defect axial velocity in the core; U_0 is negative. It is also observed that breakdown of tip vortices is unusual but that delta wing vortices of sufficient strength commonly break down.

13.15 CONCLUSIONS

Vorticity vectors and their associated vortex lines give us additional concepts for interpreting fluid-flow patterns. This viewpoint emphasizes viscous effects, since pressure does not play a direct role in the equation governing vorticity dynamics. Pressure nevertheless does have some important influences in at least two respects: (1) pressure forces help determine the velocity field, which in turn convects the vortex lines and stretches them;

(2) pressure gradients along a solid wall are related directly to the flux of vorticity from the wall into the fluid. Moreover, the wall is the only place where vorticity can originate.

Helmholtz's laws, which allow us to think of vortex lines as stringing together a set of material particles, are applicable whenever viscous diffusion (i.e., the net viscous force) is negligible. Such flows are ideal flows carrying vorticity. In these flows, stretching vortex lines increases the vorticity in direct proportion to the increase in length of the vortex line.

PROBLEMS

13.1 (A) A disk of radius R is spinning about its axis at a speed Ω. What is the vorticity of the particles at $r = 0$, $r = \frac{1}{2}R$, and $r = R$?

13.2 (A) Burgers vortex in cylindrical coordinates has the velocity components $v_r = -ar$, $v_z = 2az$, and $v_\theta = (\Gamma/2\pi r)[1 - \exp(-ar^2/2\nu)]$. What is the vorticity field for this flow?

13.3 (B) Compute the vorticity for the von Kármán pump problem. Leave your answer in terms of the functions F, G, and their derivatives. What relations of F and G determined the fluid vorticity at the wall? Contrast with Problem 13.1.

13.4 (A) Compute each term in the vorticity equation 13.3.5 for Problem 13.2.

13.5 (B) Prove relation 13.7.5 between the wall shear stress and the vorticity for a smooth curved wall.

13.6 (B) Find the equation of the "cross-curve" that marks the path of two counterrotating line vortices as they approach a wall in an inviscid flow.

13.7 (B) Consider an airfoil that is stationary in an infinite fluid. At time zero, the airfoil starts to move with a constant speed U_0. How does the vorticity and circulation in the starting vortex compare to that over the airfoil?

13.8 (A) Compare the vorticity distribution for Stokes's oscillating plate and the oscillating freestream above a fixed plate. The velocity profiles are Eqs. 11.4.16 and 11.5.7.

13.9 (B) Derive the global form of the vorticity equation. Interpret each term.

$$\frac{d}{dt}\int \omega_i \, dV = \int [n_j(w_j - v_j)\omega_i + n_j\omega_j v_i + \nu n_j \partial_j \omega_i] \, dS$$

13.10 (C) The amount of vorticity, without regard to direction, is measured by $\omega \cdot \omega$, called the *enstrophy*. Take $\omega \cdot$ (vorticity equation) to find

$$\frac{D\frac{1}{2}\omega^2}{Dt} = \omega_i \omega_j S_{ji} + \nu \partial_j \partial_j (\tfrac{1}{2}\omega^2) - \nu \partial_j \omega_i \partial_j \omega_i$$

Interpret each term.

13.11 (C) The quantity $\mathbf{v} \cdot \boldsymbol{\omega}$ is called the *helicity*. Form an equation for $\mathbf{v} \cdot \boldsymbol{\omega}$ by taking $\boldsymbol{\omega} \cdot$ (vorticity equation) and $\boldsymbol{\omega} \cdot$ (momentum equation) and combining.

13.12 (C) Stuart (1967) vortices are an infinite row of vortices that undergo inviscid motion. Because the motion is inviscid, $\omega_z = F(\psi)$. Show that if $F(\psi) = \exp(-2\psi)$ the inviscid equation $\nabla^2\psi = -\omega$ is satisfied by

$$\psi = \ln(C \cosh y + \sqrt{C^2 - 1} \cos x)$$

Here $1 \le C \le \infty$. Find the velocity components. With the use of a computer plot the streamlines for $C = 2$.

13.13 (C) Show that in Problem 13.12 the limit $C = 1$ gives the uniform shear layer $u = \partial\psi/\partial y = \tanh y$.

13.14 (C) Show that the limit $C \Rightarrow \infty$ in Problem 13.13 gives a row of point vortices with spacing 2π and circulation $\Gamma = -4\pi$. Find the streamfunction; namely,

$$\hat{\psi} \equiv \psi - \ln C \sim \ln(\cosh y + \cos x)$$

13.15 (C) Sullivan's vortex is an example where flow has a two-cell structure. The velocity profiles are

$$v_\theta = \frac{\kappa}{r} \frac{H(\eta^2)}{H(\infty)} \quad \text{where} \quad \eta^2 \equiv \frac{ar^2}{2\nu}$$

$$v_r = -ar + \frac{6\nu}{r}[1 - \exp(-\eta^2)]$$

$$v_z = 2az[1 - 3\exp(-\eta^2)]$$

and $H(\eta^2) \equiv \int_0^{\eta^2} \exp[-t + 3\int_0^t (1 - e^{-s})s^{-1} \, ds] \, dt$ with $H(\infty) = 37.905$. Sketch the velocity profiles and the streamlines in the r–z plane.

14

Flows at Moderate Reynolds Numbers

Flows where inertia, pressure forces, and viscous forces are all significant occur at moderate Reynolds numbers. Moderate Reynolds numbers cannot be defined as a precise range of values. For one thing, the numerical values depend on the particular flow situation and the way the Reynolds number itself is defined. For flow over a circular cylinder, moderate Reynolds numbers are from $VD/\nu = 0.5$ to about 200. For flow into the entrance of a slot, moderate Reynolds numbers might be 0.5 to 50.

The other difficulty in specifying an exact range for moderate Reynolds numbers is that there is no abrupt change in the flow at either end of the spectrum. Low-Reynolds-number flows, where inertia effects are unimportant, make a rather smooth transition into moderate-Reynolds-number flows. Similarly, the confinement of viscous effects to the wall regions occurs progressively at the high end of the moderate-Reynolds-number regime. To assign a particular number to these transitions is a matter of personal judgment.

Regardless of the difficulties in defining them precisely, we can characterize moderate-Reynolds-number flows as those where both pressure and viscous forces contribute importantly to fluid accelerations *over a major part of the flow.* We need this last proviso to exclude boundary layers.

The momentum and vorticity equations for moderate-Reynolds-number flows are

$$\frac{D\mathbf{v}}{Dt} = -\nabla p + \frac{1}{\text{Re}} \nabla^2 \mathbf{v}$$

and

$$\frac{D\omega}{Dt} = \omega \cdot \nabla \mathbf{v} + \frac{1}{\text{Re}} \nabla^2 \omega$$

The variables in these equations have been nondimensionalized using a characteristic velocity, a characteristic length, and the density as in Chapter 11. The highest-order terms, $\nabla^2 \mathbf{v}$ and $\nabla^2 \omega$, give these equations an elliptic nature. We therefore expect that conditions in one part of the flow will influence all other parts and, in particular, there will be an upstream influence. An important distinguishing feature of these flows is that Re occurs as a parameter. As the Reynolds number changes, we not only get a different balance of terms, but in many cases the flow patterns take on different and unusual forms. In some instances the patterns evolve, whereas in other situations the transition is abrupt and hysteresis possible.

14.1 SOME UNUSUAL FLOW PATTERNS

Figure 14.1 shows a circular cylinder as it joins a flat wall, much like a bridge support intersecting the river bottom or an airplane wing joining the fuselage. Intuition would lead us to expect that the flow would neatly divide and pass around the obstacle with a minimum of complication. In fact, this does not happen quite so simply. One of the major features of this quite complex flow is a horseshoe-shaped vortex that is looped around the cylinder in the front and trails off behind. The vortex is next to the wall and continuously entrains more fluid as it proceeds around the cylinder and downstream. The intense velocities of these vortices are responsible for scouring the river bottom around the sides of bridge supports and for making the distinctive patterns in the snow around telephone poles. Figure 14.1 is a photograph of the vortices illuminated on the center plane of the

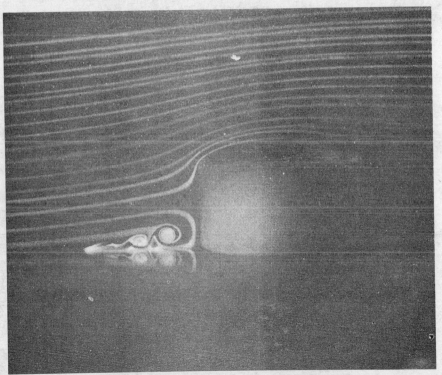

Figure 14.1 Several horseshoe vortices formed at the junction of a cylinder and a wall are made visible by smoke and illuminated on the centerline. The boundary layer in the approach flow contains vorticity that is ultimately organized into horseshoe vortices. Reprinted from Thwaites (1960).

cylinder. At this Reynolds number there are not one but several horseshoe vortices adjacent to each other. At higher Reynolds numbers, the pattern becomes unsteady. A vortex is born upstream, and convects toward the cylinder, where it merges or amalgamates with the vortex nearest the cylinder. Many patterns can occur. Figure 14.2 shows a high Reynolds number where the vortex pinches off and will reconnect downstream.

It is difficult to imagine the complicated interaction of inertia, pressure forces, and viscous forces that produces this flow. Although a detailed explanation is not possible, we can observe some major effects. One important aspect is the shear region on the wall far ahead of the cylinder. The thickness of this shear layer and the fact that it contains transverse vorticity are essential to the development of organized vortices. Far away from the shear layer the flow is simply pushed away from the cylinder and made to go around either side by pressure forces. This motion is accompanied by straining deformation of the particles. Next to the wall, within the shear layer, there is a transverse vorticity component. When this vorticity undergoes a straining motion, the term $\omega \cdot \nabla v$ in vorticity equation 13.3.5 turns the vorticity vector to give ω a large streamwise component and also intensifies it by stretching. If the flow is at a modest Reynolds number, the viscous forces of one vortex can induce another vortex of the opposite sign next to it. The final flow pattern is a delicate balance of inertia, pressure forces, and viscous forces.

As a second example, consider the flow under a sluice gate as shown in Fig. 14.3. Again our intuition would lead us to the wrong flow pattern. We might imagine that the

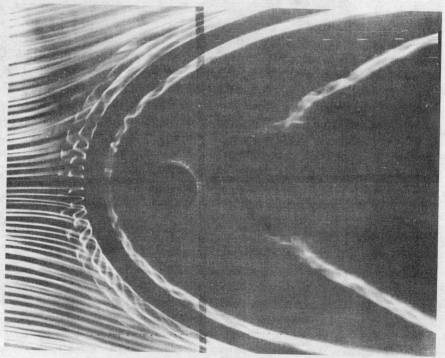

Figure 14.2 Plan view of horseshoe vortex formation. This flow is at a higher Reynolds number than Fig. 14.1, giving an unsteady pattern where the vortices pinch off and reconnect downstream of the cylinder. Courtesy of A. Thomas, Lockheed-Georgia Co. Reprinted with permission.

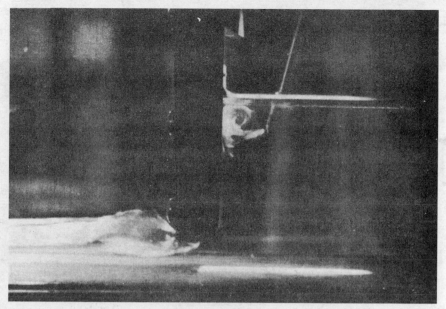

Figure 14.3   Vortex at the top of a sluice gate. The flow is visualized with fluorescent dye from a probe and a slit of light on the center plane. Courtesy of D. G. Bogard and L. N. Goenka, University of Texas.

flow would smoothly drain under the gate from all parts of the upstream area. In particular, the flow could smoothly accelerate down the gate, with the pressure dropping until at the exit the pressure would be atmospheric and the velocity correspondingly high. Figure 14.3 is a photograph of the streaklines that actually occur. A separated region exists near the top of the gate and extends downward for a considerable distance. The circular flow within this region is sometimes accompanied by an outward flow toward the sidewalls, but this is not necessary.

Another unexpected pattern occurs at the corners where the gate and the walls meet. Near the wall a vortex is formed, which has its axis nearly vertical at the surface. The vortex core is marked by a stream of bubbles in the photograph (Fig. 14.4). The core trails under the gate and turns in the streamwise direction as it enters the tailwater flow. A little reflection will reveal the analogy between this vortex and the horseshoe vortices of the first example.

14.2   ENTRANCE FLOWS

The events that occur in the entrance region of a tube or slot connected to a large reservoir were described in Section 7.1. At high Reynolds numbers, the flow was divided into several parts. Near the entrance the fluid is accelerated from the reservoir into the tube by pressure forces. This acceleration produces a velocity profile at the entrance to the straight section that is flat except for thin viscous regions next to the walls. Downstream from the entrance there is a hydrodynamic entrance region where the flat profile is trans-

Figure 14.4   Corner vortices forming from the wall boundary layer as the flow dives under a sluice gate. Air bubbles are carried downstream in the vortex core. Photograph by the author and L. N. Goenka.

formed into the parabolic profile. The last region is characterized by a fully developed profile at any downstream station.

This same flow at a moderate Reynolds number cannot be so easily divided into separate parts. There is upstream influence as the diffusion of vorticity extends into the entrance and even a slight distance into the reservoir itself. A uniform profile at the beginning of the straight section is no longer an acceptable assumption. Because of the elliptic nature of the equations, we need to formulate the problem with the reservoir, the entrance, and part of the tube connected together.

Such a flow is sensitive to geometry, and we need to specify the exact shape of the entrance contour. As an academic problem that illustrates moderate-Reynolds-number effects, yet avoids assigning a definite shape to the entrance, we consider the flow into a cascade of channels. Figure 14.5 depicts the arrangement. The essential idea is to contrive a physical arrangement where 100% of the flow coming from a uniform stream at infinity is accepted into the tube. Physically, we must have some external method to suck the flow into the cascade. Once it is there, vorticity is generated on the walls. Because the Reynolds number is low, the vorticity may diffuse out of the entrance and modify the flow in front of the entrance. Geometric symmetry allows us to assume that the streamlines that stagnate at the edges of the plates are straight. Far downstream within the cascade, the velocity profile develops into the parabolic profile of fully developed flow.

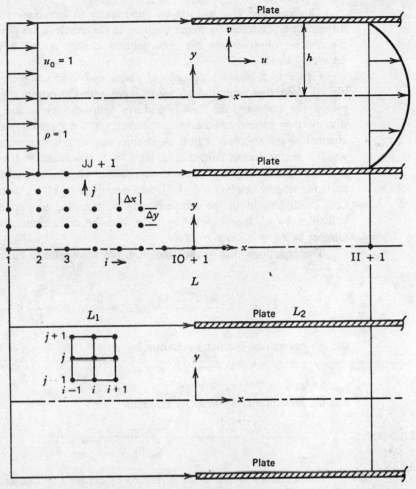

Figure 14.5   Flow into a cascade of thin plates. The flow in each cell is similar; in this diagram the top cell shows the coordinate system, the middle cell shows the i, j finite-difference grid for one-half cell, and the bottom cell contains a typical finite-difference molecule.

14.3   ENTRANCE FLOW INTO A CASCADE OF PLATES: COMPUTER SOLUTION BY THE STREAMFUNCTION–VORTICITY METHOD

Numerical methods are well suited to moderate-Reynolds-number flows. A computer can take on the added complication of having all terms in the equation present without undue effort. Although it is quite feasible to solve problems using the pressure and velocities as unknown, this particular problem is most easily formulated in terms of the stream-function and vorticity. Recall that the vorticity–streamfunction method applies only when the flow is plane or axisymmetric. Emmons (1949) was one of the first to use this method in a finite-difference solution. This particular problem was first done numerically by Wang and Longwell (1964).

This example also affords an opportunity to introduce some rudiments of finite-difference procedures. Its major purpose is nevertheless the physics of entrance flow. In the end we observe how the flow patterns change as the Reynolds number takes on different values.

Figure 14.5 shows a cascade of plates with a spacing $2h$. A coordinate system is placed along the centerline of one channel with the origin aligned wit the edge of the plates. Far upstream, the flow is uniform with velocity u_0 and a density ρ. We assume that the flow pattern has the same symmetry as the geometry and select one-half of one channel as the solution region. A simple way to nondimensionalize is to let the half-width h be the length unit; that is, let $h = 1$, choose $u_0 = 1$ as a velocity unit, and let $\rho = 1$ be the density unit (from the standpoint of dimensional analysis we are choosing units for length, velocity $v = L/T$, and density $\rho = M/L^3$, instead of the traditional M, L, T). All lengths in the problem may be regarded as nondimensionalized by h, all velocities by u_0, the vorticity by u_0/h, and the streamfunction by $u_0 h$. The Reynolds number is $\mathrm{Re} = u_0 2h/\nu = 2/\nu$.

The equations that govern the flow are the vorticity equation for the component $\omega_z = \omega$,

$$\frac{\partial \omega}{\partial t} = -\frac{\partial}{\partial x}(u\omega) - \frac{\partial}{\partial y}(v\omega) + \frac{2}{\mathrm{Re}}\nabla^2\omega \tag{14.3.1}$$

the streamfunction–vorticity equation,

$$\nabla^2\psi = -\omega \tag{14.3.2}$$

and the streamfunction–velocity relations

$$u = \frac{\partial \psi}{\partial y}, \qquad v = -\frac{\partial \psi}{\partial x} \tag{14.3.3}$$

The variables ψ and ω are governed by coupled second-order equations. We could eliminate the velocity relations 14.3.3 from the problem; however, because of their physical importance it is useful to keep them as an intermediate calculation.

We shall solve the problem as if the flow were time dependent. Then, once the solution becomes steady, we take the steady-state solutions as the answer. The general scheme will be to assume a flow field and calculate values of ω for the next instant in time using Eq. 14.3.1 with the right side known. The new ω values are then carried to Eq. 14.3.2, where the corresponding ψ values are found. In this way the calculation procedures decouple the equations. Velocities are determined from Eq. 14.3.3 to complete the step at this time level. Taking the new flow properties back to Eq. 14.3.1 starts the process over again. When the values of ω at the new time are nearly the same as those at the last time, we stop the process and consider the steady-state flow solved. It is of interest to note that the initial conditions are not necessarily a realistic flow pattern.

Since ψ and ω are the primary variables, we need to specify boundary and initial conditions on these variables. The far stream is uniform [$u(x \rightarrow -\infty, y) = 1$] and without vorticity; hence,

$$\omega(x \rightarrow -\infty, y) = 0$$

$$\psi(x \rightarrow -\infty, y) = \int \frac{\partial \psi}{\partial y} \, dy + F(x) = \int_0^y u \, dy + F(x) \tag{14.3.4}$$

But since $u(x \rightarrow -\infty, y)$ is unity, we have

$$\psi(x \rightarrow -\infty, y) = y \tag{14.3.5}$$

where the arbitrary function $F(x)$ has been chosen so that the centerline $y = 0$ is the streamline:

$$\psi(x, y = 0) = 0 \tag{14.3.6}$$

The centerline is also a line of symmetry with $du/dy = 0$ and $v = 0$. These conditions require that the vorticity be zero, that is,

$$\omega(x, y = 0) = -\frac{\partial u}{\partial y} + \frac{\partial v}{\partial x} = 0 \tag{14.3.7}$$

The position $y = 1$ consists of a stagnation streamline for $x < 0$ and a solid wall for $x > 0$. Along both sections the streamfunction is constant and equal to the nondimensional flow rate. Hence, we have

$$\psi(x, y = 1) = \frac{Q}{u_0 h} = 1 \tag{14.3.8}$$

The stagnation streamline is also a line of symmetry; so in a manner similar to Eq. 14.3.7 we find that for $x < 0$,

$$\omega(x < 0, y = 1) = 0 \tag{14.3.9}$$

Vorticity is generated on the solid wall $x > 0$, but we do not know exactly how much. The most we know is that because $v = 0$ on the wall, Eq. 14.3.2 reduces to

$$\omega(x > 0, y = 1) = -\frac{\partial^2 \psi}{\partial y^2}\bigg|_{y=1} \tag{14.3.10}$$

This is another place where ψ and ω are coupled in the problem.

Far downstream the flow becomes a fully developed parabolic profile. Hence, as $x \rightarrow \infty$, the velocity is

$$u = \tfrac{3}{2}(1 - y^2), \qquad v = 0$$

The corresponding streamfunction equation is

$$\psi(x \rightarrow \infty, y) = \tfrac{3}{2}y - \tfrac{1}{2}y^3 \tag{14.3.11}$$

and the vorticity is

$$\omega(x \rightarrow \infty, y) = 3y \tag{14.3.12}$$

Equations 14.3.4 to 14.3.10 are the boundary conditions for the steady-flow problem.

The mathematical problem we have laid out above needs to be rewritten in a finite-difference form. Several issues arise in this process. First, does the finite-difference algorithm converge? In many cases, what looks like a reasonable scheme does not converge. The second issue is accuracy: Do the answers from the computer give a good approximation of the answer to the continuous problem?

The first step in converting the problem to a form suitable for finite-difference calculation is to define a grid for the domain. An arbitrary point on the grid will be labeled i, j. In the y-direction, grid points run uniformly from $j = 1$ to $j = \text{JJ} + 1$ (Fig. 14.5). Thus, the increment in y is

$$\Delta y = \frac{1}{\text{JJ}} \tag{14.3.13}$$

and the y-position of point j is

$$y = (j - 1)\,\Delta y \tag{14.3.14}$$

The x-direction presents a slight problem in that the range is $-\infty$ to $+\infty$. It is necessary in finite-difference solutions to approximate an infinite domain with a finite one. The x length of the domain is called L (actually, the x-domain length/half-width h): L_1 is the portion in front of the plates and L_2 is the plate length. Grid points are numbered from $i = 1$ to $\text{II} + 1$. Let IO be the number of Δx intervals in front of the plate $L_1 = (\text{IO}/\text{II})L$. The length of the plate in the computation domain is then $L_2 = L\,(\text{II} - \text{IO})/\text{II}$. The increment in x is the length of the field divided by the number of intervals,

$$\Delta x = \frac{L}{\text{II}} \tag{14.3.15}$$

The x-coordinate origin is at $\text{IO} + 1$ and an arbitrary point is then

$$x = (i - \text{IO} - 1)\,\Delta x \tag{14.3.16}$$

The mesh aspect ratio is

$$\beta \equiv \frac{\Delta x}{\Delta y} = \frac{\text{JJ}}{\text{II}}\,L \tag{14.3.17}$$

By way of summary, observe that the grid is defined by four numbers II, JJ, IO, and L. With these numbers Δx, Δy, and β may be determined.

Next, we take on the task of translating the differential equations into difference equations. Consider an arbitrary point i, j and all points in the immediate neighborhood as shown in Fig. 14.5. We denote the value of some arbitrary function f at a given point by subscripts. For any y-level, a Taylor expansion gives f_{i+1} as

$$f_{i+1} = f_i + \left.\frac{\partial f}{\partial x}\right|_i \Delta x + \left.\frac{\partial^2 f}{\partial x^2}\right|_i \frac{\Delta x^2}{2} + \cdots \tag{14.3.18}$$

The value f_{i-1} is given in a similar manner as

$$f_{i-1} = f_i + \left.\frac{\partial f}{\partial x}\right|_i (-\Delta x) + \left.\frac{\partial^2 f}{\partial x^2}\right|_i \frac{(-\Delta x)^2}{2} + \cdots \tag{14.3.19}$$

A *centered finite-difference formula* for the second derivative is found by adding Eqs. 14.3.18 and 14.3.19 and solving:

$$\left.\frac{\partial^2 f}{\partial x^2}\right|_{ij} = \frac{1}{\Delta x^2} (f_{i+1,j} - 2f_{ij} + f_{i-1,j}) \qquad (14.3.20)$$

Similarly, for the y-direction at any x-level i, we have

$$\left.\frac{\partial^2 f}{\partial y^2}\right|_{ij} = \frac{\beta^2}{\Delta x^2} (f_{i,j+1} - 2f_{ij} + f_{i,j-1}) \qquad (14.3.21)$$

The sum of Eqs. 14.3.20 and 14.3.21 is the Laplacian in finite-difference form.

One of the equations we want to solve is Eq. 14.3.2,

$$0 = \nabla^2 \psi + \omega$$

The finite-difference form of this equation at the point i, j is found by substituting Eqs. 14.3.20 and 14.3.21 and multiplying by Δx^2. The result is

$$0 = \psi_{i+1,j} + \psi_{i-1,j} + \beta^2 \psi_{i,j+1} + \beta^2 \psi_{i,j-1} - 2(\beta^2 + 1)\psi_{ij} + \omega_{ij} \Delta x^2$$

$$= D(\psi; \omega) \qquad (14.3.22)$$

where $D(\psi; \omega)$ is defined as the right-hand side of the first line. In the decoupled problem we assume that we know the values of ω_{ij} and that all the ψ values are to be found.

One of many methods of solving Eq. 14.3.22 for the values of ψ is by iteration. Let ψ^n be the last known value and ψ^{n+1} the next estimate. An iteration formula (where F is some number) is constructed as

$$\psi^{n+1} = \psi^n + \frac{F}{2(\beta^2 + 1)} D(\psi^n; \omega) \qquad (14.3.23)$$

When $D(\psi; \omega)$ is zero, Eq. 14.3.22 is satisfied and no change in ψ should occur. Equation 14.3.23 says that ψ should be changed in accordance with how far away we are from satisfying $D(\psi; \omega) = 0$. This method is known as *successive overrelaxation* (SOR). The parameter F is called the *relaxation parameter*. If $1 \le F \le 2$, the method is convergent. Theory also shows that convergence can be optimized on a rectangular domain if one chooses

$$F = \frac{2}{\xi} (1 - \sqrt{1 - \xi})$$

where

$$\xi = \frac{1}{(\beta^2 + 1)^2} \left(\cos \frac{\pi}{L_x / \Delta x} + \beta^2 \cos \frac{\pi}{L_y / \Delta y} \right)^2$$

Of course, an iteration method never satisfies Eq. 14.3.22 exactly. In application we must establish a convergence criterion. For a chosen error E_ψ and normalizing value ψ_{max} the iteration is stopped when

$$\frac{D(\psi; \omega)}{\psi_{max}} < E_\psi \qquad \text{for all } i,j \qquad (14.3.24)$$

Equation 14.3.24 must be satisfied at all points in the domain.

There is one last trick in applying the iteration formula Eq. 14.3.23. Consider for a moment how the calculation for ψ^{n+1} would proceed. Begin with the line $i = 1$ in Fig. 14.5. This is the far stream, where boundary data $\psi = y$ are specified; so we move immediately to $i = 2$. In order, we compute Eq. 14.3.23 for $j = 2$ to $j = JJ$. Next, we go to $i = 3$ and again sweep across the slot in j. For the sake of argument, say that we are computing for the point $i = 3$, $j = 4$. We already know ψ for all $i < 3$ and for $i = 3$ if $j < 4$. Some of these points are included in $D(\psi; \omega)$ for the computation of $\psi_{3,4}^{n+1}$. We can use the updated values of ψ whenever they are available by redefining the operator $D(\psi; \omega)$ as

$$D^*(\psi; \omega) \equiv [\psi_{i+1,j}^n + \psi_{i-1,j}^{n+1} + \beta^2 \psi_{i,j+1}^n + \beta^2 \psi_{i,j-1}^{n+1} - 2(\beta^2 + 1)\psi_{ij}^n + \omega_{ij}^n \Delta x^2]$$

(14.3.25)

Using D^* in the iteration formula 14.3.23 speeds the convergence somewhat and also allows us to use only one storage array for ψ. We do not need to have storage for ψ^n and for ψ^{n+1}, but only for the current values of ψ, that is, ψ^{n+1} or ψ^n as the case may be.

The vorticity equation 14.3.1 is expressed in finite-difference form using similar arguments. First, we multiply by Δt to get

$$\frac{\partial \omega}{\partial t} \Delta t = \Delta t \left[-\frac{\partial}{\partial x}(u\omega) - \frac{\partial}{\partial y}(v\omega) + \frac{2}{Re} \nabla^2 \omega \right]$$

(14.3.26)

All terms on the right-hand side are considered known at the last time step n. We can explicitly compute a new set of ω_{ij}^{n+1} for the new time $n + 1$ using the formula

$$\frac{\partial \omega}{\partial t} \Delta t = \omega_{ij}^{n+1} - \omega_{ij}^n$$

(14.3.27)

For the Laplacian term on the right-hand side of Eq. 14.3.26, we use Eqs. 14.3.20 and 14.3.21:

$$\frac{2\Delta t}{Re} \nabla^2 \omega = \frac{2\Delta t}{Re \, \Delta x^2} [\omega_{i+1,j}^n + \omega_{i-1,j}^n + \beta^2 \omega_{i,j+1}^n + \beta^2 \omega_{i,j-1}^n - 2(\beta^2 + 1)\omega_{ij}^n]$$

(14.3.28)

All of the ω values in this expression are old values at time level n.

Special care is needed for the convective terms in Eq. 14.3.26. We have at least three choices to estimate the first-derivative forms needed in the convective terms. If we truncate Eq. 14.3.18 and solve for $\partial f/\partial x|_i$, we get a *forward-difference formula*,

$$\left.\frac{\partial f}{\partial x}\right|_i = \frac{1}{\Delta x}(f_{i+1} - f_i)$$

(14.3.29)

If we truncate Eq. 14.3.19 and solve, we get a *backward-difference formula*,

$$\left.\frac{\partial f}{\partial x}\right|_i = \frac{1}{\Delta x}(f_i - f_{i-1})$$

(14.3.30)

In forming both of the equations above we have neglected a term of order Δx^2. The *centered-difference formula* is found by subtracting Eq. 14.3.19 from Eq. 14.3.18 and solving. This leads to an expression that is accurate through order Δx^2:

$$\left.\frac{\partial f}{\partial x}\right|_i = \frac{1}{2\Delta x}(f_{i+1} - f_{i-1})$$

Experience has shown that there is not one best formula, but that we should change the difference formula in accordance with the direction of the flow. We want to carry information into the point ij from points upstream of ij (streamlines are subcharacteristics of the equations). The *upwind-differencing formulas* are

$$\Delta t \frac{\partial}{\partial x}(u\omega) = \frac{\Delta t}{\Delta x} \times \begin{cases} (u\omega)_{ij}^n - (u\omega)_{i-1,j}^n & \text{if} \quad u > 0 \\ (u\omega)_{i+1,j}^n - (u\omega)_{ij}^n & \text{if} \quad u < 0 \end{cases} \qquad (14.3.31)$$

$$\Delta t \frac{\partial}{\partial y}(v\omega) = \frac{\beta \Delta t}{\Delta x} \times \begin{cases} (v\omega)_{ij}^n - (v\omega)_{i,j-1}^n & \text{if} \quad v > 0 \\ (v\omega)_{i,j+1}^n - (v\omega)_{ij}^n & \text{if} \quad v < 0 \end{cases} \qquad (14.3.32)$$

Using upwind differencing gives an unconditionally stable computation scheme for the vorticity equation. Upwind differencing is mathematically stable. For this reason it is used in some commercial fluid-flow computer codes. It always gives an answer even for high Reynold numbers, where fine resolution is required. The other side of the coin is that the answer may look right, but be wrong. For this reason the American Society of Engineering's *Journal of Fluids Engineering* does not accept research papers that use this method.

Another expression that the reader will run across in the literature on finite differences is *artificial viscosity*. This is a numerical effect that occurs because we have truncated the second-order terms in formulating Eqs. 14.3.21 and 14.3.32. This error causes an effect that is equivalent to modifying the viscosity coefficient of the second-order diffusion terms; hence the name.

Another noteworthy point is that there are two ways to write the convective terms:

$$\frac{\partial}{\partial x}(u\omega) + \frac{\partial}{\partial y}(v\omega) \quad \text{or} \quad u\frac{\partial \omega}{\partial x} + v\frac{\partial \omega}{\partial y}$$

When written as finite-difference equations these forms are not equivalent, because the approximating equations throw away slightly different parts. Experience has shown that in general the version on the left-hand side, called the *conservative form*, is to be preferred.

The final vorticity equation is a relation for ω_{ij}^{n+1} obtained by substituting Eqs. 14.3.27, 14.3.28, 14.3.31, and 14.3.32 into Eq. 14.3.26. Only known values of ω^n, u^n, and v^n occur on the right-hand side. After each new vorticity value is computed, it is compared with the old value to see if a steady state has been reached. The calculation is stopped once all values change less than a specified amount E_ω:

$$\max_{ij} \frac{|\omega_{ij}^{n+1} - \omega_{ij}^n|}{\omega_{max}} < E_\omega \qquad (14.3.33)$$

We now have, in principle, the methods for finding ψ and ω for the problem.

The velocities must be calculated as an intermediate step after the ψ_{ij} values are determined. At all interior points the center-difference formula for Eq. 14.3.3 gives

$$u_{ij} = \frac{\psi_{i,j+1} - \psi_{i,j-1}}{2\Delta x/\beta}, \qquad v_{ij} = -\frac{\psi_{i+1,j} - \psi_{i-1,j}}{2\Delta x} \qquad (14.3.34)$$

These formulas cannot be used along the boundaries, because one ψ point would be outside the computation region. Along the centerline, the forward-difference version is used:

$$u_{i1} = \frac{\psi_{i,2} - 0}{\Delta x/\beta}, \qquad v_{i1} = 0 \qquad (14.3.35)$$

And along the stagnation streamline, the backward-difference formula is applied; that is, for $i = 2$, IO,

$$u_{i,JJ+1} = \frac{1 - \psi_{i,JJ}}{\Delta x/\beta}, \qquad v_{i,JJ+1} = 0 \qquad (14.3.36)$$

The values of u on the inflow boundary, the outflow boundary, and the wall are specified conditions and do not change during the calculation.

You should not expect the calculation to produce complete consistency between ψ, ω, u, and v. In different parts of the problem, different types and levels of approximation are used. For example, if a backward-difference formula similar to Eq. 14.3.36 is used on the wall, a value $u \neq 0$ will result. On the other hand, the centered-difference formula could be applied at the wall if we were to place a phantom point inside the wall. At the phantom point the value of ψ would be defined as $\psi_{i,JJ+2} = \psi_{i,JJ}$, so Eq. 14.3.34 would produce $u = 0$, the proper value.

Values of ψ are fixed on all boundaries, and values of ω are fixed on all boundaries except the wall. At the wall ψ and ω are related by Eq. 14.3.10, an equation for which we need a finite-difference equivalent. Consider the following Taylor expansion of ψ from the wall ($j = JJ + 1$) to the first interior point $j = JJ$:

$$\psi_{i,JJ} = \psi_{i,JJ+1} + \left.\frac{\partial \psi}{\partial y}\right|_{i,JJ+1} (-\nabla y) + \left.\frac{\partial^2 \psi}{\partial y^2}\right|_{i,JJ+1} \frac{(-\Delta y)^2}{2} + \cdots$$

Substituting $\psi_{\text{wall}} = 1$, $u_{\text{wall}} = \partial \psi/\partial y = 0$, $\omega_{\text{wall}} = -\partial^2 \psi/\partial y^2$ and solving gives

$$\psi_{i,JJ+1} = (1 - \psi_{i,JJ})\frac{2\beta^2}{\Delta x^2} \qquad \text{for} \quad i = \text{IO} + 2, \ldots, \text{II} \qquad (14.3.37)$$

This relation determines ω at the wall for known values of ψ. The coupling condition at a wall between vorticity and the streamfunction has been a major issue in the ψ–ω method (see Gresho, 1991). Although many other equations have been proposed, Eq. 14.3.37 still seems to be reasonable. For a major improvement, one needs a more sophisticated approach, as, for example, that of Daube (1992).

At the leading edge of the plate, the vorticity is singular. Approaching the point along the stagnation streamline gives $\omega = 0$, whereas approaching along the wall gives $\omega \Rightarrow \infty$. Unfortunately, the vorticity at this point is needed in the computation of the Laplacian in formula 14.3.28. To circumvent this problem, a special equation for the

Laplacian is employed for the point $i = IO + 1$, $j = JJ$. This formula does not involve vorticity at $i = IO + 1$, $j = JJ + 1$ (see Problem 14.8).

A flowchart of the computer program is given in Fig. 14.6. After the customary statements to dimension the variables and set the format, the input parameters are specified. Next, the known boundary conditions on ψ, ω, u, and v are fixed and the initial conditions for the interior points are specified. The program in Appendix F employed initial conditions $u = 1$, $v = 0$, $\omega = 0$, and $\psi = y$ on all interior points, while the initial wall vorticity was taken as $\omega = 3$. The main calculation consists of two loops. The outside loop of the program solves the vorticity equation 14.3.26 at all interior points. These vorticity values are used as known quantities in the inner loop for streamfunction equation 14.3.23. This equation needs only to be supplied with ω on interior points. The inner-iteration loop on ψ is complete once Eq. 14.3.24 has been satisfied. Next, velocities at all interior points, the centerline, and the stagnation streamline are found by using Eqs. 14.3.34 to 14.3.36. The final calculation uses Eq. 14.3.37 to evaluate the wall vorticity. This completes one pass through the program. The resulting flow pattern is taken back to the top of the loop, where we begin again by calculating the interior vorticity at the next time step. One successive vorticity values are within the tolerance set by Eq. 14.3.33, the calculation is halted and the last values sent to the output.

The stability and accuracy of the solution are determined by the choices we make about the mesh size and the time step. The diffusion of vorticity is not described accurately if the mesh size becomes too large. We need several mesh points to resolve any steep velocity gradients accurately. A useful rule of thumb is that the Reynolds number of grid cells should be somewhat less than 10. This translates into a mesh spacing,

$$\Delta y < \frac{10}{\text{Re}}, \qquad \text{Re} = \frac{u_0(2h)}{\nu} \qquad (14.3.38)$$

In this equation Δy is nondimensionalized by $2h$, the same length as used in Re. For small Reynolds numbers, meshes much finer than Eq. 14.3.38 are used for better resolution.

Stability considerations will fix the largest value of the time step that you can choose. It has already been noted that the equation for ψ is convergent for any mesh size as long as $1 \leq F \leq 2$. The vorticity equation offers a more stringent stability criterion. Roache (1972) gives the maximum time step for stability as

$$\Delta t < \cfrac{1}{\dfrac{|u|}{\Delta x} + \dfrac{|v|}{\Delta y} + \dfrac{4}{\text{Re}}\left(\dfrac{1}{\Delta x^2} + \dfrac{1}{\Delta y^2}\right)} \qquad (14.3.39)$$

Note that neglecting the terms containing u and v gives a larger estimate of Δt. As Ames (1977) points out, this time step is only a guide: Some problems may require larger or smaller steps than Eq. 14.3.39 would indicate. This seems to be especially true at the higher Reynolds numbers, where smaller steps are needed.

14.4   ENTRANCE FLOW INTO A CASCADE OF PLATES: PRESSURE SOLUTION

The ψ–ω method of solution does not give any information about the pressure field. A separate calculation for the pressure is needed. There are two major ways this can be approached. The first method is to do a numerical quadrature of the relation

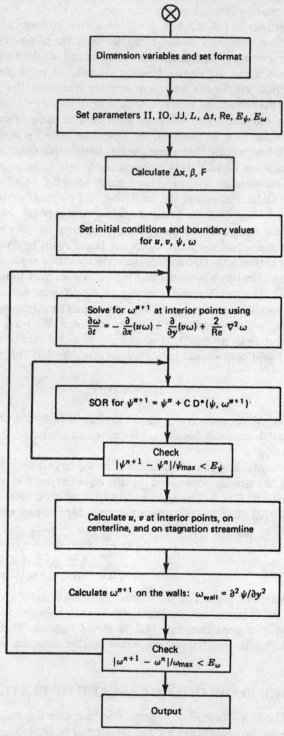

Figure 14.6 Flowchart for $\psi-\omega$ computer solution. A sample program is given in Appendix F.

$$dp = \frac{\partial p}{\partial x} dx + \frac{\partial p}{\partial y} dy \qquad (14.4.1)$$

where the derivatives are given by the momentum equations,

$$\frac{1}{\rho} \frac{\partial p}{\partial x} = -u \frac{\partial u}{\partial x} - v \frac{\partial u}{\partial y} + \nu \nabla^2 u \qquad (14.4.2)$$

$$\frac{1}{\rho} \frac{\partial p}{\partial y} = -u \frac{\partial v}{\partial x} - v \frac{\partial v}{\partial y} + \nu \nabla^2 v \qquad (14.4.3)$$

Since u and v are known at every point, the derivatives on the right-hand sides of Eqs. 14.4.2 and 14.4.3 can be expressed in finite-difference formulas. In an alternative procedure, the right-hand sides can be formulated entirely in terms of the streamfunction, which is also known.

In many instances we are only seeking a drag force, and therefore only need the pressure on the surface of the body. The quadrature of Eq. 14.4.1 is an effective method in these problems.

In Section 15.5, the pressure on the upper and lower flow boundaries will be given. These pressures were found by quadrature of Eq. 14.4.1 in a simplified form. On these streamlines $dy = 0$, so Eq. 14.4.1 becomes

$$dp = \frac{\partial p}{\partial x} dx = \rho \left[-\frac{\partial}{\partial x} \left(\frac{1}{2} u^2 \right) + \nu \nabla^2 u \right] dx$$

By noting that on the upper and lower boundaries $\nabla^2 u = -\partial \omega / \partial y$ (since $\nabla^2 u = -\nabla \times \omega$), this equation reduces to

$$\frac{1}{\rho} (p - p_\infty) = -\frac{1}{2} (u^2 - u_\infty^2) - \nu \int_\infty^x \frac{\partial \omega}{\partial y} dx \qquad (14.4.4)$$

For these special streamlines the viscous effect is all that needs to be integrated numerically (special care must be taken at the leading edge, where $\partial \omega / \partial y$ is singular).

The second method of finding the pressure is to find a numerical solution to the differential equation for the pressure field. The equation is

$$-\frac{1}{\rho} \nabla^2 p = \left(\frac{\partial u}{\partial x} \right)^2 + 2 \left(\frac{\partial u}{\partial y} \frac{\partial v}{\partial x} \right) + \left(\frac{\partial v}{\partial y} \right)^2 \qquad (14.4.5)$$

With a known velocity field, Eq. 14.4.5 is a Poisson equation and can be solved by exactly the same method as that used to solve the streamfunction equation 14.3.2. The boundary conditions on the pressure are more complicated, however.

In most instances we do not know the pressure on the complete boundary (unless we solve Eq. 14.4.1), so the problem is one of mixed-boundary conditions. Along any solid wall the pressure gradient is given by Eq. 13.7.8. When this relation is evaluated in the normal direction, we have

$$\frac{\partial p}{\partial n} = \mu \frac{\partial \omega}{\partial s}$$

where n is normal and s is along the wall. On all flow boundaries we know the value of either the pressure or the pressure gradient.

14.5 ENTRANCE FLOW INTO A CASCADE OF PLATES: RESULTS

Figure 14.7 shows the streamline patterns in the entrance for several values of the Reynolds number. These results were obtained from the computer program in Appendix F. At any Reynolds number, streamlines that are equally spaced far upstream become pinched toward the center as the fully developed profile is reached far downstream. The final location of the streamlines is always the same. The pinching process itself is the only thing that changes as the Reynolds number varies. At low Reynolds number, the pinching begins outside the plates and is completed a short distance into the channel. As the Reynolds number increases, this pattern shifts downstream and extends. As a matter of fact, as the Reynolds number becomes large, the length it takes to establish the final profile grows in direct proportion to the Reynolds number.

Velocity profiles at several x stations are given in Fig. 14.8. From the profiles in front of the plate it is evident that the upstream influence is much stronger at the lower Reynolds numbers. In fact, when Re = 100, there is practically no upstream influence; the u velocity is still very close to 1 even at $x = -0.2$. Profiles at the downstream stations confirm that the fully developed parabolic profile is established very rapidly for a low Reynolds number, whereas a much longer entrance length is required at a high Reynolds number. A different perspective of these same trends is given in Fig. 14.9, where the velocity on the centerline is plotted as a function of x. This figure also gives the velocity on the stagnation streamline. The extent to which viscous diffusion can progress against the oncoming stream is seen to be greater as the Reynolds number becomes lower.

Figure 14.10 displays the pressure coefficient along the boundaries of the flow. On the centerline, the pressure always decreases. At first the decrease is an inviscid effect;

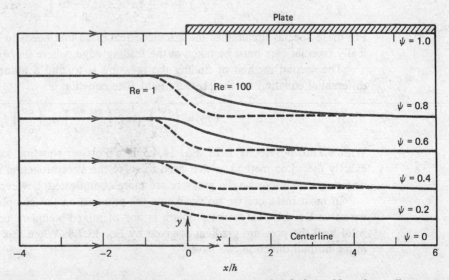

Figure 14.7 Streamlines for entrance flow into a cascade of plates. Note that x-distances are a factor of 1:5 shorter than y-distances.

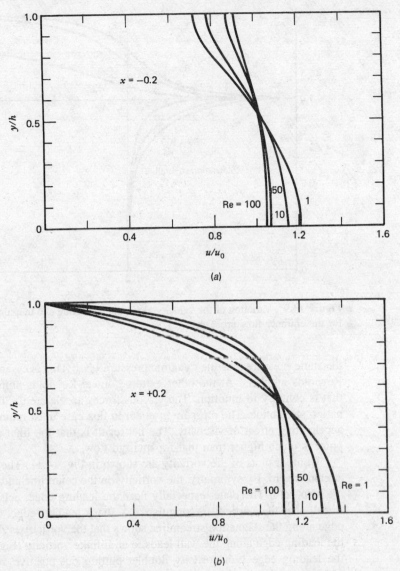

Figure 14.8   Velocity profiles for entrance flow: (a) $x = -0.2$; (b) $x = +0.2$.

the pressure gradient is needed to accelerate the core flow. The pressure continues to drop beyond the entrance length in order to balance the viscous forces retarding the flow. The final steady-state pressure gradient is $-12/\text{Re}$.

The pressure on the stagnation streamlines increases as we approach the leading edge because the flow is slowing down. In a purely inviscid process the pressure force would slow the flow to zero velocity and the pressure coefficient would be unity. Then the stagnation pressure, as given by Eq. 14.4.4 with $v = 0$ and $u = 0$, would simply be

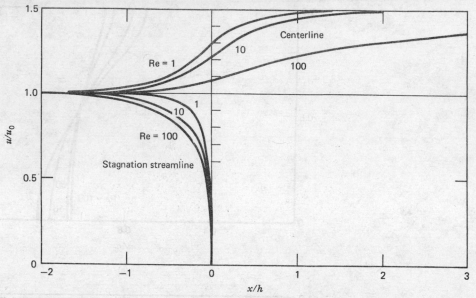

Figure 14.9   Variation of the velocity along the centerline and that along the stagnation streamline for the entrance flow problem.

the static pressure plus the dynamic pressure $\frac{1}{2}\rho u_0^2$. This is essentially what occurs at high Reynolds numbers. At the other extreme, lower-Reynolds-number flows show an effect that is contrary to intuition. The viscous forces accelerate the fluid particles on the stagnation streamline. The pressure gradient in this case must retard the particles against the accelerating effect of viscosity. The net result is that the final pressure at the stagnation point is much higher than that for inviscid flow.

Contour plots of the vorticity are shown in Fig. 14.11. The initial vorticity in the far stream is zero. By symmetry, the vorticity on the centerline and the stagnation streamline are also zero. The plate, especially near the leading edge, acts as a source of vorticity. Recall that the vorticity is singular at a sharp leading edge. Approaching the leading edge along the stagnation streamline shows that the vorticity is zero, whereas approaching the leading edge along the wall leads to an infinite vorticity (Fig. 14.12). Mathematically, the leading edge is a vorticity doublet putting out positive vorticity on one side and negative vorticity on the other.

Recall that generation of vorticity on a solid wall is related to the pressure gradient along the wall. The flux of vorticity out of the wall (in dimensional variables) is (Eq. 13.7.9)

$$-\frac{\partial \omega}{\partial y}\bigg|_{\text{wall}} = \frac{1}{\mu}\frac{\partial p}{\partial x}\bigg|_{\text{wall}}$$

Far downstream, the pressure gradient becomes constant and the flux of vorticity from the wall also becomes constant. The vorticity flux out of the upper wall is absorbed at the lower wall (see Section 13.6).

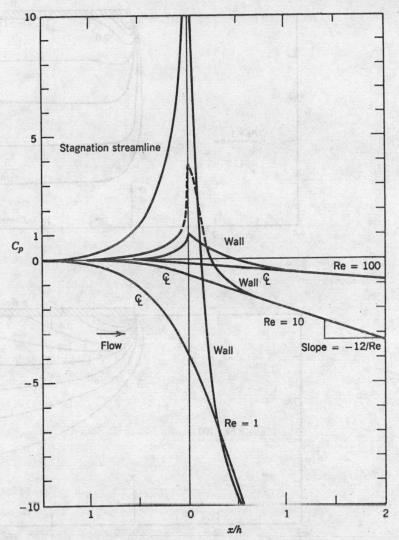

Figure 14.10 Pressure on the centerline and the wall for entrance flow. Pressure coefficient $C_p = (p - p_\infty)/\frac{1}{2}\rho u_0^2$.

Within the fluid the value of the vorticity is determined by a balance of diffusion and convection. This being a plane flow, there is no vortex line stretching. When the fully developed flow is established, the vorticity equation shows that both effects, the net convection term and the net diffusion term, are identically zero. Within the entrance region these two effects compete to distribute the vorticity that is generated at the walls. As the Reynolds number increases, the vorticity generated at the walls becomes higher and tends to stay closer to the wall for a longer distance. In the entrance region the downstream convection is faster than the cross-stream diffusion.

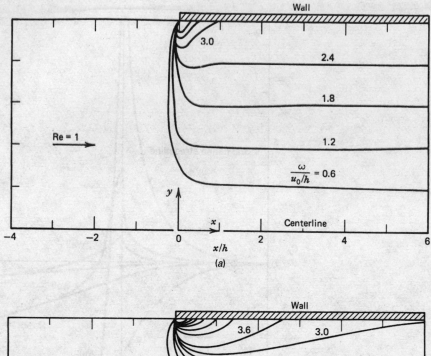

Figure 14.11   Vorticity contours for entrance flow: (a) Re = 1; (b) Re = 100. Distortion is x:y 1:5.

14.6   FLOW AROUND A CIRCULAR CYLINDER

A circular cylinder mounted perpendicular to a steady stream is a flow situation of fundamental interest. It gives us a chance to observe the flow patterns that develop around a smooth body with a finite thickness.

In an actual test we might mount a cylinder across the test section of a wind tunnel. The walls of the test section constrain the flow and make the streamlines conform to the

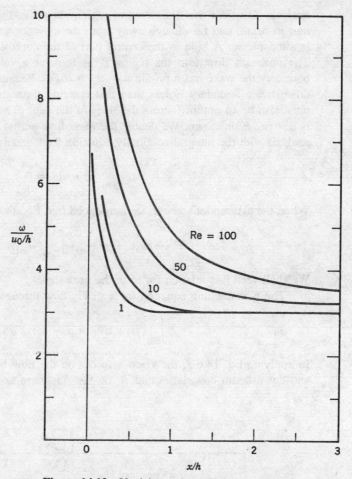

Figure 14.12 Vorticity at the wall for entrance flow.

wall at a finite distance away from the cylinder. The first question is: Does the presence of the walls modify the flow in a substantial way? Can we make the walls so far away that the flow around the cylinder can be isolated and the walls thought of as infinitely far? The answer depends on the Reynolds number. If the Reynolds number is zero, the answer is no; the walls will always influence the flow when they are a finite distance away. However, for any Reynolds number Re > 0, it is thought that the flow may be isolated and the presence of the walls ignored. The flow disturbance caused by the cylinder does not extend to infinity either upstream or on the sides, but is confined to a wake, which trails off downstream and grows slowly. The *wake* is a region where the velocity is still lower than the free-stream value u_0. Viscous stresses cause the wake to spread out, and they also accelerate the fluid to bring the velocity back up toward u_0.

The net force of the fluid on the cylinder is a drag force aligned with the flow direction. There is an important relation between the drag on the cylinder and a property of the wake called the *momentum thickness*. We find this relationship by an integral analysis. Consider the fixed control region shown in Fig. 14.13. It is rectangular, one unit in depth, and far enough away from the cylinder so that the pressure at both ends is atmospheric. A hole in the central part of the control region surrounds the cylinder. The upstream flow into the region is uniform at a value u_0, and at the downstream boundary the wake has a profile $u = u_w = u_w(y)$. Because the volume flow through the downstream boundary is less than that entering through the upstream boundary, there must also be an outflow across the sides of the control region. The velocity on the sides is $u = u_0$, v unknown. We denote the mass flow across both sides as $\dot{m}$ and begin the analysis with the integral continuity equation for a steady flow (Eq. 5.13.2):

$$\int_{FR} \rho v_i n_i \, dS = 0 \tag{14.6.1}$$

When the assumptions above are introduced into Eq. 14.6.1, we have

$$-\rho u_0 \ell + \dot{m} + \rho \int_{-l/2}^{+l/2} u_w \, dy = 0 \tag{14.6.2}$$

We shall need this relation for $\dot{m}$ in the next step.

The x-momentum equation for a steady flow through a fixed region is Eq. 5.14.1,

$$\int_{FR} (\rho n_i v_i u + n_x p - n_i \tau_{ix}) \, dS = 0 \tag{14.6.3}$$

In applying Eq. 14.6.3, the viscous forces on the flow boundaries (τ_{xx} on the upstream and downstream boundaries and τ_{yx} on the sides) are assumed to be zero. The pressure

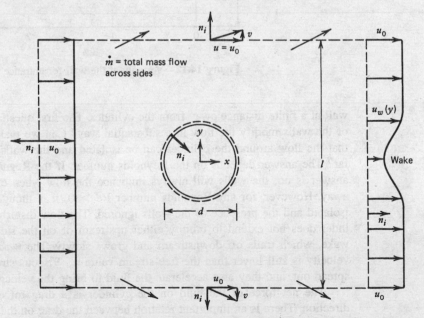

Figure 14.13 Drag analysis for flow around a two-dimensional object.

and viscous forces on the surface of the cylinder (cyl) are by definition the drag force; that is,

$$F_D \equiv \int_{\text{cyl}} (n_x p - n_i \tau_{ix}) \, dS \qquad (14.6.4)$$

These facts, together with previous assumptions, allow Eq. 14.6.3 to reduce to

$$-\rho u_0^2 \ell + \dot{m} u_0 + \rho \int_{-\ell/2}^{+\ell/2} u_w^2 \, dy + F_D = 0$$

Substituting from Eq. 14.6.2 for $\dot{m}$ and rearranging produces

$$F_D = \rho u_0^2 d \int_{-\ell/2d}^{+\ell/2d} \left[\frac{u_w}{u_0} - \left(\frac{u_w}{u_0} \right)^2 \right] d\left(\frac{y}{d} \right) \qquad (14.6.5)$$

Here we have introduced the diameter of the cylinder as a characteristic length. Note that the integrand in Eq. 14.6.5 goes to zero as y becomes large. Hence, we let $\ell \to \infty$ and define the *momentum thickness* of the wake as

$$\theta = d \int_{-\infty}^{\infty} \left[\frac{u_w}{u_0} - \left(\frac{u_w}{u_0} \right)^2 \right] d\left(\frac{y}{d} \right) \qquad (14.6.6)$$

The momentum thickness is an integral property of the wake profile. The drag is found from Eq. 14.6.5 as

$$F_D = \rho u_0^2 \theta \qquad (14.6.7)$$

The customary way to nondimensionalize the drag is by dividing by the kinetic energy of the flow, $\frac{1}{2} \rho u_0^2$, and the cross-sectional area of the body, $1 \times d$. Equation 14.6.7 expressed as a drag coefficient is

$$C_D = \frac{F_D}{\frac{1}{2} \rho u_0^2 d} = 2 \frac{\theta}{d} \qquad (14.6.8)$$

The drag coefficient as a function of Reynolds number is given as Fig. 14.14.

We summarize the picture at this stage as follows. The effect of a cylinder on the flow far away is concentrated in the wake. The velocity in the wake, u_w, gradually approaches the free-stream velocity; however, it must do so in such a way that there is always a deficit in momentum. The momentum deficit is measured by the momentum thickness, which is constant as the wake decays. The drag force on the cylinder is directly proportional to θ.

In the case where the wake becomes turbulent—the most common case in practice—the arguments above are still valid if the velocity u_w is taken as a time-averaged value. The only other effect is that the decay is dominated by turbulent stresses instead of viscous stresses.

Next, we move closer to the cylinder and examine the rich variety of flow patterns that have been observed. Several of these patterns are shown schematically in Fig. 14.15 and in flow-visualization experiments of subsequent figures.

At zero Reynolds number (Figs. 14.15a and 14.16a), the flow divides and reunites smoothly in a symmetric pattern for and aft. The drag is quite high, as shown in Fig.

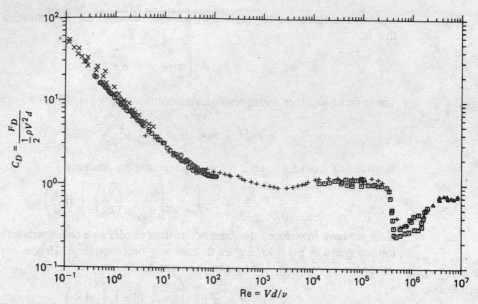

Figure 14.14 Drag curve for a cylinder. Data from Wieselsberger (1921), Delany and Sorenson (1953), Finn (1953), Tritton (1959), and Roshko (1961).

14.14. A change occurs in the flow patterns at about Re = 4. The flow separates on the downstream side, and two steady standing eddies are formed (Figs. 14.15c and 14.16b). These eddies are stable and remain attached to the body.

When the Reynolds number is about 40 the next flow pattern develops. The wake behind the cylinder become unstable. Oscillations in the wake grow in amplitude and finally roll up into discrete vortices with a very regular spacing. This trail of vortices in the wake is known as the *von Kármán vortex street*. The vortices travel downstream at a speed slightly less than u_0. They are not turbulent, and the flow near the cylinder remains steady with two attached eddies. If we placed a velocity-measuring instrument in the wake, it would show a regular oscillation with one cycle corresponding to the distance between two vortices of the same sign. The frequency of this oscillation, f, when nondimensionalized by the diameter and the free-stream speed, is called the *Strouhal* (St) *number*. It is defined as

$$\text{St} \equiv \frac{fd}{u_0}$$

The Strouhal number varies slightly with Re but is roughly 0.2 over a wide range in Re. More specific information on St(Re) is given by Williamson (1988).

As the Reynolds number increases, the vortex street forms closer to the cylinder, until finally the attached eddies themselves begin to oscillate. Ultimately, the attached eddies give way to eddies that alternatively form and then shed. Depending on the details of the experiment, this first occurs at a Reynolds number somewhere between 60 and 100. Figure 14.17a shows the vortex street development. As one goes farther downstream,

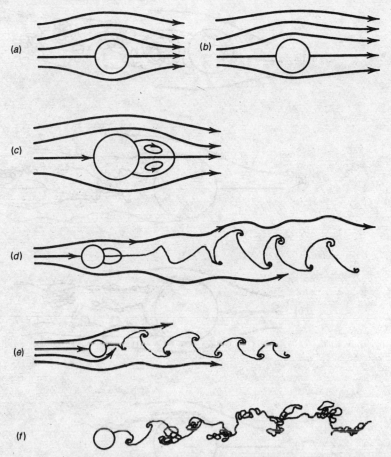

Figure 14.15   Flow regimes for a cylinder: (*a*) Re = 0, symmetrical; (*b*) 0 < Re < 4; (*c*) 4 < Re < 40, attached vortices; (*d*) 40 < Re < 60–100, von Kármán vortex street; (*e*) 60–100 < Re < 200, alternative shedding; (*f*) 200 < Re < 400, vortices unstable to spanwise bending.

the circular motion of the vortices is stopped by viscous forces. In an experiment such as Fig. 14.17 it is difficult to see when this happens as the flow visualization marker retains its distinctive pattern even after the vortices have stopped. The first picture in Fig. 14.18 shows a vortex pattern, the same as in Fig. 14.17, extending a distance of 200 diameters behind the (very small) cylinder. The pathline streaks in the figure were produced by smoke from vaporizing oil on a hot wire located at the cylinder station. After some downstream distance the pattern of smoke is no longer dynamic and the vortices have decayed. Note the picture in Fig. 14.18*d*. Here the smoke is introduced at a location 150 diameters downstream from the cylinder and no vortices exist. The earlier patterns in the picture in Fig. 14.18*a* are fossils of events that occur where the smoke was introduced. Cimbala et al. (1988) have not only shown the vortex street decay, but they have also vividly demonstrated how our eyes can be deceived by inactive flow visualization patterns.

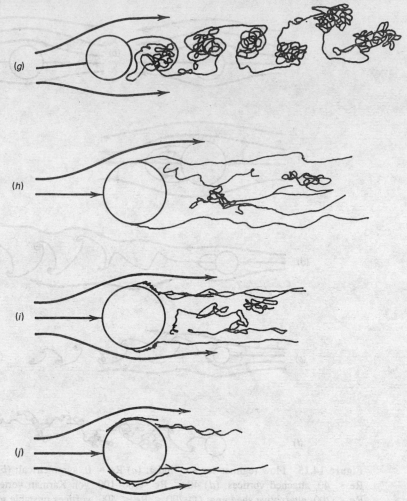

Figure 14.15 (*Continued*) (*g*) 400 < Re, vortices turbulent at birth; (*h*) Re < 3×10^5, laminar boundary layer separates at 80°; (*i*) 3×10^5 < Re < 3×10^6, separated region becomes turbulent, reattaches, and separates again at 120°; (*j*) 3×10^6 < Re, turbulent boundary layer begins on front and separates on back.

Vortex formation near the cylinder is an unsteady flow, and the drag force oscillates with the formation of each eddy. In addition, the top-to-bottom asymmetry of the flow gives rise to an oscillating lift force. As the flow forms a clockwise eddy, it rushes past the top of the cylinder somewhat faster than the flow across the bottom. This causes the pressure on the top to be less, resulting in a lift force toward the top of the page. When the clockwise eddy breaks away, the opposite pattern develops on the bottom and the lift force reverses its direction. The shedding process is very regular and coherent in the spanwise direction.

Oscillations in the lift and drag forces on bluff bodies sometimes take on great importance. Figure 14.19 shows an oil platform with spiral strakes attached to the legs

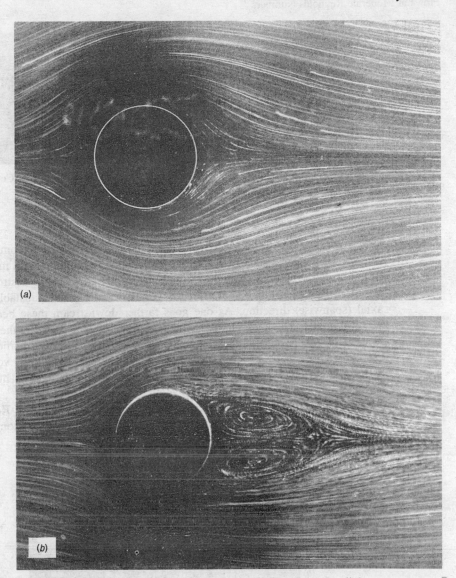

Figure 14.16   Flow over the circular cylinder is from left to right: (*a*) slight asymmetry at Re = 1.54, but flow is still attached; (*b*) standing vortices at Re = 26. Reprinted with permission from Taneda (1979).

(shown in the jacked-up position). If the bending frequency of the legs is nearly the same as the shedding frequency of the vortices, the oscillating force may, over the course of several cycles, build up to destructive magnitude. The purpose of the spiral strakes is to break up the spanwise coherence of the vortices by forcing them to tear away at different times along the length of the leg. Then different parts of the leg are in different phases of the force oscillation, and a destructive motion is avoided. Similar phenomena can occur on transmission lines, heat-exchanger tubes, and even suspension bridges. You may

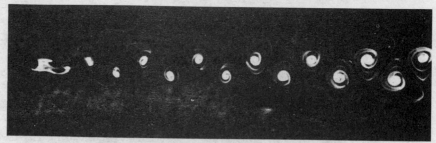

Figure 14.17 Development of the von Kármán vortex street at Re = 105. Courtesy of S. Taneda, Kyushu University, Japan. Reprinted with permission.

have seen the widely distributed movie of the collapse of the Tacoma Narrows bridge (the last of about 50 such major bridge accidents). Here, a torsional mode of oscillation in the bridge structure synchronized with the vortex shedding to destroy the bridge.

At a Reynolds number of 200, the vortex street becomes unstable to bends in the axial (spanwise) direction. As one goes farther downstream these bends grow and the wake ultimately becomes turbulent. In the range 200 < Re < 400 the Strouhal number loses its regular, well-defined character. Somewhere in the neighborhood of Re = 400 the vortices themselves become turbulent. The turbulence within the vortices gives them a different velocity profile and restores the spanwise coherence. This restabilizes the Strouhal number, and it returns to its value 0.2.

Over the higher Reynolds number range (except for $3 \times 10^5 < \text{Re} < 3 \times 10^6$) the vortex shedding becomes somewhat irregular and in flow-visualization experiments it is

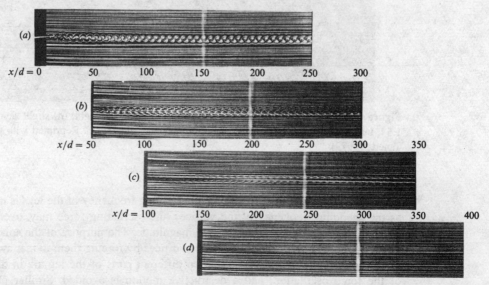

Figure 14.18 Wake of a circular cylinder at Re = 93. A smoke wire shows different patterns when inserted at different locations. Research described in Cimbala et al. (1988).

Figure 14.19   "Jack-up rig" for offshore drilling. Note spiral strakes on the legs at the top of the picture. Photograph taken by Bethlehem Steel, and supplied by O. Griffin Naval Research Lab. Reprinted with permission.

difficult to see vortex shedding. Nevertheless, a time history of the velocity at any point has a large spectral component at the Strouhal frequency of 0.2.

The time-averaged drag coefficient for the cylinder (Fig. 14.14) drops to a value of about 1 at Re ~ 100 to 200 and then remains relatively constant with increasing Reynolds number. This indicates that pressure forces dominate the drag; viscous forces are negligible. From here on we are in the high Reynolds range. Viscous forces and vorticity are confined near the surface of the cylinder in a boundary layer region. The abrupt drop in the drag coefficient at Re $= 3 \times 10^5$ is due to another change in the flow pattern. Although this is a high-Reynolds-number phenomenon, we discuss it in a qualitative way for the sake of completeness.

Below Re $= 3 \times 10^5$, the boundary layer on the cylinder is laminar and separates on the front half of the cylinder (80°) with a shallow angle as depicted in Fig. 14.15.

The pressures in the separated region on the downstream side are nearly constant, but much lower than the free-stream pressure. This causes the high drag. The *critical Reynolds number* 3×10^5 marks the point where the laminar boundary itself becomes unstable just after it separates. In a very short distance the shear layer becomes turbulent and then reattaches to the cylinder. The actual thickness of the boundary layer, the separation bubble, and the reattachment zone is greatly exaggerated in Fig. 14.15 so that we may see it. The turbulent boundary layer itself separates from the cylinder at about the 120° position. The net result is that the area of the large separation region has decreased and the pressure in this region has almost come back to the free-stream value. Accordingly, a dramatic drop in the drag (over 70%) is realized.

With a slight further increase in Reynolds number to about 3×10^6, the drag increases again. As far as experiments have gone, this is the final flow pattern. The boundary layer now becomes turbulent on the front half of the cylinder while it is still attached. Separation of the turbulent layer occurs a little earlier than before, and the pressure is somewhat lower. As a result, the drag is moderately increased.

Boundary layer separation and transition to turbulence are sensitive to many things. If the surface is rough or the free stream contains a little turbulence, the critical Reynolds number will change slightly. Even the presence or absence of sound can change the critical Reynolds number.

The pattern of flows described above is common for smooth, bluff bodies; only the values of the transition Reynolds number change. Elliptical cylinders, spheres, ellipsoids,

Figure 14.20   Subcritical flow over a sphere is shown at Re = 15,000. Laminar separation occurs forward of the equator. Courtesy of H. Werlé, ONERA, Chatillon, France. Reprinted with permission.

and so on all show similar behavior. Figures 14.20 and 14.21 show flow-visualization experiments on a sphere at subcritical and supercritical Reynolds numbers.

Many moderate Reynolds number calculations of the flow patterns have been done. Almost all of them use a $\psi-\omega$ numerical method, more or less like the one studied in the entrance flow problem. Thom (1933) (30 years before the electronic calculator) did the first published cylinder calculations at Re = 10 and 20. Many, but not all, of the flow patterns around cylinders have been reproduced by numerical solutions. Figures 14.22a and 14.23a show streamline patterns from calculations by Fornberg (1980). At Re = 2, some fore–aft asymmetry of the flow can already be detected. Higher-Reynolds-number solutions show the attached eddies and delineate their growth together with the forward movement of the separation point as the Reynolds number increases. This particular calculation method has forced symmetry. Instabilities in the wake and vortex shedding are prevented by computing only one-half of the flow. Nevertheless, the results are of theoretical interest as a solution, albeit an unstable solution, of the Navier–Stokes equations. The surface pressures from these calculations are given in Fig. 14.24, and the vorticity results are given in Figs. 14.22b and 14.23b. When Re = 2, vorticity diffuses some distance away from the cylinder with only a slight asymmetry caused by convection. As the Reynolds number increases, the intensity of the vorticity increases, an indication of sharper velocity gradients near the cylinder. A most pronounced effect is that the vorticity is concentrated near the front and sides of the cylinder and swept downstream

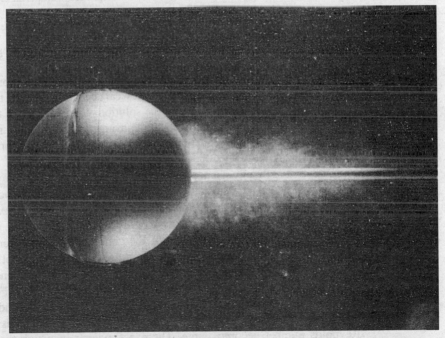

Figure 14.21 Supercritical flow at Re = 30,000. Normally, this flow is subcritical, but a small trip wire has induced transition to a turbulent boundary layer. Separation is now downstream of the equator, and the wake is smaller. Photograph from ONERA by Werlé (1980). Reprinted with permission.

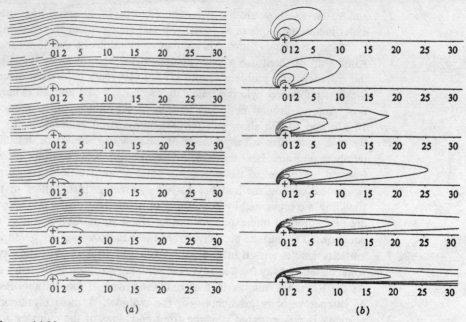

Figure 14.22   Flow over a cylinder: (*a*) streamlines; (*b*) vorticity contours. Reynolds numbers from top to bottom are 2, 4, 10, 20, 40, and 100. Reprinted with permission from Fornberg (1980).

into the wake. These patterns show that convection is becoming more important than diffusion as the Reynolds number increases.

Performing truly accurate numerical calculations becomes more difficult as the Reynolds number is increased. The difficulties can be grouped into three classes: adequate resolution of small sharp changes in the solution, adequate size of the computation region for unbounded problems, and adequate convergence rate for the numerical iterations. If the flow has turbulent regions, there is the added problem of a proper turbulence model in the computations.

The first difficulty demands that the computation mesh be refined in those areas where the gradients are severe; this is especially difficult if the locations are unknown at the outset. Putting more mesh points into a calculation can soon tax the computer storage, especially in a three-dimensional problem. The computer storage capacity also bears on the second difficulty, adequate size of the computation region for unbounded domains. Transforming the unbounded domain into a finite domain does not really solve this problem, but it helps. Although gross qualitative behavior may be found with small domains, very large domains are needed to get even three-place accuracy. Fornberg (1980) used a domain with a distance of 300 cylinder diameters to the outer boundary. The last difficulty is that the rate of convergence of the numerical schemes tends to deteriorate as the Reynolds number becomes large. The exact manner in which the convective terms are linearized and the equations decoupled when they are transcribed into a numerical form determines the convergence rate for the iteration process. For example, at Reynolds numbers approaching 300, Fornberg's calculation shows that the attached vortices are becoming slightly shorter. This unexpected result is a numerical problem. In subsequent

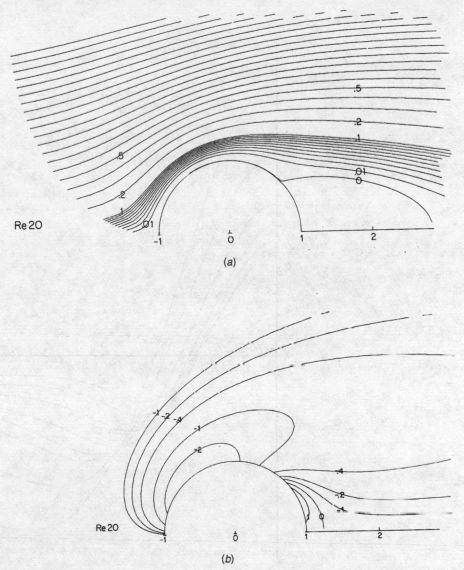

Figure 14.23 Details of (*a*) streamlines and (*b*) vorticity contours at Re = 20. Reprinted with permission from Fornberg (1980).

calculations with 64-bit accuracy, Fornberg found that the vortex length increased linearly with the Reynolds number. The moral is that very accurate calculations at a high Reynolds number need extreme care. Even large-scale features such as vortex length can be given incorrectly by apparently valid calculations. Calculations for Reynolds numbers up to 600 are given in Fornberg (1985).

Of course, the steady laminar calculations are not realistic for Re > 40 when the wake becomes unsteady. To compute the vortex shedding and wake numerically, one must have a Navier–Stokes computer program that is time accurate; the program con-

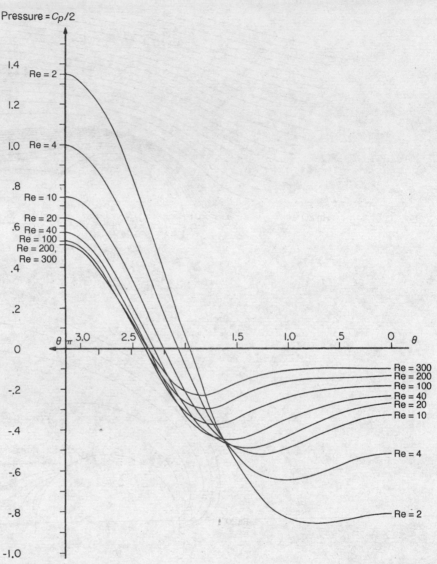

Figure 14.24 Pressure distribution over a cylinder. Pressure axis is $(p - p_\infty)/\rho u_\infty^2$. Reprinted with permission from Fornberg (1980).

verges at each time step to a correct answer. When turbulence, say Re > 200, develops, this task is overwhelming. Complete accurate Navier–Stokes calculations can be done only for simple geometries such as a flat plate or channel at relatively small Reynolds numbers. A compromise approach is to omit calculation of small-scale turbulence but retain a time-dependent calculation of larger events. The scheme must contain a model of how the small scales effect larger events. This approach is called a *large eddy simulation*. Results of such a calculation are shown in Fig. 14.25 for flow over a cylinder at Re = 3900. From Fig. 14.14 we see that this is in the region of subcritical flow, where

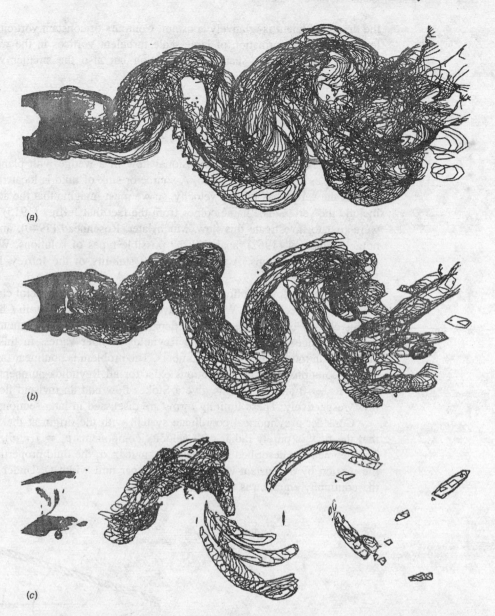

Figure 14.25 Large eddy simulation of flow over a cylinder at Re = 3900. Contours of vorticity are depicted: (a) $|\omega d/V| = 1$; (b) $|\omega d/V| = 4$; (c) $|\omega d/V| = 6$. From Beaudan and Moin (1994).

the drag coefficient is relatively constant. Contours of constant vorticity at three different levels depict the formation of large-scale turbulent vortices in the wake. Note that not only the vortices with spanwise orientation but also the smaller vortices aligned in roughly the streamwise direction.

14.7 JEFFREY–HAMEL FLOW IN A WEDGE

This analysis is for the two-dimensional flow in a wedge with plane walls at a given angle $\pm \alpha$ as shown in Fig. 14.26. A source or sink of fluid is located at the vertex. The flow at the vertex has infinite velocity, so we must imagine that the actual flow does not include the vertex. The name comes from the fact that Jeffrey (1915) and Hamel (1917) were first to investigate this flow. Much later, Rosenhead (1940), among many others, notably Fraenkel (1962), analyzed the possible types of solutions. We shall focus only on symmetric solutions. A reference to the stability of the Jeffrey–Hamel solutions is Banks et al. (1988).

The wedge flow solution is exact and illustrates many general characteristics of the Navier–Stokes equations. We could have discussed wedge flow in Chapter 11 but do so in this chapter because the solutions depend explicitly on the Reynolds number, and the profiles change qualitatively as the Reynolds number varies. In this way it illustrates variations in moderate Reynolds numbers. The problem is nonlinear (and it does not have unique solutions); however, solutions exist for all Reynolds numbers. In particular, the limits Re $\rightarrow$ 0 and Re $\rightarrow -\infty$ give a Stokes flow and an inviscid flow–boundary layer flow, respectively. These limiting forms are discussed in later sections.

Consider a cylindrical coordinate system with the origin at the vertex and assume that the flow is purely radial with velocity components $v_r = f(r, \theta)$, and $v_\theta = v_z = 0$. The geometry is described by the wedge angle $\pm \alpha$, the fluid properties by ρ and ν, and the motion by a constant-volume flow rate per unit width Q. Under these assumptions the continuity equation is integrated to give

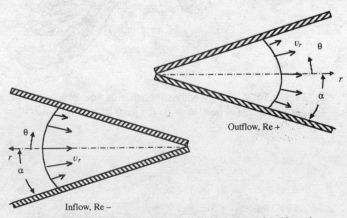

Figure 14.26 Jeffrey–Hamel flow in a wedge of half-angle α.

$$\frac{1}{r}\frac{\partial}{\partial r}(rv_r) = 0$$

(14.7.1)

$$rv_r = f(\theta)$$

Let the centerline velocity at $\theta = 0$ be denoted by

$$v_0 = \frac{f(0)}{r} = \frac{C_0}{r}$$

(14.7.2)

For outflow, v_0 and C_0 are positive; for inflow, they are negative. The nondimensional velocity $F(\theta)$ is defined as the ratio with the centerline velocity:

$$v^* \equiv \frac{v_r}{v_0} = \frac{f(\theta)}{C_0} = F(\theta)$$

(14.7.3)

So

$$v_r = v_0 F(\theta) = \frac{C_0}{r} F(\theta)$$

(14.7.4)

The volume flow rate is

$$Q = \int_{-\alpha}^{+\alpha} v_r r\, d\theta = C_0 \int_{-\alpha}^{+\alpha} F(\theta)\, d\theta$$

(14.7.5)

Since the constants C_0 and Q are related, either can be used to characterize the flow. Favoring C_0 makes the math simpler.

Other quantities of interest are the stresses and the vorticity:

$$\tau_{\theta\theta} = 2\mu \frac{v_r}{r} = 2\mu \frac{C_0 F(\theta)}{r^2}$$

$$\tau_{rr} = -\tau_{\theta\theta}$$

(14.7.6)

$$\tau_{r\theta} = \frac{\mu}{r}\frac{\partial v_r}{\partial \theta} = \frac{\mu C_0}{r^2} F'(\theta)$$

$$\omega_z = -\frac{1}{r}\frac{\partial v_r}{\partial \theta} = -\frac{1}{\mu}\tau_{r\theta} = -\frac{C_0}{r^2} F'(\theta)$$

The θ-direction momentum equation is a balance between the net $\tau_{\theta\theta}$ viscous force and the θ-direction pressure gradient. Note that since $\tau_{\theta\theta}$ is the normal viscous force, this equation means that the total normal surface stress (pressure minus normal viscous stress) is constant in the θ-direction:

$$0 = -\frac{\partial p}{\partial \theta} + \frac{\partial \tau_{\theta\theta}}{\partial \theta}$$

(14.7.7)

$$0 = -\frac{1}{\rho}\frac{\partial p}{\partial \theta} + \frac{2\nu C_0}{r^2} F'$$

(14.7.8)

The r-direction momentum equation shows that momentum convection is balanced by pressure and viscous shear forces:

$$v_r \frac{\partial v_r}{\partial r} = -\frac{1}{\rho} \frac{\partial p}{\partial r} + \frac{1}{r} \frac{\partial \tau_{r\theta}}{\partial \theta}$$

$$-\frac{C_0^2}{r^3} F^2 = \frac{\nu C_0}{r^3} F'' - \frac{1}{\rho} \frac{\partial p}{\partial r} \tag{14.7.9}$$

The pressure is eliminated from the problem by differentiating Eq. 14.7.8 with respect to r, differentiating Eq. (14.7.9) with respect to θ, and eliminating $\partial^2 p / \partial r\, \partial \theta$.

Two additional symbols are introduced: the independent variable η and a Reynolds number Re:

$$\eta \equiv \frac{\theta}{\alpha} \tag{14.7.10}$$

$$\mathrm{Re} \equiv \frac{v_0 r \alpha}{\nu} = \frac{\alpha C_0}{\nu}$$

The Reynolds number is based on the local centerline velocity and local half-width αr. It is constant for the entire flow.

The final equation is

$$F'''(\eta) + 2\mathrm{Re}\,\alpha F(\eta) F'(\eta) + 4\alpha^2 F'(\eta) = 0 \tag{14.7.11}$$

This is, in fact, the vorticity transport equation. The vorticity is F' when it is nondimensionalized with the centerline velocity divided by the wedge half-width.

$$\frac{\omega_z}{v_0/(r\alpha)} = -F'(\eta) \tag{14.7.12}$$

The physical meaning of the terms in Eq. 14.7.11 is as follows:

| net vorticity diffusion in the θ-direction | + | net vorticity convection in the r-direction | + | net vorticity diffusion in the r-direction | = 0 |

The convection term is preceded by the Reynolds number. A large Re value means that the convection (inertia) is more important to the solution.

Although there are many solutions, because of the nonlinear term we will consider only those that are symmetric about $\theta = 0$. The boundary conditions for this case are

$$F(0) = 1$$

$$F'(0) = 0 \tag{14.7.13}$$

$$F(1) = 0$$

This is a two-point nonlinear boundary value problem. Millsaps and Pohlhausen (1953) provided the velocity profiles given in most texts. However, with modern differential equation solvers, one can find solutions with relative ease.

The pressure is found by integrating dp along the centerline, $\eta = 0$, from $r = \infty$ to $r = r$, then from $\eta = 0$ to $\eta = \eta$:

$$p - p_\infty = \int_{\infty,0}^{r,0} \frac{\partial p}{\partial r}\, dr + \int_{r,0}^{r,\eta} \frac{\partial p}{\partial \eta}\, d\eta \qquad (14.7.14)$$

Equations 14.7.8 and 14.7.9 are solved to find the pressure derivatives. The local centerline dynamic pressure is the scale unit. The final result is

$$C_p = \frac{p_\infty - p}{\frac{1}{2}\rho v_0^2} = 1 + \frac{4\alpha^2}{\alpha\,\mathrm{Re}}\,[1 - F(\eta;\,\alpha,\,\mathrm{Re})] + \frac{1}{\alpha\,\mathrm{Re}}\,F''(0;\,\alpha,\,\mathrm{Re}) \qquad (14.7.15)$$

Viscous effects occur only in terms with Re dependence.

The viscous shear stress and normal viscous stress are scaled using the local dynamic pressure on the centerline.

$$\frac{\tau_{\theta r}}{\frac{1}{2}\rho v_0^2} = \frac{2}{\mathrm{Re}}\,F'(\eta) \qquad (14.7.16)$$

$$\frac{\tau_{rr}}{\frac{1}{2}\rho v_0^2} = \frac{\tau_{rr}}{\frac{1}{2}\rho\,v_0^2} = \frac{4\alpha}{\mathrm{Re}}\,F(\eta) \qquad (14.7.17)$$

If the wedge angle is $\alpha \neq 0$, there is a significant normal viscous stress that varies inversely with Re. Since this is a plane flow, $\tau_{zz} = 0$, and because the sum of the normal viscous stresses must be zero, $\tau_{\theta\theta} = -\tau_{rr}$.

Figure 14.27 gives solutions for a wedge of 20° ($\alpha = \pm 10°$). First consider the outflow solutions with positive Reynolds numbers of 0 to 300. The profiles for Reynolds number 100 and all higher values show a backflow near the wall. The maximum Re value for which no reverse flow occurs depends on the wedge angle. A single region of outflow can be maintained only if the wedge angle is equal to or smaller than a flat wall,

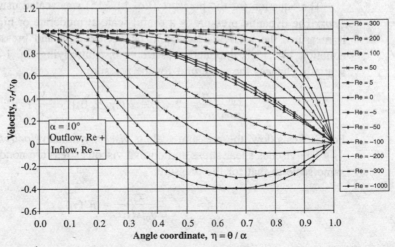

Figure 14.27 Velocity profiles for various Reynolds numbers for flow in a wedge with $\alpha = 10°$.

$\alpha = \pi/2$. For a flat wall, $\alpha = \pi/2$, pure outflow occurs only at Re $= 0$. Any smaller wedge has a finite Re above which pure outflow is impossible. As Re becomes large, the limit condition has been found as α Re ≤ 10.31. Thus, for moderate Reynolds numbers, the backflow or separation condition is a function of geometry and Reynolds number.

The Re $= 0$ solution is reversible. That is, it is either inflow or outflow. Diffusion dominates this case and convection is completely absent. When the flow is toward the apex, profiles exist for all Re and become fuller and fuller as Re increases. The curve shown for Re $= -1000$ has 70% of the channel at a uniform speed.

14.8   LIMITING CASES FOR Re $\rightarrow$ 0 AND Re $\rightarrow$ $-\infty$

As an introduction to Stokes's flow, flows with Re near zero, let us consider the case Re $= 0$ in more detail. At Re $= 0$, momentum differential equations 14.7.8 and 14.7.9 become linear equations that balance viscous and pressure forces. Inertia is negligible. Jeffrey–Hamel differential equation 14.7.11 is a balance between vorticity diffusion in the r- and the θ-directions.

$$F'''(\eta) + 4\alpha^2 F'(\eta) = 0 \qquad (14.8.1)$$

It has the exact solution

$$F = \frac{\cos 2\alpha - \cos 2\alpha\eta}{\cos 2\alpha - 1} \qquad (14.8.2)$$

In the limit $\alpha = 0$ this becomes the parabola of Poiseuille flow. The profiles for a small wedge angle are similar to Poiseuille profiles, while flow at $2\alpha = \pi$, a line source or sink on a plane wall, has zero wall shear stress. Walls within an angle $2\alpha > \pi$ show reverse-flow regions.

The equation for the pressure (Eq. 14.7.15) was scaled using the dynamic pressure, $\frac{1}{2}\rho v_0^2$. The dynamic pressure is a useful scale at moderate or high Reynolds numbers, as it measures the inviscid interaction between inertia and pressure. Obviously, pressure equation 14.7.15 is unbounded as Re $\rightarrow$ 0. Multiplying Eq. 14.7.15 through by Re essentially changes the scale unit for the pressure:

$$\frac{p_\infty - p}{\mu v_0/\alpha r} = 2\alpha[1 - F(\eta; \alpha, 0)] + \frac{1}{2\alpha} F''(0; \alpha, 0) \qquad (14.8.3)$$

For Stokes's flow, the pressure scale is *viscosity* times *velocity/length*.

The viscous shear stress and normal viscous stress are nondimensionalized using the same scale as that for the pressure:

$$\frac{\tau_{\theta r}}{v_0 \mu/\alpha r} = F'(\eta) \qquad (14.8.4)$$

$$\frac{\tau_{rr}}{v_0 \mu/\alpha r} = 2\alpha F(\eta) \qquad (14.8.5)$$

Viscous stresses by their very nature, scale with the viscosity.

In general, for flows with Re → 0, inertia effects become negligible and viscous diffusion determines the flow pattern. Normal viscous stresses, viscous shear stresses, and the pressure are all of the same magnitude and scale with $U\mu/L$.

The second important limit is for Re → −∞. Here flow is toward the apex and an inviscid flow–boundary layer character evolves. Consider rearranging the Jeffrey–Hamel (vorticity transport) equation, Eq. 14.7.11, so that the limit Re → −∞ can be taken:

$$\frac{1}{\text{Re}} F'''(\eta) + 2\alpha F(\eta)F'(\eta) + \frac{4\alpha^2}{\text{Re}} F'(\eta) = 0 \qquad (14.8.6)$$

If $\alpha \neq 0$, the convection of vorticity dominates, and the highest-order viscous term is lost.

$$F(\eta)F'(\eta) = 0 \qquad (14.8.7)$$

A solution that satisfies the centerline boundary condition $F(0) = 1$ is

$$F(\eta) = 1 \qquad (14.8.8)$$

Thus, the inviscid, outer solution, is a uniform radial flow.

Substituting $F(\eta) = 1$ into the relation for the pressure (Eq. 14.7.15), we find that in the limit Re → ∞, the pressure coefficient is unity:

$$\frac{p_\infty - p}{\frac{1}{2}\rho v_0^2} = 1 \qquad (14.8.9)$$

This is the Bernoulli equation for inviscid flow. Similarly, substituting $F(\eta) = 1$ into the stress laws, Eqs. 14.8.4 and 14.8.5, gives

$$\frac{\tau_{\theta r}}{\frac{1}{2}\rho v_0^2} = \frac{2}{\text{Re}} F'(\eta) = 0 \qquad (14.8.10)$$

$$\frac{\tau_{rr}}{\frac{1}{2}\rho v_0^2} = \frac{4\alpha}{\text{Re}} F(\eta) = \frac{4\alpha}{\text{Re}} = 0 \qquad (14.8.11)$$

The viscous stresses are zero compared to the dynamic pressure in the limit Re → −∞.

The reduced differential equation 14.8.7 cannot satisfy the no-slip boundary condition, so a complementary inner solution is needed near the wall. The η-variable must be rescaled to measure the boundary layer properly. First, the origin is shifted to the wall by introducing a translated variable, $\varphi = \alpha - \theta$. In previous sections the thickness of a viscous region was estimated by the diffusion distance $\delta \sim \sqrt{\nu t}$, where t was a convection time. The wedge-flow boundary layer is thinning as the flow approaches the origin, and a different method is employed to estimate its thickness.

To begin, the Reynolds number is redefined to be a positive quantity

$$\text{Re}_0 = -\text{Re} = \frac{-v_0 \alpha r}{\nu} \qquad (14.8.12)$$

Next, consider the wall position at r where the boundary layer thickness is δ and the flow angle with the wall is β, as depicted in Fig. 14.28; that is, $\delta = r\beta$. The velocity here is toward the origin at speed $-v_0$ and the velocity component toward the wall is $-v_0 \sin \beta \sim -v_0 \beta$. The velocity of viscous diffusion is estimated by differentiating $\delta \sim \sqrt{\nu t}$:

$$\frac{d\delta}{dt} = \frac{d(\sqrt{\nu t})}{dt} \sim \sqrt{\frac{\nu}{t}} = \frac{\nu}{\delta} \tag{14.8.13}$$

The flow velocity toward the wall is equated with the viscous diffusion velocity away from the wall.

$$-\beta v_0 = \frac{\nu}{\delta} \tag{14.8.14}$$

Noting that $\delta = r$ allows this equation to be rearranged into

$$\frac{\beta}{\alpha} = \frac{1}{\sqrt{\alpha \, \mathrm{Re}_0}} \tag{14.8.15}$$

For high Reynolds numbers, β becomes a small fraction of α. A distance variable that is of order one within the boundary layer begins with zero at the wall and is of order one at β. Therefore, the correct boundary layer variable is

$$\xi = \frac{\varphi}{\beta} = \frac{\alpha - \theta}{\beta} = (1 - \eta)\sqrt{\alpha \, \mathrm{Re}_0} \tag{14.8.16}$$

The differential equation needs to be transformed from η to ξ as the independent variable. This yields

$$\frac{d^3F}{d\xi^3} - 2F \frac{dF}{d\xi} + \frac{4\alpha}{\mathrm{Re}_0} \frac{dF}{d\xi} = 0 \tag{14.8.17}$$

For high Re_0 the equation governing the inner region is found to be

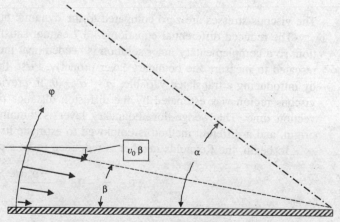

Figure 14.28   Boundary layer scaling for Jefferey–Hamel flow at Re $\rightarrow -\infty$.

$$\frac{d^3F}{d\xi^3} - 2F\frac{dF}{d\xi} = 0 \tag{14.8.18}$$

The boundary condition at the wall is the no-slip condition:

$$F(0) = 0 \tag{14.8.19}$$

The far-field boundary condition is a matching between the inviscid (outer) flow and the (inner) boundary layer flow:

$$F(\xi \to \infty) = F(\eta \to 0) = F_{\text{common part}} \tag{14.8.20}$$

$$F(\xi \to \infty) = 1$$

The third condition is that the boundary layer approaches the inviscid flow exponentially fast. In the present case we can simply require that the first derivative vanish:

$$\frac{dF}{d\xi}(\xi \to \infty) = 0 \tag{14.8.21}$$

The boundary layer problem, Eq. 14.8.18, is nonlinear; however, a closed-form solution is known to be

$$F(\xi) = 3\tanh^2\left(\frac{\zeta}{\sqrt{2}} + \operatorname{arctanh}\sqrt{\frac{2}{3}}\right) - 2 \tag{14.8.22}$$

This solution was first given by Pohlhausen (1921) as a solution to a boundary layer equation.

The pressure within the boundary layer is constant at the same value that exists in the inviscid flow; $C_p = 1$. This can be verified by showing that the pressure gradient in the normal direction is zero. Recasting Eq. 14.7.9 for $\partial p/\partial \eta$ into boundary layer variables produces

$$\frac{\partial}{\partial \xi}\left(\frac{p}{\frac{1}{2}\rho v_0^2}\right) = -\frac{4\alpha}{\text{Re}_0}\frac{dF}{d\xi} \tag{14.8.23}$$

This gradient vanishes at a high Reynolds number, $\text{Re}_0 \to \infty$.

It is interesting to form a composite asymptotic expansion for the velocity profile. A composite of the additive type (this is discussed more completely in Section 15.6) is uniformly valid for all η:

$$F_{\text{composite}}(\eta, \text{Re}_0) = F_{\text{inner}}[\xi \Rightarrow (\eta - 1)\sqrt{\alpha\,\text{Re}_0}] + F_{\text{outer}}(\eta) - F_{\text{common part}} \tag{14.8.24}$$

Since $F_{\text{outer}} = 1$ and the common part is obviously $F_{\text{common part}} = 1$, they cancel and the composite is actually the boundary layer solution with the variable changed to η. As a practical matter one does not know the lowest value of Re_0 for which the composite result is a good approximation. However, this is a case in which we know the exact answer as well as the composite result. Figure 14.29 shows a comparison of the composite and the exact result for several Reynolds numbers when the wedge angle is $2\alpha = 20°$. For this wedge angle the composite is a good approximation to the exact answer at $\text{Re}_0 = 100$, but not so good at $\text{Re}_0 = 50$. At the lower Reynolds number the centerline

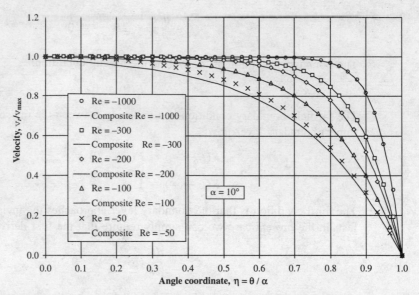

Figure 14.29 Exact and composite velocity profiles for Jefferey–Hamel flow at various high Reynolds numbers.

velocity is not unity. This indicates that viscous effects are crossing the centerline, and the boundary layer from the opposite wall should be considered.

Note that the outer inviscid flow and the boundary layer are both independent of α (and, of course, Re_0). The inviscid flow slips over a solid wall, and therefore the location of the wall is along any streamline from a radial source. Moreover, the boundary layer profile is determined by flow near the wall, so that the location of the opposite wall is immaterial. On the other hand, the composite solution (expressed in the outer variable η) depends explicitly on both α and Re_0.

14.9 CONCLUSIONS

Moderate-Reynolds-number flows are characterized by the fact that inertia, pressure (and/or gravity), and viscous forces are all important. In some cases this competition produces complicated and intricate flow patterns.

Computers are very good at predicting and confirming laminar flow patterns at moderate Reynolds numbers. When all the terms in the governing equations are about the same size, the error made in the numerical processes will be smaller than all the terms. As the Reynolds number takes on either extreme value, zero or infinity, some terms in the governing equations become very small. Under these conditions the errors in the large terms and the true size of small terms are comparable. As a result, the small-term effect is lost. You might raise the question: Does this really make any difference? Won't the small effect average itself out and be unimportant anyway? Sometimes this is true, but in fluid mechanics it is frequently not true. A small term may accumulate to give a large effect. For example, a very small force applied to a satellite over the course of a year makes a drastic change in the orbit. The problem of doing valid numerical computations at extreme Reynolds numbers, especially the practical case of high Reynolds numbers with turbulence, is a current research challenge in fluid mechanics.

The flow over a cylinder or sphere in an infinite stream shows a rich variety of flow patterns and phenomena as the Reynolds number changes. Major elements include standing vortices, the von Kármán vortex street, wake instabilities, separation bubbles, and subcritical and supercritical wake patterns. The global analysis shows the relation between the wake momentum and the drag on a body in a streaming flow. An internal flow is typified by the Jeffrey–Hamel wedge flow. Although the assumption of a single velocity component is very difficult to produce experimentally, the mathematical solution exhibits many important properties of the Navier–Stokes equations. There are multiple solutions for the same Reynolds number. Outflow (Re positive) solutions, where the pressure increases in the flow direction, show regions of reverse flow for all Reynolds numbers greater than a critical value. Inflow solutions (Re negative), where the pressure decreases in the flow direction, are quite smooth for all Reynolds numbers and exhibit a boundary layer behavior for large negative Reynolds number. In fact, the flow near the wall obeys the boundary layer equations. The other extreme limit, Re approaching zero, has the same viscous diffusion-dominated character as with the Stokes flow.

PROBLEMS

14.1 (B) The velocities for ideal flow around a cylinder are given by Eq. 18.6.3. Compute the strain rate tensor and find the principal axes. Consider a line vortex of negligible strength that is perpendicular to the free stream and to the cylinder axis. The vortex is carried into the cylinder and wraps around it. Where would it suffer the most intense stretching?

14.2 (A) Run the entrance flow program of Appendix F for $Re = 0.1$, 3.0, and 35.

14.3 (B) Do the driven cavity problem for the case where both the bottom and top lids move in the same direction at U_0. Do not assume a symmetric flow pattern to start the problem.

14.4 (B) A rectangular cavity with width L and depth $1.5L$ has a top wall that slides from left to right at velocity U. Solve for the flow field if the Reynolds number is $UL/\nu = 20$. Use a 20×30 grid. Among other information, plot the horizontal velocity profile from top to bottom at the midstation of the cavity.

14.5 (B) Repeat Problem 14.4 for various error criteria: E_ω and $E_\psi = 10^{-4}, 10^{-5}, 10^{-6}, 10^{-7}, 10^{-8}$. Assume the

results for $E = 10^{-8}$ as reference (true) values ψ_R and ω_R. For each E level, form the total errors $TE_\psi \equiv \Sigma \, |\psi - \psi_R|$ and $TE_\omega \equiv \Sigma \, |\omega - \omega_R|$, where the summation is over all grid points. Plot TE_ψ and TE_ω as functions of E.

14.6 (B) Repeat Problem 14.4 for various grid sizes: 10×15, 20×30, and 40×60 with E_ω and $E_\psi = 10^{-4}$. Assume the results for 40×60 as reference (true) values ψ_R and ω_R. For each grid form the total errors $TE_\psi \equiv \Sigma \, |\psi - \psi_R|$ and $TE_\omega \equiv \Sigma \, |\omega - \omega_R|$, where the summation is over all common grid points. Plot TE_ψ and TE_ω as functions of the number of grid points.

14.7 (B) In the cascade problem, the vorticity at the leading edge, IO + 1, JJ + 1 is needed in the five-point Laplacian for the point IO + 1, JJ. For this special situation write a five-point Laplacian using Taylor expansions to the corner points (IO, JJ − 1, IO, JJ + 1, IO + 2, JJ − 1, IO + 2, JJ + 1), thus avoiding the point IO + 1, JJ + 1. (This is equivalent to subtracting the five-point Laplacian operator from the nine-point Laplacian.)

14.8 (C) Construct a scheme for a finite-difference approximation of the equation $\omega = \nabla^2 \psi$ at a 90° corner that is concave. Repeat for a convex corner.

14.9 (A) From the numerical calculation results for steady flow, plot the pressure coefficient C_p at the stagnation point of a cylinder as a function of Re. What is the mathematical trend as Re $\rightarrow$ 0?

14.10 (A) Consider a slot where the walls are $y = \pm h + \pm A \sin(2\pi x/L)$. Find transformation $X(x, y)$, $Y(x, y)$ that will make the wave slot into a rectangle in the X–Y domain.

14.11 (B) Transform the equation $\nabla^2 \psi = \omega$ into the X–Y variables of Problem 14.10.

14.12 (B) Transform the vorticity equation into the X–Y variables of Problem 14.10.

14.13 (B) A two-dimensional body with characteristic length d is in a stream of velocity u_0. Far downstream the wake velocity is

$$u = u_0 - \frac{21\nu}{\sqrt{xd}} \exp\left(-\frac{y^2 u_0}{\nu x}\right)$$

Find the drag force per unit length and the momentum thickness.

15

Asymptotic Analysis Methods

We have already seen how incompressible flow may be considered as a flow where the Mach number, a parameter, approaches zero. This is an example of an asymptotic theory—a class of flow problems that have common characteristics as a parameter approaches zero. Alternatively, we might be interested in the behavior of a specific problem as a certain parameter or variable approaches a limiting value. For example, consider a jet issuing into a large room. What is the flow like far away from the mouth of the jet? As another example, we might ask what would be the effect on Poiseuille flow if the pipe were slightly flattened instead of round.

In this chapter we deal with several specific fluid-flow problems. These problems will be solved using asymptotic methods, also called perturbation methods. In between the sample problems are sections that give some of the formal mathematics relevant to asymptotic methods.

Before we take up the first problem, note that the variable or parameter that approaches a limit is always (or can be made into) a nondimensional variable. The expression "far away from a jet" must refer to the distance divided by the radius of the jet exit. A "slightly flattened" pipe must mean that the wall location is slightly out of round compared to the pipe radius; and of course, a low Mach number means that velocities are small compared to the speed of sound.

15.1 OSCILLATION OF A GAS BUBBLE IN A LIQUID

One of the early investigations of gas bubbles was conducted to explain the musical sounds that occur when bubbles are formed as the result of water flowing over the rocks in small streams, or a jet falling into a pool. The process of forming the bubble also sets it into oscillation. One important question is: What is the natural frequency of a bubble in a liquid? In an engineering context we might be interested in this problem with regard to the flow of a bubbly mixture or with regard to the attenuation of sound by the bubbles in the wake of a ship's propeller. A transient wave in a bubbly mixture will be strongly influenced by bubble oscillations.

In Section 12.7 we derived an equation for the change in the radius of a cavity $R(t)$ while the density of the surrounding fluid was ρ and the steady pressure at infinity was p_0. The equation is

$$R\ddot{R} + \frac{3}{2}\dot{R}^2 - \frac{1}{\rho}(p - p_0) = 0 \tag{15.1.1}$$

347

Assume that the pressure p at the liquid surface is the same as that within the bubble. This assumption ignores surface tension, which becomes important in this problem when R is less than 10^{-2} cm. Let the bubble contain a perfect gas in such an amount that if the pressure in the bubble were p_0, the volume would be V_0 and the radius R_0. For isentropic bubble oscillations thermodynamic supplies the relationship

$$\frac{p}{p_0} = \left(\frac{V_0}{V}\right)^\gamma = \left(\frac{R_0}{R}\right)^{3\gamma} \tag{15.1.2}$$

Substituting Eq. 15.1.2 into Eq. 15.1.1 gives an equation that governs $R(t)$:

$$R\ddot{R} + \frac{3}{2}\dot{R}^2 - \frac{p_0}{\rho}\left[\left(\frac{R}{R_0}\right)^{-3\gamma} - 1\right] = 0 \tag{15.1.3}$$

Every term of this oscillator equation is nonlinear. To set a definite problem, we assume that the bubble radius is initially displaced from the equilibrium position but has zero initial velocity. That is,

$$R(0) = R_0(1 + \varepsilon) \tag{15.1.4}$$

$$\dot{R}(0) = 0$$

Here ε is a nondimensional parameter that compares the initial displacement to the bubble radius. The complete problem above is so complicated that a closed-form solution is very difficult (see Plesset and Prosperetti, 1977).

Let us lower our sights a little and seek an answer for oscillations of small amplitude. Mathematically, we want the asymptotic behavior of $R(t)$ as the parameter $\varepsilon \to 0$. To start the analysis, assume that the answer has the form

$$R(t) = R_0 + \varepsilon R_1(t) + \varepsilon^2 R_2(t) + \cdots \tag{15.1.5}$$

Without any initial displacement, the solution is a constant $R = R_0$. The functions $R_1(t)$ and $R_2(t)$ are to be found. In Eq. 15.1.5 we have explicitly assumed how the answer depends on ε. An assumption of this type is the hallmark of a perturbation method.

Next, we substitute Eq. 15.1.5 into the differential equation. Taking each term in the equation separately yields

$$R\ddot{R} = \varepsilon R_0\ddot{R}_1 + \varepsilon^2(R_0\ddot{R}_2 + R_1\ddot{R}_1) + \cdots \tag{15.1.6}$$

$$\tfrac{3}{2}\dot{R}^2 = \varepsilon^2\tfrac{3}{2}\dot{R}_1^2 + \cdots \tag{15.1.7}$$

The pressure term requires some extra work. We must simplify the expression

$$\left(\frac{R}{R_0}\right)^{-3\gamma} = \left(1 + \varepsilon\frac{R_1}{R_0} + \varepsilon^2\frac{R_2}{R_0} + \cdots\right)^{-3\gamma}$$

This expression is expanded using the binomial expansion, valid for any n as long as x is small.

$$(1 + x)^n = 1 + nx + \frac{n(n-1)}{2}x^2 + \frac{n(n-1)(n-2)}{3!}x^3 + \cdots \tag{15.1.8}$$

Applying this result with $n = -3\gamma$ and x taken as the two terms containing ε and ε^2 gives

$$-\frac{p_0}{\rho}\left[\left(\frac{R}{R_0}\right)^{-3\gamma}-1\right]=\frac{p_0}{\rho}\left\{\varepsilon 3\gamma\frac{R_1}{R_0}+\varepsilon^2 3\gamma\left[\frac{R_2}{R_0}-\frac{3\gamma+1}{2}\left(\frac{R_1}{R_0}\right)^2\right]\cdots\right\} \quad (15.1.9)$$

Given enough paper, one could write out the terms of the differential equations 15.1.6, 15.1.7, and 15.1.9 and regroup them according to the powers of ε. The equation would look like this:

$$\varepsilon(\cdots)+\varepsilon^2(\cdots)+\cdots=0$$

Since ε is an independent parameter, we argue that each term in parentheses must be zero by itself. Thus, each parenthetical term produces a differential equation. The following equations are generated by collecting together terms of like powers of ε in Eqs. 15.1.6, 15.1.7, and 15.1.9:

Coefficient of ε:

$$R_0\ddot{R}_1+\frac{3\gamma p_0}{\rho R_0}R_1=0 \quad (15.1.10)$$

Coefficient of ε^2:

$$R_0\ddot{R}_2+\frac{3\gamma p_0}{\rho R_0}R_2=-R_1\ddot{R}_1-\frac{3}{2}\dot{R}_1^2+\frac{3\gamma(3\gamma+1)p_0}{2\rho}\left(\frac{R_1}{R_0}\right)^2 \quad (15.1.11)$$

We now have a sequence of problems. The first contains $R_1(t)$ as the unknown. Once this solution is found, it may be substituted into Eq. 15.1.11 and then $R_2(t)$ is the only remaining unknown.

Initial conditions for these equations are found by substituting the assumed form of the answer 15.1.5 into the conditions 15.1.4:

$$R(0)=R_0(1+\varepsilon)=R_0+\varepsilon R_1(0)+\varepsilon^2 R_2(0)+\cdots$$

$$\dot{R}(0)=0=\varepsilon\dot{R}_1(0)+\varepsilon^2\dot{R}_2(0)+\cdots$$

Again, since ε is independent, we conclude that the initial conditions on R_1 and R_2 are

$$R_1(0)=R_0, \qquad \dot{R}_1(0)=0 \quad (15.1.12)$$

$$R_2(0)=0, \qquad \dot{R}_2(0)=0$$

In principle, perturbation expansion equation 15.1.5 results in a series of problems for R_1, R_2, and so on. Usually, only the first term or the first two terms are wanted. If we have organized the problem properly, the dominant physics will be in these terms.

The solution to Eq. 15.1.10 with initial condition 15.1.2 is found to be

$$\frac{R_1}{R_0}=\cos\omega_0 t \quad (15.1.13)$$

with

$$\omega_0=\frac{1}{R_0}\left(\frac{3\gamma p_0}{\rho}\right)^{1/2} \quad (15.1.14)$$

Hence a bubble, in the first approximation, is a linear oscillator without damping. The resonant frequency equation of the bubble, as given by Eq. 15.1.14, was first proposed by Minnaert (1933) with the use of a different method. It turns out that a bubble 1 in. in diameter oscillates at middle C on the musical scale. Smaller bubbles have correspondingly higher tones.

15.2   ORDER SYMBOLS, GAUGE FUNCTIONS, AND ASYMPTOTIC EXPANSIONS

Suppose that for some physical or mathematical purpose we want to know what a certain function $f(\varepsilon)$ is like. Furthermore, $f(\varepsilon)$ is complicated in that it is not a familiar elementary function such as ε^2, $\varepsilon^{2/3}$, e^ε, or $\sin \varepsilon$. It may be defined only in terms of an integral or as the solution of a differential equation. Obviously, if we are to characterize a function by approximating it with elementary functions, we can do so only over a limited range in ε. First, we restrict our question to finding the characteristics of $f(\varepsilon)$ in the neighborhood of the point ε_0. One can take ε_0 to be zero without loss of generality: A transformation $\hat{\varepsilon} = \varepsilon - \varepsilon_0$ will shift the neighborhood of interest to the origin (in case $\varepsilon_0 = \infty$, the inversion formula $\hat{\varepsilon} = 1/\varepsilon$ can be used).

What is the shape of $f(\varepsilon)$ near the origin? One answer, if $f(\varepsilon)$ is analytic, is the Taylor series

$$f(\varepsilon) = f(0) + f'(0) + f''(0) \frac{\varepsilon^2}{2} + \cdots$$
$$= A + B\varepsilon + C\varepsilon^2 + \cdots$$

(15.2.1)

Now, this may not be the best answer. For instance, if $f = \varepsilon^{4/3}$, the Taylor series does not exist at $\varepsilon = 0$. Next, consider a slight generalization of the Taylor expansion where ε^n is replaced by a sequence of elementary functions $\delta_i(\varepsilon)$. The function $f(\varepsilon)$ is now represented by

$$f(\varepsilon) = a + b\delta_1(\varepsilon) + c\delta_2(\varepsilon) + d\delta_3(\varepsilon) + \cdots \qquad \text{as} \quad \varepsilon \to 0 \qquad (15.2.2)$$

In this equation the $\delta_i(\varepsilon)$ are called *gauge functions*. Each gauge function must be smaller than the preceding one in the following sense:

$$\lim_{\varepsilon \to 0} \frac{\delta_1(\varepsilon)}{1} = 0$$

and in general,

$$\lim_{\varepsilon \to 0} \frac{\delta_{i+1}(\varepsilon)}{\delta_i(\varepsilon)} = 0 \qquad \text{for all } i \qquad (15.2.3)$$

A sequence δ_i satisfying these relations is called an *asymptotic sequence*.

Order symbols are a shorthand notation to express how two functions compare. The function $f(\varepsilon)$ is on the order of $g(\varepsilon)$ as $\varepsilon \to 0$ if a nonzero number A exists ($0 < |A| < \infty$) such that

$$\lim_{\varepsilon \to 0} \frac{f(\varepsilon)}{g(\varepsilon)} = A \qquad (15.2.4)$$

This is written using the order symbol O as

$$f(\varepsilon) = O[g(\varepsilon)] \qquad (15.2.5)$$

The size of A in Eq. 15.2.3 is immaterial. Hence, there is no connection between *order* and *order of magnitude*. If $f = 10^4 g$, then f and g differ by four orders of magnitude, but they are still of the same order in the foregoing sense. In any physical problem that has been properly nondimensionalized, the number A will be of reasonable size, so the order of magnitude of A does not really concern us. In asymptotic analysis we are concerned about how the shape of f compares to the shape of g. The statement

$$f(\varepsilon) \sim Ag(\varepsilon), \qquad \varepsilon \to 0$$

is certainly more informative than knowing the values of $f(0)$ and $g(0)$. Some examples of the use of order symbols are given below. For $\varepsilon \to 0$,

$$\sin \varepsilon = O[\varepsilon], \qquad \tan \varepsilon = O[\varepsilon]$$

$$\sin^2 \varepsilon = O[\varepsilon^2], \qquad J_0(\varepsilon) = O[1]$$

$$\sin 2\varepsilon = O[\varepsilon], \qquad (1 + \varepsilon)^n - 1 - n\varepsilon = O[\varepsilon^2]$$

$$1000 = O[1], \qquad \sinh \varepsilon = O[\varepsilon]$$

If the value of A in Eq. 15.2.4 is zero, $f(\varepsilon)$ is said to be of smaller order than $g(\varepsilon)$. This is written with a small o:

$$f(\varepsilon) = o[g(\varepsilon)]$$

Examples are

$$\varepsilon = o\left[\varepsilon \ln \frac{1}{\varepsilon} \right], \qquad \frac{1}{\ln(1/\varepsilon)} = o[1]$$

and

$$\exp\left(-\frac{A}{\varepsilon} \right) = o[\varepsilon^n] \qquad \text{for all } n \text{ as } \varepsilon \to 0 \qquad (15.2.6)$$

Using order symbols we can now write Eq. 15.2.1 in the form

$$f(\varepsilon) = a + b\delta_1(\varepsilon) + c\delta_2(\varepsilon) + o[\delta_2(\varepsilon)] \qquad \text{as} \quad \varepsilon \to 0$$

An *asymptotic expansion* of $f(\varepsilon)$ is a finite number of terms in a series using a chosen set of gauge functions. An asymptotic expansion is written as

$$f(\varepsilon) \sim a + b\delta_1(\varepsilon) + c\delta_2(\varepsilon) \qquad \text{as} \quad \varepsilon \to 0 \qquad (15.2.7)$$

The sign $\sim$ means *asymptotically equal to*. We should not use an equal sign, because the three terms on the right only approximate f for any finite ε. The coefficients in the asymptotic expansion are defined formally by limit processes.

$$\lim_{\varepsilon \to 0} f(\varepsilon) = a$$

$$\lim_{\varepsilon \to 0} \frac{f(\varepsilon) - a}{\delta_1(\varepsilon)} = b \tag{15.2.8}$$

$$\lim_{\varepsilon \to 0} \frac{f(\varepsilon) - b\delta_1(\varepsilon) - a}{\delta_2(\varepsilon)} = c$$

and so on. In practice, the coefficients are usually determined by using some equation that governs $f(\varepsilon)$. The term *asymptotic power series* is used when the gauge functions are chosen as $1, \varepsilon, \varepsilon^2, \ldots, \varepsilon^n$ (or $1, \varepsilon^{-1}, \varepsilon^{-2}, \varepsilon^{-3}, \ldots, \varepsilon^{-n}$ if $\varepsilon \to \infty$). A Taylor series is an asymptotic power series where the coefficients are also known to be derivatives of the function.

An asymptotic expansion does not necessarily converge to $f(\varepsilon)$ as a large number of terms are taken (originally, indeed, asymptotic series were simply known as *divergent series*). This is not a disadvantage. Convergence of a series is a property of the tail end of the series. It tells nothing about how close a finite number of terms may be to the function in question. An asymptotic expansion, on the other hand, may do what we want—closely approximate the value of a function—with only a few terms.

To emphasize the difference between convergence and usefulness as an approximation, consider the example of the Bessel function $J_0(x)$. The absolutely convergent series for $J_0(x)$ is

$$J_0(x) = 1 - \frac{x^2}{2^2} + \frac{x^4}{2^2 4^2} - \frac{x^6}{2^2 4^2 6^2} + \cdots + (-1)^n \frac{x^{2n}}{2^2 4^2 \cdots (2n)^2} \tag{15.2.9}$$

This series converged for all values of x. Now, an asymptotic expansion of $J_0(x)$ as $x \to \infty$ is

$$J_0(x) \sim \sqrt{\frac{2}{\pi x}} \cos\left(x - \frac{1}{4}\pi\right) \qquad \text{as } x \to \infty \tag{15.2.10}$$

For very small x, Eq. 15.2.9 is useful, but for $x = 4$ the one-term expansion Eq. 15.2.10 gives three-place accuracy, while eight terms of Eq. 15.2.9 are needed to obtain the same accuracy. Perhaps equally as important, the asymptotic expansion immediately gives us an idea about the shape of $J_0(x)$, while the pushing and pulling of the alternating signs in Eq. 15.2.9 give no such clue.

For a certain function $f(\varepsilon)$ and a given set of gauge function $\delta_i(\varepsilon)$, we obtain one unique expansion. However, the choice of gauge functions can be changed and then a different asymptotic expansion for $f(\varepsilon)$ results. Herein lies one of the powers of asymptotic methods. The proper choice of gauge functions can lead to a very good approximation for $f(\varepsilon)$ with only a few terms. In some problems the choice is not critical; the series of gauge functions $1, \varepsilon, \varepsilon^2, \ldots, \varepsilon^n$ is fine. In other more difficult problems only a special set of gauge functions (say, $1, \varepsilon^{1/3}, \varepsilon^{2/3}, \varepsilon^1, \ldots$ or $1, \varepsilon, \varepsilon \ln \varepsilon, \varepsilon^2, \ldots$) will do the job. The best choice, or proper choice as the case may be, of gauge functions is one of the art aspects of asymptotic methods. It requires us to guess what the shape of f is as $\varepsilon \to 0$.

15.3   INVISCID FLOW OVER A WAVY WALL

In this example we study the potential flow over a way wall. The solution is approximate in two respects. First, the flow does not really slip over the wall; a viscous layer must exist next to the wall. Assume that this layer is very thin, so that it has no effect on the flow. Second, the solution will be expanded using the wall height as the perturbation parameter. Hence, we are investigating walls with small waviness. Mathematically, this problem will illustrate a perturbation analysis where it is necessary to "transfer the boundary condition." Thin-airfoil theory in aerodynamics is based on this same mathematical technique.

Figure 15.1 depicts the problem and nomenclature. The height of the wave is h, the length λ, and the free-stream speed U_∞. Velocity components are $\hat{u}$ in the $\hat{x}$-direction, $\hat{v}$ in the $\hat{y}$-direction, and the velocity potential is $\hat{\phi}$. Nondimensional variables are defined as follows:

$$\phi = \frac{\hat{\phi}}{U_\infty \lambda}, \qquad x = \frac{\hat{x}}{\lambda}, \qquad y = \frac{\hat{y}}{\lambda} \tag{15.3.1}$$

The perturbation parameter is the wall amplitude compared to the wavelength

$$\varepsilon = \frac{h}{\lambda} \tag{15.3.2}$$

Recall that the velocity potential is related to the velocity components by $v_i = \partial_i \phi$; that is,

$$u = \frac{\partial \phi}{\partial x}, \qquad v = \frac{\partial \phi}{\partial y} \tag{15.3.3}$$

where ϕ is governed by the Laplace equation (derived from continuity: $\partial_i v_i = 0$ and $v_i = \partial_i \phi$)

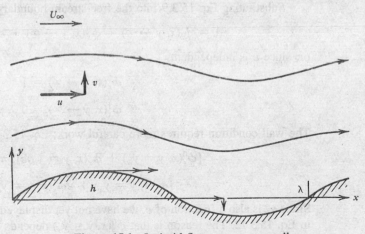

Figure 15.1 Inviscid flow over a way wall.

$$\phi_{xx} + \phi_{yy} = 0 \qquad (15.3.4)$$

The boundary condition is that there is no flow through the wall: $n_i v_i = 0$. An equivalent statement is that the direction of the velocity is tangent to the wall:

$$\frac{dy_w}{dx} = \frac{v}{u}\Bigg|_{y=y_w} \qquad (15.3.5)$$

where

$$y_w = \varepsilon \sin 2\pi x \qquad (15.3.6)$$

The second boundary condition is the free-stream condition

$$y \to \infty, \qquad u = 1 \qquad (15.3.7)$$

By using Eq. 15.3.3, we can cast the boundary conditions in terms of the velocity potential:

$$y \to \infty, \qquad \phi_x = 1$$
$$y = \varepsilon \sin 2\pi x, \qquad \phi_x \cdot 2\pi\varepsilon \cos 2\pi x = \phi_y \qquad (15.3.8)$$

The perturbation analysis is begun by assuming that the answer is an asymptotic series,

$$\phi(x, y; \varepsilon) \sim \phi^0(x, y) + \varepsilon \phi^1(x, y) \qquad (15.3.9)$$

When this is substituted into Eq. 15.3.4, we find that

$$\phi_{xx}^0 + \phi_{yy}^0 + \varepsilon(\phi_{xx}^1 + \phi_{yy}^1) = 0 \qquad (15.3.10)$$

But since ε is independent, both ϕ^0 and ϕ^1 separately satisfy the Laplace equation. Because our original equation is linear, we see that all approximations satisfy the same equation. If our original equation had been nonlinear, the first approximation, ϕ^0, might be governed by a linear or nonlinear equation; however, all higher approximations would obey linear (usually, nonhomogeneous) equations.

Substituting Eq. 15.3.9 into the free-stream boundary condition produces

$$1 = \phi_x(x, y \to \infty) = \phi_x^0(x, y \to \infty) + \varepsilon \phi_x^1(x, y \to \infty)$$

or, since ε is independent,

$$\phi_x^0(x, y \to \infty) = 1$$
$$\phi_x^1(x, y \to \infty) = 0 \qquad (15.3.11)$$

The wall condition requires more careful work; Eq. 15.3.8 becomes

$$[\phi_x^0(x, y = y_w) + \phi_x^1(x, y = y_w)\varepsilon]2\pi\varepsilon \cos 2\pi x$$
$$- [\phi_y^0(x, y = y_w) + \varepsilon\phi_y^1(x, y = y_w)] = 0 \qquad (15.3.12)$$

Since y_w is also a function of ε, we have not yet displayed the dependence on ε explicitly in Eq. 15.3.12. The reason is that $\phi_x^0(x, y = y_w)$ depends on ε through the variable y. To solve this difficulty, expand each term above in a Taylor series about $y = 0$. The term for ϕ_x^0 is

$$\phi_x^0(x, y = y_w) = \phi_x^0(x, 0) + \phi_{xy}^0(x, 0)y_w + \cdots$$

$$= \phi_x^0(x, 0) + \phi_{xy}^0(x, 0)\varepsilon \sin 2\pi x + \cdots$$

When each term in Eq. 15.3.12 is treated in this manner, one finds that

$$[\phi_x^0(x, 0) + \phi_{xy}^0(x, 0)\varepsilon \sin 2\pi x + \phi_x^1(x, 0)\varepsilon + \phi_{xy}^1(x, 0)\varepsilon^2 \sin 2\pi x]2\pi\varepsilon \cos 2\pi x$$

$$-[\phi_y^0(x, 0) + \phi_{yy}^0(x, 0)\varepsilon \sin 2\pi x + \phi_y^1(x, 0)\varepsilon + \phi_{yy}^1(x, 0)\varepsilon^2 \sin 2\pi x] = 0$$

Now, we may group together the coefficients of each power of ε and equate to zero. The wall boundary condition then becomes transferred back to the basic surface $y = 0$:

$$\phi_y^0(x, 0) = 0 \qquad (15.3.13)$$

$$\phi_x^0(x, 0)2\pi \cos 2\pi x - \phi_{yy}^0(x, 0) \sin 2\pi x - \phi_y^1(x, 0) = 0 \qquad (15.3.14)$$

After solving the problem for ϕ^0 by using Eq. 15.3.13 as a boundary condition, one can substitute into Eq. 15.3.14 to get a boundary condition on ϕ^1. Equations 15.3.10, 15.3.11, 15.3.13, and 15.3.14 constitute decoupled problems for ϕ^0 and ϕ^1.

The solution for ϕ^0 is easily found to be

$$\phi^0 = x \qquad (15.3.15)$$

This is simply a uniform stream flowing past the wall. The ϕ^1 problem is

$$\phi_{xx}^1 + \phi_{yy}^1 = 0$$

$$y = 0, \qquad \phi_y^1 = 2\pi \cos 2\pi x$$

$$y \to \infty, \qquad \phi_x^1 = 0$$

Separation of variables shows that the solution is

$$\phi^1 = -\cos 2\pi x \exp(-2\pi y) \qquad (15.3.16)$$

Hence, the complete answer is

$$\phi \sim x - \varepsilon \cos 2\pi x \exp(-2\pi y) \qquad (15.3.17)$$

From this the velocities are

$$u = \phi_x \sim 1 + 2\pi\varepsilon \sin 2\pi x \exp(-2\pi y)$$

$$v = \phi_y \sim 2\pi\varepsilon \cos 2\pi x \exp(-2\pi y)$$

The flow is a uniform stream perturbed by the presence of the waviness in the wall. Because the flow is inviscid and irrotational, the Bernoulli equation may be used to find the pressure:

$$\frac{p - p_\infty}{\frac{1}{2}\rho U_\infty^2} \sim 1 - \frac{\hat{u}^2 + \hat{v}^2}{U_\infty^2}$$

$$\sim -4\pi\varepsilon \sin 2\pi x \exp(-2\pi y) + O[\varepsilon^2] \qquad (15.3.18)$$

The pressure is in phase with the u velocity component.

Frequently, we are interested in values of the flow variables at the wall. These may be obtained by substituting the position $y = 0$, the transferred position of the wall, into the answer. When this is done we obtain wall values to the same order of accuracy with which we have solved the problem. The surface pressure and velocities are

$$u_{\text{wall}} = 1 + 2\pi\varepsilon \sin 2\pi x$$

$$v_{\text{wall}} = 2\pi\varepsilon \cos 2\pi x \qquad (15.3.19)$$

$$\frac{p_{\text{wall}} - p_\infty}{\frac{1}{2}\rho U_\infty^2} = -4\pi\varepsilon \sin 2\pi x$$

Sketches of the results are shown in Fig. 15.1. The maximum velocities are at the crest of the wave. An adverse pressure gradient decelerates the flow as it goes toward the valley, where the minimum velocity occurs. The magnitude of the velocity perturbations depends directly on the height of the wall, ε. This was built into our solution by the assumption that ε was the proper gauge function. The fact that we were able to fit the problem together using this assumption gives us confidence that this is a reasonable choice. Note that perturbations die out away from the wall as $\exp(2\pi\hat{y}/\lambda)$. The dominant influence in this term is the wavelength λ. The flow at a point y depends on influences from all parts of the wave.

15.4   NONUNIFORM EXPANSIONS: FRIEDRICH'S PROBLEM

When a function of two variables is expanded in one of the variables [for example, $f(x, \varepsilon)$ is expressed as an asymptotic expansion in ε] the expansion may not be good for all values of the other variable. Then one says that the expansion is not *uniformly valid* in x. Nonuniform expansions are very frequent in physical problems. Problems that lead to nonuniform expansions are called *singular perturbation* problems.

Friedrich's problem is a singular perturbation that illustrates boundary layer behavior. The governing differential equation (a slightly modified version of Friedrich's original problem) is

$$\varepsilon \frac{d^2u}{dy^2} + \frac{du}{dy} = -\frac{3}{2}(1 - 3\varepsilon)\exp(-3y) \qquad (15.4.1)$$

This equation is similar to the boundary layer momentum equation where u is an x-direction velocity, ε is analogous to $1/\text{Re}$, and the right-hand side represents the missing terms with x derivatives. For the boundary conditions we choose conditions that model an external flow problem:

$$u(y = 0) = 0 \qquad (15.4.2)$$

$$u(y \to \infty) = 1$$

The $y = 0$ condition is analogous to the no-slip condition at a solid wall, while the $u = 1$ condition represents a specified free stream far away from the wall.

We seek a solution to Friedrich's problem for $\varepsilon \to 0$ and y fixed, that is,

$$u = f(y, \varepsilon) \sim f^{(0)}(y) + O[\varepsilon]$$

Letting $\varepsilon \to 0$ in Eqs. 15.4.1 and 15.4.2 produces the equation and boundary conditions governing f^0:

$$\frac{df^{(0)}}{dy} = -\frac{3}{2} \exp(-3y)$$

$$f^{(0)}(0) = 0 \qquad\qquad (15.4.3)$$

$$f^{(0)}(\infty) = 1$$

Notice that the highest-order term in Eq. 15.4.2 is dropped when the limit $\varepsilon \to 0$ is applied. As a consequence we can no longer satisfy both boundary conditions. If we choose to satisfy one boundary condition, the other will not be met, and the answers become singular at that location. Losing the highest derivative always leads to a non-uniform expansion, but the converse is not true: Nonuniform expansions can still happen when the highest derivative is retained. There is no general way to know which boundary condition should be satisfied; we can try one and then the other to see which answer makes the most sense. In this case the proper boundary condition to satisfy is the one $y = \infty$. Solving Eq. 15.4.3 with $f^{(0)}(y \to \infty) = 1$ gives

$$u \sim f^{(0)} = 1 + \tfrac{1}{2} \exp(-3y) \qquad\qquad (15.4.4)$$

This is called the *outer expansion* of $u(y, \varepsilon)$.

Equation 15.4.4 gives $u \approx 1.5$ at $y = 0$. Hence, the expansion is singular at $y = 0$, since the boundary condition $u(y = 0) = 0$ is not satisfied. This deficiency is corrected by changing variables and constructing an *inner expansion*. Let a new space variable be defined as

$$Y = \frac{y}{g(\varepsilon)} \qquad\qquad (15.4.5)$$

When the transformation Eq. 15.4.5 is substituted into Eq. 15.4.1, a differential equation to govern $u(Y, \varepsilon)$ results:

$$\varepsilon \frac{d^2 u}{dY^2} + g \frac{du}{dY} = -\frac{3}{2} g^2 (1 - 3\varepsilon) \exp(-3gY) \qquad\qquad (15.4.6)$$

Now we argue that the inner expansion $u \sim F(Y, \varepsilon)$ should be governed by different physics and a different equation than the outer expansion. In particular we are interested in retaining the second-derivative term at least. Hence, choose $g(\varepsilon) = \varepsilon$. (The choice $g = O[1]$ gives the same problem as before with no magnification of y in the neighborhood $y = 0$, whereas $g = O[\varepsilon^2]$, say $g = \varepsilon^2$, gives $d^2 u/dY^2 = 0$. The solution of this equation will not match.) Letting $\varepsilon \to 0$ in Eq. 15.4.6 gives the problem

$$\frac{d^2 F^{(0)}}{dY^2} + \frac{dF^{(0)}}{dY} = 0 \qquad\qquad (15.4.7)$$

In this problem one imposes the wall boundary condition that was not satisfied in the other problem:

$$F^{(0)}(Y = 0) = 0 \qquad (15.4.8)$$

If this were a physical problem, we would have a balance between certain physical terms in the outer region (Eq. 15.4.3), and a balance between different effects in the inner region (Eq. 15.4.7). These are *distinguished limits*.

Our outer solution $f^{(0)}(y, \varepsilon)$ has already satisfied the far boundary condition $u(y \to \infty) = 1$, so we do not impose this same condition on F. Integration of Eq. 15.4.7 and application of Eq. 15.4.8 results in the answer.

$$u \sim F^{(0)}(Y) = A[1 - \exp(-Y)] \qquad (15.4.9)$$

The constant A is undetermined.

The solution to a singular perturbation problem may be represented by two *matched asymptotic expansions*. The word *matched* indicates the philosophy by which the constant A in Eq. 15.4.9 is found.

For one-term inner and outer expansions such as we have here, the simplest matching principle is that the outer answer as $y \to 0$ (the nonuniform region) is equal to the inner answer as $Y \to \infty$:

$$f^{(0)}(y \to 0) = F^{(0)}(Y \to \infty) \qquad (15.4.10)$$

As applied to our problem, Eq. 15.4.10 becomes (see Eqs. 15.4.4 and 15.4.9)

$$\tfrac{3}{2} = A = f^{(0)}_{cp} = F^{(0)}_{cp}$$

This is the common part of $f^{(0)}$ and $F^{(0)}$. Matching essentially replaces a boundary condition. A similar matching rule that applies to the u velocity in a boundary layer: The inviscid velocity at the wall is equal to the boundary layer velocity at infinity.

Figure 15.2 shows a graph of the various approximations and also the exact answer. To explain how a complicated problem might be solved, we have avoided stating the exact solution. It turns out to be

$$u = \frac{3}{2}\left[1 - \exp\left(-\frac{y}{\varepsilon}\right)\right] - \frac{1}{2}[1 - \exp(-3y)] \qquad (15.4.11)$$

By performing the outer limit ($\varepsilon \to 0$, y fixed) and the inner limit ($\varepsilon \to 0$, Y fixed) on this function you can verify that the expansions obtained, Eqs. 15.4.4 and 15.4.9, are correct.

15.5 MATCHING PROCESS: VAN DYKE'S RULE

Two functions are patched together by choosing a certain point, making the values of the functions agree at that point, and making an arbitrary number of the derivatives of the functions agree at the chosen point. We do not patch asymptotic expansions together. For example, in Friedrich's problem we had an outer expansion that was valid away from $y = 0$, and an inner expansion that was valid near $y = 0$. From Fig. 15.2 we can see that for the case $\varepsilon = 0.3$ neither of these approximations is very good in the region $0.2 < y < 0.6$. It is only asymptotically as $\varepsilon \to 0$ that the accuracy of these expansions becomes good. It is true that two or three terms in the expansions would usually give

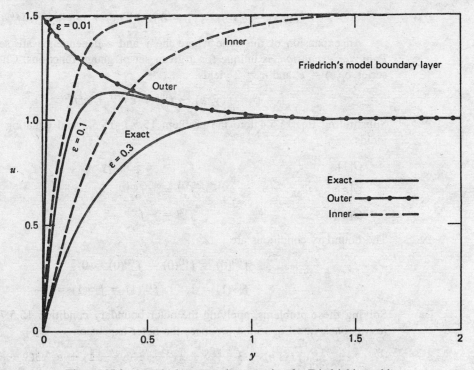

Figure 15.2 Matched asymptotic expansion for Friedrich's problem.

better accuracy, but this is beside the point. We have no good place to choose as a patching point.

The idea behind matching two asymptotic expansions is that as $\varepsilon \to 0$, there is a region in y where both expansions represent the true function. The matching region, or overlap region, is where the inner and outer expansions have the same functional form as $\varepsilon \to 0$. This is called the *common part*. *Van Dyke's rule* is a procedure to find the common part of the outer expansion and equate it to the common part of the inner expansion. The rule is

m-term inner expansion of the (n-term outer expansion)

$\qquad$ = n-term outer expansion of the (m-term inner expansion)   (15.5.1)

The integers m and n are for the gauge functions δ_n and Δ_m.

As a way of illustrating the matching technique, we shall solve Friedrich's problem to higher orders and apply Van Dyke's matching rule. Consider the new problem

$$\varepsilon f_{yy} + f_y = -\tfrac{5}{2} + \tfrac{3}{2}y^2$$

$$f(0, \varepsilon) = 0$$ (15.5.2)

$$f(1, \varepsilon) = 1$$

Assume an expansion of the form

$$f(y, \varepsilon) \sim \delta_0(\varepsilon)f^{(0)}(y) + \delta_1(\varepsilon)f^{(1)}(y) + \cdots + \delta_n(\varepsilon)f^{(n)}(y) \tag{15.5.3}$$

An expansion of this type where the y and ε dependence are separated, called a *Poincaré expansion,* is unique for a given set of gauge functions. Choosing the power series $\delta_i(\varepsilon) = \varepsilon^i$ and $n = 2$ yields

$$f(y, \varepsilon) \sim f^{(0)} + \varepsilon f^{(1)} + \varepsilon^2 f^{(2)} \tag{15.5.4}$$

Substituting Eq. 15.5.4 into the problem 15.5.1–15.5.3 and equating like powers of ε yields:

$O[1]$:
$$f_y^{(0)} = -\tfrac{5}{2} + \tfrac{3}{2}y^2 \tag{15.5.5a}$$

$O[\varepsilon]$:
$$f_y^{(1)} = -f_{yy}^{(0)} \tag{15.5.5b}$$

$O[\varepsilon^2]$:
$$f_y^{(2)} = -f_{yy}^{(1)} \tag{15.5.5c}$$

The boundary conditions are

$$f^{(0)}(0) = f^{(1)}(0) = f^{(2)}(0) = 0 \tag{15.5.6}$$

$$f^{(0)}(1) = 1, \qquad f^{(1)}(1) = f^{(2)}(1) = 0 \tag{15.5.7}$$

Solving these problems, applying the outer boundary condition 15.5.7, and putting the results back into Eq. 15.5.4 produces the outer expansion

$$f(y, \varepsilon) \sim 3 - \tfrac{5}{2}y + \tfrac{1}{2}y^3 - \varepsilon\tfrac{3}{2}(y^2 - 1) + \varepsilon^2 \cdot 3(y - 1)$$

This is called the *outer expansion* ($\varepsilon \to 0$, y fixed) truncated at term δ_2. Next, we introduce an operator notation to indicate an expansion written in inner variables and truncated at δ_n: $[\ ]_0^{\delta_n}$.

$$[f]_0^{\delta_2} = 3 - \tfrac{5}{2}y + \tfrac{1}{2}y^3 - \varepsilon\tfrac{3}{2}(y^2 - 1) + \varepsilon^2 3(y - 1) \tag{15.5.8}$$

Because the first-order equations 15.5.5 have solutions with only one arbitrary constant, these relations do not satisfy the boundary conditions at $y = 0$.

The inner expansion uses the rescaled variable

$$Y = \frac{y}{\varepsilon} \tag{15.5.9}$$

and gauge functions $\Delta_m = \varepsilon^m$:

$$f = F(Y, \varepsilon)$$
$$\sim \Delta_0 F^{(0)}(Y) + \Delta_1 F^{(1)}(Y) + \cdots + \Delta_m F^{(m)}(Y)$$
$$\sim F^{(0)}(Y) + \varepsilon F^{(1)}(Y) + \varepsilon^2 F^{(2)}(Y) \tag{15.5.10}$$

Transforming the problem into Y, substituting the expansion above, and equating coefficients of like powers of ε to zero gives

$O[1]$:
$$F_{YY}^{(0)} + F_Y^{(0)} = 0 \tag{15.5.11a}$$

$O[\varepsilon]$:
$$F_{YY}^{(1)} + F_Y^{(1)} = -\tfrac{5}{2} \tag{15.5.11b}$$

$O[\varepsilon^2]$:
$$F_{YY}^{(2)} + F_Y^{(2)} = 0 \tag{15.5.11c}$$

The solutions satisfy the inner boundary conditions

$$F^{(0)}(0) = F^{(1)}(0) = F^{(2)}(0) = 0 \qquad (15.5.12)$$

One finds the solutions and constructs the inner expansion as

$$F(Y, \varepsilon) \sim C_0(1 - e^{-Y}) + \varepsilon[C_1(1 - e^{-Y}) - \tfrac{5}{2}Y] + \varepsilon^2 C_2(1 - e^{-Y})$$

or in the operator notation for an expansion written in outer variables truncated at Δ_n: $\{ \ \}_i^{\Delta_n}$,

$$\{F\}_i^{\Delta_2} = C_0(1 - e^{-Y}) + \varepsilon[C_1(1 - e^{-Y}) - \tfrac{5}{2}Y] + \varepsilon^2 C_2(1 - e^{-Y}) \qquad (15.5.13)$$

The unknown constants must be determined by matching.

Van Dyke's matching rule is a practical recipe for matching two expansions. It offers a simple method that is easily applied (only on rare occasions does it fail). First, we consider the question: How does the three-term outer expansion behave in the inner region? To find out, write out the outer expansion (Eq. 15.5.8) and re-express it in the inner variable using $y = \varepsilon Y$:

$$\{[f]_0^{\delta_2}\}_i = 3 - \tfrac{5}{2}\varepsilon Y + \tfrac{1}{2}\varepsilon^3 Y^3 - \varepsilon \tfrac{3}{2}(\varepsilon^2 Y^2 - 1) + \varepsilon^2 3(\varepsilon Y - 1)$$

This expression is reorganized as an expansion for $\varepsilon \to 0$, Y fixed. This will show the part that is dominant in the inner region. All the terms above are algebraic; however, if we had a term like $\exp(-\varepsilon Y)$, it would be expanded in powers of ε. Finally, the expression is truncated at three terms (i.e., order ε^2):

$$\{[f]_0^{\delta_2}\}_i^{\Delta_2} = 3 + \varepsilon(-\tfrac{5}{2}Y + \tfrac{3}{2}) - \varepsilon^2 3 \qquad (15.5.14)$$

This is read: m-term (Δ_m) inner expansions of the n-term (δ_n) outer expansion. By this process we have extracted the part of the outer expansion that is most prominent in the inner region.

The matching principle is to do the same for the inner expansion and equate the results. Mathematically, the principle is

$$\{[f]_0^{\delta_n}\}_i^{\Delta_m} = [\{F\}_i^{\Delta_m}]_0^{\delta_n} = \text{common part} \qquad (15.5.15)$$

Either the integers m and n are taken the same, or one is taken as one larger than the other. In our example above, $m - n = 2$ was chosen. Equation 15.5.15 essentially defines the common parts of f^n and F^m.

Let us see how the matching principle works in Friedrich's problem. To do this we need to compute $[\{F\}_i^2]_0^2$. The $m = 2$ inner expansion of Eq. 15.5.13 is rewritten in the outer variable using $Y = y/\varepsilon$:

$$[\{F(Y, \varepsilon)\}_i^{\Delta_2}]_0 = C_0\left[1 - \exp\left(-\frac{y}{\varepsilon}\right)\right] + \varepsilon\left\{C_1\left[1 - \exp\left(-\frac{y}{\varepsilon}\right)\right] - \frac{5}{2}\left(\frac{y}{\varepsilon}\right)\right\}$$

$$+ \varepsilon^2 C_2\left[1 - \exp\left(-\frac{y}{\varepsilon}\right)\right]$$

Expanding for $\varepsilon \to 0$, y fixed, this becomes

$$\sim C_0 - \tfrac{5}{2}y + \varepsilon C_1 + \varepsilon^2 C_2 + O\left[\exp\left(-\frac{1}{\varepsilon}\right)\right]$$

Recall in Eq. 15.2.6 that the exponential term $\exp(-1/\varepsilon)$ goes to zero faster than any power of ε:

$$\exp\left(-\frac{1}{\varepsilon}\right) = o[\varepsilon^n] \qquad \text{for all } n \quad \varepsilon \to 0 \qquad (15.2.6)$$

These "exponentially small" terms are the first to drop out, as they go at the very end of any useful set of gauge functions. Next, truncate at three terms in ε:

$$[\{F\}_i^{\Delta_2}]_0^{\delta_2} = C_0 - \tfrac{5}{2}y + \varepsilon C_1 + \varepsilon^2 C_2 \qquad (15.5.16)$$

According to the matching rule, we equate Eqs. 15.5.14 and 15.5.16. To do this we need to use the same variable, either y or Y, so we convert Eq. 15.5.14 back to the inner variable:

$$\{[f]_0^{\Delta_2}\}_i^{\delta_2} = 3 - \tfrac{5}{2}y + \varepsilon\tfrac{3}{2} - \varepsilon^2 3 \qquad (15.5.17)$$

Comparing Eqs. 15.5.16 and 15.5.17 determines the constants in the inner solution as

$$C_0 = 3, \qquad C_1 = \tfrac{3}{2}, \qquad C_2 = -3 \qquad (15.5.18)$$

Matching the common parts of the two expansions replaces the boundary condition that was lost in the inner problems.

The theoretical basis of matching is a little more complicated than Van Dyke's matching rule would indicate. In case the interested student investigates this subject further, we outline what he or she is likely to find. Three types of variables and limits are defined. First, the outer limit $\varepsilon \to 0$ with y fixed. This leads to the outer expansion

$$u = f(y, \varepsilon) \sim \tilde{f}(y, \varepsilon)$$

The tilde indicates an asymptotic expansion. An inner variable has a general form

$$Y = \frac{y}{g(\varepsilon)} \qquad \text{where} \quad g(\varepsilon) \to 0 \quad \text{as} \quad \varepsilon \to 0$$

That is,

$$g(\varepsilon) = o[1]$$

When expressed in inner variables and expanded for $\varepsilon \to 0$, Y fixed, the function has the form

$$u = F(Y, \varepsilon) \sim \tilde{F}(Y, \varepsilon)$$

In addition to the inner and outer variables, there are intermediate variables defined by

$$\mathcal{Y} = \frac{y}{h(\varepsilon)} \qquad (15.5.19)$$

where $h(\varepsilon) \to 0$ as $\varepsilon \to 0$ but at a slower rate than $g(\varepsilon)$. If $g(\varepsilon) = \varepsilon$, then $h(\varepsilon)$ might be $\varepsilon^{1/2}$. The functions h and g obey the relation

$$\frac{h(\varepsilon)}{g(\varepsilon)} \to \infty \quad \text{as} \quad \varepsilon \to 0$$

The intermediate limit, $\varepsilon \to 0$ with $\mathcal{Y}$ fixed, is where the inner and outer expansions have their common region of validity. The theory, due to Kaplan (1957), indicates that when the expansions are expressed in intermediate variables, they are *asymptotically equal*, which means that with respect to a chosen set of gauge functions $\Delta_n(\varepsilon)$, the difference between the expansions is smaller than order $\Delta_n(\varepsilon)$ for all n. That is,

$$\tilde{f}(\mathcal{Y}h(\varepsilon), \varepsilon) - \tilde{F}(h(\varepsilon)\mathcal{Y}/g(\varepsilon), \varepsilon) = o[\Delta_n(\varepsilon)]$$

$$\varepsilon \to 0 \quad \mathcal{Y} \text{ fixed for all } n \quad (15.5.20)$$

In many cases the form of the expression in Eq. 15.5.20 is unchanged if the inner variable is used instead of an intermediate variable.

A more detailed approach is found in Eckhaus (1979).

15.6   COMPOSITE EXPANSIONS

The inner and outer expansions have different regions of validity and also a common form in the overlap region. In many instances it is desirable to have an expansion that is uniformly valid over the entire region. Consider what would happen if we simply added the two expansions. If y is small, F is approximately equal to the true function while f takes on values typical of the overlap region. If y is large, f is approximately equal to the true function while F takes on values typical of the overlap region. Those values common to both expansions, the values of the overlap region, are the matched parts of Eq. 15.5.15. Hence, a composite expansion for f is formed by subtracting the common part from the sum of the inner and outer expansions:

$$u \sim f_{\text{comp}}^{(n,m)} = [f]_0^{\delta_n} + \{F\}_i^{\Delta_m} - \{[f]_0^{\delta_n}\}_i^{\Delta_m} \quad (15.6.1)$$

This is called an *additive composite expansion* and is not unique. One could also form a multiplicative composite by a rule such as

$$u \sim f_{\text{comp}}^{(n,m)} = \frac{[f]_0^{\delta_n}\{F\}_i^{\Delta_m}}{\{[f]_0^{n}\}_i^{m}} \quad (15.6.2)$$

Equation 11.11.14 was an example of a composite expansion for the rotary disk problem.

We construct a composite expansion for the problem of Section 15.4 using $m = n = 0$. The outer expansion (Eq. 15.4.4) is

$$[f]_0^{\delta_0} = 1 + \tfrac{1}{2}\exp(-3y)$$

The inner expansion (Eq. 15.4.9) is

$$\{F\}_i^{\Delta_0} = \frac{3}{2}\left[1 - \exp\left(-\frac{y}{\varepsilon}\right)\right]$$

From either of the two relations above, one extracts the common part by applying the process of Eq. 15.5.15. The result is

$$\{[f]_0^{\delta_0}\}_i^{\Delta_0} = \text{common part} = \tfrac{3}{2}$$

The additive composite expansion is

$$u \sim f_{\text{comp}}^{(0,0)} = 1 + \frac{1}{2}\exp(-3y) - \frac{3}{2}\exp\left(-\frac{y}{\varepsilon}\right) \tag{15.6.3}$$

This composite expansion is actually the exact answer (Eq. 15.4.11).

Next consider a second example. In Fig. 15.3 an additive composite expansion (formed from order 1 inner and outer solutions) and the true solution are shown for the Friedrich problem of Section 15.5. The figure shows that the outer and inner solutions are very accurate, in their respective regions, only when the inner region is a small part of the outer region, say 10%, which is about $\varepsilon = 0.02$. For larger values of ε, there is an interaction between regions; that is, outer layer effects exist in the inner region (and vice versa). For $\varepsilon = 0.06$, the inner region is perhaps 20% of the outer region. An inner expansion accounts for different values of ε only by incorporating ε into the variables, $Y = y/g(\varepsilon)$. A composite expansion accounts for an interaction between the regions and is accurate to higher values of ε. Thus, a composite expansion displays the parametric effects of ε to a greater extent than does the inner expansion. When $\varepsilon = 0.15$, the composite expansion from zero-order answers is not too accurate, but it still has the proper shape. For accuracy at this level of ε, one would need a composite expression with the second or third terms in the expansions.

The accuracy of an asymptotic expansion is an important practical consideration. How large can the perturbation parameter become before a uniformly valid expansion becomes inaccurate? There is no general answer to this question. In each situation the

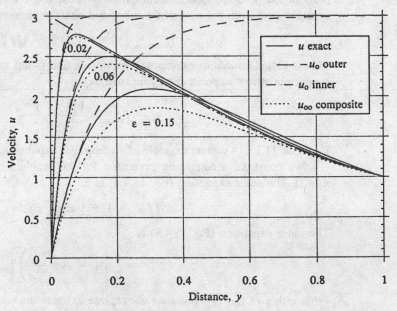

Figure 15.3 Composite expansion for Friedrich's problem (Eq. 15.5.1).

answer depends on the nature of the true function and the particular expansion used to represent it (i.e., the gauge functions chosen). If the true answer is the equation of a straight line, say $f = 6 + \varepsilon y^2$, two terms in a series give the exact answer for all values of ε. One guiding rule is that the accuracy is at least as good as the size of the next neglected term in the expansion.

Our intuition about when a parameter is large or small should be used with caution. Consider the following: Is the value $\varepsilon = 0.333$ close enough to zero for an expansion about $\varepsilon \to 0$ to apply? If we considered all possible values of ε from 0 to infinity, we might suppose that $\varepsilon = 0.333$ reasonably close to zero. Now, consider an expansion about $\varepsilon \to \infty$. Would $\varepsilon = 3$ be a reasonable number for which such an expansion would be valid? Normally, we regard 3 as a long way from infinity. Actually, an expansion about $\varepsilon \to \infty$ is completely equivalent to an expansion about $\hat{\varepsilon} \to 0$ with $\hat{\varepsilon} \equiv 1/\varepsilon$. The point $\varepsilon = 3$ with $\varepsilon \to \infty$ is equivalent to the point $\hat{\varepsilon} = 0.333$ with $\hat{\varepsilon} \to 0$. Our intuition is deceiving. In the foregoing sense, anyway, there are "just as many" points between 0 and 1 as there are between 1 and infinity. Section 15.2 compared a Taylor series for the Bessel function $J(x)$ about the point $x = 0$ with an asymptotic expansion about $x \to \infty$. The two representatives were compared at $x = 4$, where the asymptotic expansion was shown to be much superior. Another way of looking at this is that $x = 4$ for an expansion $z \to \infty$ is really the point $\hat{x} = \frac{1}{4}$ in an expansion of $\hat{x} \equiv 1/x \to 0$. This is not far from zero.

15.7   CHARACTERISTICS OF OVERLAP REGIONS

Several years ago, C. B. Millikan (1938) (and Isakson, 1937) derived the logarithmic law for turbulent wall layers using arguments about functional forms and dimensional considerations. Later, Kolmogorov (1941a,b) made somewhat similar arguments to arrive at a power law for the inertial region of the turbulent energy spectrum. After these pioneering works the concepts have been used in many other instances. This section incorporates these results in a general analysis that interprets these arguments as matching and scale-changing behavior of the leading terms of matched asymptotic expansions.

Consider a singular perturbation problem where the independent variable x and dependent variable y have the outer-dimensional scales (os) x_{os} and y_{os}:

$$x_* = \frac{x}{x_{os}}, \qquad 0 \le x_* \le \infty$$

$$y_* = \frac{y}{y_{os}} = f(x_*, \varepsilon)$$

The perturbation parameter $\varepsilon \to 0$. Let the outer problem, $0 \le x_* \le \infty$, have a Poincaré expansion

$$f \sim f^{(0)}(x_*) + \delta(\varepsilon) f^{(1)}(x_*) + \cdots \qquad \text{as } \varepsilon \to 0 \qquad (15.7.1)$$

Because we have nondimensionalized correctly, by assumption, the leading term $f^{(0)}$ is nontrivial.

Assume that the problem is singular at the origin as it gives the wrong answer there. We must have an inner expansion with a new independent variable scale (is) x_{is}:

$$X = \frac{x}{x_{is}} = \frac{x_*}{\varepsilon}$$

where

$$\varepsilon \equiv \frac{x_{is}}{x_{os}}$$

The perturbation parameter has been "normalized," so the inner region is ε smaller than the outer region. The perturbation parameter that is stated in the problem is some function of ε; that is, $\varepsilon_{problem} = g(\varepsilon)$: for example, $= \varepsilon^n$.

In some cases the dependent variable may no longer be $O[1]$ as $\varepsilon \to 0$. The outer dependent variable may approach infinity, or equally important, zero as the region near the origin is approached. These cases require rescaling the dependent variable to maintain a variable of $O[1]$. To account for this possibility, assume that the proper inner variable of order 1 is rescaled by the ratio $\gamma(\varepsilon)$ and that the first term in an asymptotic expansion is $F^{(0)}$:

$$Y \equiv \frac{y}{y_{is}} = \frac{y_*}{\gamma} = F(X, \varepsilon) \sim F^{(0)}(X)$$

(15.7.2)

$$\gamma(\varepsilon) \equiv \frac{y_{is}}{y_{os}} = \frac{y^*}{Y} = \frac{f^{(0)}}{F^{(0)}}$$

In the matching process between the inner and outer expressions, one produces the *common parts* (cp). Assume that Van Dyke's matching rule applies for $(1, 0)$ or $(0, 0)$. We consider both possibilities using the following notation for the common parts:

$$\{[f]_0^1\}_i^0 = f_{cp}^{(0)}(x_*) + \delta_1 f_{cp}^{(1)}(x_*)$$

$$[\{F\}_i^0]_0^1 = F_{cp}^{(0)}(X)$$

In each case one considers that the common parts are expressed in the original outer or inner variables as indicated. The matching equation requires inclusion of the scale-change factor γ. In the overlap region the matching rule requires that

$$f_{cp}^{(0)}(x_*) + \delta_1 f_{cp}^{(1)}(x_*) = \gamma F_{cp}^{(0)}(X)$$

(15.7.3)

Differentiating this expression with respect to x_* produces

$$\frac{df_{cp}^{(0)}}{dx_*} + \delta_1 \frac{df_{cp}^{(1)}}{dx_*} = \gamma \frac{dF_{cp}^{(0)}}{dX} \frac{dX}{dx_*}$$

(15.7.4)

Now $dX/dx_* = 1/\varepsilon = X/x_*$, so Eq. 15.7.4 can be reorganized into

$$x_* \left[\frac{df_{cp}^{(0)}}{dx_*} + \delta_1 \frac{df_{cp}^{(1)}}{dx_*} \right] = \gamma X \frac{dF_{cp}^{(0)}}{dX}$$

(15.7.5)

From these equations we can propose types or classes of common parts that connect inner and outer expansions. Furthermore, the required rescaling of the dependent variable, the proper nondimensionalization, is associated with the type of overlap function. Millikan and Kolmogorov made the opposite argument. They proposed scaling changes based on physics and derived the overlap laws (common parts).

First, consider a case where $f_{cp}^{(0)}$ is a constant. Let

$$f_{cp}^{(0)} = f_\infty \tag{15.7.6}$$

From Eq. 15.7.3 we see that the matching could be accomplished by

$$\gamma = 1$$

and

$$F_{cp}^{(0)} = f_\infty \tag{15.7.7}$$

This is the Prandtl-type matching where no rescaling of the dependent variable occurs (the term with δ_1 matches only at a higher order). The Friedrich problems and wall boundary layers have this type of matching.

As a second category, consider that the outer common part approaches zero or infinity as

$$f_{cp}^{(0)} = C_0 + C_m x_*^m, \qquad m \neq 0 \tag{15.7.8}$$

The matching equation 15.7.3 becomes

$$C_0 + C_m x_*^m = \gamma F_{cp}^{(0)}(X) \tag{15.7.9}$$

and Eq. 15.7.5 is

$$x_* C_m x_*^{m-1} = \gamma X \frac{dF_{cp}^{(0)}}{dX}$$

Reorganizing in terms of X and ε yields

$$\frac{dF_{cp}^{(0)}}{dX} = \frac{mC_m \varepsilon^m X^m}{\gamma X} \tag{15.7.10}$$

Because $F_{cp}^{(0)}$ cannot depend on ε, the solution to Eq. 15.7.10 is

$$\gamma = \varepsilon^m \tag{15.7.11}$$

$$F_{cp}^{(0)} = C_m X^m + C_i \tag{15.7.12}$$

Back-substitution of Eqs. 15.7.12 and 15.7.8 into Eq. 15.7.3 and simplifying gives $C_0 = \varepsilon^m C_i$, which implies that $C_0 = C_i = 0$ because $f_{cp}^{(0)}$ and $F_{cp}^{(0)}$ do not depend on ε.

The important conclusion is that if the common parts are proportional to x^m ($m \neq 0$), this requires a rescaling of the dependent variable by ε^m. [*Note:* It is not absolutely required to have a Poincaré outer expansion in Eq. 15.7.1. A form $f^{(0)}(x_*; \varepsilon)$ can be matched to an inner expansion that overlaps and is independent of ε.]

As an example, we consider the Kolmogorov law for the energy spectrum of turbulence. Physical arguments propose that the variables are $E(L^3 T^{-2})$, turbulent kinetic energy per unit wavenumber; $k(L^{-1})$, wavenumber; $\delta(L)$, thickness of turbulent region; $\nu(L^2 T^{-1})$, kinematic viscosity; and $e(L^2 T^{-3})$, rate of energy dissipation per unit mass.

The outer length and time scales, δ and $\delta^{2/3} e^{-1/3}$, refer to the region $k \to 0$, where viscosity is not important. In the outer region the nondimensional spectrum variables are

$$f_0(\hat{k}) = \frac{E}{\delta^{5/3} e^{2/3}}, \qquad \hat{k} = k\delta \tag{15.7.13}$$

The singular region is at $k \to \infty$. In the inner region, $k \to \infty$, the width δ is not important and the length and time scales are $x_{is} = \eta \equiv \nu^{3/4} e^{-1/4}$ and $\tau \equiv \nu^{-1/2} e^{-1/2}$. This means that the normalized perturbation parameter is

$$\varepsilon = \frac{x_{is}}{x_{os}} = \frac{\nu^{3/4}}{e^{1/4}\delta}$$

For the inner region the proper nondimensional spectrum is

$$F_0(K) = \frac{E}{\nu^{5/4} e^{1/4}}, \qquad K = k\nu^{3/4} e^{-1/4} \tag{15.7.14}$$

Now, the scaling change of the dependent variable according to Eq. 15.7.2 is

$$\gamma(\varepsilon) = \frac{F_0}{f_0} = \varepsilon^{-5/3} \tag{15.7.15}$$

Hence, $m = -\frac{5}{3}$ and the overlap region must behave as $k^{-5/3}$. Figure 15.4 shows experimental data (dimensional) that agree extremely well with Kolmogorov's energy spectrum law. The reader should note that Kolmogorov's major inspiration is in naming the list of variables; in particular, he recognized that the dissipation rate e is the proper quantity. Analysis is not as important as is inspiration.

The last case is a more delicate matching where the first term in Eq. 15.7.3 is constant ($f_{cp}^{(0)} = f_\infty$) and does not match with $F_{cp}^{(0)}$. Equations 15.7.3 and 15.7.5 become

$$f_\infty + \delta_1 f_{cp}^{(1)}(x_*) = \gamma F_{cp}^{(0)}(X) \tag{15.7.16}$$

$$x_* \delta_1 \frac{df_{cp}^{(1)}}{dx_*} = \gamma X \frac{dF_{cp}^{(0)}}{dX} \tag{15.7.17}$$

A solution here is

$$\delta_1 = \gamma \tag{15.7.18}$$

Since two of the three quantities ε, $\hat{x}$, and x_* are independent, Eq. 15.7.17 becomes a constant that is denoted by $1/\kappa$:

$$x_* \frac{df_{cp}^{(1)}}{dx_*} = X \frac{dF_{cp}^{(0)}}{dX} = \frac{1}{\kappa} \tag{15.7.19}$$

The solutions to Eq. 15.7.19 are log laws,

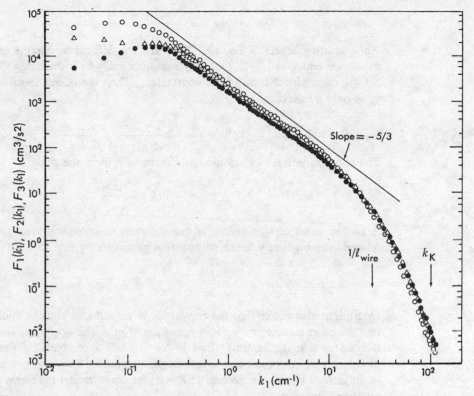

Figure 15.4 Spectrum of velocity fluctuations in a turbulent jet: ●, F_1 (longitudinal); ○, F_2 (lateral); △, F_3, (transverse). Wavenumber = k_1. Reprinted with permission from Champagne (1978), Cambridge University Press.

$$f_{cp}^{(1)} = \frac{1}{\kappa} \ln x_* + C_0 \tag{15.7.20}$$

$$F_{op}^{(0)} = \frac{1}{\kappa} \ln X + C_i \tag{15.7.21}$$

The $\gamma(\varepsilon)$ equation is found by substituting Eqs. 15.7.20 and 15.7.21 back into Eq. 15.7.16 and noting that $\varepsilon = x_*/X$:

$$f_\infty \gamma^{-1} = -\frac{1}{\kappa} \ln \varepsilon + C_i - C_0 \tag{15.7.22}$$

In this case the equation for the scale-change ratio γ has a logarithmic dependence on ε.

Some further comments on this last case are in order. In the outer expansion we had a constant for the leading term, $f^{(0)}(x_*) = f_\infty$; thus, the first important answer is the $f^{(1)}$ function. We can reorganize Eq. 15.7.1 into a *defect* form (a term used in turbulence) and insert the fact that the gauge function is known, $\delta_1 = \gamma$ (give by Eq. 15.7.18):

$$f^{(1)}(x_*) = \frac{f(x_*) - f_\infty}{\delta_1(\varepsilon)} = \frac{f(x_*) - f_\infty}{\gamma(\varepsilon)} \qquad (15.7.23)$$

An interesting aspect of Eq. 15.7.23 is that the defect law has the same scale as inner expansion equation 15.7.2. One may see this clearly by introducing the term $y_\infty \equiv f_\infty y_{os}$ for the dimensional form of the constant f_∞. Then the defect form is scaled by y_{is} and y_∞ is only a reference:

$$f^{(1)}(x_*) = \frac{f(x_*) - f_\infty}{\delta(\varepsilon)} = \frac{y(x) - y_\infty}{y_{is}}$$

The companion inner expansion has a form with the same scale:

$$F^{(0)}(X) = \frac{y(x)}{y_{is}}$$

A further result of significance is that the ratio of inner scale and the reference y_∞ are related unambiguously to the perturbation parameter by Eq. 15.7.22.

$$\frac{y_\infty}{y_{is}} = -\frac{1}{\kappa} \ln \varepsilon + C_i - C_0 \qquad (15.7.24)$$

One might also notice that the constant κ is superfluous since it could be incorporated into the other parameters: $y_{is}/\kappa \equiv \tilde{y}_{is}$, κC_i, and κC_0. The new inner scale $\tilde{y}_{is}$ is essentially defined so that the semilog slope in Eq. 15.7.21 is unity. This situation is found in turbulent wall layers and also in low-Reynolds-number flow over two-dimensional bodies in an infinite stream. In Section 15.8 we give some model problems for low-Reynolds-number flows.

15.8 LAGERSTROM'S PROBLEMS

Over several years Lagerstrom (1988) and his students developed model problems that have the essential matching characteristics of external flows at low Reynolds number, Re $\Rightarrow$ 0. Flows over a body in an infinite stream have a different character depending on whether they are two-dimensional (e.g., an infinite cylinder) or three-dimensional (e.g., a sphere). The following development is adapted from Hinch (1991), who uses Poincaré expansions in the solutions.

Consider the ordinary differential equation

$$u_{rr} + \frac{\alpha}{r} u_r + \varepsilon u u_r = 0, \qquad r > 1 \qquad (15.8.1)$$

with boundary conditions

$$u(r = 1) = 0, \qquad u(r \to \infty) \to 1 \qquad (15.8.2)$$

The constant $\alpha = 1$ models a two-dimensional flow with r from a cylindrical coordinate system, and $\alpha = 2$ models a three-dimensional flow with r corresponding to a spherical coordinate.

First, consider the three-dimensional flow with $\alpha = 2$. The straightforward expansion has a gauge function $\varepsilon \ln(1/\varepsilon)$ between $O[1]$ and $O[\varepsilon]$. Call this the *near solution*

$$u = f(r, \varepsilon) \sim f^{(0)}(r) + \varepsilon \ln \frac{1}{\varepsilon} f^{(1)}(r) + \varepsilon f^{(2)}(r) \tag{15.8.3}$$

Substituting into Eq. 15.8.1 and equating like orders in ε to zero gives linear equations and boundary conditions:

$$f_{rr}^{(0)} + \frac{2}{r} f_r^{(0)} = 0, \quad f^{(0)}(r = 1) = 0, \quad f^{(0)}(r = \infty) = 1$$

$$f_{rr}^{(1)} + \frac{2}{r} f_r^{(1)} = 0, \quad f^{(1)}(r = 1) = 0 \tag{15.8.4}$$

$$f_{rr}^{(2)} + \frac{2}{r} f_r^{(2)} = f^{(0)} f_r^{(0)}, \quad f^{(2)}(r = 1) = 0$$

The equation for $f^{(0)}$ is still second order and the solution will satisfy both boundary conditions:

$$f^{(0)} = 1 - \frac{1}{r} \tag{15.8.5}$$

The problem does not look like a singular perturbation. However, note that when the term $\varepsilon u u_r$ in Eq. 15.8.1 is approximated by $f^{(0)}$, it is $\varepsilon(1 + 1/r)/r^2 \sim \varepsilon/r^2$, while the main terms u_{rr} and $2r^{-1}u_r$ are about $2/r^3$. Thus, for some large r ($r > 1/\varepsilon$), the neglected term is actually larger than the assumed dominant terms. The singular region is at infinity. It is only fortuitous, as we will see, that the solution is uniformly valid.

Solutions for higher order are

$$f^{(1)} = A_1 \left(1 - \frac{1}{r} \right) \tag{15.8.6}$$

$$f^{(2)} = A_2 \left(1 - \frac{1}{r} \right) - \ln r - \frac{1}{r} \ln r \tag{15.8.7}$$

The constants must be determined by matching.

The singular region at infinity is examined by introducing a new variable:

$$\rho = \varepsilon r \tag{15.8.8}$$

Now the reformulated problem has a nonlinear term of first order, as in the original differential equation (Eq. 15.8.1):

$$u = F(\rho, \varepsilon) \tag{15.8.9}$$

$$F_{\rho\rho} + \frac{2}{\rho} F_\rho + FF_\rho = 0$$

Boundary conditions are

$$F(\rho = \varepsilon) = 0, \quad F(\rho \to \infty) \to 1$$

Because the singularity is at infinity, it is uncomfortable to call an expansion for F the inner expansion. Let us use the term *far solution*. The far solution will not satisfy the boundary condition $F(\rho = \varepsilon \to 0) = 0$. Assume that

$$F(\rho, \varepsilon) \sim F^{(0)}(\rho) + \varepsilon \ln \frac{1}{\varepsilon} F^{(1)}(\rho) + \varepsilon F^{(2)}(\rho) \tag{15.8.10}$$

Substituting Eq. 15.8.10 into Eq. 15.8.9 and separating like orders gives an unchanged nonlinear equation for $F^{(0)}$ and linear equations thereafter:

$$F^{(0)}_{\rho\rho} + \frac{2}{\rho} F^{(0)}_{\rho} + F^{(0)} F^{(0)}_{\rho} = 0$$

$$F^{(1)}_{\rho\rho} + \left(\frac{2}{\rho} + 1 \right) F^{(1)}_{\rho} = 0 \tag{15.8.11}$$

$$F^{(2)}_{\rho\rho} + \left(\frac{2}{\rho} + 1 \right) F^{(2)}_{\rho} = 0$$

The solutions are

$$F^{(0)} = 1$$

$$F^{(1)} = B_1 \int_{\rho}^{\infty} \frac{\exp(-\zeta)}{\zeta^2} d\zeta = B_1 \frac{E_2(\rho)}{\rho} \tag{15.8.12}$$

$$F^{(2)} = B_2 \frac{E_2(\rho)}{\rho} \sim B_2 \left(\frac{1}{\rho} + \ln \rho + \gamma - 1 - \frac{1}{2} \rho \right) \quad \text{as} \quad \rho \to \infty$$

Here E_2 is the exponential integral that has the asymptotic representation given on the second line (γ is the Euler constant). Matching gives the constants as $A_1 = 1$, $A_2 = 1 - \gamma$, $B_1 = 0$, and $B_2 = -1$.

An important result concerns the $O[0]$ near solution $f^{(0)}$. It satisfies both boundary conditions without apparent difficulty. Furthermore, if we take the $O[0]$ far solution, $F^{(0)} = 1$, and construct a composite (comp) expansion, we find that the composite is identical with the solution

$$f^{(0,0)}_{\text{comp}} = f^{(0)} + 1 - 1 \tag{15.8.13}$$

In this sense $f^{(0)}$ is uniformly valid. These results have analogues in three-dimensional Stokes ($\text{Re} = 0$) flow.

The two-dimensional flow problem is more difficult. In this case the differential equation has $\alpha = 1$ in Eq. 15.8.1. The proper near expansion proceeds slowly as

$$u = f(r, \varepsilon) \sim f^{(0)}(r) + \frac{1}{\ln(1/\varepsilon)} f^{(1)}(r) + \frac{1}{[\ln(1/\varepsilon)]^2} f^{(2)}(r) \tag{15.8.14}$$

Substituting into Eq. 15.8.1 and equating like orders in ε to zero gives the same linear equations for all orders:

$$f^{(i)}_{rr} + \frac{1}{r} f^{(i)}_{r} = 0, \qquad f^{(i)}(r = 1) = 0, \qquad i = 0, 1, 2, \ldots \tag{15.8.15}$$

The solutions will satisfy the boundary condition at $r = 1$ but not at infinity:

$$f^{(i)} = A_i \ln r \tag{15.8.16}$$

The arbitrary constant must be found by matching.

In the far region $\rho = \varepsilon r$ the problem is (again the complete equation)

$$F_{\rho\rho} + \frac{1}{\rho} F_\rho + FF_\rho = 0$$

$$F \to 1 \quad \text{as} \quad \rho \to \infty$$

(15.8.17)

Assume that

$$F(\rho, \varepsilon) \sim F^{(0)}(\rho) + \frac{1}{\ln(1/\varepsilon)} F^{(1)}(\rho) + \frac{1}{[\ln(1/\varepsilon)]^2} F^{(2)}(\rho) \qquad (15.8.18)$$

Substituting Eq. 15.8.18 into Eq. 15.8.17 and separating like orders gives an unchanged equation for $F^{(0)}$:

$$F^{(0)}_{\rho\rho} + \frac{1}{\rho} F^{(0)}_\rho + F^{(0)} F^{(0)}_\rho = 0, \qquad F^{(0)}(\rho \to \infty) = 1 \qquad (15.8.19)$$

Subsequent orders, $i = 1, 2, \ldots$, obey

$$F^{(i)}_{\rho\rho} + \left(\frac{1}{\rho} + 1 \right) F^{(i)}_\rho = 0, \qquad F^{(i)}(\rho \to \infty) = 0 \qquad (15.8.20)$$

Again a solution to the nonlinear problem is a constant, and the following answers involve the exponential integral of first order:

$$F^{(0)} = 1$$

$$F^{(1)} = B_1 \int_\rho^\infty \frac{\exp(-\zeta)}{\zeta} \, d\zeta = B_1 E_1(\rho)$$

$$F^{(2)} = B_2 E_1(\rho) + B_1^2 [2E_1(2\rho) - \exp(-\rho) E_1(\rho)]$$

The behavior of E_1 for $\rho \to 0$ is $E_1 \sim -\ln \rho - \gamma + \rho$. Matching produces the constants

$$A_0 = 0, \qquad A_1 = 1, \qquad A_2 = \gamma, \qquad B_1 = -1, \qquad B_2 = -(1 + \gamma)$$

Since $A_0 = 0$, the near expansion begins with $f^{(1)}$ and the original scaling for the dependent variable was "improper":

$$\frac{u(r, \varepsilon)}{1/\ln(1/\varepsilon)} \sim f^{(1)}(r) = \ln r$$

The far solution begins with a constant and the first important trends are given by a defect law:

$$\frac{u(r, \varepsilon) - 1}{1/\ln(1/\varepsilon)} \sim F^{(1)}(\rho) = -E_1(\rho)$$

Both the near and far solutions have the same dependent variable scaling in a form similar to the last case of Section 15.7. This problem has analogues in two-dimensional Stokes flows and turbulent wall layers.

15.9   CONCLUSIONS

The method of matched asymptotic expansion is only one of a variety of perturbation methods. It is particularly suited to several important fluid-flow problems. The reader interested in learning about other methods should consult the books by Van Dyke (1964), Nayfeh (1973), Cole and Kevorkian (1981), and Hinch (1991).

Expansions are essentially a method to simplify problems and break out the two or three most dominant aspects of the physics. Hence, they offer a viewpoint for the theoretical classifications of fluid flows. Frequently, very useful analytic expressions are formed by these methods. For example, asymptotic methods show that the drag on a sphere is given by

$$C_D = \frac{24}{\text{Re}} \left(1 + \frac{3}{16} \text{Re} + \frac{9}{160} \text{Re}^2 \ln \text{Re} + O[\text{Re}^2] \right), \qquad \text{Re} \to 0$$

In a computer solution to this same problem, it would be necessary to make a series of runs at different Reynolds numbers and then curve-fit for a drag equation. The theoretical and physical simplifications provided by an asymptotic analysis would be hidden in the computer. On the other hand, many flow problems are very complex and cannot be simplified; a large number of competing events occur without any dominant physics. Here asymptotic methods, by their nature, are inappropriate. The computer then becomes the most powerful and useful approach. Perturbation methods offer a great amount of flexibility in extracting the major elements from a problem. In this respect perturbation methods require considerable guesswork, insight, and creativity. Workers using perturbation methods are essentially doing mathematical engineering.

PROBLEMS

15.1 (A) Which of these functions goes to infinity faster when $x \to \infty$; $f_1 \sim x$ or $f_2 \sim \ln x$?

15.2 (A) Prove that when $x \to 0$, $\exp(-1/x) \to 0$ faster than x^n for any n, no matter how large.

15.3 (A) Find the limit as $\varepsilon \to 0$ for the function

$$f(y, \varepsilon) = \frac{3}{2} \left[\frac{1 - \exp(-y/\varepsilon)}{1 - \exp(-1/\varepsilon)} \right] - \frac{1}{2} [1 - \exp(-3y)]$$

Change the function by letting $Y = y/\varepsilon$ and find the limit of $F(Y, \varepsilon)$ as $\varepsilon \to 0$. In each case compare the iterated limits

$$\lim_{y \to 0} \lim_{\varepsilon \to 0} f(y, \varepsilon) \quad \text{and} \quad \lim_{\varepsilon \to 0} \lim_{y \to 0} f(y, \varepsilon)$$

15.4 (A) Solve the bubble oscillator problem to find $R_2(t)$. (*Hint:* In solving the nonhomogeneous differential equation, change squares of trigonometric functions into trigonometric functions of the double angle.)

15.5 (C) An oscillator perturbation will become invalid at large times if a term occurs such as $t \cos\omega t$, called a *secular term*. Show that secular terms will occur in $R_3(t)$ of the bubble oscillator problem.

15.6 (A) Consider a channel with wavy walls given by

$$y = \pm h \pm A \left(\sin \frac{2\pi x}{\lambda} + B \sin \frac{4\pi x}{\lambda + c} \right)$$

Solve for the viscous flow in this channel for the situation h/λ is small, A/h finite. Use the streamfunction.

15.7 (B) Do the viscous wavy wall analysis using asymptotic expansions in the variables u, v, and p.

15.8 (B) The upper surface of a thin body ($\varepsilon = h/L \to 0$) is given by the parabola $y_w/h = 1 - (x/L)^2$ for $-L \le x \le L$. The streaming flow u_0 is perturbed so that $u = u_0 + \varepsilon u_1$ and $v = \varepsilon v_1$. Transfer the wall boundary condition given below

$$\left.\frac{dy_w}{dx}\right|_{y_w} = \left.\frac{v}{u}\right|_{y_w}$$

to $y = 0$.

15.9 (A) Consider the differential equation with boundary conditions $f(0) = 0$, $f(1) = 1$.

$$\varepsilon f'' + f'' = a$$

Make an expansion for $f(x, \varepsilon)$ for $\varepsilon \to 0$. Locate the singular behavior and make a matched asymptotic expansion for the inner region.

15.10 (A) Construct a multiplicative composite expansion for Problem 15.9.

15.11 (C) Consider the flow in a slot with porous walls in Section 12.3 for the special case of large blowing;

$\alpha \to \infty$. Produce the proper nondimensional variables, equations, boundary conditions and profile results for the inner and outer problems. Construct a composition expansion.

15.12 (B) A viscous liquid jet is falling freely (pressure is atmospheric). The x-coordinate is pointing in the direction of gravity with the origin at the nozzle, where the initial uniform velocity is U. Assume that the velocity is uniform at each location, $u = u(x)$. Simplify the x-momentum equation and find nondimensional variables for u and x. Solve the problem for the limit of an inviscid jet and find the first effect of viscosity: $u = u^0(x) + u^1(x)/\text{Re}$. Plot curves for $\text{Re} = 2, 5, 10$, and 100.

16

Characteristics of High-Reynolds-Number Flows

Many engineering flows are at high Reynolds numbers. It is not unusual for the flow in a pipe to have a Reynolds number of 10^5, or the flow over the wing of a small airplane to have a Reynolds number of 10^6. In this chapter we investigate some of the main characteristics of high-Reynolds-number flows. We shall find that the flow can be divided into two parts: an inviscid flow in the major portion of the flow region, and boundary layers near the walls. Boundary layer principles also apply to thin regions of high shear (shear layers) within the main flow region.

Equations for both inviscid flow and boundary layers are derived and discussed in this chapter. The purpose in doing this rather than placing the discussions in separate chapters on inviscid flow and boundary layers is to emphasize that these subjects are not distinct but that they hold complementary positions in the theory of fluid mechanics.

16.1 PHYSICAL MOTIVATION

Viscous diffusion of momentum, or of vorticity, is often a slow process: To be specific, it is slow compared to convection. Let us again (cf. Section 13.13) consider a duct of length L and characteristic diameter D (Fig. 16.1). The flow comes from a very large reservoir connected to the entrance. On the other end of the duct, a fan or pump is placed to produce the flow. Pressure forces are responsible for accelerating the flow into the duct, and by their very nature they cannot generate a net viscous force or vorticity. Similarly, the center flow of the tube does not contain any net shear stress, because only pressure forces have acted on these particles. Once the flow is moving, the no-slip condition causes shear stresses at the wall. The imbalance in shear stress that occurs is transferred toward the center through viscous diffusion. Using Rayleigh's argument, we estimate that the thickness of the viscous effect is $\delta \sim \sqrt{\nu t}$. To find the viscous thickness at the end of the duct, we insert the flow time for t ($t_{\text{flow}} = L/U$). The final thickness of the viscous region is compared with the duct diameter:

$$\frac{\delta}{D} \sim \left(\frac{\nu}{DU} \frac{L}{D} \right)^{1/2} = \left(\frac{1}{\text{Re}} \frac{L}{D} \right)^{1/2}$$

$$(16.1.1)$$

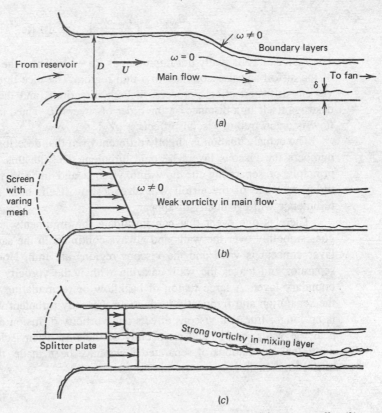

Figure 16.1 High-Reynolds-number flow in a duct: (*a*) vorticity near walls; (*b*) weak vorticity in inviscid main flow; (*c*) strong vorticity in shear layer, which must be treated as a boundary layer.

If this estimate is valid, we can expect viscous effects to be confined to a vanishingly thin region next to the wall as the Reynolds number becomes infinite. For any fixed value of L/D one could produce a high-enough Reynolds number so that $\delta/D \to 0$.

We can also make the same argument for the external flow over a body. Consider a two-dimensional flow over an airfoil. Since the airfoil may be quite thin compared to its chord length L, we compare the viscous diffusion thickness δ with L. Using the same logic as above, we find that

$$\frac{\delta}{L} \sim \left(\frac{\nu}{UL}\right)^{1/2} = \mathrm{Re}^{-1/2} \tag{16.1.2}$$

A high airfoil Reynolds number indicates that the diffusion of vorticity is confined to a thin layer next to the surface of the airfoil. Furthermore, the viscous wake of the airfoil (the region downstream where the viscous regions from the top and the bottom merge) will be thin for a distance downstream on the order of L_w. Say that $L_w = 100L$; then

$$\frac{\delta_{\text{wake}}}{L} \sim \left(\frac{L_w}{L}\frac{\nu}{UL}\right)^{1/2} = 10\,\text{Re}^{-1/2}$$

The factor of 10 is really not important as Re $\rightarrow \infty$. Thus, the viscous effects in the wake of the airfoil are also confined to a thin region. The nice thing about a wake is that the viscous-diffusion effects proceed in both directions, and the viscous part of the wake destroys itself in a distance on the order of several L. Thus, in this case, the downstream flow is again free of viscous effects.

The actual situation is slightly different from that described above. At high Reynolds numbers the viscous layers become turbulent. Despite this, they remain thin, and the principle of separating the flow into viscous and inviscid regions remains valid. The turbulent wake of the airfoil will also destroy itself; both the mean velocity and the turbulence will eventually disappear.

There is one event that can invalidate the arguments above: separation. If a flow goes smoothly over the walls and always continues in the same direction, the boundary layer concept is valid and the viscous regions are thin. However, sometimes the flow separates and leaves the wall, carrying with it the vorticity and viscous effects of the boundary layer. A large region of backflow or recirculating flow exists downstream of the separation and frequently leads to an unsteady turbulent wake. When this happens it is no longer true that viscous effects and vorticity diffusion are confined to thin regions near the walls, or that the main body of the flow is inviscid. Although some specific numerical calculations of separated flows have been made, they remain a difficult area in fluid mechanics.

16.2   INVISCID MAIN FLOWS: EULER EQUATIONS

As the Reynolds number becomes large, the viscous regions become vanishingly thin, so that almost the entire flow is governed by inviscid equations. The proper scales for these flows are the same as those used in Chapter 10 for the incompressible-flow equations: U, a characteristic velocity; L, a characteristic length of flow path or body; and ρ, the fluid density. The nondimensional continuity and momentum equations are Eqs. 10.4.4 and 10.4.5:

$$\partial_i^* v_i^* = 0 \tag{16.2.1}$$

$$\frac{Dv_i^*}{Dt} = -\partial_i^* p^* + \frac{1}{\text{Re}}\,\partial_j^* \partial_j^* v_i^* \tag{16.2.2}$$

The simplified equations when Re $\rightarrow \infty$, known as *Euler's equations,* show that acceleration results solely from pressure forces:

$$\frac{Dv_i^*}{Dt^*} = -\partial_i^* p^* \tag{16.2.3}$$

The principle of dominant balance says that solution of this equation should approximate the complete solution of Eq. 16.2.2 with Re $\rightarrow \infty$.

The second important point about Eq. 16.2.3 is that we have lost the highest-order term, $\partial_j \partial_j v_i$. This means that we can no longer stipulate as many boundary conditions as for a viscous flow. The boundary condition that must be given up is the no-slip condition at a solid wall. In general, there is no way to deduce mathematically which boundary condition must be given up. From past experience we know that the proper approach for inviscid flow is to require that the velocity normal to the wall be zero. Thus, the proper boundary condition for inviscid flow is

$$n_i v_i \big|_{\text{solid wall}} = 0 \tag{16.2.4}$$

This makes the wall into a surface containing streamlines. The velocity component along the wall is nonzero (except at stagnation points) and is a result determined by the inviscid solution. We realize that this solution is not correct in the sense that it does not satisfy the no-slip condition.

Mathematically, we may view the inviscid flow as the first term in an asymptotic expansion of the exact answer. The expansion parameter is Re $\rightarrow \infty$. The problem is a singular perturbation with the nonuniform region (i.e., the place where the answer is incorrect) next to the walls. A boundary layer exists in these regions in order to complete the solution and satisfy the no-slip condition.

The vorticity in an inviscid flow is nondimensionalized as

$$\omega^* = \frac{\omega}{U/L} \tag{16.2.5}$$

With this definition the nondimensional vorticity equation becomes

$$\frac{D\omega_i^*}{Dt^*} = \omega_j^* \partial_j^* v_i^* + \frac{1}{\text{Re}} \partial_j^* \partial_j^* \omega_i^*$$

As Re $\rightarrow \infty$, viscous diffusion becomes negligible, and we obtain the inviscid equation governing vorticity:

$$\frac{D\omega_i^*}{Dt^*} = \omega_j^* \partial_j^* v_i^* \tag{16.2.6}$$

The vorticity of a material particle changes by turning and stretching of the vortex lines. From Chapter 13 we recall that Helmholtz's theorem allows us to treat the vortex lines as material lines moving with the fluid particles. As a line stretches, the vorticity increases; as it shrinks, the vorticity decreases.

The existence of vorticity indicates that viscous forces are, or at least have been, active. In the case of inviscid flow we must choose the perfect tense in this statement. Viscous forces are not important in an inviscid flow carrying vorticity, but somewhere in the past history of the particle motion, viscous forces were active in order to generate the vorticity. As an example, suppose that we place a fine mesh screen in front of the duct entrance in Fig. 16.1b. The screen is in a low-velocity region, and the screen wires have a moderate-to-low Reynolds number. Hence, as the flow goes through the screen, viscous forces are important. Next, imagine that the screen has a very fine mesh on one end, changing gradually to a coarse mesh on the other end. The pressure drop across the screen will be the same everywhere, but the viscous forces will reduce the flow velocity where the screen has its finest mesh. The result is that flow at the entrance to the duct has a velocity profile with nonzero vorticity. The flow within the duct is an inviscid flow carrying vorticity. Stretching and turning are now the only mechanisms to change the vorticity.

Note that the scale of the vorticity in Eq. 16.2.6 must be U/L, which is relatively small. Let us consider a flow that has a larger scale for the vorticity. In Fig. 16.1c a splitter plate has been added to the entrance along with a second screen, which has a different mesh. Now, the flow contains two regions of weak vorticity with a thin layer of stronger vorticity in the shear layer formed downstream of the plate. The main flow consists of two parts with a thin shear layer between them. The shear layer is really another type of boundary layer and can be treated in a manner similar to wall boundary layers.

A special class of inviscid flows occurs when the vorticity is zero. A flow that is both inviscid and irrotational is called an *ideal flow,* or equivalently, a *potential flow* (note that irrotational flow implies inviscid flow but not the other way around). The discussion in the remainder of this section is limited to ideal flows.

The velocity field of an ideal flow is determined completely by two kinematic considerations: The rate of particle expansion and the rate of particle rotation are both zero. Mathematically, these conditions are

$$\nabla \cdot \mathbf{v} = 0 \qquad (16.2.7)$$

$$\nabla \times \mathbf{v} = \boldsymbol{\omega} = 0 \qquad (16.2.8)$$

The solution of these equations is most easily found by using the velocity potential defined by

$$\mathbf{v} = \nabla \phi \qquad (16.2.9)$$

The velocity potential ϕ exists if and only if the flow is irrotational ($\omega = 0$). The equation for ϕ is found by substituting Eq. 16.2.9 into Eq. 16.2.7. The result is the Laplace equation,

$$\nabla^2 \phi = 0 \qquad (16.2.10)$$

Boundary conditions appropriate for the solution of Eq. 16.2.10 are either to specify ϕ or to specify the normal derivative $\mathbf{n} \cdot \nabla \phi$ around a closed region. The second condition is used in fluid mechanics, as physically it corresponds to the velocity normal to the boundary:

$$n_i v_i|_{\text{boundary}} = n_i \partial_i \phi \qquad (16.2.11)$$

If the boundary is within the fluid, we must know the normal flow velocity. If the boundary is a solid wall, $n_i v_i = 0$.

We shall not go deeply or systematically into the mathematical properties of the Laplace equation. Many mathematics books cover the subject adequately. As we study several specific potential flows in Chapter 17, we bring up the required mathematical results as they are needed. Nevertheless, some general characteristics should be noted.

Potential flows are dominated by the geometry. The dimensions of length and time, but not that of mass, occur in Eqs. 16.2.7 to 16.2.11. The shape and locations of the walls of a duct or a closed body completely establish the velocities and streamlines. Except possibly for variables describing the boundary region (e.g., the aspect ratio of an ellipse), the problem contains no parameters (the characteristic values U and L are absorbed in the nondimensional variables). The fact that geometry controls the flow pattern is emphasized by noting that the velocity may be found without ever using the momentum equation. With known velocities, the momentum equation, after integration to form the Bernoulli equation, is used to find the pressure field. The actual fluid density (and mass dimension) become important at this time.

Potential flows are elliptic in their mathematical classification. Any change in a boundary condition is felt instantaneously at all points in the fluid. The influence is, of course, greatest at points closest to the place where the change was made. Any change goes upstream as well as downstream with equal intensity. If we have a sphere about which there is a streaming flow, the flow anticipates the presence of the sphere and moves aside to go around it. The flow then closes and proceeds downstream. The presence of the sphere is felt equally upstream and downstream, yielding a symmetric flow pattern. Next, let us imagine that the sphere pulsates with a sinusoidal motion about the mean radius in addition to the streaming flow. Because the governing equation and the boundary conditions are linear, we may consider the velocity solution as the sum of the steady-flow solution and the solution for an oscillating sphere in an infinite medium (a problem we solved in Chapter 14). Furthermore, the pulsating effect is transmitted instantaneously throughout the flow. There are no storage effects, as time derivatives are absent from Eqs. 16.2.7 to 16.2.11. As a result, the solution depends only on the instantaneous position and velocity of the boundaries. The past history of the boundary motion has no influence on the flow pattern. History effects occur in boundary layers, and history effects occur at moderate Reynolds numbers, but ideal flows have no memory of previous states of motion.

16.3   PRESSURE CHANGES IN STEADY FLOWS: BERNOULLI EQUATIONS

There are some general results about pressure that can be derived by inspection of the momentum equation. Consider the steady-flow momentum equation in the form used in Eq. 12.5.4:

$$\nabla\left(\frac{p}{\rho} + \frac{1}{2}v^2 + gZ\right) = \mathbf{v} \times \boldsymbol{\omega} + \nu\nabla^2\mathbf{v} \tag{16.3.1}$$

Define the *total head* as the sum of the pressure head, velocity head, and elevation head:

$$H \equiv \frac{v^2}{2g} + \frac{p}{g\rho} + Z \tag{16.3.2}$$

These terms have the dimensions of length. In some engineering disciplines, it is popular to define the head as $\tilde{H} = gH$. This head has the dimensions of energy per unit mass.

We will evaluate the momentum equation in a streamline coordinate system (see Section 4.9) with unit vectors **t**, **n**, and **b** for the tangential, normal, and binormal directions. In streamline coordinates the velocity has only one component:

$$v_t = v, \qquad v_n = 0, \qquad v_b = 0 \tag{16.3.3}$$

and the vorticity has components (Eq. 4.9.4)

$$\omega_t = v(\mathbf{t} \cdot \nabla \times \mathbf{t}), \qquad \omega_n = \frac{\partial v}{\partial b}, \qquad \omega_b = \frac{v}{R} - \frac{\partial v}{\partial n} \tag{16.3.4}$$

Here R is the radius of curvature of the streamline.

We will take the three components of the momentum equation in the **t**, **n**, and **b** directions and then proceed to discuss special cases. To evaluate the momentum equation along a streamline, take $\mathbf{t} \cdot$ Eq. 16.3.1. The term $\mathbf{t} \cdot (\mathbf{v} \times \boldsymbol{\omega})$ is zero because **v** and **t** are collinear. One can integrate $\mathbf{t} \cdot$ Eq. 16.3.1 along the streamline by noting that $t_i \partial_i H \, ds = dH$. The result is

$$gH_2 - gH_1 = g \int_1^2 t_i \partial_i H \, ds = \nu \int_1^2 t_i \partial_j \, \partial_j v_i \, ds \tag{16.3.5}$$

Now return to Eq. 16.3.1 and consider the component in the normal direction. When the $\mathbf{n} \cdot \mathbf{v} \times \boldsymbol{\omega}$ term is evaluated by using Eqs. 16.3.3 and 16.3.4, we find that Eq. 16.3.1 becomes

$$n_i \, \partial_i \left(\frac{p}{\rho} + \frac{1}{2} v^2 + gZ \right) = -\frac{v^2}{R} + \frac{d}{dn} \left(\frac{1}{2} v^2 \right) + \nu n_i \partial_j \, \partial_j v_i$$

or

$$\frac{d}{dn} \left(\frac{p}{\rho} + gZ \right) = -\frac{v^2}{R} + \nu n_i \, \partial_j \, \partial_j v_i \tag{16.3.6}$$

Recall that n is positive toward the center of curvature. Finally, the momentum equation in the binormal direction will be considered. Working out the $\mathbf{b} \cdot \mathbf{v} \times \boldsymbol{\omega}$ term for this direction reduces Eq. 16.3.1 to

$$b_i \, \partial_i \left(\frac{p}{\rho} + \frac{1}{2} v^2 + gZ \right) = \frac{d}{db} \left(\frac{1}{2} v^2 \right) + \nu b_i \, \partial_j \, \partial_j v_i$$

or

$$\frac{d}{db} \left(\frac{p}{\rho} + gZ \right) = +\nu b_i \, \partial_j \, \partial_j v_i \tag{16.3.7}$$

We are now in a position to discuss pressure changes in a general way.

For the first case we consider a steady incompressible flow. Equation 16.3.5 shows that the total head H changes along a streamline only by the action of a net viscous force. If the viscous force accelerates the particle, the head increases; if it decelerates the particle, the head decreases. Across streamlines in the **n**- and **b**-directions, Eqs. 16.3.6

and 16.3.7 show that the kinetic pressure $p_{kin} = p + \rho g Z$ also changes because of net viscous forces. In the direction normal to the streamline, the plane in which the streamline curves, there is also a centrifugal effect in the term v^2/R. One of the most useful arguments we can make concerns a flow with straight parallel streamlines, a jet exiting into a reservoir, for example. Then p_{kin} is constant across the streamlines so that the pressure in the jet is the same as that in the reservoir. This conclusion is reached by noting the R is infinite, so that the normal and binormal equations 16.3.6 and 16.3.7 have only the viscous terms. Furthermore, straight parallel streamlines mean that the **t, n,** and **b** coordinates form a rectangular system. The viscous terms are zero because v_n and v_b are always zero:

$$n_i\, \partial_j\, \partial_j v_i = \partial_t\, \partial_t v_n + \partial_n\, \partial_n v_n + \partial_b\, \partial_b v_n = 0$$

$$b_i\, \partial_j\, \partial_j v_i = \partial_t\, \partial_t v_b + \partial_n\, \partial_n v_b + \partial_b\, \partial_b v_b = 0$$

The value of p_{kin} may decrease along the streamline, as, for example, in the flow in a pipe, but it is constant across streamlines.

For the second class of flows, image that the viscous forces are negligible, but that the flow has nonzero vorticity. Equation 16.3.5 predicts the total head is constant along any streamline: the Bernoulli equation. Additional information is gained if we recall that Helmholtz's laws show that vortex lines are also material lines. Together, the streamlines and vortex lines form a set of surfaces, called *Lamb surfaces,* as shown in Fig. 16.2. Return to Eq. 16.3.1 and note that the term $(\mathbf{v} \times \boldsymbol{\omega})$ is perpendicular to both streamlines and vortex lines, and hence are perpendicular to the Lamb surface. Thus, one may integrate Eq. 16.3.1 between any points on the surface to find

$$gH = \frac{1}{2}v^2 + \frac{p}{\rho} + gZ = \text{constant on } \Psi - \omega \text{ surface} \qquad (16.3.8)$$

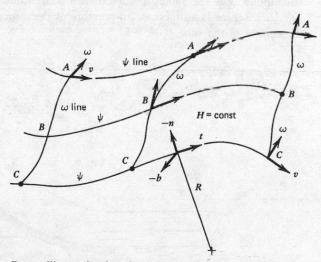

Figure 16.2 Bernoulli equation has the same constant on a Lamb surface (ψ–ω surface).

If along a streamline, p_{kin} = constant, the hydrostatic distribution of pressure exists and the velocity will be constant. On the other hand, if p_{kin} differs from one point to a subsequent point, there is an imbalance from the hydrostatic situation and an acceleration of the particle. One does not need to know the exact history of the acceleration because the net pressure force ∇p has p as an effective potential and the gravity force has a potential in $\rho g Z$. The Bernoulli equation is essentially a statement that the kinetic energy per unit mass, $\frac{1}{2}v^2$, is the difference in the potentials for the pressure and gravity forces.

Let us continue considering a steady, inviscid, incompressible flow with vorticity. Across streamlines in the normal direction, Eq. 16.3.6 becomes

$$\frac{dp_{kin}}{dn} = -\rho \frac{v^2}{R} \tag{16.3.9}$$

A curved streamline, finite R, must have a normal pressure gradient to cause the particle path to curve. The pressure decreases toward the center of curvature. This is the reason that the pressure in the core of a vortex is low. Alternatively, since streamlines curve away from a stagnation point, the pressure there is high. Across streamlines in the bi-normal direction, Eq. 16.3.7 predicts that the pressure p_{kin} is constant:

$$p_{kin} = \text{constant in the } \mathbf{b}\text{-direction} \tag{16.3.10}$$

A curve connecting binormal vectors has constant pressure.

As an example of a steady, inviscid, incompressible flow, consider the classic problem of a jet of water impacting a moving turning vane as shown in Fig. 16.3. In a coordinate system riding on the vane, the flow is steady. When the water enters and exits the vane, the streamlines are assumed to be parallel, so the radius of curvature is infinite. From Eq. 16.3.9 the pressure is constant across streamlines, and so within the jet the pressure is atmospheric since the pressure at the jet–air interface is atmospheric (neglecting gravity). Indeed, all along the free surface of the jet, the pressure is atmospheric. The streamlines near the vane are curved with some finite radius of curvature. Thus, from Eq. 16.3.9 there is an increase in pressure as one proceeds from the jet-air interface to the surface of the vane.

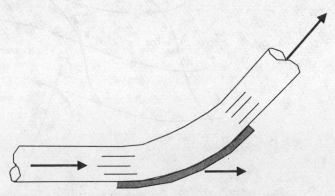

Figure 16.3   Jet of water striking a turning vane that is moving in the same direction as the jet.

The last category of flows are ideal flows where the vorticity is zero: steady, inviscid, irrotational, incompressible flows. In this case, Eq. 16.3.1 can be integrated anywhere in the field and the same constant for the total head obtained:

$$gH = \frac{1}{2} v^2 + \frac{p}{\rho} + gZ = \text{constant everywhere} \qquad (16.3.11)$$

(For the more general case of unsteady flows the Bernoulli equation was given in Eq. 12.5.5.) Subtracting Eq. 16.3.10 from Eq. 16.3.11 reveals that a curve along the binormals has a constant velocity:

$$v = \text{constant along the } \mathbf{b} \text{ curve} \qquad (16.3.12)$$

Consider a solid body in ideal flow. A streamline lies on the surface, if the normal is perpendicular to the surface, the binormal must be on the surface. Curves connecting the binormals are orthogonal to the surface streamlines and are also lines of constant pressure p_{kin}. Along these lines the velocity is constant. Therefore, in ideal flow the surface isobars are perpendicular to the streamlines and have a constant velocity.

16.4 BOUNDARY LAYERS

At high Reynolds numbers, the viscous effects are confined to thin regions. Although the regions are thin, it is very important to know the details of the flow within them. Many processes of engineering interest—such as shear stress, heat, and mass transfer—are controlled by the viscous regions. The term *boundary layer theory* applies to regions next to walls, mixing layers between two portions of the flow moving at different speeds, thin wakes behind streamlined bodies, and even jets of fluid discharging into large reservoirs. The essential characteristics of these regions are that they are thin and that they have steep velocity gradients that make the viscous effects important. Frequently, these regions become turbulent, but this does not invalidate the boundary layer concept, which need only be modified to include the turbulent characteristics. (That, however, is no small problem.)

As we look at a flow from the outside, so to speak, we see that the vorticity or viscous effects are concentrated into thinner and thinner regions as the Reynolds number increases. The first approximation is that the flow is a completely inviscid flow enclosed by the geometry of the walls. The defect in this picture is that the inviscid flow cannot satisfy the no-slip boundary conditions. It has only enough flexibility to produce streamlines that follow the wall. On the wall streamline the velocity cannot be specified but is determined as part of the inviscid solution. This error next to the wall always exists, no matter how high the Reynolds number becomes. Boundary layer theory is a complement to inviscid flow theory for the purpose of correcting the flow near the walls. The idea of treating boundary layers as a special region is due to Prandtl (1904).

Next, we derive the boundary layer equations and discuss the proper boundary conditions. For definiteness consider the boundary layer on a solid wall in a two-dimensional flow as shown in Fig. 16.4. The wall will be taken as smooth and continuous, with a radius of curvature that is always large compared to the boundary layer thickness. We

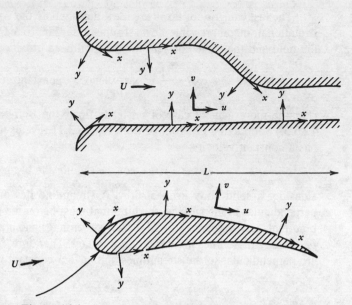

Figure 16.4   Boundary layer coordinates conform to the wall.

erect a *boundary layer coordinate system* where the surface $y = 0$ conforms to the body; the y-axis is normal to the body and the x-axis is along the body. To emphasize the physical aspects, we make two simplifications in the derivation. First, we deal only with a two-dimensional flow, so that only two velocity components are nonzero. Second, we ignore terms in the equations that come from curvature in the coordinate systems. A more detailed derivation would show that these are indeed negligible (see, e.g., Rosenhead, 1963). As far as the boundary layer is concerned, the world is flat, but three-dimensional. Figure 16.5 shows the boundary layer as it is unwrapped from the body.

Throughout the derivation keep in mind that we are making a correction to the inviscid flow so that the no-slip condition may be satisfied. We call the thickness of the boundary layer δ and note the important fact that as Re $\rightarrow \infty$, δ is approaching zero. The reason that inviscid flow theory fails near the wall is that the proper scale for viscous effects is not L. The natural scale for the y-direction is the distance δ. Let us see what happens to the u velocity component along the wall as we go across the boundary layer.

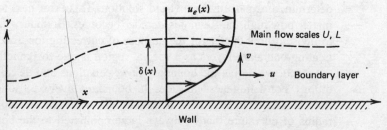

Figure 16.5   Boundary layer unwrapped from the wall.

At the wall the no-slip condition means that the velocity is always zero. On the inviscid side the slip velocity along the wall is determined by the inviscid solution. This velocity is zero at stagnation points and rises to values somewhat greater than U, the inviscid velocity scale, as a maximum. With this information we are in a position to estimate what the derivatives will be as we cross the boundary layer. A term such as $\partial u/\partial y$ would be of the order

$$\frac{\partial u}{\partial y} \sim \frac{U - 0}{\delta - 0} = \frac{U}{\delta} \tag{16.4.1}$$

In inviscid theory a term such as the one in Eq. 16.4.1 would be estimated as

$$\frac{\partial u}{\partial y} \sim O\left[\frac{U}{L}\right]$$

This is the reason that the inviscid theory failed at the wall; it contained an unreasonably low estimate of $\partial u/\partial y$.

So far we have argued that the boundary layer variables should have the following scales:

> Tangential velocity u: scale U (same as inviscid)
>
> Tangential distance x: scale L (same as inviscid)   (16.4.2)
>
> Normal distance y: scale δ (boundary layer thickness)

The boundary layer thickness is really unknown, except that we assume that it approaches zero as the Reynolds number goes to infinity.

We would expect v, the vertical or normal velocity in the boundary layer, to become zero as the boundary layer becomes thin. This is true, but it is not a precise enough estimate for our purposes. Let us introduce an unknown scale α for the vertical velocity. The nondimensional normal velocity will be

$$v^* = \frac{v}{\alpha} \tag{16.4.3}$$

Now, examine the continuity equation for the boundary layer. Below this equation we estimate the size of the terms:

$$\frac{\partial u}{\partial x} \quad + \quad \frac{\partial v}{\partial y} \quad = 0 \tag{16.4.4}$$

$$O\left[\frac{U}{L}\right] \qquad O\left[\frac{\alpha}{\delta}\right]$$

One general rule of incompressible fluid mechanics is that you should never drop a term from the continuity equation. In other words, do not let the flow gain or lose mass. (If we posed the theory in terms of the streamfunction, this rule would be enforced automatically.) Applying this principle means that α must be of order

$$\alpha \sim \frac{\delta}{L} U \tag{16.4.5}$$

When this is true, both terms in the continuity equation are the same size and no approximation to that equation occurs. The boundary layer is governed by the complete continuity equation 16.4.4.

The y-direction momentum equation will be considered next. We write the equation and then below each term our guess as to its size. We do not know the proper pressure scale, so we introduce an unknown scale P. The equation is

$$u\frac{\partial v}{\partial x} \quad + \quad v\frac{\partial v}{\partial y} \quad = \quad -\frac{1}{\rho}\frac{\partial p}{\partial y} + \quad \nu\frac{\partial^2 v}{\partial x^2} \quad + \quad \nu\frac{\partial^2 v}{\partial y^2}$$

$$O\left[U\frac{1}{L}\frac{\delta}{L}U\right] \quad O\left[\frac{\delta}{L}U\frac{1}{\delta}\frac{\delta}{L}U\right] \quad O\left[\frac{P}{\rho\delta}\right] \quad O\left[\frac{\nu}{L^2}\frac{\delta}{L}U\right] \quad O\left[\frac{\nu}{\delta^2}\frac{\delta}{L}U\right] \qquad (16.4.6)$$

Reorganizing the orders into nondimensional form produces

$$O\left[\left(\frac{\delta}{L}\right)^2\right] + O\left[\left(\frac{\delta}{L}\right)^2\right] = O\left[\frac{P}{\rho U^2}\right] + O\left[\frac{1}{\text{Re}}\left(\frac{\delta}{L}\right)^2\right] + O\left[\frac{1}{\text{Re}}\right]$$

For a moment assume that the pressure scale is the inviscid scale ρU^2 and see what happens. With this assumption, terms in the y-momentum equation will have the following orders as $\text{Re} \to \infty$:

$$O[0] + O[0] = O[1] + O[0] + O[0]$$

Thus, only one term is of order one, and the boundary layer y-momentum equation reduces to the statement that

$$0 = \frac{\partial p}{\partial y} \Rightarrow p = p(x) \qquad (16.4.7)$$

From this we conclude that the pressure is constant across a boundary layer. The pressure on the inviscid side of the layer is fixed by the inviscid flow. Whatever value occurs is impressed across the boundary layer without change. Since the proper inviscid scale for the pressure is ρU^2 and this same pressure is carried across the boundary layer, ρU^2 is also the proper boundary layer pressure scale. Our assumption that $P = \rho U^2$ leads to approximations that are consistent and reasonable.

The fact that the pressure is constant across the boundary layer is an important result. It means that pressure forces on a body are solely the result of the inviscid flow (a geometry-dominated flow). They are not modified by the boundary layer. As an example of an application of this principle, consider the lift force on an airfoil. It is a direct result of pressure forces. At high Reynolds numbers the boundary layers become so thin that the pressure forces, and hence the lift force, are determined by the inviscid flow. Further increase in the Reynolds number will not change the lift force (when nondimensionalized by inviscid scales). This principle is the basis of wind-tunnel tests. It is always impractical to take the Reynolds number of the model equal to that of the actual prototype. But if one tests at a sufficiently high Reynolds number, the lift no longer changes and the test will predict the lift of the prototype at any higher Reynolds number. This argument does not apply to the drag force, because drag is a combination of both viscous and pressure forces. The argument sometimes fails for bluff bodies, because they have regions of separated flow where boundary layer theory itself is invalid.

Now we turn to the x-direction momentum equation for the boundary layer,

$$u \frac{\partial u}{\partial x} + v \frac{\partial u}{\partial y} = -\frac{1}{\rho} \frac{dp}{dx} + \nu \frac{\partial^2 u}{\partial x^2} + \nu \frac{\partial^2 u}{\partial y^2} \qquad (16.4.8)$$

The size of each term is estimated below:

$$O\left[\frac{U^2}{L}\right] + O\left[\frac{\delta}{L} U \frac{U}{\delta}\right] = O\left[\frac{1}{\rho} \frac{\rho U^2}{L}\right] + O\left[\frac{\nu}{L^2} U\right] + O\left[\frac{\nu}{\delta^2} U\right]$$

Clearing U^2/L so that the terms are nondimensional produces

$$O[1] + O[1] = O[1] + O\left[\frac{1}{Re}\right] + O\left[\left(\frac{\delta}{L}\right)^{-2} \frac{1}{Re}\right] \qquad (16.4.9)$$

If we apply the limit $Re \rightarrow \infty$ to Eq. 16.4.9, the next-to-last term definitely vanishes and the first three terms definitely stay. The question concerns the last viscous term. It has an order that is an indeterminate form,

$$\frac{1/Re}{(\delta/L)^2} \sim \frac{0}{0} \rightarrow ? \qquad (16.4.10)$$

We have been operating up to this point on the assumption that $\delta/L \rightarrow 0$ as $Re \rightarrow \infty$, but we have not specified how fast that happens. There are three distinct possibilities: If $(\delta/L)^2$ goes to zero slower than $1/Re$, the ratio 16.4.10 becomes zero (this is, in fact, just a mathematical statement of what "slower" really means); if $(\delta/L)^2$ goes to zero faster than $1/Re$, the ratio is infinity; finally, if $(\delta/L)^2$ goes to zero at the same rate as $1/Re$, the ratio is a finite number. Let us consider the ramifications of each of these possibilities, one at a time.

If

$$\frac{1/Re}{(\delta/L)^2} \rightarrow 0 \qquad \text{as} \quad Re \rightarrow \infty$$

both viscous terms in the momentum equation are small. We are left with the same momentum equation as for the inviscid flow. Our boundary layer is governed by inviscid equations, and we cannot satisfy the no-slip conditions. This possibility must be thrown out, as it does not afford us enough flexibility to correct the inviscid flow.

The second possibility is if

$$\frac{1/Re}{(\delta/L)^2} \rightarrow \infty \qquad \text{as} \quad Re \rightarrow \infty \qquad (16.4.11)$$

This case requires us to reorganize Eq. 16.4.9 by multiplying by $(\delta/L)^2 Re$. The terms now have the following orders:

$$O\left[\frac{\delta/L)^2}{1/Re}\right] + O\left[\frac{(\delta/L)^2}{1/Re}\right] = O\left[\frac{(\delta/L)^2}{1/Re}\right] + O\left[\left(\frac{\delta}{L}\right)^2\right] + O[1]$$

Applying Eq. 16.4.11 to the relation above leads to the following result as $Re \rightarrow \infty$:

$$O[0] + O[0] = O[0] + O[0] + O[1]$$

For this case the momentum equation governing the boundary layer is the single term

$$0 = \frac{\partial^2 u}{\partial y^2} \tag{16.4.12}$$

The solution to this equation can be given immediately. It is

$$\frac{\partial u}{\partial y} = C_1(x)$$

$$\tag{16.4.13}$$

$$u = C_1(x)y + C_2(x)$$

One boundary condition is that $u = 0$ at $y = 0$; this means that $C_2 = 0$. This solution says that the boundary layer has a constant shear stress and a linear velocity profile. Such a solution will not smoothly match the inviscid flow, as it has a discontinuity in the shear stress. For these reasons we reject the second possibility.

The last possibility, and the one correct choice, is that the ratio is Eq. 16.4.10 is finite. This means that

$$\frac{\delta}{L} \sim \sqrt{\frac{1}{\text{Re}}} \tag{16.4.14}$$

From Eqs. 16.4.9 and 16.4.14 we find that the momentum equation for the boundary layer is

$$u \frac{\partial u}{\partial x} + v \frac{\partial u}{\partial y} = -\frac{1}{\rho} \frac{dp}{dx} + v \frac{\partial^2 u}{\partial y^2} \tag{16.4.15}$$

This equation differs from the inviscid momentum equation by retaining one viscous term. It offers us sufficient flexibility to meet the no-slip condition at the wall and to match smoothly to the inviscid flow.

An alternative approach to finding Eq. 16.4.14 is to use the Rayleigh argument— the diffusion of vorticity is $\delta \sim \sqrt{vt}$ and t is the flow time $t = L/U$. A physical argument such as this is often useful in pointing out the proper path to take in a complicated analysis.

Boundary layer momentum equation 16.4.15 has a much different character than the inviscid flow equations. The y-direction is dominated by the viscous diffusion term, the highest-order term in the equation. The term $u\, \partial u/\partial x$ on the left-hand side of the equation, together with the viscous term $v\partial^2 u/\partial y^2$, give the problem a parabolic mathematical character.

We encountered an example of a parabolic problem when we studied Rayleigh's problem for the impulsive motion of a fluid above a fixed flat plate:

$$\frac{\partial u}{\partial t} = v \frac{\partial^2 u}{\partial y^2}$$

$$u(y, t = 0) = u_{\text{initial}} = 0$$

$$\tag{16.4.16}$$

$$u(y = 0, t) = u_{\text{wall}} = 0$$

$$u(y \rightarrow \infty, t) = u_{\text{external}} = U$$

In particular, notice that the boundary conditions are prescribed on an open domain in the y–t plane: an initial condition $u = 0$ and the values of u at two space points $y = 0$ and $y \to \infty$. Boundary layer equation 16.4.15 is similar in character to Eq. 16.4.16 except that x in the boundary layer takes on the role of time in Rayleigh's problem. This analogy is mathematically correct, and we can use Eq. 16.4.16 as a guide to the proper boundary conditions for the boundary layer equations.

The usual boundary layer boundary conditions are an initial profile,

$$u(x = x_0, y) = u_{\text{initial}} = u_{\text{in}}(y) \tag{16.4.17}$$

the no-slip condition at the wall,

$$u(x, y = 0) = 0 \tag{16.4.18}$$

$$v(x, y = 0) = 0$$

and an external flow condition,

$$u(x, y \to \infty) = u_{\text{external}} = u_e(x) \tag{16.4.19}$$

We cannot impose a downstream boundary condition. That is prohibited for a parabolic equation. Also, a prescribed initial profile for v cannot be given, because, in principle, the continuity and momentum equations together with the initial velocity $u(y)$ could be solved to find $v(y)$. Similarly, to specify $v(x, y \to \infty)$ would overdetermine the problem. Whatever value the solution produces for $v(x, y \to \infty)$ must be accepted.

The external flow condition also deserves special comment. The exact value of $u_e(x)$ is to be determined by matching the boundary layer to the inviscid flow. As we look from the inviscid flow toward the boundary layer and allow the Reynolds number to increase, the thickness of the boundary layer decreases toward zero. Our first approximation for the inviscid flow was to neglect the thickness of the boundary layer and find a flow that slips over the surface of the body. Thus, we now argue that the external velocity of the boundary layer should be the inviscid flow evaluated at the wall,

$$u_e(x) = u_{\text{inviscid}}(\text{wall}) \tag{16.4.20}$$

This means that we must know the inviscid flow before we attempt to analyze the boundary layer.

Let us continue by considering things from the boundary layer side. The proper nondimensional y variable for the boundary layer is scaled by the boundary layer thickness:

$$y^* = \frac{y}{\delta} = \frac{y}{L/\sqrt{\text{Re}}} \tag{16.4.21}$$

The scale unit for the boundary layer becomes smaller and smaller as the Reynolds number becomes large. If you wanted to watch the events within the boundary layer, you would have to shrink yourself down in size as the Reynolds number increased. A constant unit in y^* occupies a smaller and smaller fraction of L as Re increases; $y/L = y^*/\sqrt{\text{Re}}$. The next question is: Where is the inviscid flow in terms of boundary layer variables? As far as the boundary layer is concerned, you must go out to $y^* \to \infty$ before you get to the inviscid flow. To make things clearer, we can even write subscripts on u and y in Eq. 16.4.19 to show that these are boundary layer variables. Equations 16.4.19

and 16.4.20 tell us precisely how to get the boundary condition on u by matching the boundary layer (bl) and the inviscid flow:

$$u_{bl}(x, y_{bl} \rightarrow \infty) = u_e(x) = u_{inviscid}(\text{wall}) \qquad (16.4.22)$$

The external velocity for the boundary layer—that is, the velocity as the boundary-layer distance approaches infinity—is equal to the inviscid flow velocity evaluated at the inviscid coordinates corresponding to the body surface. This is the matching between the inviscid flow and the boundary layer.

The inviscid flow supplies a major boundary condition to the boundary layer through Eq. 16.4.22. It also determines the pressure within the boundary layer. Since the inviscid streamline on the wall must obey Bernoulli's equation, we have that the boundary layer pressure is given by

$$\frac{1}{\rho} p(x) + \frac{1}{2} u_e^2(x) = \text{const} \qquad (16.4.23)$$

The boundary layer momentum equation requires that we know the pressure gradient. From Eq. 16.4.23 we find that

$$-\frac{1}{\rho} \frac{dp}{dx} = u_e \frac{du_e}{dx} \qquad (16.4.24)$$

This expression may also be derived by evaluating boundary layer momentum equation 16.4.15 as $y \rightarrow \infty$. The assumption that the boundary layer matches the inviscid flow smoothly implies that $\partial u/\partial y$, $\partial^2 u/\partial y^2$, and all other y derivatives of u becomes zero as $y \rightarrow \infty$. Equation 16.4.24 results from applying these conditions to Eq. 16.4.15.

From an analytical point of view, the inviscid flow problem is solved first. Then we can evaluate the velocity on the wall, $u_e(x)$, for use in the boundary layer calculation. Experiments may be substituted for a knowledge of the inviscid flow. To do this one makes pressure measurements on the surface of the body. In principle this pressure is the inviscid pressure, and through Bernoulli's equation 16.4.23 the inviscid velocity $u_e(x)$ is determined.

Before we discuss the physical character of boundary layers it is good to collect together in one place a complete mathematical statement of the problem. The boundary layer equations are

$$\frac{\partial u}{\partial x} + \frac{\partial v}{\partial y} = 0$$

$$u \frac{\partial u}{\partial x} + v \frac{\partial u}{\partial y} = u_e \frac{du_e}{dx} + \nu \frac{\partial^2 u}{\partial y^2}$$

$$u(x = x_0, y) = u_{in}(y) \qquad (16.4.25)$$

$$u(x, y = 0) = 0$$

$$v(x, y = 0) = 0$$

$$u(x, y \rightarrow \infty) = u_e(x)$$

Two pieces of information are needed to complete the problem: the initial velocity profile $u_{in}(y)$ and the external velocity variation $u_e(x)$. Also note that unlike the inviscid flow, where the velocity field depended only on geometry, the boundary layer equations contain ν, the kinematic viscosity, as a parameter.

The parabolic nature of the boundary layer problem means that a signal will travel across the layer at infinite speed. For example, a small pulsation at the wall or an injection of fluid at the wall instantaneously changes the entire velocity profile across the boundary layer. In the x-direction, the direction along the wall, events are convected with the flow velocity. Thus, whatever disruption the wall pulsation causes is not felt downstream until later, when fluid that was at the pulsed point arrives downstream. This means that boundary layers contain a history dependence that comes from the initial profile. (Note that from the mathematical standpoint the initial profile can be at any place we choose. We can start the boundary layer calculation at an arbitrary position. The velocity profile at that place becomes the initial profile.)

Let us consider a flat plate with a block initial profile and the external velocity $u_e = U$, which is constant over the plate (Fig. 16.6a). The boundary layer grows in a regular manner as the flow proceeds along the plate. Now, compare this problem with a second situation where a rounded leading edge is attached to the plate. Around the nose

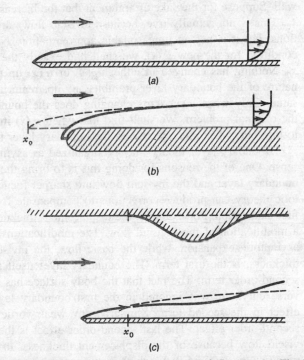

(a)

(b)

(c)

Figure 16.6 Boundary layers do not have any upstream influence. (a) The boundary layer develops on a flat plate. (b) For a boundary layer on a rounded nose, the development downstream is equivalent to (a) with a displaced effective origin. (c) The boundary layer in a flat channel develops on the dashed line. A bump on the opposite wall causes a different development after x_0.

of the plate there are pressure gradients, and only after we pass the position x_0 does the pressure become uniform and u_e take on a constant value. At x_0 a certain initial velocity profile exists, which is not the block profile. We have constructed two situations where u_e is the same but the initial profiles are different. As we go downstream, these boundary layers have different velocity profiles as a result of their different initial conditions. The boundary layer remembers its initial flow situation. The farther downstream we go, the less difference we can detect between the two boundary layers. The effect of the initial condition gradually dies out. At positions that are the same distance downstream, the two boundary layers will never be exactly the same. However, the careful observer would notice that if we shifted the origin of the rounded-nose boundary layer so that an effective position $\bar{x}_0$ was used as the origin, the two boundary layers would approach the same profile as $x \to \infty$: The effect of the initial profile is equivalent, at downstream positions, to a virtual shift in the origin of the boundary layer.

Boundary layers transfer effects only in the downstream direction; there can be no upstream influence in a boundary layer. For instance, imagine that a flat plate forms one wall of a flow channel of constant area. The external velocity u_e is constant in this case, just as in the preceding example. Now, a second test is run where a large hump is attached to the opposite wall as shown in Fig. 16.6. In this case the inviscid flow must accelerate as it goes through the area constriction, causing an increase in the velocity u_e on the flat wall. Suppose for the sake of argument that the increase in u_e begins at a certain location x_0. This is not actually true, because inviscid flows are sensitive to all boundary conditions, but it is not an unreasonable approximation. Now, if we calculate the boundary condition for the new $u_e(x)$, we shall find exactly the same solution up to the position x_0. Nothing has changed in either $u_{in}(y)$ or $u_e(x)$ up to x_0, and since the mathematical nature of the boundary layer prohibits any upstream influence, the solution must be the same. Only when $u_e(x)$ starts changing does the boundary layer become different from the original problem. We shall find that when $u_e(x)$ increases, the boundary layer tends to thin out; when $u_e(x)$ decreases, the boundary layer thickens rapidly.

Boundary layer theory may be organized as asymptotic theory in the mathematical sense. One of the reasons for doing this is to bring the matching conditions between the boundary layer and the inviscid flow into sharper focus. The other benefit is that asymptotic theory can produce corrections to compensate for things that are neglected in the first calculation. For example, the displacement thickness of the boundary layer requires a modification of the inviscid flow. The modification appears as the second term in an asymptotic expansion, while the basic flow, the inviscid flow for zero boundary layer thickness, is the first term. The boundary layer itself receives several corrections in its second-order term. The fact that the body surface has longitudinal and (possibly) transverse curvature was ignored in the first boundary layer calculation but will cause an effect in the second term. Similarly, any weak vorticity in the inviscid flow causes a second-order effect. The last second-order effect is the new external velocity in the inviscid flow because of the displacement thickness. In other words, the boundary layer modifies the inviscid flow, which in turn produces a new surface speed for the boundary layer. The different second-order effects were first investigated by several different researchers. Subsequently, Van Dyke (1962) and Maslen (1963) gave a general development of the theory.

16.5 CONCLUSIONS

Unseparated flow at high Reynolds number may be divided into two complementary flows: an inviscid flow and a boundary layer. Geometry, that is, the shape of the bounding walls and their motion, determines the inviscid flow pattern. This flow then drives the boundary layer through two effects: the boundary layer velocity at infinity must match the inviscid velocity over the wall, and the pressure gradient in the inviscid flow is imposed directly within the boundary layer. The special qualities of typical inviscid flows are given in Chapters 17 and 18; Chapter 20 concerns boundary layer theory.

PROBLEMS

16.1 (A) A jet of water traveling at a relative velocity of 50 ft/s encounters the blade of a Pelton wheel turbine. The flow path over the blade is 4 in. long. Estimate the thickness of the boundary layer at the end of the blade.

16.2 (B) Air at room temperature flows in a tube 10 cm in diameter. The tube ends 1 cm from a flat wall that is perpendicular to the flow. An end flange 30 cm in diameter is flat so that the flow turns and comes radially out along the wall exiting to the atmosphere. The flow in the tube is uniform at 15 m/s. Estimate the thickness of the boundary layers on the wall.

16.3 (B) Compute the pressure variation along the flange and in the pipe. Estimate the pressure behavior in the region where the flow turns.

16.4 (B) Find the form of each of the following equations that is appropriate for a two-dimensional boundary layer: $\boldsymbol{\omega} = \nabla \times \mathbf{v}$, $\nabla \cdot \boldsymbol{\omega} = 0$, $\nabla^2 \psi = \omega_z$, $D\boldsymbol{\omega}/Dt = \boldsymbol{\omega} \cdot \nabla \mathbf{v} + \nu \nabla^2 \boldsymbol{\omega}$.

16.5 (C) Consider a fan blade operating at a high Reynolds number. Low pressures exist on the upper surface. Pressures are especially low in the root region but not quite so low as the tip is approached. Why will contour lines of constant pressure on top of the blade have cusp shapes?

16.6 (C) Review Problem 12.12 for a steady axisymmetric vortical flow with swirl. Write Eq. 16.3.1 for an inviscid flow (carrying vorticity) introducing H. What are the three components of this equation in cylindrical coordinates? Show that $rv_\theta = \gamma$ (ψ only). Using all the relations in Problem 12.12 and this problem and considering $H = H$ (ψ only), derive the relation

$$\frac{\omega_\theta}{r} = \frac{\gamma}{r^2} \frac{d\gamma}{d\psi} - \frac{dH}{d\psi}$$

16.7 (C) Burgers vortex viewed as an inviscid flow boundary layer. Consider $v_\theta(r)$ in Burgers vortex, Eq. 11.10.8, as a function of the parameters $\Gamma(L^2/T)$, $\nu(L^2/T)$, and $a(1/T)$. Form outer-nondimensional variable for r using Γ and a but not ν. Form inner-nondimensional variables for v_θ and r using a and ν but not Γ. What is the nondimensional perturbation parameter? What is the leading term in an asymptotic expansion of Eq. 11.10.8 in outer variables? What is the common part? What rescaling of v_θ in inner variables is needed to retain the viscous term in Eq. 11.10.8?

17

Kinematic Decomposition of Flow Fields

Previously, we introduced the decomposition of fluid motion into categories of translation, solidlike rotation, and deformation. This is a local picture of the flow that is valid for the motion of particles in a vanishingly small neighborhood. In this chapter we seek to decompose the entire velocity field into parts that have kinematic significance. This can be accomplished in several different ways. We review two different methods. Helmholtz's decomposition is discussed first, as it is the most popular and best known. The second method uses Monge's potentials, which also go under the name *Clebsch variables*.

*17.1 GENERAL APPROACH

We seek to divide the velocity field into two parts as follows:

$$\mathbf{v} = \mathbf{v}^{(\omega)} + \mathbf{v}^{(\phi)} \tag{17.1.1}$$

The first part, $\mathbf{v}^{(\omega)}$, is the rotational component and accounts for all of the vorticity in the flow. As a consequence, the second part, $\mathbf{v}^{(\phi)}$, is irrotational. Mathematically, these statements imply that

$$\boldsymbol{\omega} = \nabla \times \mathbf{v} = \nabla \times \mathbf{v}^{(\omega)} \tag{17.1.2}$$

$$0 = \nabla \times \mathbf{v}^{(\phi)} \tag{17.1.3}$$

Recall that the necessary and sufficient condition for the existence of a velocity potential is simply that the flow is irrotational. Hence, we call the second part the *potential component*. It is related to a potential ϕ by

$$\mathbf{v}^{(\phi)} = \nabla \phi \tag{17.1.4}$$

The decomposition (Eq. 17.1.1) is not unique. For a given velocity field $\mathbf{v}$, we could choose any potential flow whatsoever and subtract it from the real flow to arrive at $\mathbf{v}^{(\omega)}$. To make the decomposition unique we need to apply more conditions.

In the local description of fluid motion, discussed in Chapter 4, we considered $d\mathbf{v}$, the velocity of a material particle P' with respect to the primary particle P. This velocity increment was further divided into rotational and straining components; $d\mathbf{v} = d\mathbf{v}^{(r)} + d\mathbf{v}^{(s)}$. Notice that the rotational component is denoted by $d\mathbf{v}^{(r)}$, while in Eq. 17.1.1 the rotational component is denoted by $\mathbf{v}^{(\omega)}$. These velocities are not related. As a matter of fact, $d\mathbf{v}^{(r)}$ is an inexact differential, and hence cannot be integrated to produce a function. Equation 17.1.1 is simply a splitting where one component produces the vorticity when it is differentiated. Many splittings have this property.

*17.2 HELMHOLTZ'S DECOMPOSITION

This decomposition bears Helmholtz's name because he employed it in his famous paper on vortex line behavior. As with most ideas, it developed in stages with several contributors. In fact, Stokes published a key result in a slightly different form prior to the paper of Helmholtz.

Let us impose the requirement that $\mathbf{v}^{(\omega)}$ have zero divergence (i.e., $\mathbf{v}^{(\omega)}$ is solenoidal):

$$\nabla \cdot \mathbf{v}^{(\omega)} = 0 \tag{17.2.1}$$

This cuts down the choices for $\mathbf{v}^{(\omega)}$, but it still does not produce a unique decomposition. To show this, we take any harmonic function Φ ($\nabla^2\Phi = 0$) and let $\nabla\Phi$ be another velocity potential. Now, consider a certain decomposition denoted by subscripts 1, and add and subtract $\nabla\Phi$:

$$\mathbf{v} = \mathbf{v}_1^{(\omega)} + \mathbf{v}_1^{(\phi)}$$

$$= \mathbf{v}_1^{(\omega)} + \nabla\Phi + \mathbf{v}_1^{(\phi)} - \nabla\Phi$$

$$= \mathbf{v}_2^{(\omega)} + \mathbf{v}_2^{(\phi)}$$

The combination $\mathbf{v}_2^{(\omega)} = \mathbf{v}_1^{(\omega)} + \nabla\Phi$ still satisfies all the requirements for $\mathbf{v}^{(\omega)}$, including Eq. 17.2.1, and the combination $\mathbf{v}_2^{(\phi)} = \mathbf{v}_1^{(\phi)} = \nabla\Phi$ is still a potential flow.

Equation 17.2.1 has the effect of placing the expansion motions in the potential component. We denote the rate of expansion by Δ. For a given velocity field we have

$$\Delta \equiv \nabla \cdot \mathbf{v} = \nabla \cdot \mathbf{v}^{(\phi)} = \nabla^2\phi \tag{17.2.2}$$

To keep the discussion general we allow the flow to be compressible, so the effective source distribution Δ is not zero. In incompressible flow $\Delta = 0$ and the potential ϕ will become a harmonic function.

For the sake of finding a solution to Eq. 17.2.2, let us assume that Δ is a known distribution of sources. Textbooks in mathematics show that the solution to Poisson's equation 17.2.2 is given by

$$\phi(\mathbf{x}) = \Phi - \frac{1}{4\pi} \int \frac{\Delta' \, dV}{|\mathbf{r}|} \tag{17.2.3}$$

The corresponding velocity is

$$\mathbf{v}^{(\phi)}(\mathbf{x}) = \nabla\Phi + \frac{1}{4\pi} \int \frac{\mathbf{r}\Delta' \, dV'}{|\mathbf{r}|^3} \tag{17.2.4}$$

In these equations $\mathbf{x}$ is the position of interest, while $\mathbf{x}'$ is the position of the integration element dV' and the point where Δ' is evaluated. The vector $\mathbf{r}$ is defined as $\mathbf{x} - \mathbf{x}'$. The given distribution of sources determines the integral in Eq. 17.2.4. The gradient of any harmonic function Φ may be added to the source effect. The parameter Φ is usually chosen to satisfy any boundary conditions.

Turning now to the rotational component $\mathbf{v}^{(\omega)}$, we note the result from Tensor analysis (Phillips, 1933; Brand, 1957; Aris, 1962; Batchelor, 1967), that any vector field satisfying $\nabla \cdot \mathbf{v}^{(\omega)} = 0$ (Eq. 17.2.1) may be represented by a vector potential $\mathbf{B}$. The representation is such that

$$\mathbf{v}^{(\omega)} = \nabla \times \mathbf{B} \qquad (17.2.5)$$

A unique choice for $\mathbf{B}$ is made on mathematical grounds. The vector identity

$$\nabla^2 \mathbf{B} = -\nabla \times (\nabla \times \mathbf{B}) + \nabla(\nabla \cdot \mathbf{B})$$

will simplify to

$$\nabla^2 \mathbf{B} = -\boldsymbol{\omega} \qquad (17.2.6)$$

if we make the assumption $\nabla \cdot \mathbf{B} = 0$. The solution to Eq. 17.2.6 is

$$\mathbf{B} = \frac{1}{4\pi} \int \frac{\boldsymbol{\omega}'}{|\mathbf{r}|} \, dV' \qquad (17.2.7)$$

This leads to the well-known *Biot–Savart law*:

$$\mathbf{v}^{(\omega)}(x) = -\frac{1}{4\pi} \int \frac{\mathbf{r} \times \boldsymbol{\omega}'}{|\mathbf{r}|^3} \, dV' \qquad (17.2.8)$$

A known vorticity distribution produces a specific rotational component $\mathbf{v}^{(\omega)}$ from Eq. 17.2.8. This formula is arrived at by requiring that $\nabla \cdot \mathbf{B} = 0$.

The expressions 17.2.8 and 17.2.4 give a definite decomposition of the velocity field. The ambiguity noted at the beginning amounts to adding the potential of a harmonic function to Eq. 17.2.7 and subtracting the same from Eq. 17.2.4.

With the mathematical assumptions that $\mathbf{v}$ is continuous and has bounded derivatives. The integrals in Eqs. 17.4.2 and 17.2.8 are well defined and yield well-behaved solutions. The decomposition is valid in the global sense. We have no difficulties in principle in applying the equations to the entire flow field.

*17.3 LINE VORTEX AND VORTEX SHEET

Consider a small cylindrical region of radius r_0 that contains vorticity (Fig. 17.1). The vorticity is directed along the z-axis and extends from z_1 to z_2. Outside this region the vorticity is zero. Recall that the strength of a vortex tube must be constant; hence, we let

$$\Gamma = \int_0^{r_0} \omega_z \, dA \qquad (17.3.1)$$

It is not physically possible for the vortex lines to exist only between z_1 and z_2; however, we shall consider only this piece to find the influence of a section of finite length.

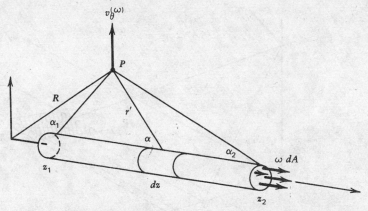

Figure 17.1 Velocity induced by a vortex element of finite length.

Without loss of generality we compute the velocity at the point P, a radial distance R from the origin. The vortex induces a velocity v_θ at this point. When R is large compared to the vortex tube radius r_0, the integral 17.2.8 becomes [note that $(\mathbf{r} \times \boldsymbol{\omega})_\theta = -R\omega_z$, $r^2 = R^2 + z^2$, $dV = dA\ dz$]

$$v_\theta = \frac{\Gamma}{4\pi} \int_{z_1}^{z_2} \frac{R\ dz}{(R^2 + z^2)^{3/2}} = \frac{\Gamma}{4\pi R} \left[\frac{z_2}{(R^2 + z_2^2)^{1/2}} - \frac{z_1}{(R^2 + z_1^2)^{1/2}} \right]$$

$$= \frac{\Gamma}{4\pi R} (\cos\alpha_2 - \cos\alpha_1) \tag{17.3.2}$$

From this equation we see that the velocity in the end plane of a semi-infinite vortex is $v_\theta = \Gamma/4\pi R$. This result has application to the downwash velocity at the wing caused by a vortex filament in the wake. A line vortex that is infinite in both directions results in the customary formula for an ideal vortex: $v_\theta = \Gamma/2\pi R$. The location of the origin becomes immaterial in this instance.

As a second example, consider a plane vortex sheet as shown in Fig. 17.2. A uniform vorticity ω exists in the region $-h < x_3 < h$, where h is very small. Integration across this layer produces a constant,

$$K = \int_{-h}^{h} \omega_2\ dx_3 \tag{17.3.3}$$

For a vortex tube dx_1 by $2h$ in cross section, the incremental circulation is

$$d\Gamma = K\ dx_1 \tag{17.3.4}$$

Thus, K is the circulation per unit length of the vortex sheet. Everywhere outside the sheet the vorticity is zero.

Since the sheet is infinite, we need only consider points on the x_3-axis to find how the velocity changes with distance from the sheet. The Biot–Savart law (Eq. 17.2.8) for these points yields

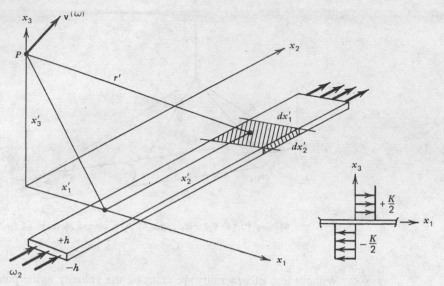

Figure 17.2   Velocity induced by a vortex sheet.

$$v_3(0, 0, x_3) = -\frac{K}{4\pi} \int\int_{-\infty}^{\infty} \frac{x_1' \, dx_1' \, dx_2'}{(x_1'^2 + x_2'^2 + x_3^2)^{3/2}} = 0$$

$$v_1(0, 0, x_3) = \frac{K}{4\pi} \int\int_{-\infty}^{\infty} \frac{x_3' \, dx_1' \, dx_2'}{[x_1'^2 + x_2'^2 + x_3'^2]^{3/2}} = \pm\frac{K}{2}$$

$(17.3.5)$

The plus sign is for $x_3 > 0$ and the minus sign for $x_3 < 0$. The velocity field associated with a vortex sheet is a uniform flow parallel to the sheet and perpendicular to the vorticity vector. The sheet separates two uniform streams: the upper with velocity $K/2$ and the lower with velocity $-K/2$. The jump in tangential velocity as the sheet is crossed is the sheet strength K.

The interpretation of K as the circulation density $d\Gamma/ds$ is especially relevant to thin-airfoil theory. Consider a small section of a thin airfoil where dx_1 is along the chord direction. The boundary layer on the upper surface has a positive vorticity as the velocity goes from zero at the wall to U_{upper} outside the boundary layer. On the lower surface the vorticity in the boundary layer is negative, with the velocity attaining a value U_{lower} outside the boundary layer. Integration across both layers gives a net strength $K = U_{upper} - U_{lower}$ at any chord position. Since $K = d\Gamma/dx$, the integration of $K \, dx_1$ from leading edge to trailing edge yields the total circulation around the airfoil, Γ. In this way the ideal flow over an airfoil may be represented as a uniform stream with a vortex sheet of varying strength inserted to represent the foil (thickness effects may be represented by sources and sinks in Eq. 17.2.4 but are usually negligible).

In the previous examples we have flows where the vorticity is concentrated in thin regions. The Biot–Savart law is not a cause–effect relationship in the sense that a force produces an acceleration. The relationship is purely kinematic. For this reason people frequently say that a vorticity distribution "induces" a certain remote velocity. We say that a vortex ring is propelled by self-induction. A similar kinematic relation occurs when a small pipe injects water in the center of a large, deep pool. The source of mass requires that a flow velocity be induced at remote positions through Eq. 17.2.4. This is a kinematic requirement. In a similar manner, changes in a vorticity distribution must be accompanied by a remote effect through Eq. 17.2.8.

When a flow is restricted by walls, as most flows are, the decomposition into rotational and potential parts is accomplished by imagining that the fluid extends beyond the walls and has fictitious sources and vortices that will produce the proper result within the real flow. This introduces another ambiguity in that many distributions of sources and vortices within the walls can produce the same flow confined between the walls.

*17.4 COMPLEX LAMELLAR DECOMPOSITION

A second method of decomposing the velocity field into a potential part $\mathbf{v}^{(\phi)}$ and a rotational part $\mathbf{v}^{(\omega)}$ is to choose $\mathbf{v}^{(\omega)}$ to be a complex lamellar field. This somewhat awkward term was applied by Kelvin and finds favor with workers in rational mechanics. (Potential flows were called *lamellar* by Kelvin.) A *complex lamellar vector field* is one that becomes a potential flow if it is divided by an integrating function σ. That is, a potential function χ exists such that

$$\frac{\mathbf{v}^{(\omega)}}{\sigma} = \nabla\chi \tag{17.4.1}$$

Substituting into Eq. 17.1.1 and using Eq. 17.1.4, we see that the three "potentials" σ, χ, and ϕ determine the velocity:

$$\mathbf{v} = \sigma\nabla\chi + \nabla\phi \tag{17.4.2}$$

These potentials are sometimes called *Clebsch's variables,* as he used them in an early application to fluid mechanics. The decomposition (Eq. 17.4.2) is not unique; several combinations of σ, χ, and ϕ can be found that give the velocity field.

Another completely equivalent definition of a complex lamellar vector is that it always is perpendicular to its own curl. Hence,

$$\mathbf{v}^{(\omega)} \cdot (\nabla \times \mathbf{v}^{(\omega)}) = 0 \tag{17.4.3}$$

$$\mathbf{v}^{(\omega)} \cdot \boldsymbol{\omega} = 0$$

In any flow where the total velocity is perpendicular to the vorticity (plane flows and axisymmetric flows), this condition is satisfied by the velocity itself. For these flows, $\mathbf{v} = \mathbf{v}^{(\omega)} = \sigma\nabla\chi$ and $\mathbf{v}^{(\phi)} = 0$ constitute an acceptable representation.

The most interesting aspect of the decomposition of Eq. 17.4.2 is revealed by computing the vorticity,

$$\boldsymbol{\omega} = \nabla \times \mathbf{v}^{(\omega)} = \nabla\sigma \times \nabla\chi \tag{17.4.4}$$

Note the similarity between this equation and Eq. 12.4.7. In Eq. 12.4.7 the incompressibility condition $\nabla \cdot \mathbf{v} = 0$ allowed the velocity to be given by streamsurfaces f and g such that $\mathbf{v} = \nabla f \times \nabla g$. Vorticity always meets the condition $\nabla \cdot \boldsymbol{\omega} = 0$, so a similar representation is possible. Equation 17.4.4 means that surfaces of $\sigma = $ const and $\chi = $ const are vortex surfaces containing the vortex lines. This is easily shown by proving that the normal at the surface σ, $\nabla\sigma$, is perpendicular to the vorticity vector: $\nabla\sigma \cdot \boldsymbol{\omega} = \nabla\sigma \cdot \nabla\sigma \times \nabla\chi = 0$. A triple vector product containing the same vector twice is always zero. Similarly, $\nabla\chi \cdot \boldsymbol{\omega} = 0$ establishes that χ surfaces also contain the vortex lines.

Since σ and χ surfaces contain the vortex lines, their intersection describes a vortex line. Thus, this decomposition offers a method of identifying vortex lines in a viscous flow. There are, however, two drawbacks that need to be pointed out immediately. First, the decomposition (Eq. 17.4.2) may not be globally valid. It may happen that a certain set of σ, χ, and ϕ surfaces cannot be extended over the entire flow. For example, this happens if the vortex lines have knots (in the same way, the streamfunction surfaces are not globally valid if the streamlines have knots). Second, the identity of the vortex lines involves an arbitrary choice of reference surfaces.

To bring out some of the details of this decomposition, consider a flow over a wall as shown in Fig. 17.3 Assume that the velocity, and hence the vorticity, are known. Also assume that the vorticity is nonzero near the wall, becomes zero on a certain surface within the flow, and is zero at all positions beyond this surface. Let the flow be regular in such a way that we may choose a certain reference plane R_0 that is pierced by all the vortex lines. All the σ and χ surfaces will also cut this plane. We may take any arbitrary set of curves on R_0 as lines where χ is constant. These lines on R_0 can be extended along the vortex lines throughout the flow to form the χ surfaces. Choosing a family of χ curves on R_0 determines the χ surfaces through the entire flow when all vortex lines pierce R_0.

In the region where $\omega = 0$ we must have $\nabla\sigma = 0$, since $\boldsymbol{\omega} = \nabla\sigma \times \nabla\chi$ and $\nabla\chi \neq 0$. Hence, $\sigma = \sigma_0$ is constant in these regions (or possibly a function of time). If we take $\sigma_0 = 0$, the component $v^{(\omega)}$ will also be zero in this region. Unlike the Helmholtz decomposition, the present decomposition can be arranged to give $\mathbf{v}^{(\omega)} = 0$ when $\omega = 0$.

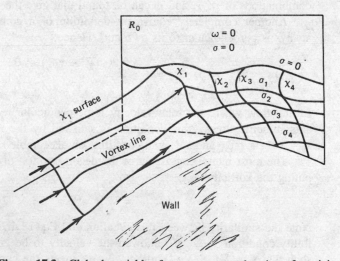

Figure 17.3 Clebsch variables for a concentrated region of vorticity.

We continue by explaining how it is possible in principle to compute σ and ϕ. Let dx be a differential line element that lies in a $\chi = $ const surface. Now

$$\omega \times d\mathbf{x} = \nabla \chi \, d\sigma \quad \text{on} \quad \chi = \text{const}$$

This vector is perpendicular to the χ surface. Take a helping unit vector that does not lie in the χ surface. For example, the surface normal $\nabla\chi$ would be suitable. We are assured that the dot product with $\omega \times d\mathbf{x}$ is nonzero:

$$\nabla\chi \cdot \omega \times d\mathbf{x} = \nabla\chi \cdot \nabla\chi \, d\sigma$$

Integrating from the region where $\omega = 0$ to any point x yields the function σ as

$$\sigma = \int^x \frac{\nabla\chi \times \omega \cdot d\mathbf{x}}{\nabla\chi \cdot \nabla\chi} \quad \text{on} \quad \chi = \text{const} \tag{17.4.5}$$

The irrotational potential is found by integrating

$$d\phi = \nabla\phi \cdot d\mathbf{x} = (\mathbf{v} - \sigma\nabla\chi) \cdot d\mathbf{x}$$

Since the right-hand side is known, the decomposition is complete.

A different choice for the family of curves on R_0 that define the χ surfaces leads to a different potential–complex lamellar decomposition. With the new choice of curves, $\mathbf{v}^{(\omega)}$ and $\mathbf{v}^{(\phi)}$ will be different.

We return now to the question of identifying vortex lines as the intersection of σ and χ surfaces with specific numbers. Obviously, the first requirement is that we have a unique decomposition defined by a certain choice of χ surfaces. Recall that in Section 12.4 we found that the shape of a family of surfaces $\chi = $ const and the numbering system for the surfaces can be chosen separately. Any function $\hat{\chi} = g(\chi)$ simply renumbers the same family of surfaces. Suppose we renumber the surfaces (even in a steady flow we could do this as a function of time). What effect would this have on the decomposition? If $\hat{\chi} = g(\chi)$, then $\nabla\hat{\chi} = g'\nabla\chi$. Substituting into Eq. 17.4.5 reveals that $\hat{\sigma} = (1/g')\sigma$. Thus, surfaces $\sigma = $ const are not the same as surfaces $\hat{\sigma} = $ const. The intersection of the σ and χ surfaces is not the same vortex line as the intersection of the $\hat{\sigma}$ and $\hat{\chi}$ surfaces with the same numbers. The history of a vortex line is ambiguous to this extent. However, even though the σ family is changed to a new set of surfaces by a simple renumbering of the χ surfaces, the vector decomposition remains the same. This is shown by noting that

$$\mathbf{v}^{(\omega)} = \sigma\nabla\chi = \hat{\sigma}\nabla\hat{\chi}$$

A numbering change of the χ surfaces gives the same decomposition but with a new family of σ surfaces and the same set of χ surfaces.

The arbitrariness in following vortex lines noted above is not at odds with Helmholtz's theorem that vortex lines follow the material particles in an inviscid flow. This theorem means only that one is *allowed* to choose the σ and χ surfaces so that an intersection follows the fluid particle [see Sudarshaw and Mukundew (1974) for a proof]. Other choices are also possible. In a steady inviscid flow we might also envision that the vortex lines are fixed in space.

*17.5 CONCLUSIONS

Many different decompositions of the velocity field are possible. The two most widely applied methods have been outlined.

Helmholtz's decomposition has global validity and many nice characteristics. The different components may be expressed as integrals of the kinematic properties of the given velocity field. The potential component $\mathbf{v}^{(\phi)}$ results from integrals of the source distribution $\nabla \cdot \mathbf{v}$, while the vortical component $\mathbf{v}^{(\omega)}$ results from integrals of $\nabla \times \mathbf{v}$. The ambiguity in this decomposition amounts to a harmonic function.

The second decomposition uses Monge's potential functions σ, χ, and ϕ. The potential component $\mathbf{v}^{(\phi)} = \nabla \phi$ is irrotational, but $\nabla \cdot \mathbf{v}^{(\phi)} \neq 0$. Not only does the vortical component $\mathbf{v}^{(\omega)} = \sigma \nabla \chi$ yields the vorticity through $\boldsymbol{\omega} = \nabla \sigma \times \nabla \chi$, but this equation also means that the σ and x surfaces intersect to determine the vortex lines. This physical interpretation is perhaps the most interesting aspect of this decomposition.

*PROBLEMS

17.1 (C) Consider a closed region where $\mathbf{B}$ is given by Eq. 17.2.7. By computing $\nabla \cdot \mathbf{B}$ from Eq. 17.2.7, show that the condition $\nabla \cdot \mathbf{B} = 0$ implies that the following surface integral over the region is zero:

$$0 = \frac{1}{4\pi} \int \frac{\mathbf{n} \cdot \boldsymbol{\omega}'}{|\mathbf{r}|} \, dS'$$

17.2 (B) Consider a square vortex of side L and strength Γ. What is the velocity induced on one side by the other three sides? Are there any singular positions? Would the square vortex remain square?

17.3 (A) A line vortex of strength Γ extends from $x = 0$ to $x = +\infty$. What is the velocity profile as a function of the distance R away from the vortex at the positions $x = +\infty$, $x = 0$, and $x = -\infty$?

17.4 (A) Consider a point in space where the velocity is in the x-direction and the vorticity is at 45° in the x–z plane. For the complex lamellar decomposition, sketch a picture of $\mathbf{v}$, $\boldsymbol{\omega}$, $\mathbf{v}^{(\omega)}$, $\mathbf{v}^{(\phi)}$, and $\mathbf{v} \cdot \boldsymbol{\omega}$ giving arbitrary magnitudes to the vectors. Sketch surfaces σ, χ, and $\phi =$ constant as they go through this point in space.

17.5 (A) Prove that Eq. 17.4.4 follows from Eq. 17.4.1.

17.6 (B) Consider the Monge potentials σ, χ, ϕ in a large region where $\boldsymbol{\omega} = 0$. How does this restrict the functions σ, χ, and ϕ, and what does this imply about $\mathbf{v}^{(\phi)}$ and $\mathbf{v}^{(\omega)}$?

17.7 (B) Consider a symmetric infinite "sheet" of vorticity $\omega_z(y^2)$ (using y^2 to ensure an even function). By noting the symmetry of the Biot–Savart integral, prove that the velocity from this distribution is of the form $u(y)$, $v = 0$, $w = 0$. Assume the potential "stagnation" flow is added; $v = -\alpha y$, $w = \alpha z$. Is the continuity equation still satisfied? Find the vorticity equation governing the flow and show that $\omega = -\omega_0 \exp(-\alpha y^2/2\nu)$ is a steady solution. This is Burgers diffusing vortex sheet intensified by straining and stabilized by a counterflow.

18

Ideal Flows in a Plane

Inviscid flows occur at high Reynolds numbers, UL/ν. The reader may hear it said that inviscid flows are situations where the fluid is frictionless or has zero viscosity. These statements are not meant to be taken literally. The questions is: Does the flow pattern have any significant unbalanced viscous forces? If not, the equations that govern the flow are those obtained by setting $\mu = 0$ in the Navier–Stokes equations. This is completely equivalent to letting the Reynolds number become infinite with a fixed velocity scale U and a fixed length scale L.

Ideal flow is a special type of inviscid flow where the vorticity is zero. The particles in an ideal flow have never experienced an unbalanced shear stress and therefore are not rotating. The pressure and gravity forces that produce the flow cannot induce any particle rotation.

Let us consider some typical situations where ideal flow is a reasonable assumption. As the first example, consider a wing mounted in a uniform airstream. The oncoming flow is without vorticity, and thus the major portion of the flow contains irrotational motion. The vorticity that is generated at the surface of the wing is confined to a thin viscous wake and to two vortices coming from the tips of the wing. A second example is an internal flow where a large reservoir supplies an irrotational flow to a duct or channel. Again the flow keeps the vorticity confined to the walls, and the main flow is an ideal flow. In this case, for any given Reynolds number UD/ν, the duct may become so long that the vorticity diffuses away from the wall to contaminate a significant region of the cross section. When this happens the flow is no longer ideal.

If flow separation occurs, either on an external flow or within an internal flow, a finite portion of the flow is occupied by the wake or recirculation region. Consequently, the flow is no longer completely irrotational. A strict application of the inviscid flow boundary layer theory fails in these cases. Nevertheless, there is a large portion of the flow where the motion remains inviscid and irrotational. The flow in these regions still obeys the ideal-flow equations. Because these equations are elliptic, the wake region exerts an upstream influence. From one viewpoint, the inviscid flow is over an effective body shape, which is the real body plus the influence of the wake. The difficulty with this approach is that the size and shape of the wake are not known beforehand. Several attempts have been made to model such flows with computer solutions. A necessary ingredient is an assumption about the nature of the wake and the way it interacts with the main flow. A general theory of this type does not exist and may not even be possible.

In this chapter we restrict ourselves to the study of unseparated ideal flows. In fact, all the flows will be two-dimensional, a mathematical convenience adopted for simplicity.

The two-dimensional simplification is not critical, as the types of flow patterns we study are also elements of three-dimensional flow patterns.

18.1 PROBLEM FORMULATION FOR PLANE IDEAL FLOWS

Ideal flows are dominated by geometry. The position and shape of the body or the confining walls determines the flow pattern. A solution for the streamlines and the velocity field may be found from the two kinematic requirements that the particles do not rotate (zero vorticity) and that they do not expand (zero divergence). The condition $\omega = 0$ is all that is required mathematically for the existence of a velocity potential. The potential ϕ is defined by

$$v_i = \partial_i \phi \tag{18.1.1}$$

Substituting Eq. 18.1.1 into the second kinematic requirement, $\nabla \cdot \mathbf{v} = 0$, shows that the velocity potential is governed by the Laplace equation,

$$\nabla^2 \phi = 0 \tag{18.1.2}$$

A function that satisfies the Laplace equation is called a *harmonic function*.

Since the flow pattern is determined completely by kinematics, what role does the momentum equation have? The momentum equation can be integrated to yield the pressures. The unsteady form of Bernoulli's equation (see Section 12.6 for a derivation) is

$$\frac{\partial \phi}{\partial t} + \frac{p}{\rho} + \frac{1}{2} \mathbf{v} \cdot \mathbf{v} + gz = C(t) \tag{18.1.3}$$

After the velocity potential is found, everything is known in this equation except the pressure. We might characterize ideal flow by the following statement: In an ideal flow the pressure adjusts itself according to Bernoulli's equation so that the fluid is accelerated to those values of velocity dictated by the geometry of the boundaries.

There is an alternative method of formulating the problem, which applies only to two-dimensional flows, either plane or axisymmetric. The streamfunction, which we studied in Section 12.1, applies to these flows, and it also obeys the Laplace equation

$$\nabla^2 \psi = 0 \tag{18.1.4}$$

Hence, ψ as well as ϕ is a harmonic function. Recall that for a plane flow, the velocity components are related to the streamfunction by

$$u = \frac{\partial \psi}{\partial y}, \qquad v = -\frac{\partial \psi}{\partial x} \tag{18.1.5}$$

Note that Eq. 18.1.4 is again a kinematic condition. It is a simplification of the mathematical identity $\nabla^2 \psi = -\omega_z$.

Most of the analysis we shall do in this chapter uses complex-variable theory, which is a very powerful mathematical method to find solutions of the Laplace equation. Unfortunately, it is restricted to the plane two-dimensional case, where the Laplace equation takes the form

$$\frac{\partial^2 \phi}{\partial x^2} + \frac{\partial^2 \phi}{\partial y^2} = 0, \qquad \frac{\partial^2 \psi}{\partial x^2} + \frac{\partial^2 \psi}{\partial y^2} = 0$$

In the remainder of this section we study the special complex-variable nomenclature that is used in ideal flows.

We begin by letting the physical plane in which the flow occurs be represented by the complex variable z. The relations between z, the Cartesian variables x, y, and the polar coordinates r, θ are

$$z = x + iy = r \exp(i\theta) \tag{18.1.6}$$

Flow properties may be expressed as complex functions of z. For example, the *complex potential* $F = F(z)$ is defined as

$$F = F(z) \equiv \phi(x, y) + i\psi(x, y) \tag{18.1.7}$$

The real part of F is the velocity potential, and the imaginary part is the streamfunction. The motive behind this definition is the fact that any analytic function of a complex variable has real and imaginary parts that are conjugate solutions to the Laplace equation.

As an example, consider the analytic function

$$F = iz^2 = -2xy + i(x^2 - y^2)$$

$$= \phi + i\psi$$

The real part of F, $\phi = -2xy$, and the imaginary part of F, $\psi = x^2 - y^2$, are both harmonic functions and have trajectories of constant ϕ and ψ that are orthogonal.

Calculus operations on an analytic function of a complex variable can be performed using the same rules that one uses for real variables. The derivative of F is known as the *complex velocity*. It is

$$W(z) \equiv \frac{dF}{dz} \tag{18.1.8}$$

The theory of complex variables shows that the derivative is related to the derivatives of the parts by

$$\frac{dF}{dz} = \frac{\partial \phi}{\partial x} + i \frac{\partial \psi}{\partial x} = \frac{\partial \psi}{\partial y} - i \frac{\partial \phi}{\partial y} \tag{18.1.9}$$

Equations 18.1.1 and 18.1.5 show that this relation may be interpreted in terms of the velocity components as

$$W = u - iv = q \exp(-i\alpha) \tag{18.1.10}$$

where q is the magnitude of the velocity and α its angle.

The complex velocity is actually the complex conjugate of the velocity vector. The complex potential and the complex velocity are the essential ideas that relate the flow quantities to the theory of complex variables. In the remainder of this section we point out some of the algebra that is especially useful in the analysis of flows.

The dependent and independent variables in a complex function can be regarded as two-dimensional vectors in a plane. Geometrically, the function $W = W(z)$ is thought of as a mapping or transformation from the z-plane to the W-plane (Fig. 18.1). Each point in the z-plane represents the tip of a vector and has, through the function $W(z)$, an associated point or vector in the W-plane. The physical flow occurs in the z-plane, while the W-plane consists of the velocity vectors.

The complex conjugate of $z = x + iy$ is found by replacing i with $-i$; the complex conjugate of z is $\bar{z} = x - iy$. One of the uses of the complex conjugate is to find the magnitude of the vector. In the case of the velocity, we have that the flow speed q is given by

$$q^2 = W\overline{W} \tag{18.1.11}$$

Another useful mathematical expression is illustrated in Fig. 18.2. Frequently, it is advantageous to work with polar coordinates r, θ. The corresponding velocity components are related to the rectangular components by the equations

$$u = v_r \cos\theta - v_\theta \sin\theta$$
$$v = v_r \sin\theta + v_\theta \cos\theta \tag{18.1.12}$$

To obtain an expression for the complex velocity, substitute these expressions into $W = u - iv$. This yields

$$W = [v_r(r, \theta) - iv_\theta(r, \theta)] \exp(-i\theta) \tag{18.1.13}$$

Working in rectangular coordinates, one finds the velocity components u and v by substituting $z = x + iy$ into $W = W(z)$ and separating the result into its real and imaginary parts. Working in polar coordinates, one substitutes $z = re^{i\theta}$ into $W = W(z)$ and arranges the equation in the form of Eq. 18.1.13. In this form the velocity components v_r and v_θ may be identified.

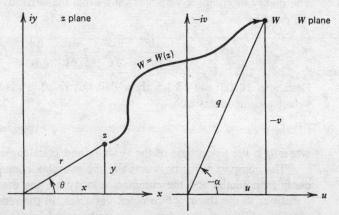

Figure 18.1   Complex function as a mapping from the z-plane to the W-plane. The example shows the complex velocity W as a function of the position in the real plane z.

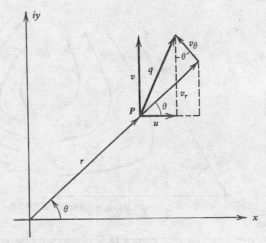

Figure 18.2 Velocity components displayed as a vector at the point P in real space in rectangular and cylindrical coordinates.

18.2 SIMPLE PLANE FLOWS

Since an analytic function represents some ideal flow, we can turn the problem around. Instead of choosing a definite flow geometry to analyze, we look at simple mathematical functions and see if they represent a practical flow situation.

We begin by noting that a complex constant may be added to F without changing the velocities. This fact is a reflection of the fact that ϕ and ψ may have an arbitrary constant added without changing the velocity. The next simplest function to a constant is $F \propto z$. In particular, we let the proportionality constant be a complex number, so that

$$F = [U \exp(-i\alpha)]z \qquad (18.2.1)$$

For this potential, the complex velocity is

$$W = \frac{dF}{dz} = U \exp(-i\alpha) = U \cos \alpha - iU \sin \alpha = u - iv \qquad (18.2.2)$$

and therefore from Eq. 18.1.10 we find that $u = U \cos \alpha$ and $v = U \sin \alpha$. This represents a uniform stream of magnitude U flowing at an angle of attack α with respect to the negative x-axis. The stream moves from left to right.

Next, consider the case where F is a power function of z. Let A and n be real constants, and take

$$F = Az^n \qquad (18.2.3)$$

Realistic flow patterns occur if $n \geq \frac{1}{2}$ (Fig. 18.3). For these flows the complex velocity is

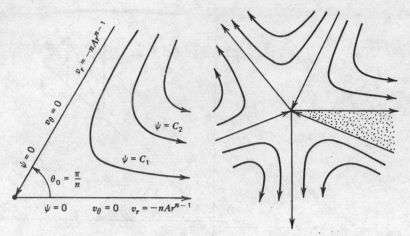

Figure 18.3   Flows with the potential $F = Az^n$.

$$W = \frac{dF}{dz} = nAz^{n-1}$$

It is most convenient to use polar coordinates to interpret this expression; hence, substitute $z = r \exp(i\theta)$ and arrange the result as

$$W = nAr^{n-1} \exp(in\theta) \exp(-i\theta) = nAr^{n-1} (\cos n\theta + i \sin n\theta) \exp(-i\theta)$$

Comparison with Eq. 18.1.13 shows that

$$v_r = nAr^{n-1} \cos n\theta, \qquad v_\theta = -nAr^{n-1} \sin n\theta \qquad (18.2.4)$$

To aid in interpreting this flow pattern, it is useful to have the streamfunction. Expanding Eq. 18.2.3 into polar form and using the definition 18.1.7, we find that

$$\phi = Ar^n \cos n\theta \qquad (18.2.5)$$

$$\psi = Ar^n \sin n\theta \qquad (18.2.6)$$

Equation 18.2.6 shows that ψ will be zero for all values of r on lines from the origin at angles where $\sin n\theta = 0$. These rays are at angles $\theta = k\pi/n$ for integer values of k. Along these radial lines Eq. 18.2.4 shows that $v_\theta = 0$, and since $\cos \pi k = (-1)^k$, the radial velocity is

$$v_r = (-1)^k nAr^{n-1} \qquad (18.2.7)$$

In particular, on the positive x-axis ($k = 0$), Eq. 18.2.7 shows that v_r is positive, indicating an outflow along the x-axis. The next line on which $\psi = 0$ is for $k = 1$, giving $\theta = \pi /n$. Here the flow v_r is negative as it comes toward the origin. The flow within the wedge $\theta = 0$, π/n first comes toward the origin and then flows away along the x-axis. This repetitive pattern may not come out even as we approach $\theta = 2\pi$. The values of W for $\theta = 2\pi$ and $\theta = 0$ are not necessarily the same. For $\theta \geq 2\pi$ we begin a second sheet of the function. By restricting the values of θ to $0 \leq \theta \leq 2\pi$, we have one unique function with a branch cut along $\theta = 0$, 2π; however, the flows at $\theta = 0$ and $\theta = 2\pi$ do not match.

An ideal flow allows the fluid to slip along the wall. In an ideal-flow solution, any streamline in the pattern may be taken to represent a solid wall. Figure 18.4 shows several different choices of walls for the same ideal-flow solution. Figure 18.5 shows some typical interpretations for different values of the parameter n. Two of the most important interpretations are the plane stagnation point where $n = 2$ and the flow over a sharp pointed wedge. In the latter case, the wedge angle is

$$\alpha = 2\pi\frac{n-1}{n} = 2\theta_{1/2} \qquad (18.2.8)$$

We would expect these solutions to be only a local approximation for a region that is a part of a much larger flow. For instance, the sharp wedge might be the most forward portion of a body. The ideal-flow solution for an infinite wedge would be valid for some small neighborhood near the nose of the body.

The corner flows are also local solutions. If any ideal flow has a corner, there is some small region near the corner where only the angle of the corner is important. In this region the local flow corresponds to the solution with $F = Az^n$. A characteristic common to all convex corners is that the velocity becomes infinite and the pressure drops to minus infinity. These flows contain a physically unrealistic singularity at the corner. In an actual flow, viscous regions would exist so that the corner would be rounded out effectively. If a convex corner is very acute, a small separated region within the viscous flow might occur.

Concave corners always have a stagnation point where the velocity is zero and the pressure is the stagnation value. As the flow comes into the corner, the pressure rises. In Chapter 19 we shall find that this situation causes the viscous boundary layer to thicken, and in some cases there may even be a separated region in these corners. If the viscous region is still thin, we can still apply the ideal-flow solution to streamlines that are slightly away from the walls.

We conclude this section with a mathematical observation. It can be proved that the only ideal flow that has a finite velocity over the entire plane is the uniform stream. Note that the wedge-shaped flows, on the other hand, have at least one point with an infinite velocity. At a convex corner the infinite velocity occurs at the corner itself, while at a concave corner the infinite velocity occurs at infinity.

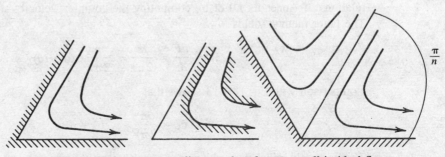

Figure 18.4   Any streamline may be taken as a wall in ideal flow.

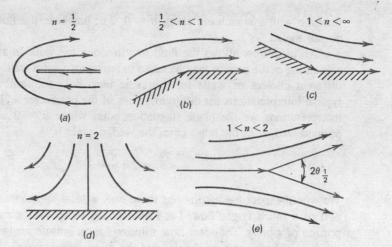

Figure 18.5 Useful values of n: (a) sharp corner; (b) convex corner; (c) concave corner; (d) $n = 2$ two flow segments giving a plane stagnation point; (e) two segments with $1 < n < 2$ giving the flow over a wedge.

18.3 LINE SOURCE AND LINE VORTEX

The complex potential for a line source located at the position $z = z_0$ is

$$F = \frac{m}{2\pi} \ln(z - z_0) \tag{18.3.1}$$

Without loss in generality we shift the origin to $z_0 = 0$ and express the potential in polar form:

$$F = \frac{m}{2\pi} \ln[r \exp(i\theta)] = \frac{m}{2\pi} (\ln r + i\theta) \tag{18.3.2}$$

Hence, by Eq. 18.1.7 we find that

$$\phi = \frac{m}{2\pi} \ln r, \qquad \psi = \frac{m}{2\pi} \theta \tag{18.3.3}$$

The velocity components are found either by differentiating Eq. 18.3.3 (employing the relations of Appendix D) or by computing the complex velocity and using Eq. 18.1.13. The latter method yields

$$W = \frac{dF}{dz} = \frac{m}{2\pi z} = \frac{m}{2\pi r} \exp(-i\theta)$$

Comparison with Eq. 18.1.13 shows that

$$v_r = \frac{m}{2\pi r}, \qquad v_\theta = 0 \tag{18.3.4}$$

This is purely radial flow, either into a sink (when m is negative) or away from a source (when m is positive).

A sketch of the flow appears in Fig. 18.6. The velocity becomes infinite at the origin as $1/r$; hence this point is unrealistic. The strength of the source is given by the constant m. A physical interpretation of m is obtained if we compute the volume flow. Taking any surface around the origin with unit depth, the flow rate is

$$\text{volume flow rate per unit depth} = \int n_i v_i \, dS$$

$$\frac{Q}{L} = \int n_r v_r \, dS = \int_0^{2\pi} \frac{m}{2\pi r} r \, d\theta = m$$

The constant m is the volume flow rate from the source per unit length.

The calculation of the volume flow m can be made in another manner by using Gauss's theorem:

$$m = \int n_i v_i \, dS = \int \partial_i v_i \, dV$$

In incompressible flow, $\nabla + \mathbf{v} = 0$, so the fact that the volume integral is not zero means that this condition is not met throughout the entire flow. The singularity in $\mathbf{v}$ at the origin is a source of zero diameter. At that point the flow does not obey the condition $\nabla \cdot \mathbf{v} = 0$.

The ideal line vortex is very similar in mathematical form to the source. It is complex potential is also the logarithmic function, but with an imaginary constant:

$$F = -i\,\frac{1}{2\pi}\ln(z - z_0) \tag{18.3.5}$$

The velocity components for this potential turn out to be

$$v_r = 0, \qquad v_\theta = \frac{\Gamma}{2\pi r} \tag{18.3.6}$$

This flow swirls in a counterclockwise direction for positive Γ and decreases in magnitude as $1/r$—the same type of decrease observed for the source.

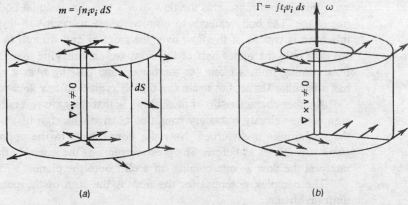

Figure 18.6   Singularities in ideal flow: (*a*) line source; (*b*) line vortex.

Again the origin has an infinite velocity, so we must exclude that point from any realistic flow. In a real vortex, the core velocity drops to zero through a viscous region where the vorticity is nonzero, a fact that was noted previously.

The strength of a vortex is given by the circulation Γ. The circulation was defined (Eq. 3.12.7) to be the counterclockwise line integral of the tangential velocity component around a closed path.

$$\Gamma \equiv \oint t_i v_i \, ds \qquad (18.3.7)$$

Recall that the circulation and the fluid vorticity are connected by an important integral relation. If Stokes's theorem is applied to Eq. 18.3.7, we find that

$$\Gamma \equiv \oint_C t_i v_i \, ds = \int_S n_i \omega_i \, dS \qquad (18.3.8)$$

In this expression, S is any simple surface bounded by the closed path C. For any circuit within a regular inviscid flow, $\omega = 0$, and hence $\Gamma = 0$. For the vortex, since Γ is not zero, there is some point in the flow (in this case, the origin) where the vorticity is not zero. The vorticity goes to infinity at the origin in such a way that the integral of Eq. 18.3.8 over the surface has a finite value.

Ideal flows satisfy the two kinematic conditions of no expansion ($\nabla \cdot \mathbf{v} = 0$) and no particle rotation ($\boldsymbol{\omega} = \nabla \times \mathbf{v} = 0$). A source is a flow that violates the first condition at one point, while a vortex is a flow that violates the second condition. These flows are the two basic types of singularities.

18.4   FLOW OVER A NOSE OR A CLIFF

The equations and boundary conditions that govern ϕ, ψ, and v_i in ideal flows are linear. Thus, potential, streamfunctions, and velocities for two flows may be added together to produce a new flow pattern. In the present example we take a source of strength m and add a uniform stream. This addition will result in the flow pattern shown in Fig. 18.7. If we take the streamline that divides the source flow from the streamflow as a solid wall, this pattern represents the flow over a two-dimensional body with a certain stream-line shape. The body extends to infinity, where it has a half-thickness h. The flow over this nose is typical of the flow over the front of any smooth two-dimensional object. If we take only the upper half of the flow, we can imagine that the pattern represents the flow coming from a plane (or the ocean) and passing over a cliff. Of course, the cliff has a peculiar shape, but again the flow is typical of any such shape.

Another characteristic of ideal flows is that they are reversible. Simply changing the sign of the velocity boundary condition changes the sign of all velocities while leaving the magnitudes undisturbed. Now the flow travels in the opposite direction along the same streamlines as before. The pressure remains the same. In the present case we could interpret the flow as one coming off a cliff onto the plane.

The complex potential for the flow is the sum of the potentials for a source and uniform stream:

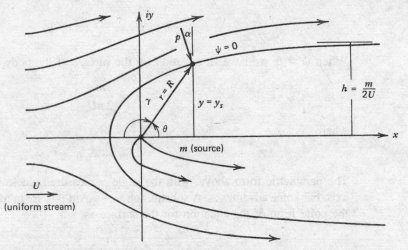

Figure 18.7   Flow over a nose or a cliff: a source in a uniform stream.

$$F = Uz + \frac{m}{2\pi} \ln z + iC \qquad (18.4.1)$$

A constant iC has been included so that we may adjust the zero of the streamfunction to correspond to the streamline separating the source and stream flows. A real constant could be included to adjust the velocity potential, but we have no need to do this. By direct calculation from Eq. 18.4.1, or by adding the results of Sections 18.3 and 18.4, we find that the streamfunction is

$$\psi = Uy + \frac{m}{2\pi} \theta + C \qquad (18.4.2)$$

The complex velocity for this flow is the derivative of Eq. 18.4.1,

$$W = \frac{dF}{dz} = U + \frac{m}{2\pi z} \qquad (18.4.3)$$

Any stagnation point will have $W = 0$, so from Eq. 18.4.3 we have one such point located at

$$z = -\frac{m}{2\pi U} \qquad (18.4.4)$$

$$x = -\frac{m}{2\pi U}, \qquad y = 0$$

This is the point on the negative x-axis where the velocity of the stream U is exactly balanced by the velocity of the source, $m/2\pi x$.

The streamline through the stagnation point is adjusted to zero by substituting $y = 0$, $\theta = \pi$, $\psi = 0$ into Eq. 18.4.2. This gives $C = -m/2$, and the streamfunction equation becomes

$$\psi = Uy - \frac{m}{2\pi}(\pi - \theta) \tag{18.4.5}$$

When $\psi = 0$, we have an equation for the surface of the body,

$$y_s = \frac{m}{2\pi U}\gamma \tag{18.4.6}$$

where

$$\gamma \equiv \pi - \theta \tag{18.4.7}$$

The parametric form above, with the angle γ measured clockwise from the negative x-axis, has some advantages. A substitution $y_s = R \sin \theta = R \sin \gamma$ into Eq. 18.4.6 produces the polar form of the equation for the surface as

$$R = \frac{m}{2\pi U}\frac{\gamma}{\sin \gamma} \tag{18.4.8}$$

From Eq. 18.4.6 we determine the half-width of the body by setting $\gamma = \pi$. The result is

$$h = \frac{m}{2U} \tag{18.4.9}$$

The point on the surface directly above the origin ($\gamma = \pi/2$) has $y_s = m/4U$; the surface has risen to one-half its final height.

One of the things we want to investigate is the pressure distribution over the surface and the drag it might produce—a sort of frontal drag typical of such bodies. We begin by finding the speed q from Eq. 18.4.3:

$$q^2 = W\overline{W} = \left(U + \frac{m}{2\pi z}\right)\left(U + \frac{m}{2\pi \bar{z}}\right)$$

Simplifying and inserting $z = -r\exp(-i\gamma)$ produces

$$q^2 = U^2 - \frac{mU}{\pi r}\cos \gamma + \left(\frac{m}{2\pi}\right)^2\frac{1}{r^2} \tag{18.4.10}$$

To obtain the surface velocity, set $r = R$ and introduce Eq. 18.4.8:

$$q_s^2 = U^2\left(1 - \frac{2}{\gamma}\sin \gamma \cos \gamma + \frac{1}{\gamma^2}\sin^2 \gamma\right) \tag{18.4.11}$$

This form is suitable for computing the pressure.

The Bernoulli equation for steady flow is

$$p + \tfrac{1}{2}\rho q^2 = p_\infty + \tfrac{1}{2}\rho U^2 \tag{18.4.12}$$

In ideal flow it is more or less natural to refer the pressure to the value at infinity; recall that the level of all pressures in an incompressible flow increases directly with the reference pressure. The natural scale for the pressure is the dynamic pressure. Hence, the nondimensional pressure or *pressure coefficient* (also known as the *Euler number*) is defined as

$$C_p \equiv \frac{p - p_\infty}{\frac{1}{2}\rho U^2} \qquad (18.4.13)$$

Inserting the Bernoulli equation into this definition results in the simple formula

$$C_p = 1 - \frac{q^2}{U^2} \qquad (18.4.14)$$

Substituting Eq. 18.4.11 gives the equation for the surface pressures:

$$C_p = \frac{2}{\gamma} \sin \gamma \cos \gamma - \frac{1}{\gamma^2} \sin^2 \gamma \qquad (18.4.15)$$

A special subscript for the surface is not used, as most of the time we use C_p only as a surface quantity. In Eq. 18.4.15, C_p is expressed as a function of the angle γ. This is not really the best form.

In boundary layer theory the distance along the body surface is a natural coordinate. Figure 18.8 shows the geometry for computing s, the distance coordinate along the surface. The triangle pictured shows that

$$(ds)^2 = (R \, d\gamma)^2 + (dR)^2 \qquad (18.4.16)$$

R is eliminated in favor of γ by employing Eq. 18.4.8. Additional algebra leads to

$$ds = \frac{h}{\pi \sin^2 \gamma} (\gamma^2 - 2\gamma \sin \gamma \cos \gamma + \sin^2 \gamma)^{1/2} \, d\gamma \qquad (18.4.17)$$

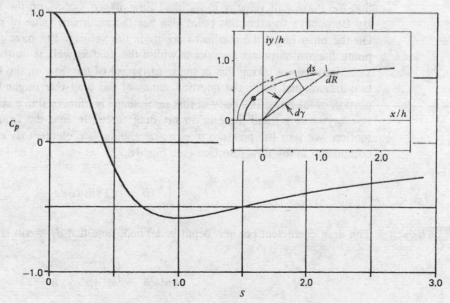

Figure 18.8 Pressure distribution on a smooth nose.

Integration of this expression produces $s = s(\gamma)$, which, together with $C_p = C_p(\gamma)$ from Eq. 18.4.15, allows one to plot $C_p(s)$ as in Fig. 18.8. The graph shown was obtained by using a computer to integrate Eq. 18.4.17

At the nose of the body, or at the base of the cliff, the stagnation pressure occurs and $C_p = 1$ results. Because of symmetry, the slope of the curve at the stagnation point is zero. As we move around the body, the fluid accelerates rapidly and the pressure drops accordingly. The velocity becomes equal to the free-stream velocity at $s = 0.42h$ ($\gamma = 1.17$ rad, $67°$). This point is noted in Fig. 18.8; it marks the end of the region where pressures are higher than p_∞. The fluid continues to accelerate and C_p continues to drop. A minimum is reached at about $s = 0.98h$ ($\gamma = 2.04$), where $C_p = -0.585$. The corresponding maximum surface speed is $q_{max} = 1.26U$. This low-pressure region continues and as $s \rightarrow \infty$ we approach p_∞ from below.

It is easy to use streamline patterns to surmise the trends in the pressure. Pressure change results from two effects: streamline convergence and streamline curvature. Converging streamlines indicate an increasing velocity and thus a decreasing pressure. Diverging streamlines, as in the region of the stagnation point, indicate an increasing pressure. Streamline curvature indicates a low pressure toward the center of curvature and a higher pressure toward the outside. The concave curvature near the shoulder of the body indicates a low pressure in this region.

The pressure and velocity patterns on this body are typical of patterns on the nose of any well-rounded body. The velocity around the shoulders always increases above the free-stream value, and the pressure always decreases below the free-stream value. The maximum and minimum values depend somewhat on the exact contour of the surface, but the trend is always the same.

It is a general mathematical result that solutions of the Laplace equation have maximum and minimum values on the boundaries. Starting with this fact, it may be proved that the maximum velocity in an ideal flow always occurs on the surface of the body. By Bernoulli's theorem this point also has the minimum value of pressure in the flow. On the other hand, the smallest magnitude the velocity can have is zero, a stagnation point. Stagnation points may occur within the fluid as well as on the surface of a body.

Since we are taking this example as typical of the flow on the forward portion of a two-dimensional body, the question arises of the drag that might be attributed to this portion of the body. If a body of this same shape is immersed in a still fluid, the pressure is everywhere p_∞ and there is no net drag force. To find the frontal drag due to the motion, we take the pressure $p - p_\infty$ on the surface element ds and resolve it into a component in the flow direction (see Fig. 18.7),

$$F_D = \int_0^\infty (p - p_\infty) \sin \alpha \, ds$$

The drag coefficient per unit depth is defined (note that $dy = \sin \alpha \, ds$) as

$$C_D \equiv \frac{F_D}{\frac{1}{2}\rho U^2 h} = \int_0^h \frac{p - p_\infty}{\frac{1}{2}\rho U^2} \frac{dy}{h} \tag{18.4.18}$$

Substituting Eqs. 18.4.6, 18.4.8, and 18.4.15 into this integral gives

$$C_D = \frac{1}{2} \int_0^\pi \left[\left(\frac{2}{\gamma} \cos\gamma \sin\gamma - \frac{1}{\gamma^2} \sin^2\gamma \right) d\gamma \right.$$

$$= \frac{1}{2} \int_0^\pi d(\gamma^{-1} \sin^2\gamma) = \frac{1}{2} (\gamma^{-1} \sin^2\gamma)_0^\pi = 0 \qquad (18.4.19)$$

Applying L'Hôpital's rule to this indeterminate form shows that the drag is zero. The drag force caused by the high pressure at the front of the body is exactly canceled out by the thrust force on the shoulders, where the pressure is less than the free-stream value. The fact that the frontal drag on a smooth slender body in ideal flow is zero is a striking result. It is valid for any smooth-shaped body; we could simulate any shape by placing sources and sinks at several positions along the x-axis, and the same zero-drag result would come out.

Our calculation has been made for a body that extends to infinity. Let us consider how this result might appear for a long slender body of finite length. We might guess that far away from the nose the pressure returns to nearly the free-stream value. At some distance downstream we may suppose that the body is terminated and has a blunt base. If the pressure in the base region is p_∞, the result above will apply and the drag force will be zero. Unfortunately, our guess that the base pressure is nearly equal to the free-stream pressure is not true. If the body has a blunt base, the flow separates and a turbulent wake is formed. The base pressure is usually fairly uniform but lower than the free-stream pressure. Hence, actual slender bodies have a finite drag, which is almost solely the result of the base drag, the frontal drag being negligible.

Since ideal flows are reversible, why don't we change the sign of the flow and consider that the pattern represents the flow at the end of a slender body? The body contour would end with the same shape as the previous nose shape. The reason this cannot be done is that the flow would need to penetrate a high-pressure region at the rear stagnation point. The ideal flow can in principle do this, but the boundary layer cannot. The particles in the boundary layer have been slowed down by wall friction and do not have sufficient momentum to move against the high-pressure gradient. The flow separates and once again we have a base region, which produces a drag force.

Separation at the rear of a body can be delayed if we decrease the height very slowly and form a sharp point at the end. Most airfoils have this shape. The slowly decreasing thickness allows the pressure to rise slowly, and more important, the streams from the upper and lower sides may merge smoothly without decreasing to zero velocity (the stagnation point is submerged within the viscous boundary layers). Shapes made in this way can have very low drag coefficients: Measured values less than $C_D = 0.1$ (based on the cross section) are not uncommon for airfoil shapes.

The zero-frontal-drag principle does not apply to shapes with sharp corners such as those shown in Fig. 18.9. When the flow separates from the shoulders, we lose the low-pressure region that provides the suction force. As a result, the high-pressure region at the nose is not counterbalanced, and the body has a substantial frontal drag. Separation always occurs if the surface has a sharp corner and is common for bodies with sharp curvature near the shoulders.

Even very smooth bodies have a region of increasing pressure once the minimum has been reached (recall Fig. 18.8). The increasing pressure is a likely candidate for

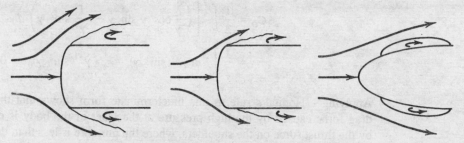

Figure 18.9 Nose drag occurs when flow separates from the sides. The last frame shows a separation bubble on a smooth nose. The size of the bubble is exaggerated.

separation, depending on the state of the boundary layer. In many cases the flow separates and then reattaches without forming a wake. Such regions are called *separation bubbles* and are very thin. We have exaggerated the thickness in the sketch so that the bubble may be seen. As far as the drag is concerned, this type of separation has a negligible effect.

18.5   DOUBLETS

The line source and line vortex are two types of singular points in the flow where the velocity is infinite and one of the kinematic conditions, either $\nabla \cdot \mathbf{v} = 0$ or $\nabla \times \mathbf{v} = 0$, is violated. There are other types of singular points that satisfy the Laplace equation everywhere except at one point. The singularity we treat in this section is called a *doublet*. Perhaps the most enlightening way to introduce the doublet is to consider it as the superposition of a source and a sink that are brought close together. Let a source of strength m be located on the negative x-axis at a point ε away from the origin, as shown in Fig. 18.10. The complex potential for the source is

$$F = \frac{m}{2\pi} \ln(z + \varepsilon)$$

Next, a sink of equal strength: m is placed at a position ε on the positive x-axis. For this combination of a source and a sink, the potential is

$$F = \frac{m}{2\pi} \ln \frac{z + \varepsilon}{z - \varepsilon}$$

$$F = \frac{m}{2\pi} \ln \frac{1 + \varepsilon/z}{1 - \varepsilon/z} = \frac{m}{2\pi} \ln \left[\left(1 + \frac{\varepsilon}{z} \right) \left(1 - \frac{\varepsilon}{z} \right)^{-1} \right]$$

(18.5.1)

As the source and sink come close together, ε becomes small. The binomial expansion (Eq. 15.2.8) says that for $\varepsilon \to 0$,

$$\left(1 - \frac{\varepsilon}{z} \right)^{-1} = 1 + \frac{\varepsilon}{z} + O\left[\left(\frac{\varepsilon}{z} \right)^2 \right]$$

Inserting this expression in Eq. 18.5.1 gives

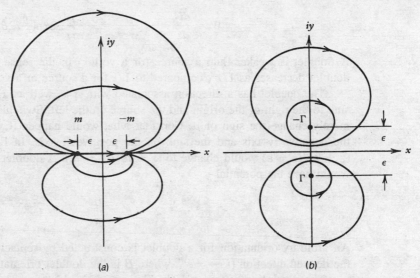

Figure 18.10 Doublet as the limit of (a) source + sink, $\varepsilon \rightarrow 0$, $m\varepsilon = \mu$; and (b) vortices on y axis, $\varepsilon \rightarrow 0$, $\Gamma\varepsilon = \mu$.

$$F = \frac{m}{2\pi} \ln \left\{ 1 + 2\frac{\varepsilon}{z} + O\left[\left(\frac{\varepsilon}{z}\right)^2\right] \right\}$$

Next, note that for small x the following expansion of $\ln x$ is valid:

$$\ln x = (x - 1) - \tfrac{1}{2}(x - 1)^2 + \cdots$$

Using this expansion results in the following relation for F:

$$F = \frac{m\varepsilon}{\pi z} + O\left(\frac{\varepsilon}{z}\right)^2$$

If we allow the source and sink to approach each other ($\varepsilon \rightarrow 0$) with a constant strength m, the result is $F = 0$; they swallow each other. However, suppose instead that as the source and sink approach each other their strengths m are increased in such a way that the product $m\varepsilon = \mu$ is a constant. The constant μ is called the *strength* of the doublet. The complex potential for a doublet is

$$F = \frac{\mu}{\pi z} \tag{18.5.}$$

One can show that the streamlines for a doublet are circles through the origin given by the equation

$$x^2 + \left(y + \frac{\mu}{2\pi\psi}\right)^2 = \left(\frac{\mu}{2\pi\psi}\right)^2 \tag{18.5.3}$$

The centers of the circles are at $y = \pm\mu/2\pi\psi$. Figure 18.10a shows the pattern.

From Eq. 18.5.2 the complex velocity is found to be

$$W = \frac{dF}{dz} = -\frac{\mu}{\pi z^2} = -\frac{\mu}{\pi r^2} \exp(-i2\theta) \qquad (18.5.4)$$

A doublet is weaker than a source (or a vortex) in the sense that the velocity of the doublet decreases as $1/r^2$, compared to $1/r$ for a source or a vortex.

The doublet has a direction associated with it as well as a strength. We placed the sink to the right of the origin and the source on the left. Switching these positions would merely change the sign of μ. Consider what would happen if we placed the source on the negative iy-axis and the sink on the positive iy-axis. In Eq. 18.5.1, the argument $(z + \varepsilon)/(z - \varepsilon)$ would change to $(z + i\varepsilon)/(z - i\varepsilon)$. A doublet aligned with the iy-axis would have the potential

$$F = \frac{i\mu}{\pi z} \qquad (18.5.5)$$

An arbitrary orientation for a doublet is constructed by replacing i by a unit vector in the desired direction ($i \rightarrow -e^{i\beta}$, where β is the doublet orientation).

The streamline pattern of a doublet was derived by considering a source and a sink brought together while the strength increased in such a way that $m\varepsilon = \mu$ was a constant. There is another physical interpretation of a doublet that is equally as valid. A doublet may be considered by merging two line vortices of opposite circulation in such a way that the strength times the separation distance, $\varepsilon\Gamma$, is a constant. If we place the vortices on the positive and negative axes, the doublet is aligned with the iy-axis, that is, Eq. 18.5.5 results. A vortex doublet is the same as a source–sink doublet turned through 90°.

From a mathematical standpoint the source and the vortex are the strongest singularities; they have potentials proportional to $\ln z$. The doublet is mathematically the derivative of the source of the vortex, having a potential $\propto 1/z$. One may continue this process and form higher-order singularities. The next singularity is constructed from a source–sink combination on the x-axis paired with another on the iy-axis. This is called a *quadrupole singularity*. In the same nomenclature sources and vortices are known as *monopole singularities,* and the doublet is called a *dipole singularity.* We have very little use in fluid mechanics for the quadrupole and higher singularities.

18.6 CYLINDER IN A STREAM

The ideal flow of a uniform stream perpendicular to the axis of a circular cylinder is given by the superposition of a doublet and a stream. The potential is

$$F = Uz + U\frac{r_0^2}{z} \qquad (18.6.1)$$

The doublet strength is taken as $\mu = \pi U r_0^2$, where r_0 is the radius of the circle. Computing the complex velocity gives

$$W = U - U\frac{r_0^2}{z^2} \qquad (18.6.2)$$

Setting Eq. 18.6.2 equal to zero shows that stagnation points are located at $z = \pm r_0$; that is, $x = \pm r_0$, $y = 0$. These are the most forward-and-aft points on the cylinder. With a little further algebra the velocity components may be found. With the use of cylindrical coordinates we have

$$W = U\left[1 - \frac{r_0^2}{r^2}\exp(-i2\theta)\right] = U\left[\exp(i\theta) - \frac{r_0^2}{r^2}\exp(-i\theta)\right]\exp(-i\theta)$$

$$= U\left[\left(1 - \frac{r_0^2}{r^2}\right)\cos\theta + i\left(1 + \frac{r_0^2}{r^2}\right)\sin\theta\right]\exp(-i\theta)$$

Comparing this form with Eq. 18.1.13 shows that the velocity components are

$$v_r = U\left(1 - \frac{r_0^2}{r^2}\right)\cos\theta, \qquad v_\theta = -U\left(1 + \frac{r_0^2}{r^2}\right)\sin\theta \qquad (18.6.3)$$

On the cylinder surface $r = r_0$ these equations show that $v_r = 0$, and hence

$$q = v_\theta = -2U\sin\theta \qquad (18.6.4)$$

The velocity at the shoulder of the cylinder is twice the free-stream value.

Figure 18.11 shows the pattern of streamlines for this flow. We disregard the doublet flow on the inside of the circle $r = r_0$ and imagine that a solid cylinder replaces this portion of the flow. A remarkable feature is the symmetry of the flow upstream and downstream of the cylinder. The symmetry of the geometry results in a symmetry of the streamlines.

The pressure force on the surface of the cylinder is obtained by substituting Eqs. 18.6.4 into 18.4.13:

$$C_p = \frac{p - p_\infty}{\frac{1}{2}\rho U^2} = 1 - \left(\frac{q}{U}\right)^2 = 1 - 4\sin^2\theta \qquad (18.6.5)$$

A plot of this function is given in Fig. 18.11. At the forward-and-aft stagnation points $C_p = 1$. At the maximum-thickness point, the point where $q = -2U$, we find that the pressure has dropped to $C_p = -3$, which is three dynamic pressure units lower than atmospheric pressure. The pressure distribution has a pattern similar to that found for flow over a rounded nose shape in Section 18.4: high pressure at the stagnation region followed by low pressure at the shoulder of the body. For the nose the minimum value of C_p was -0.585, whereas for the cylinder the lowest value is -3. If we compute the drag, we find that because of the symmetric pressure distribution, the force on the front half cancels that on the rear half to produce zero drag.

The ideal flow about a cylinder is not a realistic solution (although we shall find an important use for this solution in connection with the flow over airfoils). As discussed in Chapter 14, the flow at a high Reynolds number always separates on the sides of the cylinder. Nevertheless, the solution does give reasonable results for the front portion of the cylinder in the neighborhood of the stagnation region. From Fig. 18.11 we can see that the actual surface pressures and the ideal values given by Eq. 18.6.5 agree for a distance up to $\gamma \approx 60°$. Thereafter the separated wake flow causes a drastic change in the main flow, so the ideal solution is no longer valid.

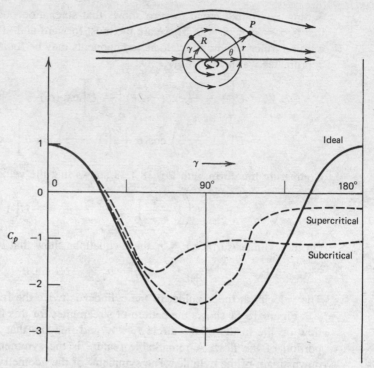

Figure 18.11 Pressure coefficient for streaming flow over a cylinder. Typical experimental trends for subcritical and supercritical Reynolds numbers are shown. After Goldstein (1965).

18.7 CYLINDER WITH CIRCULATION IN A UNIFORM STREAM

The flow discussed in Section 18.6 is not a unique solution. We can construct other ideal-flow solutions that also represent the flow on the outside of a cylinder. Consider the flow given by the potential

$$F = Uz + U\frac{r_0^2}{z} - \frac{i\Gamma}{2\pi}\ln\frac{z}{r_0} \tag{18.7.1}$$

This potential is the superposition of a uniform stream, a doublet, and a vortex of strength Γ. An imaginary constant $(i\Gamma \ln r_0)/2\pi$ has been incorporated into the potential so that the streamline on the surface of the cylinder remains the $\psi = 0$ streamline.

The addition of the vortex changes the flow pattern everywhere except at the surface of the cylinder and at infinity. That is, the streamline that represents the cylinder is still a circle; the values of the surface velocity are, of course, changed. Figure 18.12 shows several flow patterns for different values of the circulation constant. Note that the circulation constant has been changed to $\Gamma_a = -\Gamma$. It will turn out that this flow is relevant to the flow about wings and airfoils. Aeronautical engineers, in order to make the lift on an airfoil positive, define Γ as the negative of the definition given previously. Let us compute the complex velocity from Eq. 18.7.1 and insert $\Gamma = -\Gamma_a$. The result is

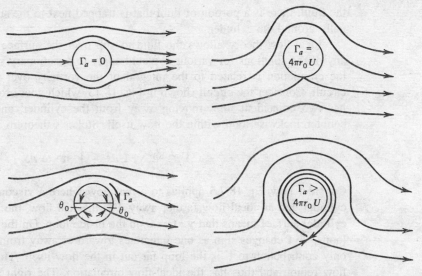

Figure 18.12   Nonuniqueness of flow over a cylinder. The circulation constant Γ_a must be specified to determine a unique flow.

$$W = \frac{dF}{dz} = U - U \frac{r_0^2}{z^2} + i \frac{\Gamma_a}{2\pi z} \qquad (18.7.2)$$

Since we may assign any value we choose to Γ_a, there are an infinite number of ideal flows for the streaming motion over a cylinder.

The velocity components v_r, v_θ are found by putting $z = r \exp(i\theta)$ into Eq. 18.7.2 and organizing the equation in the form of Eq. 18.1.13. When this is done, the components are found to be

$$v_r = U\left(1 - \frac{r_0^2}{r^2}\right) \cos \theta, \qquad v_\theta = -U\left(1 + \frac{r_0^2}{r^2}\right) \sin \theta - \frac{\Gamma_a}{2\pi r} \qquad (18.7.3)$$

The vortex only affects v_θ.

Stagnation points on the cylinder are located by setting $r = r_0$ and $v_\theta = 0$. The result is an equation for the θ_0 location of the stagnation points,

$$\sin \theta_0 = -\frac{\Gamma_a}{4\pi r_0 U} \qquad (18.7.4)$$

Without any circulation, the stagnation points are symmetrical at $\theta_0 = 0, 2\pi$, as we noted in Section 18.6. When Γ_a is less than $4\pi r_0 U$, the right side of Eq. 18.7.4 will be negative number smaller than 1. This results in stagnation points on the lower portion of the cylinder as shown in Fig. 18.12. In the case where $\Gamma_a > 4\pi r_0 U$, the stagnation points cannot be found from Eq. 18.7.4. In this case a single stagnation point moves away from the surface of the cylinder and occurs within the flow. If the stagnation point is within the fluid, there is a portion of fluid that is trapped next to the surface and rotates continually around the cylinder.

Ideal-flow theory allows the fluid to slip over the surface of a body. In principle, any of the solutions for various Γ would apply to a stationary solid cylinder. Recall that the circulation is related to the integral of the vorticity over an area enclosed by the circuit. Consider the circuit shown in Fig. 18.13, which goes around the cylinder surface, has two coincident lines moving away from the cylinder, and is finally closed by a counterclockwise loop within the flow itself. Stokes's theorem says that

$$\Gamma = \oint_C \mathbf{v} \cdot \mathbf{t} \, ds = \int_A \mathbf{n} \cdot \boldsymbol{\omega} \, dS \tag{18.7.5}$$

Consider how Eq. 18.7.5 applies to a real flow where a viscous region occurs near the cylinder and an ideal flow farther away. For the real flow, the nonslip condition on the cylinder surface means that $\mathbf{v} \cdot \mathbf{t} = 0$ on the inside loop. On the lines connecting the two loops, $\mathbf{v} \cdot \mathbf{t}$ changes sign as one integrates toward or away from the cylinder. Hence, the only contribution to Γ is the loop far out in the flow itself. This loop is in an inviscid-flow region and thus has the ideal-flow circulation. The right side of Eq. 18.7.5 is the area integral of the normal vorticity component. Since the vorticity is nonzero only in the boundary layers next to the surface, we see that the circulation constant of the ideal flow is in fact determined by the vorticity distribution in the boundary layers. Therefore, the particular value of Γ and the associated ideal flow are determined by an integrated effect from the viscous flow near the body.

18.8   LIFT AND DRAG ON TWO-DIMENSIONAL SHAPES

The ideal lift and drag force on any cylindrical body, no matter what the cross-section shape, can be related to the complex potential. From a practical standpoint, we might as well limit our thoughts to cylinders with an airfoil shape. Any bluff shape would have a wake of finite thickness, and this would invalidate the theory. The entire flow must be an ideal flow for this theory to apply. Boundary layers and wakes must be vanishingly thin.

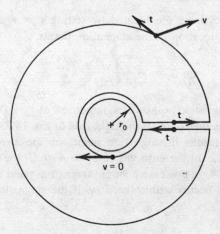

Figure 18.13 Circulation–integral circuit for flow over a cylinder.

It will turn out that the drag force is always zero and that the lift force is directly proportional to the circulation constant Γ_a. The exact relation for the lift force is

$$F_L = \rho U \Gamma_a \qquad (18.8.1)$$

This equation is called the *Kutta–Joukowski law* after the two people who discovered it independently.

To prove the statements above, consider a body of arbitrary cross section as shown in Fig. 18.14. The flow around this body is an ideal flow without any separation. Hence, the viscous forces are zero and the pressure force on the body may be divided into a lift component and a drag component. For an increment of area *ds* these components are

$$dF_L = p\ dx \qquad (18.8.2)$$

$$dF_D = -p\ dy$$

We know from Chapter 16 that the pressure is constant across a boundary layer. This means that we shall get the proper lift and drag components that arise from the pressure forces if the ideal-flow values are used in Eq. 18.8.2.

Next, form a complex vector for the conjugate of the force on the cylinder. It is

$$d(F_D - iF_L) = -p\ dy - ip\ dx = -ip\ d\bar{z} \qquad (18.8.3)$$

Integration of this expression around the contour in a counterclockwise manner will yield an expression for the total lift and drag. In this integration the pressure on the surface may be evaluated using Bernoulli's equation:

$$p = p_0 - \tfrac{1}{2}\rho q^2 = p_0 - \tfrac{1}{2}\rho W \overline{W}$$

$$= p_0 - \frac{1}{2}\rho \frac{dF}{dz}\frac{d\overline{F}}{d\bar{z}}$$

Substituting this into Eq. 18.8.3 yields

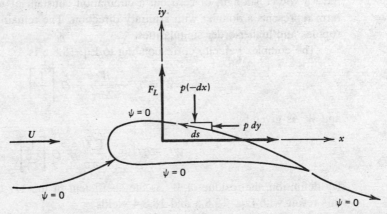

Figure 18.14   Lift and drag forces defined with respect to the flow direction at infinity. Ideal flow: $F_D = 0$, $F_L = \rho U \Gamma_a$.

$$d(F_D - iF_L) = -ip_0 \, d\bar{z} + \frac{1}{2} i\rho \frac{dF}{dz} \, d\bar{F}$$

The surface contour C is a streamline $\psi = $ const, and since $F = \phi + i\psi$, it follows that $dF = d\phi$ is real, and $d\bar{F} = dF$. Inserting this fact and noting that the integral of the constant p_0 around a closed contour is zero, we have the equation

$$F_D - iF_L = i\frac{\rho}{2} \int_C \left(\frac{dF}{dz}\right)^2 dz = i\frac{\rho}{2} \int_C W^2 \, dz \qquad (18.8.4)$$

This formula is known as the *theorem of Blasius*. The restriction of Eq. 18.8.4 to a contour on the surface of the body may be relaxed. Complex-variable theory shows that any contour of an analytic function gives the same answer as long as it loops around the same singular points of the function. If W has no singularities (sources, vortices, doublets, etc.) outside the cylinder, the contour may be enlarged to $z \rightarrow \infty$ without difficulty. Since streaming motions around airfoils are of this type, we can use a contour at infinity to evaluate the lift and drag.

Contour integrals of analytic functions are most easily evaluated by using the residue theorem, which states that

$$\int_C W^2 \, dz = 2\pi i \sum_k R_k \qquad (18.8.5)$$

where R_k are the residues of the function W^2. Residues are given by a Laurent expansion of the function. Any streaming motion must have a complex potential of the following form as $z \rightarrow \infty$:

$$F = Uz + \frac{1}{2\pi} (m + i\Gamma_a) \ln z + (a + ib) \frac{1}{z} + \cdots \qquad (18.8.6)$$

The first term is a streaming motion aligned with the x-axis. This orientation was chosen because the definitions of lift and drag are made with respect to the flow direction, and the formulation Eq. 18.8.4 implies that the stream is aligned in this way. The second term contains a source of strength m and a vortex of strength Γ. (A closed body would have a source strength of zero but a circulation constant of unknown value.) The next term represents a doublet with arbitrary direction. The remaining terms would be quadrupoles and higher-order singularities.

The complex velocity corresponding to Eq. 18.8.6 is

$$W = U + \frac{i\Gamma_a}{2\pi z} + O\left[\frac{1}{z^2}\right]$$

and W^2 is given by

$$W^2 = U^2 + i\frac{\Gamma_a U}{\pi z} + O\left[\frac{1}{z^2}\right]$$

By definition, the residue of W^2 is the coefficient of the $1/z$ term, $i\Gamma_a U/\pi$. Combining this result with Eqs. 18.8.5 and 18.8.4 yields

$$F_D = 0 \tag{18.8.7}$$

$$F_L = \rho U \Gamma_a \tag{18.8.8}$$

The first of these equations states that any airfoil has a zero drag force. The second relation shows that the lift force increases directly as the circulation increases. This formula is a little misleading in that the circulation around an airfoil is not just a function of the size and shape, but it also increases directly with the free-stream velocity. Hence, F_L is actually proportional to U^2. Equation 18.8.8 is very important in that it points out that lift can only result from a flow that has a circulation, or vortexlike behavior, in the far field away from the body.

The prediction of zero-pressure drag for a two-dimensional airfoil shape is fairly accurate. The drag of actual streamline shapes is very small and is largely caused by the viscous friction on the surface. One thing that we should take warning of is the fact that Eq. 18.8.7 applies strictly to unseparated flow about airfoil shapes that are infinitely long. This equation does not apply to shapes that are finite in length, such as an actual wing or fan blade. A finite-length wing, even in ideal theory, has a drag force caused by the pressure. This extra drag is called the *induced drag*. We consider it in Section 19.11.

The Kutta–Joukowski formula shows that the circulation Γ_a is the most important property of the flow in determining the lift. Recall the result of Section 18.7 concerning circular cylinders: There was no unique answer until we specified a value for Γ_a. Choosing Γ_a determines a specific flow pattern and at the same time establishes the value of the lift through the Kutta–Joukowski law.

18.9 MAGNUS EFFECT

The flow over a nonrotating cylinder does not look much like the ideal-flow solution for $\Gamma = 0$ even though the lift force is zero. In this case the flow separates because fluid particles in the boundary layer do not have enough momentum to penetrate into the high-pressure region at the back of the cylinder. This situation changes somewhat if the cylinder is rotated. Since the no-slip condition demands that the fluid next to the wall move with the wall velocity, the boundary-layer profiles and the separation points are greatly modified. On the top side of the cylinder, the wall and flow velocities are in the same direction. These particles have extra momentum, and as a result the flow proceeds around this side farther before it separates. The opposite effect occurs on the other side, as one can see in the photographs in Fig. 18.15.

The asymmetric flow around a rotating cylinder leads to a lift force. This is called the *Magnus effect*. The rotation parameter $r_0\Omega/U$ compares the surface velocity with the free-stream speed. As the rotation increases, the amount of lift also increases. First the increase is almost linear; then, around $r_0\Omega/U = 3$, a slower rate of increase begins.

At the higher rotation rates, separation can actually be suppressed, giving a flow pattern that is very much like the ideal-flow pattern for a single stagnation point. In this regard one should compare Fig. 18.12 with $\Gamma_a = 4\pi r_0 U$ and Fig. 18.15 with $r_0\Omega/U = 4$. The question naturally arises whether the analysis could also predict the lift force, since the actual and theoretical flow patterns are so much alike. To predict the lift force

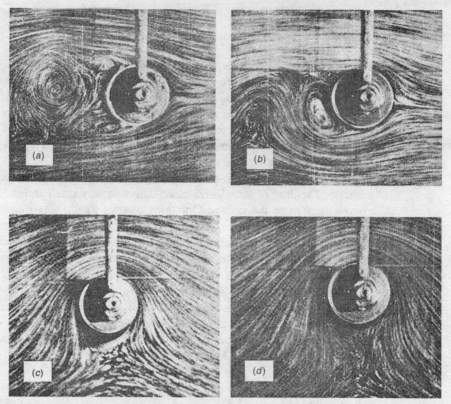

Figure 18.15   Streamlines for flow over a rotating cylinder: (a) $\Omega = 0$; (b) $r_0\Omega = U$; (c) $r_0\Omega = 4U$; (d) $r_0\Omega = 6U$. Reprinted with permission from Prandtl and Tietjens (1934).

using the theory of Sections 18.7 and 18.8, we need to make a connection between the circulation Γ_a and the cylinder rotation Ω. Several arguments and analyses have been proposed to make this connection.

The Magnus problem was investigated extensively by Prandtl; he regarded it as a fundamental question relevant to the production of lift. Prandtl started by examining the particular ideal-flow solution that has only one stagnation point, that is, the case with $\Gamma_a = 4\pi r_0 U$. In this case the ideal velocity at the wall varies from zero to a maximum of $4U$. Prandtl reasoned that if the cylinder were rotated at this speed ($\Omega = 4U/r_0$), the boundary layer would never have fluid with a lower momentum than the ideal flow. Therefore, the boundary layer would not separate, and the ideal-flow pattern, including the lift, would be realized. Prandtl thought that any higher rotation rate would give the same lift but with a slightly different boundary layer. This theory produces a lift value that is a little too high.

The Magnus lift force is not always in the same direction. At some Reynolds numbers (those near the critical value for transition from laminar to turbulent boundary layer), the Magnus effect can actually be negative. This happens only for very low rotation rates. This effect is thought to be the result of turbulent reattachment on the upwind-moving side and laminar separation on the downwind-moving side. Unless the flow is at the proper Reynolds number, the negative lift does not occur. Usually, the rotation simply shifts the separation positions asymmetrically and creates a lift force in the expected direction.

18.10   CONFORMAL TRANSFORMATIONS

A very useful geometric interpretation of an analytic function is to consider that the function maps points from the plane of the independent variable $z = x + iy$ into points on a plane of the dependent variable $\zeta = \xi + i\eta$. For every point z, the function

$$\zeta = \zeta(z)$$

gives a point in the ζ-plane. From calculus we know that the mapping is 1:1 as long as the derivative $d\zeta/dx$ is not zero. Places where $d\zeta/dz = 0$ are called *critical points* of the mapping.

As an example, consider the mapping given by the function

$$\zeta = z + \frac{r_0^2}{z} \tag{18.10.1}$$

where r_0 is a real constant. One of the best ways of visualizing a mapping is to draw lines in the z-plane and trace the corresponding lines mapped into the ζ-plane. Special choices of lines in one plane usually give simple patterns in the other plane. Figure 18.16 shows how the region in the z-plane outside of the circle $|z| = r_0$ maps into the entire ζ-plane. Points A to D are drawn in each plane. Substituting $z = r_0 \exp(i\theta)$ into Eq. 18.10.1 will give ζ coordinates corresponding to the circle. They are

$$\zeta = r_0 \exp(i\theta) + r_0 \exp(-i\theta) = 2r_0 \cos \theta$$

As θ ranges from 0 to 2π, the corresponding points in the ζ-plane are $\eta = 0$, $\xi = 2r_0 \cos \theta$. Note that points B and D in the z-plane map to the same point in the ζ-plane.

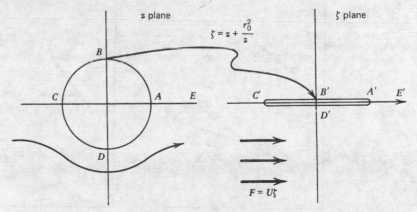

Figure 18.16   Conformal mapping of a cylinder to a flat plate.

This does not violate the $1:1$ property of the mapping: the circle $r_0 \exp(i\theta)$ merely gives a boundary in the z-plane for a region that covers the entire ζ-plane. Points on the inside of the circle map to the ζ-plane in such a way that they also cover the entire plane. The point $z = 0$ maps to the "point at infinity" ($\zeta = \infty$) according to Eq. 18.10.1.

The name *conformal transformation* denotes the fact that the angle formed by the intersection of two lines in the z-plane is unchanged when these lines are transformed into the ζ-plane. In Fig. 18.17 point P in the z-plane has a certain line going through it. Along this line the differential increment dz may be given in polar form as

$$dz = |dz| \exp(i\alpha)$$

where α is the inclination of the line at P. A certain transformation $\zeta(z)$ maps P and the increment dz into the point P' in the ζ-plane and the corresponding differential $d\zeta$:

$$d\zeta = |d\zeta| \exp(i\beta)$$

Dividing these expressions gives

$$\frac{d\zeta}{dz} = \zeta'(z) = \frac{|d\zeta|}{|dz|} \exp[i(\beta - \alpha)] \tag{18.10.2}$$

This equation presents the derivative of $\zeta(z)$ in polar form; the magnitude of $\zeta'(z)$ is the stretching factor $|d\zeta/dz|$ of a line though P, while the angle $\beta - \alpha$ is the amount of rotation the line is subjected to when it is transformed from the z-plane to the ζ-plane. Since $\zeta'(z)$ is independent of the direction of dz, all lines through P are stretched by the same amount and rotated through the same angle. Hence, any two lines through P are mapped into lines rotated by the same amount and retain the same included angle in the ζ-plane.

A critical point in the transformation occurs when $\zeta'(z) = 0$. Both the real and imaginary parts of $\zeta'(z)$ are then zero, implying that the magnitude is zero and the direction is undetermined. At critical points lines through P may be rotated by different amounts as they are transformed onto the ζ-plane. In the example furnished by Eq.

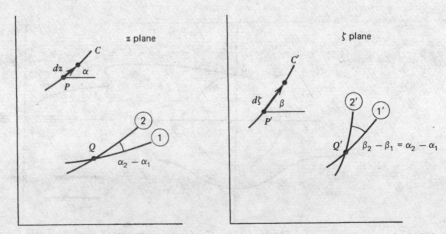

Figure 18.17   Curves mapped by a conformal transformation $\zeta(z)$ retain the same included angle.

18.10.1 and illustrated in Fig. 18.16, the critical points are $z = \pm r_0$. Lines AB and AE are rotated by different amounts and the angle between these lines is not preserved during the transformation to the ζ-plane. Note that a single line in one plane may split into several lines in the other plane at a critical point. Splitting may occur only at critical points, where the transformation is not $1:1$.

Although we shall not prove the fact, it should be stated for the record that any analytic function $F(z)$ is a conformal transformation, except at singular points of the function and at the critical points defined by $F'(z) = 0$. For example, ln z is conformal except at the origin, where it is singular, while sin z is conformal except where the derivative cos z is zero.

When conformal mapping is employed for ideal-flow problems, we shall always let z be the physical plane where the body is drawn in its true shape. In this plane we have the streamlines given by $\psi(x, y)$ and the potential lines by $\phi(x, y)$. These lines map to the ζ-plane, where there are corresponding lines $\hat{\psi}(\xi, \eta)$ and $\hat{\phi}(\xi, \eta)$. The complex potential in the physical plane is

$$F = F(z) = \phi(x, y) + i\psi(x, y) \tag{18.10.3}$$

When the inverse transformation $z = z(\zeta)$ is substituted, we call the new function $\hat{F}(\zeta)$:

$$F = F(z(\zeta)) = \hat{F}(\zeta) = \hat{\phi}(\xi, \eta) + i\hat{\psi}(\xi, \eta) \tag{18.10.4}$$

From this we see that it is perfectly reasonable to talk about an ideal flow in the z-plane, $\phi(x, y)$, and an equivalent flow in the ζ-plane, $\hat{\phi}(\xi, \eta)$.

In the example on Fig. 18.16, we considered how a cylinder in the z-plane would transform into an infinitely thin plate between A and C in the ζ-plane. Now assume that the flow in the ζ-plane is a uniform stream from right to left. This flow has the complex potential

$$F = \hat{F}(\zeta) = U\zeta \tag{18.10.5}$$

When the flat plate is transformed into a circle, we find the corresponding potential by substituting Eq. 18.10.1 into Eq. 18.10.5. The result is

$$F = U\left(z + \frac{r_0^2}{z}\right) \tag{18.10.6}$$

Thus, we have a new way of looking at the ideal flow over a cylinder. We imagine that a conformal transformation maps the cylinder into a flat plate; then the flow over the plate is a streaming motion given by Eq. 18.10.5. Equation 18.10.6 may be thought of as a composite of Eqs. 18.10.5 and 18.10.1.

The usefulness of conformal transformation is that a complicated geometry may be mapped into a simple figure in one step, and then a simple flow pattern may be imagined in the transformed plane. Streamlines and potential lines in one plane map into streamlines and potential lines in the transformed plane. The velocities, on the other hand, are modified. The original complex velocity is $W(z) = dF/dz$, while in the ζ-plane the velocity of the equivalent flow is $\hat{W} = d\hat{F}/d\zeta$. The chain rule applied to $F(z) = \hat{F}(\zeta(z))$ yields

$$\frac{dF}{dz} = \frac{d\hat{F}}{d\zeta}\frac{d\zeta}{dz}$$

This can be rewritten as

$$W(z) = \hat{W}(\zeta)\,\frac{d\zeta}{dz} \qquad (18.10.7)$$

The derivative of the mapping $\zeta(z)$ indicates the velocity ratio between the z- and ζ-planes. One important fact we see from Eq. 18.10.7 is that critical points of the transformation are always stagnation points $W(z) = 0$ of the flow in the real plane. At these points the streamlines may branch. Furthermore, stagnation points in the z-plane are not necessarily stagnation points in the ζ-plane, as $\hat{W}(\zeta)$ is not necessarily zero.

So far we have dealt exclusively with the geometric aspects of conformal transformations. How can we be sure that an ideal flow in the z-plane obeys the proper equations for a flow in the ζ-plane? Recall that the basic fact we have been using is that all analytic functions $F(z)$ have real and imaginary parts that satisfy the Laplace equation. For $F = \phi + i\psi$ we have

$$\frac{\partial^2 \phi}{\partial x^2} + \frac{\partial^2 \phi}{\partial y^2} = 0, \qquad \frac{\partial^2 \psi}{\partial x^2} + \frac{\partial^2 \psi}{\partial y^2} = 0$$

Therefore, any $F(z)$ represents a flow pattern of some sort where $\psi = \text{const}$ is a streamline and the velocity across a streamline is zero ($\partial \phi / \partial n = 0$). To establish that a flow in the z-plane is also a flow in the ζ-plane, we need another mathematical fact. It may be proved that an analytic function of an analytic function is another analytic function; that is, if $F(z)$ and $z(\zeta)$ are both analytic functions, $F(z(\zeta))$ is an analytic function of the variable ζ. Hence, $F = F(z(\zeta))$ has real and imaginary parts that satisfy the Laplace equation in terms of ξ and η. That is,

$$F = F(z(\zeta)) = \hat{\phi}(\xi, \eta) + i\hat{\psi}(\xi, \eta)$$

$$\frac{\partial^2 \hat{\phi}}{\partial \xi^2} + \frac{\partial^2 \hat{\phi}}{\partial \eta^2} = 0, \qquad \frac{\partial^2 \hat{\psi}}{\partial \xi^2} + \frac{\partial^2 \hat{\psi}}{\partial \eta^2} = 0$$

The functions $\phi(x, y)$ and $\psi(x, y)$, which satisfy the Laplace equation in x and y, also satisfy the Laplace equation in ξ and η when $x, y \to \xi, \eta$ under any conformal transformation. An analytic function of an analytic function is an analytic function.

18.11   JOUKOWSKI TRANSFORMATION: AIRFOIL GEOMETRY

The study of ideal flow over two-dimensional cylindrical objects (circular cylinders, elliptic shapes, flat plates, and a certain type of airfoil shape) is simplified by using the conformal–transformation technique. In Section 18.10 we used the example of a circular cylinder in the real plane mapped into a flat plate under the transformation $\zeta = z + r_o^2/z$. If we simply rename the planes—that is, let the flat plate be in the physical plane and the cylinder be in the transformed plane—the transformation equation is $z = \zeta +$

r_0^2/ζ. We introduce the Joukowski transformation as a generalization of this form where c replaces r_0:

$$z = \zeta + \frac{c^2}{\zeta} \qquad (18.11.1)$$

The constant c can be any real number. The inverse transformation is

$$\zeta = \frac{1}{2}z \pm \left[\left(\frac{1}{2}z\right)^2 - c^2\right]^{1/2} = \frac{z}{2} \pm \frac{z - 2c}{2}\sqrt{\frac{z + 2c}{z - 2c}} \qquad (18.11.2)$$

The second form has advantages when using a computer.

Figure 18.18 shows the flat plate $ABCD$ in the z-plane as it maps into a circle of radius $r_0 = c$ in the ζ-plane. If we let the flow in the ζ-plane [i.e., the complex potential $F(\zeta)$] be the flow over a circular cylinder, the corresponding $F(z)$ in the z-plane will be a flow over a flat plate. As a second example, consider the ellipse $EGFH$. It can be shown that this ellipse in the z-plane also maps into a circle in the ζ-plane. (If the transformation constant is c and the radius of the cylinder is R_0, the semiaxes of the ellipse are $R_0 + c^2/R_0$ and $R_0 - c^2/R_0$.) Now, if we let the flow in the ζ-plane be that for a circle of radius R_0, while the transformation constant is c, the flow in the real plane will be that over an elliptic cylinder. The reader may find the details of these flow patterns in Milne-Thomson (1960).

The useful characteristic of the Joukowski transformation is that it sends a certain airfoil-like figure in the z-plane into a circle in the ζ-plane. It turns out that the center of the circle is off axis in the ζ-plane (Fig. 18.19). Hence, the complex potential $\hat{F}(\zeta)$ for flow over an off-axis circle in the ζ-plane represents the flow over an airfoil shape in the real z-plane. This is a very important problem, as it offers a key to the flow pattern over airfoil shapes. From these solutions we can discover how various geometric parameters of the airfoil influence the lift. Of course, an airfoil does not necessarily have the

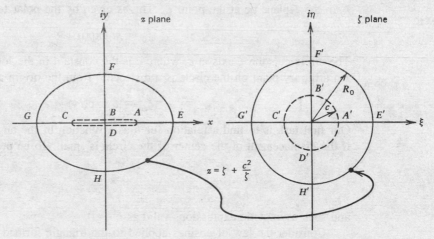

Figure 18.18 Joukowski transformation of an ellipse to a circle.

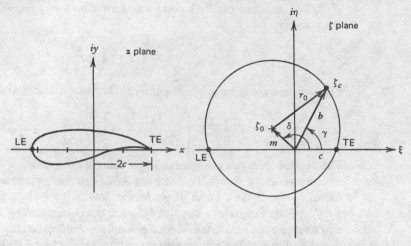

Figure 18.19   Joukowski transformation sends an airfoil shape to an off-axis circle.

same shape as a Joukowski airfoil. In fact, real airfoils are not Joukowski shapes; their contours are determined by considering viscous effects and how boundary layer separation may be avoided. Nevertheless, it is useful to study Joukowski airfoils, as the general trends for ideal flow over these shapes and for flow over actual airfoil shapes are the same.

In the remainder of this section we investigate the geometry of Joukowski airfoils. The major question is how points on an off-center circle in the ζ-plane transform into an airfoil shape in the z-plane. An exact closed-form equation for the airfoil contour in the z-plane does not exist. This is not a serious difficulty, as practical airfoils are thin, and we can find approximate equations for airfoil contours for this case. Consider the nomenclature defined for the circle on Fig. 18.19. Let the center of the circle of radius r_0 in the ζ-plane be at the point ζ_0. This is given by the polar form

$$\zeta_0 = m \exp(i\delta) \tag{18.11.3}$$

The circle cuts the ξ-axis at c, where c is the constant in the Joukowski transformation. An arbitrary point on the circle is a distance b from the origin at an angle γ,

$$\zeta_{\text{cir}} = b \exp(i\gamma)$$

Our first task is to find a relation for b as a function of the angle γ. This can be done if the displacement of the center of the circle is small. To be precise, we define

$$\varepsilon \equiv \frac{m}{c} \tag{18.11.4}$$

and seek asymptotic expressions valid as $\varepsilon \to 0$.

Consider the law of cosines applied to the triangle formed by m, r_0, and b in Fig. 18.19:

$$r_0^2 = b^2 + m^2 - 2mb \cos(\delta - \gamma) \qquad (18.11.5)$$

Next, consider the triangle formed by m, c, and another radial line from ζ_0 to TE with length r_0. The law of cosines for this triangle is

$$r_0^2 = m^2 + c^2 - 2mc \cos \delta \qquad (18.11.6)$$

Equating Eqs. 18.11.5 and 18.11.6 and solving for b gives

$$\left(\frac{b}{c}\right)^2 - 2\frac{b}{c}\varepsilon \cos(\delta - \gamma) + \varepsilon \cos \delta - 1 = 0 \qquad (18.11.7)$$

Solving and expanding for small ε yields

$$\frac{b}{c} = 1 + \varepsilon[\cos(\delta - \gamma) - \cos \delta] + O[\varepsilon^2]$$

$$= 1 + \varepsilon B + O[\varepsilon^2] \qquad (18.11.8)$$

where B stands for the bracketed expression on the first line. By introducing the trigonometric formula for $\cos(\delta - \gamma)$, the term in bracket's in Eq. 18.11.8 is expressed as

$$B = \sin \gamma \sin \delta - \cos \delta (1 - \cos \gamma) \qquad (18.11.9)$$

Equations 18.11.8 and 18.11.9 are the desired expression for b as a function of the angle γ. These relations describe the circle in the ζ-plane. The coordinate of any point on the circle is a function of the parameter γ through the equations

$$\frac{\zeta_{\text{cir}}}{c} = \frac{b}{c} \exp(i\gamma) \sim [1 + \varepsilon B(\gamma)] \exp(i\gamma) \qquad (18.11.10)$$

In the physical plane the airfoil coordinates are denoted by $z_s = x_s + iy_s$. They are found from the Joukowski transformation evaluated on the circle:

$$z_s = x_s + iy_s = \zeta_{\text{cir}} + \frac{c^2}{\zeta_{\text{cir}}}$$

Substituting Eq. 18.11.10 into this equation, dropping terms of order ε^2, and noting that $(1 + \varepsilon B)^{-1} - 1 - \varepsilon B + O[\varepsilon^2]$ yields

$$\frac{x_s}{4c} = \frac{\cos \gamma}{2}, \qquad \frac{y_s}{4c} = \frac{\varepsilon B(\gamma) \sin \gamma}{2} \qquad (18.11.11)$$

These equations are parametric relations for the airfoil coordinates in terms of γ. From Eq. 18.11.11 we find that the trailing edge is at $x_s = 2c$, while the leading edge is $x_s = -2c$. The length $4c$ is the chord of the airfoil, which is denoted by ℓ. Thus, the Joukowski transformation constant c is one-fourth of the airfoil chord:

$$c = \frac{\ell}{4} \qquad (18.11.12)$$

It is also useful to note that the leading and trailing edges correspond to the points in the ζ-plane where the ξ-axis cuts the circle ($\gamma = 0, \pi$).

The y equation for the airfoil surface, Eq. 18.11.11, can be expressed in terms of x_s. To do this we note from Eq. 18.11.11 that

$$\cos \gamma = \frac{x_s}{2c} = \frac{2x_s}{\ell}, \qquad \sin \gamma = \pm \sqrt{1 - \left(\frac{2x_s}{\ell}\right)^2}$$

When the expressions above are inserted into Eq. 18.11.11 together with Eqs. 18.11.9 and 18.11.12, the following equation results (see Fig. 18.19):

$$\frac{y_s}{\ell} = \frac{\varepsilon}{2}\left\{ \sin \delta \left[1 - \left(\frac{2x_s}{\ell}\right)^2 \right] \pm \cos \delta \left(1 - \frac{2x_s}{\ell}\right)\left[1 - \left(\frac{2x_s}{\ell}\right)^2 \right]^{1/2} \right\} \qquad (18.11.13)$$

In this form the equation of the airfoil, $y_s(x_s)$, consists of two parts. The first part is the *camber line*, given by the first term in braces. The second part, the term following the $\pm$ sign, adds and subtracts a *thickness distribution* to the camber line. The camber line reaches its maximum at $x_s = 0$; we denote this maximum as h. Inserting it into Eq. 18.11.13 gives the airfoil *camber ratio, H*:

$$H \equiv \frac{h}{\ell} = \frac{\varepsilon}{2} \sin \delta \qquad (18.11.14)$$

The thickness is zero at the leading and trailing edges and reaches a maximum, denoted by $t/2$, at $x_s/\ell = -\frac{1}{4}$. Introducing this fact into Eq. 18.11.13 shows that the *thickness ratio* is

$$T \equiv \frac{t}{\ell} = \varepsilon \frac{3\sqrt{3}}{4} \cos \delta \qquad (18.11.15)$$

By using the notation for camber and thickness ratios and $Y = y_s/\ell$ and $X = x_s/\ell$, Eq. 18.11.13 can be rewritten in the form

$$Y = H(1 - 4X^2) \pm \frac{2}{3\sqrt{3}} T(1 - 2X)(1 - 4X^2)^{1/2} \qquad (18.11.16)$$

This is the linearized Joukowski profile equation with thickness and camber parameters H and T.

The nomenclature introduced in splitting the Joukowski airfoil equation into a chord line, a camber line, and a thickness distribution is not the only accepted method for defining an airfoil shape. Figure 18.19 gives another method of constructing the definitions. First, one lays out the chord line of the proper length. The leading and trailing edges are the ends of the chord line. A camber line, sometimes also called the *mean line*, is marked off at specified distances from the chord line. There are no restrictions on the camber-line shape other than that it must begin and end at the leading and trailing edges. Joukowski airfoils described by Eq. 18.11.16 have a parabolic camber line with the maximum at the 50% chord position. Other airfoils have different shapes for the camber line. The airfoil shape is completed by adding a thickness distribution at equal distance above and below the camber line. In the alternative method, the thickness distribution must be added on a line perpendicular to the local slope of the camber line. In Eq. 18.11.16 we imply that the thickness distribution is added to the camber line in a direction perpendicular to the chord line instead of perpendicular to the mean line. This is mathematically the most convenient method, and for small camber, which incidentally most airfoils have, the two definitions are equivalent. One characteristic of all Joukowski airfoils is that they have a cusp at the trailing edge. Actual airfoils have a sharp trailing edge with a finite wedge angle. A typical Joukowski profile is shown in Fig. 18.20.

We have in Eq. 18.1.16 a complete description of the airfoil shape in the z-plane. The Joukowski transformation maps this shape into a circle in the ζ-plane. The geometry of the circle is described by c (the position where it cuts the ξ-axis) and ζ_0 (the position of the center with respect to the ζ origin). By way of summary we note that position c is given by Eq. 18.11.12:

$$\frac{c}{\ell} = \frac{1}{4}$$

The location of the center is given by Eqs. 18.11.14 and 18.11.15, which we put in a more convenient form using Eq. 18.11.3:

$$\frac{\zeta_0}{c} = \varepsilon \cos \delta + i\varepsilon \sin \delta = -\frac{4}{3\sqrt{3}} T + i2H \tag{18.11.17}$$

The camber and thickness of the airfoil are related to the vertical and horizontal displacement of the center, respectively.

18.12 KUTTA CONDITION

The ideal flow about a cylinder or other two-dimensional body is not unique because the region is doubly connected. An arbitrary circulation constant must be specified to obtain a unique flow pattern. In the case of a triply connected region, say two cylinders or two airfoils side by side, two circulation constants must be specified. For bluff bodies, such as elliptic or circular cylinders, there is no method to determine the circulation constant. This is not very important, because such bodies have large wake regions and ideal flow cannot be applied anyway. Airfoils, on the other hand, offer a situation where ideal-flow theory is very useful, and a method to determine the circulation constant is required.

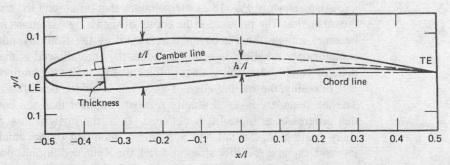

Figure 18.20 Joukowski airfoil with camber $h = 0.04\ell$ and thickness $t = 0.12\ell$. Thickness is defined as perpendicular to the camber line but is equal to vertical distance for small camber.

Figure 18.21 gives several ideal-flow patterns for airfoil shapes at the same angle of attack. Each of these patterns has a different circulation constant and, according to the Kutta–Joukowski theorem, a different lift force. The *Kutta condition* (also known as *Joukowski's hypothesis*) is the assumption that the flow cannot go around the sharp trailing edge, but must leave the airfoil so that the upper and lower streams join smoothly at the trailing edge. There is only one flow pattern and one circulation value that will do this. Formally stated, the Kutta condition says that the proper circulation constant for the flow over an airfoil is the value that causes the velocity to leave the trailing edge in a direction that bisects the angle formed by the upper and lower surfaces. An equivalent statement is that the velocity at the trailing edge cannot be infinite.

The Kutta condition is not subject to proof. It is a rule of thumb that works fairly well for most airfoils. In our theoretical analysis of flows we have, in a certain sense, oversimplified the problem by entirely neglecting viscosity and the no-slip condition. Stokes's theorem (Eq. 18.7.5) shows that circulation is equal to the integral of the vorticity in the boundary layers on the airfoil (a two-dimensional wake has no net vorticity). Thus, in some complicated way the viscous effects in the boundary layers actually go hand in hand with the circulation. At high Reynolds numbers the details of the viscous effects are no longer important and their effect on the main inviscid flow can be distilled into the Kutta condition. For these reasons it is sometimes said that the Kutta condition is the result of viscosity.

When two inviscid flow streams merge, as they do at the trailing edge of an airfoil, the pressure must be the same on either side of the streamline; it cannot be discontinuous. Since in the case of an airfoil the two streams have the same Bernoulli constant, the velocity at the trailing edge has the same value for the upper and lower streams. Figure 18.21 shows two streams merging from a cusp trailing edge such as a Joukowski airfoil would have. The velocity there is generally slightly lower than the free-stream velocity. In the case of a finite angle at the trailing edge we might envision flow patterns where one stream turns through a larger angle than the other. Such patterns are, in fact, impossible in ideal flow. Recall the wedge-flow solutions of Section 18.2 and Fig. 18.5c. The velocity along the merging streamline would be (Eq. 18.2.7) $v = nAr^{n-1}$, where the exponent n is related to the turning angle $\theta_{1/2}$ by Eq. 18.2.8. Hence, different turning angles would produce velocity variations along the stagnation streamline that would not match. The only acceptable ideal-flow solution when the streamline leaves the trailing edge is one for which it bisects the wedge angle.

Also shown in Fig. 18.21 are solutions that go around the trailing edge and flow up the other side. The pressure at the corner of such a flow is minus infinity, and the velocity becomes infinite. This behavior is ruled out by the Kutta hypothesis. Although infinite velocities are ruled out at a trailing edge, they are allowed at the leading edge of a flat plate or cambered airfoil with zero thickness (actually, separation will occur).

In reality, the trailing edge of an airfoil is hidden beneath viscous boundary layers. The top boundary layer is usually somewhat thicker than the bottom layer, a condition that progresses as more lift is obtained. Thus, the inviscid flow does not actually see a sharp trailing edge at all, but a geometry modified by the thickness of the boundary layers. Despite these difficulties in detail, the Kutta condition is one of the major working assumptions in any airfoil theory. As a first approximation it gives a remarkably good estimate of the lift as long as separation does not occur.

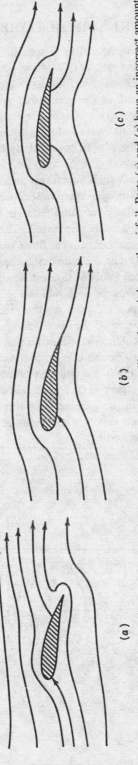

Figure 18.21 The Kutta condition requires that the streamline bisect the trailing edge as it leaves the airfoil. Parts (*a*) and (*c*) have an incorrect amount of circulation while part (*b*) satisfies the Kutta condition.

18.13   FLOW OVER A JOUKOWSKI AIRFOIL: AIRFOIL LIFT

The geometry of a Joukowski airfoil is specified by the angle of attack α, the camber ratio h/ℓ, and the thickness ratio t/ℓ. We have no control over the distributions of camber and thickness, as all Joukowski airfoils have the same distributions. In practice this is not a critical simplification, as the events that produce lift are fairly insensitive to these distributions. This is especially true at modest angles of attack.

The flow around a Joukowski airfoil is found using the ideas of Sections 18.10 to 18.12. In Section 18.10 the idea of conformally transforming one flow field into a much simpler flow field was introduced. Section 18.11 gave us a specific transformation, the Joukowski transformation, which transforms an airfoil shape in the z-plane into a circular cylinder in the ζ-plane. Since in Section 18.7 we already have in hand the solution for flow over a cylinder, the only remaining step is to reinterpret this flow after it is transformed back into the z-plane for the airfoil. The obstacle to this procedure is the fact that there are an infinite number of ideal flows over a circular cylinder and we must pick one. This difficulty is overcome by invoking the Kutta condition to select the flow that leaves the trailing edge smoothly with a finite velocity.

The cylinder in the ζ-plane is shown in Fig. 18.22. Recall that the trailing edge of the airfoil maps to the point $\zeta = c$ on the circle and that the thickness and camber determine the center position of the circle, denoted by ζ_0. To apply the Kutta condition, we must arrange the circulation constant so that the flow leaves the circle at the point marked TE; this point will be the rear stagnation point for the flow in the ζ-plane.

Before we can write down the complex potential, we need one more detail. The real airfoil is at an angle of attack α (the angle between the chord and free stream). What influence will this have in the ζ-plane? Looking at the Joukowski transformation (Eq. 18.11.1), we see that as $\zeta \to \infty$, $z \sim \zeta$. Since the functions of the complex potentials in the ζ- and z-planes are related by

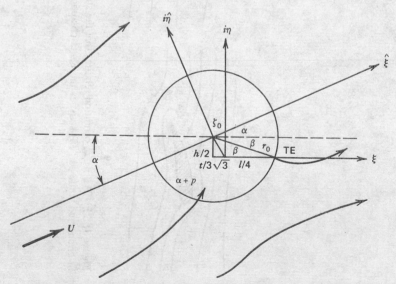

Figure 18.22   Circular cylinder off center and at angle of attack α.

$$F = \hat{F}(\zeta) = F(\hat{\zeta}(z)) = F(z) \tag{18.13.1}$$

at infinity we may set $z = \zeta$ to show $\hat{F}(z) \sim F(z)$ as $z \to \infty$. At infinity the flows have exactly the same form in either plane. This result leads us to conclude that the angle of attack for the cylinder must be the same as for the airfoil.

Return to Fig. 18.22 and introduce a $\hat{\zeta} = \hat{\xi} + i\hat{\eta}$ coordinate system that is aligned with the flow at infinity and has its origin at the center of the circle. The relation with the ζ-coordinates is given by a translation of ζ_0 and a rotation through the angle α, that is,

$$\hat{\zeta} = (\zeta - \zeta_0) \exp(-i\alpha) \tag{18.13.2}$$

The complex potential for flow about a cylinder with circulation Γ_a is given by Eq. 18.7.1. In the current notation, the potential is

$$F = U\left(\hat{\zeta} + \frac{r_0^2}{\hat{\zeta}}\right) + i\frac{\Gamma_a}{2\pi} \ln \frac{\hat{\zeta}}{r_0} \tag{18.13.3}$$

Inserting Eq. 18.13.2 gives the potential in terms of ζ:

$$F = U[(\zeta - \zeta_0) \exp(-i\alpha) + r_0^2 \exp(i\alpha)(\zeta - \zeta_0)^{-1}] + i\frac{\Gamma_a}{2\pi} \ln \frac{\zeta - \zeta_0}{r_0} \tag{18.13.4}$$

A constant term that arises from $\ln \exp(i\alpha)$ has been dropped. This merely changes the numbering system for the potentials. Equation 18.13.4 together with the inverse Joukowski transformation (Eq. 18.11.2) defines the potential $F(z)$ in the real plane.

Let us take a careful look at Eq. 18.13.4 and see how all the symbols are related to quantities that refer to the airfoil geometry and to the flow in the z-plane. The symbols U and α are obviously the free-stream speed and angle of attack. The parameter ζ is a parametric variable related to z through Eq. 18.11.2, where in turn $c = \ell/4$ (Eq. 18.11.12) introduces the airfoil chord ℓ. The displacement of the circle ζ_0 is related to camber and thickness ratios by Eq. 18.11.17. The only symbols in Eq. 18.13.4 that remain to be interpreted are the circle radius r_0 and the circulation Γ_a.

Figure 18.22 shows some of the details of the circle geometry. In this figure the right triangle that involves r_0 yields the relation

$$r_0^2 = \left(\frac{h}{2}\right)^2 + \left(\frac{\ell}{4} + \frac{t}{3\sqrt{3}}\right)^2$$

The airfoil has small h and t, so to the same degree of approximation with which we found the airfoil coordinates, we find ($T = t/\ell$)

$$r_0 = \left(\frac{1}{4} + \frac{T}{3\sqrt{3}}\right)\ell \tag{18.13.5}$$

Similarly, as $m \to 0$, the angle β in Fig. 18.22 is

$$\beta = \frac{h/2}{\ell/4} = \frac{2h}{\ell} = 2H \tag{18.13.6}$$

We need to know this angle in order to find the circulation Γ_a.

In our study of flow over a cylinder with circulation, we found that the stagnation points were moved away from the flow axis (the $\hat{\zeta}$-axis) as the circulation increased. The angular position was given by Eq. 18.7.4. To satisfy the Kutta condition, we need to position the stagnation point at an angle $\alpha + \beta$ (Fig. 18.22). Substituting $\alpha + \beta$ for $-\theta_0$ in Eq. 18.7.4 yields

$$\sin(\alpha + \beta) = \sin\left(\alpha + \frac{2h}{\ell}\right) = \frac{\Gamma_a}{4\pi r_0 U} \tag{18.13.7}$$

This equation, together with Eq. 18.13.5, gives Γ_a in terms of the airfoil geometry and flow parameters. This completes the interpretation of complex potential equation 18.13.4 in terms of variables related to the airfoil.

Velocities that occur around the airfoil are related to the velocities at corresponding points on the cylinder by Eq. 18.10.7:

$$W(x) = \hat{W}(\zeta) \frac{d\zeta}{dz}$$

$$= \frac{d\hat{F}(\zeta)}{d\zeta}\left(\frac{dz}{d\zeta}\right)^{-1} \tag{18.13.8}$$

Performing the operations indicated above, we arrive at

$$u - iv = \left\{ U[\exp(-i\alpha) - r_0^2 \exp(i\alpha)(\zeta - \zeta_0)^{-2}] + i\frac{\Gamma_a}{2\pi r_0}\frac{r_0}{\zeta - \zeta_0} \right\}\left[1 - \left(\frac{c}{\zeta}\right)^2\right]^{-1} \tag{18.13.9}$$

This expression is left with ζ as a parameter. The velocities u and v are in the z-plane at a position given by $z(\zeta)$ in Eq. 18.11.1. The factor in braces is the velocity in the ζ-plane, and the term in brackets to the -1 power is the derivative of the Joukowski transformation. This is always nonzero except at the two critical points $\zeta = \pm c$.

One critical point lies within the circle, and the other lies at the rear stagnation point on the circle. At this point both $\hat{W}$ and $dz/d\zeta$ are zero, leading to an indeterminate form in Eq. 18.13.9. This expression can be evaluated using L'Hôpital's rule. For small values of thickness and camber, the velocity at the trailing edge is found to be

$$(u - iv)_{TE} = U\left(1 - \frac{4t}{3\sqrt{3}\,\ell}\right)\left(1 + i\frac{2h}{\ell}\right) \tag{18.13.10}$$

The velocity is slightly smaller in magnitude than the free-stream velocity (an effect due to the thickness) and is directed downward in alignment with the camber line. Figure 18.23 is a sketch of how the streamlines look in the physical plane, while Fig. 18.24 displays the corresponding surface pressures.

The forward stagnation point on the cylinder maps into the forward stagnation point on the airfoil. From Fig. 18.23 we note that this position is below the leading edge. The position of the stagnation point is given approximately by

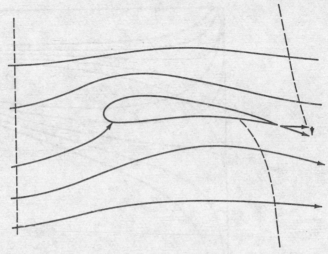

Figure 18.23   Flow over a Joukowski airfoil. Note that particles flow over the top faster than over the bottom, so that a time line is split in two as it flows over the foil.

$$X_{\text{stag}} = \left(\frac{x_s}{\ell}\right)_{\text{stag}} = -\frac{1}{2} + \alpha^2 \qquad (18.13.11)$$

The corresponding y_s position can be found from Eq. 18.1.16. As the angle of attack increases, the stagnation point moves farther away from the leading edge. The flow on the lower surface accelerates away from the stagnation point and generally has a velocity somewhat lower than the free-stream velocity. Correspondingly, through Bernoulli's equation, the pressure on the lower surface is slightly higher than the free-stream values, and hence an upward force results.

   The flow that goes over the upper surface first accelerates from the stagnation point as it moves around the leading edge. In fact, if the airfoil has zero thickness (a cambered plate), the velocity at the leading edge is infinite. With nonzero thickness the velocity is not infinite, but it does reach high values and associated low pressures, as shown in Fig. 18.24. The extremely low pressures are not sustained very long, as the flow is quickly decelerated to more modest speeds. Recall that we found a similar velocity overshoot on a nose shape (Section 18.4). Having the nose at a nonzero angle of attack intensifies the overshoot on an airfoil. Large velocities in this region are undesirable, as the subsequent deceleration may lead to boundary layer separation and airfoil stall (a type of stall known as *leading-edge stall*). The nose of a real airfoil is contoured to avoid separation by controlling the excessively low pressures near the nose. Figure 18.25 shows the streamlines over a typical airfoil in two tests at different angles of attack.

   Low pressures on the upper surface persist over the major portion of the surface, and typically they make a much larger contribution to the lift than those on the lower surface. Of course, the pressure at the trailing edge on the upper and lower surfaces must match. Since this pressure is theoretically only slightly higher than free stream, the flow on the upper surface must gradually decelerate to reach this value. Again, we have an

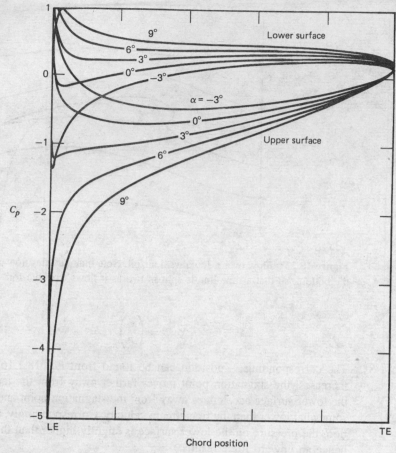

Figure 18.24 Pressure distribution over a Joukowski airfoil; $T = 9\%$, $H = 5\%$.

adverse pressure, which tends to cause the boundary layer to separate. Although the pressure gradient is not as great as in the nose region, the adverse gradient exists over a longer region. Increasing the angle of attack of the airfoil accentuates these effects, and ultimately the airfoil will stall—first at the trailing edge, and progressively farther up the surface as the angle of attack is increased. This type of stall is known as *trailing-edge stall*.

When the circulation constant for the Joukowski airfoil (Eq. 18.13.7) is substituted into the Kutta–Joukowski lift law (Eq. 18.8.1) and r_0 and β are replaced by airfoil parameters through the use of Eqs. 18.13.5 and 18.13.6, we arrive at

$$F_L = \rho U^2 4 \pi \ell \left(\frac{1}{4} + \frac{T}{3\sqrt{3}} \right) \sin(\alpha + 2H) \qquad (18.13.12)$$

In realistic situations $\alpha + 2H$ is small, so the sine term may be approximated by its argument and $T \cdot H$ neglected. With these simplifications, the lift coefficient per unit span is

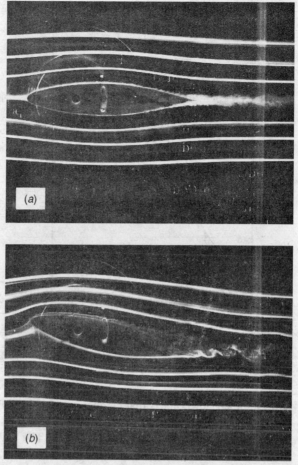

Figure 18.25   Flow over an airfoil shown by smoke filaments. Courtesy of T. J. Mueller and S. M. Batill, University of Notre Dame. Reprinted with permission.

$$C_L = \frac{F_L}{\frac{1}{2}\rho U^2 \ell} = 2\pi(\alpha + 2H) \tag{18.13.13}$$

By far, the most important geometric influences on lift are the amount of camber and the angle of attack. The thickness is not important.

A comparison with experimental results is shown in Fig. 18.26. It shows that the actual values of C_L are too low; however, the slope is nearly correct. It is customary to blame the slightly lower lift on the fact that the boundary layers, especially the thick one on the upper surface, allow the flow to leave the trailing edge at an angle smaller than the Kutta condition requires.

The lift in Eq. 18.13.13 increases directly as the sum of the angle of attack and the maximum camber parameter h/ℓ. To get more lift we need only increase the angle of attack. We might also propose to increase the lift by adding camber to the airfoil: How-

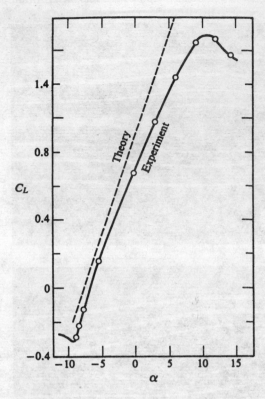

Figure 18.26   Lift curve for a Joukowski air-foil at several angles of attack. Re = 10^5; H = 14%. From Betz (1915, 1924).

ever, another viewpoint is that camber merely shifts the angle of attack at which zero lift occurs. A cambered airfoil produces some lift at $\alpha = 0$. If we are interested in large values of lift, the maximum C_L is important. The angle of attack at which the maximum occurs may not be very important. The maximum C_L is determined by stall, which in turn is related to viscous effects.

The term *linear airfoil theory* refers to an inviscid analysis that assumes an arbitrary camber curve but with a small maximum height, a thin but arbitrary thickness distribution, and a small angle of attack. The results are much like those for a Joukowski profile. The lift curve $C_L(\alpha)$ has a slope of 2π with the effective origin at zero lift displaced by an amount that depends directly on H. However, the term $2H$ in Eq. 18.13.13 has a slightly different coefficient, which depends on the exact camber distribution. Camber at the trailing edge, which is a flap, is more effective in increasing the lift than camber at the leading edge. Thickness, T, to first order makes no contribution to the lift.

18.14   NUMERICAL METHOD FOR AIRFOILS

The physical results from the Joukowski analysis suggest a numerical method to simulate an arbitrary airfoil. In the far stream all airfoils have the same flow field; equivalent to a uniform stream and a line vortex. The strength of the vortex and the lift go hand in hand. The question is: How does the shape of the airfoil and the angle of attack affect the strength of the circulation?

Consider the special case of a flat plate at an angle of attack (Fig. 18.27a). The Joukowski analysis, which is exact with $T = H = 0$, gives the circulation as (Eq. 18.13.7):

$$\Gamma = 4\pi r_0 \, U \sin \alpha \qquad (18.14.1)$$

Here $r_0 = \ell/4$ from Eq. 18.13.6 and is exact. Imagine that the plate is replaced by a vortex of strength proper to produce the correct value of lift. Let Δr be the distance from the vortex center. Flow from the vortex contributes a vertical velocity at the plate of $v = -\Gamma/2\pi\Delta r$ ($\Gamma = \Gamma_a$ in this section) while the free stream contributes a vertical velocity $U \sin \alpha$. At only one point on the plate, called the *collocation point,* can we arrange for the normal velocity of the model vortex plus free stream to have a zero component? At this point the flow is tangent to the plate:

$$v_n = U \sin \alpha - \frac{\Gamma}{2\pi \, \Delta r} = 0 \qquad (18.14.2)$$

Inserting Eq. 18.14.1 yields

$$\Delta r = \frac{\ell}{2}$$

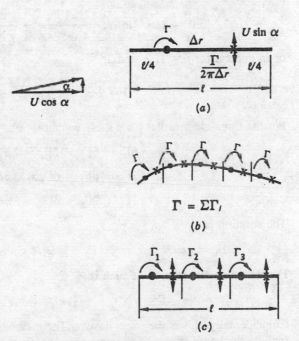

(a)

(b)

$$\Gamma = \Sigma\Gamma_l$$

(c)

Figure 18.27 Vortex model of lifting surfaces: (a) flat plate as one vortex; (b) cambered surface as five plate elements; (c) flat plate as three elements.

The collocation point should be one-half a chord away from the vortex to model the plate as a uniform stream and a vortex. It turns out that the distribution of pressure over a flat plate is such that the center of pressure (the point where a single force would act to produce the same moment) is at the quarter chord location. Thus, one can model a flat plate by a vortex located at the quarter chord point and a collocation point (a point with no normal velocity) at the three-quarter chord point and simulate the proper moment.

For an arbitrary airfoil one ignores the thickness distribution and breaks the camber line into a series of straight elements. Each element has flow along the element (no flow across the element) and contributes Γ_i to the total flow circulation. Let the flat plate model be applied to each element. The flow at a collocation point is the sum of effects from all vortex elements. Setting the normal velocity component to zero gives a linear system of equations for the strength of each vortex element.

An example where the algebra is tractable without a computer is to consider the flat plate as three elements, as shown in Fig. 18.27c. Let the vortices be located at x_{01}, x_{02}, $x_{03}(\frac{1}{12}\ell, \frac{5}{12}\ell, \frac{3}{4}\ell)$ and the collocation points at x_{c1}, x_{c2}, $x_{c3}(\frac{1}{4}\ell, \frac{7}{12}\ell, \frac{11}{12}\ell)$ with $y = 0$ for all points. A vortex element at x_0, y_0 induces velocities at x, y of

$$u = \frac{\Gamma}{2\pi}\frac{y - y_0}{(x - x_0)^2 + (y - y_0)^2}, \qquad v = \frac{-\Gamma}{2\pi}\frac{x - x_0}{(x - x_0)^2 + (y - y_0)^2} \qquad (18.14.3)$$

The normal velocity to any element is simply the v component. At any collocation point the vertical component of the free stream is $U \sin \alpha$. Summing the free-stream component and the contributions from each element at the first collocation point gives

$$0 = 2\pi U \sin \alpha - \frac{\Gamma_1}{x_{c1} - x_{01}} - \frac{\Gamma_2}{x_{c1} - x_{02}} - \frac{\Gamma_3}{x_{c1} - x_{03}}$$

or in general for $j = 1, 2,$ and 3:

$$0 = 2\pi U \sin \alpha - \sum_{i=1}^{3} \frac{\Gamma_i}{x_{cj} - x_{0i}} \qquad (18.14.4)$$

For the three-element flat plate these equations are

$$6\Gamma_1 - 6\Gamma_2 - 2\Gamma_3 = 2\pi U\ell \sin \alpha$$
$$2\Gamma_1 + 6\Gamma_2 - 6\Gamma_3 = 2\pi U\ell \sin \alpha$$
$$\tfrac{6}{5}\Gamma_1 + 2\Gamma_2 + 6\Gamma_3 = 2\pi U\ell \sin \alpha$$

The solution is

$$\Gamma_1 = \tfrac{5}{8}\pi U\ell \sin \alpha, \qquad \Gamma_2 = \tfrac{1}{4}\pi U\ell \sin \alpha, \qquad \Gamma_3 = \tfrac{1}{8}\pi U\ell \sin \alpha$$

For the entire flow the circulation is

$$\Gamma = (\tfrac{5}{8} + \tfrac{1}{4} + \tfrac{1}{8})\pi U\ell \sin \alpha = \pi U\ell \sin \alpha \qquad (18.14.5)$$

Coincidentally, this is the exact answer. The methods of this problem are generalized to include thickness effects, a necessary step to get the boundary layer behavior correctly, by using both upper and lower surfaces. They are also extended to three dimensions by considering a body to be made up of "panels."

18.15   ACTUAL AIRFOILS

The ancients, both in myth and real life, tried to copy birds in the shape of their wings. In the scientific era, Sir George Cayley (English inventor, 1773–1857), whose glider is thought to be the first heavier-than-air vehicle, conducted tests on airfoils at the end of a whirling arm. Several disadvantages of the whirling arm inspired the development of the wind tunnel. The first wind tunnel is credited to F. H. Wenham (English inventor, 1824–1908). He operated the tunnel in 1871, 30 years before the Wright brothers flight. Early airfoils up through World War I had 6 to 7% thickness and considerable camber. At low Reynolds numbers, where the tests were made, such airfoils perform well. However, actual flight Reynolds numbers were somewhat higher. Later, tests at higher Reynolds numbers indicated that wings could be considerably thicker (and thereby contain the structure necessary to support a cantilever monowing).

The Joukowski profiles we have analyzed were extensively tested in Gottingen (Prandtl et al., 1935) and Prandtl's group went on to develop other more practical shapes, for example, the Go 387. Other well-known early profiles go by the names Clark Y, RAF-34, and USA 35. National Advisory Committee on Aeronautics (NACA) conducted a systematic investigation of several series of airfoil shapes. Much of this work is reported in Abbott and Von Doenhoff (1959) for Reynolds numbers of 3 to 9×10^6. The 6-series, named for designations such as 66_3 618, were designed for extensive regions of laminar flow in the boundary layers (at low α), and hence low drag. They were employed on the later model propeller fighter planes in World War II such as the P-51. The X-15 Research Airplane, a rocket-powered airplane that flew 4100 mph (100 mph above the design value), used a NACA 66005. Several special airfoils have been developed, for example, the GA(W)-1 for General Aviation (Whitcomb). General Aviation actually means light planes for private use.

A very innovative approach was taken by Liebeck (1978). He produced a shape with a maximum lift coefficient above 3. His approach was adapted by Lissaman (1983) for the human-powered airplanes *Gossamer Condor* and *Albatross*.

The inviscid theory we used in predicting airfoil lift and (no) drag is valid for high Reynolds numbers, where the boundary layers are thin and do not separate. This theory works well for $Re > 10^6$, but the story is more complicated at lower values. This is the reason that early tests at low Reynolds numbers did not faithfully describe full-scale behavior. Figure 18.28 shows typical Reynolds numbers at sea level for various vehicles. At high altitudes the decrease in density causes Re to decrease. The crux of the problem is the nose separation bubble that can cause stall and limit lift. The behavior of the bubble and its interaction with the airfoil changes with the Reynolds number. Furthermore, the detailed shape of the airfoil, especially the nose radius and the rate at which the pressure on the upper surface increase, dictates whether boundary layer separation begins at the trailing edge or at a "burst" bubble.

Consider the enlarged view of a bubble in wall coordinates shown in Fig. 18.29. The boundary layer is laminar as it approaches the adverse pressure gradient on the upper surface. The velocity profile after separation is highly unstable and will undergo a transition to turbulence. With turbulence the cross-stream mixing of low- and high-momentum fluid promotes reattachment, and the resulting turbulent boundary layer is able to withstand a greater adverse pressure gradient without separating again. The length

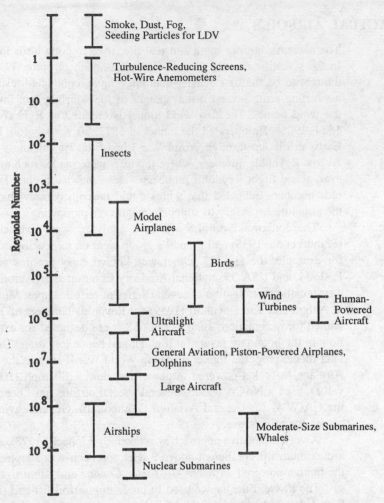

Figure 18.28 Typical flight regimes as a function of Reynolds number (items for air assume sea level conditions). Adapted from Carmichael (1981) and Lissaman (1983).

required for turbulence to develop is sensitive to the Reynolds number and is very long at low Re. The rule of thumb is that the bubble length ℓ_B compared to the chord length ℓ is $\ell_B/\ell = 50,000/\text{Re}$. Experimentally, reattachment usually does not occur if Re $<$ 70,000 and the maximum C_L is limited. For Re $= 100,000$ the bubble may be 20 to 30% of the chord and is considered long in that it changes the effective thickness of the airfoil. An order-of-magnitude increase in the Reynolds number (10^6) brings the bubble length to a few percent. Now the bubble represents a transition device and the resulting turbulent layer penetrates the adverse gradient to give the airfoil good performance. This is especially true if stall is initiated by separation progressing gradually from the trailing edge back up the upper surface. With a high Reynolds number, Re $> 10^6$, a turbulent boundary can be arranged to occur before the place where the laminar layer would separate, and hence the bubble avoided entirely. From this brief account one can see that the behavior of airfoils at a low Reynolds number or at high angles of attack at any Reynolds number

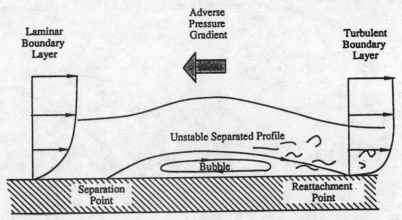

Figure 18.29 Separation bubble on the upper surface of an airfoil.

is a complicated interaction of viscous and inviscid events, sensitive to both shape and flow conditions.

*18.16 SCHWARZ–CHRISTOFFEL TRANSFORMATION

H. A. Schwarz and E. B. Christoffel, two German mathematicians, independently discovered a conformal transformation that will map the region inside a given polygon to the upper half plane. The polygonal in question must be a simple closed polygon but can have an arbitrary number of sides.

Figure 18.30 shows several examples of simple closed polygons. As shown from the figure, a polygon can have one or more sides at infinity. Indeed, polygons with some sides at infinity are the most useful ones for fluid mechanics applications. The strict definition of a simple closed polygon is that every point in the plane is either an interior point (any two interior points may be connected by a curve that never crosses a boundary), an exterior point, or a boundary point. This rules out figures where the boundary crosses itself and proceeds to form another polygon on the outside of Fig. 18.30.

If we take the polygon in the z-plane, we find that the transformation maps boundary points of the polygon to the real axis in the ζ-plane. This is one of the major aspects of the Schwarz–Christoffel transformation. As shown in the figure, a polygon boundary at infinity in the z-plane may or may not map to finite points on the ζ-plane. Similarly, the point at infinity in the ζ-plane is frequently mapped to a finite point in the z-plane, and always to a point on the polygon boundary. Let us define the vertices of the polygon as the points $A, B, C, \ldots$ in the z-plane, where the interior angles are $\alpha, \beta, \gamma, \ldots$. Under a Schwarz–Christoffel transformation these points are mapped to points on the real axis is the ζ-plane. Figure 18.30 displays this nomenclature. It is customary to take A, B, C in the counterclockwise sense, proceeding along the boundary with the interior on the left; then A', B', C' occur in the same sense on the real axis of the ζ-plane.

The transformation is expressed in the form of a differential equation, which must be integrated for any given polygon. The equation that defines the transformation $z = f(\zeta)$ is

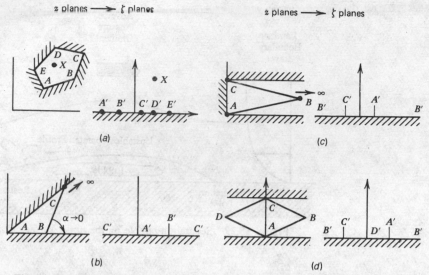

Figure 18.30 Schwarz–Christoffel transformations for several typical polygons.

$$\frac{dz}{d\zeta} = K(\zeta - \xi_a)^{\alpha/\pi-1}(\zeta - \xi_b)^{\beta/\pi-1}(\zeta - \xi_c)^{\gamma/\pi-1}\cdots \qquad (18.16.1)$$

In this equation K is an arbitrary complex constant, and ξ_α, ξ_b, ξ_c, ... are the transformed locations of the vertices in the ζ-plane. One very important fact in using Eq. 18.14.1 is that the terms corresponding to a vertex at infinity in the ζ-plane are omitted. If vertex B, located at finite z or at $z \to \infty$, is to be sent to $\xi_b \to \pm \infty$ the ζ-plane, the term $(\zeta - \xi_b)$ is left out of Eq. 18.16.1. The reason for this is explained in the following example.

To illustrate the use of the transformation, consider an infinite slit of width π. Figure 18.30d shows the slit as the limiting form of a quadrangle as points B and D go to infinity. The interior angles take on the following limiting values:

Vertex	z	Angle	(Angle/π − 1)
A	0	π	0
B	$\infty \exp(i0)$	0	−1
C	$i\pi$	π	0
D	$\infty \exp(i\pi)$	0	−1

Equation 18.16.1 for this case is

$$\frac{dz}{d\zeta} = K(\zeta - \zeta_a)^0(\zeta - \xi_b)^{-1}(\zeta - \xi_c)^0(\zeta - \xi_d)^{-1}$$

Let us choose to send the point B to $\xi_b \to \infty$. Then we can exclude the term $(\zeta - \xi_b)^{-1}$ from the transform expression. [This may be rationalized by noting that the term $(\zeta - \xi_b)^{-1}$ is dominated by ξ_b. If $dz/d\zeta$ is to be finite as $\xi_b \to \infty$, K/ξ_b must be finite. When we omit $(\zeta - \xi_b)^{-1}$ from the equation, we are essentially redefining the constant K.]

The transform equation reduces to

$$\frac{dz}{d\zeta} = K(\zeta - \xi_d)^{-1}$$

which integrates to

$$z = K \ln(\zeta - \xi_d) + L \tag{18.16.2}$$

This equation maps the degenerate quadrangle $ABCD$ to the upper half plane with the boundary points on the ξ-axis. We may still choose the mapped positions for two more vertices. Choosing $\xi_d = 0$, the transformation becomes

$$z = K \ln \zeta + L \tag{18.16.3}$$

For the second choice, we note that $z_a = 0$ and set $\zeta_a = \xi_a = 1$. This yields

$$0 = K \ln 1 + L$$

$$0 = L$$

We still must find the constant K. Note that when ζ is on the positive real axis between A' and B' (i.e., $\zeta = \mathrm{R}e^{i0}$ with $R > 1$), z must be real and positive. Thus Eq. 18.16.3 becomes real = $K \cdot$ real + $i0$, and we conclude that K is a real number. Since point D' has been sent to the origin ($\xi_d = 0$), point C' must lie on the negative ξ-axis and can be given by $\zeta_c = |\xi_c| e^{i\pi}$. Substituting this into Eq. 18.16.3 yields

$$0 + i\pi = K \ln|\xi_c| + iK\pi$$

Equating real and imaginary parts shows that $K = 1$ and that $\xi_c = -1$. The final transformation is given by

$$z = \ln \zeta \tag{18.16.4}$$

In arriving at this result we have been able to choose the ζ-plane locations of three vertices. The only restriction is that the vertices are on the real axis and retain the proper counterclockwise order. If one of the vertices is sent to infinity, this is counted as one of the arbitrary choices. The ζ location of the fourth vertex cannot be specified. In the present case the fourth vertex turns out to be located at $\xi_c = -1$. The number of arbitrary choices for vertex locations in the ζ-plane is the same for all polygons irrespective of the number of sides.

*18.17 DIFFUSER OR CONTRACTION FLOW

Consider a diffuser that connects two passages with parallel walls, as shown in Fig. 18.31. The figure shows only one diverging wall; however, we can, with equal validity, consider this as one-half of a symmetric diffuser with two diverging walls. The width of the small channel will be taken as k and that of the large channel by h. Let the flow velocity in the large channel be h. Let the flow velocity in the large channel by U. Considering the continuity equation, we must have a uniform velocity in the small channel of hU/k. In addition to h/k, a second geometrical parameter is needed to fix the diffuser geometry. We take the angle $\hat{\theta}$. Diffuser angles must be small in actual practice in order to avoid separation. (Angles of $7°$ or less are required for that purpose, so in many instances

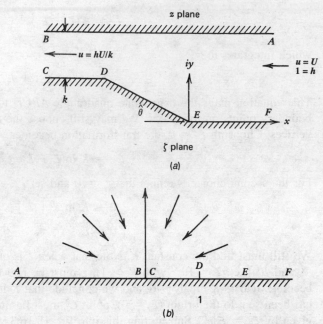

Figure 18.31   Flow in a contraction or diffuser with area ratio k and convergence angle $\hat{\theta}$. The ζ-plane flow is flow into a sink.

diffusers are in fact operated with some flow separation present.) Our solution will be valid only for situations where there is no separation and the boundary layers are thin. The answer may also represent the flow into a contraction simply by changing the sign of the velocity. Practical contraction sections have much larger angles, as flow separation is not such a critical problem in this case.

The Schwarz–Christoffel transformation maps the flow of Fig. 18.31a onto the upper half-plane as shown in Fig. 18.31b. Let us choose to map B–C to the origin, D to $\xi = 1$, and A–F to $\zeta \to \infty$. The ζ image of E is called e and cannot be specified independently. Thus, we have the following requirements:

Point	z	Angle θ	Exponent $(\theta/\pi) - 1$	ζ
A–F	$+\infty$	0	Not needed	∞
B–C	$-\infty$	0	Not needed	0
D	$(h - k)(-\cot \theta + i)$	$\pi + \hat{\theta}$	$1 + \hat{\theta}/\pi$	1
E	0	$\pi + \hat{\theta}$	$1 - \hat{\theta}/\pi$	$e = (h/k)^{\pi/\theta}$

Applying this information in the Schwarz–Christoffel equation 18.16.1, we have

$$\frac{dz}{d\zeta} = K\zeta^{-1}(\zeta - 1)^{\hat{\theta}/\pi}(\zeta - e)^{-\hat{\theta}/\pi} \tag{18.17.1}$$

The integration of Eq. 18.17.1 can be done in closed form if we take $\hat{\theta}/\pi$ as a rational fraction. Therefore, we let

$$\frac{\hat{\theta}}{\pi} = \frac{m}{2n} \qquad (18.17.2)$$

for m and n integers. Any angle can be approximated as closely as one desires by Eq. 18.17.2.

Before we actually integrate Eq. 18.17.1, it is useful to give the velocity potential and determine the constants K and e in Eq. 18.17.1. The flow in the ζ-plane is the flow from a source at the origin. Since the volume flow in the large channel is Uh, the strength of the source in the ζ-plane should be twice that amount. The complex potential is therefore

$$F = \frac{Uh}{\pi} \ln \zeta \qquad (18.17.3)$$

The corresponding velocity potential in the z-plane is

$$W(z) = \frac{dF}{d\zeta}\frac{d\zeta}{dz} = \frac{hU}{K\pi} \left(\frac{\zeta - e}{\zeta - 1}\right)^{m/2n} \qquad (18.17.4)$$

Now as $\zeta \to \infty$, $z \to A-F$, where the velocity $W = U$. For this to be true, the constant K in Eq. 18.17.4 must be

$$K = \frac{h}{\pi} \qquad (18.17.5)$$

At the other end of the channel, point $B-C$, the velocity is $W = hU/k$. Since BC maps to $\zeta = 0$, we substitute $\zeta = 0$ into Eq. 18.17.4 to obtain

$$e = \left(\frac{h}{k}\right)^{2n/m} \qquad (18.17.6)$$

With these constants the velocity becomes

$$W(z) = U \left[\frac{\zeta - (h/k)^{2n/m}}{\zeta - 1}\right]^{m/2n} \qquad (18.17.7)$$

This expression is left with $\zeta = \zeta(z)$ as a parameter.

Now, we return to the question of integrating Eq. 18.17.1. Integrals of the form Eq. 18.17.1, with rational exponents Eq. 18.17.2, can be separated into partial fractions if we make a variable change by defining s according to

$$s = \left(\frac{\zeta - e}{\zeta - 1}\right)^{1/2n} \qquad (18.17.8)$$

Solving this for ζ yields

$$\zeta = \frac{e - s^{2n}}{1 - s^{2n}} \tag{18.17.9}$$

Substitution of Eqs. 18.17.9, 18.17.5, and 18.17.2 into Eq. 18.17.1 changes the integral into

$$dz = 2n \frac{h}{\pi} \left(\frac{s^{2n-m-1}}{1 - s^{2n}} \, ds - \frac{s^{2n-m-1}}{e - s^{2n}} \, ds \right) \tag{18.17.10}$$

To simplify the notation, define

$$I_{mn}(s) = 2n \int \frac{s^{2n-m-1}}{1 - s^{2n}} \, ds \tag{18.17.11}$$

Equation 18.17.10 may now be cast into the form

$$z = \frac{h}{\pi} \left\{ I_{mn}(s) - \frac{k}{h} I_{mn} \left[\left(\frac{k}{h} \right)^{1/m} s \right] - \left(1 - \frac{k}{h} \right) I_{mn}(0) \right\} \tag{18.17.12}$$

The integrals I_{mn} in Eq. 18.17.11 can be evaluated exactly (Gradshteyn and Ryzhik, 1965):

$$I_{mn}(s) = (-1)^{2n-m+1} \ln(1 + s) - \ln(1 - s)$$

$$- \sum_{j=1}^{n-1} \cos \frac{j(2n - m)\pi}{n} \ln \left(1 - 2s \cos \frac{j\pi}{n} + s^2 \right)$$

$$+ 2 \sum_{j=1}^{n-1} \sin \frac{j(2n - m)\pi}{n} \arctan \left(\frac{s - \cos(j\pi/n)}{\sin(j\pi/n)} \right) \tag{18.17.13}$$

The transformation function $z = f(\zeta)$ is given by the combination of Eqs. 18.17.8, 18.17.12, and 18.17.13. The streamlines in the z-plane are easily found, as they are radial lines through the origin in the ζ-plane. Similarly, the potential lines are circular arcs in the ζ-plane.

The velocity potential in the z-plane is expressed by Eq. 18.17.4. A more useful form is to employ s as a parameter through Eq. 18.17.8. In terms of s the velocity potential is

$$W = u - iv = Us^m \tag{18.17.14}$$

Computation of the velocity and its position is accomplished by using ζ as the independent variable and $s(\zeta)$ as an intermediary parameter.

A plane where the points represent the complex velocity $W = u - iv$ is called a *hodograph plane*. A vector from the origin to a certain point is a mirror image of the velocity vector: The direction is $-\theta$ instead of $+\theta$. Figure 18.32 shows the hodograph plane for the flow into a contraction. Lines drawn in this figure represents the velocities that occur on a given streamline. All streamlines start from $(1, 0)$, the uniform upstream flow. Flow along the centerline goes from $(1, 0)$ to $(1/k, 0)$ while the angle remains zero. An interior streamline makes a looping path between these same two points. The loop degenerates into a series of straight lines for the streamline that follows the walls.

Figure 18.33 displays the velocity for a typical contraction as a function of the distance along the streamline. All streamlines begin at $U = 1$ in the wide section. As

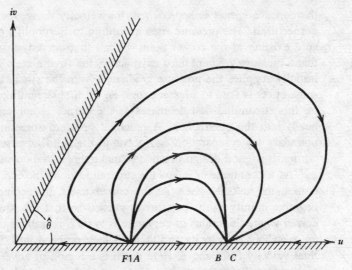

Figure 18.32 Hodograph plane $W = u - iv$ for flow in a contraction. The path of streamlines in this plane is depicted.

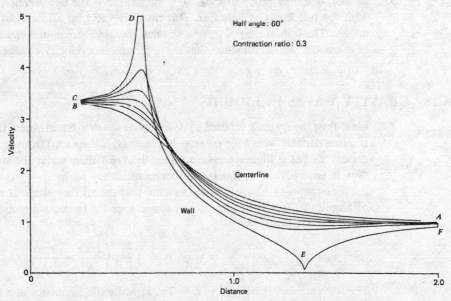

Figure 18.33 Velocities on several streamlines as a function of distance along the streamlines; $\theta = 60°$, $Kh = 0.3$. From Goenka (1982).

the concave corner is approached, the velocity decreases and must become zero at the corner itself. The pressure rises according to Bernoulli's equation, with stagnation pressure existing at the corner point. Recall that curved streamlines in inviscid flow mean that a pressure gradient must exist across the streamlines. The high pressure in the corner initially supplies the pressure gradient to turn the streamlines into the contraction. This same effect is seen to a lesser extent on the first streamline in from the wall. The velocity on this streamline first decreases as the corner is approached and then increases as it heads into the contraction. A practical problem sometimes occurs in contractions, as boundary layer separation can occur in the mild adverse pressure gradient at the first corner. It is good design practice to make this initial curvature small to avoid separation.

As we continue to follow the streamline along the contraction wall toward the convex corner, the velocity rises. At the corner itself, it becomes infinite. The corresponding negative infinity in the pressure is needed so that the streamlines can curve around the corner where the radius of curvature is zero. Streamlines that come near this corner have an overshoot in velocity and then, as they proceed into the small section, approach the final velocity from above. Here again is a region of adverse pressure and the possibility of boundary layer separation. Once more the practical solution is to make this corner gently rounded to reduce the adverse pressure gradient tending to separate the flow. Most contractions in use, even the "bell-mouth" entrance, produce a nonuniform velocity profile at the end of the geometric entrance. The velocity near the wall tends to be too high and the pressure somewhat low. This is a remnant of the curvature of the streamlines as they pack themselves into the straight section.

Note that not all the streamlines have a low velocity near the concave corner and an overshoot in velocity near the convex corner. Streamlines near the center of the flow display a monotonic increase in velocity as the flow enters the contraction. As a matter of fact, one may prove that the 50% streamline is the demarcation between streamlines with the two kinds of behavior. This result is valid for all contraction ratios and for all angles. The importance of this fact is that the 50% streamline can be used in the design of a smooth wall contraction that has a monotonic velocity change on all streamlines.

*18.18   GRAVITY WAVES IN LIQUIDS

Ideal-flow theory may be used to describe waves in a liquid where there is a free surface. If a free surface, where the pressure is constant, is displaced from its equilibrium position, gravity causes a higher pressure under the crest than under the troughs. The resulting flow is unsteady, irrotational, and incompressible.

For purposes of analysis we assume that the surface shape is a traveling sine wave of amplitude A, wavelength λ, and phase speed c in the x-direction. The y-position of the surface is given by

$$y_s \equiv \eta(x, t) = A \sin \left(\frac{2\pi x}{\lambda} - \frac{2\pi ct}{\lambda} \right) \qquad (18.18.1)$$

The wavenumber is defined as $k = 2\pi/\lambda$, while the frequency at a fixed position is $\omega = kc$. Figure 18.34 shows the wave where $y = 0$ is the equilibrium position of the free surface and the bottom is at $y = -h$.

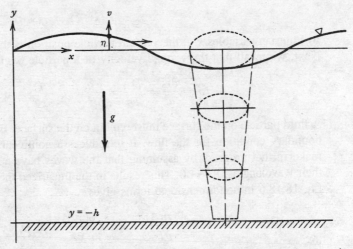

Figure 18.34 Gravity wave in a liquid. Dashed lines show particle paths at various depths.

In light of Eq. 18.18.1, we introduce nondimensional variables for x and t as

$$X = kx = \frac{2\pi x}{\lambda}$$

$$T = \omega t$$

Hence, the liquid surface is

$$\frac{\eta}{A} = \sin(X - T) \tag{18.18.2}$$

Furthermore, since ideal flow has a potential that obeys

$$\nabla^2 \phi = 0 \tag{18.18.3}$$

we should use the same nondimensional scale for y as for x, that is, $Y = ky$. Velocities are nondimensionalized by estimating that the amplitude of the motion A times the frequency indicates the particle velocity. Thus, we let

$$U = \frac{u}{A\omega}, \qquad V = \frac{v}{A\omega} \tag{18.18.4}$$

The nondimensional potential

$$\Phi = \frac{\phi}{Ac} \tag{18.18.5}$$

will render $v_i = \partial_i \phi$ consistent with the previous nondimensional forms.

The most complicated part of this problem is caused by the moving free surface. Let r_2 be the y-position of a material particle on the surface. The Lagrangian description of r_2 uses the original particle position x^0 and the Lagrangian time $\hat{t}$:

$$r_2 = r_2(x^0, \hat{t}) = \eta(x, t)$$

In Eulerian variables x, t, the vertical particle position is the equation of the free surface. Next, we recall that the vertical velocity of a particle is given by

$$v = \frac{\partial r_2}{\partial \hat{t}} = \frac{D\eta}{Dt} = \frac{\partial \eta}{\partial t} + u \frac{\partial \eta}{\partial x} \qquad \text{at} \quad y = \eta \qquad (18.18.6)$$

A fluid particle on the surface must remain on the surface. Equation 18.18.6 is a kinematic boundary condition for the flow. It introduces a nonlinearity into the problem. We can make further progress by assuming that the waves have a small amplitude compared to their wavelengths: $Ak \to 0$. This results in the linearized theory of gravity waves. Writing Eq. 18.18.6 in nondimensional terms gives

$$V = \frac{\partial (\eta/A)}{\partial T} + kAU \frac{\partial (\eta/A)}{\partial X} \qquad \text{at} \quad y = \frac{\eta}{A} kA$$

Next, we note that $V = \partial \Phi / \partial Y$ and expand the surface value in a Taylor series about $Y = 0$. This yields

$$V = \frac{\partial \Phi}{\partial Y}\bigg|_0 + \frac{\partial^2 \Phi}{\partial T}\bigg|_0 \frac{\eta}{A} kA + \cdots$$

Hence, in the limit $kA \to 0$ the two relations above yield the boundary condition at $Y = 0$ as

$$\frac{\partial \Phi}{\partial Y}\bigg|_0 = \frac{\partial (\eta/A)}{\partial T}$$

$$= -\cos(X - T) \qquad (18.18.7)$$

This equation, together with the restriction that no flow crosses the bottom,

$$\frac{\partial \Phi}{\partial Y} = V = 0 \qquad \text{at} \quad Y = -H \qquad (18.18.8)$$

constitute the kinematic condition for the solution. Separation of variables applied to $\nabla^2 \Phi$ and the boundary conditions above yields the solution as the potential

$$\Phi = \frac{\cosh(Y + H)}{\sinh H} \cos(X - T) \qquad (18.18.9)$$

The corresponding velocities are

$$U = -\frac{\cosh(Y + H)}{\sinh H} \cos(X - T)$$

$$\qquad\qquad\qquad\qquad\qquad\qquad (18.18.10)$$

$$V = \frac{\sinh(Y + H)}{\sinh H} \cos(X - T)$$

The solution above has an arbitrary wavelength and an arbitrary phase speed.

The free surface of the wave has a constant pressure. This information enters the problem through the Bernoulli equation, the only dynamic restriction in the problem. At the surface,

$$\frac{\partial \phi}{\partial t} + \frac{p}{\rho} + \frac{1}{2}(u^2 + v^2) + g\eta = C(t) \qquad (18.18.11)$$

The function $C(t)$ is equivalent to the arbitrary constant in the velocity potential (i.e., $\phi = \phi + \int C\,dt$) and may be set equal to zero. The nondimensional form of the Bernoulli equation is

$$\frac{\partial \Phi}{\partial T} + P + \frac{kA}{2}(U^2 + V^2) + \frac{g}{kc^2}\frac{\eta}{A} = 0$$

where $P = p/\rho c^2 kA$. For small amplitude ($kA \to 0$), the velocity term may be neglected. Furthermore, differentiation with respect to time eliminates the constant pressure. This yields

$$\frac{\partial^2 \Phi}{\partial T^2} + \frac{g}{kc^2}\frac{\partial (\eta/A)}{\partial T} = 0 \qquad (18.18.12)$$

The derivative of Φ is to be evaluated at the surface; however, by expanding from $Y = 0$ in a Taylor series and noting that $kA \to 0$ (the same steps that were used to arrive at Eq. 18.18.7), we can use the value at $Y = 0$. Equation 18.18.12 supplies an eigenvalue relation that determines the wave speed c. Substituting Eqs. 18.18.9 and 18.18.2 into Eq. 18.18.12 shows that

$$\frac{kc^2}{g} = \tanh kh \qquad (18.18.13)$$

The speed of propagation of a gravity wave is fixed by the wavenumber and the fluid depth. This is the central result.

For special cases we may simplify Eq. 18.18.13. In water that is shallow compared to the wavelength ($kh \to 0$), $\tanh kh \approx kh$ and we find that

$$c^2 = gh \qquad (18.18.14)$$

All waves have a speed that depends on the depth but not on the wavelength.

The second special case is when the liquid is deep compared to the wavelength ($kh \to \infty$). Now, $\tanh kh \approx 1$, so we obtain as the simplified form of Eq. 18.18.13 the relation

$$c^2 = \frac{g}{k} \qquad (18.18.15)$$

Waves have a speed that depends on their wavelength. Consider that a wave in deep water with an arbitrary shape is composed of several Fourier components. Each component, according to Eq. 18.18.15, has a different phase speed. Thus, the shape of the wave will change continually. For this reason the speed–wavenumber equation above is called the *dispersion relation*.

An important physical concept called the *group velocity* can be illustrated by water waves. Envision a disturbance that generates a train of waves composed of several wavelengths. After a while the waves sort themselves out according to their differing phase speeds, and packets of waves of nearly the same wavenumber are traveling together. For illustrative purposes, assume that two waves of equal amplitude and wavenumbers k and $k + \Delta k$:

$$\eta_1 = A \sin(kx + \omega t)$$

$$\eta_2 = A \sin[(k + \Delta k)x + (\omega + \Delta\omega)t]$$

The surface for these waves is

$$\eta = \eta_1 + \eta_2$$

$$= 2A \cos\left(\frac{1}{2}\Delta k\, x - \frac{1}{2}\Delta\omega\, t\right) \sin\left[\left(h + \frac{\Delta k}{2}\right)x + \left(\omega + \frac{\Delta\omega}{2}\right)t\right]$$

The sine part of this expression is a wave that has nearly the basic wavelength k and phase speed $c = \omega/k$. The cosine part is a much longer modulation, corresponding to a group or packet of the sine waves. This envelope moves with a *group velocity* defined by

$$c_g = \frac{\Delta\omega}{\Delta k} = \frac{d\omega}{dk}$$

or since $\omega = kc$,

$$c_g = c - k\frac{dc}{dk} \tag{18.18.16}$$

Evaluating this for water waves using Eq. 18.19.15, we find that

$$c_g = \tfrac{1}{2}c \tag{18.18.17}$$

The wave packet moves with only one-half the dominant phase speed. Physically, this is important because the energy of the group is transported at this velocity. Individual waves move within the pocket at their own speed. Individual components leave the packet at the front while others enter at the rear.

The group-velocity phenomena only occurs in a physical situation where waves of different wavelengths move with different speeds. A dispersion relation $c(k)$ must exist, or else Eq. 18.18.16 shows that $c_g = c$. Shallow-water waves, for example, travel without changing shape.

We have spent some time discussing the wave shape and how it moves. Let us now consider the motion of the fluid particles within the flow. The particle position r_i can be expressed in both Lagrangian and Eulerian variables:

$$r_i = r_i(x_i^0, \hat{t}) = r_i(x_i, t)$$

By definition, the fluid velocities are

$$v_i = \frac{\partial r_i}{\partial \hat{t}} = \frac{D r_i}{Dt} = \frac{\partial r_i}{\partial t} + u \frac{\partial r_i}{\partial x} + v \frac{\partial r_i}{\partial y}$$

Converting to nondimensional form, we have

$$\frac{\partial (r_i/A)}{\partial \hat{T}} = \frac{\partial (r_i/A)}{\partial T} + kA \left[U \frac{\partial (r_i/A)}{\partial X} + V \frac{\partial (r_i/A)}{\partial Y} \right]$$

From the equation above we see that the Lagrangian and Eulerian time derivatives are equivalent for $kA \rightarrow 0$. Therefore, we may find the particle paths by integrating Eq. 18.18.10 with respect to time. This gives

$$R_1 = \frac{r_i}{A} = - \frac{\cosh(Y + H)}{\sinh H} \cos(X - \hat{T})$$

$$R_2 = \frac{r_2}{A} = - \frac{\sinh(Y + H)}{\sinh H} \sin(X - \hat{T})$$

Here X, Y denote the average particle position and R_1, R_2 the displacement from that position. One may verify that the paths are elliptical motions obeying

$$\left(\frac{R_1}{a} \right)^2 + \left(\frac{R_2}{b} \right)^2 = 1$$

where

$$a = \frac{\cosh(Y + H)}{\sinh H}, \qquad b = \frac{\sinh(Y + H)}{\sinh H}$$

Sketches of the motion are given in Figure 18.34. Note that at the bottom, the amplitude of the motion is $1/\sinh H$. For an infinitely deep fluid this goes to zero, and furthermore the particle paths near the surface become circles.

18.19 CONCLUSIONS

Ideal-flow patterns are dominated by geometry; the streamlines adjust to the shape of an internal passage or the shape of an airfoil. When the cross section between streamlines is narrower, the velocity becomes higher, by continuity, and the pressure lower, by the Bernoulli equation. Curvature of streamlines implies that a pressure gradient exists in the normal direction with the low values toward the center of curvature. Steady unseparated external flow over a body produces no pressure drag. This fact applies to the nose of a semi-infinite body as well. Separation from the shoulders of a nose invalidates this conclusion. The lift force on an airfoil increases directly as the angle of attack, and all airfoils have the same lift curve slope of 2π. Camber offsets the angle of attack for zero lift to a negative value so that lift occurs at $\alpha = 0$. Thickness and camber distributions are important for the detailed pressure distributions, and hence the boundary layer, but the integrated effect on lift is negligible.

PROBLEMS

18.1 (A) Show that the sum of two velocity fields, potential fields, or streamfunction fields for an incompressible, irrotational flow is again an incompressible and irrotational flow.

18.2 (A) For the stagnation point flow $F = Uz^2$, find the streamlines, potential lines, and the equations for the velocity components u, v.

18.3 (A) Consider the complex function $F(z) = \phi(x, y) + i\psi(x, y) = \sin z$. Demonstrate that both ϕ and ψ satisfy the Laplace equation. Next, let $z = \zeta^2$ where $\zeta = \xi + i\eta$ and $F(z = \zeta^2) = \hat{F} = \hat{\phi}(\xi, \eta) + i\hat{\psi}(\xi, \eta)$. Show that $\hat{\phi}(\xi, \eta)$ and $\hat{\psi}(\xi, \eta)$ satisfy the Laplace equation.

18.4 (A) Verify that the streamlines from a doublet are given by Eq. 18.5.3. Find the velocity components v_r and v_θ for this flow.

18.5 (B) Consider the ideal flow over a circular cylinder where the free stream is an unsteady flow $U_\infty = a + bt$ and the pressure is $p_\infty + \frac{1}{2}\rho U_\infty^2 = $ constant. What is the velocity potential for this flow? What is the pressure at the forward stagnation point?

18.6 (A) Find the streamline equations for a line source superimposed with a line vortex both located at the origin. Determine the pressure as a function of distance from the origin.

18.7 (A) A line source of strength m is parallel to a wall at a distance h. Find the pressure distribution on the wall where p_0 is the pressure at the stagnation point.

18.8 (C) The flow in a flat slot of width h is nearly uniform at U_0, however, at x_0 it has a small deviation $U(y)$ ($0 \le y \le h$) from its previous history. How rapidly in x will the deviation die out? What Fourier modes of deviations are first and last to die out?

18.9 (B) Find the flow field potential F and velocity W for a streaming motion U over a source located at $z = -1$ and a sink of equal strength at $z = +1$. Find the stagnation points.

18.10 (A) Consider an elliptic cylinder of length five times the thickness. Find the complex potential and complex velocity for streaming flow without circulation past this object.

18.11 (B) Determine the pressure distribution over the surface in Problem 18.10 as a function of distance s from the stagnation point.

18.12 (C) Show that the exact shape of a Joukowski airfoil with zero thickness is a circular arc.

18.13 (A) Sketch the streamline patterns you would expect for ideal flow over a circular arc at angle of attack α and various values of circulation Γ.

18.14 (B) Find the pressure distribution on a Joukowski airfoil with 3% camber and 10% thickness operating at 4° angle of attack.

18.15 (B) Express the result of Problem 18.14 in terms of the surface distance from the stagnation point.

18.16 (A) According to linear theory, what is the angle of attack for zero lift for the airfoil in Problem 18.14?

18.17 (B) Determine the complex velocity for ideal streaming flow past a wall that has a thin vertical plate of height h projecting from the wall.

18.18 (A) A step in a wall is of height h. Find the complex velocity for flow into a sink located at the concave corner.

18.19 (A) Find the complex velocity for the flow from a line source of strength m located a distance h from both sides of a 90° corner.

18.20 (B) Find the pressure distribution on the walls of a 45° contraction with an area ratio of 3:1.

18.21 (B) A line vortex of strength Γ is a distance h above a plane wall. The motion of the vortex is opposed by a uniform stream U so as to be stationary. Find an expression for the pressure coefficient on the wall and plot as a function of position.

18.22 (B) Consider a step contraction of area ratio 4:1. Find the equation for the 50% streamline and plot on a true scale graph. Compute the pressure along the streamline to verify that it changes monotonically.

18.23 (C) A flat plate airfoil has a chord ℓ and trailing-edge flap of length $\ell/2$. The flap is deflected at an angle β to the chord. Formulate the solution of the problem using the method of Section 18.14.

18.24 (B) A bicylindrical (coaxial) coordinate system $\zeta = \xi + i\eta$ is related to rectangular coordinates $z = x + iy$ by

$$z = i \cot(\tfrac{1}{2}\zeta)$$

In the upper half of the z-plane, a curve of constant ξ is a circular arc with the center somewhere on the y-axis and passing through the points $(-1, 0)$ and $(1, 0)$. For instance, $\xi = n\pi/2$ is one-half of a circle (cutting through $0, 1$) when $n = 1$. If $1 < n < 2$, the arc cuts the y-axis at a value less than 1, and if $n = 2$, that is, $\xi = \pi$, the arc is a straight line between $(-1, 0)$ and $(1, 0)$. On the other hand, curves of constant η are circles in the right half-plane for $\eta > 0$ (in the left half-plane for $\eta < 0$). All centers are located on the x-axis. All circles in the right half-plane enclose the point $(1, 0)$ and those in the left half-planes enclose $(-1, 0)$. As we move along a $\xi = $ constant arc in the upper half-plane, the point $(-1, 0)$ is $\eta = -\infty$, increasing to $\eta = 0$, where the arc cuts the y-axis, and proceeding to $\eta \to \infty$ at $(+1, 0)$. Prove that the transformation above is equivalent to

$$x = \frac{\sinh \eta}{\cosh \eta - \cos \xi}, \qquad y = \frac{\sin \xi}{\cosh \eta - \cos \xi}$$

Plot the circular arc with $\xi_0 = \frac{4}{3}\pi/2$. On this arc locate the points $n = -\infty, -\pi, 0, \pi$, and $+\infty$.

A biconvex airfoil or strut shape consists of two circular arcs back to back. Consider that the symmetric streaming motion in the upper half-plane from right to left is given by the potential

$$F = U\frac{2}{n}i \cot \frac{\zeta}{n}$$

Show that the velocity is given by

$$(u^2 + v^2)^{1/2} = \frac{4U}{n^2}\frac{\sin \frac{1}{2}\zeta \sin \frac{1}{2}\bar{\zeta}}{\sin(\zeta/n)\sin(\bar{\zeta}/n)}$$

$$= \frac{4U}{n^2}\frac{\cosh \eta - \cos \xi}{\cosh(2\eta/n) - \cos(2\xi/n)}$$

18.25 (B) Consider the circular arc strut of Problem 18.24. Determine how the thickness ratio $2t/\ell$ and the nose half-angle depend on the parameter n.

18.26 (C) Find the pressure distribution on the surface of a circular arc strut with $n = \frac{5}{3}$. Given the pressure as a function of the distance from the nose measured along the surface.

18.27 (B) Consider a Joukowski airfoil with nominal (linear approximations) 3% camber and 10% thickness. Plot the exact shape and the linearized shape.

18.28 (B) Consider a uniform stream of strength U from left to right. At positions ih and $-ih$, two sources of equal strength m are located. What different types of flow patterns exist for different values of U, h, and m? When do these patterns occur? Find the velocity and pressure along the x-axis.

18.29 (B) Consider a hexagon with sides l. At each vertex a vortex of strength Γ is placed and held stationary. Adjacent vortices have opposite rotations. Where are the streamlines in this flow that are straight and could be considered as flat walls? Find the velocity and pressure distribution along one of these lines.

19

Axisymmetric and Three-Dimensional Ideal Flows

The mathematical approach to solving axisymmetric and three-dimensional ideal flows is somewhat different from that used in plane flows. No longer can we use complex-variable theory and its powerful techniques. Despite the change in the mathematical approach, the physical events and trends in three-dimensional flow are much like their plane flow counterparts. For example, we shall find that the drag on a nonlifting three-dimensional body is zero, just as it is for plane two-dimensional bodies. Nevertheless, here are some differences between plane flows and three-dimensional flows. A finite wing or other three-dimensional body that produces lift will also have a drag force. This is a three-dimensional effect.

19.1 GENERAL EQUATIONS AND CHARACTERISTICS OF THREE-DIMENSIONAL IDEAL FLOWS

Recall from Chapter 16 that any irrotational flow will allow a description in terms of the velocity potential,

$$\mathbf{v} = \nabla \phi \qquad (19.1.1)$$

By the continuity equaiton the velocity potential obeys the Laplace equation

$$\nabla \cdot \mathbf{v} = \nabla^2 \phi = 0 \qquad (19.1.2)$$

The elliptic nature of Eq. 19.1.2 implies that all parts of the flow are in communication. Changing a boundary position on one part of the field has an effect at all other points in the flow.

The boundary conditions at a solid wall require that the fluid velocity normal to the wall be the same as the wall velocity. This is expressed as

$$\mathbf{n} \cdot \mathbf{w}_{\text{wall}} = \mathbf{n} \cdot \mathbf{v} = \mathbf{n} \cdot \nabla \phi \qquad \text{at walls} \qquad (19.1.3)$$

If the wall does not move, $0 = \mathbf{n} \cdot \nabla \phi$. The mathematical problem for ϕ is completed by specifying the velocity at some arbitrarily chosen positions: The inflow and outflow boundaries for an internal flow, or $r \rightarrow \infty$ for an external flow.

By inspecting the governing equations above, we see that they are linear and may be nondimensionalized by a single length scale L and a single velocity scale U. The nondimensional potential ϕ/UL and velocities v_i/U are functions of x_i/L and the geometry of the boundaries. Thus, this is a geometry-dominated problem. Neither the reference pressure nor the fluid density has any effect on the velocity or on the flow pattern. As we noted previously, the absence of time in the differential equation means that the flow is determined completely by the instantaneous position and velocities of the walls and by the fluid velocities at prescribed boundaries. The past history of the flow is of no consequence.

The pressure field that is compatible with the velocity field is determined from the Bernoulli equation for ideal flow. It is

$$\frac{\partial \phi}{\partial t} + \frac{p}{\rho} + gh + \frac{1}{2} q^2 = C(t) \tag{19.1.4}$$

If desired, the integration function $C(t)$ may be incorporated into a redefined potential $\hat{\phi} = \phi + \int C \, dt$. From Eq. 19.1.4 we see that the proper nondimensional pressure is $p/\frac{1}{2}\rho U^2$; the actual pressure field will increase directly as the density of the fluid and directly as the kinetic energy of the flow, $\frac{1}{2}U^2$.

If the flow is axisymmetric, there are only two nonzero velocity components, which depend on only two distance variables. In these cases we may use the streamfunction theory of Chapter 12. The streamfunction $\psi(r, \theta)$ is defined as the only nonzero component of the vector potential **B**. Recall that the velocities are given by $\mathbf{v} = \nabla \times \mathbf{B}$. Furthermore, when the vorticity is zero, we may find $\psi(r, \theta)$ from the relation $0 = \nabla \cdot \nabla \mathbf{B}$. In many problems we shall find that spherical coordinates r, θ are the most useful. For further reference recall from Appendix D the working equations relating the streamfunction to the velocity components:

$$v_r = \frac{1}{r^2 \sin \theta} \frac{\partial \psi}{\partial \theta}, \qquad v_\theta = \frac{-1}{r \sin \theta} \frac{\partial \psi}{\partial r} \tag{19.1.5}$$

After some simplification, the relation for $\nabla^2 \mathbf{B} = 0$ in spherical coordinates reduces to

$$\frac{\partial^2 \psi}{\partial r^2} + \frac{\sin \theta}{r^2} \frac{\partial}{\partial \theta} \left(\frac{1}{\sin \theta} \frac{\partial \psi}{\partial \theta} \right) = 0 \tag{19.1.6}$$

This equation is not the Laplace equation in spherical coordinates. In contrast, $\nabla^2 \phi$ with $\phi = \phi(r, \theta)$ reduces to

$$\frac{\partial}{\partial r} \left(r^2 \frac{\partial \phi}{\partial r} \right) + \frac{1}{\sin \theta} \frac{\partial}{\partial \theta} \left(\sin \theta \frac{\partial \phi}{\partial \theta} \right) = 0 \tag{19.1.7}$$

The velocity components in terms of $\phi(r, \theta)$ are

$$v_r = \frac{\partial \phi}{\partial r}, \qquad v_\theta = \frac{1}{r} \frac{\partial \phi}{\partial \theta} \tag{19.1.8}$$

In axisymmetric flow we have our choice of working with $\psi(r, \theta)$ or $\phi(r, \theta)$. For general three-dimensional flows, ψ cannot be used, so ϕ is the only choice.

19.2 SWIRLING FLOW TURNED INTO AN ANNULUS

Consider a flow such as that shown in Fig. 19.1, where a stream flows radially toward an axis of symmetry. Upon approaching the axis, the stream turns and flows along the axis in an annular region. An arrangement such as this is used as the inlet section to hydraulic turbines in hydroelectric power plants. We assume that the flow is uniform at the entrance $r = R$ with an inward velocity $v_r = V_r$ and a swirling component $v_\theta = V_\theta$. The swirling velocity component is produced by vanes located far from the axis. In addition, we assume that the flow was placed in the initial condition solely by pressure and gravity forces, so that the vorticity is zero. Hence, because of Helmholtz's theorems the vorticity remains zero.

As an ideal flow, the velocity must obey the continuity condition $\nabla \cdot \mathbf{v} = 0$ and the irrotationality condition $\boldsymbol{\omega} = \nabla \times \mathbf{v} = 0$. The continuity equation in cylindrical coordinates is

$$\frac{1}{r}\frac{\partial}{\partial r}(r v_r) + \frac{1}{r}\frac{\partial v_\theta}{\partial \theta} + \frac{\partial v_z}{\partial z} = 0 \qquad (19.2.1)$$

In the entrance section, the flow has no v_z component, and v_θ depends only on r; hence, Eq. 19.2.1 is satisfied by

$$v_r = \frac{R}{r}V_r \qquad \text{(entrance region)} \qquad (19.2.2)$$

The vorticity condition is

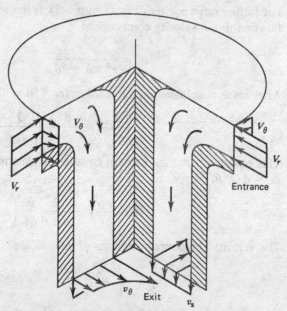

Figure 19.1 Swirling flow into an annulus.

$$\omega_r = 0 = \frac{1}{r}\frac{\partial v_z}{\partial \theta} - \frac{\partial v_\theta}{\partial z}$$

$$\omega_\theta = 0 = \frac{\partial v_r}{\partial z} - \frac{\partial v_z}{\partial r} \qquad (19.2.3)$$

$$\omega_z = 0 = \frac{1}{r}\frac{\partial}{\partial r}(rv_\theta) - \frac{1}{r}\frac{\partial v_r}{\partial \theta}$$

We shall not find out the details of the velocity profiles in the region where the flow is turned to the z-direction. However, by noting that none of the velocity components can depend on θ, we see from the first equation in 19.2.3 that $v_\theta = f(r)$ and thus is independent of z. From the last equation of 19.2.3, we find that

$$v_\theta = \frac{R}{r} V_\theta \qquad (19.2.4)$$

The fact that the vorticity is zero means that the angular momentum rv_θ is conserved as the flow moves toward the axis. If the center section is absent, the flow continues to $r = 0$ and Eq. 19.2.4 predicts that v_θ becomes infinite. This, of course, does not happen as the vorticity of the boundary layer on the back wall is swept into the core region of the resulting vortex. The core region is then not an ideal flow.

The only remaining step is to assume that the straight walls of the exit annulus force the flow into streamlines that lie on cylindrical surfaces $r = $ const. Hence, $v_r = 0$ in this region, and the continuity equation 19.2.1 is satisfied by $v_z = f(r)$. The second vorticity equation, $\omega_\theta = 0$ in Eq. 19.2.3, shows that v_z in fact cannot depend on r; so we must have a constant value of v_z at the exit. The areas of the inlet and outlet relate this constant to the inlet flow velocity V_r.

This problem illustrates how kinematic conditions determine the velocity profiles in ideal flows. By way of summary the velocities are:

At the entrance:

$$v_z = 0, \qquad v_r = \frac{R}{r} V_r, \qquad v_\theta = \frac{R}{r} V_\theta$$

In the exit annulus:

$$v_z = \frac{A_1}{A_2} V_r, \qquad v_r = 0, \qquad v_\theta = \frac{R}{r} V_\theta$$

The angular momentum RV_θ would be converted into a torque if the flow continued through a hydraulic machine.

19.3 FLOW OVER A WEIR

A weir is a device used in open-channel flows to measure the volume flow rate. A broad-crested weir is shown in Fig. 19.2, where a tranquil flow of depth z_0 occurs upstream of

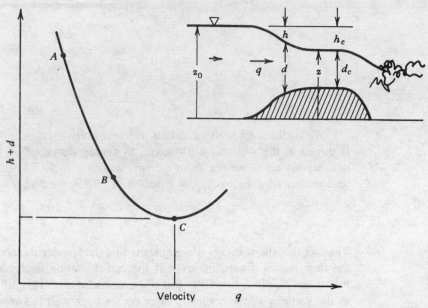

Figure 19.2   Critical flow over a broad-crested weir.

the weir. The surface is depressed an amount h_c as the flow goes over the weir. The weir is broad enough that a uniform flow is established across the top and h_c is easily measured. The water finally spills into the downstream flow as shown in the picture. If the downstream conditions prevent this pattern by backing up the water so that the free surface merely dips slightly, the weir is said to be *drowned*.

In the neighborhood of the crest, we denote the depth of the fluid by d and the position of the free surface by h, and assume that the flow changes slowly in the streamwise direction so that it is reasonable to regard the velocity q as constant across the flow. The global continuity equation requires that

$$d = \frac{Q}{q} \tag{19.3.1}$$

where Q is the total flow per unit width. The Bernoulli equation for any streamline is

$$\frac{p}{\rho} + \frac{1}{2} q^2 + gz = C \tag{19.3.2}$$

In particular, the surface streamline has a constant pressure and originates at $z = z_0$, where the velocity is negligible. For this streamline

$$\tfrac{1}{2}q^2 = g(z_0 - z) = gh \tag{19.3.3}$$

Next, solve Eq. 19.3.3 for h and combine with Eq. 19.3.1 to give the depth of the bottom measured from reference level of the free surface far upstream:

$$h + d = \frac{Q}{q} + \frac{q^2}{2g} \tag{19.3.4}$$

The behavior of Eq. 19.3.4 is shown in Fig. 19.2, where $h + d$ is plotted as a function of q for fixed Q and g. The tranquil flow upstream starts at a low value of q and high $h + d$, as at point A on the figure. As the flow approaches the crest of the weir, q increases. If the lowest value of $h + d$ is at a point such as B, the weir is drowned. In this case the velocity decreases downstream, with the flow state returning toward A. We can deduce little else about this situation, as the exact position of point B depends on the details of the downstream channel and the weir.

The case of most interest is when the flow reaches the critical point C and the velocity q continues to increase as the flow goes over the weir. The crest of the weir is the minimum of $h + d$, and from Eq. 19.3.4 we find the velocity of the water by locating the minimum point. Setting the derivative equal to zero yields

$$0 = \frac{d(h + d)}{dq} = -Qq^{-2} + \frac{q}{g} \tag{19.3.5}$$

$$q_c = (gQ)^{1/3}$$

Inserting Eq. 19.3.5 into Eq. 19.3.3 gives h_c for the crest as

$$h_c = \frac{1}{2}\left(\frac{Q^2}{g}\right)^{1/3} \tag{19.3.6}$$

From Eq. 19.3.1 the water depth at the crest is

$$d_c = \frac{Q}{q_c} = Q(gQ)^{-1/3} \tag{}$$

Finally, we solve for the flow rate Q:

$$Q = g^{1/2}d_c^{3/2} \tag{19.3.7}$$

The flow rate can be calculated from a single measurement of the fluid depth at the crest of the weir. In actual practice a coefficient is inserted in Eq. 19.3.6 to account for three dimensional effects and, in certain situations, viscous effects.

An interesting and important side result of this analysis is that point C marks the place in the flow where the Froude number Fr $= q^2/gd_c$ is equal to unity. When Fr $= 1$ the velocity of propagation of shallow water waves, c, is exactly equal to the flow velocity (see Eq. 18.18.14). Any small disturbance downstream of C that causes a wave is not felt upstream, because the wave cannot make its way beyond the crest of the weir. This divides a *subcritical* flow with $q < c$ from a *supercritical* flow $q > c$.

19.4 POINT SOURCE

The equations that govern the streamfunction, the velocity potential, and the velocity itself are all linear, and therefore a flow field may be constructed by superposition of elementary flows. One of the most useful elementary solutions is the point source.

Consider a spherical coordinate system, and assume that the flow is purely radial $v_r(r)$. Since $v_\theta = 0$, we see from Eq. 19.1.5 that ψ is a function of θ but not a function of r. Hence, the equation that governs ψ (Eq. 19.1.6) reduces to

$$\frac{d}{d\theta}\left(\frac{1}{\sin\theta}\frac{d\psi}{d\theta}\right) = 0 \tag{19.4.1}$$

Integrating Eq. 19.4.1 gives

$$\psi = -C_1 \cos\theta + C_2$$

Any radial line $\theta = $ const gives a certain value of ψ and is a streamline in the r, θ plane. When we choose the reference axis $\theta = 0$ to be $\psi = 0$, we find that $C_1 = C_2$. This choice of $\psi = 0$ also means that $Q = 2\pi\psi$ (Table D.4), where Q is the volume between the $\theta = 0$ axis and the streamsurface ψ. When $\theta = \pi$, $\psi = 2C_1$ and $Q = 4\pi C_1$. Denote the strength of the source (the volume outflow) by m. Then Eq. 19.4.1 becomes

$$\psi = \frac{m}{4\pi}(1 - \cos\theta) \tag{19.4.2}$$

The velocity of the fluid is

$$v_r = \frac{1}{r^2 \sin\theta}\frac{\partial\psi}{\partial\theta} = \frac{m}{4\pi r^2} \tag{19.4.3}$$

From Eq. 19.4.3 we see that the velocity decays as r^{-2} for a point source. This contrasts with a decay rate of r^{-1} for a line source.

It is also easy to find the velocity potential for a source. The fact that $v_\theta = 0$ coupled with Eq. 19.1.8 means that $\phi = \phi(r)$. Equation 19.1.7 shows that

$$r^2 \frac{\partial\phi}{\partial r} = C$$

Integrating this equation and evaluating the constants yields

$$\phi = -\frac{m}{4\pi r} \tag{19.4.4}$$

The correctness of this expression is easily checked by verifying that $v_r = d\phi/dr$.

In plane flow we had two first-order singularities, the line source and the line vortex. In three-dimensional flow we have a point source, but there is no such thing as a point vortex.

19.5   RANKINE NOSE SHAPE

Superposition of a uniform stream and a source located at the origin produces the flow over a smooth blunt-nosed body. In this interpretation the streamline separating the source flow and the uniform stream is the surface of a body that extends to infinity. This particular nose shape has many of the flow characteristics of any smooth blunt body.

The streamfunction is

$$\psi = \frac{1}{2} Ur^2 \sin^2 \theta + \frac{m}{r\pi} (1 - \cos \theta) + C \qquad (19.5.1)$$

The first term represents a uniform stream flowing from left to right. The second term is the source flow discussed in Section 19.4. An arbitrary constant has been added in order that we might make $\psi = 0$ on the stream surface separating the source fluid from the free-stream fluid. To do this, compute the radial velocity,

$$v_r = \frac{1}{r^2 \sin \theta} \frac{\partial \psi}{\partial \theta} = U \cos \theta + \frac{m}{4\pi r^2} \qquad (19.5.2)$$

Now, let us locate the point on the $\theta = \pi$ axis where the uniform stream velocity just cancels the source velocity. Setting $v_r = 0$ in Eq. 19.5.2, we find that the point $\theta = \pi$, $r = (m/4\pi U)^{1/2}$ is the stagnation point for the nose. The constant C is found from Eq. 19.5.1 by setting $\psi = 0$ at this point. The result is $C = -2m/4\pi$. Thus, Eq. 19.5.1 becomes

$$\psi = \frac{1}{2} Ur^2 \sin^2 \theta - \frac{m}{4\pi} (1 + \cos \theta) \qquad (19.5.3)$$

For a given streamline $2\pi\psi$ is the volume flow between that streamline and the nose-shaped surface.

An equation $R = R(\theta)$ describing the nose surface is obtained by substituting $\psi = 0$ in Eq. 19.5.3:

$$R = \left(\frac{m}{2\pi U} \frac{1 + \cos \theta}{\sin^2 \theta} \right)^{1/2} \qquad (19.5.4)$$

At $\theta = 0$, $R \to \infty$, indicating that the body is semi-infinite. Another form of the surface equation can be obtained by letting $Y(\theta)$ be the height of the surface from the reference axis. Since $y = R \sin \theta$, we see from Eq. 19.5.4 that

$$Y = \left[\frac{m}{2\pi U} (1 + \cos \theta) \right]^{1/2} \qquad (19.5.5)$$

In this form one can readily see that the body as a finite radius at $\theta \to 0$,

$$h = Y(\theta \to 0) = \sqrt{\frac{m}{\pi U}} \qquad (19.5.6)$$

Equation 19.5.6 relates the characteristic body radius h to the source constant and the free-stream velocity U.

The θ velocity in the flow is computed from Eqs. 19.5.3 and 19.1.5 It is

$$v_\theta = \frac{-1}{r \sin \theta} \frac{\partial \psi}{\partial r} = \frac{-1}{r \sin \theta} (Ur \sin^2 \theta) = -U \sin \theta \qquad (19.5.7)$$

Note that v_θ comes only from the free-stream flow; the source has $v_\theta = 0$.

Figure 19.3 shows a plot of the surface speed and the surface pressure where z is the coordinate along the reference axis measured from the nose. The trends for flow over the axisymmetric nose are the same as those we found previously for a plane nose. The maximum velocity in the axisymmetric case is $1.15U$, compared to $1.26U$ for the plane case. Corresponding pressure coefficients are $C_p = -0.333$ (axisymmetric) and -0.59 (plane) at the minimum points. Pressure curves such as Fig. 19.3 are useful in locating the static ports on pitot-static tubes.

The equation that describes the speed of the fluid on the body surface is found to be

$$\frac{q^2}{U^2} = \left(\frac{v_r}{U}\right)^2 + \left(\frac{v_\theta}{U}\right)^2 = 1 + 2\cos\theta\,\sin^2\frac{\theta}{2} + \sin^4\frac{\theta}{2} \qquad (19.5.8)$$

The parameter θ is related to the body coordinates by

$$\frac{Y}{h} = \cos\frac{\theta}{2} \qquad (19.5.9)$$

$$\frac{z}{h} = \frac{1}{2}\frac{\cos\theta}{\sin(\theta/2)} \qquad (19.5.10)$$

One can easily find the surface pressure coefficient by rearranging Bernoulli's equation into the relation

$$C_p \equiv \frac{p - p_\infty}{\frac{1}{2}\rho U^2} = 1 - \left(\frac{q}{U}\right)^2 \qquad (19.5.11)$$

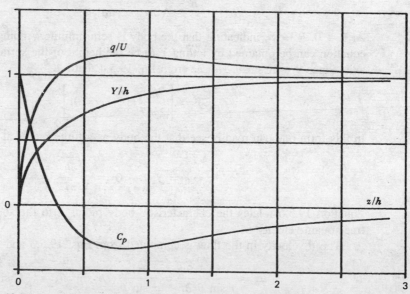

Figure 19.3   Rankine nose shape: surface speed q/U and surface pressure C_p, plotted together with the body contour Y/h as functions of the distance from the nose divided by the maximum radius h.

It is possible to integrate the surface pressure equation and show that the net force on the body is $p_\infty A$, the same force that would exist if the half-body were in a static fluid. Hence, we say that there is no net drag on the nose. There is an exact balance between the drag on the high-pressure region and the suction force on the shoulders. This result is quite general and applies to all nose shapes.

19.6 EXPERIMENTS ON THE NOSE DRAG OF SLENDER SHAPES

The drag force on an object is frequently broken out into several parts. The first separation has a rigorous physical basis in that frictin drag is easily distinguished, at least in theory, from the drag due to the pressure forces. In the present and preceding chapters we have ignored friction effects, so all of our results have actually referred to the pressure drag. Further division of the pressure drag is not so clear. When a three-dimensional body produces lift, the resulting pressure distribution also gives a drag component. Changing the attitude of a body to increase the left force also increases the drag. This drag component is known as the *induced drag* or *drag due to lift*. We discuss the origin of this drag in Section 19.11. The pressure drag that remains after the induced drag is subtracted is called *form drag,* because the shape of the body is the primary factor in determining it. Form drag also increases slightly with the angle of attack. From a practical standpoint this increase is small, and especially in the case of wings, it is common to use the term *induced drag* to represent all drag increases that come from increasing the angle of attack above that for which zero lift occurs. The combination of friction drag and form drag is called *profile drag*. At zero lift the drag on a body is all profile drag.

Ideal-flow theory predicts that the form drag on a nose of any shape will be zero as long as the flow is attached. Flow separation at the corner of the body indicates that the streamlines do not turn as sharply as the surface does. The low-pressure suction region is modified or lost completely, leaving the high-pressure region to cause a drag. The form drag for a blunt nose is shown in Fig. 19.4 to be about $C_D = 0.80$. This drag is isolated by subtracting out the base drag and friction drag of a smooth nose. The approximate form drag of several other nose shapes is also given in Fig. 19.4. The round nose actually has some drag, but it is less than 0.05. As progressively sharper corners and more side separation are encountered, the drag coefficient increases, as one would expect. What is

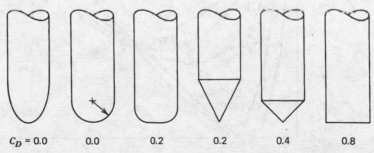

$C_D = 0.0$ 0.0   0.2   0.2   0.4   0.8

Figure 19.4 Drag coefficient of various-shaped noses. For the first two shapes $C_D < 0.05$. Adapted from Hoerner (1965).

perhaps surprising is how little rounding of the corners is needed to decrease the drag from 0.8 for a square forebody to 0.2 as for the third shape to the left.

Let us now turn to another aspect of blunt-body drag: that of interference effects. It is common knowledge that a racing car traveling very close behind another car experiences significantly less drag. A similar effect can be used advantageously in a tandem body consisting of a disk in front of the bluff main body. Figure 19.5 is a plot of the drag coefficients measured by Roshko and Koenig (1984). When the ratio of the front-disk diameter d_1 to the main-body diameter d_2 is about 0.75, the tandem body (i.e., the disk and the main body combined) has a minimum drag coefficient of about 0.02. This occurs when the space between the bodies, g, is from 0.25 to $0.5d_2$. Photographs of the flow (Fig. 19.6) show that the shear layer formed as the flow leaves the forward disk turns and attaches smoothly to the main body. In contrast, Fig. 19.7 shows the large separated regions at the corners of a body with a sharp face. When the disk is placed too far in front of the main body, the wake does not attach smoothly but sets up an oscillation where the cavity flow becomes unsteady. The drag increases in this situation.

19.7 FLOW FROM A DOUBLET

The source–sink doublet in three-dimensional flow is depicted in Fig. 19.8. The source is located a distance ε to the left of the origin and the sink an equal distance to the right. At an arbitrary field point P, the streamfunction is the sum of streamfunction equation

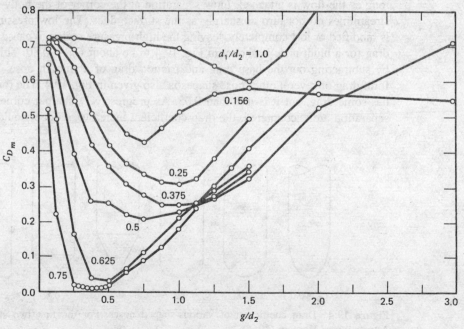

Figure 19.5 Measured drag coefficient of a tandem body. Reprinted with permission from Roshko and Koenig (1984).

Figure 19.6   Flow over tandem body at the configuration for lowest drag; $d_1/d_2 = 0.75$ and $g/d_2 = 0.375$. Reprinted with permission from Roshko and Koenig (1984).

Figure 19.7   Same as Fig. 19.6, except that $g/d_2 = 0.125$. The flow separates at the shoulder, and the drag increases. Reprinted with permission from Roshko and Koenig (1984).

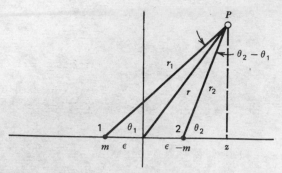

Figure 19.8   Derivation of three-dimensional doublet.

19.4.2, for the individual source and sink (in addition to spherical coordinates we use z as the position of P along the reference axis):

$$\psi = \frac{m}{4\pi}(\cos\theta_2 - \cos\theta_1) = \frac{m}{4\pi}\left(\frac{z-\varepsilon}{r_2} - \frac{z+\varepsilon}{r_1}\right)$$

$$= \frac{mz(r_1 - r_2)}{4\pi r_1 r_2} - \frac{m\varepsilon(r_1 + r_2)}{4\pi r_1 r_2} \tag{19.7.1}$$

To extract the streamfunction for a doublet, we must let $\varepsilon \to 0$, $m \to \infty$ in such a way that the product $\varepsilon m = \mu^2$ is a constant. When this limit is taken, the radii r_1, $r_2 \to r$. The first term in Eq. 19.7.1 is indeterminate, since $m(r_1 - r_2) = \infty \times 0$. We must carefully rearrange this term so that it contains μ.

Consider the law of sines applied to Fig. 19.8. This produces

$$\frac{r_1}{\sin\theta_2} = \frac{r_2}{\sin\theta_1} = \frac{2\varepsilon}{\sin(\theta_2 - \theta_1)}$$

Hence, the quantity $r_1 - r_2$ may be expressed as

$$r_1 - r_2 = \frac{2\varepsilon(\sin\theta_2 - \sin\theta_1)}{\sin(\theta_2 - \theta_1)}$$

$$= \frac{2\varepsilon 2\cos[\frac{1}{2}(\theta_2 + \theta_1)]\sin[\frac{1}{2}(\theta_2 - \theta_1)]}{2\sin[\frac{1}{2}(\theta_2 - \theta_1)]\cos[\frac{1}{2}(\theta_2 - \theta_1)]}$$

In the second relation the fact that $\sin\theta = 2\sin(\theta/2)\cos(\theta/2)$ has been used. Simplifying the expression above and multiplying by m gives

$$m(r_1 - r_2) = \frac{2\varepsilon m\cos[\frac{1}{2}(\theta_2 + \theta_1)]}{\cos[\frac{1}{2}(\theta_2 - \theta_1)]} \tag{19.7.2}$$

When the limit $\varepsilon \to 0$, $m \to \infty$ is applied to Eq. 19.7.2, this term becomes $+\mu\cos\theta$. Hence, Eq. 19.7.1 reduces to

$$\psi = \frac{\mu z \cos \theta}{4\pi r^2} - \frac{\mu}{4\pi r} = \frac{\mu}{4\pi r}(\cos^2 \theta - 1)$$

$$= -\frac{\mu}{4\pi r}\sin^2 \theta \tag{19.7.3}$$

This is the streamfunction of a doublet oriented with the sink on the positive z-axis. The corresponding expression for the velocity potential turns out to be

$$\phi = \frac{\mu}{4\pi r^2}\cos \theta \tag{19.7.4}$$

Unlike the plane case, where a doublet could be viewed as the limit of either a source–sink or two counterrotating line vortices, the three-dimensional doublet cannot be considered as the limit of a ring vortex as the diameter decreases to zero.

19.8   FLOW OVER A SPHERE

The ideal flow over a sphere is given by the superposition of a uniform stream and a doublet. Summing these contributions and including an arbitrary constant C yields

$$\psi = \frac{Ur^2}{2}\sin^2 \theta - \frac{\mu}{4\pi r}\sin \theta + C \tag{19.8.1}$$

The velocity component in the radial direction is

$$v_r = \frac{1}{r^2 \sin \theta}\frac{\partial \psi}{\partial \theta} = 2\cos \theta \left(\frac{U}{2} - \frac{\mu}{4\pi r^3}\right) \tag{19.8.2}$$

Now, on the negative axis $\theta = \pi$, the flow is purely radial and the uniform stream exactly cancels the doublet when $v_r = 0$. This occurs at the position r_0 given by

$$r_0 = \left(\frac{\mu}{2\pi U}\right)^{1/3} \tag{19.8.3}$$

Inserting this for μ in Eq. 19.8.1 and finding C by taking $\psi = 0$ at $r = r_0$, $\theta = \pi$, leads to the result

$$\psi = \frac{1}{2}r_0^2 U \sin^2 \theta \left[\left(\frac{r}{r_0}\right)^2 - \left(\frac{r}{r_0}\right)^{-1}\right] \tag{19.8.4}$$

From Eq. 19.8.4 we can verify that for arbitrary θ, $r = r_0$ is a spherical stream surface where $\psi = 0$. For future reference note that the corresponding velocity potential is

$$\phi = r_0 U \cos \theta \left[\frac{r}{r_0} + \frac{1}{2}\left(\frac{r}{r_0}\right)^{-2}\right] \tag{19.8.5}$$

The velocity components for this flow are

$$v_r = U \cos \theta \left[1 - \left(\frac{r_0}{r} \right)^3 \right] \tag{19.8.6}$$

and

$$v_\theta = -\frac{U}{2} \sin \theta \left[2 + \left(\frac{r_0}{r} \right)^3 \right]$$

As one might expect, the velocities have fore-and-aft symmetry and no evidence of a wake. On the surface of the sphere the velocity is

$$q = v_\theta = -\tfrac{3}{2} U \sin \theta \tag{19.8.7}$$

The maximum occurs at the equator, where $q = -3U/2$. Recall that for a circular cylinder the maximum was slightly higher, $q = -2U$. We might interpret this effect in terms of inserting a body into a uniform stream. A body that is finite in all dimensions allows the flow to go around in three dimensions, whereas a cylinder forces the flow to squeeze by in only two dimensions. Hence, the velocity at the shoulder of a sphere is less than the velocity at the shoulder of a cylinder.

Velocities in Eq. 19.8.6 differ from a uniform stream by a term that dies out as r^{-3}. Similar equations for a cylinder (Eq. 18.6.3) reveal that the effect of a two-dimensional body dies out as r^{-2}.

The surface pressures are found by evaluating Bernoulli's equation on the surface of the sphere, using Eq. 19.8.7 for the velocity. In terms of the pressure coefficient, the result is

$$C_p = 1 - \tfrac{9}{4} \sin^2 \theta \tag{19.8.8}$$

At the equator, the minimum pressure is $C_p = -\tfrac{5}{4}$. This is not nearly as low as the pressure predicted for ideal flow over a cylinder, $C_p = -3$. Nevertheless, the real flow over a solid body cannot penetrate the high-pressure region at the rear of the sphere, and the flow separates. The drag coefficient for a sphere follows the same trends as experienced with circular cylinders (see Section 14.6). One difference in the details of the flow is that a dominant Strouhal number and regular vortex shedding are not usually observed on spheres. In some instances a spiral shedding of the vortices is observed, but usually the wake flow is irregular and without a dominant pattern.

There are at least two situations where the potential-flow solution is in reasonable agreement with actual flows. When a sphere is started impulsively from rest (or equivalently, when the fluid is started impulsively around a stationary sphere), the initial motion is the irrotational flow given above. Another case in which the solution is valid is when a sphere undergoes small oscillations back and forth along a line. In this instance, if the frequency is high, the Stokes layer is thin, leaving the main part of the flow irrotational.

Another possible application of the ideal-flow solution is to a spherical drop in an infinite fluid. The motion of the outside fuid can engender a circulatory motion within the drop. Recall that a complete solution of the Navier–Stokes equations known as Hill's spherical vortex was discussed in Section 13.6. It is interesting that the surface velocity of Hill's vortex and the surface velocity of the ideal flow over a sphere can be exactly matched. If U is the free-stream velocity far away from the sphere, r_0 the radius of the sphere, and A the constant in the vorticity distribution $\omega_\theta = Ar_0$ for Hill's vortex, then when

$$U = \tfrac{2}{15}\, r_0^2 A$$

the surface velocity of the solutions will match. Patching these two solutions together gives a result that satisfies the Navier–Stokes equations everywhere and has continuous velocities. Its only defect is that the shear stress and the pressure at the interface of the sphere are discontinuous. Although this is an interesting result, it does not appear to have any application. High-Reynolds-number situations, such as large raindrops, seem to have separation regions similar to those of solid particles. On the other hand, many problems involving particles and droplets are also at low Reynolds numbers. Hill's vortex solution can also be matched to a low-Reynolds-number solution (Section 22.3).

19.9 KINETIC ENERGY

Consider a body moving in an infinite fluid as shown in Fig. 19.9. A control region is chosen whose boundaries are very far away (in the still fluid) and around the body, where the body has the velocity $w_i = (U(t), 0, 0)$ in the x-direction. Recall that the kinetic energy equation (Eq. 5.16.2) for an arbitrary region is

$$\frac{d}{dt}\int \frac{1}{2}\,\rho v_i v_i\, dV = -\int \rho n_i(v_i - w_i)\,\frac{1}{2}\,v_k v_k\, dS - \int n_i v_i p\, dS \qquad (19.9.1)$$

Because we are dealing with an incompressible and inviscid flow, the compression work and viscous dissipation integrals in Eq. 5.16.2 are zero. All terms on the right-hand side of Eq. 19.9.1 are neglected at the far boundary, where the fluid is still. Moreover, since flow does not cross the surface of the body, $n_i(v_i - w_i) = 0$ in the convection term. This

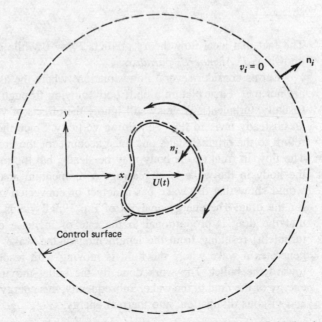

Figure 19.9 Kinetic energy analysis of a body moving through a fluid that is still at infinity.

relation also means that $n_i v_i = n_i w_i = n_x w_x = n_x U(t)$ on the body. Thus, Eq. 19.9.1 becomes

$$\frac{d}{dt} \int \frac{1}{2} \rho v_i v_i \, dV = -U \int_{S_b} n_x p \, dS$$

$$= U F_D \qquad (19.9.2)$$

The x-component of the surface pressue is defined to be the drag. The result above states that the work done by moving the body at a speed U is $U F_D$ (there being no motion and hence no work done in the direction of the lift force), and that this work must appear within an inviscid, incompressible flow as an increase in the kinetic energy of the fluid. We shall use this result in the next few sections to explain wake drag, wave drag, induced drag, and the added mass of accelerating bodies.

19.10 WAKE DRAG OF BODIES

Let us first discuss the special case when the motion U is steady. Furthermore, assume that the flow is an ideal, potential flow everywhere outside the body (a nonlifting body). The closed nonlifting ideal body does not create a wake. The flow closes smoothly behind the body and returns to the uniform flow state. A potential flow of this type may be represented by sources, sinks, and doublets distributed on and within the body. Such a flow is steady with respect to a coordinate system on the body ($\hat{v}_i$). The velocity in ground-based coordinates is $v_i = \hat{v}_i + U_i$, and $v_i v_i = \hat{v}_i \hat{v}_i + 2\hat{v}_i U_i + U^2$. Therefore, since both $\hat{v}_i$ and U are constant, the integral of $\frac{1}{2} v_i v_i$, the total energy of the fluid motion, is constant. This leads to the conclusion from Eq. 19.9.2 that the drag is zero:

$$0 = F_D \qquad (19.10.1)$$

The fact that ideal-flow theory predicts $F_D = 0$ while any real flow has a drag force is known as *D'Alembert's paradox*.

Let us consider several flow situations where the assumptions necessary for $F_D = 0$ are not met. First, picture a bluff body moving through the fluid creating a wake region (usually, turbulent). We may still ignore the effects of viscosity and consider the flow as an unsteady inviscid flow containing vorticity. Since the flow behind the body does not return to the original state, one must account for the growth or lengthening of the wake. The flow in front of the body may be steady, but the mean and turbulent energy behind the body in the wake is increasing. A momentum analysis of this flow, Section 14.6, would show that the wake has a defect of convected momentum that exactly accounts for the drag. The energy analysis of Eq. 19.9.2 yields another point of view. It shows that the drag is proportional to the rate of increase of energy (both mean flow and turbulent) resulting from the lengthening of the wake. A rifle bullet shot into still air generates a wake where the fluid is moving with respect to the ground in a direction toward the bullet. The work done by the bullet moving through the air increases the energy of the fluid in the wake. Subsequently, this energy is converted, through turbulence and viscous dissipation, into thermal energy.

Another illustration is shown in Fig. 19.10. The unexpected high drag of some "hatchback" automobiles motivated the tests shown in the figure. A rounded-nose shape was terminated with a flat base at various angles. In principle, all of the pressure drag is the result of the beveled base. When the base is square or at a modest angle, the separated region disorganized with a lot of turbulence. The pressure is somewhat lower than ambient and results in a significant drag. As the bevel angle is reduced there is a large, unexpected jump in the drag. This is caused by a change in the pattern of flow separation. Two strong vortices now attach at the top of the bevel and stay close to the surface as they follow down the base region and trail off into the wake. The low pressure and extra energy associated with these vortices is the cause of the unexpected high drag. Further reduction of the angle weakens the vortices, and the drag falls accordingly.

As remarked in Section 18.4, ideal flows are in principle reversible, and a smooth body closure would produce a flow with a pressure that increased to the stagnation value at the aft end. In Chapter 20 we will see that a boundary layer where the pressure increases will usually separate. There is a certain rate of increase of the pressure, which theoretically does not separate. This boundary layer has zero wall friction. In the case of turbulent boundary layers, the most common case, the pressure distribution for a zero friction layer is called a *Stratford* (1959) *profile.* Liebeck (1978) used a Stratford profile to close his high-lift airfoil mentioned in Section 18.15. Recently, Hammache et al. (2002) have considered the design of axisymmetric body shapes having the Stratford pressure recovery. This concept produces a body with the minimum length and avoids the drag associated with a separating wake.

For another example, consider a ship in a calm sea. At time zero the ship gets under way and shortly attains a steady speed. We study the wake of waves generated by the ship. The waves are irrotational potential motions; however, their energy is never re-

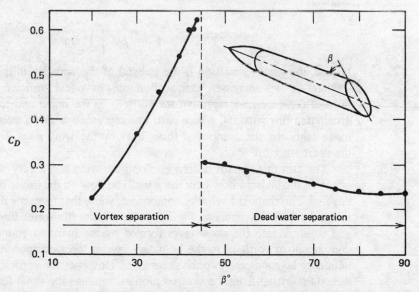

Figure 19.10 Drag of a flat base area at various angles to the flow. The jump in drag marks a change in the separated-flow pattern. Adapted from Morel (1978). Reprinted with permission.

turned. The wave system continues to grow, in principle, throughout the motion. Hence, Eq. 19.9.2 indicates that there is a wave drag equal to the rate that energy is carried out in the ever-expanding wave wake. A similar wave drag occurs in supersonic flow, where bodies generate shock waves that continually expand away from the body. In either case the waves are generated through the action of pressure at the surface of the body. The existence of the wave drag means that the integral of the x-component of these pressures is nonzero.

*19.11   INDUCED DRAG: DRAG DUE TO LIFT

Induced drag is illustrated by the flow over a lifting body such as a wing. Recall that a two-dimensional airfoil has no drag whatsoever. The case of a finite wing is much different, as we shall see.

In the first approximation, the flow over any section of a wing is just like the flow over an infinite airfoil of the same cross section. This idea needs to be refined if we are to find the drag of the wing, since the drag is much smaller than the lift. The fact that strong vortices are formed at the tip of wings, and more important, associating them with a drag force, is a contribution from the aeronautical pioneer Lanchester (1907).

Figure 19.11 shows the flow pattern over a wing of span L. Consider that the lift force produced at each chord position must change as we move along the span toward the top. Near the tip the lift drops very rapidly to zero. Now, the amount of lift at any section is related to the loal circulation $\Gamma(z)$ by generalizing the *Kutta–Joukowski law* (Eq. 18.8.1):

$$\frac{dF_L}{dz} = \rho U \Gamma(z)$$

$$F_L = \rho U \int \Gamma(z)\, dz$$

(19.11.1)

In turn, the local circulation is the integral of the vorticity in the boundary layer at that section. As $\Gamma(z)$ decreases, each section must have less vorticity. With regard to its effect in ideal flow, we may represent the vorticity in the upper and lower boundary layers by distributed line vortices, where each line represents a given strength of vorticity. As we move outboard, the number of these lines on the wing must decrease to correspond to the decreasing lift.

The fact that the lift decreases along the wing has a very slight but very important effect on the inviscid flow over the wing. The flow on the lower surface leaves the trailing edge with an outboard velocity component, while that from the upper surface has a slight inboard velocity component. Figure 19.11c depicts the vortex lines as they leave the wing and continue into the shear layer formed by the merging boundary layers. The largest component of vorticity in the boundary layers, the z-component, cancels out when the boundary layers merge into the shear layer. However, the vorticity component in the flow direction, arising from the skewed profiles, remains the same for a long distance behind the wing.

Near the tip of the wing these events are accentuated, the flow becomes three-dimensional, and the x-direction line vortices become concentrated into the wingtip vor-

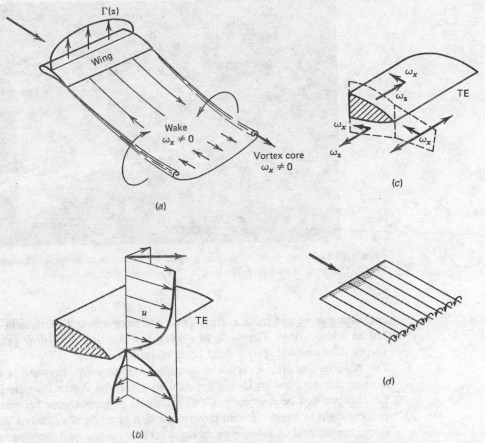

Figure 19.11 (a) Wake of a finite wing, composed of a shear layer vortex cores containing longitudinal vorticity. (b) Close-up of the trailing-edge boundary layers. (c) Skewed flow on top and bottom gives net vorticity in flow direction. (d) Wing and wake modeled as a sequence of line vortices.

tex. The core of the vortex is a finite area of dense vorticity. The overall effect of the tip vortex is to take fluid from the underside of the wake and swirl it around to the upper side. This effect accounts for the inviscid flow toward the tip on the underside and away from the tip on the upper side. Figure 19.12 is the plan view of a delta wing. In this case the tip vortices form at the apex of the delta.

With these events in mind, let us return to the question of D'Alembert's paradox and the inviscid pressure drag on a wing. The tip vortices and the wake, when idealized to zero thickness, become a singular surface in the potential flow. As we cross the shear layer, the inviscid velocity changes direction (the magnitude is the same because the pressue is constant across the shear layer and both streams have the same Bernoullli constant). A potential solution for the flow requires a distribution of vortex lines along the wake (or doublets) as well as sources, sinks, and doublets or vortices on the wing surface. Now, when we envision a wing moving in an infinite still medium, the ideal-flow problem continues to change as time goes on. The wake grows longer and longer,

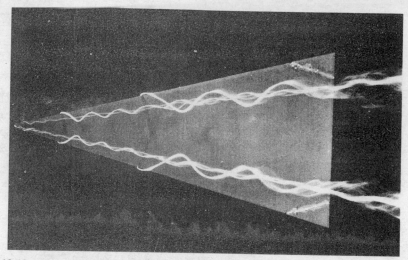

Figure 19.12 Plan view of vortices formed by a slender delta wing. Photograph courtesy of H. Werlé, ONERA, France (see Werlé, 1963). Reprinted with permission.

containing more and more energy. Thus, the wing leaves a permanent mark in the fluid, just as a bullet does. The wake of a wing is a swirling ideal flow generated by trailing vortex lines embedded in a shear layer of zero thickness.

Assume that after a certain distance behind the wing, the wake is developed to such a stage that the flow no longer depends on x and the vortex lines lie in the x-direction. Let this position be $x_1 = x_0 + Ut$. (This model is approximate because the vortex wake propels itself in the downward direction with a very slight velocity.) With these assumptions, the integral of the energy in Eq. 19.9.2 is broken into three parts: $-\infty$ to x_0, x_0 to x_1, and x_1 to $+\infty$ (Fig. 19.13). The energy in the end pieces is constant, so the only increase in energy is between x_0 and x_1. Hence,

$$UF_D = \frac{d}{dt}\int_{x_0}^{x_1=x_0+Ut} \int \int_{-\infty}^{\infty} \frac{\rho}{2} v_i v_i \, dy \, dz \, dx = \int \int_{-\infty}^{\infty} \frac{\rho}{2} v_i v_i \, dy \, dz \, \frac{d}{dt}\int_{x_0}^{x_0+Ut} dx$$

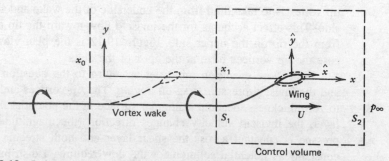

Figure 19.13 Induced drag from increasing length of the vortex wake. The wing, the plane x_1, and the control volume move through the fluid with velocity U.

Because the flow at x_1 is fully established, only the upper limit $x_1 = x_0 + Ut$ is a function of time. Hence, one finally obtains the x integration is Ut and

$$F_D = \rho \int \int_{-\infty}^{\infty} \frac{1}{2} v_i v_i \, dy \, dz \qquad \text{at } x_1 \qquad (19.11.2)$$

The drag force is equal to the kinetic energy integrated across a plane at a position where the wake flow is fully established.

It is informative to apply a momentum analysis to this problem also. We choose a region that moves along with the wing as shown in Fig. 19.13. Let $\hat{v}_i$ denote the velocity in the wing-fixed system, and retain v_i for the ground-fixed system. The flow on the inflow boundary S_2 is uniform: $\hat{v}_x = -U$ and $p = p_\infty$. The outflow is where the vortex lines, which are straight and aligned with the x-direction, penetrate the control volume. The Biot–Savart law shows that a system of straight parallel vortex lines can only induce velocities in the plane perpendicular to the lines. Hence, at the outflow boundary we have $v_x = 0$ in the gorund-based system, and since $v_x = \hat{v}_x + U$, we find that $\hat{v}_x = -U$. The x-direction flow into and out of the control volume is uniform. Moreover, this means that the net convection of momentum into the region is zero. The integral x-momentum equation 5.14.1 then reduces to a balance of pressure forces,

$$0 = -\int_{S_1} n_x p \, dS - \int_{S_b} n_x p \, dS - \int_{S_2} n_x p \, dS$$

$$0 = \int_{S_1} n_x (p_\infty - p) \, dS - F_D \qquad (19.11.3)$$

The pressure in the plane that cuts across the wake is slightly lower than the free-stream pressure. Of course, this is especially true in the vortex cores. This creates the induced drag.

We can also connect Eq. 19.11.2 to the energy equation result, Eq. 19.11.2. In wing-fixed coordinates the Bernoulli equation between points on the inlet and outlet flow planes is

$$p_\infty + \frac{1}{2}\rho U^2 = p + \frac{1}{2}\rho \hat{v}_i \hat{v}_i$$

Using $\hat{v}_x = v_x - U$, $\hat{v}_y = v_y$, and $\hat{v}_z = v_z$, we have

$$p_\infty - p = \frac{1}{2}\rho(v_i v_i - 2v_x U)$$

Noting that $v_x = 0$ on S_1 and substituting this into Eq. 19.11.3 yields the previous result (Eq. 19.11.2). Thus, the momentum analysis and the energy equation analysis give equivalent results. The low pressures on S_1 result from the swirling vortex flow giving the fluid an extra high velocity.

The induced drag on a lifting body is the result of the vortex system in the wake and the tip vortices. In turn, the wake exists because the circulation (and hence the lift) varies along the wing span and must drop to zero at the tips. Books on aerodynamics (Thwaites, 1960; Karamcheti, 1966; Kuethe and Chow, 1976; Bertin and Smith, 1979; Katz and Plotkin, 1991) solve the potential flow problem for the wake and show exactly how the induced drag depends on the distribution of lift along the wing. The result is of the form

$$F_D = C\rho\Gamma_0^2 \qquad (19.11.4)$$

where C is a constant that depends on the shape of the lift distribution over the wing, and Γ_0 is the average circulation. The remarkable aspect of Eq. 19.11.4 is that increasing the length of a wing does not increase F_D, but it does increase the lift since

$$F_L = \rho U\Gamma_0 L \qquad (19.11.5)$$

These facts may be ilustrated in another way. Assume that an airplane has a certain weight, requiring for level flight at speed U an equal lift force. We can rearrange Eqs. 19.11.4 and 19.11.5 to eliminate Γ_0 and find that

$$\frac{F_D}{F_L^2} = \frac{C}{\rho U^2 L^2} \qquad (19.11.6)$$

This shows that the longest wing will have the smallest induced drag for a given lift. For this reason sailplanes have long wings. Another point of interest is that an elliptical distribution of lift along the wing produces the smallest value of the constant C.

*19.12 LIFTING LINE THEORY

The task of predicting the lift and induced drag of a wing or blade of given shape is important in engineering design. Modern computer programs to solve this problem are quite complex and are the subject of advanced aerodynamics textbooks and research papers. The purpose of this section is to give a general discussion of the nature of the problem and indicate where assumptions and approximations are necessary to solve the problem. At the end of this discussion we outline Prandtl's lifting line theory, the first successful theory of a finite wing.

Consider the nonseparated potential flow over a given wing. Recall that even in two dimensions this problem is not unique until the Kutta condition is imposed. In three dimensions, viscosity not only determines the Kutta condition but also determines the exact details of the tip vortex formation. Most potential flow computer methods assume the Kutta condition and fix the tip vortex at the trailing edge of the wingtip. Actually, the vortex always springs from a position near midchord and slightly inboard. An exact calculation of the flow in this region involves both viscous and inviscid phenomena and hence is very difficult.

With the assumption of where and how the wake leaves the wing, the potential problem is determined uniquely. The problem consists of finding a potential flow with velocities tangent to the wing surface and obeying the Kutta condition. The strength of the vortex lines in the wake and the subsequent location of the wake in the downstream region must be calculated. The potential flow boundary conditions at the wake are (1) no flow across the wake, and (2) no change in pressure across the wake. These two conditions at the unknown wake position are equivalent to a single condition at a known location such as at a solid body.

Not only is Prandtl's lifting line theory of historical interest, but various aspects of it are incorporated in many of the more modern methods. To find the influence of the wake on the flow over the wing, Prandtl modeled the wake as a straight, flat sequence of line vortices coming back from another vortex line, the lifting line, which represents the wing (Fig. 19.11*d*).

As each vortex line peels off to form the wake, the strength $\Gamma(z)$ of the lifting line decreases. Recall from Section 19.11 that the lift distribution is proportional to the circulation distribution. The set of vortices representing the wake induces a velocity at each point of the flow (see Eq. 17.3.2). If the geometry and strength of the wake are known, it is possible to find the downwash velocity v_{dn} caused by the wake at the position of the lifting line. The lifting line induces no velocities on itself. Of course, the wake cannot really cause a flow through the wing. To remove this absurdity we suppose that the wing moves down (dn) at a velocity v_{dn}. This effectively reduces the angle of attack of the wing.

Let the true geometric angle be $\alpha = V_\infty / U_\infty$. The effective angle of attack α_e is the true angle minus the angle induced by the wake,

$$\alpha_e = \alpha - \alpha_i \approx \frac{V_\infty - v_{dn}}{U_\infty}$$

The induced angle α_i, and hence α_e, is not necessarily the same across the span of the wing. At each location the lift is computed according to two-dimensional airfoil theory using α_e as the angle of attack. The lift vector from this flow is decomposed into components with respect to the true free-stream direction α. Hence, there is a lift component and a drag component. The drag calculated in this manner is the induced drag.

The overall effect of the wake is to induce a downwash that effectively reduces the angle of attack and causes the lift vector to turn and generate a drag component along the stream direction.

*19.13　ADDED MASS OF ACCELERATING BODIES

Let us consider once more a body moving through a still fluid with a velocity $U_i(t)$. Equation 19.9.2 revealed that the work $U_i F_i$ (we now let the velocity and the force be vectors) is equal to the rate of change of the kinetic energy of the entire flow:

$$U_i F_i = \frac{d}{dt} \int \frac{1}{2} \rho v_i v_i \, dV \tag{19.13.1}$$

For example, a sphere moving at $U(t_1)$ is acclerated by an external force to a higher speed $U(t_2)$. The flow field at the second speed has more kinetic energy; hence, by Eq. 19.11.1 an additional drag force F_D was necessary to generate this motion. Even an ideal flow, where $F_D = 0$ before and after the acceleration, has a drag force during the accelrlation phase. Previously, it has been noted that ideal flows are dominated by kinematics and that the instantaneous velocity field is determined by the shape of the body and its instantaneous velocity, a quasisteady situation. The pressure field, on the other hand, is not quasisteady, as it is governed by Bernoulli's equation, which contains the unsteady term $\partial \phi / \partial t$ (Eq. 19.1.4). When a body is accelerated, the surface pressures must increase to supply the forces necessary to overcome the inertia of the fluid.

The added drag force may be found from Eq. 19.13.1, which relates the work and the rate of change of the fluid energy. A useful way to evaluate Eq. 19.13.1 is to use Green's theorem,

$$\int (\nabla \phi \cdot \nabla \phi + \phi \nabla^2 \phi) \, dV = \int \phi \frac{\partial \phi}{\partial n} \, dS$$

In potential flow $v = \nabla \phi$ and $\nabla^2 \phi = 0$, so the equation above may be used to transform the volume integral in Eq. 19.13.1 into a surface integral. The result is

$$U_i F_i = \frac{1}{2} \rho \frac{d}{dt} \int_{S_2} \phi \frac{\partial \phi}{\partial n} \, dS = -\frac{1}{2} \rho \frac{d}{dt} \int_{S_b} \phi \mathbf{n} \cdot \mathbf{v} \, dS \qquad (19.13.2)$$

The integral of $\phi \, \partial \phi / \partial n$ over the surface at infinity is zero because $\partial \phi / \partial n = -\mathbf{v} \cdot \mathbf{n}|_\infty$ is zero. The sign of the second integral of Eq. 19.13.2 has been changed so that $\mathbf{n}$ is outward from the body surface.

Before we compute the force in Eq. 19.13.2, it is good to list the transformation equations between the body-fixed system $\hat{x}_i$ and the ground system x_i:

$$U_i(t) = \text{translational velocity of the body}$$

$$x_i^0(t) = \text{location of a reference body point}$$

$$= \int U_i(t) \, dt \qquad (19.13.3)$$

$$x_i = \hat{x}_i + x_i^0$$

$$v_i = \hat{v}_i + U_i$$

The velocity potentials are defined by $\hat{\mathbf{v}} = \hat{\nabla} \hat{\phi}$ and $\mathbf{v} = \nabla \phi$. For $\nabla \phi = \hat{\nabla} \phi + \mathbf{U}$ to hold, we must have

$$\phi = \hat{\phi} + \hat{x}_i U_i \qquad (19.13.4)$$

[Actually, $\phi = \hat{\phi} + \hat{x}_i U_i + C(t)$ is acceptable, but the choice $C = 0$ is best for the Bernoulli equation.] The pressures $\hat{p}$ computed from incompressible flow equations in the moving reference frame are pseudopressures (Eq. 10.7.6). They are related to the true pressure p by

$$p = \hat{p} - \rho \hat{x}_i \frac{dU_i}{dt} \qquad (19.13.5)$$

The irrotationality and incompressibility conditions are the same in either coordinate system; however, the Bernoulli equations are

$$\frac{\partial \phi}{\partial t} + \frac{p}{\rho} + \frac{1}{2} v_i v_i = \frac{p_\infty}{\rho} \qquad (19.13.6)$$

and

$$\frac{\partial \hat{\phi}}{\partial \hat{t}} + \frac{\hat{p}}{\rho} + \frac{1}{2} \hat{v}_i \hat{v}_i = \frac{p_\infty}{\rho} + \frac{1}{2} U_i U_i \qquad (19.13.7)$$

One may verify that Eqs. 19.13.6 and 19.13.7 are compatible by using the relations 19.13.3 to 19.13.5.

As a useful example of the added-mass concept, we consider a sphere as shown in Fig. 19.13. The velocity potential for a sphere in a uniform stream was found in Eq. 19.8.5. It is rewritten in ^ variables to indicate a body-fixed system:

$$\hat{\phi} = U_\infty \hat{r} \cos \hat{\theta} + r_0^3 \frac{U_\infty \hat{r} \cos \hat{\theta}}{2 \hat{r}^2} \tag{19.13.8}$$

Now from Eq. 19.13.3 and Fig. 19.14 we get

$$v_i(\infty) = 0, \qquad \hat{v}_i(\infty) \equiv \hat{U}_i = (U_\infty, 0, 0) = -U_i, \qquad U_i = (-U_\infty, 0, 0)$$

$$U_\infty \hat{r} \cos \hat{\theta} = \hat{U}_\infty \hat{x} = \hat{U}_i \hat{x}_i = -U_i(x_i - x_i^0), \qquad \hat{r} = |\hat{x}| = |x_i - x_i^0|$$

Inserting these into Eq. 19.13.4 yields the ϕ for a sphere moving to the left $U_i = (-U_\infty, 0, 0)$. We change the sign to have a sphere moving to the right for $+U_\infty$. The potential is

$$\phi = \frac{1}{2} r_0^3 \frac{U_i(x_i - x_i^0)}{|x_i - x_i^0|^3} \tag{19.13.9}$$

To evaluate Eq. 19.13.2, note that at the surface of the body $|x_i - x_i^0| = r_0$, $(x_i - x_i^0)U_i = r_0 U \cos \hat{\theta}$, $\mathbf{v} \cdot \mathbf{n} - U \cos \hat{\theta}$, and $dS = 2\pi r_0 \times \sin \hat{\theta} r_0 \, d\hat{\theta}$. Hence Eq. 19.13.2 becomes

$$UF = -\frac{1}{2} \rho \frac{d}{dt} \int_0^\pi \pi U^2 r_0^3 \cos^2 \hat{\theta} \sin \hat{\theta} \, d\hat{\theta} \tag{19.13.10}$$

Simplifying, we arrive at

$$F = -\frac{2}{3} \pi r_0^3 \rho \frac{dU}{dt} \tag{19.13.11}$$

This is the drag force on a sphere undergoing a linear acceleration dU/dt in ideal flow. The form of this equation allows us to interpret this effect as adding a certain mass of the fluid to the true mass of the sphere. In this case the added mass is one-half the volume of the sphere times the fluid density. In other words, we may neglect the force required to accelerate the fluid if we give the sphere a virtual mass of $(\rho_0 + \frac{1}{2}\rho)V$.

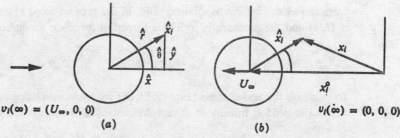

$$v_i(\infty) = (U_\infty, 0, 0) \qquad\qquad v_i(\dot{\infty}) = (0, 0, 0)$$
$$(a) \qquad\qquad\qquad (b)$$

Figure 19.14 (a) Sphere in a moving stream; (b) sphere moving in still fluid.

Let us consider the ideal flow about an arbitrary body moving in direction α_i; $U_i = U_\infty \alpha_i$. In body-fixed coordinates the potential will have a form where the space and time functions are separable, that is,

$$\hat{\phi} = \Phi(\hat{x}_i) U_\infty(\hat{t})$$

This, together with the fact that $\mathbf{v} \cdot \mathbf{n} = \mathbf{n} \cdot \mathbf{U}$ on the body surface, means that the integral in Eq. 19.13.2 will always break down into U_∞ times a surface integral that is independent of time. Hence, for all potential flows, the drag required to accelerate the fluid may always be expressed in terms of the mass of a certain volume of fluid added to the mass of the object. The size of the volume of fluid depends on the shape of the object and the direction of motion. For example, the added mass of a circular disk moving normal to its plane is $8\rho_f r_0^3/3$. Since $\frac{8}{3} \approx \pi$, this is roughly the mass of a fluid cylinder r_0 in radius and r_0 in height.

A body of a general shape has a different added mass for linear acceleration in each coordinate direction and another added mass for angular acceleration about each axis. A more general development (Landau and Lifshitz, 1959; Batchelor, 1967; Yih, 1969) leads to an added-mass tensor.

For a specific application of the theory, consider the initial acceleration of a sphere of density ρ_0 in a still fluid of density ρ_f. A bubble in a liquid or a helium balloon in air are specific examples. Let M_0 be the mass of the sphere and M_f the mass of an equal volume of fluid. The motion of the sphere is subjected to forces from its weight ($M_0 g$), its buoyancy ($M_f g$), and its added mass $\frac{1}{2} M_f$. The equation of motion is

$$M_0 \frac{dU}{dt} = -M_0 g + M_f g - \frac{1}{2} M_f \frac{dU}{dt} \tag{19.13.12}$$

Rearranging this yields

$$\frac{dU}{dt} = \frac{M_f - M_0}{M_0 + \frac{1}{2}M_f} g = \frac{\rho_f - \rho_0}{\rho_0 + \frac{1}{2}\rho_f} g \tag{19.13.13}$$

In the case of a bubble, $\rho_0 \ll \rho_f$, and the acceleration is $2g$ upward. The buoyancy force exactly supplies the force required to accelerate the liquid. The opposite extreme, a heavy ball in a light fluid, gives an acceleration of $-g$, of course.

As a second example, consider a sphere in an infinite fluid. The fluid is oscillating with $U_\infty \equiv v_x(\infty) = A \sin \Omega t$. A situation of this type is a bubble in a tank of vibrating liquid or a light particle in a sound field where the wavelength is long compared to the particle diameter. We neglect weight and buoyancy to concentrate on the motion of the particle induced by the oscillating fluid. In the ground-fixed system x_i, the sphere velocity is $U_0(t)$ and the pressure is p. The x-direction force on the sphere is

$$M_0 \frac{dU_0}{dt} = F = -\int_{S_b} n_x p \, dS \tag{19.13.14}$$

To evaluate the added mass (Eq. 19.13.14) we must introduce an $\hat{x}_i$ coordinate system in which the fluid at infinity is at rest. Velocities in the $\hat{x}_i$ system are (Fig. 19.15)

$$\hat{v}_x = v_x - U_\infty \tag{19.13.15}$$

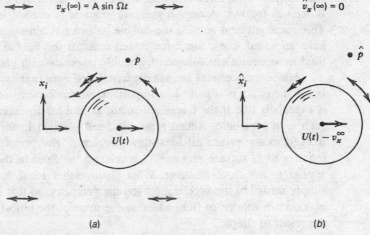

Figure 19.15   Bubble in an oscillating liquid: (*a*) ground-based system; (*b*) flow with a coordinate system chosen so that the fluid at infinity is still.

In the $\hat{x}_i$ system, the sphere moves as $U_0 - U_\infty$. Now, imagine a potential flow in the $\hat{x}_i$ system. The velocities will be related to the real flow by Eq. 19.13.15, and the pressures by Eq. 19.13.5:

$$\hat{p} = p + \rho\hat{x}\,\frac{dU_\infty}{d\hat{t}} \qquad (19.13.16)$$

The surface pressures in the imaginary flow must integrate to give the added-mass effect. Hence,

$$\frac{1}{2}\,M_f\,\frac{d(U_0 - U_\infty)}{dt} = \int_{S^+} n_x\hat{p}\,dS \qquad (19.13.17)$$

The final differential equation is obtained by multiplying Eq. 19.13.16 by n_x and integrating over S_b, combining with Eq. 19.13.17, and inserting the result into Eq. 19.13.14. These steps produce

$$M_0\,\frac{dU_0}{dt} = -\,\frac{1}{2}\,M_f\,\frac{d}{dt}\,(U_0 - U_\infty) + M_f\,\frac{dU_\infty}{dt} \qquad (19.13.18)$$

In the ground system x_i, the last term is sometimes interpreted as a buoyancy force caused by an acceleration dU_∞/dt of the fluid at infinity.

Equation 19.13.18 may be rearranged and solved to produce

$$U_0 = \frac{3\rho_f}{\rho_f + 2\rho_0}\,U_\infty \qquad (19.13.19)$$

This result is actually valid for an arbitrary time function $U_\infty(t)$. For the limiting case of a heavy particle in a light fluid, we have $U_0 = 0$; for a particle and fluid of the same density, $U_0 = U_\infty$; and for a light particle in a liquid, $U_0 = 3U_\infty$. A bubble in a liquid will oscillate with three times the amplitude of the liquid oscillation. The reason for this is seen as follows: A certain pressure gradient is needed in the liquid for acceleration. This same gradient acts on the bubble, which has almost no mass of its own but does have an added mass. Since the added mass of the bubble is only one-half that of the fluid in an equivalent volume, the bubble responds with greater acceleration.

Added-mass effects are usually associated with liquids, because the density is large. In air the effect is usually less important, but upon occasion it may be significant. This is especially true if the forces are small, as in a loudspeaker, or the object is very large, such as a parachute. Added mass has been incuded in this section because the easily worked examples are all ideal-flow problems. The principle that accelerating a body requires extra surface pressure to accelerate the fluid in the neighborhood of the body applies to any flow, however. What distinguishes ideal flow is that the extra force is simply related to the acceleration and the geometry, so that it may be related to the mass of a certain volume of fluid added to the mass of the object. Only in this special case is the result so simple.

19.14   CONCLUSIONS

Three-dimensional ideal flows have many of the same characteristics that plane two-dimensional flows have. One significant difference is in the model of thin wakes and shear layers. In plane flow a shear layer is idealized as a vortex sheet where the tangential velocity jumps and the pressure is constant. Because the net vorticity is zero, a plane two-dimensional airfoil wake has no jump in tangential velocity, hence the inviscid streamlines have exactly the same properties on either side of the wake. On the other hand, three-dimensional wakes are quite different in that the pressure and magnitude of the velocity can be the same on both sides while the direction of the velocity vectors changes. These wakes are like a plane wake in one direction and a plane shear layer in the other direction. Ideal-flow models of three-dimensional wakes must contain a surface with a longitudinal vortex sheet. Disregarding this singular surface leads to D'Alembert's paradox: The drag is predicted to be zero.

The induced drag of a lifting body comes from growth in the length of a three-dimensional wake. The work done by the drag force increases the energy of the flow by making the wake longer. The ultimate destruction of this energy is, of course, a viscous effect.

The Kutta condition was used in plane flows to select the proper circulation constant for the flow and to select a unique flow pattern. The same difficulty exists in three-dimensional flows. We must specify the location where the wake and the tip vortices leave a wing in order to have a unique solution.

PROBLEMS

19.1 (B) An ideal flow exists in a reservoir above a small hole in an infinite flat wall. The flow consists of a line vortex with the axis going through the hole and perpen- dicular to the wall plus a sink flow into the hole. Find the velocity and pressure on the wall as a function of the distance and the strength parameters of the flow.

19.2 (B) Compute the surface speed and pressure coefficient on a Rankine nose as a function of distance along the surface.

19.3 (B) Verify Eq. 19.13.9 and compute the pressure at the forward stagnation point of a sphere moving with velocity $U(t)$ in an infinite still fluid.

19.4 (A) A spherical point source of strength m is located a distance H above a flat wall. Find the velocity and pressure on the wall as a function of distance along the wall.

19.5 (A) A flat plate is moved according to $U = At$ normal to its plane. The plate is $\ell \times w$ with $\ell \gg w$. What is the initial drag?

19.6 (B) A bubble of radius r_0 is in a closed tank of water. The tank is moved according to $U = At$. What is the motion of the bubble?

19.7 (B) A buoy consists of a sphere of density ρ_s, radius R_s, which is completely submerged, and a rod of radius R_0 extending to and above the surface ($R_0 \ll R_s$). At equilibrium in seawater, ρ, the rod is submerged a distance H. The buoy is displaced slightly from the equilibrium position in a calm sea. Write an equation for the resulting motion and identify the natural frequency of oscillation.

20

Boundary Layers

Boundary layers are thin regions in the flow where viscous forces are important. Although the name *boundary layer* originally referred to the layer of fluid next to the wall, we may also apply the term to a jet or a thin shear layer between two streams of different velocities. The essential ideas are that the layer is thin in the direction across the streamlines and that viscous stresses are important only within the layer.

In Chapter 16, where the physical motivation and derivation of the boundary layer equations was given, we found that boundary layers are a high-Reynolds-number phenomenon. They constitute a correction to the main inviscid flow, which does not meet the no-slip condition at the wall. The boundary layer and the inviscid flow are coupled together through a boundary condition. The inviscid flow velocity along the wall, $u_{\text{invis}}(x)$, is equal to the boundary layer velocity, $u_e = u(x, y \to \infty)$, as the distance y from the surface, measured in boundary layer coordinates, becomes infinite. The shape of the wall does not enter directly into the boundary layer analysis. It does, of course, affect the inviscid flow that determines u_{invis} and thus, through $u_e(x)$, the boundary layer itself.

20.1 BLASIUS FLOW OVER A FLAT PLATE

The simplest boundary layer one can imagine forms when a thin flat plate is placed in a uniform stream of velocity u_0 so that it is perfectly aligned with the streamlines. Such a plate does not cause any disturbance in the inviscid flow; hence the inviscid velocity at all points of the surface has the constant value u_0. We take a coordinate system with the origin at the leading edge of the plate as shown in Fig. 20.1. For the present we assume that the plate extends to infinity.

The boundary conditions for the boundary layer equations require matching with the inviscid stream,

$$u(x \geq 0, y \to \infty) = u_e(x) = u_0 \tag{20.1.1}$$

and that the no-slip condition is met,

$$u(x > 0, y = 0) = 0 \tag{20.1.2}$$

$$v(x > 0, y = 0) = 0 \tag{20.1.3}$$

In addition, we need to specify an initial condition. For a sharp leading edge the appropriate assumption is

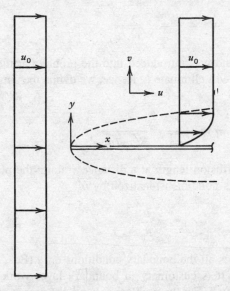

Figure 20.1   Blasius flow: flat plate in a uniform stream.

$$u(x = 0, y > 0) = u_0 \qquad (20.1.4)$$

The leading edge itself is a mathematical discontinuity in u; if we approach $x = 0$, $y = 0$ along the surface of the plate, we find that $u = 0$, but if we approach from the free stream (i.e., $x = 0$, $y \rightarrow 0$), we find that $u = u_0$.

When u_e is a constant, boundary layer equations 16.4.25 are

$$\left\{ \begin{aligned} & \frac{\partial u}{\partial x} + \frac{\partial v}{\partial y} = 0 && (20.1.5) \\[2ex] & u \frac{\partial u}{\partial x} + v \frac{\partial u}{\partial y} = \nu \frac{\partial^2 u}{\partial y^2} && (20.1.6) \end{aligned} \right.$$

The problem consisting of Eqs. 20.1.1 to 20.1.6 was solved first by H. Blasius (1908) while he was a student of Prandtl.

Blasius's problem is a nonlinear partial differential equation that does not have a simple closed-form answer. The successful approach is to look for a similarity solution. The fact that neither x nor y has a natural measuring scale in the boundary data leads us to suspect that the solution $u(x, y)$ does not depend on x and y separately but only upon some combination of them. Simple dimensional analysis of the function $u(x, y; u_0, \nu)$ does not lead us to a similarity variable, so we try another approach using a physical argument. Assume for a moment that we want to solve the problem only out to a certain distance L on the plate. Then the variable $x^* = x/L$ will be the proper nondimensional variable for this direction. As we well know, the y-direction is dominated by a diffusion process, so, according to Rayleigh's argument for viscous diffusion, we expect the non-dimensional y-distance to be scaled by the diffusion depth at $x = L$, that is,

$$y^* = \frac{y}{\delta} = \frac{y}{\sqrt{\nu L / u_0}}$$

Since L could be any position and was introduced into the problem artificially, we seek a combination of x^* and y^* that will eliminate L. Hence, we define the similarity variable as

$$\eta \equiv \frac{y^*}{\sqrt{x^*}} = \frac{y}{\sqrt{\nu x / u_0}} \tag{20.1.7}$$

The natural scale for y is the diffusion length at a distance x along the plate.

The streamwise velocity u is nondimensionalized by u_0:

$$u^* \equiv \frac{u}{u_0} \tag{20.1.8}$$

Observe that this definition makes all the boundary conditions on u (Eqs. 20.1.1, 20.1.2, and 20.1.4) into pure numbers. It is customary in boundary layer work to denote the nondimensional streamfunction by f. For the problem at hand, the proper nondimensional form is

$$f(\eta) \equiv \frac{\psi}{\sqrt{\nu x u_0}} \tag{20.1.9}$$

With Eqs. 20.1.7 and 20.1.8 it can be verified that the streamfunction relation $u = \partial \psi / \partial y$ becomes

$$u^* = \frac{df}{d\eta} = f'(\eta) \tag{20.1.10}$$

The continuity equation will be satisfied exactly if we relate v to the streamfunction. Since

$$v = -\frac{\partial \psi}{\partial x}$$

We insert Eq. 20.1.9 for ψ and use chain rules along with Eq. 20.1.7 to show that

$$v^* \equiv \frac{v}{\sqrt{\nu u_0 / x}} = \frac{1}{2} (\eta f' - f) \tag{20.1.11}$$

Equation 20.1.11 may be considered as the natural way to nondimensionalize v.

When the relations 20.1.10 and 20.1.11 are inserted into the momentum equation 20.1.6, we find that an ordinary differential equation results:

$$f''' + \tfrac{1}{2} f f'' = 0 \tag{20.1.12}$$

A successful similarity variable not only reduces the partial differential equation; it must also make the boundary conditions collapse in an appropriate way. In terms of $f(\eta)$, the boundary conditions are evaluated using Eqs. 20.1.10 and 20.1.11. They are

$$u(x, y = 0) = 0 \Rightarrow f'(\eta = 0) = 0$$

$$v(x, y = 0) = 0 \Rightarrow f(\eta = 0) = 0$$

$$u(x, y \to \infty) = u_e \Rightarrow f'(\eta \to \infty) = 1$$

$$u(x = 0, y) = u_e \Rightarrow f'(\eta \to \infty) = 1$$

(20.1.13)

The last two conditions collapse to give the same boundary condition in terms of $f(\eta)$. We still have consistency between the differential equation to be solved and the number of boundary conditions that are applied.

Blasius's problem is a nonlinear, two-point, boundary value problem and may be solved by standard techniques of mathematical analysis applications. Figure 20.2 gives the results of a computation using a value of $f''(0) = 0.33206$.

As a matter of interest, the thickness of the boundary layer, taken as the point where the u velocity becomes $0.99u_0$, occurs at $\eta = 4.9$. Hence at $y = \delta_{99}$, the definition 20.1.7 yields

$$\frac{\delta_{99}}{x} = 4.9 \sqrt{\frac{\nu}{x u_0}} = 4.9 \, \mathrm{Re}_x^{-1/2}$$

(20.1.14)

$$\mathrm{Re}_x \equiv \frac{u_0 x}{\nu}$$

(20.1.15)

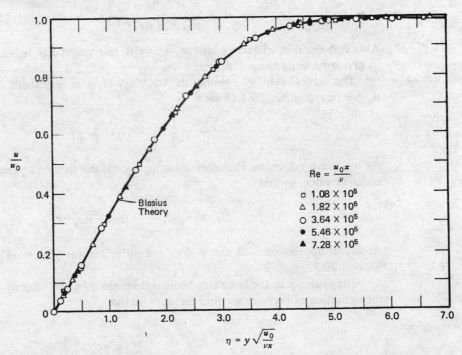

Figure 20.2   Results of experiments compared with analysis. The effective origin of the plate is found from data at two different positions. Adapted from Schlichting (1950). Nikuradse (1942) made the original measurements.

Typical values of Re_x and δ_{99} are for a stream of water at 1 m/s with x at 1 m from the leading edge, $Re_x \approx 10^6$ and $\delta_{99} = 0.5$ cm; for air under the same conditions, $Re_x \approx 6.7 \times 10^4$ and $\delta_{99} = 1.9$ cm. Even for these modest velocities, the boundary layers are very thin. The formula above is valid only for $Re_x < 3 \times 10^6$, because the flow becomes unstable for higher Reynolds numbers and transition to a turbulent boundary layer occurs.

Another result of practical importance is the wall friction. The friction coefficient is found from $f''(0)$. It is

$$C_f \equiv \frac{\tau_0}{\frac{1}{2}\rho u_0^2} = 2f''(0)\ Re_x^{-1/2} = \frac{0.664}{Re_x^{1/2}} \qquad (20.1.16)$$

Note that C_f compares the wall stress with the dynamic pressure of the flow. For a practical Reynolds number of 10^4, the shear stress is 0.0066 times the dynamic pressure. As a general rule, wall shear stresses in fluid flows are roughly 1% of the dynamic pressure (recall that the dynamic pressure indicates the range over which the normal pressure force varies on a body). This statement holds true for turbulent boundary layers as well and is the reason that friction forces may be ignored in many practical cases. Only for large surfaces or at low Reynolds numbers does the accumulated effect of wall shear stress compare with the pressure forces.

The drag force on a plate of length L may be found by integrating the friction coefficient (Eq. 20.1.16) from $x = 0$ to $x = L$. The result is

$$C_D = \frac{F_b}{\frac{1}{2}\rho u_0^2 L} = \frac{1}{L}\int_0^L C_f(x)\ dx$$

$$= 1.328\ Re_L^{-1/2} \qquad (20.1.17)$$

Although the skin friction is infinite at $x = 0$, this singularity is $\sim x^{-1/2}$ and integrates to give a finite force on the plate.

The vertical velocity v within the boundary layer is very small. To compare v with u_0, we rearrange Eq. 20.1.11 into

$$\frac{v}{u_0} = \frac{1}{2}\ Re_x^{-1/2}(\eta f' - f) \qquad (20.1.18)$$

As we move out in the boundary layer ($\eta \to \infty$), the factor in parentheses takes on a constant value, so that

$$\eta \to \infty \qquad \frac{v}{u_0} \sim 0.861\ Re_x^{-1/2}$$

At first it appears unusual that v does not go to zero as $y \to \infty$. This is explained in Section 20.7.

The vorticity in the boundary layer is dominated by the velocity profile $u(y)$. From the definition of vorticity we find for $\omega_z = \omega$ that

$$\omega = -\frac{\partial u}{\partial y} + \frac{\partial v}{\partial x} \qquad (20.1.19)$$

Converting this expression into boundary layer variables where ω is scaled by u_0/δ yields

$$\omega^* \equiv \frac{\omega}{u_0} \sqrt{\frac{\nu x}{u_0}} = -\frac{df'}{d\eta} + \frac{1}{4\mathrm{Re}_x} \left(f - \eta f' - \eta^2 f''\right)$$

$$\omega^* = -f''(\eta) + O[\mathrm{Re}^{-1}]$$

(20.1.20)

The total amount of vorticity at any x-position of the boundary layer is found by integrating Eq. 20.1.20. The result is

$$\frac{1}{u_0} \int_0^\infty \omega \, dy = \int_0^\infty \omega^* \, d\eta = -f'(\infty) + f'(0) = -1$$

The constant value means that no new vorticity is entering the flow. This agrees with our idea that a vorticity flux enters the flow only when a pressure gradient exists along the wall.

Boundary layer theory fails at a sharp leading edge. There is some small region in the neighborhood of $x = 0$ where the distance down the plate is about the same as the distance over which upstream diffusion of viscous effects can occur. In this region the assumptions made to derive the boundary layer equations are invalid. Fortunately, for engineering purposes this region is very small and does not need to be taken into account in computing the drag. However, one effect that does remain in the flow is an apparent shift in the origin of the boundary layer. The geometric origin of the plate and the apparent origin of the boundary layer do not exactly coincide.

It is usually said that the plate has a sharp leading edge. This is an idealization, of course. It might be better to imagine a plate of finite thickness h and a well-rounded leading edge. From our study of the inviscid flow over a rounded nose shape in Chapter 18 we know that the flow would stagnate to zero velocity at the front, accelerate to high velocity around the shoulder, and finally, approach u again as we moved a few h downstream from the nose. The corresponding pressures on the surface are the stagnation-point value, a value below the free-stream value, and finally, a gradual buildup back to the free-steam value (cf. Section 18.4). Through Chapter 13 we have come to expect that a vorticity flux will be produced at a surface wherever there is a pressure gradient along the surface. Hence, the nose region is a strong source of vorticity; the top has vorticity of one sign and the bottom has vorticity of the opposite sign. As we let h become small, the nose of the plate becomes a doublet of vorticity flux. Since the downstream portion of the plate has zero pressure gradient, the vorticity within the layer originates entirely at the leading edge. A detailed analysis of the flow near a sharp leading edge has been given by Davis (1972).

20.2 DISPLACEMENT THICKNESS

The thickness δ of a boundary layer, defined as the point where the u velocity becomes equal to 99% of $u_e(x)$, is useful in gauging the influence of viscous diffusion. Another thickness of importance is the *displacement thickness* δ^*. Consider the boundary layer shown in Fig. 20.3a. Let the streamline ψ_0 be located at y_0 in the inviscid flow, where the velocity is $u_e(x)$. Next, we imagine a completely inviscid flow (Fig. 20.3b, where the velocity u_e extends downward but that the flow ends at $y = \delta^*$, defined as the position

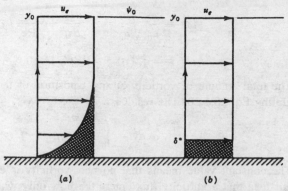

Figure 20.3 Displacement thickness. The inviscid flow above the boundary layer shown in (a) would reach to the position δ^* if it were continued toward the wall until the same flow rate was achieved.

where the ideal flow has the same mass flow as the boundary layer. Mathematically, δ^* is defined (for compressible flow the density is included, with ρ_e denoting the free-stream value) by

$$\int_0^{y_0} \rho u \, dy = \int_{\delta^*}^{y_0} \rho_e u_e \, dy \qquad (20.2.1)$$

Although the physical meaning of Eq. (20.2.1) is clear, this is not a convenient form. Note that since $u_e(x)$ does not depend on y, the following holds:

$$\rho_e u_e \, \delta^* = \int_0^{\delta^*} \rho_e u_e \, dy$$

Adding this equation to Eq. 20.2.1 and rearranging produces a definition for δ^*,

$$\delta^* = \int_0^{y_0} \left(1 - \frac{\rho u}{\rho_e u_e}\right) dy \qquad (20.2.2)$$

Of course, for incompressible flow the density cancels out. The upper limit is replaced by $y_0 \rightarrow \infty$, with the understanding that u/u_e is the velocity profile that occurs in the boundary layer.

The displacement thickness tells us the effect of the boundary layer on the inviscid flow. As a first approximation, the inviscid flow slips past a wall coinciding with the actual wall. The displacement thickness indicates how much equivalent inviscid fluid has been taken into the boundary layer. Since the boundary layer pushes the inviscid flow outward, a second approximation, if we were to require one, would be to imagine that the inviscid flow occurs over a body that has the displacement thickness added to each wall position. A completely inviscid flow between $y = \delta^*$ and $\psi(y_0)$ has the same mass flow that the actual flow has between $y = 0$ and the same location.

The exact nature of the velocity profile determines the displacement thickness, as the definition 20.2.2 shows. For the Blasius profile of Section 20.1, the displacement thickness is

$$\delta^* = 1.72 \sqrt{\frac{\nu x}{u_0}} \qquad (20.2.3)$$

Thus, δ^* is roughly one-third of the 99% thickness δ.

20.3 VON KÁRMÁN MOMENTUM INTEGRAL

In addition to the displacement thickness, boundary layers have another thickness called the *momentum thickness*. It is defined as

$$\Theta \equiv \int_0^\infty \frac{u}{u_e} \left(1 - \frac{u}{u_e}\right) dy \qquad (20.3.1)$$

and occurs in von Kármán's integral of the boundary layer equations.

Let us proceed to derive the momentum integral by integrating the boundary layer momentum equation 16.4.25 from $y = 0$ to $y = h$. The position $y = h$ is outside the boundary layer, where $u \approx u_e$ and where all derivatives $\partial u/\partial y$, $\partial^2 u/\partial y^2$, ... are zero. The equation is

$$\int_0^h \left(u \frac{\partial u}{\partial x} + v \frac{\partial u}{\partial y}\right) dy = \int_0^h u_e \frac{du_e}{dx} dy + \int_0^h \frac{\mu}{\rho} \frac{\partial^2 u}{\partial y^2} dy$$

Rearranging and integrating the shear stress term produces

$$\int_0^h \left(u \frac{\partial u}{\partial x} - u_e \frac{du_e}{dx} + v \frac{\partial u}{\partial y}\right) dy = \frac{\mu}{\rho} \frac{\partial u}{\partial y}\bigg|_0^h = -\frac{\tau_0}{\rho} \qquad (20.3.2)$$

The wall shear stress is denoted as τ_0. Now for a solid wall where $v(y = 0) = 0$, we may express v at any position y by integrating the continuity equation:

$$v = \int_0^y \frac{\partial v}{\partial y} dy' = -\int_0^y \frac{\partial u}{\partial x} dy'$$

The third term in Eq. 20.3.2, if we insert the expression above for v, becomes

$$\int_0^h v \frac{\partial u}{\partial y} dy = \int_0^h \left(-\int_0^y \frac{\partial u}{\partial x} dy'\right) \frac{\partial u}{\partial y} dy$$

This integral is of the form $\int w \, dz = wz - \int z \, dw$, where

$$w = \int_0^y \frac{\partial u}{\partial x} dy' \Rightarrow dw = -\frac{\partial u}{\partial x} dy$$

and

$$dz = \frac{\partial u}{\partial y} dy \Rightarrow z = u$$

Hence, integration by parts gives

$$\int_0^h v \frac{\partial u}{\partial y} \, dy = -u_e \int_0^h \frac{\partial u}{\partial x} \, dy + \int_0^h u \frac{\partial u}{\partial x} \, dy$$

With this, Eq. 20.3.2 becomes

$$\int_0^h \left(u \frac{\partial u}{\partial x} - u_e \frac{du_e}{dx} - u_e \frac{\partial u}{\partial x} + u \frac{\partial u}{\partial x} \right) dy = -\frac{\tau_0}{\rho}$$

Next, we add and subtract $u(du_e/dx)$ and rearrange the terms into the form

$$-\int_0^h \left[u \left(\frac{du_e}{dx} - \frac{\partial u}{\partial x} \right) + (u_e - u) \frac{\partial u}{\partial x} \right] dy - \int_0^h \left[(u_e - u) \frac{du_e}{dx} \right] dy = -\frac{\tau_0}{\rho}$$

or equivalently,

$$\frac{d}{dx} \left[u_e^2 \int_0^h \frac{u}{u_e} \left(1 - \frac{u}{u_e} \right) dy \right] + u_e \frac{du_e}{dx} \int_0^h \left(1 - \frac{u}{u_e} \right) dy = \frac{\tau_0}{\rho}$$

As $h \rightarrow \infty$ the integrals are by definition the displacement and momentum thicknesses; thus,

$$\frac{d}{dx} (u_e^2 \Theta) + u_e \frac{du_e}{dx} \delta^* = \frac{\tau_0}{\rho} \tag{20.3.3}$$

This is the integral momentum equation originally given by von Kármán (1921) using physical arguments, and subsequently derived mathematically by Pohlhausen (1921).

The momentum thickness Θ, when multiplied by ρu_e, gives an indication of the momentum of the boundary layer flow. As a typical example of momentum thickness, one can compute Θ from definition 20.3.1 using the Blasius flat-plate profile. The answer is

$$\Theta = 0.664 \sqrt{\frac{\nu x}{u_0}}$$

Very roughly, Θ is one-third of δ^*, which in turn is roughly one-third of δ. These ratios depend on the shape of the velocity profiles, of course. Only in special cases, such as the Blasius problem, are they constant.

20.4 VON KÁRMÁN–POHLHAUSEN APPROXIMATE METHOD

In the early days of boundary layer theory the electronic computer was not available and the integral method of solving boundary layer problems became highly developed. The von Kármán–Pohlhausen method was one of the first techniques used; a comprehensive survey of various methods and comparison of their accuracy is given in Rosenhead (1963). Many complicated problems, such as turbulent flows, heat transfer problems, and combustion problems are still solved using methods of the integral type. Because of these applications in other areas, it is useful to study how the method is applied to laminar flows.

An essential part of an integral method is an assumption for the form of the velocity profile. Pohlhausen assumed a fourth-order polynomial. For our example we take the cubic

$$u^* \equiv \frac{u}{u_e} = a + b\eta + c\eta^2 + d\eta^3 \tag{20.4.1}$$

where

$$\eta = \frac{y}{\delta(x)} \tag{20.4.2}$$

The profile must meet several boundary conditions. At the wall, the no-slip condition, the momentum equation, and the derivative of the momentum equation with respect to y require that

$$u = 0, \qquad -u_e \frac{du_e}{dx} = \nu \left.\frac{\partial^2 u}{\partial y^2}\right|_0, \qquad \left.\frac{\partial^3 u}{\partial y^3}\right|_0 = 0 \tag{20.4.3}$$

A smooth approach of u to u_e is enforced at the finite position $y = \delta$. This gives

$$u = u_e, \qquad \left.\frac{\partial u}{\partial y}\right|_\delta = 0, \qquad \left.\frac{\partial^2 u}{\partial y^2}\right|_\delta = 0, \qquad \ldots \tag{20.4.4}$$

For a specific boundary layer where $u_e(x)$ is given, conditions 20.4.3 and 20.4.4 together with the momentum integral (Eq. 20.3.3) allow one to find the coefficients a, b, c, and d in the assumed profile as functions of x. As profiles with more coefficients are introduced, more smoothness is required in the approach of u to u_e at $y = \delta$; that is, the higher-order derivatives $\partial^n u/\partial y^n|_\delta$ are required to be zero.

As a relatively simple example, let us solve the Blasius problem where $u_e = u_0$, a constant. Applying the first two boundary conditions of Eq. 20.4.3 and the first two of Eq. 20.4.4 shows that the profile is

$$u^* = \tfrac{3}{2}\eta - \tfrac{1}{2}\eta^3 \tag{20.4.5}$$

Inserting Eq. 20.4.5 into the definition of the displacement thickness yields

$$\delta^* = \delta \int_0^1 (1 - u^*)\, d\eta - \tfrac{3}{8}\delta \tag{20.4.6}$$

The same process applied to the definition of the momentum thickness produces

$$\Theta = \delta \int_0^1 u^*(1 - u^*)\, d\eta = \frac{117}{840}\delta \tag{20.4.7}$$

We may also use Eq. 23.4.5 to find the wall shear stress,

$$\frac{\tau_0}{\rho} = \nu \left.\frac{\partial u}{\partial y}\right|_0 = \nu \frac{3}{2}\frac{u_0}{\delta} \tag{20.4.8}$$

Now we are in a position to substitute for all terms in the von Kármán momentum integral. Equation 20.3.3 for $u_e = u_0$ becomes

$$u_e^2 \frac{d\Theta}{dx} = \frac{\tau_0}{\rho}$$

$$u_0^2 \frac{117}{840} \frac{d\delta}{dx} = \frac{3}{2} \frac{\nu u_0}{\delta}$$

Integration gives

$$\delta = \sqrt{\frac{840}{39}} \sqrt{\frac{\nu x}{u_0}} = 4.64 \sqrt{\frac{\nu x}{u_0}} \qquad (20.4.9)$$

With $\delta(x)$ known, all items in profile equation 20.4.5 have been determined. The coefficient in Eq. 20.4.9 compares well with the exact value of 4.9 in Eq. 20.1.14.

In this problem with $u_e = u_0$, the shape of the profile was constant; only the thickness δ changed with x. In the general case where $u_e(x)$ is given by a pressure gradient, the profile will contain a shape parameter, which also changes with distance along the flow.

20.5 FALKNER–SKAN SIMILARITY SOLUTIONS

In the stagnation-point flow (Hiemenz flow) or the streaming flow over a flat plate (Blasius flow), we have seen how similarity methods combine two independent variables into one. Falkner and Skan (1931) investigated the boundary layer equations to see what specific types of external flows $u_e(x)$ would allow similarity solutions.

We start the derivation of the Falkner–Skan solutions by assuming that a scaling function $u_e(x)$ makes the velocity profile similar:

$$\frac{u(x, y)}{u_e(x)} = f'(\eta) \qquad (20.5.1)$$

where $\delta(x)$ is a scaling function for y; that is,

$$\eta = \frac{y}{\delta(x)} \qquad (20.5.2)$$

At this stage $u_e(x)$ and $\delta(x)$ are undetermined functions. We analyze the boundary layer equations to determine $u_e(x)$ and $\delta(x)$. Now, at any x location the streamfunction is computed as

$$\psi(x, y) - \psi(x, 0) = \int_0^y \frac{\partial \psi}{\partial y}\, dy = \delta u_e \int_0^\eta \frac{u}{u_e}\, d\left(\frac{y}{\delta}\right) = u_e \delta \int_0^\eta f'\, d\eta = u_e \delta f(\eta)$$

Since $\psi = 0$ at $y = 0$ for all x, we have $f(0) = 0$ and

$$\frac{\psi}{u_e \delta} = f(\eta) \qquad (20.5.3)$$

An expression for the vertical velocity v is found by using its relation to the streamfunction and applying chain rules to Eq. 20.5.3. The result is

$$v = -\frac{\partial \psi}{\partial x} = -f \cdot (u_e \delta)' + \eta u_e f' \delta' \qquad (20.5.4)$$

The primes on u_e and δ stand for differentiation with respect to x. When we employ the streamfunction to compute v, we have implicitly satisfied the continuity equation.

The momentum equation for a steady boundary layer flow is

$$u \frac{\partial u}{\partial x} + v \frac{\partial u}{\partial y} = u_e u_e' + \nu \frac{\partial^2 u}{\partial y^2}$$

Performing the indicated operations on Eq. 20.5.1 and using Eq. 20.5.4 gives the momentum equation as

$$u_e f' \left(u_e' f' - \frac{\eta}{\delta} u_e \delta' f'' \right) + [\eta u_e \delta' f' - f \cdot (\delta u_e)'] \frac{u_e}{\delta} f'' = u_e u_e' + \frac{\nu u_e}{\delta^2} f''' \qquad (20.5.5)$$

This equation may be organized into the following form:

$$f''' + \alpha f f'' + \beta (1 - f'^2) = 0 \qquad (20.5.6)$$

Here, for convenience, the coefficients α and β are defined by

$$\alpha = \frac{\delta}{\nu} \frac{d}{dx} (u_e \delta) \qquad (20.5.7)$$

$$\beta = \frac{\delta^2}{\nu} \frac{du_e}{dx} \qquad (20.5.8)$$

Equation 20.5.6 will be an ordinary differential equation for $f(\eta)$ only if α and β do not depend on x but are constant. Thus, Eqs. 20.5.7 and 20.5.8 furnish relations that determine those $u_e(x)$ and $\delta(x)$ functions that result in self-similar boundary layers. The solutions of the coupled equations 20.5.7 and 20.5.8 are made easy if we recognize that

$$2\alpha - \beta = \frac{1}{\nu} \frac{d}{dx} (\delta^2 u_e)$$

Hence,

$$(2\alpha - \beta)(x - x_0) = \frac{1}{\nu} \delta^2 u_e \qquad (20.5.9)$$

The free constants in Eq. 20.5.9 are chosen as follows. We may set $x_0 = 0$; then $x = 0$ is the place where either $\delta = 0$ or $u_e = 0$. Solving Eq. 20.5.9 yields

$$\delta = \sqrt{\frac{(2\alpha - \beta)\nu x}{u_e}} \qquad (20.5.10)$$

The common situation is for u_e and x both to be positive; however, in certain situations x and u_e have opposite signs. We choose $2\alpha - \beta = 1$ or -1 according as u_e and x have the same or opposite signs. Note that any value of $2\alpha - \beta$ is acceptable. If y/δ is a similarity variable, $y/C\delta$ is also a similarity variable for any constant C. Thus, Eq. 20.5.10 becomes

$$\delta = \sqrt{\pm \frac{\nu x}{u_e}} \qquad (20.5.11)$$

[This is the original definition of δ. Several later papers and books use $\alpha = 1$, so that their δ is $(2 - \beta)^{1/2}$ times Eq. 20.5.11.]

The external velocity $u_e(x)$ is found by inserting Eq. 20.5.10 into Eq. 20.5.8. This gives

$$\beta = \pm \frac{x}{u_e} \frac{du_e}{dx} \qquad (20.5.12)$$

$$= \mp \frac{x}{\rho u_e^2} \frac{dp}{dx}$$

Integrating produces

$$u_e = u_0 \left(\frac{x}{L}\right)^m \qquad (20.5.13)$$

where the arbitrary constants u_0 and L have the same signs as u and x. The exponent m is

$$m = \left\{ \begin{array}{c} \beta \\ -\beta \end{array} \right\} \quad \text{if} \quad u_e \text{ and } x \text{ have } \left\{ \begin{array}{l} \text{the same sign} \\ \text{opposite signs} \end{array} \right.$$

Self-similar boundary layers occur when the external velocity is the simple power law (Eq. 20.5.13). The similarity variable for these flows is

$$\eta = \frac{y}{\delta} = \frac{y}{\sqrt{\pm \nu x/u_e}} = \frac{y/L}{\sqrt{\text{Re}} \left(\dfrac{x}{L}\right)^{1-m/2}} \qquad (20.5.14)$$

The equation that governs the streamfunction is Eq. 20.5.6, with α and β eliminated in favor of m. When u_e and x have the same sign, this equation is

$$f''' + \tfrac{1}{2}(m + 1)ff'' + m(1 - f'^2) = 0 \qquad (20.5.15)$$

This is known as the Falkner–Skan equation. The two arbitrary constants α and β in Eq. 20.5.6 have been reduced to one constant m by fixing the scale for the function $\delta(x)$.

For flow over a solid wall we require that $u = 0$, $v = 0$ at the wall and $u = u_e$ at $\eta \to \infty$. Equations 20.5.1 and 20.5.3 show that these conditions imply that

$$f(0) = 0$$
$$f'(0) = 0 \qquad (20.5.16)$$
$$f''(\infty) = 1$$

We refrain from specifying an initial velocity profile at $x = x_1$, as this would overdetermine the problem. Whatever profile comes out of the solution is the initial profile required for similarity. [If $x_1 = 0$, this fact is hidden by the presence of a singular point in the $\eta(x, y)$ transformation.] The Falkner–Skan equation 20.5.15 is a nonlinear differential equation, so we cannot easily know what values of m will give a solution and if that solution, once obtained, is unique.

Several typical velocity profiles for different values of m are given in Fig. 20.4. As long as $m > 0$, the solutions are known to exist, and they are also unique. As far as the boundary layer is concerned, the details of how the inviscid flow produces $u_e(x)$ are

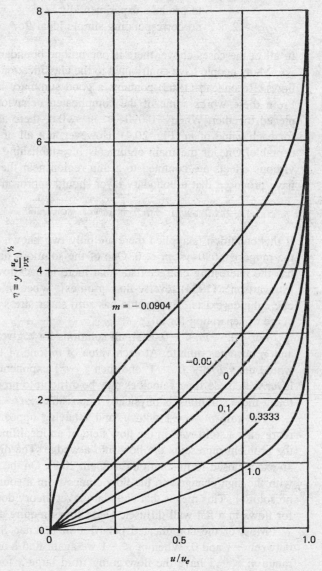

Figure 20.4 Falkner–Skan profiles. The parameter m indicates the external velocity variation through $u_e = u_0 x^m$.

inconsequential. Nevertheless, it is useful to identify several simple ideal flows that lead to Falkner–Skan boundary layers. For $m \geq 0$ they are:

$m = 0$:   Blasius flow over a flat plate with a sharp leading edge; also the local flow at any cusp leading edge

$0 < m < 1$:   flow over a wedge with half-angle $\theta_{1/2} = m/(m + 1)$ with $0 < \theta_{1/2} < \pi/2$

$m = 1$:   Hiemenz flow toward a plane stagnation point

$1 < m < 2$:   flow into a corner with $\theta_{1/2} > \pi/2$; a flow of this type may be difficult to produce experimentally

$m > 2$:   no corresponding simple ideal flow

In all of the cases above, there is one unique boundary layer profile.

Many people have contributed to the classification and computation of Falkner–Skan flows. Rosenhead (1963) contains a good summary by C. W. Jones and E. J. Watson. From these works some of the complicated behavior at negative values of m can be pieced together. When $-0.0904 < m < 0.0$, there are an infinite number of solutions for each value of m (Fig. 20.4). However, not all of these solutions are physically acceptable. One of the main arguments in establishing boundary layer theory is that the viscous effects are confined to a thin region near the wall. In light of this fact, people have proposed that a boundary layer should approach the free stream exponentially:

$$1 - u^* = 1 - f' \sim Ae^{-B\eta} \qquad \text{as} \quad \eta \to \infty$$

If this condition is applied there are only two known acceptable solutions for each m in the range $-0.0904 < m < 0$. One of the solutions has $u > 0$ for all η, while the other has the interesting characteristic that there is backflow for a small region near the wall [Stewartson's (1954) reverse-flow profiles]. When m is exactly equal to -0.0904, only one solution exists. This profile has zero shear stress at the wall and therefore is on the verge of separating for all x.

For $-1 < m < -0.0904$, all solutions for a given m tend to oscillate about $f' = 1$ and η becomes infinite. At each value of m, one of these solutions has just one region where the velocity $f' > 1$, and then $f \to 1$ exponentially. Because a laminar boundary layer with these supervelocities may be difficult to produce experimentally, some workers reject these solutions as physically impossible.

The case $m = -1$ with u_e and x having opposite signs, $u = -a_0/x$ ($u_0 = -a_0$), represents a solid wall in the flow field of an ideal line sink. When two walls are present the problem represents the flow into a wedge. The differential equation in this case has an exact closed-form solution (Problem 20.9). On the other hand, the equivalent problem with the sign changed so the flow comes from a source ($m = -1$ and $u = +u_0/x$) has no solution. This means that boundary layer theory does not produce a similarity solution for flows in a flat-wall diffuser. These flows require a nonsimilar solution.

Most of the complicated behavior in Falkner–Skan solutions happens when m is between -1 and 0. When $m < -1$ we again find a unique solution. All solutions in the range $m < -1$ have the flow going from large x toward $x = 0$. Hence, the flows are strongly accelerated with $u = -a_0(x/L)^m$, $m < -1$.

20.6 ARBITRARY TWO-DIMENSIONAL LAYERS: CRANK–NICOLSON DIFFERENCE METHOD

An arbitrary inviscid flow over a wall provides us with $u_e(x)$ as an external velocity. When $u_e(x)$ does not follow a Falkner–Skan variation, we have a nonsimilar boundary layer where $u(x, y)$ cannot be reduced to a function of a single variable η. With the aid of computers, two-dimensional boundary layers may be calculated with relative ease using finite-difference techniques.

Of the many methods that have been proposed, two methods are the most popular: the Crank–Nicolson method and the method developed by Keller and Cebeci (1971). Since the latter method is given a detailed account in the book of Cebeci and Bradshaw (1977) and in the review article of Keller (1978), we shall study the former, for which Blottner (1970, 1975) is the standard review paper. A simplified program for incompressible laminar boundary layers is given in Appendix G.

To start, consider the equations and boundary conditions that constitute a well-posed boundary layer problem on the domain $x[0, L]$, $y[0, \infty]$. We are to find u and v that satisfy the equations

$$\frac{\partial u}{\partial x} + \frac{\partial v}{\partial y} = 0 \tag{20.6.1}$$

$$u \frac{\partial u}{\partial x} + v \frac{\partial u}{\partial y} - u_e \frac{du_e}{dx} + v \frac{\partial^2 u}{\partial y^2} \tag{20.6.2}$$

No slip is allowed on the wall; hence,

$$u(x, y = 0) = 0, \qquad v(x, y = 0) = 0 \tag{20.6.3}$$

At infinity the boundary layer matches a given inviscid flow $u_e(x)$:

$$u(x, y \rightarrow \infty) = u_e(x) \tag{20.6.4}$$

The function u_e has a characteristic velocity scale u_o. The final condition is to specify the initial profile

$$u(x = 0) = u_i(y) \tag{20.6.5}$$

Equations 20.6.1 to 20.6.5 give the mathematical problem to be solved.

Since the boundary layer grows as we proceed along the surface, it is an advantage to adjust the scale of the y-axis so that the boundary layer has a nearly constant thickness. It is particularly difficult to use physical variants near a sharp leading edge. Introduce Falkner–Skan-like variables defined according to

$$\xi \equiv \frac{x}{L}, \qquad \eta = y \left[\frac{\nu x}{u_e(x)} \right]^{-1/2} = \frac{y}{L} \left(\frac{L}{x} \frac{u_e}{u_0} \frac{u_0 L}{\nu} \right)^{1/2} \tag{20.6.6}$$

Notice that L and u_0 do not occur explicitly in η but have been inserted to display the physical variables with the inviscid scales L and u_0. Velocities for the boundary layer are defined with an unusual notation where the prime refers to partial differentiation with respect to η. The nondimensional velocities are

$$f'(\xi, \eta) \equiv \frac{\partial f}{\partial \eta} \equiv \frac{u}{u_e} \tag{20.6.7}$$

$$V(\xi, \eta) \equiv \frac{v}{u_e} \left(\frac{u_e x}{\nu}\right)^{1/2} \tag{20.6.8}$$

Although $f(\xi, \eta)$ is the streamfunction, the method does not solve for f but keeps the two dependent variables defined in Eqs. 20.6.7 and 20.6.8.

In terms of the new variables, the boundary conditions corresponding to Eqs. 20.6.3 and 20.6.5 are

$$f'(\xi, 0) = 0, \qquad V(\xi, 0) = 0 \tag{20.6.9}$$

and

$$f'(0, \eta) = f_i'(\eta) \tag{20.6.10}$$

The given inviscid velocity turns out to enter the computations in two ways. The boundary condition 20.6.4 is

$$f'(\xi, \eta \to \infty) = 1 \tag{20.6.11}$$

On the other hand, within the differential equation itself $u_e(x)$ enters in the form

$$\beta(\xi) \equiv \frac{x/L}{u_e/u_0} \frac{d(u_e/u_0)}{d(x/L)} = \frac{x}{u_e} \frac{du_e}{dx} = \frac{d \ln u_e}{d \ln x} \tag{20.6.12}$$

Boundary layers differ from one another because they have different free-stream variations $\beta(\xi)$ and/or different initial velocity profiles $f_i'(\eta)$.

Transforming the differential equations 20.6.1 and 20.6.2 yields the continuity equation,

$$\xi \frac{\partial f'}{\partial \xi} + \beta f' + \frac{\eta}{2}(\beta - 1)\frac{\partial f'}{\partial \eta} + \frac{\partial V}{\partial \eta} = 0 \tag{20.6.13}$$

and the momentum equation,

$$f' \xi \frac{\partial f'}{\partial \xi} + \overline{V} \frac{\partial f'}{\partial \eta} = (1 - f'^2)\beta + \frac{\partial^2 f'}{\partial \eta^2} \tag{20.6.14}$$

A new variable $\overline{V}$ has been introduced in Eq. 20.6.14 for convenience. It is defined by

$$\overline{V} \equiv V + \tfrac{1}{2} \eta f'(\beta - 1) \tag{20.6.15}$$

The mathematical problem to be solved is now Eqs. 20.6.9 to 20.6.15.

A finite-difference grid is placed over the computation domain as depicted in Fig. 20.5, where grid points are denoted by m, n. The wall $\eta = 0$ is the grid point $n = 1$, and $\eta = \infty$ is taken to be the finite position $\eta = 8$ where $n = 81$. Thus, the mesh spacing is $\Delta \eta = 0.1$ and the formula for η is

$$\eta = 0.1(\eta - 1)$$

In the ξ-direction the grid points are denoted as $m = 1, 2, \ldots$ with an increment $\Delta \xi$, which we may specify arbitrarily.

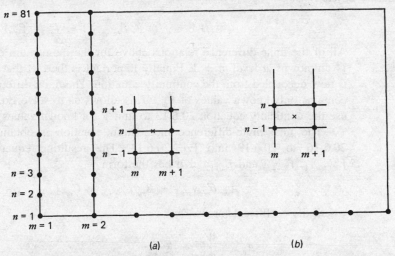

Figure 20.5   Grid and computational molecules for the Crank–Nicolson boundary layer program: (a) momentum equation molecule; (b) continuity equation molecule.

The boundary layer problem is parabolic, so the solution marches forward in ξ from a known initial profile $f_i'(\eta)$ at $m = 1$. When the solution at $m = 2$ is found, this acts as an initial condition for $m = 3$. This process continues for as long as the boundary data $\beta(\xi)$ are specified.

The finite-difference equations are written for the computational molecule shown in Fig. 20.5a. The center of the molecule is within the grid at $m + \frac{1}{2}, n$. We are essentially writing the difference equations about this point. The first term in Eq. 20.6.14 is approximated using a centered-difference formula as follows:

$$\xi f' \, \frac{\partial f'}{\partial \xi} \approx \frac{\xi_{m+1/2} f_{mn}'(f_{m+1,n}' - f_{mn}')}{\Delta \xi} \qquad (20.6.16)$$

Recall that we know all values on line m and seek values for $m + 1$. Equation 20.6.16 has been linearized by evaluating the f' coefficient at m, n, where it is known, instead of at $m + \frac{1}{2}, n$. The next convective term in Eq. 20.6.14 is also linearized by evaluating $\overline{V}$ at m, n, where it is known. In addition, for this term we find $\partial f'/\partial \eta$ by averaging the centered-difference formula at $m + 1$ and at m. The result is

$$\overline{V} \, \frac{\partial f'}{\partial \eta} \approx \frac{1}{2} \, \overline{V}_{m+1/2} \left(\frac{f_{m+1,n+1}' - f_{m+1,n-1}'}{2\Delta \eta} + \frac{f_{m,n+1}' - f_{m,n-1}'}{2\Delta \eta} \right) \qquad (20.6.17)$$

The idea of averaging $\partial f'/\partial \eta$ at m and $m + 1$ to represent $\partial f'/\partial \eta$ at $m + \frac{1}{2}$ is the essential characteristic of the Crank–Nicolson method. The same process is applied to the second-derivative term to get

$$\frac{\partial^2 f'}{\partial \eta^2} \approx \frac{1}{2} \left[\frac{f_{m+1,n+1}' - 2f_{m+1,n}' + f_{m+1,n-1}'}{(\Delta \eta)^2} + \frac{f_{m,n+1}' - 2f_{mn}' + f_{m,n-1}'}{(\Delta \eta)^2} \right] \qquad (20.6.18)$$

The last remaining term in Eq. 20.6.14 is also linearized as follows:

$$\beta(1 - f'^2) = \beta_{m+1/2}(1 - f'_{m+1,n}f'_{mn}) \qquad (20.6.19)$$

All of the finite-difference relations above for the momentum equation are linear in the f' unknowns at level $m + 1$. Equally important is the fact that the momentum equation is now decoupled from the continuity equation. The finite-difference form of Eq. 20.6.14 contains only known values of $\overline{V}_{mn}$. This allows us to solve Eq. 20.6.14 for f' and then use the continuity equation 20.6.13 to find $\overline{V}$ for known values of f'.

The final finite-difference momentum equation is obtained by substituting Eqs. 20.6.16 to 20.6.19 into Eq. 20.6.14. The resulting equation contains unknowns $f'_{m+1,n+1}$, $f'_{m+1,n}$, and $f'_{m+1,n-1}$. It has the form

$$A_{mn}f'_{m+1,n+1} + B_{mn}f'_{m+1,n} + C_{mn}f'_{m+1,n-1} = D_{mn} \qquad (20.6.20)$$

where the coefficients are

$$A_{mn} = \frac{\overline{V}_{mn}}{4\Delta\eta} - \frac{1}{2(\Delta\eta)^2}$$

$$B_{mn} = \xi_{m+1/2}f'_{mn}\frac{1}{\Delta\xi} + \beta_{m+1/2}f'_{mn} + \frac{1}{(\Delta\eta)^2}$$

$$C_{mn} = -\left[\frac{\overline{V}_{mn}}{4\Delta\eta} + \frac{1}{2(\Delta\eta)^2}\right] \qquad (20.6.21)$$

$$D_{mn} = \beta_{m+1/2} + \xi_{m+1/2}f'^2_{mn}\frac{1}{\Delta\xi} - \overline{V}_{mn}\frac{f'_{m,n+1} - f'_{m,n-1}}{4\Delta\eta}$$

$$+ \frac{f'_{m,n+1} - 2f'_{mn} + f'_{m,n-1}}{2(\Delta\eta)^2}$$

Since all f' values in Eq. 20.6.20 are at the $m + 1$ level as unknowns and all f' values in Eq. 20.6.21 are known at the m level, it is permissible to drop the m and $m + 1$ notation. In this form, Eq. 20.6.20 is

$$A_nf'_{n+1} + B_nf'_n + C_nf'_{n-1} = D_n \qquad (20.6.22)$$

The next step is to write out Eq. 20.6.22 for grid points $n = 2, 3, \ldots, 80$ across the boundary layer. This produces 79 equations in 81 unknowns as follows:

$$C_2f'_1 + B_2f'_2 + A_2f'_3 \qquad\qquad\qquad\qquad = D_2$$
$$C_3f'_2 + B_3f'_3 + A_3f'_4 \qquad\qquad\qquad = D_3$$
$$C_4f'_3 + B_4f'_4 + A_4f'_5 \qquad\qquad = D_4$$
$$\cdots \qquad \cdots \qquad \cdots \qquad\qquad \vdots$$
$$C_{79}f'_{78} + B_{79}f'_{79} + A_{79}f'_{80} \quad = D_{79}$$
$$C_{80}f'_{79} + B_{80}f'_{80} + A_{80}f'_{80} = D_{80} \qquad (20.6.23)$$

Boundary conditions on f' supply the fact that $f'_1 = 0$ and $f'_{81} = 1$, thus eliminating two unknowns. The first and last equations in Eq. 20.6.23 become

$$B_2 f_2' + A_2 f_3' = D_2 \tag{20.6.24}$$
$$C_{80} f_{79}' + B_{80} f_{80}' = D_{80} - A_{80}$$

Equations 20.6.23 are now a tridiagonal system of linear equations for f_2' through f_{80}'. The Crank–Nicolson method is implicit because we solve for all the f' values at one time. We cannot isolate a single equation for f_n' as a function of known quantities. Implicit methods are known to be very stable and allow large step sizes in the ξ direction with good accuracy.

The solution of Eq. 20.6.23 is not very difficult, primarily because the system is tridiagonal. The boundary layer program in Appendix G solves Eq. 20.6.23 by the Thomas algorithm. To understand the program completely, we briefly review the Thomas method. For a tridiagonal system of unknowns f_n' it is true that f_n' and f_{n+1}' are related by a linear equation

$$f_n' = E_n f_{n+1}' + F_n \tag{20.6.25}$$

or, with a change of subscripts,

$$f_{n-1}' = E_{n-1} f_n' + F_{n-1} \tag{20.6.26}$$

In these equations the coefficients E_n and F_n are numbers that depend on the A, B, C coefficients of Eq. 20.6.23. They are found as follows: Substitute Eq. 20.6.26 into Eq. 20.6.22 to obtain

$$A_n f_{n+1}' + B_n f_n' + C_n (E_{n-1} f_n' + F_{n-1}) = D_n \tag{20.6.27}$$

Rearrange this result into

$$f_n' = -\frac{A_n}{B_n + C_n E_{n-1}} f_{n+1}' + \frac{D_n - C_n F_{n-1}}{B_n + C_n E_{n-1}}$$

Comparing this with Eq. 20.6.25 shows that

$$E_n = -\frac{A_n}{B_n + C_n E_{n-1}} \tag{20.6.28}$$

$$F_n = \frac{D_n - C_n F_{n-1}}{B_n + C_n E_{n-1}} \tag{20.6.29}$$

These recursive relations allow us to calculate E_n and F_n from known values of E_{n-1} and F_{n-1}. Starting values E_1 and F_1 are chosen by writing Eq. 20.6.25 with $n = 1$, that is,

$$f_1' = E_1 f_2' + F_1 = 0 \tag{20.6.30}$$

In a general boundary layer f_2' takes on different values, while the boundary condition requires f_1' to be zero. The only way for Eq. 20.6.30 to be valid for arbitrary f_2' is if $E_1 = 0$ and $F_1 = 0$. With these starting values, all E_n and F_n are calculated using Eqs. 20.6.28 and 20.6.29.

The solution of the momentum equation for the $m = 2$ line can now be completed. Beginning with $f_{81}' = 1$, Eq. 20.6.26 will produce f_{80}'. Continued application of this equation gives f_n' at all positions across the boundary layer.

The continuity equation 20.6.13 is employed to find the vertical velocity V. Let the computational molecule consist of four points as shown in Fig. 20.5b. The center of the points, $m + \frac{1}{2}, n - \frac{1}{2}$, is considered as the expansion point for the finite-difference approximations. Employing centered differences and averaging as needed for the Crank–Nicolson method, we approximate the terms as follows:

$$\frac{\partial V}{\partial \eta} = \frac{1}{2}\left(\frac{V_{m+1,n} - V_{m+1,n-1}}{\Delta \eta} + \frac{V_{m,n} - V_{m,n-1}}{\Delta \eta}\right)$$

$$\frac{1}{2}\eta(\beta - 1)\frac{\partial f'}{\partial \eta} = \frac{1}{4}\eta_{n-1/2}(\beta_{m+1/2} - 1)\left(\frac{f'_{m+1,n} - f'_{m+1,n-1}}{\Delta \eta} + \frac{f'_{m,n} - f'_{m,n-1}}{\Delta \eta}\right)$$

$$\beta f' = \frac{1}{4}\beta_{m+1/2}(f'_{m+1,n} + f'_{m+1,n-1} + f'_{m,n} + f'_{m,n-1}) \tag{20.6.31}$$

$$\xi\frac{\partial f'}{\partial \xi} = \frac{1}{2}\xi_{m+1/2}\left(\frac{f'_{m+1,n} - f'_{m,n}}{\Delta \xi} + \frac{f'_{m+1,n-1} - f'_{m,n-1}}{\Delta \xi}\right)$$

Everything is known in the equations above except $V_{m+1,n}$; hence, we may substitute Eq. 20.6.31 into Eq. 20.6.13 and solve explicitly for the unknown velocity. The result is

$$V_{m+1,n} = V_{m+1,n-1} + V_{m,n-1} - V_{m,n}$$
$$+ 2\Delta\eta(A_n^c f'_{m+1,n} + B_n^c f'_{m+1,n-1} + C_n^c f'_{m,n} + D_n^c f'_{m,n-1}) \tag{20.6.32}$$

where

$$A_n^c = -\frac{1}{4}\beta_{m+1/2} - \frac{1}{2\Delta\xi}\xi_{m+1/2} - \frac{1}{4\Delta\eta}\eta_{n-1/2}(\beta_{m+1/2} - 1)$$

$$B_n^c = - \quad \cdots \quad - \quad \cdots \quad + \quad \cdots$$

$$C_n^c = - \quad \cdots \quad + \quad \cdots \quad - \quad \cdots \tag{20.6.33}$$

$$D_n^c = - \quad \cdots \quad + \quad \cdots \quad + \quad \cdots$$

Stepping across the layer from $n = 1$, where the wall condition $V_1 = 0$ is employed, to the outer edge, $n = 81$, gives all V values on line $m + 1$. The variable $\bar{V}$ is related to V by our algebraic equation 20.6.15. The finite-difference form of this equation is

$$\bar{V}_{m+1,n} = V_{m+1,n} + \frac{1}{2}\eta_n f'_{m+1,n}(\beta_{m+1} - 1) \tag{20.6.34}$$

This equation is evaluated for all n.

In principle the calculation has progressed one step from $m = 1$ to $m + 1 = 2$. The step from $m = 2$ to $m = 3$ is exactly the same as the first step, so we simply rename the data, $f'_{2,n} \rightarrow f'_{1,n}$ and $\bar{V}_{2,n} \rightarrow \bar{V}_{1,n}$, and repeat the calculation procedure using the new data as initial conditions. This process is continued for the entire ξ length of the boundary layer.

In describing the computing method, the initial conditions were glossed over by assuming that $f_i'(\eta)$ and $V_i(\eta)$ are given functions. Now we return to this question.

Assume that the initial position in the boundary layer is $\xi_i = 0$. (It is usually, but not always, permitted to set $\xi_i = 0$ at the beginning of the calculation.) With $\xi = 0$, the continuity equation 20.6.13 becomes

$$\beta_i f_i' + \frac{\eta}{2}(\beta_i - 1)\frac{\partial f_i'}{\partial \eta} + \frac{\partial V_i}{\partial \eta} = 0$$

Multiplying by $d\eta$, integrating from 0 to η, and noting that $f_i(0) = f_i'(0) = V(0) = 0$ produces

$$V_i = -\beta_i f_i - \frac{\beta_i - 1}{2}(\eta f_i' - f_i) \tag{20.6.35}$$

This equation relates V_i to the initial profile f_i. Recall that we specify initial conditions on $u = f'$, from which f may be found by integration if necessary, but no initial conditions should be given for V. The boundary layer equations themselves, in particular Eq. 20.6.35, give a restraining equation between initial values of u and v.

Next consider the momentum equation 20.6.14, evaluated at $\xi = 0$ with Eq. 20.6.15 inserted for $\bar{V}$:

$$[V_i + \tfrac{1}{2}\eta f_i'(\beta_i - 1)]f_i'' = (1 - f_i'^2)\beta_i + f_i'''$$

Introducing Eq. 20.6.35 reduces the equation above to an ordinary differential equation for f_i,

$$f_i''' + \tfrac{1}{2}(\beta_i + 1)f_i f_i'' + \beta_i(1 - f_i'^2) = 0 \tag{20.6.36}$$

Equation 20.6.36 is recognized as the Falkner–Skan equation 20.5.15, where $\beta_i = m$. [Recall that m is the power in the equation $u_e = u_0(x/L)^m$.]

If we choose $f_i(\eta)$ as one of the similarity profiles from the Falkner–Skan family and the corresponding f_i' and V_i using Eq. 20.6.35, we have a set of initial conditions that obey the differential equations, which govern the problem (although this is not actually required). The Falkner–Skan profiles supply most of the initial conditions that we might need:

$$\beta_i = 1: \quad \text{plane stagnation point}$$

$$0 < \beta_i < 1: \quad \text{wedge of half-angle } \theta_{1/2} = \beta\pi/(\beta + 1)$$

$$\beta_i = 0: \quad \text{flat plate with sharp leading edge}$$

If the body is blunt, such as the rounded nose of an airfoil, the stagnation-point solution is appropriate for starting the calculation. If the body has a pointed front, the solution corresponding to the proper wedge angle is used. If the body has a sharp or cusp leading edge, the solution for $\beta_i = 0$ is used. This is true irrespective of the pressure gradient at the leading edge. For example, consider a converging channel that causes the flow to accelerate, and suppose that we insert a flat plate in the middle of this channel. The proper initial condition for this flow is $\beta_i = 0$ even though $dp/dx \neq 0$ at the leading edge.

A flowchart for the boundary layer program of Appendix G is shown in Fig. 20.6. The program contains only the boundary layer calculation where the initial conditions f_i and f_i' are to be read in at the beginning. As the program is given, the external velocity

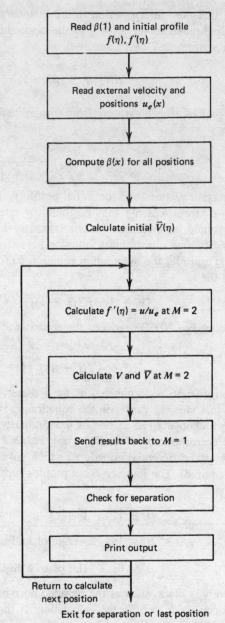

Figure 20.6   Flowchart of the boundary layer program in Appendix G.

$u_e(x/L)/u_0$ is to be read in a parametric form $u_e(m)/u_0$, $x(m)/L$ at a finite number of points. The only way in which $u_e(x)$ information enters the boundary layer equations is through the function $\beta(m)$ defined by Eq. 20.6.12. The program evaluates Eq. 20.6.12 with a forward-difference equation. since the finite-difference boundary layer equations require both β_m and $\beta_{m+1/2}$, we make the approximation $\beta_m = \beta_{m+1/2}$. If a second-order accurate method is used to determine β_m, the distinction between β_m and $\beta_{m+1/2}$ would be more appropriate. For accuracy $\Delta\beta$ should be small.

The program first reads $u_e(x)$ and the initial data $f_i(\eta)$ and $f_i'(\eta)$ and calculates $\beta(x)$. Then it starts a DO loop to advance the boundary layer profile $u/u_e = f'(\xi, \eta)$ from ξ_m to ξ_{m+1}. When this calculation is complete, the program uses the new f' values in a calculation of $V(\xi, \eta)$ and $\bar{V}(\xi, \eta)$. A check is made after each step to see if the flow has separated. If separation occurs, the calculation stops at once. If no separation occurs, the calculation continues until the last position $x = L$ is reached.

*20.7   VERTICAL VELOCITY

The vertical velocity from a boundary layer calculation needs to be interpreted carefully. Recall that during the derivation of the boundary layer equations in Section 16.4, the first guess was that v/u_0 would approach zero as $\mathrm{Re} = u_0L/\nu$ becomes infinite. Intuitively, this is reasonable. As we stand outside the boundary layer and watch the layer become thinner and thinner because $\mathrm{Re} \to \infty$, the vertical velocity vanishes. Within the boundary layer the picture is quite different. The estimate $v/u_0 \to 0$ is not good enough on the boundary layer scale. Small vertical currents convect momentum into regions where the u velocity is much different. This effect is represented by the term $v\,\partial u/\partial y$ in the momentum equation. In deriving the boundary layer equation, since $\partial u/\partial y \to \infty$ and $v \to 0$ as $\mathrm{Re} \to \infty$, we were required to make a sharper estimate of v in order to find out if the indeterminate form $0 \cdot \infty$ was zero or finite. The result was that $v\,\partial u/\partial y$ is finite and thus is important. Within the boundary layer the correct nondimensional vertical velocity is (Eq. 16.4.5)

$$v^* \equiv \frac{v}{u_0}\left(\frac{L}{\delta}\right) = \frac{v}{u_0}\,\mathrm{Re}^{1/2} \qquad (20.7.1)$$

The nondimensional v velocity used in the Crank–Nicolson program was essentially of this same form (Eq. 20.6.8):

$$V \equiv \frac{v}{u_e}\left(\frac{u_e x}{\nu}\right)^{1/2} = \frac{v}{u_0}\left(\frac{u_0 L}{\nu}\right)^{1/2}\left(\frac{x/L}{u_e/u_0}\right)^{1/2}$$

The final factor in parentheses results from the transformation to ξ, η variables.

Consider the inviscid flow near the wall. Figure 20.7 shows an outside view of a flow, where the inviscid surface velocity $u_e(x)$ is expressed in boundary layer coordinates x, y. Next to the wall the inviscid-flow continuity equation (in dimensional form) is written in boundary layer coordinates as

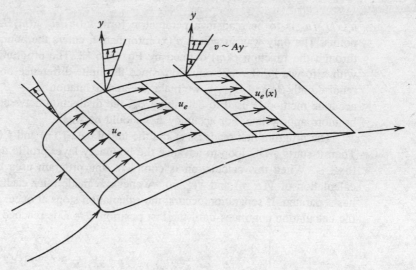

Figure 20.7 View from outside the boundary layer looking at the behavior of u and v in the inviscid flow at the top of the boundary layer.

$$\frac{du_e}{dx} + \frac{\partial v}{\partial y} = 0$$

Integrating this equation a small distance in the y-direction and considering the integrand to be constant yields

$$v_{\text{inviscid region}} = \int_0^y \frac{\partial v}{\partial y}\, dy = -\frac{du_e}{dx} \int_0^y dy$$

$$\sim -\frac{du_e}{dx} y \qquad \text{as} \quad y \to 0 \tag{20.7.2}$$

We may interpret this as the inviscid vertical velocity (expressed in boundary layer co-ordinates, however) that would exist if the boundary had zero thickness. At this point we know three things about the inviscid velocities near a wall: The velocity along the wall is $u_e(x)$, the v velocity into the wall is zero, and v grows linearly as we leave the wall in accord with Eq. 20.7.2.

Next, turn attention to the boundary layer. A more exact calculation of the vertical velocity can be made by integrating through the boundary layer. Again consider the expression for v:

$$v = \int_0^y \frac{\partial v}{\partial y}\, dy = -\int_0^y \frac{\partial u}{\partial x}\, dy = \frac{d}{dx} \int_0^y (u_e - u)\, dy - \frac{du_e}{dx} y \tag{20.7.3}$$

When y is taken in the outer portion of the boundary layer, the integral becomes the displacement thickness by Eq. 20.2.2. Hence, a boundary layer analysis gives

$$v(y \rightarrow \infty) = -\frac{du_e}{dx} y + \frac{d}{dx} (u_e \delta^*) \qquad (20.7.4)$$

This equation offers another interpretation of the influence of the displacement thickness on the inviscid flow (Lighthill, 1958). The first term represents the inviscid velocity as found in Eq. 20.7.2. The second term is the influence of the boundary layer (B.L.) profile on the v velocity in the outer regions. This is often viewed as a correction effect that the boundary layer imposes on the inviscid flow:

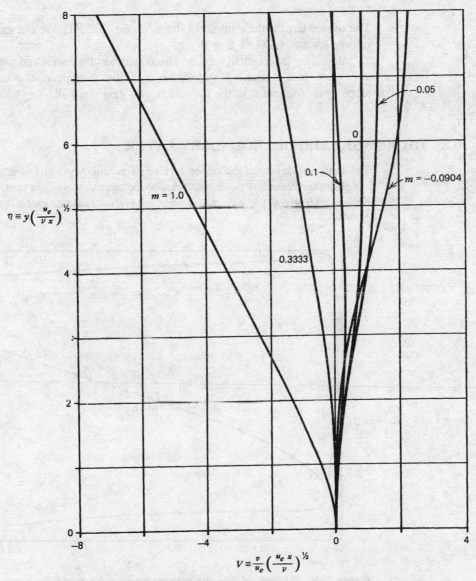

Figure 20.8 Vertical-velocity profiles for Falkner–Skan boundary layers.

$$v_{\text{B.L. inv. corr.}} = \frac{d}{dx} (u_e \delta*) \tag{20.7.5}$$

In an inviscid analysis the first-order condition is that $v = 0$ on the wall. Solving the inviscid problem with $v_{\text{wall}} =$ Eq. 20.7.5 gives a second-order solution.

Figure 20.8 gives the vertical-velocity results $v(\eta)$ for several Falkner–Skan boundary layer flows. For $\eta \to \infty$, v approaches the appropriate nondimensional form of Eq. 20.7.4, that is,

$$V(\infty) = \frac{v}{u_e} \left(\frac{u_e x}{\nu} \right)^{1/2} = -\beta\eta + \frac{x}{u_e \delta} \frac{d}{dx} (u_e \delta*)$$

The second term is the v intercept (here δ is Eq. 20.5.11). We can expect $V(\infty)$ to become infinite for any value of $\beta \neq 0$.

Boundary layers satisfy the no-slip condition at the wall and match the inviscid flow as $y \to \infty$. In this match u approaches $u_e(x)$ and v approaches a curve with the proper slope $(-du_e/dx)$ for v in the inviscid region near the wall.

20.8 JOUKOWSKI AIRFOIL BOUNDARY LAYER

The boundary layer on the upper surface of a Joukowski airfoil is a typical example of a nonsimilar boundary layer that can be computed using the method of Section 20.7. Figure 20.9 gives the external velocity $u_e(s)/u_0$ and the associated function $\beta(s)$. To

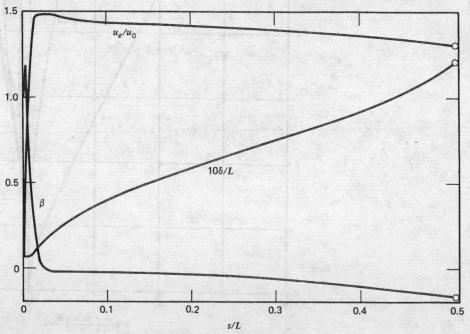

Figure 20.9 External velocity and pressure gradient function β for a Joukowski airfoil of $t/L = 0.09$ and $h/L = 0.05$ at a 3° angle of attack. The circles mark separation.

emphasize that the distance is measured along the surface, here, and also in Section 20.9, we use s instead of x. The boundary layer begins with a stagnation point, $\beta_i = 1.0$ (the surface location and flow speed for the airfoil change very rapidly in this region and must be calculated exactly without using the linearizing approximations that were employed in Section 18.11). For accuracy $\Delta\beta$ must be small. A short distance away from the stagnation point, the flow accelerates even more rapidly, as indicated by the fact that β is larger than one. β then begins a sharp fall, crossing zero when u_e/u_0 reaches its maximum value of 1.49. For this airfoil, the maximum u_e is close to the leading edge but is fairly broad. From here on, the flow gradually decelerates in an adverse pressure gradient.

Velocity profiles of $f' = u/u_e$ are shown as functions of $\eta = y(u_e/s\nu)^{1/2}$ in Fig. 20.10. The initial profile is the Hiemenz stagnation-point result ($\beta_i = m = 1$). The circle

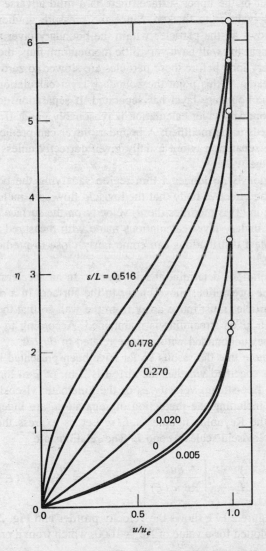

Figure 20.10   Velocity profiles for the Joukowski airfoil in boundary layer coordinates. The circles mark δ_{99}.

on the profile at $\eta = 2.36$ denotes the boundary layer thickness δ_{99}. Due to the rapid acceleration of the flow away from the stagnation point, the boundary layer becomes thinner and the profile flattens. For example, as $s/L = 0.0055$, the thickness has dropped to $\delta_{99} = 2.24$. Subsequently, the velocity u_e reaches a peak, deceleration begins, and the boundary layer thickens.

In some cases where the u_e/u_0 curve has a sharp peak, the boundary layer separates in the nose region. This would probably occur on this airfoil if the angle of attack were higher. If flow separation does occur, the boundary layer will usually become turbulent and immediately reattach to the surface (of course, at very high angles of attack the reattachment cannot be maintained and the airfoil stalls completely). A separation bubble that becomes turbulent and reattaches brings outside fluid into intimate contact with the surface. A turbine blade for a jet engine would have extremely high heat transfer at the attachment point.

Over the remainder of the upper surface, there is a mild adverse pressure gradient that causes the boundary layer to thicken. Since the pressure gradient acts uniformly through the layer, it slows all the particles within the boundary layer with equal effectiveness. The particles near the wall have very little momentum; thus, the adverse pressure does not have to act very long before these particles are slowed to zero velocity and turn around to move upstream. At this point the boundary layer calculation is stopped. It is common to say that the boundary layer has separated. If separation does not occur, we can assume that our boundary layer calculation is reasonably good. If separation is predicted, the analysis needs to be modified. A boundary layer can predict its own demise, but the location of the separation is not usually given correctly unless the pressure distribution accounts for the wake.

The separated region is no longer a thin region satisfying the boundary layer assumption. Moreover, the effective body that the inviscid flow sees includes in some way the separated-flow region. This modifies the u_e velocity on the surface and hence affects the boundary layer. Boundary layer calculations made with measured pressure distributions rather than the ideal distributions can come fairly close to predicting the location of the separation point.

Continuity considerations determine the V velocity. In an accelerating layer the velocity is negative as the streamlines move closer to the surface. In a decelerating layer, V is positive, as the particles must move away from the wall so that the same mass flow between the wall and a given streamline is maintained. According to the arguments of Section 20.7, V becomes unbounded with a slope related to du_e/ds.

It is important to note that the results so far have been presented in boundary layer variables. We have not specified whether the airfoil is 2 in. or 2 m long. Moreover, we have not specified the free-stream velocity u_0 or the kinematic viscosity ν of the fluid. All the results so far, including the prediction of separation, are independent of L, u_0, and ν, and hence of the Reynolds number $u_0 L/\nu$. Let us express the boundary layer results in terms of the inviscid scales u_0 and L. The relations are

$$\frac{s}{L} = \xi, \qquad \frac{y}{L} = \eta \left[\frac{\xi u_0}{\mathrm{Re}\ u_e(\xi)} \right]^{1/2}, \qquad \frac{u}{u_0} = \frac{u_e(\xi)}{u_0} f'(\xi, \eta)$$

where $\mathrm{Re} = u_0 L/\nu$. Figure 20.11 shows the velocity profiles and Fig. 20.9 the boundary layer thickness δ_{99}/L plotted for a value of $\mathrm{Re} = 1000$, which from a practical standpoint

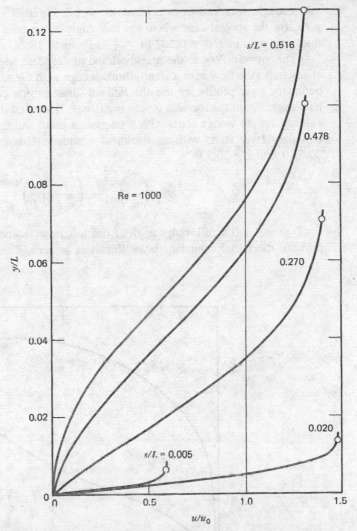

Figure 20.11   Profiles of Fig. 20.10 in physical variables u/u_0, y/L for Re = 1000.

is a very low number. The stagnation point thickness $\delta_{99}/L = 0.0075$ increases by a factor of 10 to $\delta_{99}/L = 0.122$ at the separation point. The thickness of the entire layer will decrease as $1/\sqrt{\text{Re}}$ as Re becomes larger; for Re = 10^6 the layer would be approximately $\frac{1}{30}$ as thick. Boundary layer theory is a high-Reynolds-number theory which yields profiles that are independent of Re when expressed in boundary layer variables. The actual physical variables are determined once the flow Reynolds number is given.

20.9   BOUNDARY LAYER ON A BRIDGE PILING

The inviscid flow over a section consisting of two circular arcs was given in Problem 18.24. This shape might represent a bridge piling or a streamlined strut. If the object is thin enough, it is known as a *biconvex airfoil*. Figure 20.12 gives the surface velocity u_e/u_0 for the special case where the half-angle at the nose is 30°. This corresponds to a thickness ratio of $t/\ell = 0.267$ ($n = \frac{5}{3}$ in Problem 18.26).

The inviscid flow in the neighborhood of the front edge must locally have the same character as the flow over a semi-infinite wedge with the same angle. Thus, for the initial boundary layer profile we use the Falkner–Skan profile corresponding to a 30° wedge half-angle. From the formula $\theta_{1/2} = m\pi/(m + 1)$ we find that $m = \beta_i = 0.2$. The surface velocity on the wedge starts with a stagnation point and then increases as $u_e \propto s^{0.2}$. The boundary layer starts with no thickness whatever. This is seen by substitution of Eq. 20.5.10 into Eq. 20.5.8:

$$\delta = \left(\frac{\nu s}{u_e}\right)^{1/2} = \left(\frac{\nu}{u_0 L}\right)\left(\frac{s}{L}\right)^{(1-m)/2}$$

For $0 \leq m < 1$ (i.e., all wedge angles from zero up to but not including the 90° stagnation profile), the initial boundary layer thickness is zero. This is regarded as a failure of

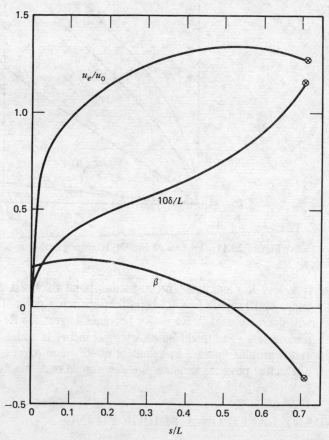

Figure 20.12 External velocity, pressure gradient function β, and resulting boundary layer thickness for flow over a biconvex strut with 30° half-angle at the nose. The ⊗s mark separation.

boundary layer theory, as there must be some small region near the leading edge where vorticity diffuses forward against the flow. The ξ, η boundary layer coordinates hide this singularity. We can view the initial profile $f_i(\eta)$ as the profile we would find if we approached the leading edge from positive values of ξ.

As shown in Fig. 20.12, the surface velocity rises rapidly at first and then slowly increases to a maximum at the midchord position. Thereafter, u_e/u_0 will fall again in a mirror image of the behavior on the front half. In contrast to the Joukowski airfoil, the bridge piling has a long acceleration region followed by a gentle deceleration. The function $\beta(\xi)$ begins at 0.2, as discussed above, and rises gently to a maximum of 0.243 at $\xi = 0.130$. The β function becomes zero at the midchord point (as it must when u_e/u_0 reaches a maximum) and then becomes negative when the flow decelerates. Although the adverse pressure gradient is very mild, the flow separates at $\xi = 0.708$. (Velocity profiles are shown in Fig. 20.13.) At this point u_e/u_0 is 1.28, only a very slight decrease from the maximum value 1.34.

The physical thickness δ_{99}/L is also shown in Fig. 20.12. The layer begins with $\delta_{99} = 0$ and grows throughout its length. Even on the forward portion, $\xi < 0.1$, the

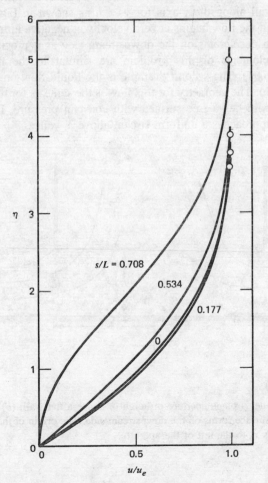

Figure 20.13 Velocity profiles in the boundary layer on a biconvex strut.

thinning of the layer by acceleration cannot overcome the thickening influence of viscosity. Take note that near separation, a rapid increase in δ_{99} occurs.

As shown by this example, laminar boundary layers separate quickly once they encounter an adverse pressure gradient. To counteract this tendency, engineers sometimes design airfoils or diffusers so that the boundary layer becomes turbulent before the adverse pressure region is reached. Turbulent layers do not separate as readily because the turbulence continually mixes high- and low-momentum fluid within the layer. This process prevents the pressure gradient from slowing a large chunk of fluid as needed for separation. Turbulent boundary layers do not always prevent separation; however, if it occurs, the position of turbulent separation is farther downstream than for a laminar layer.

20.10 BOUNDARY LAYERS BEGINNING AT INFINITY

Analysis and computation of boundary layers that come from negative infinity require some special consideration. After discussing the general idea, two examples are presented. The first example is flow on a wall that is under an aperture. The wall extends from $x = -\infty$ to $x = +\infty$ with an aperture at $x = 0$. The aperture is formed by another infinitely thin vertical wall along the y-axis for $y \geq h$ as shown in Fig. 20.14a. Ideal flow analysis predicts that the flow begins at zero velocity at negative infinity, accelerates to the aperture, and then decelerates on the downstream side as it proceeds to positive infinity. The essential elements of this problem are similar to the flow through a converging–diverging nozzle. The second example is the liquid flow on the wall under a sluice gate (Fig. 20.14b). The geometry for this flow is the same as for the first problem except that the downstream has a free surface with constant pressure. In this case the ideal flow downstream approaches a uniform stream above a wall.

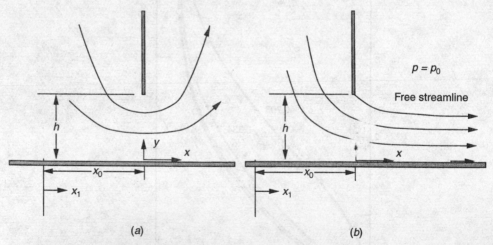

(a)   (b)

Figure 20.14   (a) Flow under a plane aperture of height h above a flat wall; (b) flow of a liquid under a sluice gate. A free surface forms on the downstream side. The origin of the boundary layer surface coordinate system is x_0 to the left of the aperture.

First we must consider the character of the flow at $-\infty$. In Section 14.7 we studied the Jeffrey–Hamel wedge flow when the flow came from infinity toward a sink at the origin. At high Reynolds numbers the flow has a boundary layer character and the velocity profile near the wall was found by Pohlhausen (1921) to be Eq. 14.8.20:

$$F(\xi_P) = 3 \tanh^2 \left(\frac{\xi_P}{\sqrt{2}} + \operatorname{arctanh} \sqrt{\frac{2}{3}} \right) - 2 \tag{20.10.1}$$

with

$$\xi_P = \frac{\phi}{\beta} = \frac{\alpha - \theta}{\beta} = \frac{\alpha - \theta}{\alpha} \sqrt{\alpha \, \mathrm{Re}_0} \tag{20.10.2}$$

and

$$\mathrm{Re}_0 = -\mathrm{Re} = \frac{-v_0 \alpha r}{\nu} \tag{20.10.3}$$

The variable ξ_P is used because this chapter has already employed $\xi = x/L$. Note that the size of the wedge angle is not important to flow near the wall.

We need to interpret these results in terms of the nondimensional boundary layer variables. Imagine that one wall of the wedge is the negative x-axis and set $y = r\,(\alpha - \theta)$. This gives

$$\xi_P = y \sqrt{\frac{-v_0}{r\nu}} \tag{20.10.4}$$

This is the proper form for a Falkner–Skan variable when the external velocity and the coordinate have opposite signs. Thus, if a boundary layer coming from negative infinity has an external velocity that behaves as $u_e \sim v_0/r$, the initial profile is the Pohlhausen (Jeffrey–Hamel) boundary layer profile.

In writing the boundary layer computer program of Section 20.6 it was assumed implicitly that the external velocity u_e/u_0 and position $\xi = x/L$ are both positive. Let us introduce a new distance variable $\hat{x}$ and set the $\hat{x}$ origin at a finite value of $r = x_0$. (This is not actually restrictive, as numerical computer programs cannot begin at infinity.) Now with $\hat{x} = x + x_0$, $r = -x = -(\hat{x} - x_0)$ and $u_e = -v_0$, we obtain

$$\xi_P = y \sqrt{\frac{u_e}{\nu \hat{x}}} \sqrt{\frac{\hat{x}}{x_0 - \hat{x}}} = \hat{\eta} \sqrt{\frac{\hat{x}}{x_0 - \hat{x}}} \tag{20.10.5}$$

Here $\hat{\eta}$ is the boundary layer variable in the y–$\hat{x}$ system. The idea is to use the Pohlhausen solution as the initial profile at a position $\hat{x} = \hat{x}_i$. If we choose $\hat{x}_i = x_0/2$, then

$$\xi_P = \hat{\eta}_i \tag{20.10.6}$$

We can summarize as follows. If a boundary layer begins at $x = -\infty$ and with the asymptotic behavior $u_e \sim 1/x$, we can shift the origin to $x = -x_0$ ($\hat{x} = x + x_0$) and begin the calculation at $\hat{x} = x_0/2$. With these choices the Pohlhausen profile is the initial profile and $\xi_P - \hat{\eta}_i$. The choice of x_0 should be large enough that the velocity behavior $u_e \sim 1/x$ is closely true at $\hat{x} = x_0/2$.

As the first example, consider the boundary layer on the wall under an aperture. The ideal flow has streamlines that are hyperbolas (see Milne-Thomson, 1960, p. 152). Any of these streamlines can be considered as a wall, so a nozzle diffuser of a hyperbolic shape could be imagined as the flow between any chosen upper and lower hyperbolas. For simplicity we consider the flow centerline as a flat wall under an aperture of height h. This streamline is typical of a nozzle-diffuser pressure distribution. The ideal inviscid velocity over the wall is

$$\frac{u_e(x)}{u_0} = \frac{1}{[1 + (x/h)^2]^{1/2}} \tag{20.10.7}$$

Here the symbol u_0 is the maximum velocity that is attained at $x = 0$. The asymptotic behavior as $x = -\infty$ is $u_e \sim 1/x$. Hence, the approach flow behaves as a sink flow, and the Pohlhausen boundary layer is the proper initial condition. The external velocity over the wall for the aperture and a sink flow are shown in Fig. 20.15. For $x/h < -5$, the aperture flow and sink flow give closely similar values ($< 2\%$ difference). It is not unreasonable to choose $x_0/h = -10$ and begin the boundary layer calculation at $\hat{x}/h = -5.0$.

The pressure gradient parameter depends on the origin of the coordinate system. For aperture flow equation 20.10.7, the parameter is

$$\beta(\hat{x}) = \frac{\hat{x}}{u_e} \frac{du_e}{d\hat{x}} = \frac{-\hat{x}(\hat{x} - x_0)}{1 + (\hat{x} - x_0)^2} \tag{20.10.8}$$

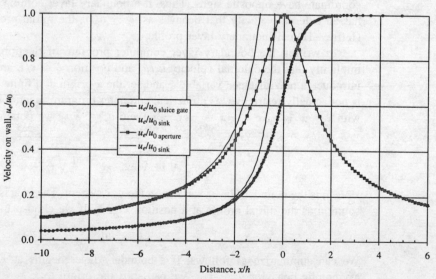

Figure 20.15 Inviscid velocity $u_e(x)$ along the wall for the aperture and sluice gate. Also shown is the $u_e(x)$ distribution for corresponding flow into a sink.

Figure 20.16 displays this β for the aperture wall problem. Beta begins at zero and climbs to a maximum of about 5 as the flow approaches the aperture. After the aperture the flow decelerates, the pressure gradient is adverse, and β changes sign.

Velocity profiles at several $\hat{x}$-positions are given in Fig. 20.17. The initial profile at $\hat{x}/h = 5$ is the Jeffrey–Hamel profile. As the flow accelerates toward the aperture, the boundary layer becomes thinner. After the aperture the profiles have an inflection point and the flow separates at $\hat{x}/h = 10.29$.

The second example is the wall under a sluice gate. Again the coordinate origin is taken at $x/h = -10$ and the boundary layer calculation initiated at $\hat{x}/h = 5.0$. The inviscid velocity is not a simple function (Kirchhoff, 1985); however, Fig. 20.15 shows that it is close to a sink flow for $x/h < -3$. The inviscid velocity approaches $u_e/u_0 = 1$ for $\hat{x}/h > 13(x/h > 3)$. Profiles of the boundary layer at several stations are given in Fig. 20.18. The initial profile at $\hat{x}/h = 5$ is the Jeffrey–Hamel profile as in the preceding example. When the flow accelerates, β increases and the profile thins. As β decreases the profile thickens, but because there is no adverse pressure gradient, there is no point of inflection. Essentially, the flow downstream is a wall under a uniform stream and the Blasius profile will ultimately develop.

The Blasius profile is shown for comparison in Fig. 20.18. Also shown is a line labeled "scaled Blasius." The computed profile at $\hat{x}/h = 15$ was adjusted to match to the Blasius profile at $u/u_e = 0.60$. The scaled Blasius and the profile computed are nearly the same for all η. This means that the profile at $\hat{x}/h = 15$ is the Blasius profile with a different scale unit. Essentially, this is equivalent to a shifted origin of the Blasius profile. The y-variable for the sluice gate wall is

$$\hat{\eta}_{\text{gate}} = y\sqrt{\frac{u_e}{\nu\hat{x}}} \qquad (20.10.9)$$

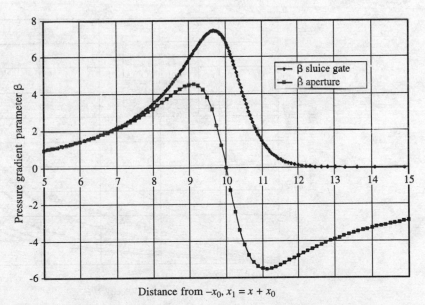

Figure 20.16 Pressure gradient parameters for aperture and sluice gate boundary layers.

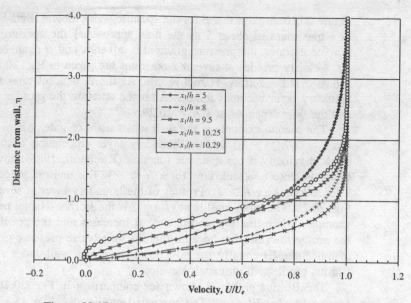

Figure 20.17   Boundary layer profiles for flow under an aperture.

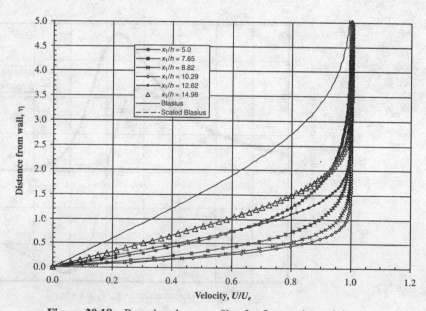

Figure 20.18   Boundary layer profiles for flow under a sluice gate.

For the Blasius profile, let the apparent origin be $\hat{x}_{B0}$. Then the Blasius variable is

$$\hat{\eta}_{\text{Blasius}} = y\sqrt{\frac{u_e}{\nu(\hat{x} - \hat{x}_{B0})}} \qquad (20.10.10)$$

Solving for the apparent origin $\hat{x}_{B0}$ and inserting numbers determined at $\hat{x}/h = 15$ with profile matching at $u/u_e = 0.60$ gives

$$\frac{\hat{x} - \hat{x}_{B0}}{h} = \frac{\hat{x}}{h}\left(\frac{\hat{\eta}_{\text{gate}}}{\hat{\eta}_{\text{Blasius}}}\right)^2 = 15\left(\frac{1.033}{1.890}\right)^2 = 4.48$$

$$\hat{x}_{B0} = 10.52h \qquad (20.10.11)$$

Since the origin of the $\hat{x}$-coordinate is 10 units upstream of the gate, the apparent origin of the Blasius boundary layer is 0.52, about $h/2$ downstream of the gate location.

20.11 PLANE BOUNDARY LAYER SEPARATION

Sections 20.8 and 20.9 displayed separation caused by pressure gradients on a smooth wall. There are other situations where discontinuities in the flow occur. The trailing edge of an airfoil is an example. Here, the finite shear stress of the upper and lower streams suddenly changes to zero in the merging stream just downstream of the edge. The exit edge of a jet into a reservoir or the edge of a splitter plate before a mixing layer are similar examples. One might also mention the situation where the wall slope is discontinuous, either concave or convex. In many of these more subtle cases, separation does not occur, but the theory of boundary layers must be modified.

The pressure force imposed on the boundary layer by the inviscid flow acts with the same magnitude on all particles within the layer. Those particles next to the wall have the least momentum and are the first to be stopped and turned around to form a region of reverse flow. In steady laminar flow, separation is identified as the place where the shear stress is zero ($\partial u/\partial y = 0$). We cannot make a general rule about when and where separation will occur. If an adverse pressure gradient of $dp/dx > 0$ acts long enough, separation is likely. No more definite statement can be made, since we know that some Falkner–Skan boundary layers with very mild adverse gradients ($-0.0906 < \beta < 0$) do not separate.

There are several important facts about the velocity profiles as they approach separation. All boundary layer profiles have a point of inflection whenever the pressure gradient is adverse. This may be deduced as follows. Consider the geometry of a velocity profile, where u is everywhere positive and at the wall $\partial u/\partial y$ is positive. Furthermore, the momentum equation evaluated at the wall shows that

$$\frac{1}{\rho}\frac{dp}{dx} = \nu\frac{\partial}{\partial y}\left(\frac{\partial u}{\partial y}\right)\bigg|_{\text{wall}}$$

A positive pressure gradient means that $\partial u/\partial y$ increases as we leave the wall. If $\tau \approx \partial u/\partial y$ increases, it must have a maximum within the flow, since $\tau \approx 0$ at infinity. A maximum in τ implies an inflection point in the velocity profile at the same position. As the wall stress becomes negative there will be a backflow near the wall. Now the boundary layer contains velocities in both directions and the layer is not independent of the region where the backflow originated.

The inviscid flow $u_e(x)$ and the resulting boundary layer profiles are independent of the Reynolds number. Hence, so is the prediction of separation. (A practical exception to this rule occurs when a boundary layer changes from laminar to turbulent flow, as in the case of a sphere or cylinder.) Even though the separation may lead to a large wake, which in turn modifies the inviscid flow, the position and occurrence of separation is fairly insensitive to the Reynolds number.

We classify separation into two types. The first occurs when a large wake, usually turbulent, forms and has a first-order effect on the inviscid flow. It changes the effective shape of the body. The second occurs when the separation causes only a local perturbation of the inviscid flow. The separation bubble and the trailing edge are in this category.

The flow in a large separated region is usually three-dimensional even if the boundary layer up to separation is roughly two-dimensional. This finding is evident in the surface streamlines made visible by putting oil on the surface of the wing shown in Fig. 20.19.

The characteristics of a steady viscous laminar separated flow (such as the circular cylinder problem of Section 15.6) as the Reynolds number becomes large are not really known. The problem centers on the wake and how it grows and interacts with the potential flow. In modeling the flow there are two main concepts. A wake with dimensions and velocities assumed to be $O[1]$ as $Re \rightarrow \infty$ has a constant vorticity. This is called the Prandtl–Batchelor assumption. Alternatively, the Kirchhoff assumption is that the wake eddy has a length $O[Re]$, width $O[Re^{1/2}]$, small eddy velocities, and a constant-pressure free streamline. A shear layer exists between the eddy and the potential flow. Both models, as well as models consisting of mixtures of the two, have defects. Turbulence in the eddy adds another complication. Although the theory is incomplete, from a practical standpoint the major need is for a model that gives the pressure on the body. Boundary layer calculations with the proper pressure distribution, obtained through ad hoc models or from experiments, give a reasonable estimate of the location of separation.

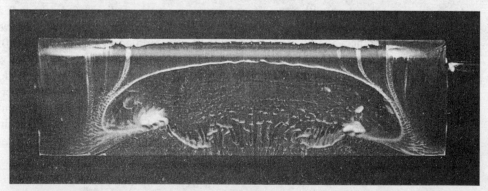

Figure 20.19   Plan view of the trailing-edge stall pattern on a Clark Y-14 airfoil. The pattern is made visible by the oil-flow technique. Flow is from top to bottom. Photography courtesy of A. Winkelmann, Department of Aerospace Engineering, University of Maryland. Reprinted with permission.

In the second category (separation with a small effect on the inviscid flow) the separation bubble is a good example. Separation bubbles can be calculated using the boundary layer equations [a review article is Williams (1977)]. The methods used are called *inverse methods* because they do not use a specified pressure gradient as the boundary condition.

When a pressure gradient is specified to calculate a boundary layer, the problem breaks down at the separation point. Goldstein (1948) solved the boundary layer equations at a separation point and found a singular solution where the vertical velocity and displacement thickness become infinite while the shear stress goes to zero in such a way that $d\tau/dx$ is infinite. Later it was found that this behavior, called the *Goldstein singularity,* is not an inherent property of the boundary layer equations but is associated with the pressure gradient specified. Catherall and Mangler (1966) modified the boundary layer problem by specifying the displacement thickness and allowing the appropriate $u_e(x)$, and hence dp/dx, to be found as part of the solution. This problem can be integrated through the separation point without any difficulty. Another inverse method, which is easier to use, is to specify the wall shear instead of the displacement thickness. The requirement for a regular solution through $\tau_0 = 0$ is that the pressure gradient be modified so that $d\beta/dx > 0$ at the separation point.

Note that even in thin separation bubbles there is an interaction between the inviscid flow and the boundary layer. Specifying the wall shear or the displacement thickness is a trick to take account of the interaction. We do not really know τ_0 or δ^* beforehand.

A minor difficulty in continuing the boundary layer calculation into the separated region of the bubble is caused by the reverse flow. Recall that the timelike term in the boundary layer momentum equation is $u\, \partial u/\partial x$. The marching direction for this parabolic equation is determined by the u coefficient of this term. Information travels downstream but not upstream. In the separated region, a very thin portion near the wall has negative u, so the proper marching direction is reversed. In formulating inverse methods, special account of this effect is taken by upwind-differencing $u\, \partial u/\partial x$ or, alternatively, even ignoring the term by setting $u\, \partial u/\partial x$ equal to zero (the convection effect is extremely small anyway).

When boundary layer theory fails because a rapid streamwise change causes a slight perturbation of the inviscid flow, one can appeal to *boundary layer interaction theory* (Messiter, 1983). The original development was to remove the Goldstein singularity of pressure-induced separation and is called triple-deck theory by Stewartson (1954). The flow consists of three layers. The lower viscous layer responding to the perturbation shifts the main portion of the middle boundary layer by an inviscid mechanism (a vortical inviscid flow) and causes a perturbation to the outer inviscid flow. The pressure is determined during the solution of the interacting layers, and hence the Goldstein singularity is avoided. Interaction theory can deal with problems such as the trailing edge, small changes in wall slope, a bump on the wall, the beginning of suction, and so on. The reader interested in turbulent flow separation should consult Simpson (1989).

20.12 AXISYMMETRIC BOUNDARY LAYERS

This section deals with boundary layers that are symmetric about an axis and have no swirl. Figure 20.20 shows the coordinate geometry of an external flow over a cylindrical

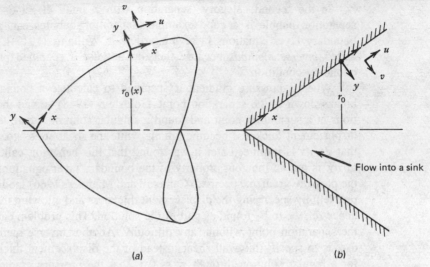

Figure 20.20 Nomenclature for Mangler's transformation: (*a*) axisymmetric boundary layer; (*b*) flow into a conical passage.

shape and an internal flow of a confined fluid. In both cases we assume that the boundary layer thickness is small compared to the radius of curvature in both the longitudinal and the lateral directions. Mangler (1945) derived the boundary layer equations for this situation. They differ from those for the plane case only by the appearance in the continuity equation r_0, the distance from the axis to the surface:

$$\frac{\partial}{\partial x}(r_0 u) + r_0 \frac{\partial v}{\partial y} = 0$$

$$\frac{\partial p}{\partial y} = 0 \qquad\qquad (20.12.1)$$

$$u \frac{\partial u}{\partial x} + v \frac{\partial u}{\partial y} = u_e \frac{du_e}{dx} + \nu \frac{\partial^2 u}{\partial y^2}$$

Mangler also gave a mathematical transformation that sends the axisymmetric problem into an equivalent plane problem. Consider the transformation defined by

$$\hat{x} = \int_0^x \left(\frac{r_0}{L}\right)^2 dx, \qquad \hat{y} = \frac{r_0}{L} y$$

$$\hat{u} = u, \qquad \hat{v} = \frac{L}{r_0}\left(v + \frac{y}{r_0} u \frac{dr_0}{dx}\right) \qquad\qquad (20.12.2)$$

where L is an arbitrary length scale. Substitution of the transformation equation 20.12.2 [note that $\partial \hat{x}/\partial x = (r_0/L)^2$ and $\partial \hat{y}/\partial x = (y/L)\, dr_0/dx$] into Eq. 20.12.1 produces the boundary layer equations for a plane flow, namely,

$$\frac{\partial \hat{u}}{\partial \hat{x}} + \frac{\partial \hat{v}}{\partial \hat{y}} = 0$$

(20.12.3)

$$\hat{u}\frac{\partial \hat{u}}{\partial \hat{x}} + \hat{v}\frac{\partial \hat{u}}{\partial \hat{y}} = \hat{u}_e\frac{d\hat{u}_e}{d\hat{x}} + \nu\frac{\partial^2 \hat{u}}{\partial \hat{y}^2}$$

One may verify that the boundary conditions also transform appropriately. A solution for an axisymmetric boundary layer may be found by considering an equivalent plane boundary layer defined by Mangler's transformation. Notice that when r_0 is constant, the transformation is trivial. The boundary layer on the outside or inside of a cylinder is the same as a plane layer as long as the boundary layer thickness is much smaller than the radius.

We consider as an example the axisymmetric stagnation point on a blunt body. The inviscid velocity near the stagnation point has the form

$$\frac{u_e}{u_0} = \frac{x}{L}$$

(20.12.4)

L is a characteristic dimension of the body, and $u_0 = \alpha u_\infty$ is related to the free-stream velocity u_∞ by a factor α that depends on the shape of the body. For this case, $r_0 = x$, and Eq. 20.12.2 becomes

$$\frac{\hat{x}}{L} = \int_0^{x/L}\left(\frac{x}{L}\right)^2 d\left(\frac{x}{L}\right) = \frac{1}{3}\left(\frac{x}{L}\right)^3$$

(20.12.5)

$$\frac{\hat{y}}{L} = \frac{r_0}{L}\frac{y}{L} = \frac{x}{L}\frac{y}{L}$$

These equations define the point $\hat{x}$, $\hat{y}$ in the plane flow, which is equivalent to the point x, y in the axisymmetric flow. Next, consider how the external velocity (Eq. 20.12.4) transforms. Using $\hat{u}_e = u_e$, we obtain

$$\frac{\hat{u}_e}{u_0} = \frac{x}{L} = \left(3\frac{\hat{x}}{L}\right)^{1/3}$$

(20.12.6)

The equivalent plane flow has the external flow $u_e \sim \hat{x}^{1/3}$, where the reference velocity constant is unchanged but the length constant is $L/3 = \hat{L}$. The solution to a boundary layer obeying Eq. 20.12.5 is the Falkner–Skan flow for $m = \frac{1}{3}$ ($\theta_{1/2} = 45°$ wedge). Assuming that this solution is known, the u velocity at the point x, y in the axisymmetric stagnation print flow would be

$$\frac{u(x, y)}{u_0} = f'\left[\frac{\hat{y}}{L} \to \frac{xy}{L^2}, \frac{\hat{x}}{L} \to \frac{1}{3}\left(\frac{x}{L}\right)^3\right]$$

A corresponding formula for v is found from Eq. 20.12.2. An axisymmetric stagnation point is about 80% as thick as a plane stagnation point.

The flow toward an axisymmetric stagnation point is a special case of the streaming flow over a cone of a given angle. Since the external flow over a cone obeys $u_e \propto x^n$ and the surface position is $r_0 = x \sin\theta_{1/2}$, Mangler's transformation produces $\hat{u}_e \propto x^{n/3}$. Again, this is one of the profiles from the Falkner–Skan group. Unfortunately, there is no simple mathematical relation between the cone angle θ and the exponent n. Whitehead and Canetti (1950) give a graphical presentation of the relation.

For a second example, consider the flow on the inside of a cone of angle θ (Fig. 20.20b). Fluid is drawn in through the orifice at the apex, and we assume that the Reynolds number is high enough so that the flow in a region somewhat removed from the orifice is a potential flow. The potential flow is modeled as the flow into a point sink. Along the cone walls

$$\frac{u_e}{-a_0} = \left(\frac{x}{L}\right)^{-2} \tag{20.12.7}$$

where a_0 and L are positive constants. The flow u_e is negative, since it is against the direction of increasing x. This formula is valid irrespective of the angle, $0 < \theta < \pi$, since the flow into a sink is independent of θ.

Mangler's transformation is computed using the fact that $r_0 = x \sin \theta$. From Eq. 20.12.2 we find that

$$\frac{\hat{x}}{L} = \frac{1}{3} \sin^2\theta \left(\frac{x}{L}\right)^3, \qquad \frac{\hat{y}}{L} = \sin \theta \frac{x}{L} \frac{y}{L} \tag{20.12.8}$$

The external velocity is obtained using the fact that $\hat{u} = u$ and $\hat{u}_e = u_e$. So from Eq. 20.12.6 we get

$$\frac{\hat{u}_e}{-u_0} = \left(\frac{3}{\sin^2\theta} \frac{\hat{x}}{L}\right)^{-2/3} \tag{20.12.9}$$

This is also a Falkner–Skan flow, with velocity scale $\hat{u}_0 = -a_0$, length scale $\hat{L} = \frac{1}{3} L \sin^2 \theta$, and exponent $m = -\frac{2}{3}$. [This is a case where the signs of u_e and x are different, so the Falkner–Skan solution would proceed with $\beta = -m = \frac{2}{3}$ (Eq. 20.5.12), and since $2\alpha - \beta = -1$, $\alpha = -\frac{1}{6}$] The nondimensional velocity profiles $\hat{f}'(\hat{\eta})$ are the same for all values of θ; however, the $\hat{x}$, $\hat{y}$ position and hence the $\hat{\eta}$ position, depend on θ through Eq. 20.12.8.

The corresponding problem where flow comes from a force and moves radially along the cone surface would result in Eq. 20.12.9 without the minus sign. Since in this case $\hat{x}$ and $\hat{u}$ have the same sign, we now have $\beta = m = -\frac{2}{3}$. A Falkner–Skan solution does not exist for this case. This means that a conical diffuser does not have a similarity boundary layer solution. In the actual case, the initial boundary layer at the entrance and the finite length determine the flow.

20.13   JETS

Figure 20.21 shows a jet of width h issuing into the same ambient fluid. The major assumption is that the Reynolds number $u_0 h / \nu$ is large, causing a long thin jet to which the boundary layer approximation may be made. We consider the plane a two-dimensional case; however, the method of analysis applies equally well to a round jet.

The flow in and near the mouth of the jet depends on the details of the flow before the fluid actually exits from the orifice. Somewhat downstream from the orifice, all jets

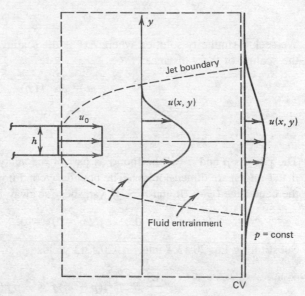

Figure 20.21 Plane laminar jet into an infinite medium.

decay in the same manner regardless of the original jet profile. Our discussion will apply only to this downstream region.

It is true that there is a contradiction in the idea of a high-Reynolds-number laminar jet. Actual jet profiles are very unstable and lead to a turbulent jet in a very short distance. This problem is nevertheless useful on at least two accounts: It supplies the laminar profile that a stability analysis shows is unstable, and it can be adapted with only a slight change to apply to the actual turbulent jet. The problem also has an interesting history. Schlichting (1933) did the original solution. At a much later date it was shown to be the high-Reynolds-number limit of an exact solution of the complete Navier–Stokes equation (Squire, 1951).

To begin, consider a control region that cuts across the exit plane of the jet and again at an arbitrary station downstream. We assume that the pressure at the two planes is the same, an assumption compatible with boundary layer analysis. The momentum equation shows that the momentum carried across any station must be a constant ($M = \rho u_0^2 h$ if we neglect flow entrained at the exit plane):

$$M = \rho u_0^2 h = \rho \int_{-\infty}^{\infty} u^2(y) \, dy \qquad (20.13.1)$$

Since the jet entrains ambient fluid, the flow rate across successive cross sections is not the same, and M is the only property of the flow at the orifice that is carried downstream. We take M as a given number and require that the jet velocity profile satisfy Eq. 20.13.1.

The boundary layer equations for a constant-pressure jet may be expressed in terms of the streamfunction. They are found by substituting Eqs. 12.2.3 into 20.1.6.

$$\psi_y \psi_{xy} - \psi_x \psi_{yy} = \nu \psi_{yyy} \qquad (20. \quad 2)$$

Recall that the velocities are

$$u = \psi_y, \qquad v = -\psi_x \tag{20.13.3}$$

We seek a similarity solution where Ax^p is the scaling of the streamfunction and Bx^q is the scaling of the y-distance:

$$\psi = Ax^p f(\eta) \tag{20.13.4}$$

$$\eta = \frac{y}{Bx^q} \tag{20.13.5}$$

The powers p and q will be found as part of the analysis, while A and B are chosen so that f and η are dimensionless. The boundary conditions require a symmetric flow about the centerline ($\psi = 0$) and $u \sim f'$ vanishes far away from centerline; thus,

$$f(\eta = 0) = 0, \qquad f''(\eta = 0) = 0, \qquad f'(\eta \to \infty) = 0 \tag{20.13.6}$$

Substituting Eq. 20.13.4 into Eq. 20.13.2 yields

$$\frac{AB}{\nu} x^{p+q-1}[(p - q)f'^2 - pff''] = f''' \tag{20.13.7}$$

For similarity the factor in front of the brackets must be independent of x. Hence, the condition $p + q = 1$ must be met. A second condition is found by substituting Eq. 20.13.4 into Eq. 20.13.1; this produces

$$M = \rho A^2 B^{-1} x^{2p-q} \int_{-\infty}^{\infty} f'^2 \, d\eta \tag{20.13.8}$$

M will be constant for all x only if $2p = q$. We satisfy these conditions if $p = \frac{1}{3}$ and $q = 2/3$.

Equation 20.13.7 now becomes

$$f''' + \frac{AB}{3\nu} (f'^2 + ff'') = 0 \tag{20.13.9}$$

The solution to this equation is

$$f = \tanh \eta \tag{20.13.10}$$

The corresponding velocity profiles are

$$\frac{u}{u_{max}} = f' = \text{sech}^2 \eta \tag{20.13.11}$$

The simple formulas 20.13.10 and 20.13.11 are obtained when

$$A = \left(\frac{9\nu M}{2\rho}\right)^{1/3}, \qquad B = \left(\frac{48\nu^2\rho}{M}\right)^{1/3} \tag{20.13.12}$$

It is informative to write the final profile in dimensional variables:

$$u = \left(\frac{3M^2}{32\rho^2 v}\right)^{1/3} x^{-1/3} \operatorname{sech}^2\left[y\left(\frac{M}{48\rho v^2}\right)^{1/3} x^{-2/3}\right] \tag{20.13.13}$$

We can now see that the maximum velocity is the coefficient of the sech function and that it decays like $x^{-1/3}$. Furthermore, if we define the jet thickness as a point where u is a certain fraction of u_{max}, the locus of such points is $yx^{-2/3} = $ const. Hence, the jet width grows as $x^{2/3}$.

The viscous forces at the edge of the jet accelerate ambient fluid and entrain it into the jet. From Eq. 20.13.13 the flow rate may be calculated as

$$Q = \int_{-\infty}^{\infty} u \, dy = \left(\frac{36Mv}{\rho}\right)^{1/3} x^{1/3} \tag{20.13.14}$$

Q grows like $x^{1/3}$, a very slow growth.

The origin is a singularity in the solution. At $x = 0$ the maximum velocity is infinite while the thickness and flow rate are zero. This breakdown in the validity of the boundary layer analysis is the same type of difficulty we encountered previously in the external flow over a wedge. In a practical application of the formulas above we should replace x by $x - x_0$, where x_0 is an unknown effective origin.

The modifications necessary to adapt the analysis to an axisymmetric jet or to turbulent jets can be found in Schlichting and Gersten (2000).

20.14   FAR WAKE OF NONLIFTING BODIES

The vorticity generated as the flow goes over a body is swept into the wake. There is just as much positive vorticity as negative vorticity, in the sense that the integral of ω over any cross section of the wake is zero. As this vorticity is carried downstream, the positive vorticity in the lower half-plane diffuses toward the centerline, where it meets with negative vorticity diffusing from the upper half-plane. Furthermore, at the outer edges of the wake, the vorticity diffuses outward to spread the wake. This effect is more than compensated for in the core of the wake, where the vorticity is being diminished. The net result is a decrease of the integral of $\frac{1}{2}\omega \cdot \omega$ over a cross section.

The results we derive in this section were first given by Tollmien (1931); for a comprehensive survey of many other aspects of wakes, the reader should consult Berger (1971). Let us propose that the boundary layer equations govern the wake flow because the Reynolds number of the body that creates the wake is large. Outside the boundary layer the velocity is u_0 (Fig. 20.22). We assume that similarity exists in terms of the velocity defect,

$$u \equiv u_0 - u_w \tag{20.14.1}$$

Here u_w is the velocity profile across the wake. In terms of u the boundary layer equation becomes

$$(u_0 - u)\frac{\partial u}{\partial x} + v\frac{\partial u}{\partial y} = v\frac{\partial^2 u}{\partial y^2} \tag{20.14.2}$$

In a manner similar to the jet analysis, we introduce a streamfunction $u = \partial\psi/\partial y$, $v = -\partial\psi/\partial x$, and assume similarity of the form

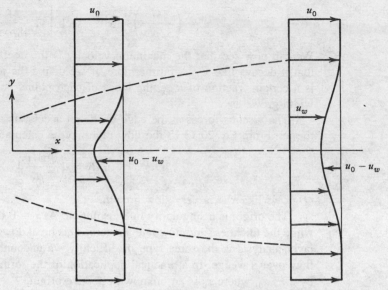

Figure 20.22 Laminar wake of a nonlifting body.

$$\psi \equiv Ax^p f(\eta) \tag{20.14.3}$$

$$\eta \equiv \frac{y}{Bx^q}$$

The constants A, B, p, and q will be chosen in the course of the analysis. Substituting Eq. 20.14.3 into Eq. 20.14.2 produces terms in the following proportions:

$$u_0 \frac{\partial u}{\partial x} \propto u_0 B^2 x^{2q-1}[(p-q)f' - qf'']$$

$$-u \frac{\partial u}{\partial x} + v \frac{\partial u}{\partial y} \propto AB^2 x^{p+q-1}[(q-p)f'^2 + 2q\eta f' f'' - pff''] \tag{20.14.4}$$

$$\nu \frac{\partial^2 u}{\partial y^2} \propto \nu f''$$

In addition to these boundary layer equations, the wake must also satisfy an integral constraint.

Recall from Section 14.6 that the drag force F_D is related to the constant momentum thickness of the wake as follows:

$$F_D = \rho u_0^2 \Theta = \rho u_0^2 \int \left[\frac{u_w}{u_0} - \left(\frac{u_w}{u_0} \right)^2 \right] dy$$

Introducing Eqs. 20.14.1 and 20.14.3 puts this expression in the form

$$F_D = \rho A x^p \int \left(u_0 - \frac{A}{B} x^{p-q} f' \right) f' \, d\eta \qquad (20.14.5)$$

The task of choosing p and q so that all terms in Eqs. 20.14.4 and 20.14.5 are independent of x cannot be accomplished. The problem does not allow similarity.

The term in Eq. 20.14.4 is independent of x if $q = \frac{1}{2}$. Similarly, the first term in the drag expression is independent of x if $p = 0$. If we assume these values, the remaining terms in both equations contain $x^{-1/2}$. Hence, we must place an additional restriction on the problem by allowing x to become infinite. For this reason the solution is called a *far-wake* solution. Formally, we are solving the problem as an asymptotic expansion where the x-coordinate is the expansion parameter.

The equations governing the far wake are

$$f''' + \frac{u_0 B^2}{2\nu} (\eta f'' + f') = 0 \qquad (20.14.6)$$

$$F_D = \rho A u_0 \int f' \, d\eta = \rho u_0 Q \qquad (20.14.7)$$

Differential equation 20.14.6 has the solution $f' = \exp(-\eta^2)$ when the coefficient in front of the bracket is 2. Thus, we choose

$$B = \left(\frac{4\nu}{u_0} \right)^{1/2} \qquad (20.14.8)$$

Inserting $f' = \exp(-\eta^2)$ into Eq. 20.14.7 reveals that A is given by

$$A = \frac{F_D}{\rho u_0 \pi} \qquad (20.14.9)$$

The final expressions are

$$\eta = y \sqrt{\frac{u_0}{4\nu x}} \qquad (20.14.10)$$

$$\psi = \frac{F_D}{2\rho u_0} \, \mathrm{erf}(\eta) \qquad (20.14.11)$$

$$u_0 - u_w = \left(\frac{F_D^2}{4\pi\rho^2 u_0 \nu x} \right)^{1/2} \exp(-\eta^2) \qquad (20.14.12)$$

As the wake decays, the velocity defect decreases as $x^{-1/2}$ while the thickness of the wake increases parabolically, $y_\delta \sim x^{1/2}$. This analysis may be extended to apply to axisymmetric and to turbulent wakes. Hence, many of the conclusions are relevant to these cases as well as to plane laminar wakes.

The drag force on a body plays a very important role in determining the wake. From previous work we found that the momentum thickness of the wake is a constant given by $\Theta = F_D/\rho u_0^2$. This same expression (Eq. 20.14.5) in the far wake reduces to $Q = F_D/\rho u_0 = u_0 \Theta$ (Eq. 20.14.7), where Q is the defect-velocity volume flow. The parameter

Q represents the flow one would observe in a quiescent fluid after a moving object, such as an automobile, had passed by. From the point of view of a fixed body in an infinite stream, the integral that gives Q is actually the displacement thickness of the wake $Q = u_0 \delta^*$. Hence, $\delta^* = \Theta = $ const in the far wake of any nonlifting body.

The wake of a lifting body differs significantly from the results above. The circulation necessary to produce the lift requires that vortices leave the body. This additional vorticity in the streamwise direction changes the picture so that the analysis given above is no longer valid.

Recall that we originally proposed to consider a body at a high Reynolds number and apply boundary layer theory to the wake. However, the resulting problem was not simple enough, so we further assumed that the distance x from the body was very large (the far wake). There is a surprise ending to this story. The answer obtained is valid for all Reynolds numbers greater than zero. The Oseen equations of slow viscous flow—low Reynolds number—give exactly the same wake solution as that found above. All bodies produce a parabolic wake for Re > 0.

20.15   FREE SHEAR LAYERS

Consider two streams that are accelerated to different velocities while being separated by a thin flat plate. Velocity profiles are shown in Fig. 20.23. At $x = 0$ the plate ends and the two streams merge. The boundary layers that build up on the plate before the streams merge are ignored, and we assume that the initial profiles are $u = u_1$ in the upper fluid $y > 0$ and $u = u_2$ in the lower fluid $y < 0$. The constant u_1 will always be greater than zero; however, u_2 can be set equal to zero. This case corresponds to the flow off the lip of a large cavity or the shear layer at the lip of a jet issuing into a large room. Lessen (1949) gave the solution for the case when the two fluids are the same, and Lock (1951) extended the analysis to apply to fluids with different densities and viscosities.

As the two streams merge to the lip of the plate, we assume that the pressure of both streams has the same value, so that the streamline leaves the plate horizontally. The subsequent position of the dividing streamline depends on the inviscid flow field. For the case of completely uniform inviscid flows u_1 and u_2, this streamline will be straight at $y = 0$. Since pressures do not change across boundary layers, subsequent growth of the layers does not modify the original inviscid position of the dividing streamline.

With the absence of a pressure gradient, the boundary layer equation is

$$u \frac{\partial u}{\partial x} + v \frac{\partial u}{\partial y} = \nu \frac{\partial^2 u}{\partial y^2} \tag{20.15.1}$$

The Blasius similarity variable is introduced:

$$\eta_\alpha = \left(\frac{u_1}{\nu_\alpha x} \right)^{1/2} y \tag{20.15.2}$$

In this section we use a subscript α to indicate a variable that may be used in either the lower fluid ($\alpha = 2$) or the upper fluid ($\alpha = 1$). The variable η_1 is used in the upper

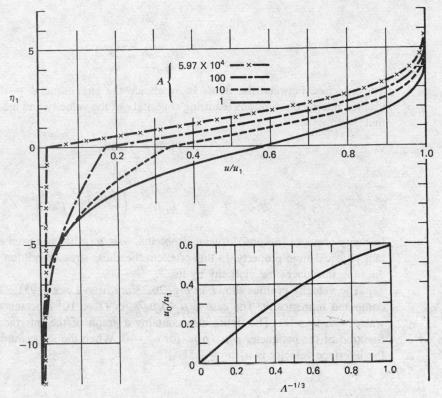

Figure 20.23 Velocity profiles between shear layers. $A = \rho_1\mu_1/\rho_2\mu_2$. Inset shows centerline velocity as a function of A. Reprinted by permission from Lock (1951) Oxford University Press.

fluid ($y > 0$), while η_2 is used in the lower fluid ($y < 0$). The reference velocity for both fluids is u_2, since u_1 may take the value of zero.

When the streamfunction

$$\psi_\alpha = (\nu_\alpha u_1 x)^{1/2} f_\alpha(\eta_\alpha) \qquad (20.15.3)$$

is introduced, the velocities are

$$u_\alpha = \frac{u_\alpha}{u_1} = f'_\alpha \qquad (20.15.4)$$

$$v_\alpha = \frac{1}{2}\left(\frac{u_1\nu_\alpha}{x}\right)^{1/2}(\eta_\alpha f'_\alpha - f_\alpha) \qquad (20.15.5)$$

and differential equation 20.14.1 transforms into the Blasius equation,

$$2f''_\alpha + f_\alpha f''_\alpha = 0 \qquad (20.15.6)$$

The boundary conditions on the far stream show that

$$f_1(\infty) = 1 \tag{20.15.7}$$

$$f_2(-\infty) = \frac{u_2}{u_1}$$

The interface between the fluids is by choice the streamline $\psi = 0$. In addition, the viscous interface conditions requiring continuity of the velocity and the shear stress imply that

$$f_1'(0) = f_2'(0) \tag{20.15.8}$$

and

$$f_1''(0) = \left(\frac{\rho_2 \mu_2}{\rho_1 \mu_1}\right)^{1/2} f_2''(0) \tag{20.15.9}$$

In many previous viscous diffusion problems, $\nu = \mu/\rho$ has occurred as the only important physical fluid property. In this problem the shear stress condition $\mu_1 \, \partial u_1/\partial y|_0 = \mu_2 \, \partial u_2/\partial y|_0$ introduces the viscosity by itself.

The velocity profiles shown in Fig. 20.23 are from Lock (1951). These results were computed numerically. The case $\rho_2 \mu_2/\rho_1 \mu_1 = 5.97 \times 10^4$ represents air flowing over water with $u_2 = 0$. The figure also contains a graph of the interface velocity u_0 as a function of the parameter $\rho_2 \mu_2/\rho_1 \mu_1$ for $u_2 = 0$. When the same fluid is in both layers, the interface velocity is $u_0/u_1 = 0.58$.

20.16   UNSTEADY AND ERUPTING BOUNDARY LAYERS

All flows must begin by some transient process. In this section we consider several boundary layer examples that illustrate the major processes. The phenomena of eruption of fluid from a boundary layer is so important that it is included in the section title.

Unsteadiness adds the term $\partial u/\partial t$ to the momentum equation

$$\frac{\partial u}{\partial t} + u\frac{\partial u}{\partial x} + v\frac{\partial u}{\partial y} = \frac{\partial u_e}{\partial t} + u_e\frac{du_e}{dx} + \nu\frac{\partial^2 u}{\partial y^2}$$

This equation is still second order and can be classified rigorously in any two variables. In x, y it is parabolic with initial data carried in the direction of u; there is no upstream influence. In t, y it is also parabolic. In t, x it is a first-order hyperbolic wave equation. The direction and speed of propagation is the flow velocity u. As an illustration consider a steady established boundary layer and at time t_0, position x_0, we make some slight change. We suck a little fluid out of the wall or wiggle a stick in the free stream to change $u_e(x, t)$. The boundary layer for $x < x_0$, $t < t_0$ is unchanged. The profile at x_0, t_0 is effected instantaneously for all y, and subsequently, viscous diffusion modifies the profile. This behavior is just like the Rayleigh impulsive plate or the Stokes oscillating plate. The boundary layer downstream of x_0 is initially unaffected for $t > t_0$. The position $x > x_0$ does not know about the event at x_0, t_0 until fluid that was at x_0, t_0 has time to flow to that point.

The first example is a semi-infinite flat plate under a static fluid. An impulsive acceleration is applied at time zero to give the fluid a uniform velocity $u_e = U_0$, $t > 0$.

Consider a position a distance x from the leading edge. At x the fluid has no "knowledge" of the leading edge, and the velocity profile develops exactly as in the Rayleigh infinite flat-plate flow of 7.7. The Rayleigh profile continues to evolve until a fluid particle that passed the leading edge arrives at x; to be exact, until $t = x/U_0$. After this time the boundary layer begins to fill with particles whose history includes flowing past the leading edge. Ultimately, for long times, we expect the profile to approach the Blasius profile.

In general, changes in the pressure gradient, $u_e(x, t)$, or wall conditions are applied instantaneously. The effects are then distributed in y across the layer by viscous diffusion. Information about the new flow situation is carried from one x position to another by the fluid particles. Usually, the fastest upstream-to-downstream communication is the velocity of the external flow u_e. The development of flow on an impulsively started airfoil would be much the same as that on the flat plate except that the external stream has some specific distribution $u_e(x)$.

Separation of the flow in a two-dimensional unsteady boundary layer is much harder to identify than is the steady case. Instantaneous streamlines are not particle paths, and the condition $\tau_{\text{wall}} = 0$ does not indicate separation in an unsteady flow. The flow is simply going in the opposite direction for that instant and may not necessarily break away from the surface. Separation, in plane unsteady flow, occurs when fluids with different regions of origin meet and move away from the surface. This is indicated by the MRS criterion (Moore, Rott, Sears; see Telionis, 1981). First, the interface between the two fluids is identified by a stagnation point with $\tau = 0$ (equivalently $\omega = 0$ or in boundary layers $du/dy = 0$). Second, this point, that is, $\omega = 0$, must move with the local flow velocity in order to remain as the interface between the streams. A further complication is that the $\omega = 0$ point occurs within the layer and not at the wall.

A body that we know has separation is the circular cylinder. Calculating the boundary layer for the impulsive motion of a circular cylinder turned out to be a formidable task. At $t > 0$ the inviscid solution (Eq. 18.6.3) is established having the external velocity $u_e/2U_\infty = \sin(x/R)$, where x is measured around the surface from the stagnation point. The boundary layer begins to grow by diffusion, but with the pressure gradient of the inviscid flow (adverse on the rear half). The central question is when and where separation starts. Fluid particles that enter the boundary layer at the front stagnation point start to modify the precise nature of the profiles. At the rear stagnation point the boundary layer from top and bottom collide and flow away to start the formation of a wake. Proudman and Johnson (1962) computed this flow and showed that separation does not begin here. Many numerical computer solutions were attempted unsuccessfully until Van Dommelen and Shen (1982) approached the problem using Lagrangian boundary layer equations. They found that separation begins after the cylinder moves about three-quarter diameter at about 111°. Furthermore, separation forms from a narrow region focusing into a singularity at a position of zero vorticity as shown in Fig. 20.24. Flow-visualization experiments at a high Reynolds number (Bouard and Coutanceau, (1980) confirm this initial behavior. The time at which the singularity develops denotes the separation time and marks the end of the validity of the boundary layer equations. As separation is approached the boundary layer splits into three parts: two shear layers, which are relatively passive, and a central portion with little vorticity, which is growing rapidly. The fluid in the center portion is being squeezed, and continuity, the equation that actually becomes singular, forces the flow outward. These central portion activities are inviscid and nonlinear. The final eruption of fluid becomes independent of the initial pressure gradient that started

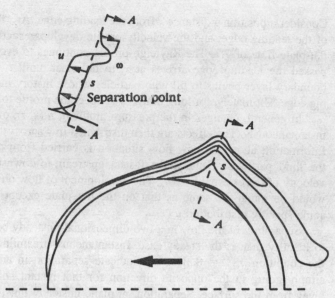

Figure 20.24 Vorticity contours in an erupting boundary layer. Section *A–A* shows the velocity and vorticity profiles.

the process. Figure 20.25 displays time frames from a complete Lagrangian Navier–Stokes calculation by Koumoutsakos and Leonard (1995).

A related problem is the interaction of a vortex and a boundary layer. Consider a vortex of strength Γ a height h above a wall. The image vortex propels the vortex to the right with a speed $\Gamma/2h$. Hence, a steady inviscid flow occurs in coordinates attached to the vortex with the wall moving left at $\Gamma/2h$. The inviscid velocity above the wall is

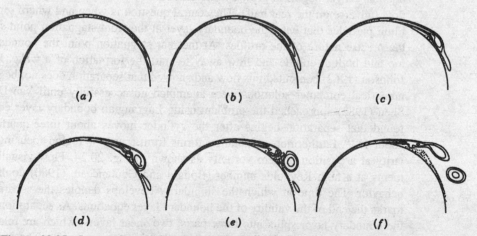

Figure 20.25 Lagrangian Navier–Stokes calculations of vorticity contours after the impulsive start of a cylinder at Re $= Ud/\nu = 9500$. Nondimensional time is $T = tU/r_0$: (*a*) $T = 0.75$; (*b*) $T = 1.50$; (*c*) $T = 1.75$; (*d*) $T = 2.00$; (*e*) $T = 2.25$; (*f*) $T = 3.00$. Reprinted with permission from Koumoutsakos and Leonard (1995).

$$\frac{u_e(x)}{\Gamma/2h} = -1 + \frac{4}{(x/h)^2 + 1}$$

For $x > 0$ the pressure gradient is adverse. One imagines that the vortex is turned on at $t = 0$ and the unsteady boundary layer on the wall begins to develop. Lagrangian computations of this problem have been done by Peridier et al. (1991). They find that a secondary vortex is developed within the boundary layer and eventually the eruption process, very similar to the cylinder problem above, takes place. Flow properties such as displacement thickness and pressure (Conlisk, 1989) develop sharp spikes. The latter stages of the eruption processes are not completely understood.

Figure 20.26 shows a ring vortex that was directed at a shallow angle toward a wall. The wall is a moving belt whose motion was started just prior to the vortex generation. Thus, a thin Rayleigh boundary layer exists near the wall. The ring vortex has "bounced" off the wall and caused a secondary vortex to be ejected. In this experiment a layer of dye was placed on the wall before the belt started. This is the marking fluid that one now sees in the ejected vortex.

There are many fluid-flow situations where the birth of vortices and the eruption of fluid from a wall are important. Formation of the vortex street behind a cylinder is the most elementary example. Unsteady airfoil stall, called *dynamic stall,* involves the growth of vortices on the suction side of the airfoil. Unsteadiness of the horseshoe vortex system has been noted (Section 14.1). Many workers noted the occurrence of vortices within turbulent boundary layers. Smith et al. (1991) in particular emphasized the vortex-induced eruption process as an element in momentum transfer (Reynolds stress) and regeneration of the vortex. For the general problem the conditions under which an ejection is abrupt or moderate are not well understood.

*20.17   ENTRANCE FLOW INTO A CASCADE

We shall study a slightly different way in which inviscid flows fail to be uniformly valid. Consider the entrance flow problem for which a complete solution was given in Section 14.4. The computer solution given there required an increasingly long computation domain as the Reynolds number became large. In fact, the size of the hydrodynamic en-

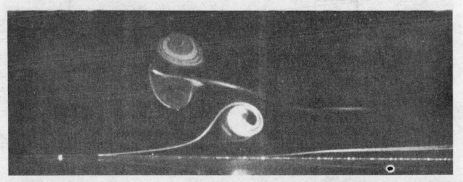

Figure 20.26   Vortex ring interacting with a boundary layer on a wall. Note the secondary vortex erupting from the wall. Photo courtesy of M. Stanislas and P. DuPont, École Centrale de Lille.

trance region increases linearly with the Reynolds number. For a high Reynolds number this problem may be broken into several parts. Van Dyke (1970) is responsible for the organization of this problem.

Figure 20.27 is a sketch of the geometry and velocity profiles. The uniform stream u_0 at $x = -\infty$ feels the presence of the plate and begins slowing down before the leading edges are reached. At the same time a slight acceleration of the centerline fluid is observed (due to continuity, of course). Within the cascade, the profiles gradually change until the parabolic profile of uniform flow is reached as $x \rightarrow \infty$.

The Re $\rightarrow \infty$ (for fixed x where u_0, ρ, and h are the scales) limit of the Navier–Stokes equations leads to the Euler equations. Any fixed point x, y is in inviscid flow when Re becomes high enough. The solution is a constant velocity $U_1 = u/u_0 = 1$, $V_1 = 0$. This answer is valid in the region marked I in Fig. 20.27, that is, upstream and into a core area within the cascade. This solution fails to meet the no-slip condition along both walls (the classic boundary layer failure), and it also fails to satisfy the parabolic profile prescribed as the downstream condition for the complete Navier–Stokes problem.

Regions II on both walls are boundary layers on a flat plate with a uniform stream. Hence, the Blasius solution gives the correction to the inviscid flow in these regions. For the sake of completeness, note that the Blasius boundary layer fails at the leading edge, the region marked 0 (see end of Section 20.1 for reference).

Region III is a new type of failure of the inviscid flow. For internal flow, the region $x \rightarrow \infty$ is described incorrectly by the solution $U_1 = u_0$. The nonuniform region is not a thin region near a wall but quite a large region within the cascade. It is true that the boundary layers of regions II would grow and ultimately fill the slot, but this is not the failure mechanism of region III. Region III begins long before the boundary layers gain any significant thickness. Region III is due to the failure of $U_1 = u_0$ to meet the parabolic profile. The position where region III begins is $x \sim 0(\text{Re})$.

A solution for region III is formulated by defining a stretched x variable,

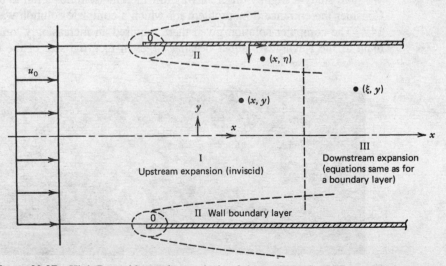

Figure 20.27   High-Reynolds-number analysis of the entrance flow into a cascade of plates.

$$\xi = \frac{x}{\text{Re}} \qquad (20.17.1)$$

Now as $\text{Re} \to \infty$, a $\xi = \text{const}$ position moves downstream proportionally. Since $\partial\psi/\partial x = -v$, we have $\partial\psi/\partial\xi = -\text{Re}\, v$, implying that the region III scaling for v should be changed by defining $v^{\text{III}} = v\,\text{Re}$. All other variables retain the nondimensional forms of the original Navier–Stokes equations. The momentum equations for region III are

$$uu_\xi + v^{\text{III}}u_y = -p_\xi + \text{Re}^{-2}u_{\xi\xi} + u_{yy} \qquad (20.17.2)$$

$$\text{Re}^{-2}uv_\xi^{\text{III}} + \text{Re}^{-2}v^{\text{III}}v_y^{\text{III}} = -p_y + \text{Re}^{-1}v_{\xi\xi} + \text{Re}^{-1}v_{yy}$$

The ordering of terms in these equations is different from that in the usual boundary layer, although the limit $\text{Re} \to \infty$ gives the boundary layer equations.

The boundary conditions for Eq. 20.17.2 are the no-slip condition on the walls and matching with the first-order inviscid flow:

$$u(\xi = 0, y) = u_0 \qquad (20.17.3)$$

Equations 20.17.2 produce the parabolic profile automatically as $\xi \to \infty$. The problem for region III is termed the *downstream expansion,* and the region I solution is called the *upstream expansion.*

We should probably not call the downstream expansion (Eqs. 20.17.2 and 20.17.3) a boundary layer. The differential equations for the problem are the boundary layer. The differential equations for the problem are the boundary layer equations, but the boundary conditions and method of matching are quite unlike those of Section 20.15. Actually, we have derived a "parabolized Navier–Stokes" equation for region III. The shear layers in this problem are thin to start out, but by the end of region III they cover the tube. The idea used in the original solution of the entrance flow problem by Schlichting (1934) was that two boundary layers on the walls grew and interacted simultaneously with an inviscid core. This must be considered as an approximate solution for the downstream expansion in the light of Van Dyke's formulation.

Van Dyke went on to calculate the second-order inviscid flow, the upstream expansion. This flow accounts for the displacement thickness of the sidewall boundary layers. Figure 20.28 gives the velocity profile at $x = 0$ calculated for $\text{Re} = 75$ with the second-order inviscid expansion and compared with a complete Navier–Stokes calculation. Because of the good agreement, we can assert that the physical event that modifies the flow ahead of the plates is inviscid. The flow is essentially the inviscid flow into a channel modified for the displacement thickness of the boundary layers. Although our complete solution in Section 14.5 at the same Reynolds number would be slightly more accurate, we would not be able to distinguish inviscid effects from viscous diffusion effects as in the $\text{Re} \to \infty$ theory.

*20.18 THREE-DIMENSIONAL BOUNDARY LAYERS

The idea that a flow has thin regions where viscous forces are important is, of course, not restricted to plane flows. There are several unique physical events that may occur in

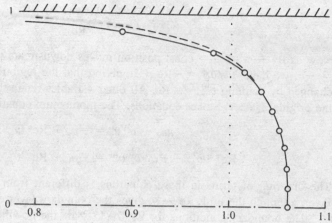

Figure 20.28 Velocity profiles at the entrance $x = 0$ for Re = 75 (Van Dyke, 1970). The dashed line is the two-term upstream expansion, the solid line is the composite expansion with Blasius boundary layer, and the circles are the Navier–Stokes numerical solution of Wang and Longwell (1964).

three-dimensional boundary layers. We discuss several of these before we introduce the three-dimensional boundary layer equations.

The first important effect is lateral convergence or divergence of the flow. An axisymmetric stagnation point illustrates this; the streamlines diverge when they move away from the stagnation point. By the continuity equation we expect that divergence will cause thinning of the boundary layer. Conversely, convergence should cause thickening. Indeed, in axisymmetric flow without swirl, streamline convergence is the only three-dimensional effect. It is tied intimately to the increase or decrease in the surface radius $r_0(x)$. Recall that r_0 occurs only in the continuity equation 20.11.1, and that this is the only way in which the axisymmetric boundary layer equations differ from the two-dimensional equations.

A second, and perhaps the most important, three-dimensional effect is the secondary flow caused by transverse pressure gradients. In plane flows the longitudinal pressure gradient causes the flow either to speed up or to slow down. Another degree of freedom exists in three-dimensional layers. Now, transverse pressure gradients are allowed to change the direction of the free stream by pushing sideways on the particles. It is still true that the pressure is constant across a boundary layer, so the full force of the transverse pressure is also applied to the low-velocity particles deep within the boundary layer. This causes the low-velocity particles to have a more tightly curved path than the high-velocity particles at the edge of the layer.

An example of this effect is found in the cyclone separator as shown in Fig. 20.29. The fluid is injected tangentially in the large-diameter portion of the chamber. The momentum of the fluid is used to establish a pressure gradient with low pressure in the core and high pressure on the outer wall. The mass flow through the machine is relatively small and is really just the secondary flow. The slanted wall is where the boundary layer

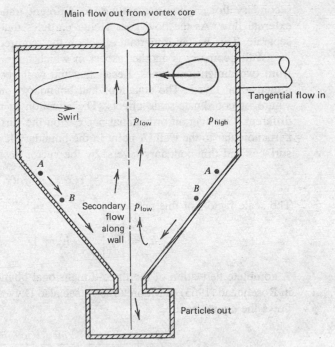

Figure 20.29   Flow in a cyclone separator.

events take place. Because the point A is farther from the rotation axis than B, it has a higher pressure. Hence, when viscous forces slow down the particles at the wall, the pressure gradient pushes them toward the apex. This boundary layer fluid, which has lost most of its swirling velocity, then turns and flows through the core and out the top through the *vortex finder*. The vortex finder is placed inside the chamber to inhibit the same process on the upper wall (it is sometimes an advantage if the flow in the top region will separate).

The chamber at the bottom has little or no flow. It is used to collect the particles that are to be separated from the fluid. As the particles enter the cyclone with the main stream, they are pushed toward the walls, since they are too dense to be turned by the pressure gradient. Once concentrated in this region, they are swept toward the apex by the secondary boundary layer flow. Now, as the flow turns to ascend through the core (and here a shallow angle to the core helps), the inertia of the particles separates them from the flow and they collect in the lower chamber. To summarize: The transverse pressure gradient in a boundary layer causes streamlines within the layer to curve more tightly than those of the free stream. Thereby a secondary crossflow develops.

Another important aspect of three-dimensional boundary layers is caused by the secondary flow itself. We might term this a spreading transverse influence. Consider all the particles in the boundary layer at a certain wall location at a certain time. As time goes on, these particles are carried downstream. Particles in the external flow follow certain streamlines to new positions, while particles within the layer, because of the secondary flow, follow streamlines to different transverse positions from those of the external flow. As the flow goes along, particles that were originally neighbors tend to separate. This has an important effect on the required initial conditions.

Wall geometry is another aspect in which three-dimensional boundary layers differ from two-dimensional ones. Recall that the wall geometry plays no direct role in two-dimensional layers. The equations and boundary conditions were free of any wall curvature or coordinate-scale effects. The situation in three-dimensional layers is slightly different. Consider an orthogonal net x, z on the surface of the body with y everywhere perpendicular to the wall. A point in the boundary layer is given (for sufficiently smooth surfaces and thin boundary layers) by the vector position.

$$\mathbf{R} = \mathbf{r}(x, z) + y\mathbf{n}(x, z) \tag{20.18.1}$$

The scale factors of this net are

$$h_x \equiv \left|\frac{d\mathbf{r}}{dx}\right|, \qquad h_y = 1, \qquad h_z \equiv \left|\frac{d\mathbf{r}}{dz}\right| \tag{20.18.2}$$

A complete derivation of the three-dimensional boundary layer equations may be found in Rosenhead (1963) or Moore (1964) (see also Dwyer, 1981; Cousteix, 1986). For steady flows the equations are

$$\frac{u}{h_x}\frac{\partial u}{\partial x} + \frac{w}{h_z}\frac{\partial u}{\partial z} + v\frac{\partial u}{\partial y} + \frac{uw}{h_x h_z}\frac{\partial h_x}{\partial z} - \frac{w^2}{h_x h_z}\frac{\partial h_z}{\partial x}$$

$$= -\frac{1}{\rho h_x}\frac{\partial p}{\partial x} + \nu\frac{\partial^2 u}{\partial y^2} \tag{20.18.3}$$

$$\frac{u}{h_x}\frac{\partial w}{\partial x} + \frac{w}{h_z}\frac{\partial w}{\partial z} + v\frac{\partial w}{\partial y} - \frac{u^2}{h_x h_z}\frac{\partial h_x}{\partial z} + \frac{uw}{h_x h_z}\frac{\partial h_z}{\partial x}$$

$$= -\frac{1}{\rho h_z}\frac{\partial p}{\partial z} + \nu\frac{\partial^2 w}{\partial y^2} \tag{20.18.4}$$

$$0 = \frac{\partial p}{\partial y} \tag{20.18.5}$$

$$\frac{1}{h_x h_z}\left[\frac{\partial}{\partial x}(h_z u) + \frac{\partial}{\partial z}(h_x w)\right] + \frac{\partial v}{\partial y} = 0 \tag{20.18.6}$$

The equations above differ from the two-dimensional counterparts by some extra convection terms (a result of the fact that the flow may now have w velocity) and the explicit appearance of the coordinate scale factors $h_x(x, z)$ and $h_z(x, z)$.

Three-dimensional boundary layers have three unknown velocities as functions of three coordinates—a considerably more complicated situation than the two-dimensional case. Moreover, surface-curvature effects now enter the equation through h_x and h_z. It is not possible to pin down the exact way in which curvature influences the boundary layer, because we still have a great deal of flexibility in placing an orthogonal net on the surface. For the most general surface $h_x(x, z)$ and $h_z(x, z)$ will exist and exert some influence in the convection terms. If a surface is developable, that is, if it can in principle be constructed from a flat sheet without stretching, it is possible to choose a coordinate system where $h_x = h_z = 1$. Hence, it is only for surfaces more complicated than developable surfaces that the curvature actually affects the boundary layer equations.

Boundary conditions for the equations are the no-slip condition and as $y \rightarrow \infty$, a match of the velocities u and w with the corresponding inviscid components u_e and w_e evaluated at the wall. The pressure in the layer is the inviscid pressure. Compatibility conditions between u_e, w_e, and the pressure are found by assuming that $u \rightarrow u_e$ and $w \rightarrow w_e$ exponentially fast in y. This is equivalent to striking all derivatives with respect to y in Eqs. 20.18.3 and 20.18.4 and replacing u and w with u_e and w_e. Unlike the two-dimensional case, the resulting compatibility equations do not lead to Bernoulli's equation for the free stream. The reason is that Eqs. 20.18.3 to 20.18.6 allow an arbitrary distribution of vertically directed vorticity ω_y at $y \rightarrow \infty$. Several interesting boundary solutions do have $\omega_y \neq 0$ in the free stream. If the inviscid flow does have $\omega_y = 0$, this extra information may be used in conjunction with the compatibility conditions to derive Bernoulli's relation.

The three-dimensional boundary layer equations are so complicated that numerical computers must be used in all but the simplest cases. Because of the need to take account of the surface geometry and the spreading transverse influence, these programs are themselves very complicated.

*20.19 BOUNDARY LAYER WITH A CONSTANT TRANSVERSE PRESSURE GRADIENT

As a simple example that contains important physics, consider a flat plate with a leading edge at $x = 0$. The flow approaching the leading edge is at an angle θ_0 (Fig. 20.30). For $x > 0$ the boundary conditions at $y \rightarrow \infty$ are

$$u \rightarrow u_e = \text{const} \tag{20.19.1}$$

$$w \rightarrow w_e = u_e(a + bx)$$

(This flow has a constant external vorticity ω_y.) The compatibility conditions show that this corresponds to pressure gradients

$$\frac{\partial p}{\partial x} = 0, \qquad -\frac{1}{\rho}\frac{\partial p}{\partial z} = u_e \frac{\partial w_e}{\partial x} = u_e^2 b \tag{20.19.2}$$

Hence, the constant b indicates the magnitude of the constant transverse pressure gradient. If $b = 0$, the external flow traverses the plate at a constant angle

$$\theta = \theta_0 = \arctan \frac{w_e}{u_e} = \arctan a \tag{20.19.3}$$

The constant a is the sweep angle of the plate with respect to the free stream. The special case $b = 0$ is of interest, as it shows the effect of sweep on a Blasius boundary layer.

Two researchers, Sowerby (1954) and Loos (1955), solved this problem independently. We give only the highlights; the reader who is interested in the details should consult the original works.

The inviscid flow streamlines $z_0(x)$ are easily found from Eq. 20.19.1:

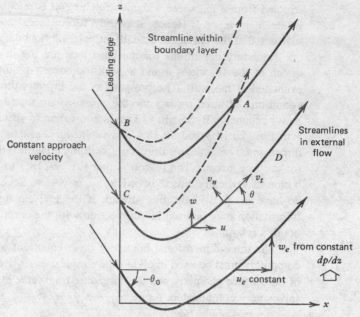

Figure 20.30   Plan view of the boundary layer on a plate with a constant transverse pressure gradient.

$$\frac{dz_e}{dx} = \frac{w_e}{u_e} = a + bx$$

$$z_e = ax + \tfrac{1}{2} bx^2 + c$$

(20.19.4)

where c is a constant that gives z_e at the leading edge. The streamlines are a system of translated parabolas as depicted in Fig. 20.30.

The boundary layer equations 20.18.3 to 20.18.6 for this problem become

$$u \frac{\partial u}{\partial x} + v \frac{\partial u}{\partial y} = \nu \frac{\partial^2 u}{\partial y^2}$$

(20.19.5)

$$u \frac{\partial w}{\partial x} + v \frac{\partial w}{\partial y} = bu_0^2 + \nu \frac{\partial^2 w}{\partial y^2}$$

(20.19.6)

$$\frac{\partial u}{\partial x} + \frac{\partial v}{\partial y} = 0$$

(20.19.7)

The x momentum and continuity equations do not contain w, and in fact, they are identical to the Blasius problem. The solution for the x direction follows immediately as

$$\frac{u}{u_e} = f'(\eta)$$

(20.19.8)

where

$$\eta \equiv y \sqrt{\frac{u_e}{\nu x}} \tag{20.19.9}$$

and $f(\eta)$ is the Blasius function obeying

$$ff'' + 2f''' = 0 \tag{20.19.10}$$

The fact that the problem separates out so that u and v may be solved without regard for w is known as the *sweep-independence principle*. It applies to any yawed cylindrical shape, no matter what the cross section (flat plate, circle, ellipse, or airfoil). In all of these flows the boundary layer for flow in the direction normal to the leading edge may be calculated as a two-dimensional boundary layer. Subsequently, this flow is used to calculate the cross-flow component parallel to the leading edge. As a practical example the secondary flow near the trailing edge of a swept wing is a strong spanwise outflow.

The transverse flow due to the constant-pressure force is a little more complicated. The assumed form of the velocity is

$$\frac{w}{u_e} = \frac{w_e(x)}{u_e} f'(\eta) + bxh(\eta) \tag{20.19.11}$$

Note that the first term is a Blasius component rescaled to match $w_e(x)$ (Eq. 20.19.1). Substitution of Eq. 20.19.11 into the different equations and considerable algebra will yield the following equation for $h(\eta)$:

$$h'' + \tfrac{1}{2}fh' - f'h + 1 - (f')^2 = 0 \tag{20.19.12}$$

Appropriate boundary conditions are $h(0) = h(\infty) = 0$. Loos (1955) realized that the equation for h was the same equation solved and tabulated previously by Mager and Hansen (1952).

An informative way to look at the results is to refer the velocities to the inviscid flow streamline. Let V_∞ be the magnitude of the inviscid velocity at any point, and v_t and v_n the velocity components along and normal to the inviscid streamline. It turns out that if one uses the local inviscid streamline angle θ as a variable, the velocity in the tangent direction is

$$\frac{v_t}{V_\infty} = f'(\eta) + \tfrac{1}{2} \sin 2\theta(\tan \theta - \tan \theta_0)h(\eta) \tag{20.19.13}$$

and the velocity in the normal direction is

$$\frac{v_n}{V_\infty} = \tfrac{1}{2} \cos^2 \theta(\tan \theta - \tan \theta_0)h(\eta) \tag{20.19.14}$$

where f' is the Blasius function and h is the solution of Eq. 20.19.12.

In discussing the results, let us first consider a uniform stream with a flat plate at a sweep angle θ_0. This is the case $b = 0$ and $\theta = \theta_0$. Equations 20.19.13 and 20.19.14 show that the boundary layer is simply a Blasius profile with no secondary flow at all. [A general statement may be made about the absence of secondary flows. If the external inviscid streamlines coincide with geodesic curves of the surface, the boundary layer streamlines have the same direction as the main stream and no secondary flow exists (Squire, 1965).]

A typical example with a transverse pressure gradient is shown in Fig. 20.31. Here tangential velocity profiles are presented as a function of θ for the case $\theta_0 = -60°$. The normal velocity profiles are not given because Eq. 20.19.14 shows that they are simply a multiplicative factor times $h(\eta)$. The first profile of Fig. 20.31b at $\theta = -60°$ is the Blasius profile. As we proceed along the flow to $\theta = -40°$ and $\theta = -20°$, the profiles show negative values of v_t near the wall. This is not separation of even a region of backflow; the normal velocity at the corresponding positions is large enough to keep the flow moving toward positive values of x.

Moving father along in the flow, that is, to higher values of θ, we see that v_t develops an overshoot. The maximum velocity is within the boundary layer. Another view is given by the polar diagram of Fig. 20.32. This very interesting phenomenon occurs frequently in three-dimensional boundary layers. To explain it, we must consider the history of particles in the upper part of the boundary layer. Near the leading edge, viscosity retards the particles into the Blasius profile while pressure begins to accelerate the flow in the transverse direction to develop the $h(\eta)$ profile. Particles in the upper part of the $h(\eta)$ profile (from the inflection point outward, to be precise) have a net transverse viscous force in the same direction as the pressure force. This aiding viscous force dies out as $y \rightarrow \infty$, where particles receive only the pressure force. Hence, there is a thin region at the top of the boundary layer where the particles experience a pressure force and a net viscous force in the same direction. These particles have more transverse acceleration than the external stream, which experiences only the pressure force. Farther along in the flow, the stream turns to higher θ, and the extra velocity from the viscous acceleration

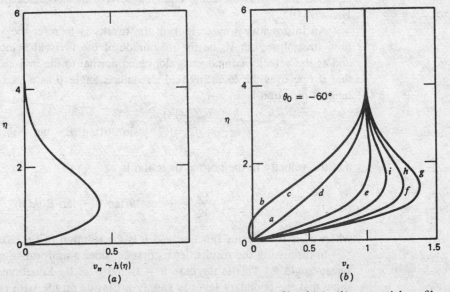

Figure 20.31 Typical velocity profiles: (a) transverse profiles $h(\eta)$; (b) tangential profiles for various flow angles: a, $\theta = -60°$; b, $\theta = -40°$; c, $\theta = -20°$ (same curve as b); d, $\theta = 0°$ (same as a); e, $\theta = 20°$; f, $\theta = 40°$; g, $\theta = 60°$; h, $\theta = 80°$ (same as f); i, $\theta = 90°$.

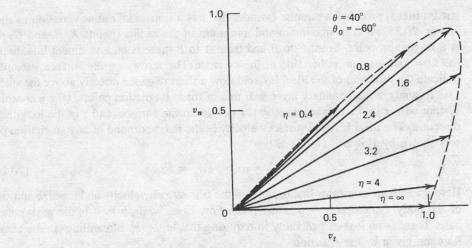

Figure 20.32 Polar diagram of velocity profile with overshoot.

appears as an overshoot in the v_t profiles. This is another example of viscous acceleration increasing the Bernoulli constant.

The surface streamlines may be computed exactly, and they are also parabolas. The equation is

$$z_s(x) = ax + \frac{1}{2} bx^2 \left[1 + \frac{h'(0)}{f''(0)} \right] + C_0 \tag{20.19.15}$$

The curvature of the surface streamlines is greater than that of the external flow by a factor $1 + h'(0)/f''(0) \approx 1\frac{1}{3}$. Note that this particular flow never separates.

One of the most important things to be learned from this problem concerns the spreading lateral influence mentioned in Section 20.18. Wang (1971) pointed out that particle paths are subcharacteristics of the three-dimensional boundary layer equations. In a sense, a particle carries its initial conditions and history wherever it goes within the boundary layer. Return to Fig. 20.30, where a surface streamline CA and two external flow streamlines CD and BA are shown. All the particles in the boundary layer at point A have come from the region ABC. Changing the initial conditions or boundary conditions anywhere in the region ABC has an effect on the velocity profile at A. From another standpoint, consider the boundary layer at point C. Particles that pass through C ultimately influence the flow within the region ACD. This is called the *region of influence* of point C. As we proceed in the flow direction, the region of influence spreads in the lateral direction. Any numerical calculation scheme for boundary layers needs to take account of the spreading lateral influence.

*20.20 HOWARTH'S STAGNATION POINT

The plane or axisymmetric stagnation point we studied previously is a very special case. To introduce a more general way in which a flow meets a body, consider a uniform stream that approaches a circular cylinder that has a sinusoidal radius variation as shown in Fig. 20.33. At each maximum and minimum of the radius (points A, B, and C) there is a stagnation point. From C to B and from A to B there is an attachment line dividing the flow that goes on either side of the cylinder. The arrows on the surface streamlines indicate the direction of the ideal inviscid flow a short distance directly above the surface.

To analyze the boundary layer near one of these stagnation points, take a coordinate system with x in the upward direction, y normal to the surface, and z in the longitudinal direction. The ideal inviscid surface velocity in the neighborhood of any stagnation point was shown by Howarth (1951) to be

$$u_e = ax, \qquad w_e = bz \qquad (20.20.1)$$

Here a and b are constants that depend on the free-stream velocity and the size and shape of the body. Note that $b = 0$ is the plane flow case, while $b = a$ is the axisymmetric case. There is no loss of generality in requiring that $|a| > |b|$. Streamlines in the external flow are given by the equation

$$x_e = cz^{1/\alpha} \qquad (20.20.2)$$

where

$$\alpha \equiv b/a \qquad (20.20.3)$$

and c is a constant that gives a specific streamline. The cases $0 < \alpha \leq 1$ display nodal attachment (stagnation) points, $\alpha = 0$ is the plane flow case (stagnation line), and the cases $-1 < \alpha < 0$ display saddle points of attachment where b is negative and a is positive. Typical patterns of streamlines are shown in Fig. 20.34.

The boundary layer equations for this flow are

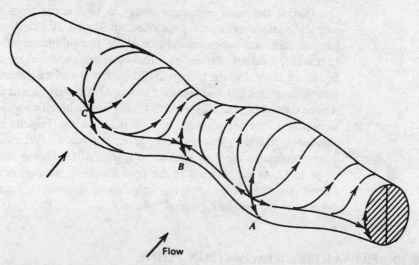

Figure 20.33   Ideal flow over a wavey cylinder. Surface streamlines emanate from nodal attachment points A and C.

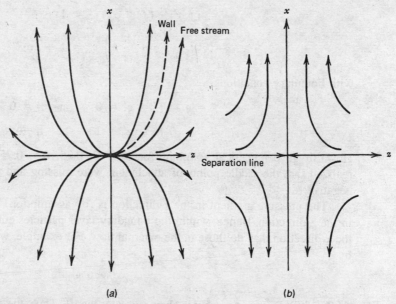

Figure 20.34 Plan view of streamlines on the surface and in the inviscid flow for a typical Howarth stagnation point: (a) nodal attachment point as points A and C of Fig. 20.33; (b) saddle attachment point as point B of Fig. 20.33.

$$u \frac{\partial u}{\partial x} + v \frac{\partial u}{\partial y} + w \frac{\partial u}{\partial z} = a^2 x + \nu \frac{\partial^2 u}{\partial y^2} \tag{20.20.4}$$

$$u \frac{\partial w}{\partial x} + v \frac{\partial w}{\partial y} + w \frac{\partial w}{\partial z} = b^2 z + \nu \frac{\partial^2 w}{\partial y^2} \tag{20.20.5}$$

$$\frac{\partial u}{\partial x} + \frac{\partial v}{\partial y} + \frac{\partial w}{\partial z} = 0 \tag{20.20.6}$$

Howarth's stagnation-point analysis is presented in variables similar to those used in the plane flow case. They are

$$\eta \equiv \left(\frac{a}{\nu} \right)^{1/2} y \tag{20.20.7}$$

$$\frac{u}{u_e} = \frac{u}{ax} = f'(\eta) \tag{20.20.8}$$

$$\frac{w}{w_e} = \frac{w}{bz} = g'(\eta) \tag{20.20.9}$$

These assumptions lead to a coupled set of equations with α as a parameter:

$$(f')^2 - (f + \alpha g)f'' = 1 + f''' \tag{20.20.10}$$

$$(g')^2 - \left(g + \frac{1}{\alpha} f\right) g'' = 1 + \frac{1}{\alpha} g''' \tag{20.20.11}$$

with boundary conditions

$$f = g = f' = g' = 0 \quad \text{at} \quad \eta = 0$$

$$f' = g' = 1 \quad \text{at} \quad \eta \to \infty$$

Howarth gave numerical solutions for $\alpha = 0$, 0.25, 0.5, 0.75, and 1. Davey (1961) realized that the saddle points of attachment were missing and produced the results for negative α.

The pressure gradient in the x-direction is (by assumption) always greater than that in the z-direction. Hence, within the boundary layer particles curve more rapidly toward the x-direction than do those in the external flow. For example, wall streamlines are given by

$$x_s = cz^{f''(0)/[g''(0)\alpha]} \tag{20.20.12}$$

$f''(0)/g''(0)$ depends on α but is always greater than 1. Thus, the exponent in Eq. 20.20.12 is greater than the exponent of Eq. 20.20.2.

We have solved for the flow in the neighborhood of points A, B, and C in Fig. 20.34. Note how important these flows, and the separation lines from C to B and from A to B, are to determining the boundary layer over the entire cylinder. Mathematically, all the inviscid surface flow from C to B and over the top of the cylinder originates at the stagnation point C (or within ε of it, to be exact). Similarly, all particles from $y = 0$ to $y = \delta$ in the stagnation point at C (or within ε of the point C) are carried out toward B and over the top of the cylinder in an ever thinning sheet near the surface of the boundary layer, the upper portions of the boundary layer being entrained from the external flow. Hence, by the effect of lateral spreading, the flow near the nodal point C has an influence, very much diminished at remote locations of course, on the entire boundary layer from C to B.

*20.21   THREE-DIMENSIONAL SEPARATION

Flows frequently take on three-dimensional patterns and separate from walls. The slightest transverse pressure gradient sends the wall streamlines on highly curved paths and makes the entire flow three-dimensional. Separation is complex and sensitive to the details of the situation. For example, Tobak and Peak (1982) describe four different patterns of separation as the angle of attack is increased on a smooth nose shape. Much of our knowledge is qualitative information gained from flow-visualization experiments. For these reasons this section deals mainly with the qualitative aspects of separation and the classification of streamline patterns.

The classification of flow patterns is first approached by looking at special planes (either flat or curved). The plane of the body surface is, of course, very important. Planes of flow symmetry or cross-flow planes are other choices. Consider the velocity components in the plane chosen. This two-dimensional vector field, say $u = dx/dt$, $v = dy/dt$, has *trajectories, y(x)*, leading to a pattern. On a solid surface these are the *surface stream-lines* or *limiting streamlines* (coincident with the shear stress lines for a Newtonian fluid). Unfortunately, the pattern of streamlines depends on the motion of the observer, an especially important consideration in unsteady flow. Vortex lines, which are invariant to translation of the observer, are also a good candidate for analysis. Recall that on a solid surface the stress and vortex lines are orthogonal. The assumption that the velocity field is continuous leads to patterns of trajectories connecting critical points. Critical points are points where the velocity (vorticity) components are zero and trajectories may split. Much of the theory and nomenclature comes from phase plane analysis of autonomous differential equations. Discussions from a fluid mechanics viewpoint are found in Tobak and Peak (1982) and Perry and Chong (1989).

At a critical point the velocity is zero; however, the derivatives can be organized into two important quantities: the Jacobian $J = (\partial u/\partial x)(\partial v/\partial y) - (\partial u/\partial y)(\partial v/\partial x)$ and the divergence $\Delta = (\partial u/\partial x) + (\partial v/\partial y)$ (in three dimensions the invariants of the strain tensor are investigated; Chong et al., 1990). Delta is the divergence in the plane of interest. In incompressible flow the continuity equation requires that $\Delta = -(\partial w/\partial z)$, where z is the direction normal to the plane. Thus, a solid wall with no slip has $\Delta = 0$. Figure 20.35 classifies critical points into three groups according to J and Δ. *Foci* are within the area above the parabola $J = \Delta^2/4$, *nodes* between the parabola and the Δ-axis, and *saddles* below the Δ-axis.

If a configuration is on the boundary it is called a *focal node* or *saddle node*. In Section 20.20 we encountered the attachment node and the attachment saddle. The special case of an attachment saddle node is a plane stagnation line, whereas the special case of an attachment focal node is an axisymmetric stagnation point. These are on the left side of Fig. 20.35 and are slightly different from Fig. 20.34 because irrotational flow has only orthogonal patterns. Patterns in the second quadrant of Fig. 20.35 are called *unstable*: an unstable node or unstable focus, for example. This name comes from the mathematical problem of integrating $u(t)$, $v(t)$ away from such a singular point. All trajectories leave this point, so such integration is not possible. Patterns in the first quadrant are stable because integration progresses toward the point. Typically, the left side of the diagram is the same pattern as the right except that the direction of flow is reversed. In the case of saddles this is unimportant, as the same pattern results from rotation of the axes. The occurrence of critical points follows certain topological rules. For instance, on a closed body the number of nodal points minus the number of saddle points is equal to 2.

Another special feature of separation patterns is a *local separation line, limit cycle line,* or *bifurcation line;* the nomenclature varies. It is a line toward which other lines asymptote. Consider the Taylor–Couette flow pattern shown in Fig. 20.36. Taylor–Couette flow (Section 7.3) is a stack of spiral vortex cells caused by a moving inner wall and a stationary outer wall. Figure 20.36 is a small section of the outer stationary wall shown as the flat lower wall. The inner cylinder wall, the upper wall of the figure, is not shown but its location is indicated. Two spiral vortex cells are depicted with the associated streamlines in the lower wall and on a vertical plane between cells. A cross-flow plane shows the swirling character of the vortex. The walls contain attachment lines and sep-aration lines to which the streamlines asymptote. As a particle of fluid on the lower wall gets exponentially close to the separation line, it becomes exponentially tall and separates.

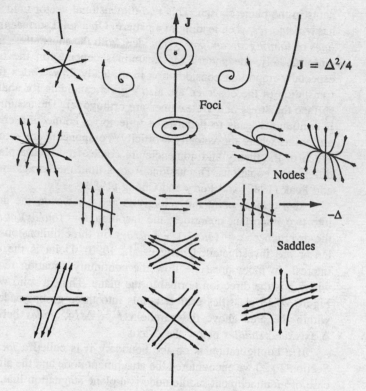

Figure 20.35   Types of critical points.

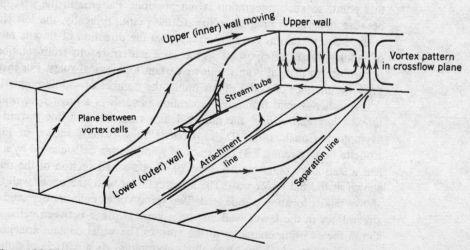

Figure 20.36   Streamlines in a Taylor vortex cell of a Couette flow. The wall and the surfaces separating vortex cells intersect in lines of separation and lines of attachment.

Attachment lines and separation lines are sometimes drawn with tangential streamlines, but this is not actually true; the lines are asymptotes. A bifurcation line only exists in a three-dimensional flow. Furthermore, they can begin and end at any place, not necessarily a critical point. The terms *separation* and *attachment* can reasonably be applied to bifurcation lines on the wall; however, within the fluid it is best to use the term *bifurcation line*.

Flow-visualization techniques cannot resolve such minute distances, and in the records from such experiments the streamlines appear to merge with the separation line. On the other side of a cell, the reverse of these events take place. The line is now a line of attachment and appears to be a source of surface streamlines. In this flow the separation surface from one wall becomes an attachment surface on the other wall. This is typical of closed separation regions.

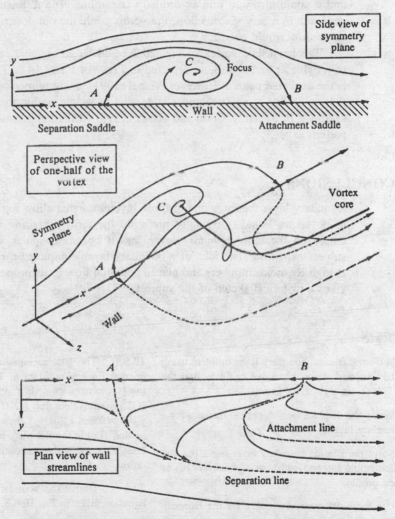

Figure 20.37 Separation pattern of a horseshoe vortex above a wall.

In more complex patterns of separation, several nodal and saddle points occur in combination with separation–attachment lines. Nodal focus points also play a role whenever a vortex flow springs from a wall. For example, the vortex that forms at the tip of a wing begins not at the trailing edge but at a point near midspan on the upper surface. A focus point must occur somewhere in this vicinity as the origin of the streamline in the core of the vortex.

We see in Fig. 20.37 one of the simplest examples of a three-dimensional separation, a steady horseshoe vortex above a solid wall. The wall is in the $x–z$ plane, and only one-half the flow is shown because of symmetry. The vortex is perpendicular to the oncoming stream at point C, a spiral focus. Point A is a separation saddle point and point B is the attachment saddle point. A bifurcation line leaves A and proceeds to bend back along the wall. At some position the line ceases to be an asymptote and becomes an ordinary wall streamline. In a similar fashion, a bifurcation attachment line is emanating from B, and it could also turn into an ordinary streamline. The ultimate fate of the vortex is not depicted. In a very viscous flow, the vortex could die out downstream and only a uniform shear flow would remain.

The horseshoe vortex in Fig. 20.2 could be an element in the flow at the juncture of a cylinder and a wall, as depicted in Figs. 14.1 and 14.2. The saddle separation at A is the expected pattern. However, Visbal (1991), using numerical computations, predicted the possibility of an attachment node at A, a saddle within the flow, and an attachment saddle at B. Recently, Coon and Tobak (1995) verified experimentally that the alternative pattern exists.

20.22   CONCLUSIONS

Boundary layer theory is one of those inventions that allow a giant step in understanding to be taken. Prandtl originally preferred the term *transition layer*, but Blasius (1908) employed the term *boundary layer*, and it became popular among researchers as the subject expanded. The idea of a boundary layer completed the theory of attached flows at high Reynolds numbers and placed potential flow in its proper perspective. Tani (1977) gives a historical sketch of the subject.

PROBLEMS

20.1 (A) Solve the Blasius boundary layer problem using $f''(0) = 0.33206$ and $\eta_\infty = 12$. Solve again to find the value of $f''(0)$ to six significant figures.

20.2 (A) Verify the displacement thickness formula for a Blasius boundary layer.

20.3 (A) Solve the Blasius boundary layer using the von Kármán momentum integral with $u = u_0 \sin(\pi y/2\delta)$ as the assumed profile.

20.4 (B) Use the K-P4 method to solve for the Howarth problem where $u_e = u_0(1 - a(L/x))$.

20.5 (C) The Blasius equation is unchanged if $f(\eta) \rightarrow af_0(a\eta)$ for any constant a. That is, f and f_0 both obey the Blasius equation. If f obeys the Blasius B.C., what B.C. is equivalent for f_0? If f_0 is found using $f_0(0) = f_0'(0) = 0$ and $f_0''(0) = 1$, how can the constant a be found so that $f(\eta)$ is the flat plate result? The solution has now been obtained without shooting to the far boundary condition.

20.6 (C) Derive the boundary layer form of the energy equation given in Eq. 10.8.8.

20.7 (B) Construct a computer program to solve the Falkner–Skan equation over the range $\eta[0, 12]$ and print out f and f' every 0.1 increment in η. Solve the case $\beta = 0.2$.

20.8 (A) Show that the Falkner–Skan equation when u_e and x have opposite signs is

$$f''' + \frac{1}{2}(\beta - 1) ff'' + \beta(1 - f') = 0$$

$$\text{with} \quad \beta = -\frac{x}{u_e}\frac{du_e}{dx}$$

20.9 (B) Verify that the exact closed-form solution to the Falkner–Skan flow along a flat wall into a line sink on the wall at $x = 0$, $y = 0$ is governed by $f''' - f'^2 + 1 = 0$ and that $f' = 3\tanh(\eta/\sqrt{2} + c) - 2$. From the boundary conditions show that $c = \tanh^{-1}(\sqrt{2/3})$.

20.10 Prove that a sharp leading edge in a pressure gradient flow has $\beta_i = 0$ just the same as the Blasius flow.

20.11 (B) Experimental measurements show that the velocity over the surface of a circular cylinder is $U = 7.151x - 0.04497x^3 - 0.0003300x^5$. In this expression U is in centimeters per second, x is in centimeters from the stagnation point ($x < 7$). The free stream of the tests was 19.2 cm/s, the cylinder diameter is 9.75 cm, and the fluid viscosity $\nu = 0.01$ cm^2/s. Compute the boundary layer.

20.12 (B) Consider the boundary layer under a stationary line source of strength m located a fixed distance h above and parallel to the wall. Locate the region of adverse pressure gradient. Solve for the boundary layer on the wall.

20.13 (B) Compute the boundary layer on an ellipse as given in Problem 18.11.

20.14 (B) Computer the boundary layer on a Joukowski airfoil as found in Problem 18.15.

20.15 (B) Computer the boundary layer on the circular arc strut of Problem 18.24.

20.16 (B) Compute the boundary layer on a semi-infinite flat plate aligned with the flow from a line source. The leading edge of the plate is a distance r_0 from the source that has a strength Q.

20.17 (C) Consider the problem of the ideal flow over a rotating cylinder (Section 18.7) for the case $\Gamma_a = 4\pi r_0 U$. Set up the boundary layer equations and boundary conditions that govern this flow.

20.18 (C) Derive the boundary layer equations for a liquid film falling down a vertical flat plate from an arbitrary initial state. State the appropriate boundary conditions.

20.19 (C) Derive the proper three-dimensional boundary layer forms for the equations $\boldsymbol{\omega} = \nabla \times \mathbf{v}$, $\nabla \cdot \boldsymbol{\omega} = 0$, and the three vorticity equations 13.3.5.

20.20 (C) The flow from a jet into a reservoir has the constant momentum M. Integrate the differential equation 20.13.7 from $-\infty$ to ∞, applying appropriate conditions, to arrive directly at Eq. 20.13.8. This demonstrates that M is a constant intrinsically associated with the similarity equation. Consider a flat wall with a jet coming out perpendicular. What are the characteristics of the flow and pressure along the wall because of entrainment. Would M exactly equal $\rho A_j u_0^2$?

20.21 (C) Consider the flow over the front of a sphere has the external stream, determined from experiments:

$$\frac{u_e}{u_0} = \frac{3}{2}(\Theta - 0.2914\Theta^3 + 0.0987\Theta^5 - 0.0282\Theta^7)$$

where Θ is the angle from the stagnation point. For what values of Θ is the stagnation point solution valid to 3% accuracy for this flow?

20.22 (C) An ideal spherical point source of fluid of strength m is located a distance H above a flat wall. Solve for the boundary layer above the wall. Plot the u velocity profile in the boundary layer as a function of y/H at the position $x/H = \frac{1}{2}$. The coordinate x begins at the point directly under the source. The Reynolds number $m/\nu 2\pi H = 20$.

20.23 (B) How will Mangler's transformation affect the shape (maximum, minimum, inflection points) of $u_e(x)$?

20.24 (A) Show that Jeffrey–Hamel flow is a Falkner–Skan flow with $\beta = 1$ in the equation for flow in opposite directions derived in Problem 20.8.

20.25 (B) A plane flow exists between two flat walls (like the walls of a diffuser) that have an angle α between them. The flow is at a high Reynolds number and is moving outward toward the larger area. A flat plate is inserted halfway between the walls and is aligned with the streamlines. The leading edge of the plate is located a distance R_0 from the effective origin of the intersection of the walls and at this location the velocity is U_0. Compute the boundary layer on the inserted plate and determine how long the plate can be if laminar boundary layer separation is to be avoided. If the Reynolds number of the flow $Re = U_0^* R_0 / \nu$ is 5000, what is the physical thickness of the boundary layer δ / R_0 at the trailing edge?

20.26 (C) A manufacturing process requires a flat area that is free of oxygen. It is proposed to have an inert gas flow over the area from two long parallel pipes with porous walls. The flow rate from each pipe is uniform in the radial direction at a value of m $(L^3/T)/L$ of pipe length. The Reynolds number $Re = m/2\pi\nu = 1000$. The pipes are located a distance ℓ apart and a distance $h = 1.25l$ above the surface. How wide (in terms of l) can the work area be? Plot velocity profiles. How will things, including the work area width, change if the Reynolds number is increased by a factor of 2?

21

Flows at Low Reynolds Numbers

Situations where the Reynolds number is very low form another class of incompressible flows having common physical events. For a domain characterized by the length L and a motion characterized by the velocity U, we can imagine that the Reynolds number $Re = LU\rho/\mu$ is small because the object is small, or the fluid is very viscous, or the velocity or density is very small. From a physical point of view we may think of $Re \to 0$ as either the flow of a massless fluid or the flow of highly viscous fluid. These flows are frequently called *creeping flows* or *Stokes flows*.

Of course, the term *creeping flow* is appropriate to many practical cases in which a high viscosity leads to slow motion. The chemical and material processing industries frequently deal with very viscous substances. In other cases, the fluid may be of modest viscosity but the length dimension is small.

A small particle of dirt or a droplet of liquid settling out of the air does so very slowly, at a low Reynolds number. The size range of engineering interest extends all the way down to aerosols, where the continuum assumption itself must be modified. As another example, the width of the gap in an oil-lubricated bearing is typically very small, 0.001 in. or less. The flow of groundwater, oil, or natural gas through porous rock formations furnishes yet another example of a low-Reynolds-number situation. When considering the flow through small passages or around tiny objects, we focus our interest on a small region in space. The physical events are those of a viscous, massless fluid.

The flows mentioned above are either confined flows or unconfined flows. Low-Reynolds-number flows can also occur as parts of larger flow fields. Consider, for example, the leading edge of a flat plate aligned with the free stream. As the flow separates to go on either side of the plate, the velocity on the stagnation streamline must become zero, and viscous diffusion can therefore extend a slight distance in front of the edge. The size of this region is ν/U, very small in most instances. In a small neighborhood near the leading edge, the flow is viscous and a local Reynolds number $x_i U/\nu$ is less than 1. The leading edge is typical of any wall irregularity, such as a corner.

The term *low Reynolds number* commonly has several meanings. Frequently, it merely designates flows where Re is lower than typical values. Here and throughout this chapter, we use the term to mean flows where inertia is negligible.

21.1   GENERAL RELATIONS FOR RE → 0: STOKES'S EQUATIONS

Consider a flow field with characteristic length L and velocity U. The proper nondimensional distance $x_i^* = x_i/L$ and velocities $v_i^* = v_i/U$ contain these scales. In previous work for moderate the high Reynolds numbers, the pressure was scaled with the dynamic pressure, $\frac{1}{2}\rho U^2$, implying that inertia and pressure effects are the same size. However, this scaling is inappropriate for Re $\rightarrow$ 0 because inertia effects, including the dynamic pressure, are becoming very small. In a very viscous flow the pressure force must become large to balance the viscous stresses. The appropriate nondimensional pressure cannot contain ρ. It is

$$p^{**} = \frac{p - p_0}{\mu U / L} = \frac{p - p_0}{\frac{1}{2}\rho U^2} \, \text{Re} \tag{21.1.1}$$

With these variables, the nondimensional momentum equation becomes

$$\text{Re} \, \frac{D\mathbf{v}^*}{Dt^*} = -\nabla^* p^{**} + \nabla^{*2}\mathbf{v}^* \tag{21.1.2}$$

For Re $\rightarrow$ 0 this simplifies to

$$\nabla^* p^{**} = \nabla^{*2}\mathbf{v}^* \tag{21.1.3}$$

The net forces on a fluid particle must add to zero (p^{**} may include the body force as in Section 10.5). Flows governed by Eq. 21.1.3 are termed *Stokes flows*. Stokes (1851) was the first to propose this simplification, in his paper concerning the motion of a pendulum.

Several other forms for Eq. 21.1.3 are (in dimensional form)

$$0 = \nabla \cdot \mathbf{T}$$
$$\nabla p = \nabla \cdot \boldsymbol{\tau} \tag{21.1.4}$$
$$\nabla p = \mu \nabla^2 \mathbf{v}$$
$$\nabla p = -\mu \nabla \times \boldsymbol{\omega}$$

The characterization of Stokes flows as the flow of a massless fluid, in contrast to its characterization as the flow of a very viscous fluid, is emphasized by noting that setting $\rho = 0$ in the dimensional equations produces the proper simplified forms for Re $\rightarrow$ 0. Furthermore, all results and conclusions arrived at for Stokes flows are independent of the fluid density. For instance, a particle of ash from a volcano settles at the same velocity at an altitude of 18,000 m that it does at sea level, despite the fact that the air density changes by a factor of 10.

In Eq. 21.1.4 the dynamic viscosity μ appears as a proportionality constant between the pressure field and velocity field or vorticity field. The magnitude of the pressure increases directly as the viscosity increases (this is, of course, the reason for the scaling Eq. 21.1.1).

Taking the divergence of Eq. 21.1.3 and using the continuity equation shows that the pressure is governed by

$$\nabla^{*2} p^{**} = 0 \tag{21.1.5}$$

Thus, whenever boundary conditions appropriate to this equation may be prescribed in a problem (and some lubrication problems are of this type), we may solve for the pressure independently of the velocity. With the pressure known, Eq. 21.1.3 furnishes a mathematical problem for the velocity field.

Consider the vorticity equation where the nondimensional vorticity is $\omega^* = \omega/(U/L)$.

$$\text{Re}\,\frac{D\omega^*}{Dt^*} = \text{Re}\,\omega^* \cdot \nabla\mathbf{v}^* + \nabla^{*2}\,\omega^* \qquad (21.1.6)$$

For low Reynolds numbers the simplified form is

$$0 = \nabla^{*2}\,\omega^* \qquad (21.1.7)$$

The velocity and vorticity fields are completely determined by viscous diffusion. The inertialike effect of convection of vorticity is absent, as is the kinematic effect of stretching the vortex lines. Low-Reynolds-number flows are so slow that these effects are of a smaller magnitude than the viscous diffusion of vorticity.

Time does not appear explicitly in the equations governing Stokes flows. Thus, these flows are quasisteady. Any time-dependent motion of a massless fluid arising from unsteady boundary conditions is quasi-steady. The validity of this conclusion rests on the assumption that the time scale in the substantial derivative term of Eq. 21.1.2 is L/U. The unsteady motion of a boundary condition introduces another independent time scale into the problem. If we use t_0 to characterize the imposed unsteadiness, then when $s = t_0 U/L$ is of order 1 or larger, our conclusion that the flow is quasisteady is valid. However, if $s = t_0 U/L$ is very small (a high-frequency case), the unsteady term $\rho\,\partial u/\partial t$ must be retained in Eq. 21.1.3. Such flows have local inertia effects but no convective inertia effects. Hence, whether a time-dependent flow at a low Reynolds number requires a momentum-storage term or not depends on the time scale of the motion imposed.

As a general feature, all properties of a Stokes flow are governed by linear equations: Eq. 21.1.5 for p, Eq. 21.1.6 for v_i or ω_i, and a linear equation for τ_{ij} arising from the viscous law for τ_{ij} and its linearity in v_i. The linear property may be used to great advantage in adding flow fields to produce new flows. We saw in Chapters 18 and 19 how two or more ideal flows could be added because the potential ϕ, the streamfunction ψ, and the velocity v_i were all governed by linear equations. Pressures in ideal flows are not additive because the Bernoulli equation is quadratic in v_i. On the other hand, in Stokes flows, pressures and viscous stresses are also governed by linear equations, and superposition is therefore allowed. Since forces are simply the integration of stresses and pressures, the superposition of forces is also allowed in a Stokes flow.

The linearity of Stokes flows leads to many nice mathematical results. For example, it is possible to show that the viscous flow with the least energy dissipation, for given geometry and boundary conditions, is the Stokes solution (this result is due to Helmholtz). Another theorem states that the solution of Eq. 21.1.6 for prescribed geometry and boundary conditions on the velocity is mathematically unique.

Perhaps one of the most useful mathematical properties of Stokes flows is a direct result of the linearity. Consider what happens if we reverse the velocity ($v_i \rightarrow -v_i$) of a certain flow problem. All equations and boundary conditions are still satisfied. The stresses change direction ($\tau_{ij} \rightarrow -\tau_{ij}$), and the pressure changes sign ($p \rightarrow -p$). Thus, Stokes flows are reversible in the sense that the reverse flow is also a Stokes flow. These facts allow one to argue that a velocity pattern about a symmetrical object or in a symmetrical flow channel must also be symmetrical. The corresponding pressure distribution is antisymmetric. An application of this principle to symmetrical objects in an infinite fluid shows that these objects have no wakes. The downstream flow has the same streamline pattern and velocity magnitudes as the upstream pattern. Viscous diffusion of the vorticity proceeds upstream and downstream with equal effectiveness. Figure 21.1 shows the symmetric flow over a block.

Confined flows in general lead to well-structured solutions to low-Reynolds-number equations. For flows where the domain is infinite, we shall find that the situation is quite different. Stokes flows on an unbounded domain are not uniformly valid from a mathematical standpoint. The difficulty is analogous to the one we discovered for high-Reynolds-number flows. Stokes flows on an infinite domain turn out to be singular at infinity. A perturbation theory that includes Stokes flows and gives the correct behavior at infinity is quite different for two- or three-dimensional objects. We discuss these equations in Sections 21.9 to 21.12.

21.2 GLOBAL EQUATIONS FOR STOKES FLOW

The integral momentum and kinetic energy equations for Stokes flows take on very simple forms. The integral momentum equation may be derived by the appropriate simplification of Eq. 5.14.1 or by integrating Eq. 21.1.4 over a volume of interest and applying the theorem of Gauss. The result by either method is

Figure 21.1 Viscous flow over a block shows symmetry at Re = 0.02. From Taneda (1979). Reprinted with permission.

$$0 = \int - n_i p \, dS + \int n_j \tau_{ji} \, dS \qquad (21.2.1)$$

The fact that there is always a local balance between pressure and viscous forces translates into a statement that the pressure and viscous forces on any finite region are also in balance.

Let us apply Eq. 21.2.1 to a body moving in an infinite fluid. For a sketch, see Fig. 21.2. The integration region consists of the fluid outside the body up to a remote boundary that we call S_∞. For n_i pointing inward the drag force is defined as

$$F_i \equiv \int_{S_b} (n_i p - n_j \tau_{ji}) \, dS \qquad (21.2.2)$$

Global force balance equation 21.2.1 becomes

$$F_i = - \int_{S_\infty} (n_i p - n_j \tau_{ji}) \, dS \qquad (21.2.3)$$

The surface forces on the remote boundary must die out very slowly. If we move S_∞ to even more remote positions, the surface forces decrease but S_∞ increases in such a way that a finite force is maintained. This is an example of one of the major characteristics of low-Reynolds-number flows: the influence of a body on the flow extends very far in all directions.

In flows at any finite nonzero Reynolds number we are able to relate the drag force to events in the wake, a specific region downstream of the body. Outside the wake the velocity and pressure are essentially the free stream values. The drag is associated with a defect in the momentum convected in the wake, or with decreased surface forces in the wake. Stokes flows, on the other hand, have no wakes, so the drag force is transmitted to remote locations in all directions as a surface force.

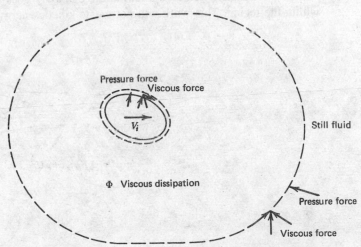

Figure 21.2 Control volume for flow over an object moving in an infinite medium.

Next, consider a body, not necessarily symmetrical, that has a certain drag force. As discussed earlier, reversing the direction of the free stream simply reverses the direction of the velocity everywhere and changes the sign of the stress and the pressure $(p - p_{ref})$. Inserting these facts into Eq. 21.2.2 shows that if the free-stream direction is reversed, the body has exactly the same drag force but with the direction reversed. In creeping flow, the drag of a body moving forward is the same as the drag of a body moving backward.

In Stokes flows the drag of an object is fairly insensitive to the exact shape. Sharp corners and sharp edges are not as important as the surface area on which the pressure and viscous forces act. A theorem due to Hill and Power (1956) states that the Stokes drag of an object must be larger than the drag of any inscribed figure but smaller than that of any circumscribed figure. A sphere circumscribed around the object has a larger drag than the object, although it has no sharp corners, whereas a sphere inscribed within the object must have a smaller drag than the object. Figure 21.3 depicts this fact.

Now we turn our attention to the work done by surface forces. Consider the following mathematical identity for the rate that work is done per unit volume by surface forces:

$$-\partial_i(pv_i) + \partial_j(\tau_{ji}v_i) = -v_i\partial_i p + v_i\partial_j\tau_{ji} + \tau_{ji}\partial_i v_j$$

The total surface force work is equal to the work to accelerate the fluid plus the viscous dissipation (Section 5.10). From Eq. 21.1.4 we see that the first two terms on the right-hand side are always balanced in Stokes flows. Integrating this equation over a finite region and using Gauss's theorem on the left-hand side yields

$$-\int (n_i v_i p - n_i \tau_{ij} v_j)\, dS = \int \Phi\, dV \tag{21.2.4}$$

where

$$\Phi \equiv \tau_{ij}\partial_j v_i$$

All the work done by surface forces at the boundary goes to produce viscous dissipation within the region. This work will not create kinetic energy of the fluid.

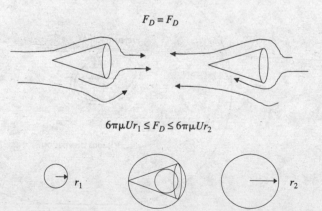

$$F_D = F_D$$

$$6\pi\mu U r_1 \le F_D \le 6\pi\mu U r_2$$

Figure 21.3 Drag in reversed flow is equal but opposite in direction. Drag is greater than inscribed sphere and less than circumscribed sphere.

Note how the work dissipation result (Eq. 21.2.4) applies to the flow field about a body moving in an infinite fluid. Again we take a region that surrounds and encloses the fluid out to a remote surface S_∞. The fluid velocity at S_∞ is approaching zero, so the surface integral in Eq. 21.2.4 becomes zero there. On the surface of the body the velocity is a uniform value V_i, so that the integral in Eq. 21.2.4 over the body becomes V_iF_i. Thus, Eq. 21.2.4 is rewritten as

$$F_iV_i = -\int \Phi \, dV \qquad (21.2.5)$$

The left-hand side is negative because the drag force and the velocity are in opposite directions. Equation 21.2.5 offers an alternative method for computing the drag force in Stokes flows.

21.3 STREAMFUNCTION FOR PLANE AND AXISYMMETRIC FLOWS

In Chapter 12 it was shown that the streamfunction is useful in any flow that has symmetry with respect to a coordinate surface. In fact, a flow can be determined completely by solving an equation for the streamfunction. The vector potential **B** defines the streamfunction:

$$\mathbf{B} = \psi\nabla g \qquad (21.3.1)$$

Here g is the coordinate with flow symmetry. Velocity and vorticity arise in the expressions

$$\mathbf{v} = \nabla \times \mathbf{B}$$
$$\boldsymbol{\omega} = \nabla^2\mathbf{B} = -\nabla \times \nabla \times \mathbf{B} \qquad (21.3.2)$$

One uses the momentum equation, or its form as a vorticity equation, to include dynamics and determine the pressure and viscous stresses in the problem:

$$0 = \nabla^2\boldsymbol{\omega}$$
$$\nabla p = -\mu\nabla \times \boldsymbol{\omega} \qquad (21.3.3)$$

Of course, in any specific case these vector equations need to be simplified to their scalar components.

Consider a plane two-dimensional Stokes flow. A solution for a general plane flow, where planes of constant z have the same flow pattern, has only the ω_z component being nonzero. Velocity components in a plane flow are given by

$$g = z, \qquad \mathbf{B} = \mathbf{i}_z\psi, \qquad \mathbf{v} = \nabla \times \mathbf{B} \qquad (21.3.4)$$

The vorticity and streamfunction are related by Eq. 12.2.10:

$$-\omega_z = \nabla^2\psi \qquad (21.3.5)$$

The vorticity equation as simplified for a Stokes flow (Eq. 21.1.7) shows that ω_z is governed by the Laplace equation

$$\nabla^2 \omega_z = 0 \qquad (21.3.6)$$

Substituting Eq. 21.3.1 into Eq. 21.3.2 reveals that the streamfunction by itself is governed by the biharmonic equation:

$$\nabla^4 \psi = 0 \qquad (21.3.7)$$

The theory of harmonic functions applies to ω_z, and the theory of biharmonic functions applies to $\psi(x, y)$. This means that the maximum and minimum values of vorticity occur on the boundaries and there is a smooth profile on the interior.

Pressure–vorticity relation 21.1.4 is useful when the pressure must be found by integration:

$$\nabla p = -\mu \nabla \times \omega_z \qquad (21.3.8)$$

In rectangular coordinates x, y the components are

$$\partial_x p = -\mu \partial_y \omega_z = \mu \partial_y (\nabla^2 \psi)$$

$$\partial_y p = \mu \partial_x \omega_z = -\mu \partial_x (\nabla^2 \psi) \qquad (21.3.9)$$

Alternatively, the pressure also satisfies Laplace equation 21.1.5:

$$\nabla^2 p = 0 \qquad (21.3.10)$$

Therefore, $p(x, y)$ is a harmonic function. In fact, ω_z and p/μ are conjugate harmonic functions, so that the complex variable $\omega_z + ip/\mu$ is an analytic function of $z = x + iy$.

In the theory of biharmonic functions, one can show that the streamfunction $\psi(x, y)$ can be represented by two analytic functions, $f(z)$ and $g(z)$, where $z = x + iy$. A reference giving the derivation with a fluid mechanics viewpoint is Langlois (1964, p. 157). The result is

$$\psi(x, y) = -\mathcal{R}_e \, [\bar{z} f(z) + g(z)] \qquad (21.3.11)$$

Here $\bar{z}$ is the complex conjugate $x - iy$, and $\mathcal{R}_e$ indicates the real past. With this formulation the velocities, vorticity, and pressure are

$$u + iv = i[f(z) + z \, \overline{f'(z)} + \overline{g'(z)}] \qquad (21.3.12)$$

$$\omega + \frac{ip}{\mu} = 4f'(z)$$

As a sidelight, for ideal inviscid flows, $f(z) = 0$, $\psi = \mathcal{R}_e \, g(z)$, and $v + iu = g'(z)$.

For axisymmetric flows the situation is different. Let θ be the asymuthal coordinate in a rotational system q_1, q_2, θ with metric coefficients h_1, h_2, h_θ. All planes of constant θ have the same flow pattern. The vector potential has only one component:

$$g = \theta, \qquad \nabla g = i_\theta h_\theta, \qquad B_\theta = h_\theta \psi$$

$$\mathbf{v} = \nabla \times i_\theta B_\theta \qquad (21.3.13)$$

$$\omega_\theta = (\nabla^2 \mathbf{B})_\theta = -\nabla \times \nabla \times i_\theta B_\theta$$

The mathematics motivates the definition of the E^2 operator (Eq. 12.5.14):

$$E^2\ (\ ) \equiv \frac{h_1 h_2}{h_\theta} \left\{ \frac{\partial}{\partial q_1} \left[\frac{h_1 h_\theta}{h_2} \frac{\partial(\ )}{\partial q_1} \right] + \frac{\partial}{\partial q_2} \left[\frac{h_2 h_\theta}{h_1} \frac{\partial(\ )}{\partial q_2} \right] \right\} \tag{21.3.14}$$

With this definition Eq. 12.5.15 shows that the vorticity–streamfunction relation is

$$\omega_\theta = -h_\theta E^2 \psi \tag{21.3.15}$$

The Stokes flow vorticity equation $\nabla^2 \omega_\theta = 0$ reduces to

$$E^2 E^2(\psi) = 0 \tag{21.3.16}$$

This fourth-order differential equation governs Stokes flows in rotational coordinate systems. These relations are given for the common coordinate systems in Appendix D. The $E^2 E^2$ equation is found by inserting the $-\boldsymbol{\omega} = \nabla^2 \mathbf{B}$ relation into the given vorticity equation.

Other quantities of interest are related to the streamfunction. The velocity (Eq. 12.5.12) is

$$\mathbf{v} = \nabla \times \mathbf{B} = \mathbf{i}_1 h_2 h_\theta \frac{\partial \psi}{\partial q_2} - \mathbf{i}_2 h_1 h_\theta \frac{\partial \psi}{\partial q_1} \tag{21.3.17}$$

The pressure can be computed by integration from

$$dp = \frac{\partial p}{\partial q_1} dq_1 + \frac{\partial p}{\partial q_2} dq_2 \tag{21.3.18}$$

To employ this equation one finds the pressure derivatives from Eq. 12.5.16:

$$\nabla p = \mu \nabla^2 \mathbf{v} = -\mu \nabla \times \omega \tag{21.3.19}$$

$$\mathbf{i}_1 h_1 \frac{\partial p}{\partial q_2} - \mathbf{i}_2 h_2 \frac{\partial p}{\partial q_1} = \mu \left[\mathbf{i}_1 h_2 h_\theta \frac{\partial}{\partial q_2} (E^2 \psi) - \mathbf{i}_2 h_\theta h_1 \frac{\partial}{\partial q_1} (E^2 \psi) \right]$$

In light of these relations, much of the Stokes flow is centered around finding the streamfunction.

21.4   INTERNAL FLOWS: PLANE

There are a variety of interesting plane flow situations with different geometric conditions. If a closed region containing the fluid has prescribed wall motion, a cavity with a moving lid, for example, the Stokes flow is a unique result. If the walls are stationary, the fluid is stationary. Regions where the flow comes from infinity and returns to infinity, a channel of infinite length, for example, have a flow if there is a driving pressure difference. On the other hand, Stokes solutions for the streaming flow, a uniform stream at infinity flowing over a plane finite object, cannot meet the uniform flow boundary condition. This fact is called *Stokes's paradox*. The velocity grows logarithmically at large distances from the object. This is a manifestation of the fact that on infinite domains the Stokes problem is a singular perturbation of the Navier–Stokes problem.

In Section 14.7 we studied the Jeffrey–Hamel flow through a wedge with plane walls at angles $\pm \alpha$ that converge to the origin. The Stokes flow version of this problem, Re = 0, has an exact solution in r, θ coordinates:

$$\frac{v_r}{v_0} = \frac{\cos 2\alpha\eta - \cos 2\alpha}{1 - \cos 2\alpha} \tag{21.4.1}$$

Recall that the centerline velocity $v_0 = C_0/r$ and that $\eta = \theta/\alpha$. Velocity profiles for various wedge angles are shown in Fig. 21.4. It is interesting that for a line sink on a plane wall, $2\alpha = \pi$, the solution has zero wall shear stress. For convex walls with $2\alpha > \pi$, there is a reverse flow near the wall.

The equation for the pressure $p(r, \theta)$ (Eq. 14.8.3) becomes

$$C_p^{**} \equiv \frac{p_\infty - p}{\mu \, v_0/\alpha r} = \frac{-2\alpha \cos 2\alpha\eta}{1 - \cos 2\alpha} \tag{21.4.2}$$

while the normal viscous stress is

$$\frac{\tau_{rr}}{v_0\mu/\alpha r} = 2\alpha F(\eta) = 2\alpha \frac{\cos 2\alpha\eta - \cos 2\alpha}{1 - \cos 2\alpha} \tag{21.4.3}$$

These relations illustrate one of the typical characteristics of Stokes flows. The normal surface stress, $\tau_{rr} - p$, is not predominately the pressure but has a major contribution from the normal viscous stress. In all Stokes flows, $\partial_i(-p\delta_{ij} + \tau_{ij}) = 0$. At a solid wall the normal viscous stresses are always zero (for a Newtonian fluid); however, within the flow away from the walls, the normal viscous stress are comparable to the pressure.

$$\frac{\tau_{rr} - p + p_\infty}{v_0 \, \mu/\alpha r} = \frac{2\alpha \cos 2\alpha}{1 - \cos 2\alpha} \tag{21.4.4}$$

In this particular flow the normal surface stress happens to be constant everywhere.

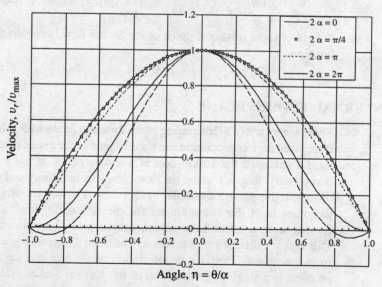

Figure 21.4   Velocity profiles for Stokes flow in a plane wedge.

As another example, consider the flow through a slot aperture in an infinite wall. The wall is located at $x = 0$, $y \geq h$ and the flow is driven by a pressure difference on either side of the wall. At $x \to -\infty$ the pressure is $p_0 - \Delta p/2$ and at $x \to +\infty$ the pressure is $p_0 + \Delta p/2$. The solution for the streamfunction may be represented as the sum of two harmonic functions in the form discussed in Eq. 21.3.11:

$$\psi(x, y) = -\mathscr{R}e\,[\bar{z}f(z) + g(z)]$$

$$\psi = -\mathscr{R}e\left(\frac{-2i}{\pi}\,\bar{z}\,\sqrt{z^2 + 1} + \frac{2i}{\pi}\,\text{asinh}\,z\right) \qquad (21.4.5)$$

$$f(z) = \frac{-2i}{\pi}\,\sqrt{z^2 + 1}$$

$$g(z) = \frac{2i}{\pi}\,a\,\sinh z$$

Here z is made nondimensional by h and ψ by $U_{ave}h$, with U_{ave} as the average velocity through the aperture. Figure 21.5 displays the streamlines. The flow is symmetric with

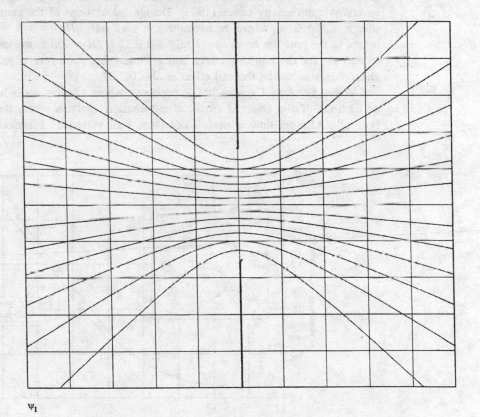

ψ_1

Figure 21.5 Streamlines for flow through a plane aperture.

no separation on the downstream side. Hasimoto (1958) published the solution to this problem and gave the velocity expressions as

$$\frac{u}{\Delta p/4\mu} = \mathscr{R}e \; \frac{z^2 + 1 - xz}{\sqrt{z^2 + 1}}$$

$$\frac{v}{\Delta p/4\mu} = \mathscr{R}e \left(-\frac{ixz}{\sqrt{z^2 + 1}} \right)$$

(21.4.6)

In the plane of the aperture, $x = 0$, $z = iy$, the velocity profile is the ellipse $u \sim y^2 + 1$. In his solution method, which borrows from elasticity theory, Hasimoto relates the Stokes flow to an ideal inviscid flow through a conjugate wall (a vertical flat plate in the case of a slot aperture). He also presents results for an elliptical aperture and an infinite set of slits.

Next consider the flow into a *Borda mouthpiece*. The geometry is a plane channel formed from infinitely thin walls a width H apart and extending from $x \geq 0$. The remainder of the plane outside the channel is its source of fluid. The entrance effect for flow into a reentrant channel shows that viscous effects damp the flow to the Poiseuille profile in a short distance. An approximate calculation was given by Dean (1951) and an analytic answer by Green (1943). Dean's calculations of the centerline pressure are shown in Fig. 21.6, where the asymptote is $p/(2\,\mu U_{max}/h^2) = x/h + 0.64$. Hence, with regard to the pressure drop, one should add $0.32\,H$ ($H = 2h$) to the length of the channel to account for the entrance effect. Since Stokes flows are reversible, the flow out of a channel is similar and the exit effect is also $0.32H$.

There are several approaches to problems where channel walls have various shapes or motions. If the effect is small, a perturbation analysis where the base flow is the Poiseuille channel flow is useful. For large wall variations Fraenkel (1962) suggested

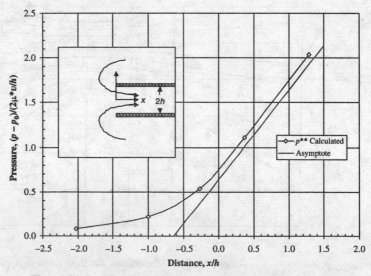

Figure 21.6   Pressure along the centerline of a plane entrance.

using the Jeffrey–Hamel wedge flow as a local approximation. The idea was developed further by Langlois (1964). More sophisticated computational approaches have appeared using boundary integral methods (see, e.g., Pozrikidis, 1992). Figure 21.7 gives the streamline pattern for the upper half of a channel with a symmetric sinusoidal wavy wall. Nahas (1989) performed these calculations. He used the ψ–ω finite-difference scheme in a coordinate system transformed so that the walls are flat, and he clustered the grid near the walls. An interesting feature is the recirculating eddy trapped in the trough of the wall under certain circumstances. Such recirculating zones were first described by Dean (1944) in the shear flow over a wall with an asymmetric cusp shape. As the trough becomes deeper, a second eddy of opposite rotational sense appears. The appearance of a sequence of eddies is a general phenomenon called *Moffatt vortices*. The occurrence of eddies as a function of the wall amplitude and wavelength is given in Fig. 21.8a. The increase in pressure drop (per wavelength) compared to the pressure drop in a straight channel of the same average width is displayed in Fig. 21.8b. Detailed results for channels with one wavy wall and a stationary or moving flat wall are presented in Pozrikidis (1987).

Another flow of interest is the internal flow between two rotating circular cylinders. When the cylinders are coaxial, this is the Couette flow problem. Several authors have presented the case of eccentric cylinders. Ballal and Rivlin (1976) solve the general situation where both inner and outer cylinders are rotating. Their reference to previous work is complete. A reference in the engineering literature is Kamal (1966) and, in the lubrication texts, Tipei (1962). The problem is solved in bipolar coordinates (discussed in Section 12.5) When the gap between the cylinders becomes small, this is the journal-bearing problem. In that case the pressure distribution is a quantity of engineering interest. This is discussed further in Chapter 22. An example of a wide-gap annulus flow is shown in Fig. 21.9. Here both inner and outer cylinders are rotating and there are four regions of closed streamlines. Note that the internal stagnation points have streamlines meeting at an angle.

A closely related problem is the flow engendered by a rotating cylinder of radius R a height X_0 above a plane stationary wall. Let the plane of the flow be described by cylindrical bipolar coordinates as shown in Fig. 12.7. Recall from Section 12.5 that bipolar coordinates ξ, η with the scale parameter c are described by

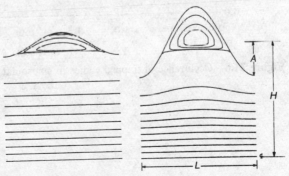

Figure 21.7 Streamlines in the upper half-plane of a channel with sinusoidal wavy walls. Computed by Nahas (1989).

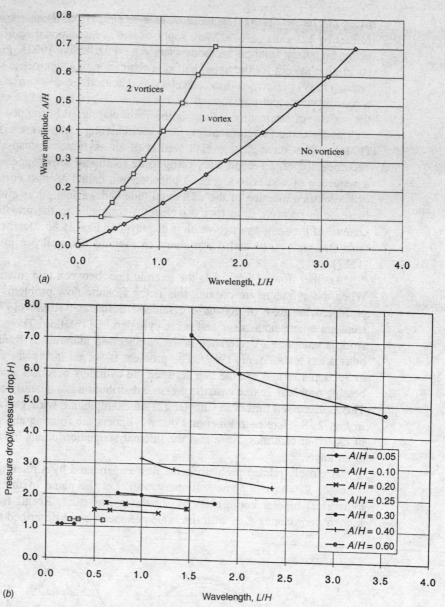

Figure 21.8 Occurrence of trapped eddies in sinusoidal channel. Computed by Nahas (1989).

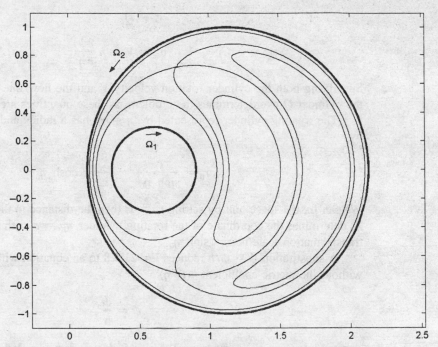

Figure 21.9   Flow in an eccentric annulus computed by Qu (2004) using the method of Ballal and Rivlin (1976). $R_2/R_1 = 0.3$, eccentricity $= 0.75$, $\Omega_2/\Omega_1 = 20$. Note the internal stagnation points with skewed streamlines.

$$x + iy = ic \cot(\xi + i\eta)$$

$$x = \frac{c \sinh \eta}{\cosh \eta - \cos \xi}, \qquad y = \frac{c \sin \xi}{\cosh \eta - \cos \xi} \qquad (21.4.7)$$

$$h_1 = h_2 = h = \frac{\cosh \eta - \cos \xi}{c}, \qquad h_3 = 1$$

A vertical wall along the y-axis is the coordinate $\eta = 0$ and the rotating cylinder $\eta = \eta_0$. For such a system the metric coefficients are $h_3 = 1$ and $h_1 = h_2 = h$. The equation governing the streamfunction is

$$0 = \nabla^2 \nabla^2 \psi = E^2 E^2 \psi = \left(\frac{\partial^2}{\partial \xi^2} + \frac{\partial^2}{\partial \eta^2} \right) \left[h^2 \left(\frac{\partial^2 \psi}{\partial \xi^2} + \frac{\partial^2 \psi}{\partial \eta^2} \right) \right] \qquad (21.4.8)$$

Appropriate boundary conditions are on the stationary wall, $\eta = 0$:

$$\psi = 0$$

$$v_\eta = 0 = h \frac{\partial \psi}{\partial \eta} \qquad (21.4.9)$$

and on the rotating cylinder, $\eta = \eta_0$:

$$\psi = Q$$

$$v_\eta = V = h\, \frac{\partial \psi}{\partial \eta} \tag{21.4.10}$$

Specifying both the cylinder rotation velocity V and the flow rate between the wall and the cylinder Q overdetermines the problem, as these quantities are actually related.

The rotating cylinder represented by $\eta = \eta_0$ has a radius and center location given by

$$r_0 = \frac{c}{\sinh \eta_0}, \qquad \frac{X_c}{r_0} = \cosh \eta_0 \tag{21.4.11}$$

We can fix the space unit by setting $r_0 = 1$: then the distance to the center from the wall X_c determines the coordinate of the rotating cylinder, $\eta_0 = a \cosh X_c$, and the coordinate transformation scale is $c = \sinh \eta_0$.

A substitution $\psi = \phi/h$ reduces Eq. 21.4.8 to an equation with constant coefficients without the metric coefficient $h(\xi, \eta)$:

$$\psi = \frac{\phi}{h}$$

$$0 = \frac{\partial^4 \phi}{\partial \xi^4} + 2\frac{\partial^4 \phi}{\partial \xi^2\, \partial \eta^2} + \frac{\partial^4 \phi}{\partial \eta^4} - 2\frac{\partial^2 \phi}{\partial \xi^2} + 2\frac{\partial^2 \phi}{\partial \eta^2} + \phi \tag{21.4.12}$$

This remarkable result is unique to bipolar coordinates. It appears in Jeffrey (1922) and perhaps earlier. The complete solution, which is periodic in ξ, is

$$\frac{\psi}{Q} = \frac{2VR/Q}{\cosh \eta - \cos\xi} [K_1 \sinh \eta + K_2 \cosh \eta + K_3\, \eta \sinh \eta + K_4\, \eta \cosh \eta$$

$$+ (L_1 + L_2\eta + L_3 \sinh 2\eta + L_4 \cosh 2\eta) \cos \xi] \tag{21.4.13}$$

For the present problem of a cylinder rotating above a wall, the coefficients that satisfy the boundary conditions are

$$K_1 = \frac{\cosh \eta_0}{\sinh \eta_0}, \qquad L_1 = \tfrac{1}{2}$$

$$K_2 = 0, \qquad L_2 = K_1$$

$$K_3 = 0, \qquad L_3 = -\frac{K_1}{2} \tag{21.4.14}$$

$$K_4 = -K_1, \qquad L_4 = -L_1$$

The connection between the cylinder rotation velocity V and the flow rate Q is found by requiring that the vorticity (or pressure) be periodic around the cylinder ($L_2 = -K_4$). This gives

$$\frac{VR}{Q} = \frac{\sinh \eta_0}{2(\eta_0 \cosh \eta_0 - \sinh \eta_0)} \tag{21.4.15}$$

A typical solution is shown in Fig. 21.10. A portion of the fluid near the cylinder rotates with the cylinder, while in the far field there is a flow toward the cylinder in one half-plane and away from the cylinder in the other half-plane. The streamline separating these flows intersects the y-axis at $y_s/R = c/R = \pm \sinh \eta_0$.

21.5   INTERNAL FLOWS: THREE-DIMENSIONAL AND AXISYMMETRIC

Flow in a tube with straight, parallel streamlines, but of arbitrary cross section, was discussed in Sections 11.1 to 11.3. These flows are driven by a pressure gradient that is in equilibrium with the viscous shear stresses; $dp/dz = \mu \nabla^2 v_z$. Inertia effects are absent

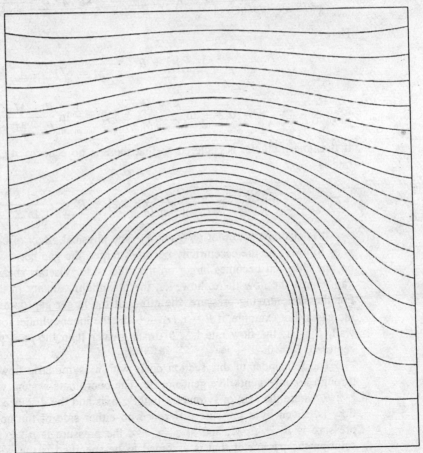

Figure 21.10   Streamline pattern for flow caused by a circular cylinder rotating above a stationary wall.

(as well as the Reynolds number) because the particles are never accelerated in any direction. In essence, they are a special class of Stokes flows. The normal viscous stresses, τ_{xx}, τ_{yy}, and τ_{zz}, which are important in any three-dimensional Stokes flow, are zero because the flow pattern has parallel streamlines.

An interesting example of a unidirectional flow is the pressure-driven flow in an eccentric annulus formed by a cylinder of radius r_0 inside a cylinder of radius r_1. The radius ratio is $R = r_0/r_1$ and the pressure gradient dp/dz is constant. The distance between the cylinder centers, the eccentricity, is e with a value $E = e/(r_1 - r_0)$ compared to the average gap or $B = e/r_1$ compared to the outer cylinder. As in Section 11.1 the velocity variable is transformed, $v_z = f(x, y) + C(x^2 + y^2)$, with the result that $f(x, y)$ satisfies the Laplace equation. The exact velocity profile is found by a conformal transformation of the region. The following form of the flow rate versus pressure drop relation below was first given by Piercy et al. (1933):

$$\frac{Q}{(\pi/8\mu)(-dp/dz)} = 1 - R^4 - \frac{4B^2M^2}{\beta - \alpha} - 8B^2M^2 \sum_{n=1}^{\infty} \frac{n \exp[-n(\beta + \alpha)]}{\sinh[n(\beta - \alpha)]} \quad (21.5.1)$$

Here

$$F = \frac{1 - R^2 + B^2}{2B}, \qquad M = \sqrt{F^2 - 1}$$

$$\alpha = \frac{1}{2} \ln \frac{F + M}{F - M}, \qquad \beta = \frac{1}{2} \ln \frac{F + M - B}{F - M - B} \quad (21.5.2)$$

If the inner cylinder is centered so that there is no eccentricity, the corresponding flow rate is

$$\frac{Q_e}{(\pi/8\mu)(-dp/dz)} = 1 - R^4 + \frac{(1 - R^2)^2}{\ln R} \quad (21.5.3)$$

It is customary to plot $Q/Q_e(E; R)$. The physical effect of changing the eccentricity is as follows. As the eccentricity becomes larger, the gap between the cylinders narrows on one side and becomes larger on the other side. Viscous shear stresses in the narrow gap retards the flow there; however, the maximum velocity in the larger gap increases. For the same driving pressure, the effect of the larger gap dominates and the flow rate increases. For example, if $R = r_0/r_1 = \frac{1}{2}$ and the inner cylinder touches the outer cylinder wall, $B = 1$, the flow rate is 2.5 times greater than the case where the cylinders are centered, $B = 0$.

The remainder of this section deals with axisymmetric flows. The first is the flow through a convergent–divergent nozzle. The coordinate system will be a rotated system z, r, θ, where the axis of symmetry is the z-axis and the distance from this axis is r. The flow is driven by a pressure difference on either side of the nozzle. As $z \Rightarrow -\infty$, the pressure is $p_0 - \Delta p/2$, and at $z \Rightarrow +\infty$, the pressure is $p_0 + \Delta p/2$. However, in the solution the parameter that is assumed to be specified is the volume flow rate Q. The book of Happel and Brenner (1983) contains complete details of the solution without reference to other articles. It is possible that their presentation is the original publication of this solution.

The problem is transformed into oblate–spherodial coordinates ξ, η, θ as shown in Fig. 21.11 The coordinate transformation is

$$z + ir = c \sinh(\xi + i\eta) \qquad (21.5.4)$$

Here the ranges are $0 \le \xi \le \infty$, $0 \le \eta \le \pi$, and $0 \le \theta \le 2\pi$. Coordinate lines where ξ is constant are ellipses. The transformation parameter $c > 0$ (distance scale unit) is the focal point of the ellipses. A line of constant η is a hyperbola given by

$$-\frac{z^2}{c^2 \cos^2 \eta} + \frac{r^2}{c^2 \sin^2 \eta} = 1 \qquad (21.5.5)$$

Any chosen value of $\eta = \eta_0$ is the wall of the tube. The throat of the nozzle is

$$r_0 = c \sin \eta_0 \qquad (21.5.6)$$

The figure shows r_0/c for $\eta_0 = \pi/3$. The shape of the nozzle depends on the value of η_0; the value $\eta_0 = 0$ is a straight tube and the value $\eta_0 = \pi/2$ is an orifice in a flat wall.

A Stokes flow has a streamfunction that satisfies the equation $E^2 E^2 \psi = 0$ (Eq. 12.5.14). Boundary conditions on the wall, $\eta = \eta_0$, require that the streamfunction equal the volume flow rate, $\psi = Q/2\pi$ and that the no-slip condition $v_\xi \sim d\psi/d\eta = 0$ be satisfied. A separation of variables solution for ψ depends only on η and is most easily represented in variables that are transformed by the relations

$$\lambda = \sinh \xi, \qquad \zeta = \cos \eta \qquad (21.5.7)$$

Happel and Brenner (1983) give the streamfunction relation as

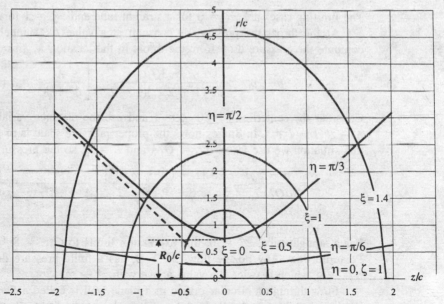

Figure 21.11 Oblate spheroidal coordinates for flow through a tube with hyperbolic w.

$$\psi = \frac{Q}{2\pi} \frac{(1 - 3\zeta_0^2) - \zeta(\zeta^2 - 3\zeta_0^2)}{(1 + 2\zeta_0)(1 - 2\zeta_0)^2} \qquad (21.5.8)$$

The wall coordinate $\zeta_0 = \cos\eta_0$ is now the nozzle shape parameter. The radius of the throat is also a shape parameter since

$$\mathscr{R} \equiv \frac{r_0}{c} = (1 - \zeta_0^2)^{1/2} \qquad (21.5.9)$$

Thus, the throat area is $\pi r_0^2 = c^2(1 - \zeta_0^2)$.

Velocities can be computed using the formulas of Section 12.5. The maximum velocity occurs on the centerline at the throat. It is related to the shape parameter as follows:

$$\frac{v_{max}}{Q/A} = \frac{3}{2} \frac{(1 + \zeta_0)^{1/2}}{1 + 2\zeta_0} \qquad (21.5.10)$$

The velocity normalized with the maximum velocity is

$$\frac{v_\xi}{v_{max}} = \frac{\zeta_0^2 - \zeta^2}{(\lambda^2 + \zeta^2)(1 + \lambda^2)(\zeta_0^2 - 1)} \qquad (21.5.11)$$

The velocity profile across the throat, $\lambda = 0$, is best displayed using the radial coordinate

$$r^* = \frac{r}{r_0} \qquad (21.5.12)$$

The profile is

$$\frac{v_\xi}{v_{max}} = \frac{1 - r^{*2}}{(1 - \mathscr{R}^2 r^{*2})^{1/2}} \qquad (21.5.13)$$

The limiting cases are $\mathscr{R} = 0$ for a straight tube and $\mathscr{R} = 1$ for an orifice.

At the throat the pressure is constant at a value p_0. Happel and Brenner (1983) compute the pressure drop from the throat to the location λ, ζ as

$$p - p_0 = \frac{-3Q\mu}{\pi c^3(1 + 2\zeta_0^2)(1 - \zeta_0)^2} \left[\frac{\lambda}{\zeta^2 + \lambda^2} + a \tan(\lambda) \right] \qquad (21.5.14)$$

Consider the centerline $r = 0$, $\zeta = 1$ and use the distance variable $z^* = z/r_0$ so that $\lambda = z^*(1 - \zeta_0^2)^{1/2}$. In Stokes flows the proper pressure scale is of the form $\mu\, U_0/L$. For this situation we use $U_0 = v_{ave} = Q/A$ and $L = r_0$, so the pressure coefficient is

$$C_p^{**} = \frac{p - p_0}{\mu Q/\pi r_0^2} = \frac{-3\,[1 + (1 - \mathscr{R}^2)^{1/2}]}{3 - 2\mathscr{R}^2} \left[\frac{z^*}{1 + \mathscr{R}^2 z^{*2}} + \frac{1}{\mathscr{R}} a \tan(\mathscr{R}\, z^*) \right]$$

$$(21.5.15)$$

For a straight tube, $\mathscr{R} = 0$, this expression limits to $C_p^{**} = 8z^*$, which is correct for Poisuille flow. Any nozzle flow, $\mathscr{R} > 0$, has a finite pressure drop from $z = -\infty$ to $z = +\infty$, which is twice the value above with $z^* \to \infty$.

Flow through a circular orifice in a plane wall is called a *Sampson* (1891) *flow*, as he presented the first detailed solution. Here we can consider a Sampson flow as a special case of the hyperbolic nozzle flow with $\mathcal{R} = r_0/c = 1$ ($\zeta_0 = 0$). The result for the streamfunction is (Eq. 21.5.8 with $\zeta_0 = 0$)

$$\psi = \frac{Q}{2\pi}(1 - \zeta^3) = \frac{Q}{2\pi}(1 - \cos^3\eta) \qquad (21.5.16)$$

The velocity profile across the orifice is (Eq. 21.5.13 with $\mathcal{R} = 1$)

$$\frac{v_\xi}{v_{max}} = (1 - r^{*2})^{1/2} \qquad (21.5.17)$$

The pressure drop from the orifice to infinity is (Eq. 21.5.15 with $\mathcal{R} = 1$)

$$C_p^{**}(\infty) = \frac{p_\infty - p_0}{\mu Q/\pi r_0^2} = \frac{-3\pi}{2} \qquad (21.5.18)$$

The total pressure drop across the orifice is $\Delta p = 3\mu Q/r_0^2$.

Finally, a comment on flow through tubes with a sinusoidal variation in diameter. The flow has the same character as the flow in a channel with wavy walls. If the wave height becomes large enough, Moffatt vortices appear in the troughs. Some typical references here are the analyses of Deiber and Showalter (1979) and Ralph (1987).

21.6 LOCAL FLOWS: PLANE (MOFFATT VORTICES)

For the purposes of mathematical analysis we idealize bodies to have sharp edges and corners. The fact that the velocity on the wall is zero means that there is a small neighborhood near the corner where convection effects are negligible and the Navier–Stokes equations simplify to the Stokes form. If r is the distance from the corner and U is a characteristic velocity, the creeping flow equations are valid in some region where Ur/ν is small. To be more precise, one must examine the ratio of convective to diffusion effects in each problem. It is convenient in plane flows to use the streamfunction in polar coordinates. Recall that ψ satisfies the biharmonic equation:

$$\nabla^4\psi = 0 \qquad (21.6.1)$$

The vorticity equation is

$$\nabla^2\psi = -\omega$$

and the velocity components are

$$v_r = \frac{1}{r}\frac{\partial\psi}{\partial\theta}, \qquad v_\theta = -\frac{\partial\psi}{\partial r}$$

In solving corner flow problems, one seeks separation-of-variables solutions. The solutions appropriate for these problems have the following forms [Michael and O'Neil (1977); Hasimoto and Samo (1980)]. For n any number except 0, -1, or $+1$,

$$\psi(r, \theta) = r^{n+1}[A\cos(n + 1)\theta + B\sin(n + 1)\theta + C\cos(n - 1)\theta + D\sin(n - 1)\theta]$$

while for the special cases $n = -1$, 0, and $+1$,

$$\psi(r, \theta) = A \cos 2\theta + B \sin 2\theta + C\theta + D \qquad (n = -1)$$

$$\psi(r, \theta) = r(A \cos \theta + B \sin \theta + C\theta \cos \theta + D\theta \sin \theta) \qquad (n = 0) \qquad (21.6.2)$$

$$\psi(r, \theta) = r^2(A \cos 2\theta + B \sin 2\theta + C\theta + D) \qquad (n = 1)$$

Because the problem is linear, solutions may be superimposed.

An interesting example is the flow in a corner where a stationary wall and a moving wall intersect. Figure 21.12 gives the geometry where the wall along the x axis is moving at speed U and the stationary wall is at an arbitrary angle α. Boundary conditions are

$$\psi(r, \theta = 0) = 0, \qquad \psi(r, \theta = \alpha) = 0$$

$$v_r(r, \theta = 0) = U = \frac{1}{r} \frac{\partial \psi}{\partial \theta}, \qquad v_r(r, \theta = \alpha) = 0 = \frac{1}{r} \frac{\partial \psi}{\partial \theta}$$

The solution from Eq. 21.6.2 with $n = 0$ will satisfy these conditions. After some algebra to solve four linear equations for the coefficients, the result is

$$\psi(r, \theta) = \frac{-Ur}{\sin^2\alpha - \alpha^2} [\alpha^2 \sin \theta - (\sin^2\alpha)\theta \cos \theta + (\sin \alpha \cos \alpha - \alpha)\theta \sin \theta]$$

$$(21.6.3)$$

As shown in the first figure, the flow is the deposition of a fluid on a moving plane. Since Stokes flows are reversible, the same streamline pattern results when U is reversed. Now, the upper wall is scraping across the moving wall. This could also represent a window wiper or a piston moving into a cylinder. One important result is that the shear stress at the origin becomes infinite as $\tau_{r\theta} \sim 1/r$. The sliding force is the integral of $\tau_{r\theta}$ over r and is infinite when the limit $r = 0$ is inserted. The origin of this nonphysical result is the discontinuity in the boundary condition at $r = 0$; that is, v_r $(r \Rightarrow 0, \theta = 0)$ $= U$ and $v_r(r \Rightarrow 0, \theta = \alpha) = 0$. The remedy is to solve another problem that allows for a finite but small gap at the junction.

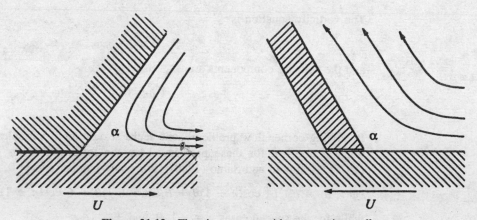

Figure 21.12 Flow in a corner with one moving wall.

Other flows of this type that have been solved include symmetric walls swinging about a pivot at $r = 0$, and a source or sink located at the apex of two walls meeting at an angle. This latter flow is a special case of the Jeffrey–Hamel flow and was discussed in Section 21.4.

To continue, let us consider corners with stationary solid walls. In general, the solutions in Eq. 21.6.2 can be divided into symmetric and antisymmetric functions with respect to the centerline of the corner. Several examples are shown in Fig. 21.13. First, consider the flat wall where the separating streamline leaves at the angle α. Michael and O'Neil (1977) rule out all solutions of Eq. 21.6.2 for $n \le 0$ because they cause infinite

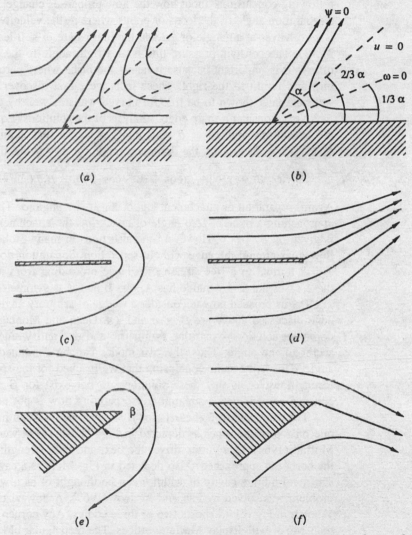

Figure 21.13 (a, b) Separation from a wall; (c, d) flow around and separation from a sharp cusp edge; (e, f) flow around and separation from a sharp corner.

point forces at $r = 0$. Turning to the $n = 1$ equation and applying the no-slip conditions leaves $\psi \sim Ar^2 \cos 2\theta$. This represents a uniform shear that does not separate. Applying the boundary conditions to the general form in Eq. 21.6.2 reveals that $n = 2, 3, 4, \ldots$ are suitable. The strongest solution $n = 2$ can be written with two constants:

$$\psi_2(r, \theta) = r^2[A(\cos 3\theta - \cos \theta) + B(\sin 3\theta - 3 \sin \theta)] \qquad (21.6.4)$$

Thus, the solution can accommodate any angle or separation α. The value of α is a function of A/B. The exact angle is determined by the flow outside the region of the Stokes flow and depends on the global structure of that flow.

Analysis of the flow in the region of separation from a plane wall leads to the following conclusions about how the flow properties change. If the global flow produces a separation angle α, the locus of points where u (the velocity component along the wall) is zero leaves at an angle of $\frac{2}{3}\alpha$ and the line where $\omega = 0$ leaves at an angle of $\frac{1}{3}\alpha$ (Fig. 21.13). The constant-pressure line is at a right angle to the vorticity line. The location of $u = 0$ is important because it marks the place where particles coming from the right turn and return to the right. These facts were first discovered by Oswatitsch for a flat wall and later shown to be true for curved walls as well by O'Brian (1977).

Next, consider a sharp edge. Analysis of the solutions (Eq. 21.6.2) and no-slip boundary conditions applied at $\theta = 0$ and 2π shows that admissible solutions have $n = \frac{1}{2}, 1, \frac{3}{2}, 2, \frac{5}{2}, 3, \frac{7}{2}, \ldots$. the dominant mode for $n = \frac{1}{2}$ has the solution

$$\psi_{1/2}(r, \theta) = r^{3/2}[A_{1/2}(\cos \tfrac{3}{2} \theta - \cos \tfrac{1}{2} \theta) - B_{1/2}(\sin \tfrac{3}{2} \theta - 3 \sin \tfrac{1}{2} \theta)] \quad (21.6.5)$$

Again, separation or attachment can occur at any angle α. The case of a uniform stream approaching a plate at zero angle of attack has the attachment streamline at $\alpha = \pi$ and is given by $B_{1/2} = 0$. However, one also finds in many Stokes flow solutions where the flow goes around the edge without separation. Separation does not occur at the edge of a disk normal to a free stream or a fence protruding from a wall into a shear flow. In these cases the $n = \frac{1}{2}$ mode has $A_{1/2} = 0$ and ψ is symmetric about $\theta = \pi$.

Let us proceed now to consider a wedge of arbitrary angle β. The flat wall and sharp edge discussed above are $\beta = \pi$ and 2π. Dean and Montagnon (1949) found that two dominant solutions exist: one symmetric and one antisymmetric with respect to the bisector of the angle. Thus, the two modes can be combined to give separation at any angle. This is the same conclusion that we reached for the special cases above. The new result, however, is that these solutions do not exist for $\beta < \beta^* = 146.3°$. For these concave corner flows a streaming or separating flow is not possible.

The flow pattern that exists for $\beta < \beta^*$ consists of an infinite sequence of vortices, one on top of the other as depicted in Fig. 21.14. These were predicted analytically by Moffatt (1964). One vortex drives the next and their strength decreases exponentially as the corner is approached. Also depicted in Fig. 21.14 is a cavity driven by a moving lid. The semi-infinite cavity of width h can be thought of as a wedge of angle $\beta = 0$. This problem was solved by Pan and Acrivos (1967). A flow-visualization experiment of the V notch in Fig. 21.15 shows two or three eddies. Any corner with an included angle less than 146.3° will display Moffatt vortices. The rectangular block in Fig. 21.1 has an initial angle with the wall of $\beta = \pi/2 < \beta^*$, and thus the vortex we see in the flow visualization is the first of the sequence.

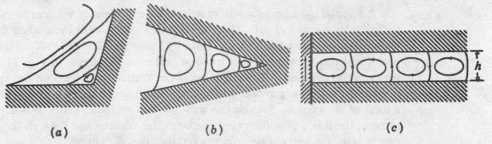

Figure 21.14   Moffatt vortices (*a, b*) in corners; (*c*) in semi-infinite driven cavity.

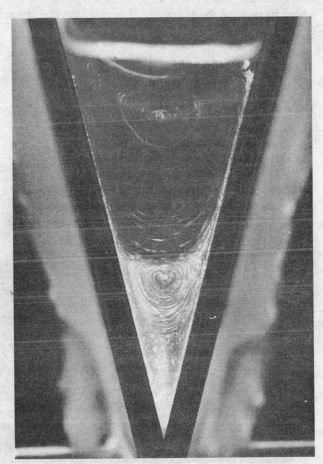

Figure 21.15   Moffatt vortices formed by rolling a cylinder over a V-shaped notch. The Reynolds number is 0.17. A 90-min exposure was required for this photograph. From Taneda (1979). Reprinted with permission.

A circular cylinder on a wall must also have systems of vortices in the corners where the cylinder meets the wall. There are vortices on the wall even when the cylinder is a slight distance above the wall, as shown by Davis and O'Neil (1977). Taneda (1979) also performed this experiment and the flow pattern is as shown in Fig. 21.16. As the gap between the cylinder is decreased, two more vortices will form on the cylinder. Continuing to decrease the gap will produce two additional vortices on the wall. There will be a total of six vortices, four on the wall and two on the cylinder. For any gap not equal to zero, there is a flow that winds between the vortices and through the gap. When the gap is zero, the vortices become stacked into the Moffatt set.

21.7   LOCAL FLOWS: AXISYMMETRIC

Axisymmetric flows allow us to use a streamfunction in spherical coordinates r, θ, ϕ, where because of the symmetry $\psi = \psi(r, \theta)$. The streamfunction equation $0 = \nabla^2 \omega = E^2 E^2(\psi)$ is (see Eq. 12.5.19)

$$E^2 E^2 \psi = \left[\frac{\partial^2}{\partial r^2} + \frac{\sin \theta}{r^2} \frac{\partial}{\partial \theta} \left(\frac{1}{\sin \theta} \frac{\partial}{\partial \theta} \right) \right]^2 \psi = 0 \qquad (21.7.1)$$

The velocity components are related to the spherical streamfunction by

Figure 21.16   Re = 0.011 shear flow over a cylinder near a wall. Vortices form on the upstream and downstream sides. Photograph reprinted with permission from Taneda (1979).

$$v_r = \frac{1}{r^2 \sin\theta}\frac{\partial\psi}{\partial\theta}, \qquad v_\theta = -\frac{1}{r\sin\theta}\frac{\partial\psi}{\partial r} \qquad (21.7.2)$$

The details of an analysis of Eq. 21.1.1 employing separation of variables are in Leal (1992).

The first result we study is the flow into or out of a cone of angle θ_0. The flow rate $Q = 2\pi\psi_0$ is a parameter in the solution. The velocity is

$$v_r = \frac{3Q}{2\pi r^2}\frac{\cos^2\theta - \cos^2\theta_0}{(1 + 2\cos\theta_0)(1 - \cos\theta_0)^2}$$

The corresponding pressure varies as $1/r^3$:

$$\frac{p - p_\infty}{\mu Q} = -\frac{1 - 3\cos^2\theta}{\pi r^3}$$

These expressions are not valid near the origin, where the velocities are high and a Stokes approximation is invalid.

It was only recently that the problem of flow from a reservoir into a tube of finite length was solved by Dagan et al. (1982). The results show that the Poiseuille velocity profile is established, within 1.5%, after the flow proceeds only one-half the orifice radius into the tube; in other words, $L_{\text{entrance}}/D = \frac{1}{4}$. Thus, after a very short distance the length of the tube becomes immaterial as the Poiseuille profile continues. Because Stokes flows are reversible, the solution also represents the flow from a tube into a reservoir. Therefore, one also has a solution for the flow from one reservoir to another through a tube or orifice of finite length. With regard to the pressure drop, it turns out that the pressure drop from a Sampson flow added to the Poiseuille pressure drop gives an approximation to the exact answer to within 1%:

$$\frac{p_1 - p_2}{\mu Q / r_0^3} = 3 + \frac{16L}{\pi r_0} \qquad (21.7.3)$$

Among other things, this problem has application to transport and filtering processes in synthetic membranes.

If a constriction such as a thin orifice is in a round tube, it causes an extra pressure drop, which has been computed by Davis (1991). Results adapted from this paper are shown in Fig. 21.17. The length L_e is the length of pipe that has the same pressure drop as the extra pressure drop caused by the orifice. A contraction ratio of 0.7 causes a pressure drop equal to a pipe one diameter in length.

The fact that Moffatt vortices form in cracks and cavities lead workers to inquire about the effect of "fluid" walls. Consider the pipe or channel shown in Fig. 21.18. The barriers of height h are spaced a distance ℓ apart. Small vortices occupy each cavity and if the cavity is deep enough a series of Moffatt vortices would exist. Essentially, the walls of a pipe of diameter d *would* be moving fluid. There is a slight advantage in that, for the same pressure drop, the flow in the tube with fluid walls is greater than that in a Poiseuille flow in a tube of diameter d. However, there is no optimum configuration (a pipe of diameter D has less pressure drop). As one increases ℓ, the situation becomes a

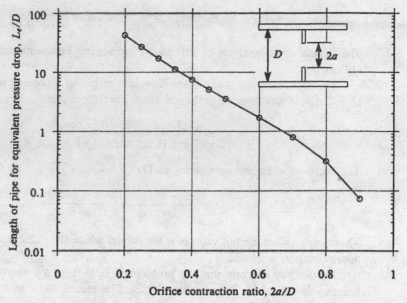

Figure 21.17 Pressure drop of an orifice in a pipe.

tube with widely spaced orifices and the pressure drop approaches that in a smooth pipe of diameter D. The other limit, $\ell = 0$, is a smooth pipe of diameter d.

A more fundamental approach is to consider a "fluid" wall in an unbounded shear flow. The configuration is a wall with cavities of height h, length ℓ, in a shear flow, characterized by gradient u_0/ℓ. Davis (1993) solved this problem and introduced the concept of a slip velocity (Fig. 21.18). Far away from the wall the velocity profile asymptotes to

$$u \sim \frac{u_0}{h} y + u_{\text{slip}} \qquad (21.7.4)$$

Here the slip velocity u_{slip}/u_0 is a function of ℓ/h. The concept is that the boundary condition for such a wall is equivalent to a slip boundary (Section 6.4). That is,

$$u_{\text{slip}} = L_{\text{slip}} \left. \frac{du}{dy} \right]_{\text{wall}} \qquad (21.7.5)$$

Davis approximated his exact numerical calculations for $\ell/h < 2$ by $L_{\text{slip}} = 0.17\ell$.

One should note that the theory we are discussing is valid for low Reynolds numbers. In this instance the height of the cavity is the appropriate length and the velocity is that determined from the wall shear:

$$\text{Re} = \frac{u_0 h}{\nu} = \frac{h^2}{\nu} \left. \frac{du}{dy} \right]_{\text{wall}} \ll 1$$

Solutions of cavity configurations have been extended to include large periodic barriers in channels and pipes.

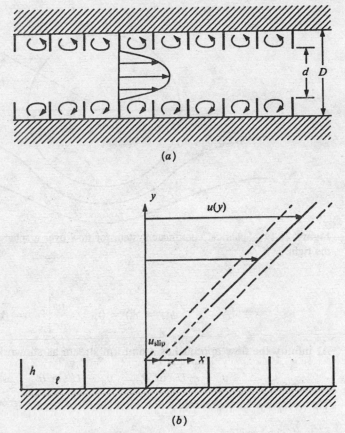

Figure 21.18   Walls with trapped vortices: (a) channel flow; (b) slip velocity for shear flow over a wall with cavities $h \times 1$.

21.8   EXTERNAL FLOW: SPHERE IN A UNIFORM STREAM

The streaming motion of a flow over a body when the Reynolds number becomes small has some interesting but complicated characteristics. At infinity the uniform stream has no vorticity, but as $\mathrm{Re} \equiv U2r_0/\nu \to 0$, viscous diffusion is dominant and sends vorticity very far from the body. The analysis of these flows produces a singular perturbation problem where the singularity is at infinity. We will find that the consequence of the singular behavior is severe for two-dimensional flows but relatively benign in three-dimensional flows.

The best plan is to begin with the study of streaming flow over a sphere. The streamfunction is governed by the fourth-order equation given previously as Eq. 21.7.1. Geometry and nomenclature are depicted in Fig. 21.19. Recall that the velocity components are related to ψ by Eq. 21.7.2:

$$v_r = \frac{1}{r^2 \sin \theta} \frac{\partial \psi}{\partial \theta}, \qquad v_\theta = -\frac{1}{r \sin \theta} \frac{\partial \psi}{\partial r} \qquad (21.8.1)$$

From these relations one sees that the no-slip condition at the surface is satisfied by

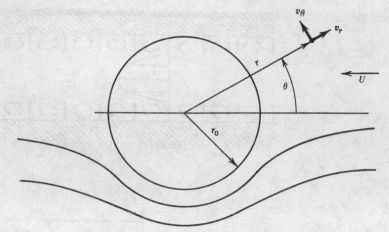

Figure 21.19 Spherical coordinate system for flow over a sphere. The free stream comes from the right.

$$\psi(r = r_0) = 0, \qquad \left. \frac{\partial \psi}{\partial r} \right|_{r=r_0} = 0 \tag{21.8.2}$$

At infinity the flow approaches a uniform stream as shown in Fig. 21.19:

$$v_r \sim -U \cos \theta, \qquad v_\theta \sim U \sin \theta \qquad \text{as} \quad r \to \infty \tag{21.8.3}$$

The corresponding streamfunction for a uniform stream is

$$\psi \sim -\frac{r^2}{2} U \sin^2 \theta \qquad \text{as} \quad r \to \infty \tag{21.8.4}$$

The mathematical problem consisting of Eq. 21.7.1, $E^2 E^2 \psi = 0$, and boundary conditions 21.8.3 and 21.8.4 can be solved by separation of variables. Let us assume that the stream-function is of the form

$$\frac{\psi}{r_0^2 U} = \sin^2 \theta \, F\!\left(\frac{r}{r_0}\right) \tag{21.8.5}$$

This has the same θ dependence as the free-stream boundary condition 21.8.4. The $\sin^2\theta$ term is all that is needed for sphere problems. Objects with other shapes would need additional terms. See Leal (1992) for a complete separation-of-variables solution. Substituting into Eq. 21.7.1 yields Euler's differential equation:

$$F^{(\text{iv})} - \frac{4}{(r/r_0)^2} F'' - \frac{8}{(r/r_0)^3} F' - \frac{8}{(r/r_0)^4} F = 0 \tag{21.8.6}$$

This equation has solutions of the form $F \sim C_n (r/r_0)^n$. Inserting this form into Eq. 21.8.6 shows that the values of n are -1, 1, 2, and 4. The interim answer is

$$\frac{\psi}{r_0^2 U} = \sin^2\theta \left[C_{-1} \left(\frac{r}{r_0}\right)^{-1} + C_1 \left(\frac{r}{r_0}\right) + C_2 \left(\frac{r}{r_0}\right)^2 + C_4 \left(\frac{r}{r_0}\right)^4 \right] \qquad (21.8.7)$$

To match the free-stream boundary condition 21.8.4, $C_2 = -\frac{1}{2}$ and $C_4 = 0$. The term with coefficient C_{-1} is the ideal flow doublet, while C_1 is unique to viscous flow and called a *Stokeslet*. Since the surface of the sphere is $\psi = 0$, an equation relating the coefficients is

$$0 = C_{-1} + C_1 - \tfrac{1}{2} \qquad (21.8.8)$$

The other condition is the no-slip condition $v_\theta \sim \partial\psi/\partial r|_{r_0} = 0$. It yields

$$0 = C_{-1} + C_1 - 1 \qquad (21.8.9)$$

Solving these relations shows that $C_{-1} = -\frac{1}{4}$ and $C_1 = \frac{3}{4}$. The final result is

$$\frac{\psi}{r_0^2 U} = \sin^2\theta \left[-\frac{1}{4}\left(\frac{r}{r_0}\right)^{-1} + \frac{3}{4}\left(\frac{r}{r_0}\right) - \frac{1}{2}\left(\frac{r}{r_0}\right)^2 \right] \qquad (21.8.10)$$

The corresponding velocity components are

$$\frac{v_r}{U} = 2\cos\theta \left[C_{-1}\left(\frac{r}{r_0}\right)^{-3} + C_1\left(\frac{r}{r_0}\right)^{-1} - \frac{1}{2} \right]$$

$$= \cos\theta \left[-\frac{1}{2}\left(\frac{r}{r_0}\right)^{-3} + \frac{3}{2}\left(\frac{r}{r_0}\right)^{-1} - 1 \right] \qquad (21.8.11)$$

$$\frac{v_\theta}{U} = -\sin\theta \left[-C_{-1}\left(\frac{r}{r_0}\right)^{-3} + C_1\left(\frac{r}{r_0}\right)^{-1} - 1 \right]$$

$$= \sin\theta \left[-\frac{1}{4}\left(\frac{r}{r_0}\right)^{-3} - \frac{3}{4}\left(\frac{r}{r_0}\right)^{-1} + 1 \right] \qquad (21.8.12)$$

The velocity is symmetric and without a wake. At Re = 0, three-dimensional closed bodies do not have wakes. Viscous effects extend equally upstream and downstream.

The vorticity is calculated as the simple formula

$$\frac{\omega_\phi}{U/r_0} = 2\sin\theta\, C_1 \left(\frac{r}{r_0}\right)^{-2}$$

$$= \frac{3}{2}\sin\theta \left(\frac{r}{r_0}\right)^{-2} \qquad (21.8.13)$$

The vorticity is zero at the forward stagnation point, rises to a maximum at the sholders, and then drops to zero at the aft stagnation point, $\theta = \pi$. As the free stream is approached, the vorticity dies out as r^{-2}.

It is interesting to compute the surface forces, which according to the general remarks of Section 21.1 dominate the flow. The pressure may be computed by integrating $dp = \nabla p \cdot d\mathbf{x}$, where $\nabla p = \nabla^2 \mathbf{v}$ is used with the known velocity components. An alternative method is to employ $\nabla p = -\mu \nabla \times \boldsymbol{\omega}$. One finds that

$$(\nabla p)_r = \frac{\partial p}{\partial r} = -\mu(\nabla \times \omega)_r = -4C_1 \cos \theta \left(\frac{r}{r_0}\right)^{-3}$$

$$(\nabla p)_\theta = \frac{1}{r}\frac{\partial p}{\partial \theta} = -\mu(\nabla \times \omega)_\theta = -2C_1 \sin \theta \left(\frac{r}{r_0}\right)^{-3}$$

$$p - p_\infty = \int_{\infty, \theta=0}^{r} \frac{\partial p}{\partial r} dr + \int_{0,r}^{\theta} \frac{\partial p}{\partial \theta} d\theta \tag{21.8.14}$$

$$= 2C_1 \cos \theta \left(\frac{r}{r_0}\right)^{-2}$$

$$= \frac{3}{2} \cos \theta \left(\frac{r}{r_0}\right)^{-2}$$

The pressure in the flow approaching the sphere, $0 \le \theta \le \pi/2$, rises to a value higher than p_∞, since $\cos \theta$ is positive in this quadrant. On the downstream side of the sphere, pressures are always lower than p_∞. This antisymmetrical behavior is typical of Stokes flows. Note that the pressure gradient is never adverse. The fluid is sucked toward the aft stagnation point by the low pressure.

The pressure reaches a maximum at the forward stagnation point and a minimum at the rear stagnation point. The values are

$$p_0 - p_\infty = \pm \frac{3}{2}\frac{\mu U}{r_0} \tag{21.8.15}$$

This equation illustrates the fact that the pressures in a given velocity field increase directly with the viscosity of the fluid. For comparison we may cast Eq. 21.8.15 in the form of the pressure coefficient

$$\frac{p_0 - p_\infty}{\frac{1}{2}\rho U^2} = \frac{6}{Re} \tag{21.8.16}$$

Although this nondimensional form is appropriate only for moderate or high Reynolds numbers, it reveals that low-Reynolds-number effects cause the forward stagnation pressure on a sphere to become much larger than ideal-flow value of unity.

The viscous stresses in the flow are given by

$$\tau_{rr} = -2\tau_{\theta\theta} = -2\tau_{\varphi\varphi} = \frac{\mu U}{r_0} 4 \cos \theta \left[-3C_{-1}\left(\frac{r}{r_0}\right)^{-4} - C_1 \left(\frac{r}{r_0}\right)^{-2} \right]$$

$$= 3\frac{\mu U}{r_0} \cos \theta \left[\left(\frac{r}{r_0}\right)^{-4} - \left(\frac{r}{r_0}\right)^{-2} \right]$$

$$\tau_{r\varphi} = 0$$

$$\tau_{r\theta} = -\frac{\mu U}{r_0} 6C_1 \sin \theta \left(\frac{r}{r_0}\right)^{-4} = \frac{3}{2}\frac{\mu U}{r_0} \sin \theta \left(\frac{r}{r_0}\right)^{-4} \tag{21.8.17}$$

As r becomes large, the shear stress dies out much faster that the normal stress and the pressure.

It is apparent from these equations that the shear stresses, normal viscous stresses, and pressure are all about the same magnitude. In Stokes flows, normal viscous stresses play an important role in determining the flow patterns. Because we are dealing with a Newtonian flow, the viscous stress vector at the surface of a body must lie on the surface. Therefore, at r_0 all the normal viscous stresses in Eq. 21.8.17 vanish.

Another way to find the drag is to use the global force balance (similar to Eq. 21.2.3 except for a stationary body in a moving stream). Let the far boundary be a sphere in spherical coordinates. The area element is a disk of radius $r \sin\theta$ and width $r\, d\theta$. The pressure and surface stresses have an x-direction component f_x.

$$dS = 2\pi r \sin\theta\, r\, d\theta$$

$$f_x = (-p + \tau_{rr})\cos\theta - \tau_{r\theta}\sin\theta \tag{21.8.18}$$

The drag force is

$$F_D = -\mu r_0 U \lim_{r\to\infty} \int_0^\pi \frac{f_x r_0}{\mu U}\frac{dS}{r_0^2} = \mu U r_0 \cdot 12 C_1 \pi \int_0^\pi \cos^2\theta \sin\theta\, d\theta \tag{21.8.19}$$

$$F_D = 8\pi\mu r_0 U C_1$$

This is actually a special case of a more general formula.

The drag force on any body with cylindrical symmetry has a special relation to the limiting behavior of the stream function at infinity. Payne and Pell (1960) proved that

$$F_D = 8\pi\mu \lim_{r\to\infty} \frac{\psi - \psi_\infty}{r \sin^2\theta} \tag{21.8.20}$$

Evaluating Eq. 21.8.20 with the streamfunction equation 21.8.7 produces Eq. 21.8.19. Any body in a streaming flow that has cylindrical symmetry can be represented in the form of a separation-of-variables solution such as Eq. 21.8.7. The coefficient C_1 of the series is the only term important to the drag. Other coefficients that are sensitive to the small shape contours of the body do not influence the drag. For the solid sphere $C_1 = \frac{3}{4}$ and the result is

$$F_D = 6\pi\mu r_0 U \tag{21.8.21}$$

This equation is called *Stokes's law*. It is known from experiments to be very good for Re < 0.5. It is accurate to about 10% at Re = 1. For a higher Reynolds number the accuracy is lost very rapidly, but Stokes's law is still a lower bound. Theoretical considerations show that any flow where the convective terms are important must have a higher drag than Eq. 21.8.21. The proper drag law for Stokes flows over any three-dimensional body is $F/\mu r_0 U = $ const. If we insist on comparing drag with high-Reynolds-number theories and cast Eq. 21.8.21 in the usual nondimensional form, we find that

$$C_D = \frac{F}{\frac{1}{2}\rho U^2 \pi r_0^2} = \frac{24}{\text{Re}}\left(1 + \frac{3}{8}\text{Re}\right) \tag{21.8.22}$$

The inverse dependence on the Reynolds number is required because the density does not actually influence the drag. The correction term $\frac{3}{8}$ Re comes from a higher approximation. The effects of unsteady, nonuniform flow on particle motion is discussed by Maxey and Riley (1983).

21.9   COMPOSITE EXPANSION FOR FLOW OVER A SPHERE

The mathematical structure of low-Reynolds-number flows was illustrated by a model problem in Section 15.8. Here we outline the sphere problem formulation and results. This approach is due to Proudman and Pearson (1957) and Kaplun (1957), and the reader can find further discussions in Van Dyke (1964) and Hinch (1991). The sphere is typical of any three-dimensional body. The complete Navier–Stokes equations for a nondimensional streamfunction ($\psi = \psi_{\text{dim}}/r_0^2 U$, $r = r_{\text{dim}}/r_0$) is

$$\frac{\text{Re}}{r^2 \sin \theta} \left(\psi_\theta \frac{\partial}{\partial r} - \psi_r \frac{\partial}{\partial \theta} + 2 \cot \theta\, \psi_r - \frac{2}{r} \psi_\theta \right) E^2 \psi = E^2 E^2 \psi \qquad (21.9.1)$$

Here E^2 is given by 12.5.19. Boundary conditions become

At $r = 1$: $\qquad\qquad\qquad\qquad \psi = 0, \qquad \psi_r = 0$

As $r \to \infty$: $\qquad\qquad\qquad\qquad \psi \sim \dfrac{r^2}{2} \sin^2 \theta$

If one assumes that the solution is the asymptotic expansion $\psi \sim \psi_0 + \Delta_1(\text{Re})\psi_1$, the limit $\text{Re} \to 0$ gives $E^2 E^2 \psi_0 = 0$, which is solved by Eq. 21.9.4, as given previously:

$$\psi_0 = \tfrac{1}{4}(2r^2 - 3r + r^{-1}) \sin^2 \theta \qquad (21.9.2)$$

Let us call this the *near problem*. The term $2r^2$ is a uniform stream, the term r^{-1} is a doublet, both being irrotational, while the term $-3r$ is the rotational component called a *Stokeslet*. A second approximation in the series, ψ_1, will not meet the boundary condition at infinity. Historically, this fact, mentioned earlier, is known as *Stokes's paradox*.

Next consider a *far problem*. the singular region at infinity is retained at the same relative position if we rescale the independent variable by defining

$$R \equiv \text{Re}\, r \qquad (21.9.3)$$

Moreover, the boundary condition at infinity is independent of Re if we set $\psi^* \equiv \text{Re}^2 \psi$:

$$\psi^* \equiv \text{Re}^2\, \psi \sim \frac{R^2}{2} \sin^2 \theta \qquad \text{as} \quad R \to \infty \qquad (21.9.4)$$

In the *far variables* (also called *Oseen variables*) the body $r = 1$ shrinks to a point as $\text{Re} \to 0$. The flow is like a point force in an infinite fluid: At $R = \text{Re}\, r \to 0$, $\psi^* = 0$ and $\psi_R^* = 0$. We do not require the far answer to satisfy this condition because the near problem has already done so. One replaces the boundary conditions with the requirement that the far problem must match the near problem.

The differential equation in Oseen variables is the complete Navier–Stokes without simplification:

$$\frac{1}{R^2 \sin \theta} \left(\psi_\theta^* \frac{\partial}{\partial R} - \psi_R^* \frac{\partial}{\partial \theta} + 2 \cot \theta\, \psi_R^* - \frac{2}{R} \psi_\theta^* \right) E_R^2 \psi^* = E_R^2 E_R^2 \psi^* \qquad (21.9.5)$$

Assuming that, $\psi^* \sim \psi_0^* + \delta_1(\text{Re})\psi_1^*$, the first answer is simply a uniform stream. It makes each term in Eq. 21.9.5 identically zero. This is not only the answer for a sphere, but is the answer for any three-dimensional shape. Thus, our analysis is relevant to all closed bodies. It is only the near solution that depends on the exact shape of the body.

$$\psi_0^* = \frac{R^2}{2} \sin^2 \theta$$

Furthermore, the uniform stream matches the near solution since the solution 21.9.2 is dominated by the uniform stream term as $r \Rightarrow \infty$.

Let us proceed to produce a uniformly valid answer. The common part of matching is the entire free stream $\psi_{cp}^* = \psi_0^*$. An additive composite solution is the sum of the near and far solutions minus the common part:

$$\psi_{0 \text{ comp}} = \psi_0 + \text{Re}^{-2} \, \psi_0^* - \text{Re}^{-2} \, \psi_{cp}^* = \psi_0 \qquad (21.9.6)$$

Thus, we have the nice result that the Stokes near solutions in three-dimensional flows are uniformly valid to first order. The far solution is canceled by the common part. This is the same result as that found in the model problem, Eq. 15.7.13.

The important conclusion from this section is as follows. As a general rule, the singular behavior of Stokes flows in three-dimensional infinite domains can be ignored because the first approximation near solution is uniformly valid.

21.10   STOKES FLOW NEAR A CIRCULAR CYLINDER

Our good fortune with three-dimensional flows disappears when we consider the two-dimensional case. For the plane flow over a cylinder the governing differential equation (Navier–Stokes) and boundary conditions in terms of the nondimensional streamfunction ($\psi = \psi_{\text{dim}}/r_0 U$, $r = r_{\text{dim}}/r_0$ Re $= 2r_0 V/\nu$) are

$$\frac{\text{Re}}{r} \left(\psi_\theta \frac{\partial}{\partial r} - \psi_r \frac{\partial}{\partial \theta} \right) \nabla^2 \psi = \nabla^2 \nabla^2 \psi \qquad (21.10.1)$$

Boundary conditions become

At $r = 1$: $\qquad\qquad\qquad \psi = 0, \qquad \psi_r = 0$

As $r \to \infty$: $\qquad\qquad\qquad \psi \sim r \sin \theta$

The structure of this problem is not obvious, as the model problem 15.8.14 reveals. Assume that the solution is $\psi \sim \psi_0 + \Delta_1(\text{Re})\psi_1$. The limit Re $\to 0$ gives $\nabla^2 \nabla^2 \psi_0 = 0$, which is solved and satisfies the wall boundary conditions, but when matched to the far solution becomes zero; that is, $\psi_0 = 0$. We now have $\psi \sim \Delta_1(\text{Re})\psi_1$. Matching to the far solution shows that $\Delta_1(\text{Re}) = [\ln(1/\text{Re})]^{-1}$. That means in the near region a variable of order 1 is

$$\hat{\psi} = \frac{\psi}{[\ln(\text{Re})]^{-1}} \sim \psi_1 \qquad (21.10.2)$$

The near problem for $\hat{\psi}$ is Stokes's equation,

$$0 = \nabla^2 \nabla^2 \hat{\psi}$$

At $r = 1$: $\qquad\qquad\qquad \hat{\psi} = 0, \qquad \hat{\psi}_r = 0$

which has the answer

$$\hat{\psi} = (r \ln r - \tfrac{1}{2}r + \tfrac{1}{2}r^{-1}) \sin \theta \qquad (21.10.3)$$

The term $r \ln r$ is vortical (called an *Oseenlet*) and the last two terms are irrotational.

The far problem again uses the variable $R \equiv \mathrm{Re}\, r$, and the boundary condition at infinity is independent of Re if we set $\psi^* \equiv \mathrm{Re}\, \psi$:

As $R \to \infty$: $\qquad\qquad \psi^* \equiv \mathrm{Re}\, \psi \sim R \sin \theta \qquad (21.10.4)$

Changing into Oseen variables produces the complete unchanged equation for the far problem:

$$\frac{1}{R}\left(\psi_\theta^* \frac{\partial}{\partial R} - \psi_R^* \frac{\partial}{\partial \theta}\right)\nabla_R^2 \psi^* = \nabla_R^2 \nabla_R^2 \psi^* \qquad (21.10.5)$$

Next, one assumes the expansion $\psi^* \sim \psi_0^* + \delta_1(\mathrm{Re})\psi_1^*$ and substitutes into the differential equation and far boundary condition to find that $\psi_0^* = R \sin \theta$, a uniform stream. This result does not match the near answer because the term $r \ln r$ is dominant as $r \to \infty$. Recall that this is a situation similar to Eq. 15.7.16, where two terms of the far solution are needed to match one term of the near solution. The matching also fixes the gauge function as $\delta_1(\mathrm{Re}) = [\ln(1/\mathrm{Re})]^{-1}$. The form of ψ_1^* is that of a defect law or perturbation from a uniform free stream:

$$\psi_1^* = \frac{\psi^* - \psi_0^*}{[\ln(1/\mathrm{Re})]^{-1}} \qquad (21.10.6)$$

When Eq. 21.10.6 is substituted into Eq. 21.10.5, one finds that

$$\left(-\cos\theta\, \frac{\partial}{\partial R} + \frac{\sin\theta}{R}\frac{\partial}{\partial \theta}\right)\nabla_R^2 \psi_1^* = \nabla_R^2 \nabla_R^2 \psi_1^* \qquad (21.10.7)$$

The is a form of the *Oseen equation*. the convective terms have been linearized by a uniform stream. Simple closed-form answers have not been found.

All low-Reynolds-numbers flows over two-dimensional bodies have this nonuniform character where logarithmic terms in the inner layer must match a far solution that is a defect from the uniform stream. Calculations of Kaplun give the drag formula as

$$C_D = \frac{F}{\rho U^2 r_0} = \frac{4\pi}{\mathrm{Re}}\left[\left(\ln \frac{3.703}{\mathrm{Re}}\right)^{-1} - 0.87\left(\ln \frac{3.703}{\mathrm{Re}}\right)^{-3} + \cdots\right] \qquad (21.10.8)$$

This formula diverges as $\mathrm{Re} \to 0$. Notice that unlike three-dimensional flows, the drag per unit length ($F/\mu U \sim C_D\, \mathrm{Re}$) never becomes independent of the density (i.e., Re); inertia is always important in the far field. This is an important general result about external two-dimensional low-Reynolds-number flows.

*21.11 AXISYMMETRIC PARTICLES

The influence of the geometry of a particle on the creeping flow drag force is of interest for practical reasons. In many engineering or natural situations, fine particles are suspended in air or water. They may be spherical, angular, rodlike, or platelike.

The general motion of a setting particle can be quite complicated. Odd-shaped particles tumble and spin as they move in erratic paths. Since the drag force is different when the flow approaches the particle in different orientations, the velocity and direction of motion are constantly changing. Particles with somewhat regular but asymmetric shapes can make a graceful spiral as they settle through a fluid.

As examples of falling particles we consider spheroids (ellipsoids of revolution) as depicted in Fig. 21.20. The reference axis, about which the generating line is rotated to form the spheroid, makes an angle ϕ with respect to the gravity vector. Let a be the maximum radius and $2b$ be the length of the spheroid. If $e \equiv b/a > 1$, the figure is a *prolate* spheroid; if $e < 1$, it is an *oblate* spheroid. The value $e = 0$ indicates a disk of radius a, $e = 1$ a sphere of the same radius, and $e \rightarrow \infty$ a needle of length $2b$.

The fact that the equations governing pressure and stress are linear is used to great advantage in this problem. It means that we may consider the flow as the superposition of a flow aligned with the reference axis with magnitude $U \cos \theta$ and a flow normal to the axis of magnitude $U \sin \theta$. The angle θ is the direction of motion of the particle with respect to the reference axis; consequently, $\phi \rightarrow \theta$ gives the direction of motion with respect to gravity. The force on the particle is decomposed into F_1 aligned with the reference axis and F_2 normal to the reference axis:

$$F_1 = C_1 \mu U \cos \theta$$

$$F_2 = C_2 \mu U \sin \theta$$

(21.11.1)

The constants C_1 and C_2 depend only on the particle geometry. Exact relations for the constants may be found by analysis. [Indeed, Stokes flow is one of the oldest areas in analytical fluid dynamics; this problem was first solved by Oberbeck (1876).] Useful approximations are (see Clift et al., 1978)

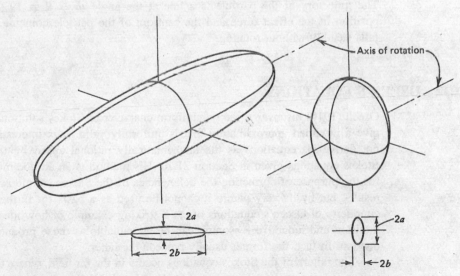

Figure 21.20   Ellipsoids of revolution. The maximum radius is a; the length is $2b$.

$$C_1 = 6\pi a \left(\frac{4+e}{5} \right)$$

(21.11.2)

$$C_2 = 6\pi a \left(\frac{3+2e}{5} \right)$$

These relations can be applied in the range $0 \le e \le 5$ with less than 10% error. At $e = 1$ they are exact.

Needlelike objects ($e \to \infty$) are described by the following approximate formulas:

$$C_1 = \frac{2\pi b}{\ln 2e - 0.5}$$

(21.11.3)

$$C_2 = \frac{4\pi b}{\ln 2e + 0.5}$$

The drag of a very thin needle falling normal to its axis is twice the drag of the same needle falling along its axis.

As a specific example, consider a thin needle falling so that $\theta = 30°$. Since $C_2 = 2C_1$, the ratio of the normal force to the axial force is found from Eq. 21.11.1 to be

$$\frac{F_2}{F_1} = 2 \frac{1/2}{\sqrt{3}/2} = \frac{2}{\sqrt{3}}$$

At equilibrium the net force is balanced by the weight and thus must be in the vertical direction. This means that the inclination of the particle is

$$\phi = \arctan \frac{F_2}{F_1} = 49.1°$$

The trajectory of the particle is a line at the angle $\phi - \theta = 19.1°$. In this case the position of the effect force and the centroid of the particle coincide. Thus, the particle falls steadily without rotating.

*21.12 OSEEN'S EQUATIONS

Oseen (1910) discovered the nonuniform character of Stokes solutions and proceeded to give a modified approximation that is uniformly valid. It is interesting that Oseen did not derive his equations as the mathematically rational approximation to the Navier–Stokes equations given in Section 21.10. His method is an ad hoc intuitive construction for the purpose of correcting the deficiencies of the Stokes solutions. It gives improved results, but by its very nature it cannot be used as a basis for further refinements. The simplicity of Oseen's equations offers a striking example of how ideas constructed with intuition and inductive reasoning can be as valuable as those produced by rational deduction. In fact, the former usually precede the latter.

The failure of the Stokes equations occurs in the far field, where the convective term is just as large as the viscous term. Oseen reasoned that he could replace $(\mathbf{v} \cdot \nabla)\mathbf{v}$ by the linear approximation $U \, \partial v_i / \partial x$, where U is the free-stream velocity. Thus, he proposed the momentum equation

$$\rho U \frac{\partial v_i}{\partial x} = -\partial_i p + \nu \partial_j \partial_j v_i \qquad (21.12.1)$$

This equation, or its equivalent form in terms of the streamfunction, gives answers that are uniformly valid for the whole flow field as Re → 0. Near the body the viscous terms are dominant and the linearized convective term in Eq. 21.12.1 makes very little contribution to the flow. In fact, the Oseen approximation of $U \partial v_i / \partial x$ and the Stokes approximation of zero are errors of the same order in comparison with the true $(\mathbf{v} \cdot \nabla)\mathbf{v}$ term; therefore, both equations are acceptable in this region. Far away from the body the velocity differs only slightly from U, so Oseen's linearized convection term is a valid approximation. Thus, Oseen achieved a remarkable improvement over the Stokes equations.

We may verify the statements above by looking at Oseen's solution for flow over a sphere. The streamfunction in spherical coordinates for this flow is

$$\frac{\psi}{Ur_0^2} = \frac{1}{4}\left[2\left(\frac{r}{r_0}\right)^2 + \left(\frac{r_0}{r}\right) \right] \sin^2 \theta$$

$$- \frac{3}{2 \operatorname{Re}} (1 + \cos \theta) \left\{ 1 - \exp\left[-\frac{\operatorname{Re}}{2} \frac{r}{r_0} (1 - \cos \theta) \right] \right\} \quad (21.12.2)$$

(Note that the nondimensional form of Oseen's equations contains the Reynolds number.) Near the surface of the sphere, r/r_0 is small, so the exponential term in the last term in brackets may be expanded in a series. The result shows that Eq. 21.12.2 is identical to the Stokes solution to order one:

$$\frac{\psi}{Ur_0^2} = \frac{1}{4}\left[2\left(\frac{r}{r_0}\right)^2 - 3\left(\frac{r}{r_0}\right) + \frac{r_0}{r} \right] \sin^2 \theta + O[\operatorname{Re}]$$

Equation 21.12.2 is not the true Oseen solution for flow over a *sphere* in that it does not satisfy the no-slip condition at the wall exactly but only to $O[\operatorname{Re}]$. Nevertheless, we should consider this adequate, as the Oseen equations themselves are valid to this order only near the sphere.

As a matter of practical interest, the Oseen theory produces the drag law for a sphere as

$$F_D = 6\pi\mu Ur_0(1 + \tfrac{3}{8}\operatorname{Re})$$

Researchers have shown that the matched asymptotic theory of Section 21.9 gives the next term as $\frac{9}{40} \operatorname{Re} \ln \operatorname{Re}$.

*21.13 INTERFERENCE EFFECTS

Viscous diffusion causes the influence of a particle to be felt at large distances. To see this, recall the radial velocity relation 21.8.11 for flow over a sphere:

$$v_r = -\frac{1}{2} U \cos \theta \left[2 - 3 \frac{r_0}{r} + \left(\frac{r_0}{r}\right)^3 \right] \qquad (21.13.1)$$

The three terms in brackets show the behavior as we go away from the particle. The constant 2 produces the undisturbed uniform stream, while the other two terms show the remote influence of the particle. Creeping flow effects decay at the slow rate of r_0/r. In contrast, in ideal flow the velocity decays as $(r_0/r)^3$.

As the first example we consider two spherical particles a distance ℓ apart. The flow field around each particle alters the flow at the location of the other. The net effect can be summarized by noting a change in the drag coefficient of the particle. Let λ denote the ratio of the drag of the particle to the drag of a sphere in an unbounded fluid:

$$F = \lambda 6\pi\mu r_0 U \qquad (21.13.2)$$

Experimental and theoretical information on $\lambda(\ell/2r_0)$ is given Fig. 21.21 for two cases: spheres moving parallel and perpendicular to the line of centers.

Due to the reversibility of Stokes flows, the flow pattern must be symmetric and there is no tendency for the particles to move toward or away from each other. Mutual interaction causes the spheres to rotate as they fall. As shown in the figure, the drag of a sphere in the presence of another sphere is reduced slightly.

Strong interference effects occur when a particle is in a closed vessel or near a wall. Approximate formulas for λ show that the wall has a retarding effect (increases the drag). For example, a plane wall a distance ℓ from the particle gives

$$\lambda = \begin{cases} 1 + \dfrac{9}{8}\dfrac{r_0}{\ell} & \text{for motion perpendicular to the wall} \\[4mm] 1 + \dfrac{9}{16}\dfrac{r_0}{\ell} & \text{for motion parallel to the wall} \end{cases}$$

In the latter case there is no tendency for the particle to move toward or away from the wall, but the particle does experience a torque, which induces a rotation.

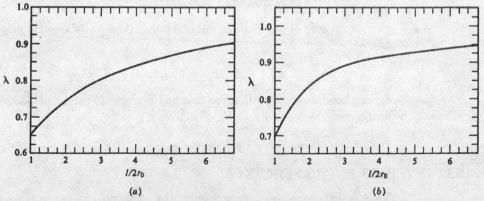

(a)   (b)

Figure 21.21 Influence coefficient λ (drag/drag in infinite medium) for a sphere influenced by another sphere a distance ℓ away: motion (a) along and (b) perpendicular to the line of centers. Adapted from Happel and Brenner (1983). Reprinted with permission.

Swarms of bubbles or suspensions of particles usually experience an increase in drag. Whereas a pair of particles in an infinite fluid may fall faster than a single particle, a suspension of particles falls slower. This effect is called *hindered settling*. Consequently, in a fluid from which particles are settling, one frequently observes a sharp demarcation separating clear fluid and particle-laden fluid. Particles in the flow settle slower than isolated particles, so that any particle that is left behind has ample opportunity to catch up. Brownian motion causes diffusion of the particles, which tends to smear out the interface. Competition between these effects determines the sharpness of the concentraton interface.

21.14   CONCLUSIONS

Flows at low values of the Reynolds number are free of inertia, and thus the fluid density is irrelevant. In such flows the pressure is properly scaled by the quantity $\mu U/L$ and can reach quite high values. The normal viscous stresses, although zero at solid walls, are substantial within the flow field itself. Since the governing equations are linear and symmetric, reversing the direction of flow causes a reversal of velocities and pressures without altering the streamline pattern. For this reason the flow about a symmetric object must be symmetric. A striking phenomenon occurs at flows in concave corners. The flow cannot go smoothly into and out of a corner; a series of nested vortices called Moffatt vorticies must occupy the corner.

External flows about objects have quite different behavior, depending on whether the flow is two- or three-dimensional. In both instances the problem is a singular perturbation with the nonuniform region at infinity. In a three-dimensional flow, this causes no trouble, as the first-order solution is uniformly valid (the common part and the far solution are identical). On the other hand, two-dimensional problems are essentially singular and the far flow will introduce a Reynolds number effect into any uniformly valid solution.

PROBLEMS

21.1 (A) What is the ratio of p^{**} to p^*?

21.2 (A) Prove that the vorticity flux $\mathbf{n} \cdot \nabla\boldsymbol{\omega}$ through any closed surface is zero when Re $\rightarrow 0$.

21.3 (A) Verify that Eq. 21.8.5 is a solution to the low-Reynolds-number equations and that it produces the velocity components and the vorticity relation given in the text.

21.4 (A) What is the terminal velocity in still air of a water droplet 0.01 mm in diameter?

21.5 (A) Compare the E^2 and ∇^2 operators.

21.6 (A) A spheroid with $4b = a$ has its axis at 50° to the horizontal. What is its angle of decent?

21.7 (A) Compute $\mathbf{n} \cdot \nabla\boldsymbol{\omega}$ at the surface of a sphere. Find its integral over the surface.

21.8 (B) Show that the Jeffrey–Hamel flow for Re = 0 (Eq. 21.4.1) gives plane Poiseuille flow in the limit $\alpha r \rightarrow h$ and $\alpha \rightarrow 0$.

21.9 (A) For Jeffrey–Hamel flow at Re = 0, find the relation between C_0 and the flow rate Q.

21.10 (A) Find flow rate–ΔP relation for the plane aperture problem.

21.11 (B) Find the pressure distribution along the centerline of the flow through a plane aperture.

21.12 (A) Consider the parallel flow in an eccentric annulus. If the inner cylinder is centered so there is no eccentricity, find the flow rate.

21.13 (A) Consider the parallel flow in an eccentric annulus. Plot Q/Q_e (E; R).

21.14 (A) Find the velocity profile across a circular orifice.

21.15 (B) Consider the local Stokes flow in the neighborhood of a sharp leading edge. The flow attaches smoothly at zero angle of attack. Find the velocity, vorticity and stress fields.

21.16 (B) How does the drag coefficient law $C_D(Re)$ vary with the Reynolds number (first term only) for three- and two-dimensional bodies in an infinite stream?

22

Lubrication Approximation

In previous chapters we have dealt with special simplifications of the flow when the Reynolds number takes on various values: low, moderate, or high. This chapter is slightly different in that a geometric parameter of the flow is small. We study situations where the flow region is thin transverse to the flow direction. If h is a characteristic length across the flow and L a characteristic length along the flow, the lubrication approximation is the case $\varepsilon \equiv h/L \ll 1$ or $\varepsilon \to 0$. A second requirement is that the Reynolds number be small or moderate. The exact definition of *moderate* depends on the problem, of course. Re $= 2000$ might be moderate in some cases, but Re $= 10^5$ is not moderate. Lubrication flows are like Stokes flows (and unlike boundary layer flows) in that the inertia terms in the momentum equation are negligible. The flows are quasisteady, although an imposed time scale from the boundary motion can modify this conclusion (as discussed in the Stokes flow, Chapter 11). Lubrication flows are like boundary layers in that the transverse pressure gradient is small and the longitudinal pressure is important. The pressure (and viscous stress) scale differently in lubrication problems than in boundary layers or Stokes flows, and this is a central distinction of these flows.

The name *lubrication approximation* obviously comes from the fact that this approximation was originally done in that field. However, in many other situations, porous media, filtration, adhesion, biological flows, and some manufacturing flows, this approximation is useful. The major characteristics of this approximation are illustrated by the problem in the next section.

22.1 BASIC CHARACTERISTICS: CHANNEL FLOW

Consider a two-dimensional slot as shown in Fig. 22.1. Assume a very long channel across which the imposed pressure drop per unit length is $\Delta p/L$. Allow the width of the channel to vary slowly but in an arbitrary manner $h(x)$. The slot has a typical width h_0. The x-direction length over which a significant change in the cross section occurs is L. The lubrication approximation is $\varepsilon = h_0/L \to 0$.

Let us proceed to estimate the order of magnitude of the flow-field quantities. Since the flow is assumed to be driven by the pressure gradient, the velocity scale for the x-direction is similar to that for flow in a plane slot, that is,

$$u_s = \frac{\Delta p h_0^2}{\mu L}$$

Let us turn this around and assume that a velocity scale u_s is prescribed. Then the pressure scale would be

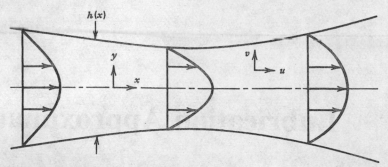

Figure 22.1 Flow in a slot with a slowly changing area is locally a Poiseuille flow.

$$p_s = \Delta p = \frac{\mu u_s}{h_0 \varepsilon} \qquad (22.1.1)$$

This is just like the viscous-dominated Stokes flow pressure scale but divided by ε. Hence, pressures in the lubrication approximation are a factor of $1/\varepsilon$ higher than in Stokes flows.

The transverse velocity v has a much smaller scale than u_s. Denote the v velocity scale by v_s, and estimate the terms in the continuity equation as follows:

$$\frac{\partial u}{\partial x} + \frac{\partial v}{\partial y} = 0$$

Since the area changes occur on the length scale L, we estimate the terms as (omitting the order symbols)

$$\frac{u_s}{L} + \frac{v_s}{h_0} = 0$$

By requiring that the continuity equation have both terms the same size, we find that the vertical velocity scale is

$$v_s = \frac{h_0}{L} u_s = \varepsilon u_s \qquad (22.1.2)$$

where u_s is given by Eq. 22.2.1. From another viewpoint, Eq. 22.2.2 is simply a statement that the slope of a streamline is about the same as the wall slope.

Next, consider the transverse momentum equation. From this equation we can estimate the size of the transverse pressure gradient. The equation is

$$\rho u \frac{\partial v}{\partial x} + \rho v \frac{\partial v}{\partial y} = -\frac{\partial p}{\partial y} + \mu \frac{\partial^2 v}{\partial x^2} + \mu \frac{\partial^2 v}{\partial y^2}$$

The terms have the following sizes:

$$\rho u_s \frac{\varepsilon u_s}{L} + \rho \varepsilon u_s \frac{\varepsilon u_s}{h_0} = \frac{\mu u_s}{h_0 \varepsilon h_0} + \mu \frac{\varepsilon u_s}{L^2} + \mu \frac{\varepsilon u_s}{h_0^2}$$

With $Re \equiv u_s h_0/\nu$, the estimates are

$$Re\ \varepsilon^3 + Re\ \varepsilon^3 = 1 + \varepsilon^4 + \varepsilon^2$$

Thus, if the Reynolds number is moderate, the limit $\varepsilon \to 0$ shows that the transverse momentum equation is

$$0 = \frac{\partial p}{\partial y} \tag{22.1.3}$$

The pressure is constant across the flow: $p = p$ (x only).

The x-momentum equation is considered next. The equation is

$$\rho u\ \frac{\partial u}{\partial x} + \rho v\ \frac{\partial u}{\partial y} = -\frac{dp}{dx} + \mu\ \frac{\partial^2 u}{\partial x^2} + \mu\ \frac{\partial^2 u}{\partial y^2}$$

Estimates for the size of each term are

$$\rho u_s\ \frac{u_s}{L} + \rho \varepsilon u_s\ \frac{u_s}{h_0} = \frac{\mu u_s}{h_0 \varepsilon L} + \mu\ \frac{u_s}{L^2} + \mu\ \frac{u_s}{h_0^2}$$

$$Re\ \varepsilon + Re\ \varepsilon = 1 + \varepsilon^2 + 1$$

Thus, as $\varepsilon \to 0$, a balance between pressure and a viscous force is obtained:

$$0 = -\frac{dp}{dx} + \mu\ \frac{\partial^2 u}{\partial y^2} \tag{22.1.4}$$

At this point, to simplify the algebra, we assume that the wall is symmetrical about the centerline. Then the solution is

$$u = -\frac{h^2}{8\mu}\ \frac{dp}{dx}\left[1 - \left(\frac{2y}{h}\right)^2\right] \tag{22.1.5}$$

This is Poiseuille flow, determined by the local slot width and local pressure gradient.

Global continuity requires that the flow rate be constant. Integration of Eq. 21.1.5 yields

$$Q = -\frac{h^3}{12\mu}\ \frac{dp}{dx} \tag{22.1.6}$$

With the use of this equation, we can write Eq. 21.1.5 in terms of Q and h and eliminate dp/dx. The overall pressure drop over the distance L is

$$p_2 - p_1 = \int_0^L \frac{dp}{dx}\ dx = -12\mu Q \int_0^L h^{-3}\ dx$$

or inserting h_0,

$$\frac{(p_1 - p_2)/L}{\mu Q/h_0^3} = \int_0^1 \left(\frac{h_0}{h}\right)^3 d\left(\frac{x}{L}\right) = \text{constant} \tag{22.1.7}$$

This is a typical pressure drop flow-rate relation for inertialess flow. The right-hand side of Eq. 22.1.7 is a constant that depends on the geometry of the passage. Similar results are obtained for passages of arbitrary shape (see Section 11.1) and modest curvature.

It is interesting to contrast the lubrication approximation with Stokes flows. In Stokes flows the normal stresses, shear stresses, and pressure are all of the same importance. They all have $\mu u_s / h_0$ as the scale for a flow field of size h_0. On the other hand, in the lubrication approximation, for a flow field of size h_0 by L, the scales are $\tau_{xx} \sim \varepsilon \mu u_s / h_0$, $\tau_{yx} \sim \mu u_s / h_0$, $p \sim \mu u_s / \varepsilon h_0$. The net forces from viscous shear stress ($\partial \tau_{yx} / \partial y$) and pressure ($\partial p / \partial x$) are now stronger by a factor of $1/\varepsilon$ compared to Stokes flow.

Both flows are quasisteady and reversible in the sense that if u, v, $p - p_{\text{ref}}$ is a solution then $-u$, $-v$, $-(p - p_{\text{ref}})$ is also a solution. Also, both flows are quasisteady.

22.2 FLOW IN A CHANNEL WITH A POROUS WALL

Consider the flow in a channel of width h_0 where fluid is withdrawn along a porous lower wall. The situation is depicted in Fig. 22.2. Place the coordinate system origin on the lower wall where the porous section begins. Prior to this point the walls are solid and the Poiseuille profile has developed. The withdrawal (or addition) of fluid takes place over a length L. If the channel is thin, $\varepsilon = h_0 / L \to 0$, we can use the lubrication approximation. This also implies that the withdrawal velocity is small compared to the average longitudinal velocity.

Let u_s be the initial average velocity and serve as a scale for the $u(x, y)$ profiles. As in Section 22.1, the continuity equation shows that the vertical velocity scale is $v_s = u_s h_0 / L = \varepsilon u_s$. Define nondimensional variables as

$$x^* = \frac{x}{L}, \qquad y^* = \frac{y}{h_0}, \qquad u^* = \frac{u}{u_s}, \qquad v^* = \frac{v}{\varepsilon u_s}$$

$$p^* = \frac{p - p_{\text{ref}}}{\mu u_s / h_0 \varepsilon}, \qquad \text{Re} = \frac{u_s h_0}{\nu}$$

(22.2.1)

Note that the pressure scale is like the Stokes flow scale increased by $1/\varepsilon$.

Substituting these definitions into the Navier–Stokes equations and taking the limit $\varepsilon \to 0$ produces the lubrication equations:

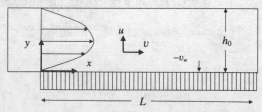

Figure 22.2 Plane channel with a porous wall withdrawing fluid at velocity $-V_w(x)$.

$$\frac{\partial u^*}{\partial x^*} + \frac{\partial v^*}{\partial y^*} = 0$$

$$0 = \frac{\partial p^*}{\partial y^*} \tag{22.2.2}$$

$$0 = -\frac{\partial p^*}{\partial x^*} + \frac{\partial^2 u^*}{\partial y^{*2}}$$

An immediate consequence of Eq. 22.2.2 is that $p^* = p^*(x^*$ only).

The initial profile is

$$u^*(0, y^*) = \frac{u}{u_s} = 6(y^* - y^{*2}) \tag{22.2.3}$$

Boundary conditions include a specified withdrawal velocity along the lower wall v_w (x^*).

$$u^*(x^*, 0) = 0, \qquad u^*(x^*, 1) = 0 \tag{22.2.4}$$

$$v^*(x^*, 0) = v_w^*(x^*), \qquad v^*(x^*, 1) = 0$$

For fluid withdrawal, $v_w^*(x^*)$ will be negative.

One can readily verify that the solution is a Poiseuille flow profile which changes its strength, that is, a changing average value $u_0(x)$, at different x locations.

$$u^*(x^*, y^*) = 6u_{ave}^*(x^*)(y^* - y^{*2}) \tag{22.2.5}$$

where

$$\frac{dp^*}{dx^*} = -12u_{ave}^* \tag{22.2.6}$$

The initial value is $u_{ave}^*(0) = 1$. By applying the global continuity equation between the positions $x^* = 0$ and $x^* = 1$, a relation between the average velocity and the wall velocity is obtained:

$$u_{ave}(x^*) = 1 + \int_0^{x^*} v_w^* \, dx^* \tag{22.2.7}$$

The vertical velocity profile is found by integrating $\partial v^*/\partial y^*$ and substituting the continuity equation:

$$v(x^*, y^*) - v_w(x^*) = \int_0^{y^*} \frac{\partial v^*}{\partial y^*} \, dy^*$$

$$= -\int_0^{y^*} \frac{\partial u^*}{\partial x^*} \, dy^* \tag{22.2.8}$$

Performing the algebra indicated in Eq. 22.2.7 (observing that Eq. 22.2.6 implies that $du_{ave}^*/dx^* = v_0^*$) yields

$$v(x^*, y^*) = v_w(x^*)(1 - 3y^{*2} + 2y^{*3}) \tag{22.2.9}$$

The location of the porous wall, bottom, top, or both walls affects the $v^*(y^*)$ profile; however, it has no effect on the $u^*(y^*)$ profile.

The velocity profiles $v^*(y^*)$ and $u^*(y^*)$ do not explicitly contain the x^* position. This effect is in the $v_w^*(x^*)$ withdrawal velocity and its effect on $u_{\text{ave}}^*(x^*)$. For an example, we can assume a constant withdrawal and integrate Eq. 22.2.7 to find that

$$u_{\text{ave}}(x^*) = 1 + v_w^* x^* \tag{22.2.10}$$

Recall that for fluid withdrawal $v_w^*(x^*)$ will be negative. Say that a porous section that is just long enough for average velocity is depleted to zero when the channel ends. The distance for this to happen is $x^* = 1 = -1/v_w^*$. In dimensional terms,

$$\frac{L}{h_0} = -\frac{u_s}{v_w} \tag{22.2.11}$$

In other words, $-Q_W = -Lv_w = Q = h_0 u_s$. This confirms the statement made at the beginning of the problem that the withdrawal velocity must be small for the lubrication approximation $\varepsilon = h_0/L \rightarrow 0$ to apply. If the channel is longer than this, we would need to supply fluid from both right and left sides.

22.3 REYNOLDS EQUATION FOR BEARING THEORY

The dominant events in lubrication problems involve pressure, viscosity, and moving walls at a slight incline angle. A typical bearing has a gap width of 0.001 in. or less, and the convergence between the walls may be as small as 1/5000. Unlike Section 21.2, where the pressure gradient is imposed to cause the flow, the pressure gradients in a

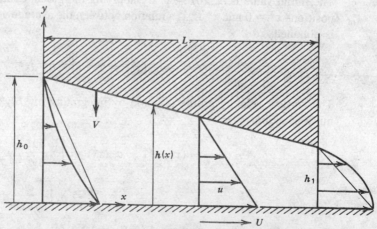

Figure 22.3 Flow in a slipper-pad bearing is locally the sum of a Couette flow and a Poiseuille flow.

bearing are generated by two events. First, the moving wall on one side sweeps fluid into a narrowing passage through the action of viscous shear forces. The local velocity profile from this effect is the Couette profile $u = Uy/h$. A local flow rate due to the Couette motion, $Q_c = \frac{1}{2}Uh$, would be large where h is large and small where h is small. This, of course, cannot happen, because continuity demands that the overall flow rate be constant. Hence, the flow sets up a pressure gradient to supply a Poiseuille component that redistributes the fluid and maintains a constant flow rate.

The pressure equation appropriate for lubrication theory is known as the Reynolds equation. Several ideas from Section 22.1 on channel flow are used to derive it. Figure 22.3 shows a channel of height $h(x, t)$. For simplicity, let the upper wall have only a vertical velocity $v(t)$, which may be a function of time, and the lower wall a steady horizontal velocity U. Although the lower wall moves only in the x-direction, we allow for a z-direction flow that may be set up by the pressure gradient. The following scales are appropriate:

$$x, z \sim L$$
$$y \sim h_0$$
$$t \sim L/U$$
$$u, w \sim U \tag{22.3.1}$$
$$v \sim \frac{Uh_0}{L}$$
$$p \sim \frac{\mu UL}{h_0^2}$$

If the scales given in Eq. 22.3.1 are used to estimate the terms in the y-momentum equation and the limit $h_0/L \to 0$ is taken, one finds that $\partial p/\partial y = 0$. Thus, the pressure is only a function of x and z.

A similar process applied to the x- and z-momentum equation yields the quasisteady equations

$$0 = -\frac{\partial p}{\partial x} + \mu \frac{\partial^2 u}{\partial y^2}$$
$$0 = -\frac{\partial p}{\partial z} + \mu \frac{\partial^2 w}{\partial y^2} \tag{22.3.2}$$

Partial integration over y and application of boundary conditions

$$u(y = 0) = U, \qquad u(y = h) = 0$$
$$w(y = 0) = 0, \qquad w(y = h) = 0$$
$$v(y = 0) = 0, \qquad v(y = h) = V$$

produces the velocity profiles

$$u = \frac{1}{2\mu} \frac{\partial p}{\partial x} (y^2 - yh) + \left(1 - \frac{y}{h}\right) U \qquad (22.3.3)$$

$$w = \frac{1}{2\mu} \frac{\partial p}{\partial z} (y^2 - yh) \qquad (22.3.4)$$

In all bearing problems the local profiles are a combination of a Couette flow and a Poiseuille flow given by the local gap and pressure gradient. The only remaining question, but the crucial one with regard to supporting a load with the bearing, is to determine the pressure distribution.

The Reynolds equation for the pressure is derived by integrating the continuity equation over the y-direction to find that

$$\int_0^h \frac{\partial u}{\partial x} \, dy + \int_0^h \frac{\partial w}{\partial z} \, dy = -\int_0^h \frac{\partial v}{\partial y} \, dy = -V \qquad (22.3.5)$$

This equation is changed by noting that $V = \partial h / \partial t$ and that Leibnitz's theorem requires that

$$\frac{\partial}{\partial x} \int_0^h u \, dy = \int_0^h \frac{\partial u}{\partial x} \, dy + u(y = h) \frac{\partial h}{\partial x} = \int_0^h \frac{\partial u}{\partial x} \, dy$$

Substituting these relations into Eq. 22.3.5 and employing velocity profiles (Eqs. 22.2.3 and 22.2.4) allows the integrals to be evaluated. The result is

$$\frac{1}{\mu} \left[\frac{\partial}{\partial x} \left(h^3 \frac{\partial p}{\partial x} \right) + \frac{\partial}{\partial z} \left(h^3 \frac{\partial p}{\partial z} \right) \right] = 6U \frac{\partial h}{\partial x} + 12 \frac{\partial h}{\partial t} \qquad (22.3.6)$$

This is the Reynolds equation for lubrication in a channel $h(x, t)$ with the lower wall moving at velocity U. It is the basic equation in lubrication theory. The pressure distribution may be found by knowing the geometry and motion of the walls. Once the pressure is known, the proportion of Poiseuille and Couette components in the velocity profiles of Eq. 22.3.3 is fixed.

22.4   SLIPPER PAD BEARING

The principles of bearing lubrication are demonstrated nicely by the slipper pad. Figure 22.3 shows a flat pad inclined at an angle α. The pad length is L, the entrance gap is h_0, and the exit gap is h_1. One assumes that the reservoirs on each side of the bearing are at the same pressure p_0. Let the lower wall move with a velocity U. In accord with Eq. 22.3.1, we define nondimensional variables as

$$p^* = \frac{p - p_0}{\mu UL / h_0^2} \qquad (22.4.1)$$

$$x^* = \frac{x}{L}, \qquad h^* = \frac{h}{h_0}$$

The wall location is given by

$$h^* = 1 - Ax^* \qquad \text{where} \quad A = \frac{\alpha L}{h_0} = \frac{h_0 - h_1}{h_0} \tag{22.4.2}$$

For an infinitely wide bearing, the flow is assumed to be one-dimensional. This allows Eq. 22.3.6 to be integrated once to yield

$$h^{*3} \frac{dp^*}{dx^*} = 6(h^* - h_m^*)$$

Here the constant of integration has been denoted as h_m^* and is physically the gap width at the location where the pressure gradient is zero. This particular point is where the pressure is a maximum and the velocity profile is the linear Couette profile without any Poiseuille component. This being the case, the flow rate through the bearing is simply

$$Q = \frac{U h_m}{2} \quad \text{or} \quad Q^* = \frac{2Q}{U h_0} = h_m^* \tag{22.4.3}$$

A second integration of the pressure equation, together with the boundary condition that $p^* = 0$ at $h^* = 1$, yields

$$p^* = 6A^{-1}(h^{*-1} - 1) - 3A^{-1} h_m^*(h^{*-2} - 1) \tag{22.4.4}$$

Inserting $p^* = 0$ at $h^* = 1 - A$ gives

$$h_m^* = 2 \frac{1 - A}{2 - A} \tag{22.4.5}$$

We now insert Eqs. 22.4.5 and 22.4.2 into Eq. 22.4.4 to obtain the pressure as a function of x^*:

$$p^* = \frac{6x^*}{1 - Ax^*} \left(1 - \frac{1 - A}{2 - A} \frac{2 - Ax^*}{1 - Ax^*} \right) \tag{22.4.6}$$

The pressure curves (Fig. 22.4), contain the slope parameter A. We can show that the maximum pressure is

$$p_m^* = \frac{3A}{2(2 - A)(1 - A)} \tag{22.4.7}$$

From Eqs. 22.4.5 and 22.4.2 this occurs at

$$x_m^* = \frac{1}{2 - A} \tag{22.4.8}$$

To interpret these results, consider the case $A = 0$, implying that the upper and lower walls are parallel. This flow is simply a Couette flow with a constant pressure along the pad. If a small convergence is added, so that $A > 0$, a maximum pressure $p_m^* \approx 3A/4$ occurs at $x_m^* \approx \frac{1}{2}$. For the first one-half of the pad, the pressure rises, indicating a Poiseuille component opposing the flow into the bearing. The Poiseuille component changes sign for $x^* > x_m^*$ and causes an increase in the flow as the gap narrows. We can roughly describe the situation by saying that the fluid dragged into the converging channel by the viscous shear forces piles up to create high pressure near the center $x^* = \frac{1}{2}$. The

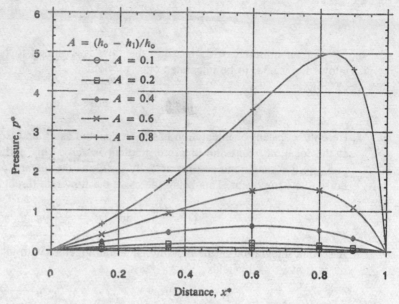

Figure 22.4 Pressure in a slipper-pad bearing.

pressure gradient between the center and either end induces a Poiseuille flow toward both ends of the bearing. The Poiseuille component subtracts from the Couette flow for the first one-half of the bearing length and then adds for the other one-half.

The magnitudes of pressure generated by this mechanism are truly remarkable. In dimensional terms

$$p_m - p_0 = \frac{\mu U_0 L}{h_0^2}\left(\frac{3}{4}A + O[A^2]\right)$$

This shows that h_0 plays the strongest role in fixing the pressure.

22.5 SQUEEZE-FILM LUBRICATION: VISCOUS ADHESION

There is an intriguing physical similarity between the "wringing" together of smooth surfaces and the operation of a crankshaft bearing in an automobile. In the latter case, the power stroke of the piston causes a normal motion $V(t)$ between the crankshaft and the bearing (this effect is actually dominant over the hydrodynamic journal-bearing effect). The case of attempting to separate smooth surfaces by pulling in the normal direction is just the opposite, as we are trying to generate a normal motion $V(t)$ that increases the gap height. Suppose that two highly polished flat surfaces with a liquid coating are brought together. If the fluid gap is small, it is impossible to pull them apart in the normal direction, although the sliding motion is quite easy.

Recall that when the Reynolds equations were derived in Section 22.3, a normal motion of the upper surface $V(t)$ was allowed. Consider a bearing plate of length L with a uniform but time-dependent gap $h(t)$. The Reynolds equation 22.3.6 becomes

$$\frac{1}{\mu}\frac{d}{dx}\left(h^3\frac{dp}{dx}\right) = 12\frac{dh}{dt}$$

Let the origin be halfway from either end of the bearing pad. Integration of the equation above gives

$$\frac{dp}{dx} = \frac{12\mu}{h^3}\frac{dh}{dt}\,x$$

The Poiseuille component is zero at $x = 0$, where there is no flow at all, and is a maximum at the ends ($x = \pm L/2$). All of the flow into or out of the gap must cross the ends.

The pressure distribution is found by further integration:

$$p - p_0 = \frac{6\mu L^2}{h^3}\frac{dh}{dt}\left[\left(\frac{2x}{L}\right)^2 - 1\right]$$

Note that the pressure varies as h^{-3}. Smoothly polished materials allow h to become very small, and the pressures are consequently very large.

22.6   JOURNAL BEARING

Hydrodynamic bearings come in a large variety of sizes. However, in all cases the thickness of the fluid film is very small compared to the length of the flow. In addition, the curvature of the flow is also small, allowing the film to be analyzed as a flat region. A rotating shaft, or journal, of radius R_1 is shown in Fig. 22.5 in the bearing housing of radius R_2. The journal bearing length is L and the aspect ratio is L/R_1. Bearings with $L/R_1 < 0.5$ are considered short, and $L/R_1 > 2$ are considered long. During operation the center of the journal is offset from the center of the bearing (bushing) by a distance e, called the *eccentricity*. The difference in radii, $c = R_2 - R_1$, is called the *clearance* and the ratio $\varepsilon = e/c$ is the *eccentricity ratio*. Note that the minimum channel width is $c - e$ and the maximum width is $c + e$. Thus, the eccentricity ratio is a measure of how much the height of the film changes. The journal rotates in a counterclockwise direction so that it drags fluid from the wide section into a narrowing passage. This creates a high pressure that supports the journal. The amount of the load to be supported determines

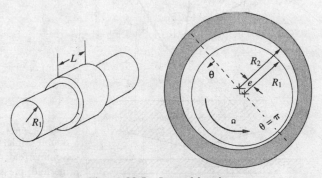

Figure 22.5   Journal bearing.

the eccentricity and the angle at which it occurs. The intent in this section is to cover the major physical events. Actual bearing design involves many practical details that cannot be covered here.

The physical processes in the journal bearing can be interpreted by considering the events in the slider bearing of Section 22.4. Imagine that the converging-diverging passages of the journal bearing are equivalent to two slider bearings placed back to front as shown in Fig. 22.6. Recall that the equations for the lubrication approximation are reversible so that if the direction of motion of a slider is reversed, as it is in the diverging portion of our Fig. 22.6, the velocity profiles are reversed and the pressure–distance curve is the negative of the original (the pressure gradient changes sign). Curve I in Fig. 22.6 follows this trend. Such a curve for a bearing is called the *full Sommerfeld condition*, and it has unrealistically large negative pressures. Actually, in the diverging section some of the fluid vaporizes or cavitates and a three-dimensional flow sets up with liquid and gaseous phases.

A better engineering analysis is to model the three-dimensional flow in the diverging portion as a region of constant pressure. This is called a *half Sommerfeld* or *Gumbel condition* and is shown by the dashed line labeled II in Fig. 22.6. In solving the slider bearing problem, the pressure was set to p_0 at the ends. An alternative is to specify two conditions at an unknown location. The *Swift–Stieber* or *Reynolds condition* specifies that at the cavity beginning, the pressure and the pressure gradient will be zero, $p = p_{cavity} = 0$, $dp/d\theta = 0$. Thereafter the flow is imagined to consist of a liquid film and a gaseous cavity at constant pressure. This is labeled III in Fig. 22.6. The Swift–Stieber condition is often used in numerical calculations and gives reasonable agreement with experiments.

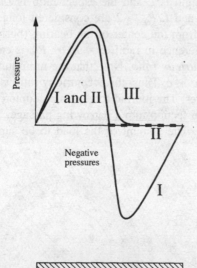

Figure 22.6 Similarity of journal bearing and double slider block. Pressure distribution I, full Sommerfeld; pressure distribution II, half Sommerfeld; pressure distribution III, Swift–Steiber.

It is traditional to place the origin of the θ coordinates at the journal center with $\theta = 0$ at the maximum film width. The z-coordinate origin is at the center of the bearing, so the ends are $z = \pm L/2$. Books on lubrication show that because the gap is very thin compared to R_1, a reasonable approximation for the channel width distribution is

$$h = c(1 + \varepsilon \cos \theta) \quad \text{where} \quad x = R_1\theta \quad (22.6.1)$$

This approximation is exact at $\theta = 0$ and π.

We will consider the two special cases of long and short bearings: first, the short bearing case where $L/R_1 \ll 1$. Nondimensional variables are

$$\theta = \frac{x}{R_1}, \qquad h^* = \frac{h}{c}, \qquad z^* = \frac{z}{L/2}$$

$$\bar{p} = \frac{p - p_0}{\mu\Omega L^2/c^2} \quad (22.6.2)$$

Using these variables in Reynolds equation 22.3.6 gives

$$\frac{1}{4}\left(\frac{L}{R_1}\right)^2 \frac{\partial}{\partial\theta}\left(h^{*3}\frac{\partial\bar{p}}{\partial\theta}\right) + \frac{\partial}{\partial z^*}\left(h^{*3}\frac{\partial\bar{p}}{\partial z^*}\right) = \frac{3}{2}\frac{\partial h^*}{\partial\theta} \quad (22.6.3)$$

For the short bearing limit this simplifies to

$$\frac{\partial}{\partial z^*}\left(h^{*3}\frac{\partial\bar{p}}{\partial z^*}\right) = \frac{3}{2}\frac{\partial h^*}{\partial\theta} \quad (22.6.4)$$

If we assume that the pressure at either end of the bearing is p_0, the solution is

$$\bar{p} = \frac{3}{4}\frac{1}{h^{*3}}\frac{\partial h^*}{\partial\theta}(z^{*2} - 1) \quad (22.6.5)$$

This solution indicates that there is flow in both the θ- and z^*-directions.

The long bearing problem is more widely relevant to applications. The nondimensional variables are the same except that the pressure variable uses R_1 instead of L in the scale. Since this case $R_1/L \ll 1$, we expect a two-dimensional flow without any dependence on L:

$$p^* - \frac{p - p_0}{\mu\Omega R_1^2/c^2} \quad (22.6.6)$$

Using these variables in Reynolds equation 22.3.6 gives

$$\frac{\partial}{\partial\theta}\left(h^{*3}\frac{\partial p^*}{\partial\theta}\right) + 4\left(\frac{R_1}{L}\right)^2 \frac{\partial}{\partial z^*}\left(h^{*3}\frac{\partial p^*}{\partial z^*}\right) = 6\frac{\partial h^*}{\partial\theta} \quad (22.6.7)$$

For a long bearing this simplifies to

$$\frac{\partial}{\partial\theta}\left(h^{*3}\frac{\partial p^*}{\partial\theta}\right) = 6\frac{\partial h^*}{\partial\theta} \quad (22.6.8)$$

Integrating twice gives the pressure distribution in a symbolic form:

$$p^*(\theta) = 6 \int_0^\theta \frac{h^*(\xi) - C}{[h^*(\xi)]^3} \, d\xi \qquad (22.6.9)$$

The constant of integration C is determined by the type of boundary conditions assumed: Sommerfeld, half Sommerfeld, or Swift–Stieber.

Recall that the Sommerfeld condition is a solution periodic in θ, $p^*(0) = p^*(2\pi)$ [and we can specify that $p^*(\theta = 0) = 0$]. For these cases the integration constant is

$$C = \frac{\int_0^{2\pi} d\xi / [h^*(\xi)]^2}{\int_0^{2\pi} d\xi / [h^*(\xi)]^3} \qquad (22.6.10)$$

The solution was first given by Sommerfeld (1904), who devised an ingenious transformation that allows Eq. 22.6.9 to be integrated exactly. He replaced $h^*(\theta) = 1 + \varepsilon \cos \theta$ using a new angle ψ defined by the relation

$$\cos \psi = \frac{\varepsilon + \cos \theta}{1 + \varepsilon \cos \theta} \qquad (22.6.11)$$

The details are given in all books on lubrication theory. His final answer is

$$p^*(\theta) = \frac{6\varepsilon \sin \theta (2 + \varepsilon \cos \theta)}{(2 + \varepsilon^2)(1 + \varepsilon \cos \theta)^2} \qquad (22.6.12)$$

The half Sommerfeld is a Sommerfeld solution with the pressure in the diverging section set to zero.

The Swift–Stieber (Reynolds) condition is that the pressure and the pressure gradient will be zero, $p = p_{\text{cavity}} = 0$, $dp/d\theta = 0$ when the vapor cavity forms, $\theta = \theta_{\text{cav}}$. These conditions determine the front location of the cavity. Differentiating Eq. 22.6.9 and applying $dp^*/d\theta = 0$ shows that the constant C in Eq. 22.6.9 is the film thickness at the cavity inception:

$$C = h^*(\theta_{\text{cav}}) \qquad (22.6.13)$$

Casting Eq. 22.6.9 in terms of the Sommerfield angle ψ and evaluating at $\theta = \theta_{\text{cav}}$ gives an implicit relation for ψ_{cav}:

$$\varepsilon(\sin \psi_{\text{cav}} \cos \psi_{\text{cav}} - \psi_{\text{cav}}) + 2(\sin \psi_{\text{cav}} - \psi_{\text{cav}} \cos \psi_{\text{cav}}) = 0 \qquad (22.6.14)$$

The angle at which the cavity forms is found using the inverse of Eq. 22.6.11.

$$\cos \theta = \frac{\cos \psi - \varepsilon}{1 - \varepsilon \cos \psi} \qquad (22.6.15)$$

Szeri (1980) computes these angles and finds that for $\varepsilon = 0.1$, $\psi_{\text{cav}} = 4.44510$ and $\theta_{\text{cav}} = 4.34974$ (249.2°). Figure 22.7 shows pressure curves computed for an eccentricity ratio of $\varepsilon = 0.5$. In this case, $\theta_{\text{cav}} = 3.834338$ (219.7°).

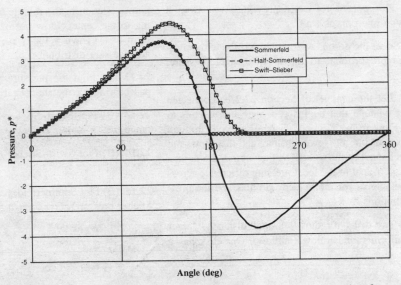

Figure 22.7 Pressure distributions in journal bearing for eccentricity ratio of $\varepsilon = 0.5$.

22.7 CONCLUSIONS

Lubrication flows are thin and change slowly in the flow direction. In the lubrication limit the transverse length scale of the flow is small compared to the length scale in the flow direction. The pressure and viscous forces dominate, and unlike boundary layers, inertia effects are negligible. The flows are quasisteady and the Poiseuille and Couette flow velocity profiles are established in the main flow direction. The scale of the pressure is $\mu U/(h_0^2/L)$. This is a viscous scale like that for Stokes flows except it is stronger by the factor h_0/L. The pressure is constant across the width of the flow, and the wall shape and its motion determine variation along the flow. Vertical wall motion produces squeeze-film lubrication and viscous adhesion.

PROBLEMS

22.1 (B) Find the pressure drop versus flow rate relation for steady flow in a slot with width given by $h = h_0 + A \sin(2\pi x/L)$, where A/h_0 is small.

22.2 (B) Consider a V-shaped wedge as in Fig. 22.6, where $U = 0$. Allow for a squeeze film motion $V(t)$. What is the Reynolds equation for this situation? If the pressure at the left end is p_0. Find the pressure distribution.

22.3 (B) Find the pressure distribution for a step bearing, $0 \leq x \leq L$, with a constant gap h_0 for $0 \leq x < L/2$ followed by a smaller constant gap h_1 over the last half of the bearing. The pressure at $x = L/2$ is continuous.

22.4 (A) Find the load-carrying capacity and the drag force for Problem 21.3.

22.5 (A) Find the drag force on the plane slipper-pad bearing. Compute the power required by the bearing.

22.6 (B) A circular rod with a flat end is a distance $h(t)$ above a flat wall. Derive the lubrication equations for the squeeze-film problem for this geometry. Solve for the pressure distribution and total force on the rod.

22.7 (A) Let the channel of Section 22.2 be porous on the upper as well as the lower wall. Solve the problem for this configuration.

22.8 (A) Plot $p^*(x^*)$ for constant withdrawal from a channel with one porous wall.

22.9 (A) Solve the porous wall problem if the withdrawal velocity is proportional to the local channel pressure; $v_w = kp$.

22.10 (B) Let the channel of Section 22.2 be connected to a lower channel that begins at $x = 0$ and extends to the right. Flow from the upper channel proceeds through the porous wall into the lower channel and then flows out the lower channel to the right. The flow across the porous wall is proportional to the local pressure difference across the channel. Solve for the velocity profiles and the pressure distributions.

22.11 (B) Two disks of radius R_0 a small distance h_0 apart have a uniform radial inflow (outflow). One disk has a porous section in the middle beginning at R_i and extending to the center. Flow out of the porous section is uniform at a known velocity v_z. Find the velocity profiles and pressure distribution.

22.12 (A) Find the pressure and forces on the Michell pad bearing for the short bearing approximation.

22.13 (B) Plot Swift–Stieber $\Psi_{cav}(\varepsilon)$ and $\theta_{cav}(\varepsilon)$ for the range $0 \leq \varepsilon \leq 1$.

22.14 (B) Plot Swift–Stieber $p^*(\theta)$ for $\varepsilon = 0, 0.25, 0.5, 0.75,$ and 1.

22.15 (B) Plot Sommerfeld, half Sommerfeld, and Swift–Stieber pressure curves $p^*(\theta)$ for $\varepsilon = 0.8$.

23

Surface Tension Effects

Surface tension is important in determining the shape of interfaces and in certain instances promoting flow within the bulk phases. First, we discuss some kinematic and mathematical aspects of surfaces. This is followed by the application of mass and momentum conservation laws and will result in relations between the flow properties on either side of the interface. In several sections we present analysis of the static menisci shapes. Stokes flow over a bubble and capillary waves is followed by the basic problem of flows, the drag-out problem. Coating flows contain moving contact lines, a subject that requires extra discussion. The chapter ends with the presentation of three Marangoni flows, flows that are driven by surface tension.

23.1 INTERFACE CONCEPTS AND LAWS

The interface between a flowing liquid and a gas is difficult to define in an unambiguous manner. In general, there are absorbed molecules of various species and complex interactions that are not easily characterized with continuum properties. Moreover, the mathematics of a two-dimensional world embedded and interacting with a three-dimensional world is more advanced than we have been using (Aris, 1962; Slattery, 1990). Nevertheless, many useful engineering analyses can be accomplished with a simple model of the interface (see Table 23.1).

Assume that there is a surface with gas on one side and liquid on the other. The jump in density is a mathematical discontinuity and the density function is not defined at the interface. It is, in a certain sense, contrary to the assumption that fluid properties are continuously distributed in space. Essentially, we must make some special assumptions about the behavior of interfaces. A major assumption is that the interface itself contains no mass. This is not suitable for mixtures with surface chemical reactions, as a mass per unit surface area needs to be envisioned.

A mathematical equation describing an interface surface is

$$x_3 = f(x_1, x_2) \tag{23.1.1}$$

Of course, such an explicit form might not actually exist for a complicated surface. Nevertheless, most surfaces amenable to analysis can be placed in this form. Equation 23.1.1 is not as theoretically useful as the more general implicit form

23.1 Properties of Interfaces in Various Coordinate Systems[a]

	Coordinates			
Interface	x, y, z $z = h(x, t)$	r, θ, z $z = h(r, t)$	r, θ, z $r = R(z, t)$	r, θ, ϕ $r = R(t)$
n_1	$n_x = -n_z \dfrac{\partial h}{\partial x}$	$n_r = -n_z \dfrac{\partial h}{\partial r}$	$n_r = \left[1 + \left(\dfrac{\partial R}{\partial z}\right)^2\right]^{-1/2}$	$n_r = 1$
n_3	$n_z = \left[1 + \left(\dfrac{\partial h}{\partial x}\right)^2\right]^{-1/2}$	$n_z = \left[1 + \left(\dfrac{\partial h}{\partial x}\right)^2\right]^{-1/2}$	$n_z = -n_r \dfrac{\partial R}{\partial z}$	$n_\theta = 0$
Curvature, $2\mathcal{H}$	$n_z^3 \dfrac{\partial^2 h}{\partial x^2}$	$\dfrac{1}{r}\dfrac{\partial}{\partial r}\left(r n_z \dfrac{\partial h}{\partial r}\right)$	$\dfrac{n_r^3}{R}\left[R\dfrac{\partial^2 R}{\partial z^2} - \left(\dfrac{\partial R}{\partial z}\right)^2 - 1\right]$	$-\dfrac{1}{R}$
Interface Velocity, $\mathbf{n \cdot w}$	$n_z \dfrac{\partial h}{\partial t}$	$n_z \dfrac{\partial h}{\partial t}$	$n_r \dfrac{\partial R}{\partial t}$	$\dfrac{dR}{dt}$
$(\nabla_{(s)}\sigma)_1$	$n_z^2 \dfrac{\partial \sigma}{\partial x}$	$n_z^2 \dfrac{\partial \sigma}{\partial r}$	$n_r^2 \dfrac{\partial R}{\partial z}\dfrac{\partial \sigma}{\partial z}$	$\dfrac{1}{R}\dfrac{\partial \sigma}{\partial \theta}$
$(\nabla_{(s)}\sigma)_3$	$n_z^2 \dfrac{\partial h}{\partial x}\dfrac{\partial \sigma}{\partial x}$	$n_z^2 \dfrac{\partial h}{\partial r}\dfrac{\partial \sigma}{\partial r}$	$n_z^2 \dfrac{\partial \sigma}{\partial z}$	$\dfrac{1}{R \sin \theta}\dfrac{\partial \sigma}{\partial \phi}$

[a] n_z is used to simplify terms.

$$F = F(x_1, x_2, x_3) = x_3 - f(x_1, x_2) \tag{23.1.2}$$

There is a separate surface for each value of F. Now F is defined for the entire domain and the interface that we are interested in can be $F = 0$. Consider the differential

$$dF = d\mathbf{x} \cdot \nabla F \tag{23.1.3}$$

Specifically restrict $d\mathbf{x}$ to be within a certain surface. On this surface F is constant, so $dF = 0$. For any $d\mathbf{x}$ within the surface $d\mathbf{x} \cdot \nabla F = 0$, and thus the gradient ∇F is always perpendicular to the surface $F = $ constant. For the interface the local unit normal vector is

$$\mathbf{n} = \pm \frac{\nabla F}{|\nabla F|} \quad \text{for } F = 0 \tag{23.1.4}$$

The sign is determined once the inside and outside of the interface are specified.

Next consider that the interface may move with velocity $\mathbf{w}$ as shown in Fig. 23.1a. Following the moving interface F is constant, so the "substantial" derivative, modified to contain the interface velocity, is zero.

$$\frac{\partial F}{\partial t} + \mathbf{w} \cdot \nabla F = 0 \tag{23.1.5}$$

Dividing by $|\nabla F|$ and noting Eq. 23.1.4 gives

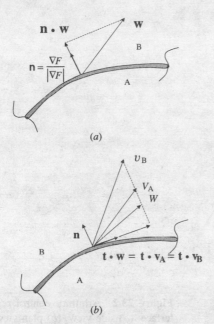

Figure 23.1   Interface between two fluids, A and B: (*a*) interface moves with velocity **w**; (*b*) velocities of A and B with no-slip assumption.

$$\frac{1}{|\nabla F|} \frac{\partial F}{\partial t} + \mathbf{w} \cdot \mathbf{n} = 0 \qquad \text{for } F = 0 \qquad (23.1.6)$$

This equation essentially relates the interface velocity in the normal direction to the surface equation. The tangential component of the interface velocity **w** does not appear in physical laws, and we may prescribe it in any convenient manner.

Now consider a small neighborhood of the interface as shown in Fig. 23.1*b*. Let **t** be a unit vector tangent to the surface. The fluid on side A just next to the interface has velocity $\mathbf{v}_A$ while fluid on side B has velocity $\mathbf{v}_B$. The viscous no-slip condition, an empirical result, is that the tangential component of the velocity is continuous across the interface:

$$\mathbf{v}_A \cdot \mathbf{t} = \mathbf{v}_B \cdot \mathbf{t} \qquad (23.1.7)$$

If we like, we can set the tangential interface velocity equal to the fluid velocities; $\mathbf{w} \cdot \mathbf{t} = \mathbf{v}_A \cdot \mathbf{t} = \mathbf{v}_B \cdot \mathbf{t}$. You will notice that the normal velocity components in the figure are not equal. This implies that fluid from side A is moving into the interface, where it is vaporizing to become part of fluid B. The normal components of the velocities are governed by the mass balance, which we now consider.

Prescribe an "arbitrary" control region around the interface area S and slightly into the fluids on either side, as shown in Fig. 23.2. On side A the volume is V_A with surface S_A, outward normal $\mathbf{n}_A$, and fluid properties ρ_A, $\mathbf{v}_A$. Similarly, on side B the properties are V_B, S_B, $\mathbf{n}_B$, ρ_B, $\mathbf{v}_B$. Conservation laws will be applied to this region assuming that continuum properties can be defined everywhere. Then we will limit the regions toward the interface so that the volumes vanish and only the surface remains: $V_A \Rightarrow 0$, $V_B \Rightarrow 0$ (S finite) $S_A = S_B = S$ and $\mathbf{n} = \mathbf{n}_B = -\mathbf{n}_A$.

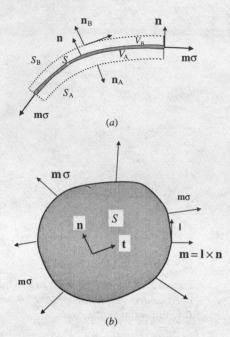

Figure 23.2 Arbitrary control region includes interface: (a) side view; (b) plan view.

Recall that the integral mass balance for a region with arbitrary motion is (Eq. 5.13.2)

$$\frac{d}{dt} \int_{AR} \rho \, dV + \int_{AR} \rho \, \mathbf{n} \cdot (\mathbf{v} - \mathbf{w}) \, dS = 0 \qquad (23.1.8)$$

Apply this to a small region on the interface as depicted in Fig. 23.2. Substitute for the volume integrals an average value times the size of integration region (neglect any flow across the end pieces).

$$\frac{d}{dt}(\rho_A V_A + \rho_B V_B) + \int_A \rho_A \mathbf{n}_A \cdot (\mathbf{v}_A - \mathbf{w}) \, dS + \int_B \rho_B \mathbf{n}_B \cdot (\mathbf{v}_B - \mathbf{w}) \, dS = 0 \quad (23.1.9)$$

Assume that the limit $V_A \to 0$, $V_B \to 0$ (S finite) leaves no mass within the interface.

$$-\int [\rho_A \mathbf{n} \cdot (\mathbf{v}_A - \mathbf{w}) - \rho_B \mathbf{n} \cdot (\mathbf{v}_B - \mathbf{w})] \, dS = 0 \qquad (23.9.10)$$

Since the region of surface integration is arbitrary, the integrand must be zero at all points on the interface.

$$\rho_A \mathbf{n} \cdot (\mathbf{v}_A - \mathbf{w}) - \rho_B \mathbf{n} \cdot (\mathbf{v}_B - \mathbf{w}) = 0$$

$$\dot{m} = \rho_A \mathbf{n} \cdot (\mathbf{v}_A - \mathbf{w}) = \rho_B \mathbf{n} \cdot (\mathbf{v}_B - \mathbf{w}) \qquad (23.1.11)$$

The result is that the mass flux across the interface relates the jump in the normal velocities and densities.

The special case when there is no mass transfer gives continuity of the normal velocities

$$\mathbf{n} \cdot \mathbf{v}_A = \mathbf{n} \cdot \mathbf{v}_B = \mathbf{n} \cdot \mathbf{w} \qquad (23.1.12)$$

In this case the viewpoint may be taken that the fluids on either side and the interface itself have a single velocity. Equation 23.1.6 is then written replacing $\mathbf{w}$ with $\mathbf{v}$:

$$\frac{1}{|\nabla F|} \frac{\partial F}{\partial t} + \mathbf{v} \cdot \mathbf{n} = 0 \qquad \text{for } F = 0 \qquad (23.1.13)$$

This is known as the *kinematical interface condition*.

Apply momentum equation 5.14.1 to the same region:

$$\frac{d}{dt} \int_{AR} \rho \mathbf{v} \, dV + \int_{AR} \rho \mathbf{n} \cdot (\mathbf{v} - \mathbf{w}) \, \mathbf{v} \, dS = \int_{AR} \mathbf{n} \cdot \boldsymbol{\tau} \, dS - \int_{AR} \mathbf{n} p \, dS + \int_{AR} \rho \mathbf{F} \, dV$$

$$(23.1.14)$$

Once again, substitute for the volume integrals an average value times the size of the integration region. (Neglect any momentum carried by flow across the end pieces.) For the ends of the region, have a length element $\mathbf{l} \, ds$ and outward unit vector $\mathbf{m} = \mathbf{l} \times \mathbf{n}$. Surface forces in the end pieces have been condensed into a surface tension σ. This force per unit length is assumed to act in the direction tangent to the interface and perpendicular to $\mathbf{l} \, ds$; the direction is $\mathbf{m} = \mathbf{l} \times \mathbf{n}$. Surface tension is the pressure concept for a two-dimensional world. Surface tension is regarded as a thermodynamic property of the materials on either side of the interface and is sensitive to the temperature. Increasing temperature generally decreases the tension.

$$\frac{d}{dt} (\rho_A \mathbf{v}_A V_A + \rho_B \mathbf{v}_B V_B) + \int_A \rho \mathbf{n}_A \cdot (\mathbf{v}_A - \mathbf{w}) \, \mathbf{v}_A \, dS + \int_B \rho \mathbf{n}_B \cdot (\mathbf{v}_B - \mathbf{w}) \, \mathbf{v}_B \, dS$$

$$= \int_A [\mathbf{n}_A \cdot \boldsymbol{\tau}_A - \mathbf{n}_A p_A] \, dS - \int_B [\mathbf{n}_B \cdot \boldsymbol{\tau}_B - \mathbf{n}_B p_B] \, dS$$

$$+ \rho_A g V_A + \rho_B g V_B + \oint \mathbf{m} \sigma \, ds \qquad (23.1.15)$$

Again assume that the limit $V_A \to 0$, $V_B = 0$ (S finite) leaves no momentum within the interface. Recall that $S_A = S_B = S$ and $\mathbf{n} = \mathbf{n}_B = -\mathbf{n}_A$. Thus, Eq. 23.1.15 simplifies to

$$-\int [\rho \mathbf{n} \cdot (\mathbf{v}_A - \mathbf{w}) \, \mathbf{v}_A - \rho \mathbf{n} \cdot (\mathbf{v}_B - \mathbf{w}) \, \mathbf{v}_B] \, dS$$

$$= -\int [(\mathbf{n} \cdot \boldsymbol{\tau}_A - \mathbf{n} p_A) - (\mathbf{n} \cdot \boldsymbol{\tau}_B - \mathbf{n} p_B)] \, dS + \oint \mathbf{m} \sigma \, ds \qquad (23.1.16)$$

Now there is a surface tension force $\oint \mathbf{m} \sigma \, ds$ around the edge that must be considered.

There is an integral formula, similar to Stokes's theorem, that will transform the line integral into a surface integral [for a summary, see Leal (1992) or Dean (1998)]. For a closed circuit bounding a surface S, the theorem states that

$$\oint \mathbf{m}\sigma \, ds = \int [\nabla_{(s)}\sigma + 2\mathcal{H}\mathbf{n}\sigma] \, dS \qquad (23.1.17)$$

Here $\nabla_{(s)}(\ \ )$ is the surface gradient operator. It is the derivative operation for functions defined on a surface. For any curve in the surface with distance coordinate s and a function $f(s)$, the differential is

$$df = d\mathbf{s} \cdot \nabla_{(s)} f \qquad (23.1.18)$$

The symbol $\mathcal{H}$ in Eq. 23.1.17 stands for the mean curvature of the surface. Geometrically, the mean curvature is the sum of the radii of curvature for any two curves in S formed by the intersection of S with orthogonal planes containing $\mathbf{n}$. This is independent of the choice of orthogonal planes and is equal to $-\frac{1}{2}\nabla \cdot \mathbf{n}$:

$$2\mathcal{H} = -\left(\frac{1}{R_1} + \frac{1}{R_2}\right) = -\nabla_{(s)} \cdot \mathbf{n} = -\nabla \cdot \mathbf{n} \qquad (23.1.19)$$

The curvature $\mathcal{H}$ is negative when $\mathbf{n}$ is outward on a convex surface.

To continue the derivation of the momentum equation, insert Eq. 23.1.17 together with Eqs. 23.1.19 into 23.1.16 and note that since the integration region may be chosen in any manner, the integrand must be zero everywhere. This yields

$$\int [\rho\mathbf{n} \cdot (\mathbf{v}_A - \mathbf{w})\mathbf{v}_A - \rho\mathbf{n} \cdot (\mathbf{v}_B - \mathbf{w})\mathbf{v}_B - (\mathbf{n} \cdot \boldsymbol{\tau}_A - \mathbf{n}p_A) + (\mathbf{n} \cdot \boldsymbol{\tau}_B - \mathbf{n}p_B)$$

$$+ \nabla_{(s)}\sigma + \sigma\mathbf{n} \cdot 2\mathcal{H}] \, dS = 0$$

$$\rho\mathbf{n} \cdot (\mathbf{v}_A - \mathbf{w}) \, \mathbf{v}_A - \rho\mathbf{n} \cdot (\mathbf{v}_B - \mathbf{w}) \, \mathbf{v}_B$$

$$= (\mathbf{n} \cdot \boldsymbol{\tau}_A - \mathbf{n}p_A) - (\mathbf{n} \cdot \boldsymbol{\tau}_B - \mathbf{n}p_B) - \nabla_{(s)}\sigma - \sigma\mathbf{n} \cdot 2\mathcal{H}$$

Or if the mass flux is identified, we have

$$\dot{m}(\mathbf{v}_A - \mathbf{v}_B) = (\mathbf{n} \cdot \boldsymbol{\tau}_A - \mathbf{n}p_A) - (\mathbf{n} \cdot \boldsymbol{\tau}_B - \mathbf{n}p_B) - \nabla_{(s)}\sigma - \sigma\mathbf{n}2\mathcal{H} \qquad (23.1.20)$$

With no mass flow across the interface this becomes a balance of forces at the interface.

To interpret Eq. 23.1.20, consider two curves within the interface that are locally perpendicular. At a point on the interface the unit vectors are $\mathbf{n}$, normal; $\mathbf{t}$, tangent; and $\mathbf{b} = \mathbf{n} \times \mathbf{t}$ tangent. The orthogonality conditions are $\mathbf{n} \cdot \mathbf{t} = \mathbf{n} \cdot \mathbf{b} = \mathbf{b} \cdot \mathbf{t} = 0$. The components of Eq. 23.1.20 tangent to the interface are computed by taking $\mathbf{t} \cdot$ and $\mathbf{b} \cdot$ Eq. 23.1.20. Let the viscous stress components be denoted by $\mathbf{t} \cdot (\mathbf{n} \cdot \boldsymbol{\tau}) = \tau_{nt}$, and note that $\mathbf{t} \cdot \nabla_{(s)}\sigma = d\sigma/dt$.

t-direction force balance:

$$0 = (\tau_{ntA} - \tau_{ntB}) - \frac{d\sigma}{dt} \qquad (23.1.21)$$

b-direction force balance:

$$0 = (\tau_{nbA} - \tau_{nbB}) - \frac{d\sigma}{db} \qquad (23.1.22)$$

For interfaces where the surface tension is uniform, these equations show a balance of shear stress across the interface. If the surface tension changes along the surface, then, to maintain equilibrium, there must be a difference in the fluid stresses on either side.

The force balance in the normal direction is $\mathbf{n} \cdot$ Eq. 23.1.20.

n-direction force balance:

$$0 = (\tau_{nnA} - \tau_{nnB}) - (p_A - p_B) - 2\sigma\mathcal{H} \tag{23.1.23}$$

A curvature of the interface $\mathcal{H}$ produces a normal component to the surface tension that is balanced by a jump in the normal stress. In general, the normal stress has the pressure and the normal viscous stress as components. Neglecting the viscous component yields the famous Young–Laplace equation.

$$[p_A - p_B] = -2\sigma\mathcal{H} = \sigma\left(\frac{1}{R_1} + \frac{1}{R_2}\right) \tag{23.1.24}$$

The common situation of a static bubble or drop is well known. The interior pressure is higher by an amount related to the tension and the radius. The curvature $2\mathcal{H} = -2/R$, and since there is no motion, the Laplace equation reduces to

$$p_A - p_B = \frac{2\sigma}{R} \tag{23.1.25}$$

When R is very small, as it is for the inception of a boiling water bubble, the continuum model predicts an extremely high pressure. A soap bubble has two surfaces, and so the interior pressure is twice as high:

$$p_A - p_B = \frac{4\sigma}{R} \tag{23.1.26}$$

The drop and bubble are closed surfaces. Many important situations have an interface that contacts a solid wall.

The intersection of a fluid–liquid interface with a solid is called a *contact line* or *triple junction*. A static contact line is analyzed by postulating a surface tension in the solid–fluid interfaces. Consider the contact line shown in Fig. 23.3, where the liquid A, fluid B, and solid phases are shown. The second phase B could be imagined as a gas or a liquid without a change in the physics. The interfacial tensions use subscripts to indicate

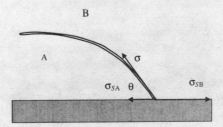

Figure 23.3   Interface and contact line on solid wall.

the phases to which they refer, σ_{SA}, σ_{SB}, and just σ for the fluid–liquid interface. A force balance the wall direction introduces the contact angle as an unknown:

$$\sigma_{SB} - \sigma_{SA} - \sigma \cos \theta = 0 \qquad (23.1.27)$$

This is Young's equation, and it indicates that the contact angle θ, measured through the liquid, is a property of the materials (and the temperature).

The concept of solid surface tension has some difficulties. Note that the normal component of the forces at the contact line do not balance. In writing Eq. 23.1.27 we have assumed that the surface tension for the liquid–gas away from the contact line is also applicable at the contact line. It is easy to imagine that the molecular state of the interfaces when they meet at the triple line is modified. In addition to this we have not included wall roughness as an influence. The contact angle θ is a macroscopic property and the contact line a geometric idealization. Effectively immeasurable interface contamination from foreign molecules can cause a variation in θ of several degrees.

23.2   STATICS: PLANE INTERFACES

A basic problem in static interface behavior is the rise (or depression) of a meniscus of a semi-infinite horizontal liquid–gas interface as it meets a vertical solid wall. Let the wall be at $x = 0$ and the height of the interface in the y-direction be $h = h(x)$, with $h = h' = 0$ as $x \rightarrow \infty$, as shown in Fig. 23.4. The other boundary condition is $h'(0) = -\cot \theta$, where θ is the given contact angle at $x = 0$. The pressure in the liquid along $x = 0$ is the hydrostatic rise $\rho g h$ minus the pressure jump caused by the curved meniscus:

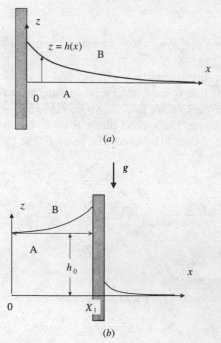

Figure 23.4   Meniscus between liquid A and gas B rising near a plane solid wall: (a) exterior problem; (b) interior problem showing one half of a capillary channel of width $2X_1$.

$$-2\sigma\mathcal{H} + \rho g h(x) = \sigma\left(\frac{1}{R_1} + \frac{1}{R_2}\right) + \rho g h(x) = 0 \qquad (23.2.1)$$

The radii of curvature are $1/R_1 = 0$ and $1/R_2 = -h''(1 + h'^2)^{-3/2}$. Hence,

$$\frac{h''}{(1 + h'^2)^{3/2}} - \frac{\rho g h}{\sigma} = 0 \qquad (23.2.2)$$

Introduce the nondimensional variables

$$X = \frac{x}{\sqrt{\sigma/\rho g}} \quad \text{and} \quad H = \frac{h}{\sqrt{\sigma/\rho g}} \qquad (23.2.3)$$

The combination $\sqrt{\sigma/\rho g}$ is called the *capillary length scale*. For water–air the tension is about 70×10^{-3} N/m and the capillary length about 2.7 mm. Using these variables, Eq. 23.2.2 becomes free of parameters:

$$\frac{H''}{(1 + H'^2)^{3/2}} - H = 0 \qquad (23.2.4)$$

Let $(1 + H'^2) = u$; then $du = 2H'dH' = 2H'H''\,dX$. Multiplying Eq. 22.2.4 by $2H'\,dX$, and integrating once yields

$$\frac{1}{(1 + H'^2)^{1/2}} + \frac{H^2}{2} = C \qquad (23.2.5)$$

Applying the boundary conditions $H = H' = 0$ as $X \to \infty$ gives $C = 1$. The boundary condition of a known contact angle θ at the wall gives $1 + H_0'^2 = 1 + \cot^2\theta = 1/\sin^2\theta$. Putting this into Eq. 23.2.5 yields the rise in the meniscus at the wall $h(0) = h_0$. In dimensional terms the result is

$$H_0 = \sqrt{2(1 - \sin\theta)} \qquad h_0 = \sqrt{\frac{2\sigma}{\rho g}(1 - \sin\theta)} \qquad (23.2.6)$$

One can solve Eq. 23.2.5 for H' and integrate again

$$X = \cosh^{-1}\frac{2}{H} - \cosh^{-1}\frac{2}{H_0} - \sqrt{4 - H^2} + \sqrt{4 - H_0^2} \qquad (23.2.7)$$

This is an implicit relation for $H(X)$ with the contact angle information hidden in H_0.

The problem of a capillary rise of liquid in a plane wall channel of width $2x_1$ is slightly more complicated from a mathematical standpoint. There are two parameters in this problem: the contact angle θ and the wall location x_1. Place the origin of x coordinates at the centerline of the channel as shown in Fig. 23.4b. Equation 23.3.5 still governs the meniscus shape with the boundary conditions $h'(x = 0) = 0$, $h'(x = x_1) = -\cot\theta$. The constant C in Eq. 23.3.6 is no longer unity and must be retained and found later. Using the same nondimensional variables as in Eq. 22.3.8, the second integration of Eq. 22.3.6 is (let $\hat{H}$ be the dummy integration variable)

$$X = \int_{H_0}^{H} \frac{C - \hat{H}^2/2}{\sqrt{1 - (C - \hat{H}^2/2)^2}} \frac{1}{\sqrt{2}} \, d\hat{H} \qquad (23.2.8)$$

Here the integration limits are $H(X)$, the interface height position, and $H_0 = H(0)$, the unknown centerline height. From Eq. 23.2.5 we see that

$$H_0 = \sqrt{2(C - 1)} \qquad (23.2.9)$$

It is customary (Landau and Lifshitz, 1959) to make a variable change by defining ζ with the equation

$$\cos \zeta = C - \frac{H^2}{2}$$

$$H = \sqrt{2(C - \cos \zeta)} \qquad (23.2.10)$$

Thus, $H_0 = \sqrt{2(C - 1)}$ implies that $\zeta_0 = 0$. Transforming the integral produces

$$X = \frac{1}{2} \int_0^\zeta \frac{\cos \hat{\zeta}}{\sqrt{C - \cos \hat{\zeta}}} \, d\hat{\zeta} \qquad (23.2.11)$$

Let us use $H_1 = H(X_1)$ as the meniscus height at the wall where $h' = H'_1 = \cot \theta$. Inserting these conditions into Eq. 23.2.5 at X_1 gives $H_1 = \sqrt{2(C - \sin \theta)}$. On the other hand, from Eq. 23.2.10, $H_1 = \sqrt{2(C - \cos \zeta_1)}$. Comparing these results shows that the wall is $\zeta_1 = \pi/2 - \theta$. Employing the fact that the width of the channel X_1 is known in Eq. 23.2.11 gives an implicit relation for the constant $C(X_1, \theta)$:

$$X_1 = \frac{1}{2} \int_0^{\pi/2 - \theta} \frac{\cos \hat{\zeta}}{\sqrt{C - \cos \hat{\zeta}}} \, d\hat{\zeta} \qquad (23.2.12)$$

The interface curve is given in parametric form by Eqs. 22.2.10, $H(\zeta)$, and 22.2.11, $X(\zeta)$. The integrals above are tabulated as elliptic integrals; however, with modern mathematics software they may be evaluated numerically with ease.

The interior problem has an extra parameter, introduced by the channel width x_1, that is absent in the exterior problem. The nondimensional distance is related to the *Bond number*; $X_1^2 = x_1^2 (\sigma/\rho g) = $ Bo. The Bond number is the square of a typical geometric length compared to the capillary length. A useful approximation can be made when Bo $\Rightarrow 0$. This can be thought of as a very thin channel compared to the capillary length. In this case X_1 is small and the integrand in Eq. 23.2.12 must be dominated by a very large C. This is consistent with the fact that we expect that H_0 is large, and Eq. 23.2.9 shows that $H_0 = \sqrt{2(C - 1)}$. Thus, approximating the integrand in Eq. 23.2.12 by $\cos \zeta/\sqrt{C}$ and integrating gives

$$X_1 = \frac{\sin(\pi/2 - \theta)}{\sqrt{2C}} = \frac{\cos \theta}{\sqrt{2C}}$$

This result, together with approximations to Eq. 23.2.5 and 23.2.6, means that $H \sim H_0 \sim H_1 \sim \sqrt{C} = \cos \theta/2X_1$. In dimensional variables the height of capillary rise is

$$h_0 = \frac{\sigma \cos \theta}{\rho g x_1} \qquad (23.2.13)$$

The elementary way to derive this same result is to assume that the walls are close together and that the meniscus is a circular arc with contact angle θ. Then by geometry $\cos \theta = x_1/R_1$. The pressure decrease across the curved surface is $p_B - p_A = \sigma/R_1$, while the decrease because of the hydrostatic equation is $p_B - p_A = \rho g h_0$. Equating these expressions results in Eq. 23.2.13.

23.3   STATICS: CYLINDRICAL INTERFACES

The capillary problems in cylindrical geometries are slightly different. The exterior problem (Fig. 25.5a) is a vertical cylinder in an infinite bath, and the interior problem (Fig. 25.5b) is the meniscus rise (or fall) in a round vertical tube. Both of these problems have a geometric length scale, the tube radius r_0. Comparing r_0 with the capillary length scale introduces the Bond number as a parameter:

$$\text{Bo} = \frac{r_0^2 \rho g}{\sigma} \tag{23.3.1}$$

Force balance equation 23.2.4 for the meniscus height $h(r)$ in cylindrical coordinates is

$$\frac{\sigma}{r} \frac{\partial}{\partial r} [r(1 + h'^2)^{-1/2} h'] - \rho g h = 0 \tag{23.3.2}$$

Introduce nondimensional coordinates with r_0 as the length scale; $R = r/r_0$, $H = h/r_0$:

$$\frac{1}{R} \frac{\partial}{\partial R} [R(1 + H'^2)^{-1/2} H'] - \text{Bo } H = 0 \tag{23.3.3}$$

For a given Bo value, the equation needs two boundary conditions.

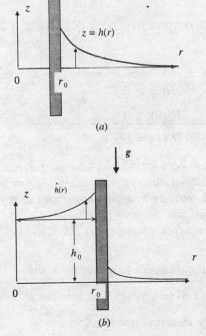

(a)

(b)

Figure 23.5   Meniscus between liquid A and gas B rising near a cylindrical solid wall: (a) exterior problem; (b) interior problem showing one half of a capillary channel of radius r_0.

Boundary conditions for the exterior problem are conditions on the meniscus slopes; $H'(1) = \cot \theta$ and $H'(\infty) = 0$. The case of a thin needle, $\text{Bo} \to 0$, has been solved by Lo (1983) as a singular perturbation problem (see also Lagerstrom, 1988). The solution is interesting in that the matching of two asymptotic expansions has logarithmic common parts. This is similar to the matching in turbulent wall layers or in two-dimensional Stokes flow over a cylinder.

For the interior problem, a round capillary tube, the boundary conditions are $H'(R = 0) = 0$ and $H'(R = 1) = \cot \theta$. Numerical solutions for a variety of Bond numbers and contact angles are presented in Concus (1968). A useful special case is the regular perturbation expansion for small Bond numbers. As a first step, let us transfer the coordinate origin to the free surface at the tube center $r = 0$. At $R = 0$, let $h = \hat{h} + h_0$, where h_0 is the height of the meniscus above the bath in which the capillary tube is placed. This height h_0 does not scale on r_0. As Bo becomes small, h_0 becomes large. We need a nondimensional variable that is of order one as $\text{Bo} \to 0$. Consider that the pressure decrease at the meniscus due to the hydrostatic effect is $\rho g h_0$ and that the pressure decrease because of the curved interface is about σ/r_0 (the radius of curvature is somehow related to the contact angle and r_0). Equating these pressures means that $h_0 \sim \sigma/\rho g r_0$. Hence, we define a nondimensional centerline meniscus height that will be of order one as

$$H_0^* = \frac{h_0}{\sigma/(\rho g r_0)} = \frac{h_0}{r_0}\,\text{Bo} = H_0\,\text{Bo} \tag{23.3.4}$$

The equation to transfer the coordinate origin to the surface is

$$\text{Bo}\,H = \text{Bo}\,\hat{H} + H_0^* \tag{23.3.5}$$

When this is substituted into Eq. (23.3.3), we arrive at

$$\frac{1}{R}\frac{\partial}{\partial R}\left[R(1 + \hat{H}'^2)^{-1/2}\,\hat{H}'\right] - \text{Bo}\,\hat{H} - H_0^* = 0 \tag{23.3.6}$$

Now the boundary conditions are

$$\hat{H}(0) = 0$$
$$\hat{H}'(0) = 0 \tag{23.3.7}$$
$$\hat{H}'(1) = \cot \theta$$

An extra unknown constant H_0^* has been introduced into the differential equation; however, it will be fixed be an additional boundary condition $\hat{H}(0) = 0$. Taking the limit $\text{Bo} \to 0$, solving Eq. 23.3.6, and applying boundary conditions at $R = 0$ yields

$$(1 + \hat{H}'^2)^{-1/2}\,\hat{H}' = H_0^*\,\frac{R}{2} \tag{23.3.8}$$

Evaluating at $R = 1$ determines the meniscus height at the wall:

$$H_0^* \cdot \tfrac{1}{2} = [1 + (\cot \theta)^2]^{-1/2}\cot \theta = \cos \theta \tag{23.3.9}$$

In dimensional terms the capillary meniscus rise is

$$h_0 = \frac{2 \cos \theta \; \sigma}{\rho g r_0} \tag{23.3.10}$$

Integrating Eq. 23.3.8 gives the meniscus curve:

$$\hat{H}(R) = \frac{\hat{h}}{r_0} = \frac{1}{\cos \theta} \{1 - [1 - (R \cos \theta)^2]^{1/2}\} \tag{23.3.11}$$

For the limit Bo $\rightarrow$ 0 the height of the meniscus is influenced by the surface tension σ and the contact angle θ, while the meniscus shape is only influenced by θ.

23.4   STATICS: ATTACHED BUBBLES AND DROPS

Meniscuses with axisymmetric shapes have methods of analysis with common features. Figure 23.6 shows the different configurations. A sessile drop on top of a flat surface is mathematically equivalent to a captive bubble under a flat surface. Actually, the solid surface could also have conical symmetry. For example, a captive bubble in a conical crack is shown in the figure. With regard to tubes, the pendant drop and the emerging bubble have similar boundary conditions. The situation here is different in that the contact line is pinned to the solid. Because of the sharp corner, the contact line can leave the wall at any angle. The exact angle depends on the volume of fluid in the drop or bubble. A consolidated analysis of all these problems is presented by Slattery (1990). All of these situations can be used for the measurement of surface tension and contact angles. Analysis and computer results for a wide range of parameters are tabulated for this purpose in Hartland and Hartley (1976); however, specific calculations on a case-by-case basis are now feasible. Their analysis method uses a set of variables adapted to these problems. The sessile drop will be discussed as an illustrative case.

A cylindrical coordinate system is placed at the top of the liquid drop with the z-axis pointing downward as shown in Fig. 23.7. For simplicity the drop will be considered

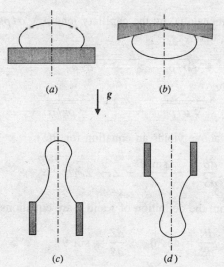

(a)

(b)

g

(c)

(d)

Figure 23.6   Meniscus shapes for bubbles or drops attached to solid walls: (a) sessile drop; (b) captive bubble; (c) emerging bubble; (d) pendant drop.

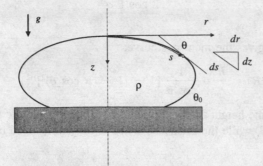

Figure 23.7 Cylindrical coordinates r, z and coordinates s, θ on a sessile drop.

to be in a gas of negligible density. Convenient variables are s, the distance along the surface, and θ, the angle of the surface with the horizontal. The radii of curvature are

$$R_1 = -\frac{ds}{d\theta} \qquad R_2 = -\frac{r}{\sin\theta} \qquad (23.4.1)$$

The gauge pressure at the top of the liquid drop is

$$p_{A0} = -2\sigma\mathscr{H}_0 \qquad (23.4.2)$$

Here $\mathscr{H}_0$ is the curvature at the top of the drop, and along with θ_0, is used as a parameter to characterize the drop. At any point on the surface the gauge pressure in the liquid is

$$p_A = p_{A0} + \rho g z \qquad (23.4.3)$$

We can also compute the local gauge pressure by the Young–Laplace equation with the local curvature:

$$p_A = -2\sigma\mathscr{H} = \sigma\left(\frac{1}{R_1} + \frac{1}{R_2}\right) \qquad (23.4.4)$$

Lengths will be made nondimensional by the capillary length $\sqrt{\sigma/\rho g}$.

$$Z = \frac{z}{\sqrt{\sigma/\rho g}} \qquad R = \frac{r}{\sqrt{\sigma/\rho g}}$$

$$S = \frac{s}{\sqrt{\sigma/\rho g}} \qquad \mathscr{H}_0^* = \frac{\mathscr{H}_0}{\sqrt{\rho g/\sigma}} \qquad (23.4.5)$$

Combining all the equations above yields an equation for $\theta(S)$:

$$\frac{d\theta}{dS} = -\frac{\sin\theta}{R} + Z - 2\mathscr{H}_0^* \qquad (23.4.6)$$

The companion equations from the definition of s and θ are equations for $R(S)$ and $Z(S)$.

$$\frac{dR}{dS} = \cos\theta \qquad \frac{dZ}{dS} = \sin\theta \qquad (23.4.7)$$

The solution strategy is to specify the initial curvature $\mathcal{H}_0^*$ and compute the functions $R(S)$, $Z(S)$, and $\theta(S)$ using Eqs. 23.4.6 and 23.4.7. Then one can plot $Z(R)$ as in Fig. 23.8. For a specific case identify the edge of the drop by the contact angle θ_0. This gives the associated contact radius and drop height. Typical solutions are shown in Fig. 23.8 for four values of $\mathcal{H}_0^*$. Each curve represents sessile drops of a variety of contact angles θ_0. The solutions proceed past $\theta_0 = 180°$, although such solutions are physically unreasonable.

23.5   CONSTANT-TENSION FLOWS: BUBBLE IN AN INFINITE STREAM

A liquid droplet in a different liquid and a gas bubble in a liquid are common situations of practical importance. Frequently, the problem is at steady state where the weight force, the buoyancy force, and the drag force are all in balance and the bubble has a constant velocity and a very low Reynolds number. The solution proceeds under the assumption that the bubble is spherical. At the end we will check this assumption.

Consider a fluid sphere of radius r_0 at the origin of a spherical coordinate system as shown previously in Fig. 21.8. The problem is similar to Stokes flow over a solid sphere (Section 23.5) except that the boundary conditions are different. The streamfunction in spherical coordinates for Stokes flow is governed by $E^2 E^2 \psi = 0$. From Eq. 12.5.19 (also Eq. 21.7.1) this is

$$0 - \left[\frac{\partial^2}{\partial r^2} + \frac{\sin \theta}{r^2} \frac{\partial}{\partial \theta} \left(\frac{1}{\sin \theta} \frac{\partial}{\partial \theta} \right) \right] \left[\frac{\partial^2 \psi}{\partial r^2} + \frac{\sin \theta}{r^2} \frac{\partial}{\partial \theta} \left(\frac{1}{\sin \theta} \frac{\partial \psi}{\partial \theta} \right) \right] \quad (23.5.1)$$

The flow outside the bubble will simply be called ψ and that within the bubble denoted by ψ^i.

The boundary condition of a uniform stream at infinity (Eq. 21.8.4) is retained. The condition of no flow across the surface of the droplet gives

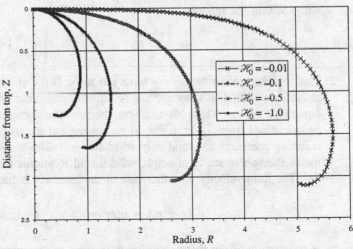

Figure 23.8   Solutions for sessile drops. $\mathcal{H}_0$ is the initial curvature at the top of the drop.

$$\psi(r = r_0) = \psi^i(r = r_0) = 0 \qquad (23.5.2)$$

The interface fluid may have a tangential velocity v_θ, but in accord with 23.1.7, we require that both sides have the same value. From Eq. 21.8.1 this leads to the condition on the streamfunction that

$$\left. \frac{\partial \psi}{\partial r} \right|_{r_0} = \left. \frac{\partial \psi^i}{\partial r} \right|_{r_0} \qquad (23.5.3)$$

In addition, we assume that the surface tension is constant, so the shear stress is also required to match on either side of the interface.

$$\mu \left. \frac{\partial}{\partial r} \left(\frac{1}{r^2} \frac{\partial \psi}{\partial r} \right) \right|_{r_0} = \mu^i \left. \frac{\partial}{\partial r} \left(\frac{1}{r^2} \frac{\partial \psi^i}{\partial r} \right) \right|_{r_0} \qquad (23.5.4)$$

The boundary conditions demanding continuity of v_θ and $\tau_{r\theta}$ across the interface replace the usual condition that the surface velocity of a solid is known. The shear-stress expression 23.5.4 introduces the viscosity ratio

$$\alpha = \frac{\mu_i}{\mu} \qquad (23.5.5)$$

as a parameter in the problem. Gas bubbles in a liquid are modeled by $\alpha \rightarrow 0$, while the results for rigid spheres are retrieved by $\alpha \rightarrow \infty$.

The problem for Stokes flow over a fluid bubble was first solved independently by Rybczynski (1911) and Hadamard (1911). Just as in the case of the rigid sphere, the technique of separation of variables leads to a solution. The streamfunction for the outer flow is

$$\psi = -\frac{1}{2} U r^2 \sin^2\theta \left[1 - \left(\frac{r_0}{r} \right) \frac{3\alpha + 2}{2(1 + \alpha)} + \left(\frac{r_0}{r} \right)^3 \frac{\alpha}{1 + \alpha} \right] \qquad (23.5.6)$$

while within the sphere

$$\psi^i = \frac{1}{4} U r^2 \sin^2\theta \frac{1}{1 + \alpha} \left[1 - \left(\frac{r}{r_0} \right)^2 \right] \qquad (23.5.7)$$

The solution within the sphere turns out to be Hill's spherical vortex, which was given in Section 13.6. Hill's vortex is a solution to complete unapproximated Navier–Stokes equations. At low Reynolds numbers, the pressure corresponding to Hill's solution may be calculated from $\nabla p = \mu \nabla^2 \mathbf{v}$. Since we neglect the inertia terms in this equation, the resulting pressures are valid only when $\text{Re} \rightarrow 0$. The vorticity and velocity distributions inside the sphere are in principle valid for all Reynolds numbers.

The fluid velocity on either side of the interface is found using Eq. 21.8.1. It is

$$v_\theta(r = r_0) = v_\theta^i(r = r_0) = \frac{1}{2} U \sin\theta \frac{1}{1 + \alpha} \qquad (23.5.8)$$

A calculation of the shear stress on both sides of the interface reveals that

$$\tau_{r\theta}(r = r_0) = \tau_{r\theta}^i(r = r_0) = \frac{3}{2}\frac{\mu U}{r_0}\sin\theta\frac{\alpha}{1 + \alpha} \qquad (23.5.9)$$

Equation 23.5.9 shows that the special case of a gas bubble in a liquid, $\sigma \to \infty$, has no shear at the interface.

Next, let us investigate the normal forces, both pressure and viscous, that act at the interface. In formulating the problem it was not necessary to specify any conditions on the normal stresses because the interface shape was assumed. On the outside of the sphere, a pressure reference p_0 is taken at the equator, while p_0^i is a similar reference for the inside motion. These reference values may be functions of time, as would be the case for a sphere moving in a liquid where the hydrostatic pressure gradient is significant. The pressure and normal viscous stress on the outside are

$$p = p_0 + \rho g r_0 \cos\theta + \frac{\mu U}{r_0}\cos\theta\frac{3\alpha + 2}{2(1 + \alpha)} \qquad (23.5.10)$$

$$\tau_{rr} = -2\frac{\mu U}{r_0}\cos\theta\frac{1}{1 + \alpha} \qquad (23.5.11)$$

It is apparent that p and τ_{rr}, are of comparable size, so that the normal viscous force contributes strongly to the total drag force on the sphere. In fact, for a gas bubble ($\sigma \to 0$), the contribution to the drag from the normal viscous force is twice that of the pressure. The other extreme case is the rigid particle. Equation 23.5.10 shows that $\tau_{rr} = 0$ when $\sigma \to \infty$. This is, of course, just an example of the fact that Newtonian fluids cannot have normal viscous stresses at a solid wall.

The total drag force on the outside of the spherical interface is found by integrating the surface forces. A simpler way is to use the force balance result (Eq. 21.8.20; $F_D = 8\pi\mu r_0 U C_1$), which relates the drag to streamfunction cooefficient C_1 in Eq. 21.8.9. Comparing Eqs. 23.5.6 and 21.8.9 shows that $C_1 = (3\alpha + 2)/4(\alpha + 1)$. The resulting formula is called the *Hadamard–Rybcyznski draw law*. It is

$$F_D = 6\pi\mu r_0 U\frac{3\alpha + 2}{3(\alpha + 1)} \qquad (23.5.12)$$

If $\sigma = \infty$, Stokes's drag law is obtained for rigid spheres, while for the gas bubble limit $\sigma \to 0$, the coefficient of 6π becomes 4π.

A frequent application of the Hadamared–Rybczynski formula is to the case where a fluid sphere of density ρ^i rises or falls through a still fluid of density ρ. At equilibrium the weight, drag, and bouyancy forces balance. The resulting expression can be solved to yield the terminal velocity equation,

$$U_t = \frac{2}{9}\frac{g r_0^2}{\mu}(\rho' - \rho)\frac{3\alpha + 1}{3\alpha + 2} \qquad (23.5.13)$$

This equation offers an experimental method to verify the drag formula 23.5.12. Overall, the experiments confirm the theory as long as the fluid sphere is reasonably large; a considerable amount of practical information is summarized in Clift et al. (1978). The situation changes for very small spheres; they show little internal circulation and have a drag force approaching that of rigid particles. The cause of this deviation is thought to be an accumulation of surface-active molecules in the interface. Such molecules contaminate most liquids and are very difficult to purge. As the drop or bubble moves through the fluid, the contaminant molecules collect on the interface. This gives the interface a viscous characteristic of its own. Small spheres, because of their relatively small surface area, are more susceptible to this effect.

In the calculations above we have dealt exclusively with the pressures and stresses on the outside of the interface. The normal stresses that act on the inside surface of the interface are calculated from Hill's vortex solution. They turn out to be

$$p^i = p_0^i + \rho^i g r_0 \cos \theta - 5 \frac{\mu^i U}{r_0} \cos \theta \frac{1}{1 + \alpha} \tag{23.5.14}$$

$$\tau_{rr}^i = -2 \frac{\mu^i U}{r_0} \cos \theta \frac{1}{1 + \alpha} \tag{23.5.15}$$

To compare the normal forces on either side of the interface, we let $F_n \equiv p - \tau_{rr}$. The change in F_n is found from Eqs. 23.5.10, 22.5.11, 23.5.14, and 23.5.15. It is

$$F_n - F_n^i = p_0 - p_0^i + (\rho - \rho^i) r_0 \cos \theta + \frac{\mu U}{r_0} \cos \theta \frac{9\alpha + 6}{2\alpha + 2} \tag{23.5.16}$$

According to the elementary theory for an interface, surface tension should account for this jump. Hence,

$$F_n - F_n^i = \frac{\alpha}{2r_0} \tag{23.5.17}$$

From Eq. 23.5.16 we see that when ρ, ρ^i, and U take on arbitrary values, the surface tension musst be a function of θ in order to maintain a spherical shape. We would not expect this to be the normal situation, and the surface would distort from our assumed spherical shape.

When a bubble or drop is falling or rising through an infinite fluid at its terminal velocity, a very striking result is obtained. Substitution of Eq. 23.5.13 into Eq. 23.5.16 shows that the imbalance of hydrostatic pressure across the interface is balanced exactly by the normal stress. The result is a constant jump in the normal force across the interface,

$$F_n - F_n^i = p_0 - p_0^i = \frac{\alpha}{2r_0} \tag{23.5.18}$$

A bubble or droplet at its terminal velocity can have a constant surface tension and therefore has no tendency to distort from its spherical shape. Experiments confirm that bubble and drop retain a spherical shape for all low-Reynolds-number flows.

23.6   CONSTANT-TENSION FLOWS: CAPILLARY WAVES

A free liquid surface that is disturbed can be represented by Fourier sine and cosine components. Because the surface tension and curvature change the pressure in the liquid, a traveling wave flow is engendered. These are inviscid, irrotational flows that have much in common with gravity waves. In fact, the analysis of Section 18.18 needs to be modified only slightly to describe capillary waves. Consider a traveling wave of wavelength λ (wavenumber k), phase speed c, and amplitude A. The vertical direction is y and the wave travels in the x-direction. With the origin placed at the mean wave height, the wave surface is

$$y_s = \eta(x, t) = A \sin \frac{2\pi(x - ct)}{\lambda}$$

$$= A \sin[k(x - ct)] \qquad (23.6.1)$$

We can use the same nomenclature as in Section 18.18. The kinematics of irrotational, inciscid flow determines the velocity field, so the analysis of Section 18.18 is valid through Eq. 18.18.10. The Bernoulli equation must be modified to reflect the jump in pressure across the interface because of surface tension. The pressure in the liquid next to the interface is the atmospheric value p plus the surface tension effect. Since we assumed in Section 18.18 that the wave amplitude is small compared to λ, it is appropriate to express the curvature as $2\mathcal{H} = \eta_{xx}[1 + (\eta_x)^2]^{-3/2} \sim \eta_{xx}$:

$$p + \sigma \frac{1}{R} = p + \sigma\left(-\frac{\partial^2 \eta}{\partial x^2}\right)$$

$$= p + \sigma k^2 \eta \qquad (23.6.2)$$

Modifying the Bernoulli equation 18.18.11 yields

$$\frac{\partial \phi}{\partial t} + \frac{p}{\rho} + \frac{\sigma k^2 \eta}{\rho} + \frac{1}{2}(u^2 + v^2) + g\eta = 0 \qquad (23.6.3)$$

Notice that the hydrostatic gravity effect and the surface tension effect have the same dependence on η. Hence, it is possible to define an effective gravity and use the previous analysis of Section 18.18:

$$g_{\text{eff}} = \left(\frac{\sigma k^2}{\rho g} + 1\right) g \qquad (23.6.4)$$

The wavelength of the surface tension effect is nondimensionalized by the capillary length scale $\sqrt{\sigma/\rho g}$. If the wavelength ($\lambda = 1/2\pi k$) is long compared to the capillary length, surface tension effects are not important. On the other hand, very short wavelengths are dominated by surface tension. The wavelength for equal gravity and surface tension effects for water–air is about 1.7 cm.

From Section 18.18 we find the dispersion relation between wavenumber k and wavespeed c (Eq. 18.18.13):

$$\frac{kc^2}{(\sigma k^2/\rho) + g} = \tanh kh \qquad (23.6.5)$$

Here h is the depth of the liquid. Special cases of deep and shallow liquid depths parallel those of Section 18.18. For example, the phase speed in a deep liquid is

$$c^2 = \frac{\sigma k}{\rho} + \frac{g}{k}$$ (23.6.6)

For large k the gravity effect is negligible. For small k the surface tension effect is negligible.

23.7 MOVING CONTACT LINES

In many fluid flows the contact line moves over the surface of a solid. The spreading of a drop on a flat wall is a simple situation, yet has several physical models. An industrially important situation is the slide-coating apparatus shown in Fig. 23.9. A web to be coated is moving over a roller. The coating fluid comes from a reservoir and the flow rate is metered by the Poiseuille flow in a long slot. The coating fluid exits to the slide, flows along the slide, and then attaches itself to the web by a moving contact line. The speed of the process is controlled by events at the moving contact line.

The physics of moving (also called dynamic) contact lines is not clearly understood. The contact angle is modified by the flow situation and its exact value depends on the degree of magnification of the measurement. Experimental observations on nominally the same system can differ by 10° (see, e.g., Hayes and Ralston, 1993). Some of this may be attributed to contamination, but other deviations are attributed to different methods of measurement. One proposal is that on a microscopic scale, the dynamic contact angle is the same as the static angle except that the flow field distorts the angle and the angle observed is at the macroscopic scale. Figure 23.10 shows the typical trends for a dynamic contact line plotted as a function of velocity. For an advancing line the contact angle increases with velocity until a maximum value is reached where the angle is effectively 180° and air is entrained. At very small velocities the contact line does not move smoothly but advances in sporadic jumps. Many empirical representations of the advancing contact angle θ_A are used. They can be special cases of the general relation

$$\theta_A = \theta_{SA} + \left(\frac{U}{k_A}\right)^{1/m}$$ (23.7.1)

Here θ_{SA} is the static angle just before motion is initiated; k_A and m are constants. If the line is moved in the receding direction, motion does not start until a lower contact angle

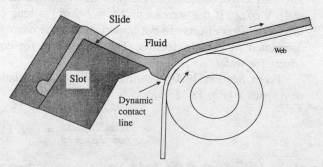

Figure 23.9 Slide-coating process to attach fluid continuously to a moving web material.

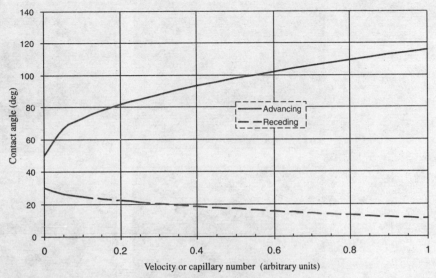

Figure 23.10 Trends from a model of contact angle of advancing and receding contact lines.

θ_{SR} is attained. This difference is termed *contact-angle hysteresis*. It is thought to be the result of surface roughness and surface contamination. The receding contact angle decreases with speed and a speed is reached where the angle is effectively zero with a film left on the solid. An equation of form similar to Eq. 23.7.1 is used to model the receding contact angle.

Dussan V. and Davis (1974) focused attention on the rolling motion that occurs at a moving contact line. They illuminated the importance of this motion and deduced properties of the flow in the contact line neighborhood. One of their experiments is shown in Fig. 23.11. In part (a) two drops of glycerin, one dyed a dark color, are placed on a flat beeswax surface. The surface is tilted and the drops merge in part (b). Further motion to the left is shown in part (c), where the advancing contact line on the left is clear fluid and the receding line on the right is dark fluid. At a later time, shown in part (d), the dark fluid has rolled over the light fluid and the contact line consists of dark fluid. The receding line on the right is now entirely light fluid. In their analysis of the flow pattern Dussan V. and Davis (1974) deduced that the streamlines near a moving contact line must have the pattern shown in Fig. 23.12. In a coordinate system moving with the contact line, the flow is steady, with fluid A rolling over the wall. Fluid B is ejected from the contact line and joins fluid B that comes from the interface. Which fluid is ejected depends on the contact angle and the viscosity ratio of the fluids. Note that at the contact line several streamlines join. From the continuum point of view, this is a stagnation point with zero velocity. On the other hand, the no-slip boundary condition would require that the wall velocity would exist at this point. Thus, from a continuum kinematic point of view, there must be slip at the contact line. We are accustomed to accepting jumps in velocity boundary conditions (multi-valued points; for instance, the lid of a driven cavity); however, this case is more serious. The paper of Dussan V. and Davis (1974) shows that the shear stress in not only infinite but is not integrable to give

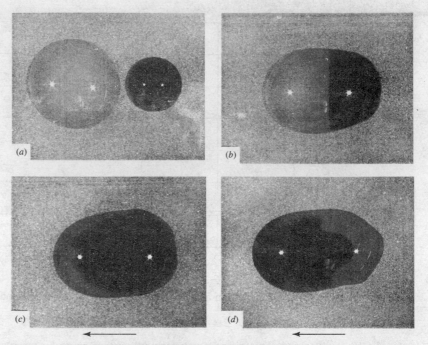

Figure 23.11   Rolling motion of moving contact line: (*a*) two drops of glycerin, one colored, on a flat surface; (*b*) drops move to the left and merge; (*c*) advancing line is clear fluid, receding is dark fluid; (*d*) dark fluid has rolled over the light fluid. Reprinted with permission from Dussan V. and Davis (1974), Cambridge University Press.

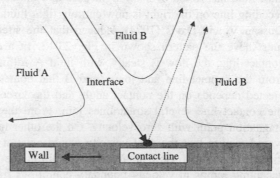

Figure 23.12   Streamlines near a moving contact line as seen moving with the contact line.

a finite force. Any type of slip boundary condition (e.g., slip velocity ~ shear stress) will remedy this situation with regard to continuum calculations.

Well-posed continuum calculations with moving contact lines need only a specified contact angle and a slip law for the region near the contact line. The simple situation of the spreading of a certain quantity of liquid over a plane solid is the canonical problem. A review of several theories is given in Davis (2000). An introductory review of dynamic contact line behavior is Dussan V. (1977). The physics of dynamic contact line behavior is not settled, but progress has been made. The next level of complexity from the continuum viewpoint is Shikhmurzaev (1997). He endows the solid–liquid interface with a "pressure" and absorbed surface density that are related by an equation of state. Similarly, the liquid–liquid interface is two surfaces with "surface pressures" and absorbed "surface densities." Calculations using kinetic theory and molecular interaction models are also successful. The spreading of a drop on a solid as calculated by de Ruijter et al. (1999) produces the proper macroscopic behavior.

23.8 CONSTANT-TENSION FLOWS: COATING FLOWS

There are various processes for applying coatings of materials to surfaces. In many instants the thickness of the material is determined by fluid-flow events in the process. Many processes can be described in three parts. First, there is the flow path of the bulk fluid as it brought to the coating area, then there is the formation of the coating meniscus, and finally, there is an adjustment to a solid form by cooling, drying, chemical reaction, or a similar process. Of critical interest in any case is the thickness of the coating. Ruschak (1985) describes two general categories. In premetered flows the film thickness is controlled by events upstream of where the meniscus is formed. In self-metered flows the meniscus formation process itself determines the film thickness. Industrially relevant processes are discussed in Weinstein and Ruschak (2004).

Examples of premetered coatings are the slide coating shown in Fig. 23.9 and the wire coating shown in Fig. 23.13a. In slide coating the pressure drop that produces the

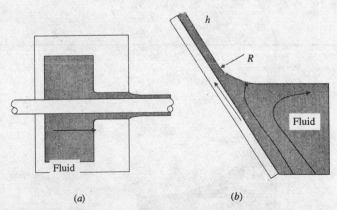

(a)   (b)

Figure 23.13 Classification of coating flows: (a) premetered flow; (b) self-metered flow.

Poiseuille flow in the die determines the volume flow rate. Similarly, the wire coating has a pressure-driven flow from the reservoir, and in addition, a Couette flow, because of the wire motion.

The common flow element in the self-metered processes is the *dip coating* or *drag out* process shown in Fig. 23.14. Here the web or machine part is withdrawn from a bath of the coating liquid. Surface tension effects at the withdrawal point frequently dominate the process. This process is relevant to any situation where a film is formed from a liquid pool. For example, a bubble rising in a tube leaves a film on the walls.

The nomenclature for the analysis is depicted in Fig. 23.14. Let the x-axis be along the plate and the y-axis be normal to the plate at the level of the free surface. Unlike the meniscus problem of Section 23.2, the film thickness is measured from the web $h(x)$, which has the drag-out velocity U_0. For a very low velocity U_0, the meniscus remains static. Hocking (2001) has found that there is a critical capillary number, $Ca^* = \mu U_0 / \sigma$, which also depends on the slip coefficient of the contact line, for which the contact line simply moves over the web and coating does not occur. Here we are interested in the case where a coating is produced.

The original approximate analysis was given in Landau and Levich (1942); a summary is in Levich (1962). Their reasoning is that the coating is very thin compared to the region where the capillary rise occurs, and that the capillary rise is described by the static meniscus problem of Section 23.2. This implicitly neglects the approach flow engendered within the bath by the moving web. Where the static meniscus would apparently contact the web, there is a flow region that produces the coating film. Since the flow region replaces the contact line, the effective contact angle of the static meniscus is assumed to be zero. The solution (Eq. 23.2.5) for a static meniscus is shown in Fig. 23.15 for $\theta_0 = 0$. The meniscus height at the web is Eq. 23.2.6:

$$x_0 = \sqrt{\frac{2\sigma}{\rho g}} \tag{23.8.1}$$

The slope of the static meniscus at the web, $y = 0$, is by assumption infinite; however, there is a finite radius of curvature R_0 given by Eq. 23.3.3:

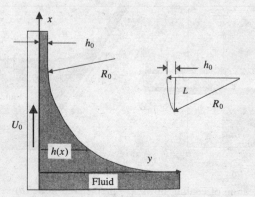

Figure 23.14 Dip or drag-out coating problem.

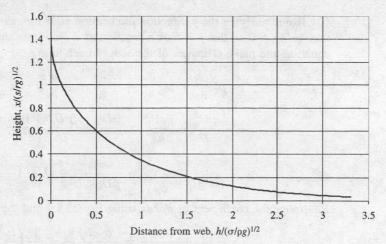

Figure 23.15   Solution for a static meniscus with a contact angle of $\theta = 0$.

$$R_0 = \sqrt{\frac{2\sigma}{\rho g}} \qquad (23.8.2)$$

This radius is used to connect the meniscus region to the flow region. In the terminology of a singular perturbation problem, it is the common part from an overlap region.

The flow region is analyzed employing the lubrication approximation; the flow-direction length scale is much longer than the transverse length scale. Temporarily, let L be the x-direction scale. The final film thickness h_0 is the y-direction scale and their ratio $\varepsilon = h_0/L$ is a small parameter. Flow direction velocity u is scaled by U_0 and transverse velocities v by εU_0 (so that the continuity equation is satisfied). The pressure scale in the lubrication approximation with a free surface is different from that for the lubrication approximation with confined flows. The pressure scaling is imposed by the surface tension and surface curvature. Here we use the characteristic curvature from the meniscus, so $p \sim \sigma/R_0$. The scales, Reynolds number, and capillary number are

$$x \sim L, \qquad y \sim h_0 = \varepsilon L, \qquad u \sim U_0, \qquad v \sim \varepsilon U_0, \qquad p \sim \frac{\sigma}{R_0}$$

$$\mathrm{Re} = \frac{\rho U_0 h_0}{\mu}, \qquad \mathrm{Ca} = \frac{\mu U_0}{\sigma} \qquad (23.8.3)$$

To be more specific about the x-scale, consider the inset of Fig. 23.14, where the arc of a circle of radius R_0 is shown. Consider the lubrication approximation for this region. If the meniscus increases by an amount $\sim h_0$, the chord length L is given by geometry as

$$L \sim \sqrt{2h_0 R_0 - h_0^2} \sim \sqrt{h_0 R_0} \qquad (23.8.4)$$

The fact that h_0/L is small indicates that the lubrication approximation has been used. This relates R_0, h_0, and L for later use.

If one analyzes the y-direction momentum equation, as in Section 21.1, it turns out that $\partial p/\partial y = 0$, so that p is only a function of x. Now consider the x-direction momentum equation and make estimates of the size of each term.

$$\rho u \frac{\partial u}{\partial x} + \rho v \frac{\partial u}{\partial y} = -\frac{\partial p}{\partial x} + \mu \frac{\partial^2 u}{\partial x^2} + \mu \frac{\partial^2 u}{\partial y^2} - \rho g$$

$$\frac{\rho U_0^2}{L} + \frac{\rho \varepsilon U_0^2}{h_0} = \frac{\sigma/R_0}{L} + \frac{\mu U_0}{L^2} + \frac{\mu U_0}{h_0^2} + \rho g \tag{23.8.5}$$

$$\varepsilon \, \text{Re} + \varepsilon \, \text{Re} = \frac{\sigma h_0^2}{\mu U_0 R_0 L} + \varepsilon^2 + 1 + \frac{\rho g h_0^2}{\mu U_0}$$

Rearrange the coefficient of dp/dx using Eq. 23.8.4 and the definition of Ca gives

$$\frac{\sigma h_0^2}{\mu U_0 R_0 L} = \frac{\sigma}{\mu U_0} \frac{h_0}{R_0} \frac{h_0}{L} = \frac{1}{\text{Ca}} \left(\frac{h_0}{L}\right)^3 \tag{23.8.6}$$

In the limit $\varepsilon \to 0$ the viscous term and the pressure term will be the same size if the coefficient (Eq. 23.8.6) is of order one. Hence, let L be defined by

$$\frac{h_0}{L} = \varepsilon = (3\text{Ca})^{1/3} \tag{23.8.7}$$

The factor of 3 is included to make the subsequent algebra simpler. As a matter of interest, the size of the gravity term is

$$\frac{\rho g h_0^2}{\mu U_0} \sim \text{Ca}^{1/3} = \varepsilon \tag{23.8.8}$$

Gravity does not influence the film coating process except through its effect on the static meniscus.

Momentum equation 23.8.5 in the lubrication approximation $\varepsilon \to 0$ with the Laplace equation $p = \sigma/R$ inserted for the pressure is

$$0 = -\frac{d(\sigma/R)}{dx} + \mu \frac{\partial^2 u}{\partial y^2} \tag{23.8.9}$$

For a rectangular coordinate system the radius of curvature is

$$\frac{1}{R} = h''(1 - h'^2)^{-2/3} \tag{23.8.10}$$

Equation 23.8.10 is substituted into Eq. 23.8.9 and the nondimensional variables below are inserted.

$$X = \frac{x}{L}, \qquad Y = \frac{y}{h_0}, \qquad H = \frac{h}{h_0}, \qquad U = \frac{u}{U_0} \tag{23.8.11}$$

Solving with boundary conditions $U(Y = 0) = 1$ and $dU/dY(Y = 1) = 0$ gives the velocity profile:

$$U = 1 - 3H'''(YH - \tfrac{1}{2}Y^2) \qquad (23.8.12)$$

Note that far downstream the coating is fully developed, the pressure gradient vanishes, $H''' = 0$, the velocity profile is $U = 1$, and the volume flow rate $Q = UH = 1$. At any upstream station X the flow rate is

$$Q = 1 = \int_0^H U \, dY = H^3 H''' + H \qquad (23.8.13)$$

$$H^3 H''' = 1 - H$$

This is the differential equation governing the meniscus shape in the flow region. Boundary conditions are

$$H(-\infty) = 1, \qquad H'(-\infty) = 0, \qquad H''(-\infty) = 0 \qquad (23.8.14)$$

Probstein (2003) notes that the as $X \Rightarrow -\infty$ the equation becomes $H''' = 1 - H$ and a solution is $H = 1 + Ae^{-X}$. Furthermore, the origin of the X-axis can be adjusted so that $A = 1$. This solution provides starting values for integration from a finite negative value of X toward positive X. Results for the meniscus $H(X)$ and the curvature $H''(X)$ are given in Fig. 23.16.

A condition that completes the problem is the matching between the curvature of the flow region as $X \rightarrow \infty$ and the static meniscus at the wall:

$$\left. \frac{d^2 h}{dx^2} \right|_{x \rightarrow -\infty} = 2\mathcal{H}_{\substack{\text{static} \\ \text{at wall}}} = \frac{1}{R_0} \qquad (23.8.15)$$

In nondimensional terms this is

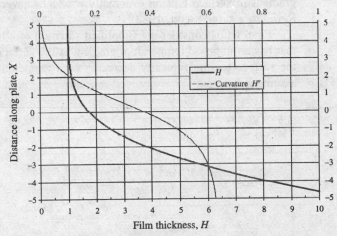

Figure 23.16   Solution for the coating thickness H and meniscus curvature H'' as a function of distance X along the moving wall (arbitrary origin). Alternatively, meniscus height X as a function of distance from the wall H.

$$C = H''|_{X \to -\infty} = \frac{L^2}{h_0}\frac{d^2h}{dx^2}\bigg|_{x \to -\infty} = \frac{L^2}{h_0 R_0} \tag{23.8.16}$$

The solution of Eq. 23.8.13 yields $H''(-\infty) = C = 0.643$, so the film thickness equation is

$$\frac{h_0}{R_0} = C(3\text{Ca})^{2/3} = 0.643(3\text{Ca})^{2/3} = 1.34\text{Ca}^{2/3} \tag{23.8.17}$$

A comparison of this equation with experimental data by Ruschak (1985) shows that the validity is for $0.01 < \text{Ca}$ ($\text{Ca}^{2/3} = 0.046$, $h_0/R_0 = 0.06$). Inserting Eq. 23.8.2 for R_0 completes the formula for h_0.

Recall that the lubrication approximation, $\varepsilon = h_0/L \to 0$, was used to find the $H(X)$ solution in the flow region (Fig. 23.16). It is a little disappointing that the asymptotic value of $H''(-\infty) = C = 0.643$ is only reached at about $X = -5$, where $h_0/X = 11$.

23.9   MARANGONI FLOW

Marangoni flow is a term to indicate that a gradient in the surface tension (Eq. 23.1.21) is the driving force for the flow. The surface tension may vary because of electrical effects, because the interface has various concentrations of absorbed foreign molecules, or simply because the temperature, and therefore σ, of the interface is varying. If the flow is caused by temper variations it is called a *thermocapillary flow*. Some liquid interfaces are not prone to collecting foreign molecules; others are, however. Unfortunately, water–air interfaces are easily contaminated. One may observe that a stick or obstacle in a slow-moving stream will collect contamination on the upstream side. This gradient in surface tension eventually produces a very small ripple or wave known as *Reynolds's ridge* (Scott, 1982).

First, let us consider the simplified situation of a liquid film of constant thickness h_0 that has an imposed temperature gradient at the surface as shown in Fig. 23.17. Because the surface tension typically decreases with temperature, there is a gradient, which we assume is constant:

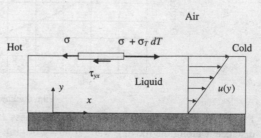

Figure 23.17   Marangoni flow of a film of constant thickness with surface tension gradient σ_T.

$$\frac{d\sigma}{dx} = \sigma_x = \frac{d\sigma}{dT}\frac{dT}{dx} = \sigma_T\frac{\Delta T}{h_0} \qquad (23.9.1)$$

Here we have introduced the temperature sensitivity of the surface tension $d\sigma/dT = \sigma_T$ and a characteristic temperature difference ΔT over the distance h_0. The interface boundary condition at $y = h_0$ is Eq. 23.1.21.

$$0 = \tau_{xyA} - \tau_{xyB} - \frac{d\sigma}{dx} \qquad (23.9.2)$$

$$\tau_{xyA} = \mu\left.\frac{du}{dy}\right|_{h_0} = \sigma_x$$

Make the usual assumption that the stress in the air $\tau_{yxA} = 0$. The no-slip condition $u(y = 0)$ will be used at the wall. If we assume a parallel flow $u(y)$, the simplified x-direction momentum equation is

$$0 = \mu\frac{d^2u}{dy^2} \qquad (23.9.3)$$

Integration and applying boundary conditions gives the linear velocity profile:

$$u = \frac{\sigma_x}{\mu}y = \frac{\sigma_T\Delta T}{\mu}\frac{y}{h_0} = u_s\frac{y}{h_0} \qquad (23.9.4)$$

The important point about Eq. 23.9.4 is the velocity scale:

$$u_s = \frac{\sigma_x}{\mu} = \frac{\sigma_T\Delta T}{\mu} \qquad (23.9.5)$$

This is the thermocapillary velocity scale and is used in various nondimensional numbers when thermocapillary events are important.

For example, the *Marangoni number* compares fluid convection to heat conduction, Ma $= Lu_s/\alpha$ (here α is the thermal diffusitive). A low Marangoni number means that the temperature field is dominated by conduction and unaffected by the flow field. This is a good situation to study thermocapillary effects without the complications of heat transfer effects. Additionally, we assume that the interface has its assumed shape without being deformed by the flow. This is true if the capillary number, Ca $= \mu u_s/\sigma$, is small. The surface tension is so strong that the interface is not deformed.

As a typical thermocapillary problem, consider a liquid cylinder in air with the ends held at different temperatures. This might be a model for a molten solder cylinder between a chip and a substrate. A closed-form solution exists (Xu, 1984) for the Stokes flow case of Re $= 0$. The temperature at the interface varies linearly and causes a gradient in surface tension [Davis (1989) considers arbitrary surface temperature profiles]. The interface flows toward the colder end, where the tension is higher. By Eq. 23.9.2 a viscous stress is generated in the liquid and diffuses into the liquid to produce a flow that because the cylinder is closed, must recirculate as shown schematically in Fig. 23.18. Nondimensional variables are formed with the cylinder height L, radius r_0, temperature difference ΔT, and the thermocapillary velocity scale (Eq. 23.9.5):

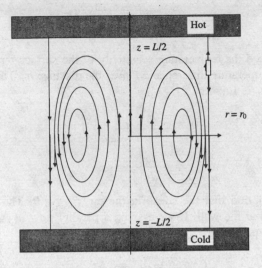

Figure 23.18 Streamlines in a cylinder of liquid with ends at different temperatures.

$$z^* = \frac{z}{L}, \qquad r^* = \frac{r}{L}, \qquad R = \frac{r_0}{L}$$

$$v_r^* = \frac{v_r}{\sigma_T \Delta T / \mu}, \qquad v_z^* = \frac{v_z}{\sigma_T \Delta T / \mu} \qquad (23.9.6)$$

$$\psi^* = \frac{\psi}{\sigma_T \Delta T L^2 / \mu}$$

Note that the aspect ratio of the cylinder is $R = r_0/L$. In cylindrical coordinates the velocity components are

$$v_r^* = \frac{-1}{r^*} \frac{\partial \psi^*}{\partial z^*}, \qquad v_z^* = \frac{1}{r^*} \frac{\partial \psi^*}{\partial r^*} \qquad (23.9.7)$$

The equation governing ψ for Stokes flow in cylindrical coordinates is $E^2 E^2 \psi^* = 0$.

$$\left(\frac{\partial^2}{\partial r^2} - \frac{1}{r} \frac{\partial}{\partial r} + \frac{\partial^2}{\partial z^2} \right)^2 \psi = 0 \qquad (23.9.8)$$

Boundary conditions are $\psi = 0$ on the cylinder centerline, outside interface, and the ends; symmetry in v_z at $r = 0$ ($\partial v_z/\partial r = 0$); no-slip conditions on the ends; and the stress–surface tension condition 23.9.2 on the interface.

$$\psi(r = 0, z) = 0, \qquad \psi(r = r_0, z) = 0, \qquad \psi(r, z = \pm L/2) = 0$$

$$\frac{\partial^2 \psi}{\partial r^2}(r = 0, z) = 0, \qquad \frac{\partial \psi}{\partial z}(r, z = \pm L/2) = 0 \qquad (23.9.9)$$

$$\mu \frac{\partial v_z}{\partial r}(r = r_0, z) = -\sigma_x \Delta T \quad \text{or} \quad \mu \frac{\partial}{\partial r}\left(\frac{1}{r} \frac{\partial \psi}{\partial r} \right)(r = r_0, z) = -\sigma_x \Delta T$$

The nondimensional solution by the separation-of-variables method is

$$\psi^* = -\frac{1}{8R}(r^{*4} - R^2 r^{*2}) + 2R \sum_{m=1}^{\infty} \frac{rJ_1(k_m r^*/R)}{k_m^2 J_0(k_m)}$$

$$\times \left[\left(\cosh \frac{k_m}{2R} + \frac{2R}{k_m} \sinh \frac{k_m}{2R} \right) \cosh \frac{k_m z^*}{R} - 2z^* \sinh \frac{k_m}{2R} \sinh \frac{k_m z^*}{R} \right]$$

$$\times \left(\frac{k_m}{R} + \sinh \frac{k_m}{R} \right)^{-1} \tag{23.9.10}$$

Here k_m are the zeros of Bessel functions $J_1(k_m) = 0$ arranged in ascending order. This series solution gives sufficient accuracy with 18 terms. For certain large aspect ratios $R = r_0/L$ and interface temperature profiles, this flow develops cylindrical Moffatt vortices.

Another cylinder problem of interest is when both ends of the cylinder are at the same temperature but the side is heated by radiation. This is called a *liquid bridge* and is important to manufacturing processes. As is easily imagined, this flow has two vortices on either side of the symmetric temperature profile.

An interesting example of a local Marangoni flow is the stagnation point (line) in a bath of liquid with the surface heated in a prescribed manner. The heating could be by thermal radiation, for instance. Figure 23.19 shows the geometry of the problem. The surface tension in the hot region decreases and the interface is pulled toward the cold regions by the higher surface tension. Viscous diffusion promotes a flow within the liquid in the direction away from the stagnation point. Mass conservation then requires a flow toward the surface from deep within the liquid bath. The analysis closely parallels the stagnation-point problem of Section 11.9. Boundary conditions for the present problem are

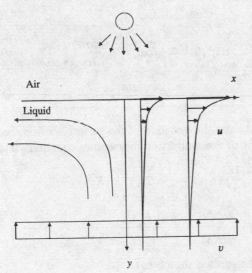

Figure 23.19 Local stagnation region at a surface with a local minimum in the surface tension.

$$u(x, \infty) = 0$$

$$\tau_{xyA}(x, \infty) = 0$$

$$v(x, 0) = 0 \qquad (23.9.11)$$

$$p(x, 0) = p_0$$

No conditions on the interface velocity $u(x, 0)$, the stress $\tau_{yx}(x, 0)$, or the surface tension gradient $d\sigma/dx$ are specified. We will accept whatever distribution produces a solution of simple form. As in Section 11.9, assume that the profiles are given by a function $f(y)$ such that

$$u(x, y) = xf'(y)$$

$$v(x, y) = -f(y) \qquad (23.9.12)$$

$$\tau_{yx}(x, y) = \mu x f''(y)$$

In terms of f the boundary conditions are

$$f'(x, \infty) = 0$$

$$f''(x, \infty) = 0 \qquad (23.9.13)$$

$$f(x, 0) = 0$$

Thermocapillary interface condition 23.1.21 for this problem is $\tau_{yxA} = -d\sigma/dx$.

Let

$$f''(0) = -a \qquad (23.9.14)$$

then

$$\tau_{yxA} = -\frac{d\sigma}{dx}$$

$$\mu x f''(0) = -\mu x a = -\frac{d\sigma}{dx} \qquad (23.9.15)$$

$$\sigma = \sigma_0 + \frac{\mu a}{2} x^2$$

The coefficient a, which indicates the variation of the surface tension, becomes a parameter in the analysis. Analysis of the x-direction momentum equation yields (Eq. 11.9.11)

$$\frac{1}{\rho} p(x, y) = \frac{1}{2} x^2 H(y) + K(y) \qquad (23.9.16)$$

where

$$-H(y) = f'^2 - ff'' - \nu f''' \qquad (23.9.17)$$

Evaluating Eq. 23.9.14 at the surface shows that

$$K(0) = p_0, \qquad H(0) = 0 \qquad (23.9.18)$$

The y-direction momentum equation is the same as Eq. 11.9.12 except that the gravity force must be added.

$$f(y)f'(y) = -\tfrac{1}{2}x^2H'(y) - K'(y) - \nu f''(y) + g \qquad (23.9.19)$$

This equation can be true only if $H'(y) = 0$, hence using Eq. 23.9.18, $H(y) = 0$. Furthermore, evaluating Eq. 23.9.19 at $y = \infty$ gives $K'(y) = g$. Together with Eq. 23.9.16 this means that the hydrostatic pressure distribution exists:

$$\frac{1}{\rho}p(x, y) = \frac{1}{\rho}p_0 + gy \qquad (23.9.20)$$

Moreover, the fact that $H(y) = 0$ simplifies differential equation 23.9.17 to

$$0 = f'^2 - ff'' - \nu f''' \qquad (23.9.21)$$

The two parameters in the problem $a(1/LT)$ and ν (L^2/T) are used to introduce nondimensional variables as follows:

$$\eta \equiv \frac{y}{(\nu/a)^{1/3}}, \qquad F \equiv \frac{f}{(\nu^2 a)^{1/3}}, \qquad F' \equiv \frac{f'}{(\nu a^2)^{1/3}}, \qquad F'' \equiv \frac{f''}{a} \qquad (23.9.22)$$

The nondimensional version of Eq. 23.9.21 is free of parameters:

$$0 = F'^2 - FF' - F''' \qquad (23.9.23)$$

The solution subject to boundary conditions $F(0) = 0$, $F''(0) = -1$, and $F'(\infty) = 0$ is

$$F = 1 - \exp(-\eta) \qquad (23.9.24)$$

Inserting this result into Eq. 23.9.12 gives dimensional answers:

$$u(x, y) = xf'(y) = xa^{2/3}\,\nu^{1/3}\exp\left[\frac{-y}{(\nu/a)^{1/3}}\right]$$

$$v(x, y) = -f(y) = -a^{1/3}\,\nu^{2/3}\left\{1 - \exp\left[\frac{-y}{(\nu/a)^{1/3}}\right]\right\} \qquad (23.9.25)$$

$$\tau_{yx}(x, y) = \mu x f''(y) = -xa\mu\exp\left[\frac{-y}{(\nu/a)^{1/3}}\right]$$

The flow toward the stagnation point from infinity is $v(x, \infty) = -a^{1/3}\nu^{2/3}$; the surface flow away from the point is $u(x, 0) = xa^{2/3}\nu^{1/3}$. One can find the corresponding heat transfer problems in Chan et al. (1988).

The final example of a Marangoni flow is the self-propulsion of a bubble or drop when the continuous liquid has a temperature gradient. The temperature gradient is imposed on the bubble interface, and this engenders variation in the surface tension. A motion of the surface from the hot end to the cold end is the result. Viscosity then produces a flow inside and outside the bubble, and the bubble moves toward the hot portion of the continuous phase.

For simplicity we will consider the bubble to be spherical in shape and in a Stokes flow situation where fluid inertia is negligible (Fig. 23.20). For the heat transfer, the compatible assumption is that convection is neglected and conduction completely determines the temperature field. Flow variables referring to inside the bubble will have an i superscript, and variables referring to the bulk continuous fluid will not have superscripts. First, consider the temperature field. The governing equations for heat conduction are

$$\nabla^2 T = 0, \qquad \nabla^2 T' = 0 \qquad (23.9.26)$$

There is a known gradient ∇T_∞ at infinity that is aligned with the axis of the spherical coordinates r, θ, ψ. The radius of the sphere is r_0 and at the equator level, $\theta = \pi/2$, the far-field temperature at infinity is T_0. The boundary conditions for the temperature field are

$$r \rightarrow \infty: \qquad T = T_0 + \nabla T_\infty z = T_0 + \nabla T_\infty r \cos \theta \qquad (23.9.27)$$

$$r = r_0: \qquad T = T^i$$

$$q_r = q_r^i \qquad (23.9.28)$$

$$\frac{\partial T}{\partial r} = \beta \frac{\partial T^i}{\partial r}$$

where the ratio of thermal conductivities is

$$\beta = \frac{\kappa^i}{\kappa} \qquad (23.9.29)$$

The temperature solutions are

$$T = T_0 + \nabla T_\infty \cos \theta \left(r + \frac{C_1}{r^2} \right)$$

$$C_1 = \frac{1 - \beta}{2 + \beta} r_0^3 \qquad (23.9.30)$$

$$T^i = T_0 + \nabla T_\infty \frac{3}{2 + \beta} r \cos \theta$$

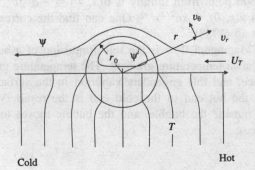

Figure 23.20 Self-propulsion of a spherical bubble in a liquid that has a linear temperature gradient. Lower half shows the isotherms; streamlines are depicted in the upper half.

A typical isotherm pattern is sketched in the lower half of Fig. 23.20. Within the bubble the isotherms are always vertical. If $\beta < 1$ ($\kappa^i < \kappa$), bulk fluid isotherms pinch in and intensify the thermal gradient at the interface. For $\beta > 1$ ($\kappa^i > \kappa$), the opposite effect occurs. It is this interface temperature gradient, acting through the surface tension thermal sensitivirty $\sigma_T = d\sigma/\delta T$, that drives the flow.

The Stokes velocity problem is governed by Eq. 23.5.1; $E^2E^2 \psi = 0$ in spherical coordinates. At infinity there is a uniform flow of unknown magnitude U_T. An important result of the analysis is an expression for U_T:

$$r \rightarrow \infty: \qquad \qquad \psi = \tfrac{1}{2} U_T r^2 \sin^2 \theta \qquad \qquad (23.9.31)$$

On the assumed spherical interface the velocity $v_r = 0$ and there is a difference inn the shear stresses caused by the gradient in the surface tension.

$$r = r_0: \qquad v_r = \frac{\partial \psi}{\partial \theta} = 0, \qquad v_r^i = \frac{\partial \psi^i}{\partial \theta} = 0$$

$$\tau_{r\theta} = \mu r \frac{\partial}{\partial r}\left(\frac{v_\theta}{r}\right) = \mu r \frac{\partial}{\partial r}\left(\frac{-1}{r^2 \sin\theta}\frac{\partial \psi}{\partial r}\right) \qquad (23.9.32)$$

$$\tau_{r\theta} - \tau_{r\theta}^i = \frac{1}{r_0}\frac{\partial \sigma}{\partial \theta} = \frac{1}{r_0}\sigma_T \frac{\partial T}{\partial \theta}$$

Scales that would be used for nondimensionalizing are the radius and the thermocapillary velocity scale:

$$r_0: \qquad \qquad u_s = \frac{\sigma_T \nabla T_\infty r_0}{\mu} \qquad \qquad (29.3.33)$$

Important property ratios appear in the solutions.

$$\alpha = \frac{\mu^i}{\mu}, \qquad \beta = \frac{\kappa^i}{\kappa}, \qquad A = \frac{1}{(2+3\alpha)(2+\beta)} \qquad (23.9.34)$$

In a typical problem of streaming flow over a body, the free stream is considered as specified and the drag force required to hold the body in place is found. In this problem the free-stream velocity is unknown. However, this velocity can be determined by imposing the condition that the bubble is not restrained in any manner, but has drag force. With this condition the solution (Subramanian and Balasubramaniam, 2001) in the bulk fluid is

$$\frac{\psi}{r_0^2 u_s} = A\left(\frac{r}{r_0}\right)^2 \sin^2\theta\left[1 - \left(\frac{r_0}{r}\right)^3\right]$$

$$\frac{v_r}{u_s} = -2A\cos\theta\left[1 - \left(\frac{r_0}{r}\right)^3\right] \qquad \qquad (23.9.35)$$

$$\frac{v_\theta}{u_s} = 2A\sin\theta\left[1 + \frac{1}{2}\left(\frac{r_0}{r}\right)^3\right]$$

$$p = p_\infty$$

The solution inside the bubble is

$$\frac{\psi^i}{r_0^2 u_s} = -\frac{3}{2} A \sin^2\theta \left[\left(\frac{r}{r_0}\right)^2 - \left(\frac{r}{r_0}\right)^4 \right]$$

$$\frac{v_r^i}{u_s} = 3A \cos\theta \left[1 - \left(\frac{r}{r_0}\right)^2 \right] \qquad (23.9.36)$$

$$\frac{v_\theta}{u_s} = -3A \sin\theta \left[1 - 2\left(\frac{r}{r_0}\right)^2 \right]$$

Streamlines computed from these equations are shown in Fig. 23.21. The self-propelling velocity is found to be

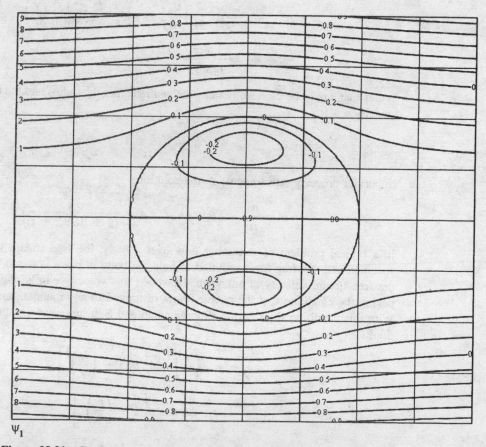

Figure 23.21   Computed streamlines with coordinates following the bubble. Increments between streamlines outside the bubble are one-fourth those on the inside of the bubble.

$$\frac{U_T}{u_s} = 2A = \frac{2}{(2 + 3\alpha)(2 + \beta)}$$

$$U_T = \frac{2}{(2 + 3\alpha)(2 + \beta)} \frac{\sigma_T \nabla T_\infty r_0}{\mu}$$

(23.9.37)

For a gas bubble in a liquid the approximation $\alpha = \beta = 0$ is often made. This leads to $U_T = 2u_s$.

Since Stokes flows are linear, the Marangoni solution and other sphere solutions can be superposed. An example of this is the rising of a bubble because of the buoyancy force in a gravitational field. If the fluid also has a temperature gradient, the self-propulsion flow should be added. If the temperature gradient is arranged so that the motions are opposed, the bubble can be made stationary. Such an experiment was first preformed by Young et al. (1959). For a more complete discussion of the motion of bubbles, drops, and particles, the reader is referred to Leal (1992), Antar and Nuotio-Antar (1993), and Subramanian and Balasubramaniam (2001).

23.10   CONCLUSIONS

The simplified continuum concept of an interface is a surface with no mass but with continuous tangential velocity and temperature. Surface tension acts within the interface and results in a pressure jump across a curved interface. Constant surface tension leads to continuity of the viscous shear stresses on either side of the interface. Hence, a bubble rising in a fluid develops an internal flow. Although the pressure within the bubble is higher, there is no tendency for the bubble to deform in Stokes flow. Deformation occurs at higher Reynolds numbers when inertia effects are important. Another effect of the jump in pressure across a curved interface is the existence of capillary waves. These waves have the same characteristics as gravity waves but have small wavelengths. A variation in surface tension along the surface is accompanied by a jump in the viscous shear stresses on either side of the interface. Flows produced by this effect, such as bubble self-propulsion, are called *Marangoni flows*. A contact line formed by the intersection of an interface with a solid wall has, from the continuum viewpoint, a definite angle that depends on the materials. In flow situations where the contact line moves over the solid, a rolling motion is observed. Such a motion leads to a singularity in the shear stress that is not integrable to give a finite force. Allowing slip between the fluid near the contact line and the wall remedies this problem with negligible effect on the overall flow.

PROBLEMS

23.1 (A) Calculate the pressure in air bubble in atmospheric water for the size range 1 mm $< r_0 <$ 1 μm.

23.2 (B) Two flat glass rectangular plates $L \times H$ form a wedge of a very small angle with a line of contact along side L. On the other side of the contact line, a distance H away, the distance between the plates is h. The plates are dipped into a liquid bath with the line of contact aligned vertically with the gravity vector. This forms a capillary of varying width. Derive an equation for the meniscus height as a function of distance from the contact line if the Bond number $h^2/(\sigma/\rho g)$ is small.

23.3 (B) Reproduce the calculations needed for Fig. 23.8.

23.4 (A) What is the phase speed of a capillary wave in air–water if the wavelength is 5 mm?

23.5 (B) Consider the vertical drag-out problem for a thick coating where the fully established flow is a balance between viscous and gravity forces. If the film is too thick, part of the fluid is moving upward with the web and part is falling downward. Derive an equation for the largest film thickness when all of the fluid is moving upward. If this film ultimately solidifies, what is its thickness?

23.6 (B) A plane sheet of copper has a film of liquid on it that is h_0 thick everywhere $|x/L| > 1$. For $|x/L| < 1$, the interface surface tension varies because the temperature of the copper sheet varies. The tension is $\sigma = \sigma_0 + A[1 + \cos(\pi x/L)]$. What nondimensional parameters enter the problem for the height of the meniscus as a func-

tion of x? Compute a typical curve for $h(x)$. When will the meniscus have zero thickness? Neglect any Marangoni flow in your calculations.

23.7 (B) A circular spot on a surface is heated so that the Marangoni effect produces an axisymmetric stagnation point flow. Find the velocity profile and surface distribution of surface tension

23.8 (B) In Section 20.19 we analyzed Howarth's stagnation point where the external velocities are $u_e = ax$ and $w_e = bz$. The solution has the form $u \sim x\,F(y)$, $w \sim z\,G(y)$. Is there a distribution of surface tension that will produce a Marangoni stagnation point flow of a similar mathematical form?

23.9 (B) Consider the self-propelled Marangoni flow caused by a temperature gradient ∇T_∞ on a bubble that is in Earth's gravitational field. The Marangoni flow and the flow from bubble buoyancy are opposing each other so that the bubble is stationary. For this situation prove that the gradient must be $|\nabla T_\infty| = gr_0(\rho^i - \rho)(1 + \alpha)(2 + \beta)/3\sigma_T$.

24

Introduction to Microflows

This chapter deals with flows where the depth of the flow is small. As the title suggests, the dimension is on the order of micrometers or even nanometers. Flows of this size bring into question the appropriateness of the Navier–Stokes equations and the no-slip boundary condition. The molecular structure of the fluid must also be considered, and we therefore need to consider gas and liquid flows separately. In gas flows a very large pressure difference will be required to drive the flow, so despite the title of this book, we will need to study the compressible flow of a perfect gas. In microflows the surface area of the walls is very large compared to the volume of fluid (to be precise, $A/V^{2/3}$ is large). The molecular interactions at the interface are more important, and this introduces a need for the field of interfacial science. Arbitrarily, the important topic of electrical effects will be omitted. In the first part of this chapter the general characteristics of molecules, compressible flows, and slip flows are discussed. Flow of gases are taken up next, and finally, liquid flows are considered.

24.1 MOLECULES

As the reader knows, molecules come in all sizes and shapes. The lightest, hydrogen, has a molecular mass of 2.016 g/gmol and a radius of $\sigma = 2.915$ Å (1 angstrom unit $= 10^{-10}$ m $= 0.1$ nm); the smallest, helium, has a molecular mass of 4.003 g/g mol and a radius of $\sigma = 2.576$ Å. Two molecules that are far apart attract each other, but as they come closer, the force changes to a repulsion. This force can be represented by a potential as shown in Fig. 24.1. A measure of the size of the molecule is the crossover point, where the potential changes sign. The noble gases, simple polyatomic molecules, and hydrocarbon molecules are relatively spherical with molecular weights of less than 200 and radii of less than 8 Å. On the other hand, the polymeric fluids, or macromolecules, have molecular weights of 10^4 to 10^6 g/g mol and sizes as large as 25 μm. Similarly, biological molecules are quite large and diverse in shape. These fluids are non-Newtonian and are outside the scope of the present discussion.

A basic concept that must be used in kinetic theory is the force between two molecules as a function of the distance between them. If the force does not depend on the orientation of the molecules, the molecules are said to be *nonpolar*. Most simple molecules are nonpolar; however, water, ammonia, methanol, and methyl chloride are examples of polar molecules. The forces between molecules are the result of the activities of the charged electrons. They are represented by potentials $\phi(r)$ such that $F = -d\phi/dr$.

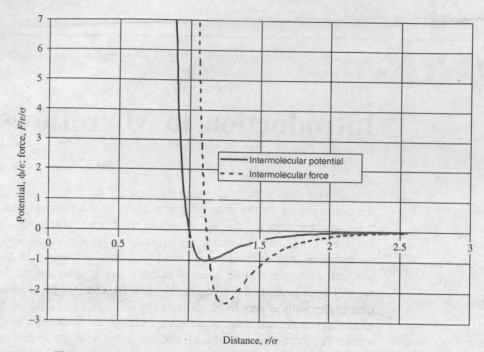

Figure 24.1 Intermolecular potential and force for Lennard-Jones potential.

Of minor interest are the electrostatic Coulomb and dipole forces between charged molecules and the induced charges from their motion. In the encounter of two essentially neutral molecules the two most important forces are the attractive dispersion (van der Waals) force and the repulsion force. The approaching molecule has moving electrons that instantaneously form an asymmetric (dipole) electric field. This field induces a dipole in the other neutral molecule that dies away as $-1/r^{-6}$. The repulsion force is thought to be the consequence of the electron orbits of the two molecules coming into overlapping range. It is represented as $1/r^{-k}$, with $9 \leq k \leq 15$. The most popular nonpolar potential is the *Lennard-Jones equation*:

$$\phi = 4\varepsilon \left[\left(\frac{\sigma}{r} \right)^{12} - \left(\frac{\sigma}{r} \right)^{6} \right] \tag{24.1.1}$$

The length scale σ is an effective radius of the molecule, and the energy parameter ε indicates the strength of the forces. Figure 24.1 plots the Lennard-Jones potential and the corresponding force as functions of the distance between molecules. A significant attraction force does not extend beyond 2.4σ, while the repulsion force begins at 1.122σ and rises very rapidly.

The molecular mass and the Lennard-Jones parameters can be used to form a time scale:

$$\tau = \sigma \left(\frac{m}{\varepsilon} \right)^{1/2} \tag{24.1.2}$$

This is the period of oscillation about the potential well. For nitrogen the time scale is 2.3×10^{-12} s. When molecules are very close together, as in a liquid or solid, this time scale measures the interaction motions.

There are numerous other models for the intermolecular potential. The Sutherland potential, square-well potential, and Buckingham potential are all nonpolar and have various mathematical advantages. The most often used polar potential is the *Stockmayer potential*. The molecules are imagined to be dipoles of strength μ:

$$\phi = 4\varepsilon \left[\left(\frac{\sigma}{r} \right)^{12} - \left(\frac{\sigma}{r} \right)^{6} \right] - \frac{\mu^2}{r^3} g(\theta_1, \theta_2, \phi_2 - \phi_1) \tag{24.1.3}$$

where

$$g(\theta_1, \theta_2, \phi_2 - \phi_1) = 2 \cos\theta_1 \cos\theta_2 - \sin\theta_1 \sin\theta_2 \cos(\phi_2 - \phi_1)$$

The angle θ is the angle between the molecule dipole axis and the line connecting the molecule centers. The angle ϕ is the azimuthal angle in a plane perpendicular to the line of centers. If the molecules are randomly oriented and one averages over all angles, the factor g becomes unity and the averaged potential is an attractive force, $\sim -\mu/r^3$. This force attracts farther out than the van de Waals force.

24.2   CONTINUUM DESCRIPTION

The continuum description of a fluid requires that we form average properties of a collection of molecules. Conceptually, this can be done in several ways. There are certain philosophical objections to most averaging methods, but we will not be overly rigorous. In Chapter 1 we formed density, velocity, and internal energy averages by imagining that the flow was a frozen snapshot in time. The test volume contained molecules whose properties were averaged. Alternatively, we could watch the test volume for a considerable length of time and sum the events. This would work only for a steady flow and is useful in a rarefied gas. A more sophisticated concept is to imagine a series of flow systems that are similar to the system in which we are interested. Each system in this ensemble has the same continuum properties, but the molecules are in different microscopic arrangements. The continuum properties are averages over all the member systems of the ensemble.

Consider a property X for a group of N molecules. The theory of statistics shows that the relative dispersion, the root mean square divided by the mean, for N molecules is proportional to $1/\sqrt{N}$:

$$\frac{\sigma_X}{\overline{X}} \sim \frac{1}{\sqrt{N}} \tag{24.2.1}$$

For example, if the principle of equal partition of energy holds with D as the degrees of freedom, a statistical mechanics calculation shows that the relative dispersion of energy is

$$\frac{\sigma_E}{E} \sim \sqrt{\frac{2}{D}} \frac{1}{\sqrt{N}} \qquad (24.2.2)$$

An ideal monatomic gas has $D = 3$, $\sqrt{2/3} = 0.82$, whereas an Einstein solid has $D = 6$, $\sqrt{2/6} = 0.57$. For fluctuations in the density of a perfect gas, Eq. 24.2.1 holds with a unity coefficient, whereas for pressure the coefficient is 0.82.

Consider a cubic volume with side L containing N molecules. For purposes of illustration, imagine that the molecules are spaced apart equally in a rectangular array. The average number of molecules along a side is $n_L = N^{1/3}$. This is known as the *mean molecular spacing*. Figure 24.2 is a graphical display of the relative dispersion (say, of density) as a function of the number of molecules on a side of length L. This gives an indication of the size of a volume needed to have negligible fluctuations in thermodynamic properties. For example, a liquid volume with 40 molecules on a side would have less than 0.5% fluctuation in the density. However, this volume needs to be located where the fluid (liquid or gas) is in thermodynamic equilibrium. Molecules immediately next to a wall might be in a different state because of the interaction with the wall.

24.3 COMPRESSIBLE FLOW IN LONG CHANNELS

Many microdevices have long channels or tubes with very small widths or diameters. The pressures required to overcome viscous effects are quite large because the surface area for viscous friction is large compared to the cross section on which the pressure

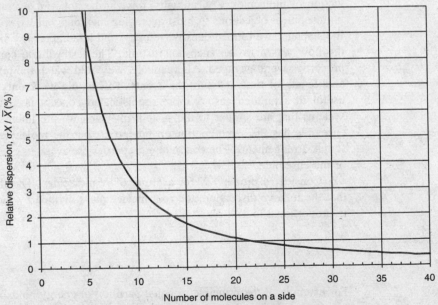

Figure 24.2 Relative dispersion as a function of sample size.

acts. The pressure drop required to produce appreciable flow is so large that a change in the density may occur. This is especially true in gases but is important less frequently in liquids. The second aspect of these flows is that the very large wall area for heat transfer and the massive container combine to keep the flow at the same temperature.

In this section we derive a simplified form of the Navier–Stokes equations that apply to compressible flows. These equations will be specialized to flow regions that are long and thin. This is essentially the lubrication approximation used in Chapter 22, except that compressibility is retained.

Consider a flow where the flow region is long in the x-direction with scale L and small in the transverse y-direction with scale h. Nondimensional variables are

$$\hat{x} = \frac{x}{L}, \qquad \hat{y} = \frac{y}{h}, \qquad \varepsilon = \frac{h}{L} \tag{24.3.1}$$

A reference position in the flow (e.g., the entrance or exit) is denoted by the subscript 0. The characteristic velocity at the reference is u_0. The general low-speed compressible equations derived in Section 10.8 used the dynamic pressure $\rho_0 u_0^2$ as the pressure scale, and the difference between the flow reference and the wall temperature, $T_w - T_0$, as the temperature scale. Those scale units are inappropriate here. If $T_w \sim \overline{T}_0$, heat conduction is small and the absolute temperature is needed to describe thermodynamic effects. The pressure also has a thermodynamic role, where the scale would be p_0, but in addition it has a force role where the pressure scale is $\mu u_0 / h\varepsilon$ (Eq. 22.2.1). Viscous forces rather than inertia (convective) effects dominate the pressure. The force scale $\mu u_0 / h\varepsilon$ is appropriate to the lubrication limit and reflects the fact that the pressure drop is the result of wall friction. The algebra is somewhat clearer if we choose that force scale. Define nondimensional variables as

$$\hat{p} = \frac{p}{\mu u_0 / \varepsilon h}, \qquad \hat{T} = \frac{T}{T_0}, \qquad \hat{\rho} = \frac{\rho}{\rho_0} \tag{24.3.2}$$

We will work with steady, plane Cartesian coordinates, although it is obvious that the lubrication approximation can be applied in other systems. The distance and velocity variables for each direction are

$$\hat{u} = \frac{u}{u_0}, \qquad \hat{v} = \frac{v}{\varepsilon u_0} \tag{24.3.3}$$

Because the flow field is long and slender, the transverse v velocity must be scaled by εu_0 so that the continuity equation is satisfied without approximation:

$$\frac{\partial(\hat{\rho}\hat{u})}{\partial \hat{x}} + \frac{\partial(\hat{\rho}\hat{v})}{\partial \hat{y}} = 0 \tag{24.3.4}$$

The asterisk will be retained for variables that have the same definition as in Chapter 10.

$$t^* = \frac{t}{L/v_0}, \qquad c_p^* = \frac{c_p}{c_{p0}}, \qquad \gamma_0 = \frac{c_{p0}}{c_{v0}}$$

$$\mu^* = \frac{\mu}{\mu_0}, \qquad \kappa^* = \frac{\kappa}{\kappa_0}, \qquad \alpha^* = \frac{\alpha}{\alpha_0}, \qquad \beta^* = \frac{\beta}{\beta_0}$$

$$A = \alpha_0 \rho_0 c_{p0} T_0, \qquad B = \beta_0 T_0 \qquad\qquad (24.3.5)$$

$$\Phi^* = \frac{\Phi}{\mu_0 v_0^2/L^2}, \qquad \mathrm{Pr} = \frac{\mu_0 c_{p0}}{\kappa_0}, \qquad Z = \frac{p_0}{\rho_0 \mathscr{R} T_0}$$

$$\mathrm{Re} = \frac{\rho_0 v_0 L}{\mu_0}, \qquad M^2 = \frac{v_0^2}{a_0^2} = \frac{v_0^2}{\gamma_0/\rho_0 \alpha_0}$$

In addition to those parameters that appeared in Chapter 10, the universal gas constant $\mathscr{R}$ and the compressibility factor Z have been introduced.

Written in these variables, energy equation 10.2.6 becomes

$$\varepsilon^2 \hat{\rho} c_p^* \left(\hat{u} \frac{\partial \hat{T}}{\partial \hat{x}} + \hat{v} \frac{\partial \hat{T}}{\partial \hat{y}} \right) = \frac{1}{\mathrm{Re}\,\mathrm{Pr}} \left[\left(\varepsilon \frac{\partial}{\partial \hat{x}} + \frac{\partial}{\partial \hat{y}} \right) \left(\varepsilon \kappa^* \frac{\partial \hat{T}}{\partial \hat{x}} + \kappa^* \frac{\partial \hat{T}}{\partial \hat{y}} \right) \right]$$

$$+ \varepsilon^2 \left[\frac{\gamma_0 M^2}{A\,\mathrm{Re}} \Phi + BZ \frac{\mathscr{R}}{c_{p0}} \left(\hat{u} \frac{\partial \hat{p}}{\partial \hat{x}} + \hat{v} \frac{\partial \hat{p}}{\partial \hat{y}} \right) \right] \qquad (24.3.6)$$

If all the variables are nondimensionalized properly to be of order one, the limit $\varepsilon \to 0$ gives

$$0 = \frac{\partial}{\partial \hat{y}} \left(\kappa^* \frac{\partial \hat{T}}{\partial \hat{y}} \right) \qquad\qquad (24.3.7)$$

The solution for a constant wall temperature is $\hat{T} = \hat{T}_w$. The isothermal assumption is consistent with the lubrication approximation.

The thermodynamic equation of state for isothermal flow is

$$\frac{1}{\hat{p}} \frac{D\hat{p}}{Dt^*} = \alpha^* \alpha_0 p_0 \frac{D\hat{\rho}}{Dt^*} \qquad\qquad (24.3.8)$$

The nondimensional number $\alpha_0 p_0$ is unity for perfect gases but very small for most liquids. Water has a value of 4.7×10^{-5}, whereas most hydrocarbons have 2 to 20 10^{-5}. It is unlikely for liquids that compressibility is significant.

The viscous stresses are normalized in different ways for different components.

$$\nabla \cdot \mathbf{v} = \frac{\partial u}{\partial x} + \frac{\partial v}{\partial y} \sim \frac{u_0}{L} + \frac{\varepsilon u_0}{h} \sim \frac{u_0}{L}$$

$$\tau_{xx} = 2\mu \left(\frac{\partial u}{\partial x} - \frac{1}{3} \nabla \cdot \mathbf{v} \right) \sim \mu_0 \frac{u_0}{L}, \qquad \hat{\tau}_{xx} = \frac{\tau_{xx}}{\mu_0 u_0/L}$$

$$\tau_{yy} = 2\mu \left(\frac{\partial v}{\partial y} - \frac{1}{3} \nabla \cdot \mathbf{v} \right) \sim \mu_0 \frac{u_0}{L}, \qquad \hat{\tau}_{yy} = \frac{\tau_{xx}}{\mu_0 u_0/L} \qquad (24.3.9)$$

$$\tau_{yx} = \tau_{yx} = 2\mu \left(\frac{\partial u}{\partial y} + \frac{\partial v}{\partial x} \right) \sim \mu_0 \frac{u_0}{\varepsilon L}, \qquad \hat{\tau}_{yx} = \frac{\tau_{yx}}{\mu_0 u_0/\varepsilon L}$$

Introducing these scalings into the y-direction momentum equation yields

$$\varepsilon^3 \, \text{Re} \, \hat{\rho}\left(\hat{u} \, \frac{\partial \hat{v}}{\partial \hat{x}} + \hat{v} \, \frac{\partial \hat{v}}{\partial \hat{y}} \right) = -\frac{\partial \hat{p}}{\partial \hat{y}} + \varepsilon^2 \frac{\partial \hat{\tau}_{xy}}{\partial \hat{x}} + \varepsilon^2 \frac{\partial \hat{\tau}_{yy}}{\partial \hat{y}} \qquad (24.3.10)$$

Thus, the limit $\varepsilon \to 0$ gives $0 = \partial \hat{p}/\partial y$, so $\hat{p} = \hat{p}(\hat{x})$.

The x-direction momentum equation is

$$\varepsilon \, \text{Re} \, \hat{\rho}\left(\hat{u} \, \frac{\partial \hat{u}}{\partial \hat{x}} + \hat{v} \, \frac{\partial \hat{u}}{\partial \hat{y}} \right) = -\frac{\partial \hat{p}}{\partial \hat{x}} + \varepsilon^2 \frac{\partial \hat{\tau}_{xx}}{\partial \hat{x}} + \frac{\partial \hat{\tau}_{yx}}{\partial \hat{y}} \qquad (24.3.11)$$

Here, the limit $\varepsilon \to 0$ is

$$0 = -\frac{d\hat{p}}{d\hat{x}} + \frac{\partial \hat{\tau}_{yx}}{\partial \hat{y}} = -\frac{d\hat{p}}{d\hat{x}} + \mu^* \frac{\partial^2 \hat{u}}{\partial \hat{y}^2} \qquad (24.3.12)$$

This is essentially the same equation as that derived in Section 22.2. Compressibility enters through state equation 24.2.4 and continuity equation 24.2.8. Additionally, it is assumed that the viscosity is only a function of temperature and therefore that because the flow is isothermal, $\mu^* = 1$. Note that the derivation includes the possibilities of a slightly variable channel width or a slightly porous wall.

24.4 SIMPLE SOLUTIONS WITH SLIP

The first modification to describe flows in regions of small length dimensions is in the boundary condition at solid walls. Within the bulk fluid, either liquid or gas, the Navier–Stokes equations are still valid. The average fluid velocity as we approach a wall is not zero but a finite value. This is known as the *slip velocity* u_s. An equivalent concept is the slip length β. If the velocity profile is extended into the wall, the velocity is zero at a depth equal to the slip length:

$$\beta = \frac{u_s}{du/dy|_0} \qquad (24.4.1)$$

The slip velocity is a manifestation of local molecular events at the wall and thus is customarily related to the velocity gradients at the wall. Since liquids and gases have different physical interactions with walls, a more detailed discussion of slip is given in those sections.

Any previous Navier–Stokes solution that has a constant shear stress at the wall can easily be modified to become a slip-flow profile. Two simple flows that have a constant stress at the wall, and therefore a constant slip velocity u_s, are Poiseuille pipe or channel flow and Couette flow. The velocity profiles for those cases are shown in Fig. 24.3. For flow in a channel of width h with the coordinate origin on the bottom wall, the profile is

$$u = 4u_p \left[\left(\frac{y}{h} \right) - \left(\frac{y}{h} \right)^2 \right] + u_s \qquad (24.4.2)$$

where

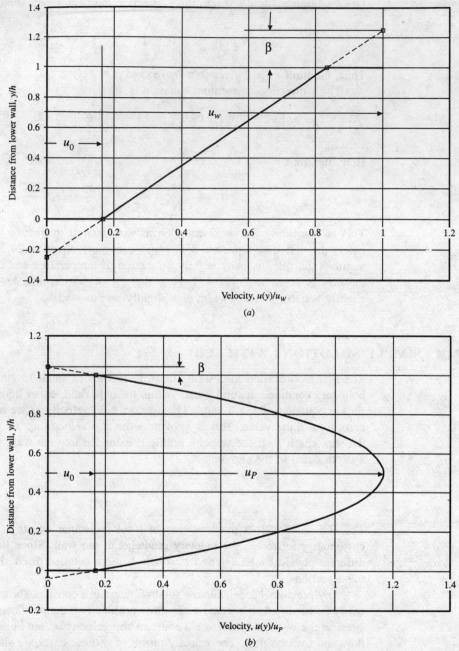

Figure 24.3 (*a*) Couette flow with slip; (*b*) Poiseuille flow with slip.

$$u_P \equiv -\frac{h^2}{8\mu}\frac{dp}{dx}$$

$$\dot{m} = \rho h(\tfrac{2}{3}u_P + u_s)$$

The constant u_P is the centerline velocity that would occur without slip. For flow in a pipe with the coordinate origin in the center, the profile is

$$v_z = v_P\left[1 - \left(\frac{r}{r_0}\right)^2\right] + v_s$$

where

$$v_P \equiv -\frac{r_0^2}{4\mu}\frac{dp}{dz}$$

$$\dot{m} = \rho\pi r_0^2(\tfrac{1}{2}v_P + v_s) \qquad (24.4.3)$$

Again the constant v_P is the centerline velocity that would occur without slip.

The velocity profile for Couette flow in a channel where the lower wall at $y = 0$ is stationary and the upper wall at $y = h$ moves with velocity $u = u_w$ is

$$u = (u_w - 2u_s)\frac{y}{h} + u_s$$

$$\dot{m} = \tfrac{1}{2}u_W \qquad (24.4.4)$$

The amount of slip depends on an empirical slip law, as noted before.

The Couette and Poiseuille flows are unidirectional flows independent of the stream-wise coordinate. For this reason the inertia terms vanish and the flows are independent of the Reynolds number. Flow over a sphere is two-dimensional and therefore dependent on the Reynolds number. Microflows have small dimensions and we can usefully limit our discussion to the small-Reynolds-number case. This leaves out the rarefied gas dynamics situation, where the sphere may be large but the gas is at such a low density that the mean free path is comparable with the sphere radius.

From the literature it appears that Basset (1888) first gave the drag formula for Stokes flow over a solid sphere with slip. Consider the streamfunction solution in spherical coordinates given in Eq 21.8.7. Here the boundary condition matching the free stream has been applied: $C_2 = -\frac{1}{2}$, $C_4 = 0$.

$$\frac{\psi}{r_0^2 U} = \sin^2\theta\left[C_{-1}\left(\frac{r}{r_0}\right)^{-1} + C_1\left(\frac{r}{r_0}\right) - \frac{1}{2}\left(\frac{r}{r_0}\right)^2\right] \qquad (24.4.5)$$

The condition of $\psi(r = r_0) = 0$ gives

$$0 = C_{-1} + C_1 - \tfrac{1}{2} \qquad (24.4.6)$$

The second condition is the slip law. For a curved surface it is assumed that

$$v_\theta(r = r_0) = \frac{\Lambda}{\mu}\tau_{r\theta}(r = r_0) \qquad (24.4.7)$$

Here Λ is a nondimensional slip coefficient $\Lambda = \beta r_0$. In terms of the streamfunction at $r = r_0$, this is

$$\left.\frac{\partial \psi}{\partial r}\right|_{r_0} = \Lambda \left.\frac{\partial}{\partial r}\left(r^{-2}\frac{\partial \psi}{\partial r}\right)\right|_{r_0} \tag{24.4.8}$$

Inserting Eq. 24.4.5 leads to a second equation for C_{-1} and C_1:

$$-C_{-1} + C_1 - 1 = \Lambda(4C_{-1} - 2C_1 + 1) \tag{24.4.9}$$

Solving Eqs. 24.4.5 and 24.4.9 gives

$$C_{-1} = \frac{-1}{4 + 12\Lambda}, \qquad C_1 = \frac{3}{4}\left(\frac{1 + 2\Lambda}{1 + 3\Lambda}\right) \tag{24.4.10}$$

The drag force is found using the previously derived formula 21.8.19; $F_D = 8\pi\mu U r_0 C_1$:

$$F_D = 6\pi\mu U r_0 \frac{1 + 2\Lambda}{1 + 3\Lambda} \tag{24.4.11}$$

For $\Lambda = 0$ the solid sphere result is reproduced. This formula is nearly the same as the no-slip formula. Even at $\Lambda = 0.1 F_D$ is $1.2/1.3 = 0.92$ times the drag of a solid sphere.

24.5 GASES

In the gaseous state the molecules are so far apart that the force of attraction is negligible. The motion of a molecule is a free flight until an encounter with another molecule. After a brief collision, the molecule is again in free flight. During the collision, mass, momentum, and energy are conserved. A continuum property that describes the gas is the number of molecules per unit volume, n. The gas density is

$$\rho = nm \tag{24.5.1}$$

At standard temperature and pressure the number density $n = 3 \times 10^{25}$ molecules per cubic meter. This gives an average distance between molecules of 2.5×10^{-9} m or 2.5 nm (roughly 10 molecular radii). A channel 1 μm high would have about 400 molecules across the height.

According to the statistical theory of Eq. 24.2.1, the density in a given volume fluctuates according to the equation

$$\frac{\sigma_\rho}{\rho} = \frac{1}{\sqrt{N}} \tag{24.5.2}$$

If we consider a region with $10 \times 10 \times 10 = 1000$ molecules, the fluctuation in density is 0.031, or 3%. Thus, it does not take too many molecules to form reasonable averages. The thermodynamic variables of a dilute gas are related by the well-known perfect gas laws,

$$\rho = \frac{p}{RT} \qquad n = \frac{p}{kT} \qquad e = c_v(T)T \tag{24.5.3}$$

Here k is the gas constant per molecule or Boltzmann constant, 1.38×10^{-16} erg/K.

Kinetic theory relates the mean square of the translational molecular velocities ($\mathbf{v}$) and the thermodynamic temperature by the formula

$$\tfrac{1}{2} m(\overline{\mathbf{v} \cdot \mathbf{v}}) = \tfrac{3}{2} kT \qquad (24.5.4)$$

The overbar indicates the average over all molecules. Temperature indicates the mean kinetic energy of translation of the molecules. Additional energy in the internal modes of molecular vibration and rotation is described by the internal energy equation of state. Several formulas for the molecular behavior of gases will be quoted without reference. They are all contained in any textbook on the kinetic theory of gases [a classic is Kennard (1938)]. The root-mean-square molecular velocity is

$$v_{\mathrm{rms}} = \sqrt{\overline{\mathbf{v} \cdot \mathbf{v}}} = \sqrt{\frac{3kT}{m}} \qquad (24.5.5)$$

An interesting calculation is to compare this velocity to the speed of sound, a. The result is

$$\frac{v_{\mathrm{rms}}}{a} = \sqrt{\frac{3}{\gamma}} \qquad (24.5.6)$$

For diatomic gases such as air, $\gamma = 1.4$ and the ratio is 1.46. The speed of sound is about 70% of the rms velocity. The propagation of events through a gas is related directly to the molecular translation velocity.

The statistical nature of molecular events means that there is a distribution of velocities among the molecules. Of course, in a still gas the average speed is zero. Maxwell proposed a distribution function for the distribution of molecular speeds that was later derived by Boltzmann. The average molecular speed without regard to the direction is

$$\bar{v} = \sqrt{\frac{8kT}{\pi m}} \qquad (24.5.7)$$

Comparing this to Eq. 24.5.5 shows that $\bar{v} = 0.921 v_{\mathrm{rms}}$. Typical values of molecular speed at standard conditions are: hydrogen, 1740 m/s; xenon, 174 m/s; and air, 459 m/s. The molecular speed is useful in computing a molecular flux. If one considers a unit area in the flow or on a wall, the flux of molecules from one side of the surface to the other is

$$Z = \tfrac{1}{4} n\bar{v} \qquad (24.5.8)$$

The dimensions of Z are molecules per unit area per unit time.

In a gas undergoing a process, thermodynamic equilibrium is maintained by collisions. It is of interest to know how far, on average, a molecule travels between collisions. This depends on the projected area that the molecule presents to other molecules, the collision cross section, as it moves through the spatial array of molecules. This distance is known as the *mean free path*. It is related to an effective molecular diameter and the number density:

$$\lambda \sim \frac{1}{d^2 n} \qquad (24.5.9)$$

Only in the case of a hardball model of the molecules can a precise calculation of λ be made. A fairly simple argument leads to the equation

$$\lambda = \frac{1}{\sqrt{2}\ \pi d^2 n} \tag{24.5.10}$$

$$= \frac{m}{\sqrt{2}\ \pi d^2}\frac{1}{\rho} = \frac{m}{\sqrt{2}\ \pi d^2}\frac{RT}{p}$$

For air at standard conditions the value is $\lambda \sim 65$ nm. Thus, a channel with width 1 μm is about 15 mean free paths in width, and since there are 400 molecules across the channel, a molecule that is directed directly across the channel passes about 25 molecules before colliding with another molecule. There are other formulas for λ that account for the relative motion of molecules or for the distribution of molecular speeds. Hence, although an important parameter in rarefied gas flows, λ is not uniquely defined.

The time scale of the Lennard-Jones potential (Section 24.2) is not important for gases because collisions are rapid compared to the flight time between collisions. A time scale formed with the mean free path and the mean speed is called the *time between collisions;* the inverse is the *collision frequency:*

$$\theta = \frac{\lambda}{v}$$

$$\theta = \frac{\sqrt{m}}{4\pi d^2}\frac{\sqrt{kT}}{p} \tag{24.5.11}$$

Air at standard conditions has a time between collisions of 1.5×10^{-10} s. This is about three orders of magnitude slower than the Lennard-Jones time scale. Since collisions are necessary to maintain thermodynamic equilibrium, the time scale shows that engineering processes are relatively long-term events where there is adequate time to maintain thermodynamic equilibrium.

The most important dimensionless number in rarefied gas flows is the *Knudsen number*. Knudsen made pioneering measurements of rarefied gas flow through tubes. His number is the ratio of the mean free path to a dimension of the flow field.

$$Kn = \frac{\lambda}{h} \tag{24.5.12}$$

The limit of Knudsen number Kn $\rightarrow$ 0 is continuum flow, and the limit Kn $\rightarrow \infty$ is free molecular flow. An equivalent equation for the Knudsen number relates it to the traditional Mach and Reynolds numbers using perfect gas relations:

$$Kn = \frac{\lambda}{h} = \sqrt{\frac{\gamma\pi}{2}}\frac{M}{Re} \tag{24.5.13}$$

The Knudsen number plays an important role in classifying flows.

The no-slip boundary condition was found in Section 6.4 to be the continuum approximation valid for Kn $\rightarrow$ 0. Kinetic theory equation 6.4.9 is

$$u_s = \frac{2-\sigma}{\sigma}\frac{2}{3}\lambda\frac{du}{dy}\Big|_0 \tag{24.5.14}$$

The factor $\frac{2}{3}$ is the apparent origin of the incoming molecules and is taken as unity in many derivations. Together with the ambiguity in defining the mean free path, the $\frac{2}{3}$ factor is usually lumped into the Knudsen number:

$$u_s = \frac{2 - \sigma}{\sigma} \text{Kn} \left. \frac{du}{d(y/h)} \right|_0 \qquad (24.5.15)$$

The tangential momentum accommodation coefficient σ accounts for the microscopic nature of the wall: that is, the type of solid and gas molecules and the smoothness and contamination of the surface. Measurements, which show considerable scatter, generally give values of σ from 0.85 to 1.0. Measurements in microchannels of silicon by Arkilic et al. (2001) yielded values from 0.75 to 0.85. A concept that combines the accommodation coefficient and the Knudsen number is slip length, defined as

$$\beta = \frac{u_s}{du/dy|_0} = \frac{2 - \sigma}{\sigma} \left(\frac{2}{3} \right) \lambda \qquad (24.5.16)$$

Many theoretical treatments begin by assuming that $\sigma = 1$, so that $\beta = \lambda$, and the precise effect of the accommodation coefficient and the Knudsen number are not separated.

Equation 24.5.14 is known as a first-order slip equation, as it can be considered as the first term in a truncated Taylor series. Second-order slip equations keep a term of order d^2u/dy^2. An effect that is missing from Eq. 24.5.14 is the situation where the wall itself has a temperature gradient. This effect results in an additional term proportional to dT_W/dx. A fuller discussion of this effect can be found in Karniadakis and Beskok (2002).

The state of molecules very near the wall is not described well by the Navier–Stokes equations. Within a distance of about one mean free path the velocity profile has what is called a *Knudsen layer* or *kinetic boundary layer*. This layer is independent of the flow farther out—hence the name *kinetic boundary layer*. Figure 24.4 is a schematic of a calculation of this layer. This layer is often ignored in engineering. The Knudsen layer makes a second-order contribution to the slip equation, but other non Navier–Stokes effects that are problem specific also contribute a second-order slip term. When the Knudsen number is about unity, the layers fill the flow, so to speak, and the flow is a truly transitional or free molecular flow. The Knudsen layer concept then loses its validity.

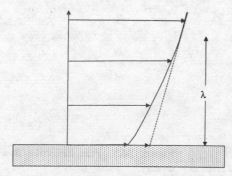

Figure 24.4 Knudsen layer where Navier–Stokes equations do not apply. Data from Cercignani (2000).

The second form of the Knudsen number equation, $\mathrm{Kn} = (\gamma\pi/2)^{1/2}M/\mathrm{Re}$, is especially useful to aeronautical engineers. They encounter slip flows at high altitudes where vehicles are usually traveling at finite Mach numbers. Schaaf and Chambre (1961) codified the flow regimes in terms of M/Re. They noted several previous classifications, the first of which is that of Tsien (1948). Ignoring the factor $(\gamma\pi/2)^{1/2}$, their classifications are

$0 \leq \mathrm{Kn} \leq 0.01$: "continuum" flow (Navier–Stokes equations with no-slip boundary conditions)

$0.01 \leq \mathrm{Kn} \leq 0.1$: slip flow (Navier–Stokes equations with slip boundary conditions)

$0.1 \leq \mathrm{Kn} \leq 3$: transitional flow (Navier–Stokes equations are not valid)

$3 \leq \mathrm{Kn} \leq \infty$: free molecular flow (molecules interact only with walls)

Schaaf and Chambre (1961) also define a Knudsen number based on the boundary layer thickness δ. Since $\delta \sim 1/\sqrt{\mathrm{Re}}$, $\mathrm{Kn}_\delta \sim M/\sqrt{\mathrm{Re}}$. These classification numbers can only be used as a guide. The situation is analogous to trying to specify that boundary layer theory is valid above a certain Re. The exact values for transition from one regime to another depend on the problem under consideration and the choice of length scale.

24.6 COUETTE FLOW IN GASES

As the first step we consider the free molecular flow situation depicted in Fig. 24.5. When the mean free path becomes large compared to the channel width, a molecule that leaves one wall arrives at the other wall without colliding with any other molecules. From the definition of the accommodation coefficient (Eq. 6.4.5) we have

$$u_r = (1 - \sigma)u_i + \sigma u_w$$

$$u_i = \frac{u_r - \sigma u_w}{1 - \sigma}$$

(24.6.1)

Here the tangential velocity components of the incoming molecules are u_i, reflected molecules u_r, and the wall u_w. Consider wall a as shown in Fig. 24.5. The average tangential molecular velocity leaving wall a is u_a and that leaving wall b is u_b. At a, $u_w = 0$, $u_i = u_b$, $u_r = u_a$, and $\sigma = \sigma_a$; hence, from Eq. 24.6.1,

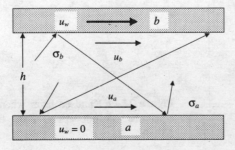

Figure 24.5 Free molecular flow in Couette geometry.

$$u_a = (1 - \sigma_a)u_b \tag{24.6.2}$$

Similarly, at b, $u_w = u_w$, $u_i = u_a$, $u_r = u_b$, and $\sigma = \sigma_b$; hence, again from Eq. 24.6.1,

$$u_a = \frac{u_b - \sigma_b u_w}{1 - \sigma_b} \tag{24.6.3}$$

Solving Eqs. 24.6.2 and 24.6.3 gives the molecular velocities in terms of the wall velocity:

$$u_a = \frac{(1 - \sigma_a)\sigma_b}{\sigma_a + \sigma_b - \sigma_a\sigma_b} u_w$$

$$\tag{24.6.4}$$

$$u_b = \frac{\sigma_b}{\sigma_a + \sigma_b - \sigma_a\sigma_b} u_w$$

Half the molecules in the gap are coming from wall a and half from wall b. The flow in the gap is constant at the mean value of Eqs. 24.6.4:

$$u = \frac{u_w}{2} \frac{2\sigma_b - \sigma_a\sigma_b}{\sigma_a + \sigma_b - \sigma_a\sigma_b} \tag{24.6.5}$$

If the two walls have the same accommodation coefficient, the velocity is one-half the wall velocity. To compute the wall stress, consider the lower wall, where the incoming tangential velocity is u_b and the outgoing is u_a:

$$\tau_{FM} = \text{net flux of momentum} = (\text{net flux of mass})(u_a - u_b)$$

$$= \frac{1}{4} nm\bar{v} \frac{\sigma_a\sigma_b}{\sigma_a + \sigma_b - \sigma_a\sigma_b} u_w$$

$$= \frac{1}{4} nm\bar{v} \frac{\sigma}{2 - \sigma} u_w \qquad \text{for } \sigma_a = \sigma_b \tag{24.6.6}$$

Recall that the mean molecular speed is related to the temperature by Eq. 6.5.7, $\bar{v} = \sqrt{8kT/\pi m}$.

Now consider the Couette flow as described by the Navier–Stokes equations with slip boundary conditions. It is interesting that this solution is a good approximation for all Knudsen numbers $\text{Kn} = \lambda/h$, including the limit to free molecular flow, $\text{Kn} \Rightarrow \infty$. The velocity profile is (Eq. 24.4.4)

$$\frac{u}{u_w} = \left(1 - 2\frac{u_s}{u_w}\right) Y + \frac{u_s}{u_w} \tag{24.6.7}$$

We will use the first-order slip law for gases:

$$\frac{u_s}{u_w} = \frac{2 - \sigma}{\sigma} \text{Kn} \frac{d(u/u_w)}{dY} \tag{24.6.8}$$

Inserting the Couette profile (Eq. 24.6.7) into the slip law gives the slip velocity as a function of the Knudsen number:

$$\frac{u_s}{u_w} = \frac{[(2 - \sigma)/\sigma]\mathrm{Kn}}{1 + 2\,[(2 - \sigma)/\sigma]\mathrm{Kn}} \qquad (24.6.9)$$

The velocity profiles are found by inserting Eq. 24.6.9 into Eq. 24.6.7. For the limiting cases, one obtains

$$\mathrm{Kn} \to 0: \frac{u_s}{u_w} = 0, \qquad \frac{u}{u_w} = Y$$

$$\mathrm{Kn} \to \infty: \frac{u_s}{u_w} = \frac{1}{2}, \qquad \frac{u}{u_w} = \frac{1}{2} \qquad (24.6.10)$$

In the free-molecular limit the mean velocity is half the wall velocity, as found previously.

The wall shear stress is computed as

$$\tau_{\mathrm{slip}} = \mu \left.\frac{du}{dy}\right|_0 = \frac{\mu u_w}{h} \left(1 - 2\frac{u_s}{u_w}\right) \qquad (24.6.11)$$

It is useful to normalize this with the free-molecular value, and to do this, recall that the viscosity is given by Eq. 6.2.6:

$$\mu = \tfrac{1}{3}\, mn\bar{v}\lambda = \tfrac{1}{3}\, \rho\bar{v}\lambda \qquad (24.6.12)$$

Let $\Lambda = [(2 - \sigma)/\sigma]\,(\lambda/h)$. This is a convenient grouping of the Knudsen number and the accommodation·coefficient and is actually a nondimensional slip length $\Lambda = \beta/h$. For diffuse reflections, $\Lambda = \mathrm{Kn}$. Substituting Eqs. 24.6.12 and 24.6.9 into Eq. 24.6.11 yields

$$\tau_{\mathrm{slip}} = \frac{1}{4}\,\rho\bar{v}u_w\,\frac{\sigma}{2 - \sigma}\frac{2\Lambda}{1 + 2\Lambda} \qquad (24.6.13)$$

Comparing with Eq. 24.4.6 yields

$$\frac{\tau_{\mathrm{slip}}}{\tau_{\mathrm{FM}}} = \frac{2\Lambda}{1 + 2\Lambda} \qquad (24.6.14)$$

The shear stress is plotted as a function of Knudsen number in Fig. 24.6. Admittedly, the wall shear stress is not as sensitive a flow parameter as the velocity profile; however, the Navier–Stokes solution with a slip boundary condition gives an engineering approximation throughout the Knudsen number range. A solution to the Boltzmann equation by Willis (1962), which in theory is valid for all Kn, is also shown. Cercignani (1990) discusses this problem and other Boltzmann solutions. Typical definitions for flow regimes were given in Fig. 24.5. The fact that these numbers do not apply to Fig. 24.6 very well illustrates how these limits depend on the problem and the variable of interest.

24.7 POISEUILLE FLOW IN GASES

Pressure-driven flow through tubes was the original problem that Knudsen studied. Consider a tube of constant cross section and length with the pressure difference between

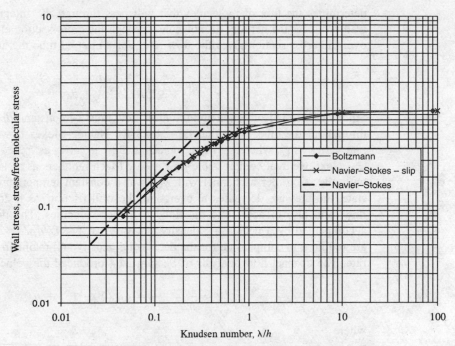

Figure 24.6   Shear stress in Couette flow.

the ends maintained at the same value. The gas is a perfect gas with constant temperature. As the mean pressure is decreased, the Knudsen number increases until the flow becomes a free molecular flow. First, we consider the free molecular flow.

In free molecular flow the molecules interact only with walls. Because the mean free path is so long, there are no collisions within the fluid. A sketch of the analysis (Kennard, 1938) is as follows. Consider a cross section of the flow at $x = 0$ with area element dS as shown in Fig. 24.7. All the molecules passing through dS come from the walls, where there are area elements dS_w. As the wall element moves away from the cross section under consideration, the pressure and therefore the number density of molecules changes. Both p and n decrease if we move in the flow direction. For any wall element one

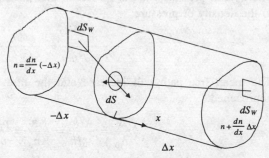

Figure 24.7   Free molecular flow in a tube.

determines the flux of molecules that will pass through dS. Integrating over the entire wall produces the net flux of molecules through the cross-section element dS. Integrating over the cross section gives the flow rate. For a circular tube the answer is

$$\dot{m} = \frac{4}{3} \sqrt{\frac{2\pi}{RT_0}} \, r_0^3 \left(-\frac{dp}{dx} \right) \tag{24.7.1}$$

Since the tube is isothermal and the mass flow must be constant, dp/dx must be constant throughout the tube. Note that Eq. 24.4.3 for Navier–Stokes flow shows that the flow rate varies as r_0^4, whereas in free molecular flow it varies as r_0^3.

Next, we treat compressible flow at low Mach numbers as a Navier–Stokes problem with slip. Consider a channel with walls at a constant temperature. From the entrance state, the pressure decreases to overcome the wall friction, as it does in incompressible flow, and also to accelerate the flow to higher velocities. The decreasing pressure is accompanied by a decreasing density since $dp/dx = RT_0 \, d\rho/dx$. The higher velocities are required to compensate for the decreasing density and maintain a constant mass flow rate. The channel flow analysis of Section 24.4 produced the velocity profile

$$Y = \frac{y}{h}, \qquad u = 4u_P(Y - Y^2) + u_s \tag{24.7.2}$$

where

$$u_P \equiv -\frac{h^2}{8\mu} \frac{dP}{dx}$$

$$u_s = \frac{2 - \sigma}{\sigma} \frac{\lambda}{h} \frac{du}{dY}\bigg|_0 = \Lambda \frac{du}{dY}\bigg|_0$$

The flow rate consists of a pressure gradient component plus a slip component:

$$\dot{m} = \rho h \left(\tfrac{2}{3} u_P + u_S \right) \tag{24.7.3}$$

Let the inlet at $x = 0$ be designated by i and the outlet at $x = L$ be 0. The pressure and density follow the perfect gas law and will be nondimensionalized by the outlet value:

$$p = \rho RT_0, \qquad P = \frac{p(x)}{p_0}, \qquad P_i = \frac{p_i}{p_0} \tag{24.7.4}$$

The overall pressure ratio is P_i. Recall that the mean free path is inversely proportional to the density or pressure:

$$\lambda = \frac{m}{\sqrt{2}\,\pi d^2 nm} = \frac{m}{\sqrt{2}\,\pi d^2 \rho} = \frac{mRT_0}{\sqrt{2}\,\pi d^2 p} \tag{24.7.5}$$

The mean free path will increase and the flow become more rarefied as the exit is approached.

$$\frac{\Lambda}{\Lambda_0} = \frac{\lambda/h}{\lambda_0/h} = \frac{\mathrm{Kn}}{\mathrm{Kn}_0} = \frac{p_0}{p} = \frac{\rho_0}{\rho} = \frac{1}{P} \tag{24.7.6}$$

Mass flow equation 24.7.3 can be integrated to find $P(x)$ since u_P contains the pressure gradient (Eq. 24.7.3). It is convenient to use the following group as a nondimensional mass flow rate:

$$\dot{m}_* = \frac{h^3 p_0^2}{8\mu R T_0 L} \qquad (24.7.7)$$

Substituting and placing Eq. 24.7.3 in nondimensional form yields

$$\dot{m}\, d\left(\frac{x}{L}\right) = -\dot{m}_* P(x)\left(\frac{2}{3} + 4\,\frac{\Lambda_0}{P(x)}\right) dP(x) \qquad (24.7.8)$$

Integrating from $x = 0$ to $x = L$ gives the flow rate in terms of the $\dot{m}_*$ parameter, overall pressure ratio, and outlet Knudsen number:

$$\dot{m} = \dot{m}_* \left[\tfrac{1}{3}(P_i^2 - 1) + 4\Lambda_0(P_i - 1)\right] \qquad (24.7.9)$$

Integrating from $x = 0$ to and x gives the pressure distribution $P(x)$ by the implicit equation

$$\frac{x}{L} = 1 - \frac{[P^2(x) - 1] + 12\Lambda_0[P(x) - 1]}{(P_i^2 - 1) + 12\Lambda_0(P_i - 1)} \qquad (24.7.10)$$

The average velocity and the "pressure" velocity increase as the pressure decreases:

$$u_{\text{ave}}(x) = \frac{\dot{m}}{\rho h} = \frac{\dot{m}_*}{\rho_0 h}\frac{1}{P(x)}\left[\frac{1}{3}(P_i^2 - 1) + 4\Lambda_0(P_i - 1)\right] \qquad (24.7.11)$$

$$\frac{u_p(x)}{u_{p0}} = \frac{1}{P(x)} \qquad (24.7.12)$$

The ratio of the pressure velocity and the slip velocity are constant for the length of the pipe, depend on the overall pressure, and are directly proportional to the Knudsen number:

$$\frac{u_s(x)}{u_p(x)} = 8\Lambda_0\,\frac{P_i - 1}{P_i^2 - 1} \qquad (24.7.13)$$

Pressure distributions for several Knudsen numbers are shown in Fig. 24.8 for an overall pressure ratio of 3.5. The pressure gradient increases toward the outlet, where changes in the flow are more rapid.

The pressure distributions and mass flow rates of the analysis are in general agreement with experiments (e.g., Arkilic et al., 1997; Pong et al., 1994) up to Kn = 0.1. The velocity profiles found using the first-order slip equation also compare well to DSMC and Boltzmann solutions (see, e.g., Karniadakis and Beskok, 2002) up to Kn = 0.1.

The Navier–Stokes analyses with either no-slip or slip boundary conditions are valid only for low Knudsen numbers. The Boltzmann equation, which in principle is valid throughout the range of Knudsen numbers, can be solved for channel flow by a number of techniques. This calculation needs only the local pressure gradient and local Knudsen number. In the analysis above, dp/dx and Kn were not independent but were determined

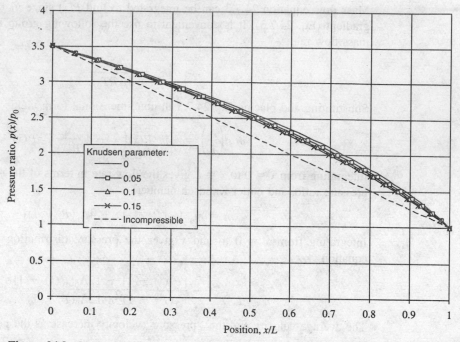

Figure 24.8 Low-speed, isothermal, compressible flow in a tube with pressure ratio 3.5.

for a pipe of given length and given overall pressure ratio. Calculations of Cercignani and Daneri (1963) in Fig. 24.9 show a plot of the mass flow rate through a channel as a function of Knudsen number. The mass flow is normalized according to

$$\dot{m}_* = \frac{\dot{m}}{\dot{m}_{\text{ref}}} = \frac{\dot{m}}{-(dp/dx)\ h^2(2RT_0)^{-1/2}} \qquad (24.7.14)$$

The reference velocity is a group that occurs in the Boltzmann formulation of the problem and avoids any mention of viscosity. There are two special aspects to Fig. 24.9. There is minimum flow rate as the gas is rarified. This occurs around Kn = 1 and is common to any tube flow. This is called *Knudsen's minimum* and was also produced experimentally in his experiments in round tubes. The second aspect is that the curve increases without bound in the free molecular limit, Kn → ∞. This phenomenon is specific to a flat channel of infinite aspect ratio. For a channel with a finite aspect ratio, the curve shown in Fig. 24.9 bends over to a finite limit as Kn → ∞. The curve moves to infinity, as ln (Kn), as the aspect ratio becomes large. The physical reason is that in free molecular flow the flow rate is an integral over the upper, lower, and side walls of the molecules emitted. This integral diverges as the aspect ratio becomes infinite. The idea that a molecule can come off a sidewall and travel a very long distance, several mean free paths, before hitting the upper or lower wall is inconsistent with the free molecular concept.

Gaseous flow in channels has become so important that Karniadakis and Beskok (2002) have developed an engineering model to describe the entire range of Knudsen numbers. In essence, velocity profiles (Eq. 24.4.2) are used where the scale u_P contains

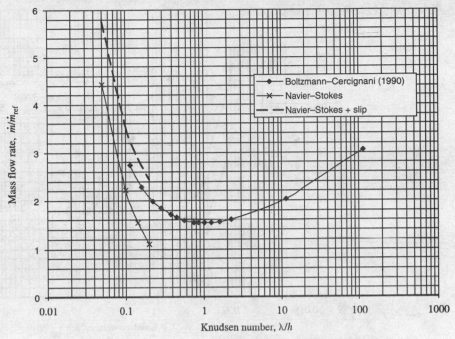

Figure 24.9   Mass flow in plane Poiseuille channel flow.

an empirical function of Kn that will give the proper flow rate. They propose a slip velocity of the form

$$u_s = \frac{2 - \sigma}{\sigma} \frac{\text{Kn}}{1 - b\,\text{Kn}} \left.\frac{du}{d(y/h)}\right|_0 \tag{24.7.15}$$

By comparing the velocity profiles with profiles determined by Boltzmann and DSMC calculations, they have concluded that $b = -1$ is the best choice. The choice $b = -1$ works also for round-tube velocity profiles, and a slightly different formula is needed to model the flow rate. Boltzmann equation calculations for a round tube are shown in Fig. 24.10. Here a finite limit for the free molecular flow is reached as the Knudsen number increases.

24.8   GAS FLOW OVER A SPHERE

In free molecular flow over a closed body the oncoming stream is a Maxwellian distribution at the temperature of the free stream. These molecules interact with the wall and are reemitted after being modified by the nature of the wall and its temperature. We consider only the case of a body temperature equal to the free stream so that an accommodation coefficient and a Knudsen number can describe the interaction. Calculations of the free molecular flow over bodies were done by aeronautical engineers (see, e.g., Schaff and Chambre, 1961) for problems concerning space vehicles. They do not compute the

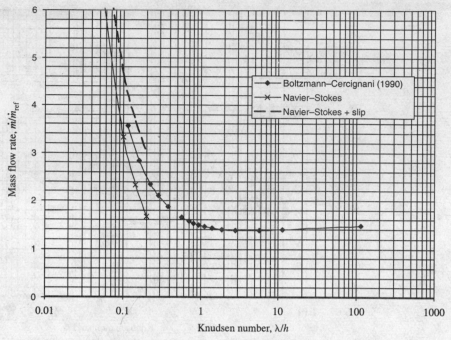

Figure 24.10 Mass flow in round Poiseuille tube flow.

velocity profiles but integrate the molecular interactions with the surface to find the drag directly. As is customary in aeronautics, the drag is placed in the form of a drag coefficient based on the dynamic pressure. The result is

$$C_{D,\text{FM}} = \frac{F_D}{\frac{1}{2}\,\rho U^2 A_x} = \frac{12}{\text{Re}}\frac{1}{1.22\text{Kn}} \tag{24.8.1}$$

Here A_x is the projected area of the sphere. The theoretical scaling for a drag coefficient in Stokes flow is the combination

$$\frac{F_D}{\mu U A_x / \bar{r}_0} = \frac{\text{Re}\; C_D}{2} = 12 \tag{24.8.2}$$

Note that the drag coefficient for free molecular flow actually approaches zero as Kn → ∞.

Results are normalized by the drag in free molecular flow. The Stokes flow equation is

$$\frac{F_D}{F_{D,\text{FM}}} = 1.22\text{Kn} \tag{24.8.3}$$

The dependence on Kn actually comes from the behavior of the free molecular limit. From an analysis of slip flow (Eq. 24.4.9) we arrive at the relation for Stokes flow with slip:

$$\frac{F_D}{F_{D,FM}} = 1.22\text{Kn}\,\frac{1 + 2\text{Kn}}{1 + 3\text{Kn}} \tag{24.8.4}$$

In his famous oil drop experiments, Millikan (1923) produced an empirical formula to fit the experiments:

$$\frac{F_D}{F_{D,FM}} = \frac{A\,\text{Kn}}{1 + \text{Kn}[A + B\exp(-C\,\text{Kn})]}$$

$$A = 1.22, \qquad B = 0.41, \qquad C = 0.875 \tag{24.8.5}$$

It turns out that this equation is also a good fit to calculations of the Boltzmann equation as given in Cercignani (2000). Hence, we can consider the Millikan equation as an excellent approximation for the Boltzmann results. Finally, there is an interpolation equation proposed by Sherman (1963):

$$\frac{F_D}{F_{D,FM}} = \frac{1}{1 + 0.773/\text{Kn}} \tag{24.8.6}$$

All of the formulas above are plotted on Fig. 24.11.

The Sherman formula is a special case of a general formula that he proposed for streaming flow over any object. His proposal is that any property of the flow F divided by its value in the free molecular limit can be estimated by

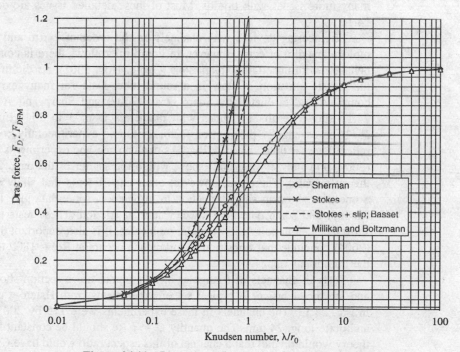

Figure 24.11   Drag on a sphere at low Reynolds numbers.

$$\frac{F}{F_{FM}} = \frac{1}{1 + F_{FM}/F_{NS}} \tag{24.8.7}$$

Here F_{NS} is the continuum behavior from the Navier–Stokes equations.

24.9   LIQUID FLOWS IN TUBES AND CHANNELS

The density of liquids is 800 to 100 times that of the typical gaseous state. The molecules are closely packed and surrounded by other molecules. Since the molecules are continuously in collision, the concept of a mean free path is not used for liquids. An analogous idea is the mean spacing between molecules, which is given by the cube root of the number density:

$$\delta_L = \frac{1}{n^{1/3}} \tag{24.9.1}$$

This length is on the order of the molecular diameter, and the molecular diameter is most often used as a scale, especially in calculations. Because the mean free path for a gas is roughly 20 times the molecular diameter, the length scale for significant molecular effects to occur in a liquid is correspondingly smaller than that for a gas. However, next to a wall there are many molecules in intimate interaction with the wall. Whereas in a gas the accommodation coefficient described all the important wall interactions, there are many more issues with liquids. Most of these detailed issues are deferred until Section 24.10.

Engineering devices with channels on the order of 2 μm and larger do not suffer molecular (slip) effects. However, in liquid microflows there is considerable anomalous behavior with uncertain explanations (Gad-el-Hok, 2001). As the first example, consider the classic situation of flow in a round tube. Data for many experiments have been compiled and evaluated by Sharp et al. (2002) and Sharp and Adrian (2004). Figure 24.12 shows results for tubes with diameters from 3 to 254 μm. Here the quantity $P_0/16$ is essentially the friction factor measured experimentally compared to the theoretical laminar flow value $64/Re_D$. As one can see, the experiments of Sharp and Adrian (2004) and Judy et al. (2002) show, within the scatter of the data, that the laminar flow theory is valid. There are, however, other experiments that show anomalous behavior. Some data show an early transition to turbulence, some data give higher than expected friction, and some data give lower values of friction. These tests included a variety of substances, both polar and nonpolar molecules. It is also important that Sharp and Adrian (2004) conclude that transition to turbulence occurs at Re = 1800 to 2000, more or less the traditional values.

Tests in channels of triangular or rectangular cross section show even more scatter and are inconclusive. A typical set of experiments from Hsieh et al. (2004) are shown in Fig. 24.13. The channels in these experiments were 115 by 200 μm in cross section and quite long, 24 mm. The quantity $C = f\,Re$ should be constant for laminar flow, and theory would predict that a channel of this aspect ratio would have $C = 60.9$. The average for Fig. 24.13 is 64.3 if Re < 240. Thus, these experiments confirm the traditional laminar flow but also show an early transition at Re = 240. For higher Reynolds numbers

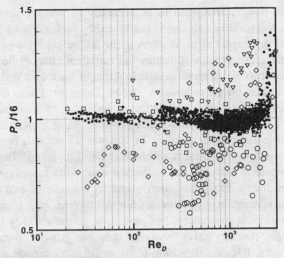

Figure 24.12   Liquid flow in round tubes. $P_0/16$ is unity when the flow confirms to laminar theory without slip. Re_D is the Reynolds number based on diameter. •, Sharp and Adrian (2004), (50–247 μm in diameter; ∇, Mala and Li (1999), 50–254 μm; o, Yu et al. (1995), 19–102 μm; $\diamond$, Choi et al. (1991), 3–18 μm; $\square$, Judy et al. (2002), 15–150 μm. From Sharp and Adrian (2004).

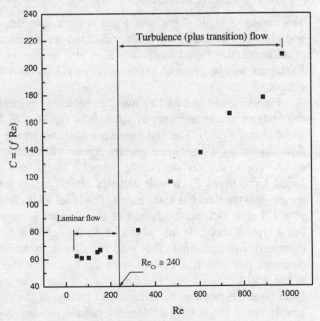

Figure 24.13   Early transition in liquid channel flow. Data from Hsieh et al. (2004).

the flow is confirmed to be unsteady by particle image velocimetry. The friction factor in the turbulent region is considerably higher, up to 3.5 times, than conventional values for this aspect ratio. Workers in the microchannel area call these flows *turbulent,* implying that they compare to traditional turbulent channel flows; however, it would probably be better to call them *unsteady*. In terms of the traditional turbulent wall variable, the channel width is on the order of $h^+ = hu_*/\nu = 30$. These flows would show little resemblance to traditional wall turbulence, as indicated by their higher than usual friction.

Other workers have also reported early transition, but there is no agreement on the critical Reynolds number. In Chapter 25 we will find that traditional laminar–turbulent transition has been a difficult issue. Linear stability theory predicted boundary layer transition that was not confirmed until wind tunnels with very smooth free streams were produced. Early transition occurred because of external disturbances from free-stream turbulence, acoustic interactions with joints, wall roughness, or unsteadiness in the flow-producing machinery. For pipe flow, linear stability theory predicted complete stability. Only recently has a theory of transient growth given results that correspond to experiments. Because transition is so sensitive to outside influences, free-stream disturbances, vibration, wall roughness, inlet geometry, and so on, the term *bypass transition* was invented as a means of classifying these events. In microchannels the early transitions do not scale with the Reynolds number, indicating that the events are unique to each facility. Furthermore, the fact that in round pipes some authors find the traditional transition Reynolds number indicates that early transition in pipes is also a facility-dependent event.

24.10 LIQUID FLOWS NEAR WALLS

The nature of liquid flows near walls is more complex than that of gases. The physical and chemical nature of the walls and liquid are significant. Dissolved gases or mixtures of different size liquid molecules also play important roles in fluid–wall interactions. Examples will be given of experiments or calculations that illustrate the most important effects.

Figures 24.14 and 24.15 show the molecular dynamics calculations of Koplik. These calculations are refinements of the results reported in Koplik et al. (1989) and Koplik and Banavar (1995). The first figure is a snapshot of the molecular positions in a channel flow driven by a horizontal gravity force. All molecules are superimposed across the width. The molecules are simple nonpolar atoms, one unit in diameter, with Lennard–Jones force fields. Each wall consists of 968 atoms tethered to a position with a stiff spring, and the fluid has 8000 atoms. The inner wall molecules are located along positions $y = 1.3$ and 19.2, so the height of the channel is approximately 18 atomic diameters. For a typical molecule this would be on the order of 10 nm. Thus, we are looking at an extremely small channel. This wall is molecularly smooth, and liquid molecules cannot penetrate the wall. It is evident from the figure that the liquid in the immediate vicinity of the wall forms a layer. The force field of this layer induces a second layer, and so on. Each layer becomes more diffuse, and finally, in the center, no layering is observed. A simple liquid might have five layers, but the number depends on the chemical nature of the wall and the liquid. Within the layers, complex molecules with oblong structures

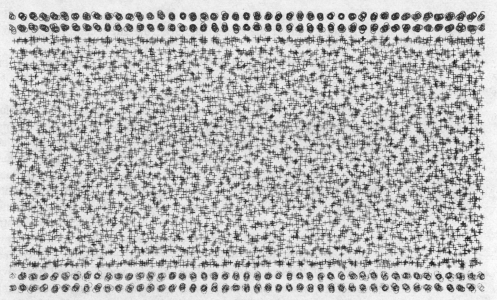

Figure 24.14   Snapshot from molecular dynamics calculation of Poiseuille channel flow. Courtesy of J. Koplik.

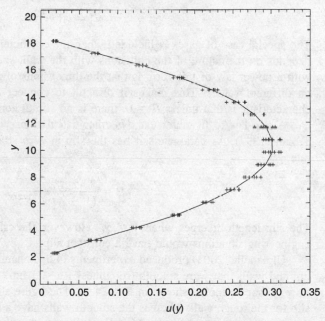

Figure 24.15   Velocity profiles from molecular dynamics calculation of Poiseuille channel flow. Courtesy of J. Koplik.

would arrange themselves with their axes in a preferred orientation. With this organized angular momentum at the molecular level, the stress tensor would no longer be symmetric, $T_{ij} \neq T_{ji}$.

Figure 24.15 is a parabola fitted to the molecular velocities. Within the uncertainty of the wall location, the profile shows little if any slip. Outside 10 molecular diameters the velocity and stress fields are essentially those predicted by the Navier–Stokes equations with essentially no-slip boundary conditions. This is the conclusion for simple Lennard–Jones molecules and smooth walls of the same density. Thompson and Robbins (1990) have investigated variations of the wall and fluid using molecular dynamics. The walls have a periodic force field structure with a certain intensity. If the strength of the force field is increased, the fluid layers next to the wall lock and mimic the structure of the wall. Then a negative slip is observed. For walls with higher density than the fluid, the period of the wall structure is shorter and the liquid molecules do not readily mimic the wall. Slip is then observed. Similarly, changing the force potential strength compared to the liquid force potential alters the slip. A weak wall potential promotes slip.

In experimental liquid flows there are further considerations. Near the walls the effects of wall–fluid chemistry, wall roughness, and dissolved gases will be important. The molecular model for gas slip has no relevance to liquids. Purely empirical equations are used for the slip length β or the slip velocity u_0 (e.g., Choi et al., 2002; Ulmanella, 2003). Here the wall velocity gradient is denoted as

$$\left.\frac{du}{dy}\right|_0 = \dot{\gamma}$$

$$\beta = A(\dot{\gamma})^B \tag{24.10.1}$$

$$u_0 = A(\dot{\gamma})^{B+1}$$

The special case of gases is included when the coefficient $B = 0$, and the coefficient A depends on the nature of the collisions with the wall, specular or diffuse. The difficulty with a power law of this form is that the dimensions of A change as the power B takes on different values. This makes it difficult to connect A with the physics. A second characteristic is that unless $B = 0$, there is no slip at zero strain rate.

A slip law to fit molecular dynamics calculations was proposed by Thompson and Troian (1997). As parameters it has the slip at zero strain rate β_0 and a critical strain rate $\dot{\gamma}_C$:

$$\beta = \frac{\beta_0}{(1 - \dot{\gamma}/\dot{\gamma}_C)^{1/2}} \tag{24.10.2}$$

The slip length diverges when $\dot{\gamma} = \dot{\gamma}_C$. However, the critical value is quite high. Many engineering situations would have a constant slip.

Ulmanella (2003) produced experiments in five channels with heights of 350 to 1270 nm and walls that were smooth (roughness Ra < 1 nm) and rough (Ra $= 8.4$ nm). The flow of isopropanol is shown in Fig. 24.16. The figure shows that there is essentially no slip for the rough wall, whereas the smooth walls have a slip of up to 35 nm. To validate that these events are dominated by the wall, note that the results are independent of the channel height. Contrary to the molecular dynamics predictions, the curve has a convex

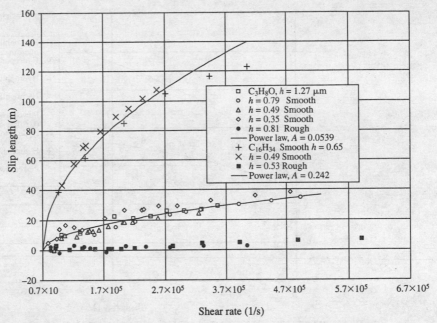

Figure 24.16   Slip in liquid flow with smooth and rough walls. Data from Ulmanella (2003).

curvature with increasing strain rate. The wall with a roughness height of 8.5 nm has no slip for all strain rates. This agrees with Zu and Granick (2002), who place the critical roughness for no slip at 6 nm.

There are many chemical factors that establish interactions between the fluid and the walls. The simplest overall indication is the wettability or nonwettability of the wall and the fluid. The terms *hydrophilic* and *hydrophobic* are also in common use. A second overall pattern is that polar molecules interact more strongly with the wall than do non-polar molecules. Figure 24.17 shows data of a polar molecule, C_3H_8O, and a nonpolar molecule, $C_{16}H_{34}$, flowing over the same hydrophilic wall. The nonpolar substance, with less wall interaction, has more slip. This same graph shows experiments by Choi et al. (2002) with water on a hydrophilic wall and then on a hydrophobic wall. The constants as determined by the experimenters are listed in Table 24.1. Choi et al. (2002) note that the power B is essentially $\frac{1}{2}$ and that the fit to the data is not decreased significantly with this value.

An important issue in the liquid–slip problem is the occurrence of gas in the liquid–solid interface. The gas may be left in rough walls as part of the history of liquid displacing a gas-filled tube, or the gas may come out of the liquid from a dissolved state. There are proposals that shear may induce nucleation of gas that preferentially forms a layer near the wall and promotes slip. Figure 24.18a shows measurements with liquid tetradecane that contained two dissolved gases. Carbon dioxide is readily dissolved in tetradecane, whereas argon has a low solubility. In these experiments the liquid is between two surfaces that are close together. One surface is vibrated in the normal direction so that the fluid is squeezed out (or in) as in the squeeze-film lubrication problem (Section

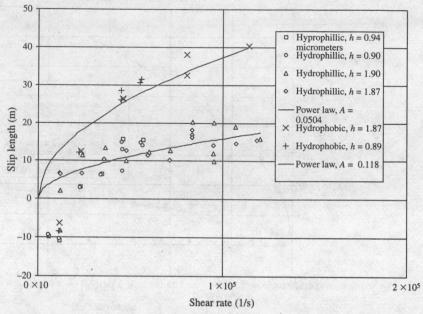

Figure 24.17   Slip in liquid flow with hydrophilic and hydrophobic walls. Data from Ulmanella (2003) and Choi et al. (2002).

22.5). The velocity amplitude of the motion, v, divided by spacing between the walls D, is termed the *flow rate* in the graph. It is a typical strain rate. If the force between the walls increases linearly with the flow rate, there is no slip. The fluid with argon undergoes slip at a flow rate of about 1 unit, whereas the liquid with CO_2 goes an order of magnitude higher without significant slip. This is taken as an indication that argon, which has low solubility, is segregating near the wall, forming a lower-viscosity fluid. In Fig. 24.18b the same experiment was done with water. The hatched region represents a series of tests where the gases dissolved in the water were uncontrolled. The curves for CO_2 and argon represent liquids saturated with those gases, respectively. In this case the gases gave slip behavior at nearly the same level. The question of gas accumulating at the interface is another unresolved issue in microflows. An engineering model of this behavior was analyzed by Lauga and Stone (2003). They simulated a flow where regions of no slip and regions of slip are periodic along the wall.

Table 24.1   Results of Experiments

Liquid	Molecular weight	Molecular size (Å)	Polar moment (Db)	Boundary	A (Å/10^{-11})	B
Isoproponal	60	4.35	1.66	Hydrophilic	3.94	0.52
n-Hexadecane	178	23.0	Nonpolar	Hydrophilic	51.9	0.42
Water	18	2.83	1.84	Hydrophilic	5.9	0.485
Water	18	2.83	1.84	Hydrophobic	19.2	0.460

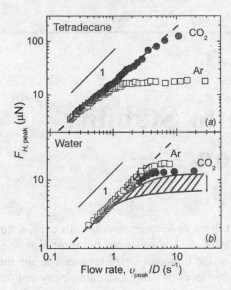

Figure 24.18 Effect of dissolved gases on liquid slip: (*a*) argon and CO_2 dissolved in tetradecane; (*b*) argon and CO_2 dissolved in water. From Granick et al. (2003) with permission.

24.11   CONCLUSIONS

Microflow of gases is characterized by the Knudsen number, the mean free path divided by the height of the flow. Four regions are identified. Low-Knudsen-number flows, where the Navier–Stokes equations and no-slip boundary conditions apply, are called *continuum flows*. However, in all flows we envision continuum properties such as density, velocity, and energy. Next, at slightly higher Knudsen numbers, the slip boundary condition and Navier–Stokes equations are applicable. At higher Knudsen numbers, a region called *translational,* the Navier–Stokes equations are no longer valid and flow is described by the Boltzmann equation. The limit of large Knudsen numbers is free molecular flow, where molecules only interact with walls. The Knudsen number can become large because the mean free path is large (rarefied gas dynamics) or the width of the flow is small (microflows). Microflows have a large surface and are typically isothermal, compressible flows.

A length scale for liquid flows is the average spacing between molecules or the molecular diameter. A nondimensional number similar to the Knudsen number is not commonly used. In liquid flows, slip is detectable only when the flow width is less than 2 μm. Flows in larger tubes have traditional characteristics, although experiments are very difficult and sensitive to extraneous effects. The Navier–Stokes equations are reasonable at a distance of about 10 molecular diameters away from the wall. Slip in liquids is on the order of 10 to 100 nm. If walls are rough, there is no slip. Other important influences on slip are the density of the wall compared to the liquid, the chemical characteristics of the wall and liquid, and the effects caused by dissolved or residual gases. The physics of liquid slip is complex and not completely understood.

25

Introduction to Stability and Transition

It is the perverse nature of fluid flows to become unstable. To exist, a flow pattern must not only be a solution to the Navier–Stokes equations but must also be stable. Any real flow contains slight deviations in the boundaries, irregularities in the incoming stream, or any of many other possible imperfections that cause the velocity and pressure to depart slightly from the nominal steady-state values. Situations where the departure is damped out and the flow returns to its steady values are stable. Typically, flows at low Reynolds numbers, where the damping effect of viscosity is strong, are stable. Most ideal inviscid flows (free of vorticity) are also stable.

Several things may happen to unstable flows. The most prominent is turbulence. In Reynolds's famous experiments on pipe flow, he noted that the transition from a stable laminar flow to a turbulent flow depended on exceeding a critical value of the Reynolds number. Pipe flows, wall boundary layers, jets, and shear layers are examples of flows that directly become turbulent. A second type of behavior of an unstable flow was characterized by Taylor's famous experiments on Couette flow. When a cylindrical Couette flow becomes unstable, it makes a transition to a new pattern containing Taylor vortices. The new pattern itself may at some point become unstable and give way to yet another pattern. Ultimately, at high enough Reynolds number, turbulence develops.

The classification of a flow as *open* or *closed* has important consequences on its stability. A closed flow is one where the particles travel on closed streamlines and stay in the domain of interest; the Taylor–Couette flow between concentric cylinders mentioned above is an example. Such flows tend to pass through a series of flow states as the Reynolds number (or equivalent) increases. The theory of dynamical systems has had success in describing these transitions. On the other hand, a fluid particle in an open flow enters the field and is convected through and passes out a downstream boundary. An open flow is in a sense isolated from events far from the field of interest. Boundary layers, jets, and mixing layers are in this category.

The purpose of *linear stability analysis,* described more fully in Section 25.1, is to indicate the flows patterns that are unstable. In this regard it is only partially successful. There are cases of flows that are linearly stable but which develop turbulence: for example, Poiseuille flow in a round pipe and plane Couette flow. In other cases, such as plane Poiseuille flow, turbulence develops at Reynolds numbers far below that where the flow theoretically becomes linearly unstable. As a general rule, turbulence develops rapidly in free-shear flows, jets, and mixing layers, but much slower in wall-bounded flows.

Stability theory is a mathematically complex subject. It has seen slow development because of great difficulty in solving its problems. In many instances heuristic and imaginative methods have been employed to solve stability problems. Recently, the computer has aided in resolving some issues, however, the reader should realize that there are distinct approaches that sometimes are complementary and sometimes contradictory. An open mind should be maintained as this subject progresses. The purpose of this chapter is to give the reader an introduction to the approaches, special nomenclature, and a survey of major results.

25.1   LINEAR STABILITY AND NORMAL MODES AS PERTURBATIONS

Hydrodynamic stability theory deals with predicting if a given flow pattern is or is not stable. The first approach is to consider a given steady flow V_i, which satisfies the governing equations. A perturbation of some type is added. The velocity is then

$$v_i(x_i, t) = V_i(x_i) + v_i'(x_i, t)$$

In linear theory v_i' is taken to be much smaller than V_i. (We could put a small-amplitude parameter ε in front of v_i' in the equation above, but since we work only to first order in ε, it is easy to keep track of the proper order of terms without this parameter. This follows the customary notation employed in this field.) When the equation $v_i = V_i + v_i'$ is substituted into the governing equations, they become a system to determine v_i' with a known basic flow V_i. In generating these equations, products of terms containing v_i' are discarded because they are of order ε^2. Thus, the small-amplitude assumption results in a linear system of equations for v_i'. The term *linear stability theory* is employed to indicate this approach. A theory of this nature can only mark the beginnings of any instability, as the growth of the disturbance soon invalidates the linearity assumption. The most we can expect of linear stability theory is that it will tell us what types of disturbances will grow, the amplification rate, and the critical values of the Reynolds number, or equivalent parameter, at which this will happen.

Since the equations for a small disturbance are linear, it is natural to draw on our experience with simple equations and propose that a disturbance can be decomposed into normal modes of various wavelengths. Although they are almost always used, it is only in a few special flows that the normal modes can be shown to form a complete set. Consider a basic flow in the x-direction that is parallel and depends only on the y-coordinate, that is, $V_i = (V_x(y), 0, 0)$. A normal-mode disturbance is a traveling wave with an amplitude that depends on y. For this flow it is assumed to be the real part of

$$v_i' = \hat{v}_i(y) \exp[i(\alpha x + \beta z - \alpha c t)] \qquad (25.1.1)$$

Here $\hat{v}(y)$ is a complex amplitude function, α (real) is the wavenumber in the x-direction, β (real) is the wavenumber in the z-direction, and c is a complex wave speed. The total wavenumber has the magnitude

$$k = (\alpha^2 + \beta^2)^{1/2} \qquad (25.1.2)$$

[The wavevector $\mathbf{k} = (\alpha, 0, \beta)$.]

It is useful to separate the complex wave speed into parts as

$$c = c_R + ic_I \qquad (25.1.3)$$

With this notation Eq. 25.1.1 becomes

$$v_i' = \hat{v}_i(y) \exp[i(\alpha x + \beta z - \alpha c_R t)] \exp(\alpha c_I t) \qquad (25.1.4)$$

The physical importance of c is evident in this form. At a fixed point in the flow the disturbance mode oscillates with a frequency $\omega = \alpha c_R$ as waves with wavenumber α, β pass by. The phase velocity of the mode is in the direction α, β with magnitude

$$c_\varphi = \frac{\alpha c_R}{k} = \frac{\omega}{k} = \frac{2\pi f}{2\pi/\lambda} = \lambda f \qquad (25.1.5)$$

A disturbance in the flow direction ($\beta = 0$, so that $k = \alpha$) has the phase velocity c_R.

For the stability question, the most important quantity is c_I (assuming $\alpha > 0$). The growth or decay of Eq. 25.1.4 occurs in time as follows:

$$c_I < 0: \qquad \text{flow is stable}$$

$$c_I > 0: \qquad \text{flow is unstable}$$

$$c_I = 0: \qquad \text{flow is neutrally stable}$$

A point where $c_I = 0$, but where a small change in a flow parameter, say the Reynolds number, moves it into a region where $c_i > 0$, is called *marginally* or *neutrally stable*. Such points are important because their locus marks the boundary between stable and unstable conditions. An analysis with c complex is called a *temporal stability analysis*.

Consider a second possibility in Eq. 25.1.1, where c is real and $\alpha = \alpha_R + i\alpha_I$ is complex. The perturbation now grows in x:

$$v_i' = \hat{v}_i(y) \exp[i(\alpha_R x + \beta z - \alpha_R ct)] \exp(\alpha_I x)$$

If this perturbation is used, the problem is known as a *spatial stability problem*.

25.2 KELVIN–HELMHOLTZ INVISCID SHEAR LAYER INSTABILITY

When the basic flow and the perturbation are governed by the Euler equations, the stability problem is called an *inviscid stability problem*. The Kelvin–Helmholtz instability of an inviscid shear layer is an important example of this type of flow. Figure 25.1 shows a shear layer and the resulting growth of the instability. In this particular experiment a splitter plate separates the flows so that the age of the perturbation increases in the downstream direction. The mathematical problem is posed in a slightly different form where two uniform streams in the x-direction slip past each other with the velocity discontinuity in the $y = 0$ plane, as shown on Fig. 25.2.

In inviscid flow theory, the slip surface constitutes a vortex sheet of uniform density. Let us consider the equations that govern the flow, including any perturbation. The flow above the sheet has a velocity potential ϕ_2 and that below the sheet ϕ_1. Incompressible, irrotational flows satisfy

$$\nabla^2 \phi_1 = 0 \quad \text{and} \quad \nabla^2 \phi_2 = 0 \qquad (25.2.1)$$

with boundary conditions

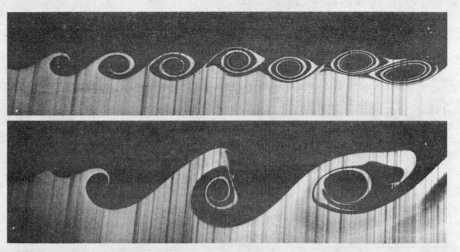

Figure 25.1 Kelvin–Helmholtz instability of a shear layer. The lower water stream, which contains a fluorescent dye, moves slower than the upper stream. A perturbation is introduced to initiate the growth in a regular pattern. Frequency is halved in the lower picture. Courtesy of F. A. Roberts, P. E Dimotakis, and A. Roshko, California Institute of Technology.

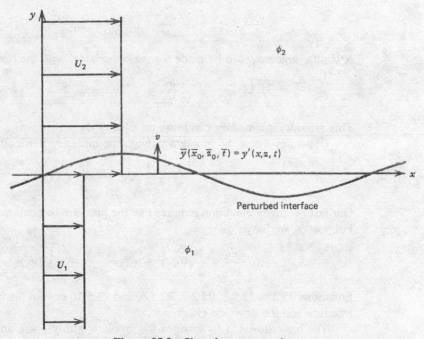

Figure 25.2 Shear layer nomenclature.

$$\nabla \phi_1 = U_1 \quad \text{as} \quad y \to -\infty \tag{25.2.2}$$

$$\nabla \phi_2 = U_2 \quad \text{as} \quad y \to +\infty$$

These conditions require that the perturbations die out far from the interface.

The interface is displaced slightly by the perturbed flow. Let the interface have the vertical position

$$F(x, y, z, t) = y - f(x, z, t) \tag{25.2.3}$$

The interface may move with velocity w, and one form of the kinematic interface condition was given as Eq. 23.1.5:

$$\frac{\partial F}{\partial t} + w \cdot \nabla F = 0 \tag{25.2.4}$$

Evaluating this equation for the form Eq. 25.2.3 gives

$$-\frac{\partial f}{\partial t} + w_y - w_x \frac{\partial f}{\partial x} - w_z \frac{\partial f}{\partial z} = 0 \tag{25.2.5}$$

The interface velocity w is not defined completely by Eq. 23.1.5. We can assume that a surface fluid particle in the lower fluid remains in the interface at later times. Then $w = v_1$ and Eq. 25.2.6 becomes

$$-\frac{\partial f}{\partial t} + v_1 - u_1 \frac{\partial f}{\partial x} - w_1 \frac{\partial f}{\partial z} = 0 \tag{25.2.6}$$

Solving for v_1 and noting that $f = y'$ and $v_1 = \partial \phi_1/\partial y$ results in

$$\frac{\partial \phi_1}{\partial y} = v_1 = -\frac{\partial y'}{\partial t} + u_1 \frac{\partial y'}{\partial x} + w_1 \frac{\partial y'}{\partial z} \quad \text{at} \quad y = y' \tag{25.2.7}$$

A similar argument can be made for the upper side, with the result that

$$\frac{\partial \phi_2}{\partial y} = v_2 = -\frac{\partial y'}{\partial t} + u_2 \frac{\partial y'}{\partial x} + w_2 \frac{\partial y'}{\partial z} \quad \text{at} \quad y = y' \tag{25.2.8}$$

This provides a boundary condition on ϕ_1 and ϕ_2.

Dynamics enters the problem through the unsteady Bernoulli equation,

$$\frac{\partial \phi}{\partial t} + \frac{1}{2} (\nabla \phi)^2 + \frac{p}{\rho} = C(t) \tag{25.2.9}$$

Our last boundary condition requires that the pressure be continuous across the interface. For $y = y'$ we have

$$\frac{\partial \phi_1}{\partial t} + \frac{1}{2} (\nabla \phi_1)^2 - C_1 = \frac{\partial \phi_2}{\partial t} + \frac{1}{2} (\nabla \phi_2)^2 - C_2 \tag{25.2.10}$$

Equations 25.2.1, 25.2.2, 25.2.7, 22.5.8, and 22.5.10 govern the inviscid motion of a slip interface and the flows on either side.

The basic flow U_1, U_2 satisfies the problem with $y' = 0$, and the Bernoulli relation then reduces to

$$C_1 - \tfrac{1}{2}U_1^2 = C_2 - \tfrac{1}{2}U_2^2 \qquad (25.2.11)$$

Perturbations from the basic flow are denoted by a prime. Thus, the potentials are

$$\phi_1 = U_1 x + \phi_1'$$

$$\phi_2 = U_2 x + \phi_2'$$

When these relations are substituted into Eq. 25.2.1 we find that

$$\nabla^2 \phi_1' = \nabla^2 \phi_2' = 0 \qquad (25.2.12)$$

While Eq. 25.2.2 shows that the perturbations die out at infinity:

$$\nabla \phi_1' = 0 \qquad \text{as} \quad y \to -\infty$$
$$\nabla \phi_2' = 0 \qquad \text{as} \quad y \to +\infty \qquad (25.2.13)$$

The surface conditions 25.2.7 and 25.2.8 are transferred back to the basic surface $y = 0$ (see Section 15.3) and linearized by dropping products of primed quantities. This results in

$$\left.\frac{\partial \phi_1'}{\partial y}\right|_0 = \frac{\partial y'}{\partial x} + U_1 \frac{\partial y'}{\partial x} \quad \text{and} \quad \left.\frac{\partial \phi_2'}{\partial y}\right|_0 = \frac{\partial y'}{\partial t} + U_2 \frac{\partial y'}{\partial x} \qquad (25.2.14)$$

In a similar manner the perturbation quantities are introduced into the Bernoulli equation 25.2.9, the relation is expanded about the basic surface $y = 0$, and the steady-flow relation 25.2.11 is subtracted. The final equation is

$$\frac{\partial \phi_1'}{\partial t} + U_1 \frac{\partial \phi_1'}{\partial x} = \frac{\partial \phi_2'}{\partial t} + U_2 \frac{\partial \phi_2'}{\partial x} \qquad \text{at} \quad y = 0 \qquad (25.2.15)$$

The mathematical problem for y', ϕ_1', and ϕ_2' consists of Eqs. 25.2.12 to 25.2.14.

The flow has been divided into a steady basic flow and a time-dependent perturbation. Next, assume that the perturbation can be represented by a composition of normal modes of the form

$$\begin{Bmatrix} y' \\ \phi_1' \\ \phi_2' \end{Bmatrix} = \begin{Bmatrix} \hat{y} \\ \hat{\phi}_1\,(y) \\ \hat{\phi}_2\,(y) \end{Bmatrix} \exp[i(\alpha x + \beta z - \alpha c t)] \qquad (25.2.16)$$

As discussed in Section 25.1, $c = c_R + i c_I$ is a complex wave speed. Note that $\hat{y}$ is a constant that gives the original amplitude of the interface displacement. It keys the size of all perturbed quantities. When $c_I > 0$, this displacement is unstable and grows exponentially in time.

Substituting Eq. 25.2.16 into 25.2.12 with boundary conditions 25.2.13 shows that the amplitude functions are

$$\hat{\phi}_1\,(y) = A_1 \exp(+\,ky)$$
$$\hat{\phi}_2\,(y) = A_2 \exp(-\,ky) \qquad (25.2.17)$$

where $k = (\alpha^2 + \beta^2)^{1/2}$. Substituting Eqs. 25.2.16 and 25.2.17 into the interface conditions 25.2.14 yields

$$A_1 = i\alpha \frac{\hat{y}}{k} (U_1 - c) \tag{25.2.18}$$

$$A_2 = -i\alpha \frac{\hat{y}}{k} (U_2 - c)$$

The final relation is obtained by inserting Eqs. 25.2.16 to 25.2.18 into the Bernoulli relation 25.2.15. This gives

$$(U_1 - c)^2 = -(U_2 - c)^2$$

The last step is to solve for the complex wave speed:

$$c = \tfrac{1}{2}(U_1 + U_2) \pm i\tfrac{1}{2}|U_2 - U_1|$$

$$= c_R + ic_I \tag{25.2.19}$$

A flow with $c_I > 0$ is unstable. Hence, waves of all wavenumbers α, β are unstable if we take the plus sign in Eq. 25.2.19 (the possibility of stable decay for the minus sign exists; however, we are more interested in situations that allow instability). All shear layers $U_1 \neq U_2$ are inviscidly unstable to disturbances of all wavelengths.

Consider a disturbance of a certain wavelength $k = (\alpha^2 + \beta^2)^{1/2}$ and an arbitrary orientation. Since the growth rate is $\exp(\alpha c_I t)$, the wave of given $|k|$ that is oriented in the flow direction $k = \alpha$ will grow the fastest. The phase speed of this wave is

$$c_\varphi = \frac{\alpha c_R}{k} = c_R = \frac{1}{2}(U_1 + U_2) \tag{25.2.20}$$

The disturbance travels at the average speed of the main flows.

Kelvin–Helmholtz instability is extremely common, as many flows are essentially thin free shear layers (e.g., the initial region of a jet). Viscous effects in a shear layer, which spread the velocity profile over a finite thickness, stabilize perturbations with wavelength comparable to the shear layer thickness. Waves much longer are still governed by the analysis we have just completed.

25.3 STABILITY PROBLEM FOR NEARLY PARALLEL VISCOUS FLOWS

When viscous effects are included, the stability equations become much more complicated. A degree of simplicity can be restored if we consider a flow with two components $U(x, y)$, $V(x, y)$. An introduction to the stability of three-dimensional flows is Reed and Saric (1989). First, it is assumed the flow is nearly parallel: $V \ll U$ and $\partial U / \partial x \ll \partial U / \partial y$. Velocity and pressure perturbations v' and p' are added to the main flow, so that

$$v = (U + u', V + v', w')$$

$$p = P + p' \tag{25.3.1}$$

Both the steady main flow U, V, P and the flow with the perturbation satisfy the Navier–Stokes equations. The variables in Eq. 25.3.1 are nondimensional. Typical scales U_∞, L, ρ will be specified for each particular problem.

The x-component of the momentum equation for the flow is

$$\frac{\partial u'}{\partial t} + (U + u') \frac{\partial}{\partial x} (U + u') + (V + v') \frac{\partial}{\partial y} (U + u')$$

$$= -\frac{\partial}{\partial x} (P + p') + \frac{1}{\text{Re}} \nabla^2 (U + u') \qquad (25.3.2)$$

The same equation for the main flow is

$$U \frac{\partial U}{\partial x} + V \frac{\partial U}{\partial y} = -\frac{\partial P}{\partial x} + \frac{1}{\text{Re}} \nabla^2 U \qquad (25.3.3)$$

Equation 25.3.2 is expanded and linearized by dropping products of u', v', w', V, and $\partial U / \partial x$. When Eq. 25.3.3 is subtracted, we arrive at an x-momentum equation for the perturbation:

$$\frac{\partial u'}{\partial t} + U \frac{\partial u'}{\partial x} + v' \frac{\partial U}{\partial y} = -\frac{\partial p'}{\partial x} + \frac{1}{\text{Re}} \nabla^2 u' \qquad (25.3.4)$$

The y- and z-direction momentum equations are found by similar steps:

$$\frac{\partial v'}{\partial t} + U \frac{\partial v'}{\partial x} = -\frac{\partial p'}{\partial y} + \frac{1}{\text{Re}} \nabla^2 v' \qquad (25.3.5)$$

and

$$\frac{\partial w'}{\partial t} + U \frac{\partial w'}{\partial x} = -\frac{\partial p'}{\partial z} + \frac{1}{\text{Re}} \nabla^2 w' \qquad (25.3.6)$$

Applying the same process to the continuity equation yields

$$\nabla + \mathbf{v}' = 0 \qquad (25.3.7)$$

Relations 25.3.4 to 25.3.7 are a linear system of equations for $\mathbf{v}'$, p' when a specified main flow $U(y)$ is given. The dependence of the main flow in the x-direction has been suppressed by the "nearly parallel" assumption. Essentially, we are treating any chosen location x as if the profile at that station continued upstream and downstream without changing.

If the flow is confined between two walls, the no-slip condition requires that the perturbation $\mathbf{v}'$ vanish at both walls. If the flow extends to infinity, we require that the perturbation velocity vanish there also. No boundary conditions on the pressure are required.

Next, we note that the problem is linear and propose that an arbitrary disturbance may be decomposed into normal modes described by

$$v_i' = \hat{v}_i(y) \exp[i(\alpha x + \beta z - \alpha c_R t)] \cdot \exp(\alpha c_I t)$$

$$p' = \hat{p}(y) \exp[i(\alpha x + \beta z - \alpha_R c t)] \cdot \exp(\alpha c_I t) \qquad (25.3.8)$$

For a chosen wavenumber α, β (both real) and specified Reynolds number Re, the substitution of Eq. 25.3.8 into Eqs. 25.3.4 to 25.3.7 produces an eigenvalue problem where certain solutions $\hat{v}_i(y)$, $\hat{p}(y)$, the eigenfunctions, occur for specific values of c (complex for temporal instability), the eigenvalue. Performing the substitution just described produces the following set of equations:

$$i\alpha(U - c)\hat{u} + \hat{v}\,\frac{dU}{dy} = -i\alpha\hat{p} + \frac{1}{\text{Re}}\left[\frac{d^2\hat{u}}{dy^2} - (\alpha^2 + \beta^2)\hat{u}\right]$$

$$i\alpha(U - c)\hat{v} = -\frac{d\hat{p}}{dy} + \frac{1}{\text{Re}}\left[\frac{d^2\hat{v}}{dy^2} - (\alpha^2 + \beta^2)\hat{v}\right]$$

$$i\alpha(U - c)\hat{w} = -i\beta\hat{p} + \frac{1}{\text{Re}}\left[\frac{d^2\hat{w}}{dy^2} - (\alpha^2 + \beta^2)\hat{w}\right]$$

$$(25.3.9)$$

$$i\alpha\hat{u} + i\beta\hat{w} + \frac{d\hat{v}}{dy} = 0$$

These equations govern the viscous stability of a normal mode in any nearly parallel flow.

A remarkable simplification of the stability problem was revealed by Squire (1933). He showed that for any *unstable* three-dimensional disturbance, there is a corresponding two-dimensional disturbance ($\hat{w} = 0$) that is more unstable. This allows us to seek the stability boundary of the flow with a two-dimensional disturbance $\hat{u}$, $\hat{v}$ and be assured that this is sufficient to find the lowest limit of linear stability. To prove Squire's theorem, consider the following transformation of variables:

$$\alpha^* = (\alpha^2 + \beta^2)^{1/2}, \qquad c^* = c$$

$$\alpha^* u^* = \alpha\hat{u} + \beta\hat{w}, \qquad v^* = \hat{v} \qquad (25.3.10)$$

$$\frac{p^*}{\alpha^*} = \frac{\hat{p}}{\alpha}, \qquad \alpha^*\,\text{Re}^* = \alpha\,\text{Re}$$

These relations are used to transform the set 25.3.9. The first and third equations in Eq. 25.3.9 are added together, whereas the second and fourth are simply transformed. The result is the three equations

$$i\alpha^*(U - c^*)u^* + v^*\,\frac{dU}{dy} = -i\alpha^* p^* + \frac{1}{\text{Re}^*}\left(\frac{d^2 u^*}{dy^2} - \alpha^{*2} u^*\right) \qquad (25.3.11a)$$

$$i\alpha^*(U - c^*)v^* = -\frac{dp^*}{dy} + \frac{1}{\text{Re}^*}\left(\frac{d^2 v^*}{dy^2} - \alpha^* v^*\right) \qquad (25.3.11b)$$

$$i\alpha^* u^* + \frac{dv^*}{dy} = 0 \qquad (25.3.11c)$$

These equations are identical with Eq. 25.3.9 when $\beta = 0$ and $\hat{w} = 0$ are taken in the former set. Through Squire's transformation 25.3.10, any solution for a two-dimensional disturbance u^*, v^* of wavenumber α^* and wave speed c^* may be used to describe an equivalent three-dimensional disturbance of wavenumber α, β, and wave speed c.

Recall from Eq. 25.1.4 that the temporal growth rate of a disturbance is $\exp(\alpha c_i t)$. Thus, for any three-dimensional disturbance of wavenumber α, β and wavespeed $c = c_R + ic_I$, the equivalent two-dimensional disturbance has a larger x-direction wavenumber, since $\alpha^* = (\alpha^2 + \beta^2)^{1/2}$, and is more unstable in the sense that $\alpha^* c_I^* > \alpha c_I$ (note that $c_I^* = c_I$ in Squire's transformation). Moreover, the Reynolds number of the equivalent flow is lower because Re* = Re · α/α^*. In seeking the marginal stability curve of a flow, we are usually interested in the smallest Reynolds number for which any disturbance is unstable. Squire's transformation shows that if this value is found for a two-dimensional disturbance, we have, in fact, determined the smallest value for both two- and three-dimensional disturbances. As a matter of convention, in further work we shall use the notation of Eq. 25.3.9 in the two-dimensional problem 25.3.11. This is equivalent to setting $\beta = \hat{w} = 0$ in Eq. 25.3.9.

25.4 ORR–SOMMERFELD EQUATION

Incompressible, two-dimensional flows may be formulated in terms of a streamfunction. Since the perturbations satisfy $\nabla \cdot \mathbf{v}' = 0$, it is permissible to introduce a perturbation streamfunction ψ' defined by

$$u' = \frac{\partial \psi'}{\partial y}, \qquad v' = -\frac{\partial \psi'}{\partial x} \qquad (25.4.1)$$

The normal-mode assumption for the streamfunction is

$$\psi' = \phi(y) \exp[i(\alpha x + \beta z - ct)] \qquad (25.4.2)$$

Where $\phi(y)$ is the complex amplitude function for the streamfunction. (This is the universally accepted symbol. The reader should carefully note that this ϕ has no connection with the velocity potential.) Substituting Eq. 25.4.2 into Eq. 25.4.1 and using Eq. 25.1.4 gives

$$\hat{u} = \frac{d\phi}{dy}, \qquad \hat{v} = -i\alpha\phi \qquad (25.4.3)$$

These relations reduce the continuity equation in Eq. 25.3.11 to an identity.

A single equation for $\phi(y)$ is found by substituting Eq. 25.4.3 into equation 25.3.11a, differentiating with respect to y so that $d\hat{p}/dy$ occurs, and then eliminating $d\hat{p}/dy$ in Eq. 25.3.11b. The result may be written as

$$(U - c)\left(\frac{d^2\phi}{dy^2} - \alpha^2\phi\right) - \phi\frac{d^2U}{dy^2} = \frac{1}{i\alpha\,\mathrm{Re}}\left(\frac{d^2}{dy^2} - \alpha^2\right)^2\phi \qquad (25.4.4)$$

This equation is the cornerstone of linear hydrodynamic stability theory. It was derived first by Orr (1907) and Sommerfeld (1908). Although the equation is linear, it is notoriously difficult to solve. Consider, for example, the Blasius boundary layer profile. The first successful solutions of the Orr–Sommerfeld equation for this flow were by Tollmien (1929) and Schlichting (1933), more than 20 years after the equation was discovered. These first attempts were approximations. A significantly different approach was taken by Lin (1945), and finally, what might be called an exact solution was found by Jordinson (1970) over a one-half century after the equation was first established. Mack (1984) is a recommended reference for the linear stability of boundary layers.

The Orr–Sommerfeld equation, with no-slip boundary conditions $\phi = d\phi/dy = 0$ at two locations in the flow, is to be solved for a given velocity profile $U(y)$, Reynolds number Re, and wavenumber α. The equation determines not only the eigenfunction $\phi(y)$ but also the complex wave speed $c = c_R + ic_I$ as the eigenvalue. A bounded flow has, for fixed Re and α, a discrete set of eigenvalues $c_1, c_2, c_3, \ldots$. A boundary layer flow that is unbounded has a discrete set and an additional continuous spectrum. Consider the eigenvalues as a function of α and Re (for a given flow):

$$c_R = c_R(\alpha, \text{Re})$$

$$c_I = c_I(\alpha, \text{Re})$$

(25.4.5)

Recall that the perturbation growth is $\exp(\alpha c_I t)$ and that the flow is unstable for $c_I > 0$. If at least one neutral stability mode $c_I = 0$ exists, then setting $c_I = 0$ in Eq. 25.4.5 gives a curve of neutral stability $c_I(\alpha, \text{Re}) = 0$. If, in addition, it is possible to show that c_I changes sign as one crosses the neutral curve, this is also the curve of marginal stability. It separates a stable and an unstable region in α, Re space. The neutral curve established by spatial stability theory, that is, $\alpha = \alpha_R + i\alpha_I$, is where $\alpha_I = 0$ and is the same as that found from a temporal analysis.

25.5 INVISCID STABILITY OF NEARLY PARALLEL FLOWS

When Re $\to \infty$ the Orr–Sommerfeld equation, we have a simplified form known as Rayleigh's equation:

$$\frac{d^2\phi}{dy^2} - \left(\alpha^2 + \frac{1}{U-c} \frac{d^2U}{dy^2} \right)\phi = 0$$

(25.5.1)

Since an inviscid flow slips past a wall, only the boundary condition $\phi = 0$ is enforced at two places in the flow. It is particularly important to realize that Rayleigh's equation describes a perturbation that behaves in an inviscid manner. The main flow profile $U(y)$ may be a viscous-dominated flow. Thus, it is perfectly reasonable to talk about the inviscid stability of the Blasius boundary layer profile. This is, in fact, the behavior of the marginal stability curve $c_I(\alpha, \text{Re}) = 0$ as Re $\to \infty$.

Rayleigh proved two characteristics of inviscid stability that are of general utility in predicting stability characteristics. The first is known as *Rayleigh's point-of-inflection theorem*. It may be stated as follows: A necessary (but not sufficient) condition for inviscid instability is that the basic profile $U(y)$ has a point of inflection. This is a very powerful result, as we may conclude that any profile without a point of inflection is stable as Re $\to \infty$. Poiseuille flow, plane Couette flow, the Blasius boundary layer, and all boundary layers with favorable pressure gradients are therefore stable as Re $\to \infty$.

A slightly stronger result is known as *Fjørtoft's theorem*. It may be stated as follows: If y_0 is the position of a point of inflection [$d^2U/dy^2 = 0$ in the basic profile $U(y)$ and $U_0 = U(y_0)$], then a necessary (but not sufficient) condition for inviscid instability is that $(d^2U/dy^2)(U - U_0) < 0$ somewhere in the flow. Figure 25.3 illustrates this theorem. Both profiles a and b have points of inflection, and hence by Rayleigh's theorem they are possibly unstable. The stronger theorem of Fjørtoft shows that the first case (Fig. 25.3a) is also stable because $(d^2U/dy^2)(U - U_0) > 0$. The second case is possibly unstable by both criteria.

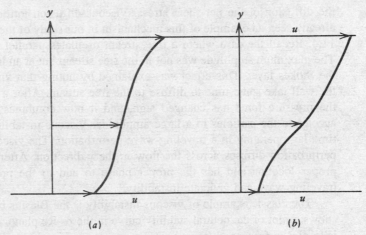

Figure 25.3 Inviscid instability of shear flows. Both cases are possibly unstable by Rayleigh's theorem, but only (b) is possibly unstable by Fjørtoft's theorem.

Rayleigh's second result concerns the neutral stability mode with $c_I = 0$. For this mode $c = c_R$ and the denominator $U - c$ in Eq. 25.5.1 is real. Rayleigh proved that the phase speed c_R must lie between the maximum and minimum values of the profile $U(y)$. Thus, $U - c = 0$ at some point within the flow. This position is called the *critical layer*, because the inviscid equation 25.5.1 is singular at this location. The wave propagation velocity and the flow velocity are matched at the critical layer.

When we regard Rayleigh's equation 25.5.1 as the asymptotic form of the Orr–Sommerfeld equation 25.4.4 as Re $\rightarrow \infty$, we note that the inviscid eigenfunctions $\phi(y)$ cannot be uniformly valid. Two boundary conditions ($d\phi/dy = 0$) have been dropped. Since Eq. 25.5.1 is of second order while Eq. 25.4.4 is of fourth order, viscous effects on the perturbation must occur at both walls (or at the wall and the free stream in an unbounded flow). Another nonuniform region occurs at the critical layer. Here $U - c = 0$ causes singular behavior in the Rayleigh equation, whereas the Orr–Sommerfeld equation has no difficulty at this point. The critical layer, where the wave speed of the inviscid perturbation matches the flow speed, is another place where viscous effects on the perturbation are important. Lin (1945) showed that when a profile has a point of inflection, the critical layer is located there.

25.6 VISCOUS STABILITY OF NEARLY PARALLEL FLOWS

Inertia and pressure forces must be in balance in an inviscid flow. An unstable velocity perturbation, say an increase in speed, through the Bernoulli equation must produce a pressure gradient. Intuitively, the addition of viscosity to this picture would be expected to be stabilizing. Indeed, a direct retarding force is one effect of viscosity. For any basic profile, one can usually find complete stability if the flow Reynolds number is low enough.

A second and somewhat unexpected effect of viscosity is destabilizing. A slight amount of viscosity can destabilize an otherwise stable profile. The reason has to do with the diffusion of the net shear stress. Viscous diffusion introduces a time lag. We have already seen an example of this mechanism in our study of the Stokes problem in Section 11.4. Recall the case where a free stream oscillates parallel to and above a fixed wall. The maximum amplitude was not in the free stream but at an intermediate distance within the Stokes layer. This effect was explained by noting that viscous stresses generated at the wall take some time to diffuse to the free stream. After a time lag of one-half cycle, the pressure force has changed sign, and it now combines with the viscous force to accelerate the particles to a large amplitude. Viscous instability is this same diffusional time lag operating in a traveling-wave perturbation. The viscous stress generated by the perturbation diffuses across the flow in the y-direction. After a certain time it is in the proper location and has the proper phase to add to the pressure mechanisms of the traveling wave and generate instability.

The classic example of viscous instability is the Blasius boundary layer. Figure 25.4 shows a plot of the neutral-stability curve in the α–Re plane. Another form of this graph is to plot in frequency ($\omega = \alpha c_R$)–Re space (see Fig. 25.6). This curve divides the plane into stable and unstable regions. The flow is stable to disturbances of all wavenumbers at a low Reynolds number. This is the stabilizing effect of viscous damping. Similarly, as Re $\rightarrow \infty$ by Rayleigh's point-of-inflection theorem, the flow is completely stable for all α. Within the loop of the marginal stability curve is a range of wavenumbers that are unstable. These unstable waves are called *Tollmien–Schlichting* (TS) *waves*. The point on the neutral curve with the lowest Reynolds number is called the *critical point*. The Blasius boundary layer has a critical Reynolds number of Re $= U\delta^*/\nu = 520$. The boundary layer is completely stable until this Reynolds number is reached. At this point

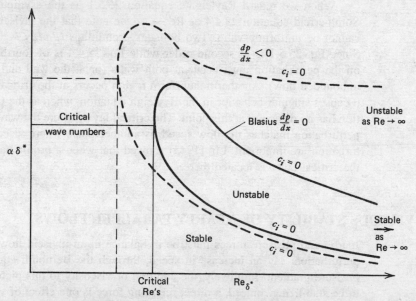

Figure 25.4   General shape of the neutral stability curve (locus of $c_i = 0$ in wavenumber–Reynolds number space) for a Blasius boundary layer and for layers with adverse pressure gradients.

the layer is unstable to a TS wave with $\alpha \delta^* = 0.30$. The wavelength of this unstable mode is $L = 2\pi/\alpha = 2\pi\delta^*/0.3 \approx 18 \, \delta^* \approx 6\delta$. Thus, the first unstable wave has a very long wavelength. The boundary layer is always stable to short wavelengths. As the boundary layer grows, Re increases and the band of unstable wavelength becomes larger. Of course, the loop closes and stability returns as Re $\rightarrow \infty$. The boundary layer never actually reaches this state, because the end result of the previous instability is a turbulent flow.

Boundary layers in an adverse pressure gradient must have a point of inflection. By Fjørtoft's theorem these profiles may have inviscid instability. Indeed, it turns out that they do. The upper branch of the neutral stability curve (see Fig. 25.4) now has a finite limit α_∞ as Re $\rightarrow \infty$. Tollmien–Schlichting waves with $0 < \alpha < \alpha_\infty$ (long wavelengths) are unstable to inviscid mechanisms. Perhaps more important from a practical standpoint is the fact that the critical Reynolds number is now lower and the range of unstable wavenumbers is greater. Adverse pressure gradients rapidly promote the transition to turbulence.

As a final example in this section, we consider the marginal stability curve for a shear layer. Figure 25.5 was computed by Betchov and Szewczyk (1963) for a shear layer profile $U = \tanh(y/L)$. This is actually a model of a shear layer making a transition from U_1 to U_2 as seen by an observer moving at $(U_1 + U_2)/2$. Only at Re $= 0$ is the profile completely stable for all wavenumbers. At Re $\rightarrow \infty$ the flow is unstable to long wavelengths ($0 \leq \alpha L \leq 1$). This is essentially the Kelvin–Helmholtz instability. The only new aspect is that the actual profile of the shear layer causes wavelengths shorter than the shear layer thickness L to be stable. Between these extremes of Reynolds numbers the neutral stability curve has a smooth monotonic variation. Viscosity has a purely stabilizing effect in this flow.

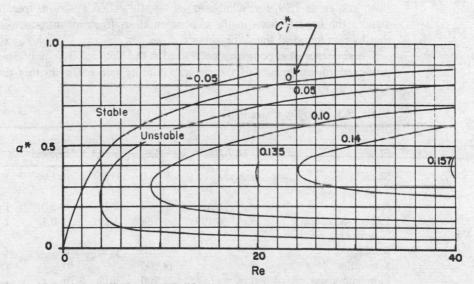

Figure 25.5   Curves of constant amplification $c_i^* = c_i \alpha L / U_0$ in the wavenumber $\alpha^* = \alpha L$ versus Re plane for a shear layer $u = U_0 \tanh(y/L)$. Neutral stability is given by $c_i^* = 0$. Viscosity makes the flow completely stable only at Re $= 0$. Reproduced with permission from Betchov and Szewczyk (1963). Graph courtesy of A. Szewczyk, Notre Dame University.

Table 25.1 gives stability characteristics of several common flows. The first three flows have points of inflection in the profiles. They are unstable as Re $\rightarrow \infty$ for the range of wavenumbers denoted as $0 - \alpha_\infty^* L$. The critical Reynolds numbers are very low for these flows. Furthermore, the stability curve is somewhat insensitive to the shape of the main velocity profile $U(y)$. All the remaining flows are stable as Re $\rightarrow \infty$; they do not have a point of inflection. In these flows the viscous instability mechanism operates. They have a larger critical Reynolds number and show more sensitivity to the form of the basic flow profile. Note in the last entry that plane Couette flow and cylindrical Poisuille flow are completely stable. This is an obvious failure of linear stability theory.

25.7   EXPERIMENTS ON BLASIUS BOUNDARY LAYERS

The usual historical sequence in fluid mechanics is that phenomena are observed, documented experimentally, and subsequently explained by analysis and theory. Linear stability theory is an interesting reversal of this sequence. The prediction of the existence of TS waves and the neutral stability curve lacked verification for many years. Finally, experiments on the Blasius boundary layer confirmed the theory.

The Blasius boundary layer is known to become turbulent at $Re_\delta^* \approx 3000$. Because an unstable wave grows very slowly at first, the critical Reynolds number for stability, 520, is much lower than this value. Moreover, TS waves are only the first stage in a natural transition. The waves slowly change form, become three-dimensional, and nonlinear processes determine the final transition. Depending on the details of the flow situation, there are several different mechanisms and events that can lead ultimately to turbulence. The idealized transition beginning with the linear instability of a TS wave (also known as TSS, for Schubauer) is usually called a *natural transition*. In most instances the imperfections in the experimental arrangement introduce large disturbances that bypass the ideal transition process.

A sequence of experiments conducted at the National Bureau of Standards ultimately produced measurements of the neutral stability curve. To do this they constructed a

Table 25.1   Stability Characteristics

Flow	$U(y)/U_0$	$U_0 L/\nu$ $= Re_c$	$\alpha_c L$ $= \alpha^*$	$0 - \alpha_\infty^*$ Inviscid	Remarks
Shear layer	$\tanh(y/L)$	0	0	0–1.0	Kelvin–Helmholtz, Re $\rightarrow \infty$
Jet	$\operatorname{sech}^2(y/L)$	4	0.2	0–2.0	Even mode
Falkner–Skan separating profile	$\beta = -0.199$	64	1.24	0–0.8	$L = \delta^*$
Blasius	$\beta = 0$	520	0.30	0	$L = \delta^*$
Stagnation	$\beta = 1$	14,000		0	$L = \delta^*$
Flow into a sink	$\beta = \infty$	21,700	0.17	0	$L = \delta^*$
Poiseuille (plane)	$1 - (y/L)^2$	5,780	1.02	0	$L =$ half-width
Poiseuille (cylindrical)	$1 - (r/R)^2$	∞		0	Stable
Couette (plane)	y/L	∞		0	Stable

special wind tunnel which had a very low turbulence level in the free stream. The root-mean-square velocity fluctuation averaged in three directions was less than 0.03% of the free-stream velocity. Figure 25.6 gives the stability curve determined by vibrating a ribbon in the boundary layer and observing the stability of the disturbance. The frequency of the disturbance ($\omega = \alpha c_R$) is plotted, as this is experimentally easier to determine than the wavenumber. Also shown in the figure are the original stability curves of Schlichting (1933) using approximate methods and some improved calculations by Shen (1954). The agreement between theory and experiment at this time was close. With the development of computers, more exact methods of solving the Orr–Sommerfeld equations became possible. Exact solutions revealed that the previous curves are slightly wrong; $Re_c = 520$ in the exact calculations, compared to an experimental value of 450.

Attempts to resolve the discrepancy have centered on accounting for the growth of the boundary layer. Several nonparallel stability calculations, involving quite different

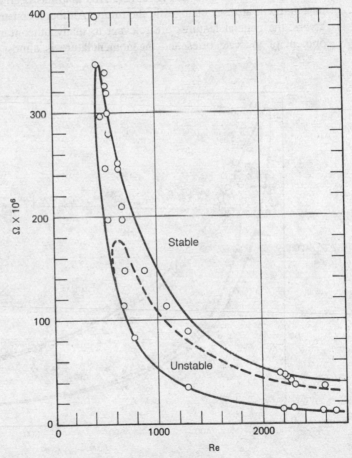

Figure 25.6 Blasius boundary layer neutral stability curves, $C_i = 0$, in the wavenumber–Re plane. Experimental points, Schubauer and Skramstad (1947); solid line, Shen (1954); dashed line, Schlichting (1933). $Re = U\delta^*/\nu$ and $\Omega = \alpha c_r/Re$.

approximations and approaches, have been done. All nonparallel theories give a correction in the proper direction; however, the amount of the correction varies widely. The subject still remains controversial. Figure 25.7 shows the work of Saric and Nayfeh (1977).

The flow pattern in a TS wave is sketched in Fig. 25.8. Flow visualization of these waves requires extreme care to avoid extraneous disturbances. A view looking down on the flow over a flat plate in Fig. 25.9 shows a pattern of TS waves. This figure also shows the formation of Λ-shaped structures. The TS waves are even more clearly seen in Fig. 25.10 as cylindrical bands.

25.8 TRANSITION, SECONDARY INSTABILITY, AND BYPASS

Transition in wall turbulence is also a complex story that can be summarized briefly by a *Morkovin map,* shown in Fig. 25.11. This map has been modified several times in the past and will also see changes in the future. Although constructed primarily for boundary layers, the general features are relevant to many other transition problems. The development of the categories and the nomenclature is almost as important as the details.

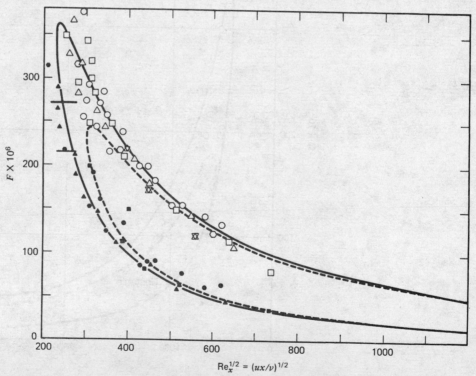

Figure 25.7 Later results for Blasius flow. Experimental results from various sources. theory; – – – linear, — nonparallel theory of Saric and Nayfeh (1977). This graph was plotted using $Re_x^{1/2}$ instead of Re_δ. $F = 2\pi f \nu / U^2$. Courtesy of W. Saric, Arizona State University.

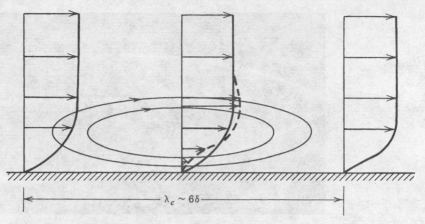

Figure 25.8 Flow pattern in the critical TS wave. Perturbation streamlines are given in a coordinate system moving with the wave.

Figure 25.9 Plan view of smoke visualization of TS waves in a Blasius boundary layer. Flow is left to right. Note the development of three-dimensional secondary instabilities. Courtesy of A. Thomas, Lockheed-Georgia Co. See Thomas (1983).

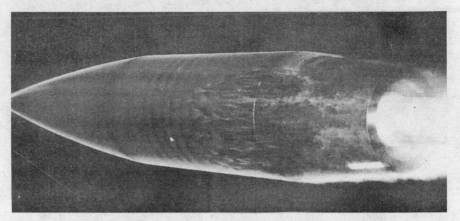

Figure 25.10 Smoke in the flow over a cylindrical body shows natural transition. The TS waves (light–dark bands) form Λ shapes that ultimately break down. Courtesy of T. J. Mueller and R. C. Nelson, University of Notre Dame. Reprinted with permission.

Starting with a base flow at the top, one proceeds to the location and type of disturbances at the next level. Disturbance strength is not noted explicitly but is very important.

Along the right side is what might be called the *natural* or *ideal path* taken by flows with disturbances of low intensities. The primary instability is a linear, usually viscous mode that grows very slowly—in boundary layers, the TS mode. On Fig. 25.7 a TS disturbance of a certain frequency, say $F \times 10^6 = 200$, would only become amplified at a position on the plate where $\mathrm{Re}_x = 300^2$. The amplification ceases completely at $\mathrm{Re}_x = 450^2$. In fact, a pure TS wave would die by viscosity at larger x-positions. However, in natural transition there is a secondary instability. Note on Fig. 25.9 that the smoke concentrates into Λ-shaped patterns aligned one behind the next. Sometimes the terms *hairpin vortex* or Λ *vortex* are applied to these structures, as they are in fact concentrations of vorticity near the critical layer. The same Λ vortices are evident in Fig. 25.10, but observe here the tendency for the Λ vortices to be staggered. Very quickly the Λ vortices themselves show a disturbance, *spikes,* and break up into complete turbulence.

The two extreme arrangements of Λ vortices are depicted in Fig. 25.12. In the aligned case the wavelength is the same as the TS fundamental and the signal sharpens at the vortices, a process called *peak–valley splitting*. On the other hand, in the staggered arrangement the wavelength is twice the TS wavelength, a subharmonic signal, as confirmed by Saric and Thomas (1984).

Several theories have addressed the formation of Λ vortices. Craik (1971) found a resonance between three Orr–Sommerfeld modes: a TS $(\alpha, 0)$ and two oblique waves $(\alpha/2, \pm\beta)$ with wavelengths twice the TS wave. *Secondary instability* is the most productive approach and is reviewed, including historical notes on transition research in general, by Herbert (1988). At a sufficient finite amplitude, the primary TS mode together with the base flow constitute a new quasisteady base flow that has a periodic character in the flow direction. This new periodic flow is unstable (secondary instability), allowing the rapid inviscid growth of secondary three-dimensional modes. The analysis is a linear problem that goes under the mathematical term *Floquet analysis*. As an historical note

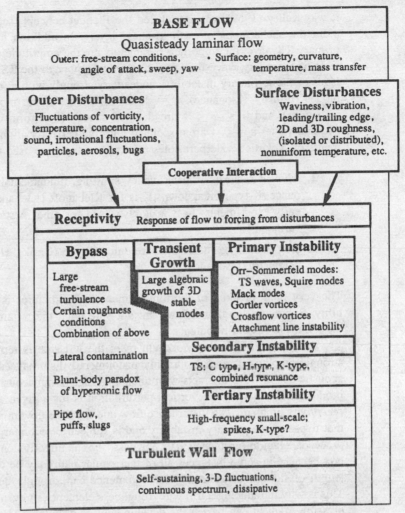

Figure 25.11 A Morkovin map of the roads to wall turbulence.

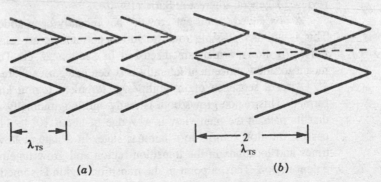

Figure 25.12 Secondary instabilities of TS waves: (a) aligned mode, $\varepsilon = 0$; (b) staggered mode, $\varepsilon = 1$.

it was Kelley (1967) who introduced the Floquet concept (secondary instability) to explain the subharmonic growth in shear layers. In addition to the wavenumber of the primary TS wave, the important parameters are the amplitude of the TS wave and ε (the ratio of secondary wave flow-direction wavenumber to the TS wavenumber). Characteristics of the secondary instability modes vary strongly with ε; $\varepsilon = 0$ are the fundamental modes (primary resonance), $\varepsilon = 1$ are the subharmonic modes (principal parametric resonance), and $0 < \varepsilon < 1$ are detuned modes (that form combination modes). The extreme values $\varepsilon = 0, 1$ are associated with the perfectly aligned and staggered arrangements of Λ vortices. Herbert notes that many names are used for these two phenomena.

1. *Aligned Λ vortices:* peak–valley splitting, fundamental resonance, primary resonance, K-type breakdown [K is for Klebanoff (Klebanoff et al., 1962), who did early experiments; K type is also used for other perturbations with a spanwise variation.]

2. *Staggered Λ vortices:* subharmonic, C-type (Craik), H-type (Herbert), principal parametric resonance

The very rapid breakup of the three-dimensional structures is possibly a tertiary instability. Subsequently, although we are not sure what the requirements are, the flow has the ability to sustain turbulence.

Returning now to the Morkovin map, the left side is termed "bypass" and is for stronger-amplitude, more commonly encountered disturbances. For example, when an acoustic sound wave interacts with a leading edge, a nonacoustic vortical perturbation is produced. How strong the vortical perturbation is for a given acoustic wave is a typical *receptivity* problem. The disturbance flow and the base flow now combine to form a flow that bypasses the primary instability and is subject to secondary instabilities. Hence, one proceeds again to turbulence. The "bypass" box is directly connected to the "turbulent" box because in some instances all of the regular path may be completely bypassed. The length of flow required to develop turbulence can strongly depend on the path taken. This is why introducing a trip wire, roughness elements, or even a short region of adverse pressure gradient can hasten the development of turbulence. External free-stream turbulence, which is of engineering interest, has been reviewed by Reshotko (1994). Another review of general interest is Saric (1994b).

A box called "transient growth" has recently been added beside the "bypass" box. This is another possible route to turbulence and is especially relevant to Couette and Poiseuille flows, which are discussed in Section 25.11. The shaded vertical lines are meant to allow movement laterally between categories there.

After a sequence of instabilities, a turbulent region known as a *turbulent spot* is formed. This region grows both laterally and longitudinally and is swept downstream so that its path in the plan view is a wedge of about $10°$ to $11°$ half-angle. After the spot passes, the flow returns to a laminar state. In a natural flow spots are born at random times and locations in the transition region and grow together to produce the fully turbulent region. Thus, a point in the transition region is sometimes turbulent or sometimes laminar, depending on whether a spot is currently located at that point. Details of the flow, wall roughness, pressure gradient, free-stream turbulence, and so on, determined the birth rate of spots. In a highly unstable flow, spots are so numerous and frequent that they merge to form a turbulent front before they mature.

25.9   SPATIALLY DEVELOPING OPEN FLOWS

The temporal Orr–Sommerfeld analysis (α real, $c = c_R + ic_I$) is an investigation of the local stability of a parallel flow profile. Similarly, the spatial stability analysis (c real, $\alpha = \alpha_R + i\alpha_I$), which has the same neutral curve, deals with a local profile. A more general approach is to question the progress in both space and time of an impulse inserted into the flow. Gaster (1965) raised this issue with regard to boundary layers. If the perturbation grows but is swept downstream, leaving an unperturbed main flow, the flow is called *locally convectively unstable*. Alternatively, as shown on Fig. 25.13, the flow is called *locally absolutely unstable* if the disturbance grows at a fixed position. In general, boundary layers are in the locally convectively unstable class while the mixing layer shown in Fig. 25.1 is locally absolutely unstable. It is not intuitive into which class a given flow will fall. For example, a shear layer is absolutely unstable for $(U_1 - U_2)/(U_1 + U_2) \geq 1.315$. Huerre and Monkewitz (1990) offer a review and tabulate many of the known results.

Steady subsonic flows are mathematically elliptic (or from another viewpoint, an unsteady flow has characteristics that propagate upstream). The flow at any point depends globally on the flow states at all remote points. The local convective-absolute classification depicted in Fig. 25.13 assumes something of a parabolic character and seeks to determine if the dominant perturbation physics has a positive convection (group) velocity. This is a relevant question in many situations. In contrast, the entire flow field (or a substantial region) may have global instability modes. Formation of the von Kármán vortex street behind a cylinder is such an example. In simplistic terms the movement of the downstream vortices sends pressure signals upstream to the cylinder where the vortices are forming. Questions of global stability are difficult and experimental answers are often sought.

25.10   TRANSITION IN FREE SHEAR FLOWS

Free shear layers are inviscidly unstable to the Kelvin–Helmholtz type of instability, which grows rapidly to amplitudes where nonlinear effects are important. Nevertheless, experiments confirm that linear Orr–Sommerfeld theory is correct for the initial stage. Michalke (1964) found that the initial process is much better described by the spatial analysis than by a temporal analysis. Linear theory predicts the most amplified frequency f_n correctly, but this lasts a very short distance (about eight wavelengths) from the splitter plate until a subharmonic $f_n/2$ becomes dominant. The Floquet concept (secondary instability; Kelley, 1967) helps explain the subharmonic growth in shear layers. Some features of transition are seen on the left side of Fig. 25.5. Farther along two (and sometimes three) adjacent vortices merge in a *pairing process*. Also evident on Fig. 25.5 are the longitudinal striations that have been confirmed to be associated with small-scale streamwise vortices (Bernal et al., 1980). Ho and Huerre (1984) review various aspects

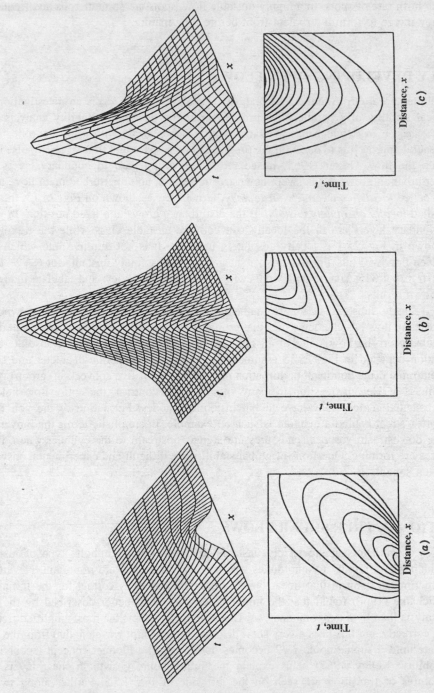

Figure 25.13 Time–distance history of a disturbance. Flow is left to right: (a) stable; (b) convectively unstable; (c) absolutely unstable. Courtesy of L. Paulon and P. A. Monkewitz, Ecole Polytechnique Federale de Lausanne. Reprinted with permission.

of the growth of subharmonics, pairing, and the instability that leads to longitudinal striations. Schoppa et al. (1995) investigate the importance of core variations in the spanwise vortices.

Jets, either plane or round, are initially shear layers near the lip of the exit. However, if the flow is forced by plane acoustic waves, the shear layer perturbation has coherence around the complete circumference. As the shear layers merge to form a jet, the flow becomes a spatially developing flow and the question of global instability (note the spiral mode in Fig. 25.11) of Section 25.9 becomes relevant.

25.11   POISEUILLE AND PLANE COUETTE FLOWS

Three flows for which linear Orr–Sommerfeld theory predictions fail are plane Couette flow and Poiseuille flow, either plane or in a round tube. Couette and Poiseuille tube flow are apparently completely stable in an Orr–Sommerfeld analysis. Pipe flow experiments show a variety of critical Reynolds numbers. The nominal transition in engineering work is Re = 2000, however, Reynolds himself attained laminar flow at 14,000, and more modern experiments produced laminar flow at Re = 40,000. Plane Couette flow has become unstable at Reynolds numbers as low as 360 (Tillmark and Alfreddsson, 1992). Plane Poiseuille flow has received considerable attention because the geometry is so simple. Orr–Sommerfeld theory (see Fig. 25.14) gives a critical Reynolds number (based on half channel height) of 5772, but experiments have become turbulent as low as Re = 1000 or as high as 8000. Even when plane Poiseuille flow is unstable, the growth rates are extremely slow. Nevertheless, with great care, Nishioka and Asai (1984) have produced TS waves in Poiseuille flow.

For these flows no complete theory or experimental verification exists even for the primary instability. Of course, Morkovin's bypass concept is a general framework that cautions us not to look for just one transition mechanism. There are probably three main theoretical themes that should be outlined: two-dimensional nonlinear theory, secondary instability (Floquet theory), and transient (pseudospectrum) growth.

The nonlinear theory seeks solutions of the Navier–Stokes equations for two-dimensional streamwise disturbances that have a certain specified energy level but maintain the correct wall stress on average. This implies that the average pressure gradient is unchanged. Using this approach, Herbert (1976) found that a critical Reynolds number of 2935 occurred for $\alpha = 1.32$ at a certain finite energy level.

The second approach is the secondary instability analysis similar to that described for boundary layers (Bayly et al., 1988). A finite-amplitude two-dimensional wave is added to the steady flow. This combination is quasisteady, and three-dimensional unstable perturbations are sought. The difference between the Poiseuille case and the Blasius boundary layer is that the boundary layer used TS waves as the finite perturbation. The production of the three-dimensional secondary instability is a linear event.

Recently, attention has turned toward growth of three-dimensional transients. Even when the Orr–Sommerfeld problem has no eigenmodes with exponential growth rates, there can be ε-pseudomodes that grow by factors of 10^3 to 10^4 (sometimes called *algebraic growth;* Trefethen et al. 1993). On the Morkovin map these modes are the "transient growth" box. The fastest growing pseudomodes are three dimensional. This is not a

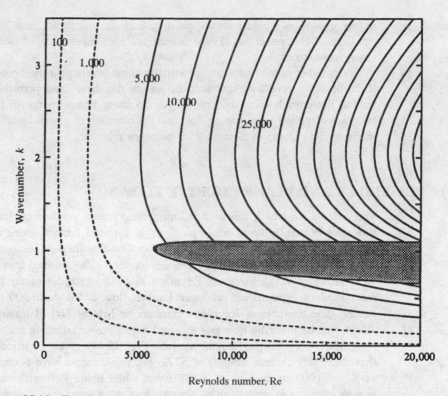

Figure 25.14 Transient growth in plane Poiseuille flow. Contour lines depict the maximum energy growth factors for a disturbance. Here the wavenumber is $k = \sqrt{\alpha^2 + \beta^2}$. The shaded area is unstable for TS waves. This is a different version of the amplification factor map of Trefethen et al. (1993).

violation of Squire's theorem because that theorem only relates to exponentially unstable modes. Figure 25.14 shows the stability map for plane Poiseuille flow. The wavenumber of the graph is $k = (\alpha^2 + \beta^2)^{1/2}$. The unstable region of the Orr–Sommerfeld analysis ($k = \alpha$) begins at Re = 5772, but this is not as important as the lines representing the maximum amplification of three-dimensional pseudomodes. Values of energy amplification of 1000 are possible for Re > 2260. Theoretically, pseudomodes grow inviscidly until viscous forces become great enough to shut off growth and initiate a slow decay. At higher Reynolds numbers the time for viscous forces to become active is longer.

The form of the pseudomodes is not uniquely determined. A study of the optimal perturbation reveals that a streamwise vortex pattern is most favorable (Butler and Farrell, 1992). A single or pair of streamwise counterrotating vortices in a shear layer transport low-velocity fluid into regions of high velocity (and vice versa). This intensifies the shear and tends to generate inflectional profiles. The conjecture is that the new flow state is unstable and breaks down into turbulence. A study of secondary instability of a slowly developing three-dimensional base flow does not seem to have been accomplished. The only firm confirmation of these theories is the fact that they are able to produce critical

Reynolds numbers that are, in agreement with experiment, lower than the Orr–Sommerfeld value.

25.12 INVISCID INSTABILITY OF FLOWS WITH CURVED STREAMLINES

Streamlines of the main flow usually curve because a pressure gradient exists in the direction across the streamlines. This pressure gradient supplies the centripetal force to turn the particle trajectories. A particle disturbed in a curved flow can disrupt the balance between the pressure gradient and the centrifugal effect to such an extent that the flow becomes unstable. This instability mechanism is inviscid.

The main result on this topic is *Rayleigh's circulation criterion.* It gives a necessary and sufficient condition for the stability to axisymmetric disturbances of a velocity profile with circular streamlines. The fact that the streamlines are circles is not too restrictive, as we might imagine that a flow with a local radius of curvature R is somewhat like a circular flow with the same radius of curvature. Consider an axisymmetric flow in cylindrical coordinates. The θ-momentum equation for a flow where $\partial(\ )/\partial\theta = 0$ is

$$\frac{\partial v_\theta}{\partial t} + v_r \frac{\partial v_\theta}{\partial r} + \frac{v_r v_\theta}{r} + v_z \frac{\partial v_\theta}{\partial z} = 0 \qquad (25.12.1)$$

Multiplying this equation by r and rearranging shows that the *reduced circulation* $\gamma \equiv r v_\theta$ for a particle is constant, that is,

$$\frac{D\gamma}{Dt} = 0 \qquad (25.12.2)$$

Any axisymmetric disturbance must occur in such a way as to maintain $\gamma = \text{const}$ for each material element.

Let us assume that a ring of fluid at location r_1, z_1 is disturbed so that it is interchanged with a ring of equal volume at r_2, z_2. The kinetic energy of the elements (per unit volume) is $\text{KE} = \frac{1}{2}\rho v_\theta^2 = \frac{1}{2}\rho\gamma^2/r^2$. In the unperturbed state the energy of both elements is

$$\text{KE}_A = \frac{\rho}{2}\left[\left(\frac{\gamma_1}{r_1}\right)^2 + \left(\frac{\gamma_2}{r_2}\right)^2\right]$$

Since the perturbation must occur at constant γ, the energy of the perturbed state is

$$\text{KE}_B = \frac{\rho}{2}\left[\left(\frac{\gamma_1}{r_2}\right)^2 + \left(\frac{\gamma_2}{r_1}\right)^2\right]$$

Next, we calculate the change in energy of the flow:

$$\text{KE}_B - \text{KE}_A = \frac{1}{2}\rho(\gamma_2^2 - \gamma_1^2)(r_1^{-2} - r_2^{-2}) \qquad (25.12.3)$$

If the energy in state B is larger than that of state A, the perturbation requires a finite amount of energy. We would not expect this to be available internally, and thus this situation is stable. Conversely, a disturbance that leads to a lower total energy liberates energy, which can be used to make the disturbance grow. Without loss of generality we assume that $r_2 > r_1$. Hence, for a stable flow, where Eq. 25.12.3 is positive, we must have

$$\gamma_2^2 > \gamma_1^2 \qquad \text{for} \quad r_2 > r_1 \qquad (25.12.4)$$

The square of the reduced circulation increases outward in a stable swirling flow. In terms of the velocity or angular velocity profiles, Eq. 25.12.4 is

$$(r_2 v_{\theta 2})^2 > (r_1 v_{\theta 1})^2$$
$$(r_2^2 \Omega_2)^2 > (r_1^2 \Omega_1)^2 \qquad (25.12.5)$$

Rayleigh's criterion is a useful method of estimating inviscid instability, even though it tells nothing about stability of the flow with respect to three-dimensional disturbances.

The rotary flow between coaxial cylinders offers an example to which Rayleigh's criterion may be applied. We consider the general situation where the inner cylinder and the outer cylinder may both be rotated: r_i, Ω_i for the inside and r_o, Ω_o for the outside. The laminar viscous flow solution may be expressed in terms of the angular velocity as

$$\frac{\Omega(r)}{\Omega_i} = A + B\left(\frac{r_i}{r}\right)^2$$

where

$$A = \frac{\Omega_o/\Omega_i - (R_i/R_o)^2}{1 - (R_i/R_o)^2}$$

$$B = \frac{1 - \Omega_o/\Omega_i}{1 - (R_i/R_o)^2}$$

It is customary to consider that the outer cylinder has positive rotation while the inner cylinder can have either sign. Consider first the case when both cylinders rotate in the same direction. The quantity $r^2\Omega$ will always increase with r as long as the outer speed satisfies

$$\Omega_o \geq \left(\frac{r_i}{r_o}\right)^2 \Omega_i \qquad (25.12.6)$$

Equation 25.12.6 is called the *Rayleigh line*. If the inner cylinder is fixed and the outer is rotated, the flow is stable. If the outer cylinder is fixed and the inner rotated, Rayleigh's criterion indicates instability. Viscosity does, however, stabilize this situation until a certain speed is reached. More is said on this in Section 25.13.

Situations where the cylinders rotate in opposite directions are always unstable to inviscid disturbances. In this case, where Ω_2 is positive and Ω_1 is negative, Ω_2 decreases in a region near the inner cylinder until the radius where $\Omega = 0$ is reached. From this point outward Ω increases. The flow is unstable in the inner region $\Omega < 0$, but stable in the outer region.

25.13 TAYLOR INSTABILITY OF COUETTE FLOW

Viscosity plays only its stabilizing role in Taylor–Couette flows. A chart of the stability characteristics is given as Fig. 25.15. The viscous stability of these flows was first determined by Taylor (1921, 1923) both experimentally and theoretically. The theoretical problem is quite difficult, and most work is done using a thin-gap assumption. This assumption takes centrifugal effects out of the main flow but retains them partially in the disturbance equations. The problem, simplified for axisymmetric disturbances, contains a parameter called the *Taylor* (Ta) *number*. Several definitions are in use. A typical one is

$$\mathrm{Ta} \equiv \frac{r_i(r_o - r_i)^3(\Omega_i^2 - \Omega_o^2)}{\nu^2} \tag{25.13.1}$$

In Eq. 25.13.1, r is the cylinder radius, Ω the angular velocity, and the subscripts i and o refer to inner and outer, respectively.

Essentially, Ta represents the centrifugal effect divided by the viscous effect. Upon crossing Taylor's first stability boundary, one encounters a second stable laminar flow pattern with toroidal vortices. For inner rotation only, $\Omega_0 = 0$, this boundary is Ta = 1708. The new flow pattern is an example of the principle of *exchange of stabilities*. Taylor vortices and Couette flow are both stable laminar flow patterns.

Taylor vortices themselves become unstable at higher rotation rates, where they give way to wavy Taylor vortices as shown in Fig. 25.16a. Many states of different mode numbers can be attained in the wavy patterns. Moreover, when the outer cylinder is

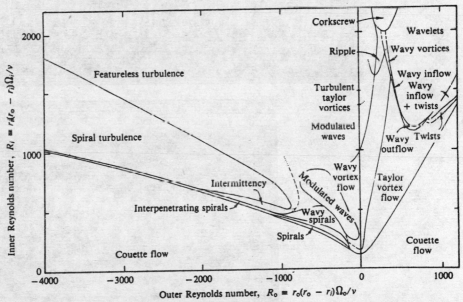

Figure 25.15 Stability chart for Taylor vortex behavior. Reprinted with permission from Anderreck et al. (1986).

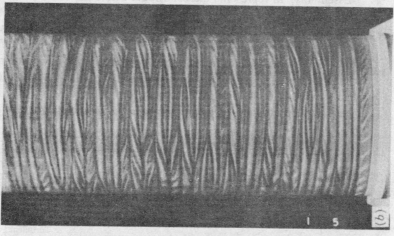

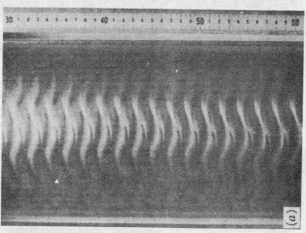

Figure 25.16 (a) Wavy Taylor vortices. Reprinted with permission from Koschmieder (1979). (b) Braided Taylor vortices. From Andereck et al. (1983). (c) Turbulent Taylor vortices. Courtesy of Zhang and Swinney (1985), University of Texas. Reprinted with permission.

allowed to rotate, one can achieve extremely complex flows, such as the braided pattern of Fig. 25.16b. For the highest rotation rates, turbulent flow finally ensues. Figure 25.16c shows turbulent Taylor vortices. If the inner cylinder rotates at very high rates (Lathrop et al., 1992), an apparently completely turbulent flow without vortices exists. Such a flow has boundary layers of angular momentum on each wall and a core of constant angular momentum (Panton, 1992) in the center. A review of Taylor vortices is given by Koschmieder (1993).

25.14   STABILITY OF REGIONS OF CONCENTRATED VORTICITY

We have seen many examples where an inviscid flow is determined by a distribution of vorticity in a small isolated region. The velocity field in these flows can in principle be found by the Biot–Savart law:

$$v = \frac{1}{4\pi} \int \frac{\boldsymbol{\omega} \times d\mathbf{r}}{|\mathbf{r} - \mathbf{r}_0|^3}$$

From this point of view, the Helmholtz instability of a vortex sheet is caused by warping the sheet so that the integral is in a new location, with a rearrangement of the vorticity within the sheet. The sheet is no longer of uniform vorticity, but has a lumpy distribution. Both of these effects cause a new velocity field through the equation above. In particular, a certain point on the sheet has a new velocity induced by the remainder of the sheet. If this self-induction mechanism causes further growth, the vorticity distribution is unstable.

Since a vortex sheet is unstable, what about a line vortex? A small perturbation of a vortex line is neutrally stable. There are two modes. In one mode a displacement travels down the vortex in the form of a helix, while in the second mode the vortex remains in a plane as a spinning sine wave. Neutral stability means that there is no tendency for these perturbations to either grow or decay. Because we are dealing with small perturbations, the problem is linear and disturbances of different wavelengths behave independently. The problem is actually nonlinear for finite disturbance. In this case different wavelengths interact and unstable growth occurs.

Next, consider a plane two-dimensional flow that contains several line vortices. These vortices move with the local fluid velocity in conformity with Helmholtz's laws. We have previously calculated (Section 13.11) how two counterrotating vortices are self-propelled. This situation is neutrally stable in the sense that a small disturbance simply produces a new configuration, which propels itself in a new direction or with a new speed. There is no tendency for the perturbation to grow or die. Two corotating vortices form a similar situation except that the vortices rotate around each other.

Several line vortices lead to an unstable configuration in the following sense. A perturbation of the location or strength of a vortex alters the effect that it produces on the motion of all the others. The subsequent motion goes through a different history than if the perturbation were absent. A famous exception to this statement is the Von Kármán vortex street. Von Kármán found that an infinite array of counterrotating point vortices will be neutrally stable only if the spacing between the vortices and the rows is $b/h = 3.56$. In any other configuration the vortex street is unstable. Saffman's (1992) book discusses many aspects of vortex dynamics.

Another inviscid line–vortex instability is called the *Crow* (1970) *instability*. It was first studied in connection with the trailing vortex wake of airplanes. Figure 25.17 shows a vortex trail made by an airplane at very high altitude in smooth, stable air. The plane, weighing 3000 kg and flying at 54 m/s, has pyrotechnic smoke grenades that mark the core of the vortex from each wingtip. Crow considered that the wake was like two infinite line vortices separated by a given distance b. His analysis showed that the vortices were most unstable to a symmetric oscillation in the vortex location with wavelength $8.6b$. The pictures clearly show the steady growth of a long-wavelength disturbance. The growth continues until the vortices touch and pinch off to form vortex rings. It is necessary to have a very smooth atmosphere to observe this sequence of events. Contrast Fig. 25.17 with Fig. 1.2, where atmospheric turbulence has formed kinks of various wavelengths in each vortex. Self-induction and interaction of these several wavelengths will soon scramble these vortices before the Crow mode has a chance to develop.

25.15   OTHER INSTABILITIES: TAYLOR, CURVED PIPE, CAPILLARY JETS, AND GÖRTLER

Brief mention of a few additional instabilities in fluids will be made. Another instability named after Taylor (1950), also called the *Rayleigh–Taylor instability,* occurs in the acceleration of two fluid layers with different densities. For example, in Earth's gravitational field, the heavier fluid must be on the bottom for stability: Removing the cover from a jar of water held upside down would lead to a disaster. Taylor proved that a density discontinuity in a fluid was unstable to any acceleration from the light fluid into the heavy fluid and stable for acceleration in the opposite direction.

A capillary instability is illustrated in Fig. 25.18. This is essentially an inviscid instability where a cylinder of liquid from a jet is so thin that surface tension is important. The surface tension law is $p = p_\infty + \sigma(R_1^{-1} + R_2^{-1})$, where R_1 and R_2 are the radii of curvature of the surface. When the surface is deformed, the pressure distribution within the liquid changes. The primary effect is that the fiber has a higher internal pressure where the radius is smaller. The resulting pressure gradient then drives the fluid toward the regions of larger radii. The jet is unstable to all axisymmetric disturbances with wavelengths greater than the circumference of the jet. The wavelength that grows the fastest is $\lambda = 9.0r$. Note in the figure that the final breakup of the jet into droplets produces two distinct sizes. Small satellite drops are formed between the large drops.

Centrifugal effects in combination with viscous damping can lead to some striking flow patterns. Two other flow situations with curved streamlines are worthy of a brief description. One is the flow in a curved pipe or channel, and the other is the flow of a boundary layer over a concave wall.

Consider a curved channel where the radius of curvature is much larger than the channel width. The flow is driven by a pressure gradient, and when the radius of curvature is large, the velocity profile is nearly the parabolic Poiseuille profile. Rayleigh's criterion shows that the flow on the inside half of the channel is stable, whereas that on the outer half is unstable. This situation is very much like the Taylor problem, in that viscosity stabilizes a profile that is inviscidly unstable. The parameter that measures the curvature effect compared to viscous effects is called the *Dean number*. Exceeding a critical value

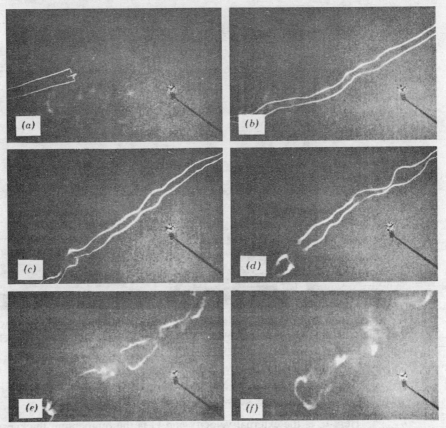

Figure 25.17 The inviscid instability of a pair of line vortices is known as the Crow instability. The time lapse between each picture is 10 s. Reprinted with permission from Tombach (1974).

of the Dean number results in an instability and the development of a second stable laminar flow pattern with a toroidal vortex, or in some cases several vortices, superimposed on the main flow. This centrifugal instability is the origin of the secondary flow in curved pipes and channel bends.

A somewhat similar flow situation exists when a boundary layer flows over a concave wall. The case of interest is when the curvature is in the longitudinal direction, as shown in Fig. 25.19. If the boundary layer is thin compared to the radius of curvature R, a condition required for our standard boundary layer analysis, the pressure is constant through the layer and centrifugal stability is not important. On the other hand, if δ is a reasonable fraction of the radius of curvature, the first effect on the boundary layer equations is simply to modify the transverse momentum equation from $\partial p / \partial y = 0$ to $\partial p / \partial y = -\rho u^2 / R_0$. The possibility of centrifugal instability now exists in this boundary layer. Once again we have a flow that is inviscidly unstable according to Rayleigh's criterion, and viscosity plays a stabilizing role. In this flow the parameter comparing the centrifugal effect with the viscous effect is called the *Görtler number:*

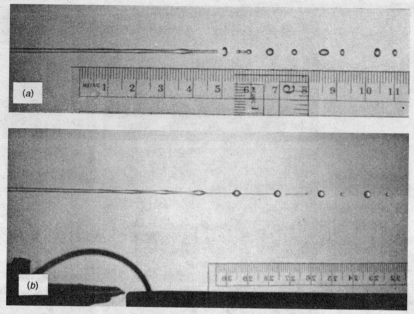

Figure 25.18   Capillary instability of a liquid jet. Photograph (*a*) is water while (*b*) is a more viscous glycerine–water solution. Reprinted with permission from Donnelly and Glaberson (1966).

$$G = \frac{u_e \Theta}{\nu} \left(\frac{\Theta}{R_0}\right)^{1/2}$$

Here u_e is the external velocity and Θ is the momentum thickness. Görtler vortices (the secondary flow pattern shown in Fig. 25.19) occur when G exceeds about 0.3. This number is not very sensitive to the shape of the velocity profile; $G_c = 0.311$ for the Blasius profile, and $G_c = 0.278$ for a straight-line profile between u_e and the wall value

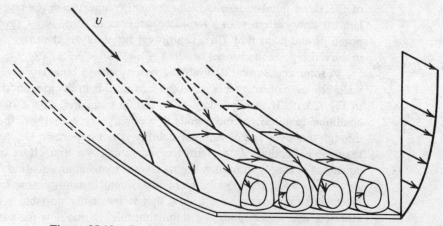

Figure 25.19   Görtler vortices in a boundary layer on a concave wall.

zero. Görtler vortices and their role in secondary instabilities and transition are discussed by Saric (1994*b*).

25.16   CONCLUSIONS

It is interesting to note that potential flows of a homogeneous fluid are stable. Instabilities arise when regions of the flow carry vorticity. The exact distribution of vorticity is not as important as its existence in many instances, for example, in the Kelvin–Helmholtz instability of a shear layer or the Crow instability of two line vortices. In these cases the amplification of disturbances occurs through inviscid processes; nevertheless, the existence of the vortical region is an essential element.

Viscous instability is a counterexample to the expectation that viscosity is a stabilizing force. Viscous instability is a time-delay phenomenon. In several instances we have observed viscous forces accelerating a fluid to a higher velocity than would be achieved by the pressure forces acting alone. In these cases, and in the case of viscous instability, a net shear stress generated at one time diffuses slowly through the flow. At some later time it is in the proper position to add to a net pressure force. The result is an overshoot in the velocity profile or a growth in the instability wave. Viscous instability is the only theoretical reason that a Blasius boundary layer is unstable.

There are many routes from initial disturbance to self-sustaining turbulence. Some of these routes involve the transient growth of disturbances that are theoretically ultimately damped by viscosity. However, these configurations may themselves be unstable to other modes. Much progress has been made in describing secondary instabilities, but bypasses and the various transition routes to turbulence remain a challenge.

26

Introduction to Turbulent Flows

Instability in a fluid flow will result in another stable laminar flow pattern, an example of the exchange of stabilities, or in a turbulent flow. Turbulent flows contain self-sustaining velocity fluctuations in addition to the main flow. Many flows in industry and in nature are at high enough Reynolds numbers that they are turbulent.

Consider for a moment the turbulent flow in a pipe or over a flat plate. As we view positions farther and farther downstream, we expect that the state of the flow will become independent of the inlet or leading-edge conditions. The particular events that occurred at the inlet and during the transition process will be forgotten. The final local flow state will have universal characteristics that are the result of the local turbulent processes in the immediate neighborhood of the point in question. This type of reasoning—that is, seeking universal characteristics—is behind all turbulence research. We only have experimental assurance that our proposition of a single asymptotic turbulence state actually exists. Experiments have shown that effects from initial conditions last considerably longer than one might anticipate. In fact, in the case of the bifurcating jet, to be discussed later, the initial conditions result in a completely different downstream flow.

Turbulence as a field of study has many facets. Some come to the field needing only to know the wall shear stress and the mean velocity profiles. Others wish to have a knowledge of mass diffusion and concentration statistics. Many wish to know the details of turbulent motions and how they interact. At the most abstract level, there is an effort to connect turbulence to the mathematical theory of chaos. An introduction cannot hope to cover such a large field. Our purpose is to treat several typical topics, usually in only a descriptive way. The reader should gain a vocabulary and the proper orientation to proceed to more thorough treatments.

26.1 TYPES OF TURBULENT FLOWS

Turbulent flows are not all alike. The universal characteristics of a turbulent jet and those of flow in a pipe display certain differences. We can classify turbulent flows roughly into three groups: gridlike flows, free-shear layers (mixing layers), and wall layers.

Grid turbulence is a special type of turbulence that violates the definition because it is not self-sustaining. To generate this flow, a grid of (say) circular cylinders is placed perpendicular to a uniform stream. The vortices generated by the cylinders interact, and after a certain distance, a homogeneous, isotropic field of turbulence is achieved. The turbulence exists without preference for direction, and it decays so slowly that the variations in flow direction are not important to the decay process. Many experiments have been carried out on grid turbulence to see how decay occurs in this idealized situation.

Free-shear layers include not only the typical mixing layer between two fluids moving at different speeds, but also all sorts of jets and wakes. A transition region near the origin of these flows precedes the turbulent region. Downstream, the extent of the turbulent region always grows. It is thought that these flows develop universal characteristics at distances far from the origin. Flows that develop a state that depends only on the local flow quantities (e.g., the local value of the mean velocity and local jet thickness) are said to be *self-preserving* or *self-similar*. Different turbulence characteristics may become self-preserving at different stages. The mean velocity profile in a jet becomes self-preserving about eight diameters downstream. On the other hand, the turbulence properties (i.e., the first-order statistics of the fluctuations) are self-preserving after a distance of 40 diameters.

Wall layers are the last class. The presence of a wall has a dominant effect on the processes that produce turbulence. For example, the turbulent characteristics of flow in a pipe are determined by the wall. The core region and the presence of the wall on the other side have only a minor influence. Boundary layers and all internal flows are also in this category.

26.2   CHARACTERISTICS OF TURBULENT FLOWS

It is probably not wise to make a rigid definition of a turbulent flow. On the other hand, the flows we call turbulent do have certain properties in common. For example, waves on the surface of water should not be classified as turbulence. They do not possess the mechanisms and characteristics of the types of flows mentioned in Section 26.1. Next, we describe the major qualities of turbulent flows, with the reservation that some of these characteristics are not found in every turbulent flow.

Turbulent flows have irregular fluctuations of velocity in all three directions. The intensity of the fluctuations is variable, but the maximum is customarily 10 to 30% of the mean velocity. A time history of the velocity at a point looks like a random signal. Nevertheless, there is structure to the fluctuations, so it is not absolutely accurate to say that the fluctuations are random (mathematicians have a definition of the term *random variable* which turbulent irregularities do not meet).

The irregularities in the velocity field have certain spatial structures known as *eddies*. This is a vague term that may be applied to any spatial flow pattern that persists for a short time. An eddy may be like a vortex, an embedded jet, a mushroom shape, or any other recognizable form. Large eddies are quite evident in the picture of the boundary layer in Fig. 26.1. Eddies are not isolated; small eddies exist inside larger eddies, and even smaller eddies exist inside the small eddies. Such small-scale motions are also visible in Fig. 26.1. One of the main characteristics of turbulence is a continuous distribution of eddy sizes. A flow where the irregularities are limited to a few separated frequency bands does not qualify as a turbulent flow.

The turbulence in a flow is self-sustaining. Processes that are not well de'   1 or understood occur that generate more turbulence and maintain the irregular moti   nce a flow becomes unstable and turbulence develops, it does not simply die out and   peat

Figure 26.1   Smoke wire flow visualization of a turbulent boundary layer at Re = 3500. Flow is from right to left. Courtesy of T. Corke, Y. Guezennec, and H. Nagib, Illinois Institute of Technology.

the process as a limit-cycle oscillation. Turbulence once initiated continues and perpetuates itself without diminishing. Thus, the transition mechanisms, the original instability, do not necessarily play a role in sustaining turbulence.

A gradient in the mean velocity profile is another characteristic. This *mean shear* must exist for the turbulence to be self-sustaining (we verify this fact later). In shear layers, boundary layers, jets, and wakes, the region where turbulence exists coincides with the region of mean shear. The reason that grid turbulence decays is that it has no mean shear.

In confined flows, turbulence may grow to cover the entire flow, but in all other cases the turbulent region has a limited extent. This is not to say that some fluid is always turbulent and other fluid is always nonturbulent. Another characteristic of turbulent flows is that they *entrain* nonturbulent fluid, so that the extent of the turbulent region grows. Consider the jet as an example. The fluid that composes the jet continues to increase by entrainment as the jet extends farther from the origin.

The rigorous way to decide whether fluid is turbulent or nonturbulent is based on vorticity. By definition, turbulent fluid has vorticity and nonturbulent fluid does not. Figure 26.2 shows a jet of dye submerged in a uniform laminar flow of lower velocity

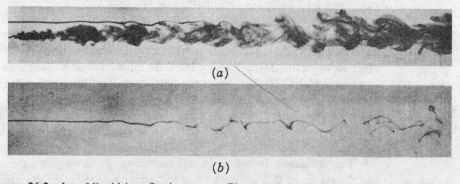

(a)

(b)

Figure 26.2   Jet of liquid in a flowing stream. Photograph (a) shows an external dye streak and a dyed jet and (b) shows a jet without dye. From Tritton (1977), by permission of Van Nostrand-Reinhold Ltd.

(this spreads out the events for better visualization). A filament of fluid outside the jet is also marked. The figure shows that the outside filament oscillates slowly for a while and then is entrained into the jet. Once within the jet, the streak is subjected to straining motions from eddies of all sizes. The irregular motions when the streak is outside the jet are nonturbulent, nonvortical potential fluctuations. The interface between the turbulent and nonturbulent fluid is very sharp. It is easy to see in Fig. 26.2 that the unsteady potential motions have only large-scale motions, whereas the turbulent motions have a continuous range of eddy sizes, as stated. Figure 26.3 shows the wake of a bullet and the sharp interface between the turbulent and nonturbulent fluid.

Turbulent flows are diffusive. Just as random molecular motions in a gas are responsible for viscous diffusion, thermal diffusion, and mass diffusion, a turbulent eddy can transport fluid from a region of low momentum and deposit it in a region of high momentum. Although the actual process is more complicated than that, it is clear that turbulence tends to mix fluid and thereby has a diffusive effect. The term *eddy diffusion* is frequently used to distinguish this effect from molecular diffusion. Eddy diffusion can be 10 or 100 times stronger than molecular diffusion.

All turbulent flows involve processes that change the length scale of the eddies. Once again, not much is actually known about these processes, but there is no doubt that they are a major characteristic of turbulent flows. These processes act in both directions. A modest-size irregularity or eddy grows and becomes a large eddy. The largest eddies in a flow are about as large as the thickness of the turbulent region. The size of the largest eddies in a boundary layer is about 3δ long by 1δ wide, and that of the largest eddies in a jet is about equal to the local jet diameter.

Processes also occur that reduce the eddy size. Turbulent eddies are formed continually with smaller and smaller length scales. There is also a limit to this process. When

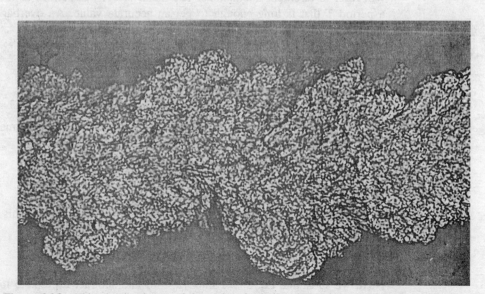

Figure 26.3   This classic picture of the wake of a bullet shows the sharp interface between turbulent and nonturbulent fluid. Photograph supplied by S. Corrsin from an experiment conducted by Ballistic Research Laboratory, Aberdeen Proving Ground.

the spatial extent of an eddy becomes very small, viscous forces, because of the steep velocity gradient, become very important. They tend to destroy the smallest eddies, and hence viscosity puts a lower limit on the eddy size.

The last major characteristic of turbulent flows is that they are *dissipative*. Any flow with viscosity has viscous dissipation, but turbulent flows have much more of it because the small-scale eddies have sharp velocity gradients. The energy dissipated in the small eddies dominates that dissipated in the largest eddies and in the mean flow. Since the small eddies dissipate energy and tend to destroy themselves, the scale-changing process that produces smaller eddies is a necessary element of self-sustaining turbulence.

26.3 REYNOLDS DECOMPOSITION

Computers are not able to solve the Navier–Stokes equations for all the detailed unsteady velocity profiles of a turbulent flow at high Reynolds numbers. However, some calculations at low Reynolds numbers exist (Kim et al., 1987), and with the aid of models of turbulent processes, one can compute the large-scale turbulent events. The simplest engineering approach today is the same as the one Reynolds used when he decomposed the instantaneous velocity into a mean part and a fluctuation (turbulence literature generally uses u_i rather than v_i for the velocity):

$$\tilde{u}_i(x_i, t) = U_i(x_i) + u_i(x_i, t)$$

(26.3.1)

$$\tilde{p}(x_i, t) = P(x_i) + p(x_i, t)$$

In the final equations, capital letters will refer to main quantities and lowercase letters will refer to turbulent fluctuations. The mean velocity is defined as the time average for a period T that is long enough to get an accurate value. An overbar denotes the time average:

$$U_i(x_i) \equiv \frac{1}{T} \int_0^T \tilde{u}_i(x_i, t)\, dt$$

(26.3.2)

$$= \bar{\tilde{u}}_i$$

We assume that differentiation and time averaging are commuting mathematical operations. For example,

$$\overline{\partial_i \tilde{u}_j} = \partial_i \bar{\tilde{u}}_j = \partial_i U_i$$

The time average of a fluctuation is, of course, zero: $\bar{u}_i = 0$.

Consider the continuity equation $\partial_i \tilde{u}_i = 0$. If we time average this equation, we find that the mean velocities also obey an equation of the same form:

$$\partial_i U_i = 0$$

(26.3.3)

Next, we substitute Eq. 26.3.1 into $\partial_i \tilde{u}_i = 0$ and subtract Eq. 26.3.5 to arrive at the fact that the fluctuations themselves are incompressible,

$$\partial_i u_i = 0 \qquad\qquad (26.3.4)$$

Both the mean flow and the fluctuations satisfy the continuity equation separately.

Let us turn to the momentum equation next. It is

$$\rho\ \partial_0 \tilde{u}_i + \rho\ \partial_j(\tilde{u}_j \tilde{u}_i) = -\partial_i \tilde{p} + \mu\ \partial_j \partial_j \tilde{u}_i$$

Inserting Eq. 26.3.1 and time averaging leads to

$$\rho\ \partial_j(U_j U_i) + \rho\ \partial_j(\overline{u_j u_i}) = -\partial_i P + \mu\ \partial_j \partial_j U_i \qquad\qquad (26.3.5)$$

This momentum equation governs the time-averaged properties of the flow. It contains a new effect, $-\rho \overline{u_j u_i}$, called the *Reynolds stresses*. Through this term the details of the turbulence make their imprint on the mean velocity profile U_i. Note that the Reynolds stresses come from the nonlinear convection terms.

As an illustration, consider the Reynolds stress $-\rho \overline{u_2 u_1}$ in a mean flow $U_1(x_2)$. If a slight excess velocity u_1 has a tendency to occur at the same time that a positive transverse velocity u_2 occurs, extra u_1 momentum is being transported across the flow. This is the diffusion characteristic of turbulent flows. Something in the turbulent processes of the flow causes a correlation, so that the time average $-\overline{u_1 u_2}$ is not zero. Note that Reynolds stresses are obviously not a fluid property and can depend on the position in the flow.

When we time average the Navier–Stokes equations, we lose information about the details of the flow. The effect of the turbulent structure has been distilled into the Reynolds stresses. However, the Reynolds stresses are not known. We have generated new unknowns, and the number of equations is insufficient to solve the problem. This is called the *closure problem*. An ad hoc, special assumption must be made about the nature of the turbulent flow. This assumption is equivalent to determining the Reynolds stresses. All turbulent calculation techniques contain such an assumption at some stage in their formulation.

26.4 REYNOLDS STRESS

Turbulence affects the mean velocity through the Reynolds stresses, $-\rho \overline{u_i u_j}$. In general, there are both normal, say $-\rho \overline{uu}$, $u_i = (u, v, w)$, and tangential, say $-\rho \overline{uv}$, components to this stress. The tangential components are of greater interest, as they usually play a larger role in determining the mean velocity profile. From experience we know that the large-scale turbulent eddies are the most important in transporting momentum across the flow. These motions are driven by pressure fluctuations and inertia interactions and are so large that viscosity is not at all important. Consider a local portion of a simple flow $U(y)$ with a mean shear dU/dy. Let the major Reynolds stress $-\rho \overline{uv}$ be caused by a turbulent eddy with a transverse size ℓ and an intensity characterized by the velocity scale u_0. In Fig. 26.4 assume the fluid originates near point A and is carried toward point B, where it interacts and merges with the local flow. Similarly, fluid originating at B may be carried toward point A, where it merges with the existing fluid. Let us assume that the Reynolds stress is a function of the density, the eddy size and strength, and the mean shear:

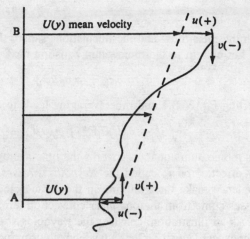

Figure 26.4 Mean velocity profile and the fluctuations that contribute most to the Reynolds stresses.

$$-\rho\overline{uv} = f(\rho, \ell, u_0, dU/dy)$$

Dimensional analysis produces

$$-\frac{\overline{uv}}{u_0^2} = f\left(\frac{\ell}{u_0}\frac{dU}{dy}\right)$$

If we further assume a linear relation between these variables and introduce the Boussinesq (1877) eddy diffusivity ν_t we arrive at

$$-\overline{uv} = \nu_\tau \frac{dU}{dy} \tag{26.4.1}$$

where

$$\nu_t \equiv C\ell u_0 \tag{26.4.2}$$

The eddy diffusivity is the product of a turbulence length scale and velocity scale. The development can be continued with a physical argument. The time scale for the turbulence, an eddy turnover time, is ℓ/u_0. A time scale for the mean flow is $(dU/dy)^{-1}$. Since the turbulence produces the gradient, we propose that the time scales are proportional:

$$\frac{\ell}{u_0} \sim \left|\frac{dU}{dy}\right|^{-1}$$

This relation allows one to eliminate u_0 from Eq. 26.4.2. At the same time we eliminate the proportionality constant and rename ℓ as the mixing length:

$$\nu_t = \ell^2 \left|\frac{dU}{dy}\right| \tag{26.4.3}$$

This expression was originally derived from vorticity by Taylor (1915), and independently for momentum by Prandtl (1925), both men using arguments that drew an analogy with the molecular model of gas viscosity.

Closing the turbulence problem for a simple flow rests on prescribing the mixing length through the field. For free turbulence, jets, wakes, and shear layers, the size of the largest eddies is related to the lateral extent of the shear. For these flows we assume that the mixing length is constant across the flow and proportional to the width of the shear. It is not necessary to require that ℓ dies out at the edge of the turbulence because dU/dy becomes zero there. Turbulent wall layers are somewhat different. They have two regions. The outer regions are very much like free turbulent flows, and these regions have a constant mixing length. The inner region next to the wall has turbulence of decreasing scale (while $dU/dy \neq 0$). At a given y location the vertical velocity is restricted by the wall and the assumption that ℓ is proportional to the distance from the wall has been found to be appropriate; $\ell = \kappa y$.

It is possible to derive an exact equation that governs the Reynolds stresses $\overline{u_i u_j}$. An equation for u_i is produced by subtracting the time-averaged equation 26.3.5 from the Navier–Stokes equation, where $\tilde{u}_i = U_i + u_i$. This equation is multiplied by u_j. The process is repeated with the roles of i and j reversed to yield a second equation. Adding these equations and time averaging yields the final result:

$$U_k \partial_k (\overline{u_i u_j}) = -\partial_k (\overline{u_k u_i u_j}) - \frac{1}{\rho} [\partial_i (\overline{u_j p}) + \partial_j (\overline{u_i p})]$$

diffusion terms

$$- (\overline{u_i u_k} \partial_k U_j + \overline{u_j u_k} \partial_k U_i) + \frac{1}{\rho} (\overline{p \partial_j u_i} + \overline{p \partial_i u_j})$$

production terms

$$+ \nu (\overline{u_j \partial_k \partial_k u_i} + \overline{u_i \partial_k \partial_k u_j}) \qquad (26.4.4)$$

destruction terms

The nine equations above can only be solved when closure assumptions are made about the effects on the right-hand side. Our main interest is in interpreting the various effects that change the Reynolds stresses. The first two terms are called diffusion effects because the quantities of interest are differentiated. They are imagined to redistribute turbulence, because their integrated effect (over a region where fluctuations on the boundary vanish) must be zero.

The net production of Reynolds stress is due to the terms containing $\partial_k U_\ell$. Mean shear is an essential part of turbulence. Without it the turbulence decays. As an example, consider a plane mean flow $U(y)$. The turbulence production term would be $\overline{uv}\, dU/dy$. It is often said that turbulence is sustained by the Reynolds stress working with the mean shear. This is, of course, a time-averaged interpretation and cannot be regarded as an instantaneous process.

Production also occurs through the pressure–strain correlation. Note that the pressure diffusion and pressure–strain production actually combine mathematically into only one group: $\overline{u_i \partial_j p} + \overline{u_j \partial_i p}$. This form emphasizes that the actual pressure force that generates or destroys a fluctuation u_j is $\partial_j p$.

The last term in Eq. 26.4.4 is the viscous destruction of Reynolds stress. Implicit in this name is the assumption that viscous forces only affect the small eddies and are mainly a retarding influence.

Turbulence calculations where the terms on the right-hand side of Eq. 26.4.4 are modeled are called second-order closure models. They are quite complicated in their most general form.

26.5 FREE TURBULENCE: PLANE SHEAR LAYERS

A plane shear layer, also called a *mixing layer,* is formed when a high-speed stream and low-speed stream meet downstream of a splitter plate.

Figure 26.5 is a Schlieren photograph of the shear layer between two different gases. Flow is from left to right with the upper stream faster. A splitter plate separating the streams ends on the left side just out of view. The density difference between the gases aids the photography but does not affect the flow pattern. The dominant features are the large coherent vortex eddies that are very regular and go entirely across the shear layer. This very regular growth and two-dimensional character of the large-scale eddies continues for some distance downstream as the shear layer grows. As one goes downstream the eddies are not only larger but are also fewer in number.

Figure 26.5 Growth of a free-shear layer between streams with different speeds. The lower portion of the photo is a side view; a plan view is reflected in a mirror in the upper portion. Large coherent eddies continue to grow for all downstream distances. Reprinted with permission from Brown and Roshko (1974).

The large eddies grow by two mechanisms: They entrain fluid outside the shear layer into their edges, and they swallow up vortices that are already in the shear layer. The latter process is called *vortex pairing* and is illustrated in Fig. 26.6, where the camera moves to follow the same eddies. It is obviously the mechanism by which the number of vortices is reduced.

Small-scale eddies within the large eddies are also evident in Fig. 26.6. The beginning of three-dimensional structures can be seen as longitudinal striations, produced by a secondary instability, in the plan view of Fig. 26.7 and in the side-view cross section (normal to the flow) of Fig. 26.5. Another view of the mixing layer is shown in Fig. 26.7. On a horizontal cut through the layer, the dark regions are high-speed fluid and the light areas lower low-speed fluid. Compressed portions of the vortices show up as a fine scale mixture of light and dark.

The shear layer grows by entraining fluid from both sides. The large eddies sweep fluid in and wind it around. Molecular viscosity then completes the mixing process. Many practical situations exist where different fluids are to be mixed (and possibly reacted) so the shear layer has been studied extensively.

Let $\Delta(x)$ be a characteristic width of the shear layer, $U_0 = U_2 - U_1$ be the velocity difference, and $U_{ave} = (U_1 + U_2)/2$. When downstream similarity is achieved, the mean velocity profile has the form

$$U(x, y) = U_1 + U_0 F(\eta) \qquad \text{with} \quad \eta = y/\Delta$$

Analysis Tennekes and Lumley (1972) of the global momentum equation shows that the width of the layer must increase linearly, $\Delta = ax$, or alternatively,

$$\frac{\delta}{x} = C \frac{U_0}{U_{ave}} \tag{26.5.1}$$

A closed-form answer for $F(\eta)$ does not come out of the analysis, however, the hyperbolic tangent or the integral of the error function (Townsend, 1976) is a reasonable approximation.

The type (laminar or turbulent) and age of the boundary layers on the splitter plate are important to the initial development of the shear layer and the length required before similarity is achieved. Several hundred initial momentum thicknesses may be needed to arrive at mean flow similarity. Bradshaw (1966) emphasized the sensitivity to initial conditions. The growth rate constant C in Eq. 26.5.1 is between $0.25 \le C \le 0.45$ if the layer is not forced by external excitations, but C is not a unique function. The growth rate even 1000 momentum thicknesses downstream is dependent on the initial conditions.

26.6 FREE TURBULENCE: TURBULENT JET

Consider a reservoir with a plane jet of width H from which fluid of viscosity ν issues at average velocity U_0. To make things definite, assume that the jet is produced by an orifice that connects a plenum to the reservoir. The profile at the jet exit is a uniform block profile. Where the jet and reservoir fluids meet there is a thin shear layer that is unstable and vortices are formed as in Figs. 26.5 and 26.6. The inviscid flow in the core is gradually entrained into the vortices as is fluid from the reservoir. The shear layers on either side grow larger and eventually consume the core entirely. Afterward the jet be-

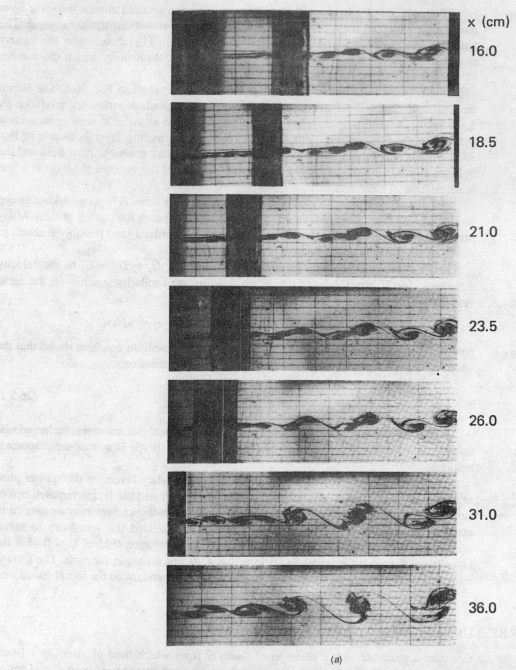

x (cm)

16.0

18.5

21.0

23.5

26.0

31.0

36.0

(a)

Figure 26.6 Vortex pairing shown in a step-by-step sequence. Reprinted with permission from Winant and Browand (1974), Cambridge University Press. Numbers indicate downstream distance of the camera.

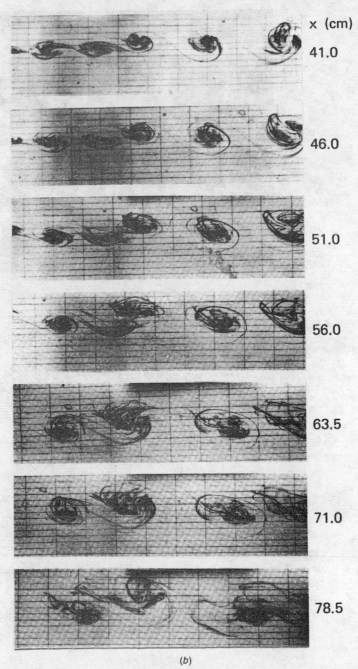

(b)

Figure 26.6   (continued)

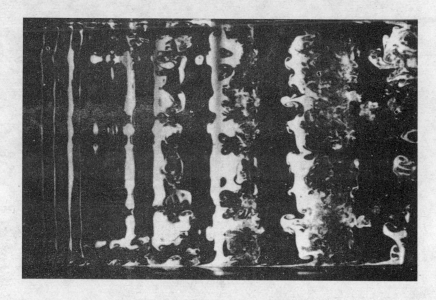

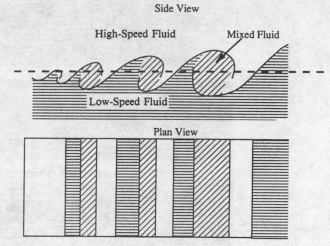

Figure 26.7 Flow visualization of a mixing layer in a plan view. Lower low-speed fluid is marked with fluorescent dye and illuminated by a sheet of light, as indicated by the dashed line in the pictorial side view. The pictorial plan view indicates regions of fluid corresponding to the photograph. The regions on the right show counterrotating vortices (mushroom shapes) on the braids between vortices. Reprinted with permission from Bernal and Roshko (1986), Cambridge University Press.

comes completely turbulent and grows in width while the centerline velocity decreases. Ultimately, the mean velocity is destroyed completely by turbulence and subsequently, destroyed by viscosity.

Let us focus attention on the region far downstream and assume that the jet velocity profile $U(x, y)$ becomes self-preserving (similar). The scale of development in the flow direction is the distance from some virtual origin, $L = x$. The width of the jet is thin in the sense that the cross-stream scale $\delta(x)$ is small compared to $x = L$. This is similar to the boundary layer assumption and is approximately true as the Reynolds number Re $=$ $U_0 H/\nu \to \infty$. Experiments actually show that $\delta = Cx$, where C approaches a small number $C = 0.110$ for Re $\to \infty$. Let $U_S(x)$ be the local maximum centerline velocity and $u_0(x)$ a scale for the turbulence. The continuity equation for the mean flow is

$$\frac{dU}{dx} + \frac{dV}{dy} = 0 \tag{26.6.1}$$

As the U profile changes in the streamwise direction, there must be a mean vertical velocity spreading the jet in the interior and bringing fluid into the jet from the outside.

The Reynolds averaged x momentum equation 26.3.5 is

$$U\frac{dU}{dx} + V\frac{dU}{dy} = -\frac{d\overline{uv}}{dy} - \frac{d(\overline{u^2})}{dx} - \frac{dP}{dx} + \nu\frac{d^2U}{dy^2} + \nu\frac{d^2U}{dx^2} \tag{26.6.2}$$

A rational analysis shows that many terms above are modest contributors to the jet dynamics. For illustrative purposes we can take a coarse approach and select the terms that are most prominent. We are guided by the knowledge that viscous stresses are typically much smaller than Reynolds stresses and that the pressure is approximately constant everywhere. We assume that the decay of the jet is the result of turbulent stresses and is governed by

$$U\frac{dU}{dx} + V\frac{dU}{dy} = -\frac{d\overline{uv}}{dy} \tag{26.6.3}$$

To Eq. 26.6.3 one can add U times the continuity equation and rearrange into

$$\frac{dU^2}{dx} + \frac{dUV}{dy} = -\frac{d\overline{uv}}{dy}$$

Integrating this equation in y at any x station and noting that both V and $\overline{uv}$ vanish at infinity produces the constraint that the momentum flux across any x-plane is constant. The same result comes from a control region analysis across planes perpendicular to the jet:

$$\frac{d}{dx}\int_{-\infty}^{\infty} U^2\, dy = 0 \quad\text{or}\quad \int_{-\infty}^{\infty} U^2\, dy = U_0^2 H \tag{26.6.4}$$

Since the momentum in the jet is a constant, the mass flow is not. The jet continually entrains ambient fluid and grows.

Now, formally introduce a streamfunction and the similarity assumptions

$$\psi = U_s F(\eta), \qquad \eta = \frac{y}{\delta} \tag{26.6.5}$$

Noting that $\partial \eta / \partial y = 1/\delta$ and $\partial \eta / \partial x = -\eta \delta' / \delta$ (' denotes differentiation), one can use chain rules to compute

$$U = \frac{\partial \psi}{\partial y} = U_s F' \tag{26.6.6}$$

$$V = -\frac{\partial \psi}{\partial x} = (U_s \delta)' F + U_s \delta' \eta F'$$

Substituting into the momentum equation 26.6.3 produces

$$F'^2 - \frac{(U_s \delta)'}{U_s' \delta} FF'' = \frac{1}{U_s U_s' \delta} \frac{d\overline{uv}}{d\eta} \tag{26.6.7}$$

The Reynolds stresses are assumed to be represented using an eddy viscosity

$$-\overline{uv} = \nu_t \frac{dU}{dy} \tag{26.6.8}$$

In turn, the eddy viscosity is proportional to the scale of the velocity fluctuations. From experiments we also find that the turbulence scale u_0 is a constant fraction of the centerline velocity U_s:

$$\nu_t(x) = c u_0 \delta = C U_s \delta \tag{26.6.9}$$

Here again we have the physical picture that the transport of momentum is determined by the larger eddies of intensity u_* that are of a scale comparable with the extent of the turbulent region. This is inviscid activity.

Equation 26.6.7 now becomes

$$F'^2 - \frac{(U_s \delta)'}{U_s' \delta} FF'' = \frac{C U_s}{U_s' \delta} F''' \tag{26.6.10}$$

For similarity the coefficients must be set to constants. Because U_s' is negative we set the first group to -1, and for a simple answer we set the second to $-\frac{1}{2}$.

$$\frac{(U_s \delta)'}{U_s' \delta} = -1, \qquad \frac{C U_s}{U_s' \delta} = -\frac{1}{2} \tag{26.6.11}$$

Solving Eq. 26.6.11 produces the growth of the jet and decay of the velocity as required by similarity. Experimentally determined coefficients are given below:

$$\delta = 4Cx = 0.110x$$
$$U_s = Ax^{-1/2} = 2.7 U_0 (H/x)^{1/2} \tag{26.6.12}$$

One can verify that a solution of Eq. 26.6.10 which satisfies boundary conditions $F(0) = 0$, $F'(0) = 1$, $F''(0) = 0$, and $F'(\pm\infty) = 0$ is

$$F(\eta) = \tanh \eta \tag{26.6.13}$$

$$\frac{U}{U_s} = \frac{U}{Ax^{-1/2}} = \mathrm{sech}^2\, \eta$$

This profile is called the *Bickley jet*. It is a reasonable approximation to the profiles measured. Round jets have a similar profile with a linear growth in width but a faster decay of the centerline velocity: $U_s \sim 1/x$.

26.7 BIFURCATING AND BLOOMING JETS

It was remarked earlier that the growth of jets and shear layers is sensitive to initial conditions. Experimenters found that even acoustic perturbations at the edge, where the jet or shear layer is formed, can have large effects. The regular perturbations can lock in and control the initial vortex formation, growth, and pairing processes. There is perhaps no more dramatic example of this than the bifurcating and blooming jets produced by Reynolds and co-workers.

Consider a jet issuing from a round tube into a reservoir. Superposition of a plane axial acoustic perturbation (Zaman and Hussain, 1980) locks the formation of the vortex rings to the excitation frequency, causing subsequent growth and spreading of the jet by vortex pairing to be altered. Onto the axial perturbation Juvet and Reynolds (1989) added a helical perturbation that causes the vortex rings to leave the nozzle lip eccentrically. If the ratio of axial-to-helical frequency is about 2, the jet bifurcates into two somewhat distinct branches that emerge at an angle to the jet axis. If the ratio of frequencies is incommensurate but between 1.7 and 3.5, the vortex rings are sent in all directions and the velocity profile is very broad. This is called a *blooming jet*. Figure 26.8 is the original blooming jet produced by Reynolds in 1984. The jet Reynolds number was about 5000 and the axial–orbital frequency ratio 2.3. Axial amplitude of 10% free-stream velocity was estimated. One might expect that these phenomena would be limited to modest Reynolds numbers; however, bifurcating jets have even been produced with Reynolds numbers of 100,000. As the Reynolds number increases, the intensity of the acoustic perturbations must be increased.

*26.8 CORRELATIONS OF FLUCTUATIONS

The statistical approach to uncovering the structure of turbulence uses space–time correlations. Let $X(x_i, t)$ and $Y(x_i, t)$ be two fluctuating properties of the turbulent flow. For simplicity assume that X and Y have been normalized by their root-mean-square (rms) values. Is there a relation between X at the point x_i^A and Y at another point x_i^B in the flow? If a turbulent process occurs that tends to produce a relationship, we can express this fact by means of the integral that defines the *correlation coefficient*:

$$R_{XY}(x_i^A, x_i^B) \equiv \frac{1}{T} \int_0^T X(x_i^A, t) Y(x_i^B, t)\, dt \tag{26.8.1}$$

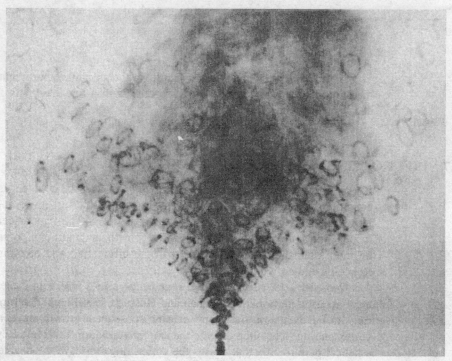

Figure 26.8   Blooming jet with a spreading angle of about 75°. Photograph by W. C. Reynolds, Stanford University.

Another notation is to replace x_i^A, x_i^B by x_i, r_i, where $x_i = x_i^A$ and $r_i = x_i^B - x_i^A$. Equation 26.8.1 shows the average instantaneous correlation of events at two points in space. In many cases the event at point A does not arrive at point B until sometime later. This is especially true at large separations where the event is convected between A and B by the flow velocity. Such events can be extracted if we delay one variable by a time τ. Allowing τ to range over different values will show if a delayed correlation exists. Thus, the more general definition of a space–time correlation is

$$R_{XY}(x_i, r_i, \tau) \equiv \overline{X(x_i, t)Y(x_i + r_i, t + \tau)} \tag{26.8.2}$$

The Reynolds stresses are (proportional to) such correlations, where X and Y are velocity fluctuations and $r_i = 0$, $\tau = 0$.

When X and Y are the same variable, R_{XX} is the *autocorrelation*. Figure 26.9 shows the autocorrelation of the pressure fluctuations on the wall under a turbulent boundary layer. Curves for several fixed distances $r_i = \xi, 0, 0$ are drawn as a function of the delay time. The autocorrelation at $r_i = 0$, $\tau = 0$ is by definition unity. If we let $\tau = 0$, Eq. 26.8.2 indicates, as a function of r_i, the spatial structure of the turbulence. In general, eddies with scales longer than r_i contribute to this correlation, whereas scales much shorter than r_i do not. As r_i increases to become larger than the largest eddies, the autocorrelation approaches zero. An indication of the largest eddies that cause the fluctuation X is given by defining an *integral length scale:*

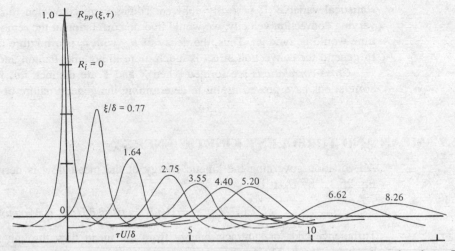

Figure 26.9   Autocorrelation of wall pressure fluctuations under a turbulent boundary layer. The distance between microphones is ξ/δ and the time lag is τ. Reprinted from Panton et al. (1980), Cambridge University Press.

$$L_{XX_1} \equiv \int R_{XX}(x_i, r_1, \tau = 0) \, dr_1$$

Correlations tend to emphasize large-scale effects and to hide smaller-scale effects.

From a practical standpoint it is difficult to hold $\tau = 0$ and vary the measurement position r_i. The concept of *convection velocity* sometimes overcomes this difficulty. Many turbulent flows have a large mean velocity and much smaller fluctuations. *Taylor's hypothesis* is the assumption that a large convection velocity U_c sweeps a frozen turbulent state past the position of interest. This connects the flow-direction space separation and time by $r_1 = U_c t$. Invoking the convection hypothesis allows us to interpret $R_{XX}(x_i = 0, r_i = 0, \tau)$ as indicating the spatial structure of the turbulence in the flow direction. Referring to Figure 26.9, we use the convective hypothesis to interpret the spatial size of turbulent eddies that cause the largest wall pressure fluctuations; that is, let

$$R_{pp}(x_i = 0, r_i = 0, \tau) \approx R_{pp}(x_1 = U_c\tau, 0, 0)$$

Since the extent of the positive region of R_{pp} (at $r_i = 0$) is about $\tau U/\delta \approx 2$, we surmise that the spatial extent of the large turbulent eddy is probably twice this size:

$$L_E \approx U_c\tau \approx \frac{U_c}{U} \frac{U\tau}{\delta} \delta \approx \frac{U_c}{U} 4\delta \approx 3\delta$$

Here the convective velocity has been taken as about 0.8 of the free velocity.

Next, we consider the correlation R_{pp} for large separation in the microphone separation distance. The decay of the correlation is caused by two effects. First, the pressure-producing eddies change their structure as they traverse the distance r_1. To the extent that this modification is random, it will drive R_{pp} toward zero. Second, the convection process over the distance r_1 may not be uniform. The convection velocity itself is a statistical variable. If perfectly coherent eddies were convected to long distances by a varying convection velocity, we would find no correlation at the remote point. The arrival time would be random. Thus, the decay of R_{pp} with r_1 is a mixture of these two effects. In general the convection effect is much more important (Panton and Robert, 1994).

Cross-correlations are formed when X and Y are distinct: $\overline{uv}$, for example. Cross-correlations have proved useful in determining the general nature of large-scale eddies.

*26.9   MEAN AND TURBULENT KINETIC ENERGY

An equation governing the kinetic energy of the mean flow is derived by multiplying Eq. 26.3.5 by U_i. It is

$$\rho U_j \partial_j (\tfrac{1}{2} U_i U_i) = -U_i \partial_i P + \mu U_i \partial_j \partial_j U_i - U_i \partial_j (\rho \overline{u_i u_j}) \qquad (26.9.1)$$

Turbulence adds or subtracts energy from the mean flow through the gradient of the Reynolds stress. The total overall effect is to decrease the mean energy. To show this, consider the identity

$$\partial_j (\rho U_i \overline{u_i u_j}) = \rho \overline{u_i u_j} \partial_j U_i + U_i \partial_j (\rho \overline{u_i u_j})$$

We integrate this over a thin slice of boundary layer or pipe flow where changes in the flow direction are negligible. After applying Gauss's theorem to the left-hand side, the result is

$$\int n_j \rho U_i \overline{u_i u_j} \, dS = \int \rho \overline{u_i u_j} \partial_j U_i \, dV + \int U_i \partial_j (\rho \overline{u_i u_j}) \, dV$$

The left-hand side is zero, since the Reynolds stress is zero on the wall or in the free stream and the integrals on the ends of the slice cancel each other. Hence, the overall mean kinetic energy production by turbulence is

$$-\int U_i \partial_j (\rho \overline{u_i u_j}) \, dV = \int \rho \overline{u_i u_j} \partial_j U_i \, dV < 0 \qquad (26.9.2)$$

In a typical shear layer, $\overline{u_i u_j}$ is always negative and $\partial_j U_i$ is always positive; thus the net effect is negative. On balance, the Reynolds stress effect tends to decrease the mean kinetic energy in Eq. 26.9.1.

A *turbulence intensity* can be defined for each velocity component as the root mean square referenced to a characteristic mean flow velocity U_0. It is given by

$$I_x \equiv \frac{(\overline{u_1 u_1})^{1/2}}{U_0}$$

The overall turbulence intensity is defined as the average of I_x, I_y, and I_z:

$$I \equiv \frac{(\tfrac{1}{3} \overline{u_i u_i})^{1/2}}{U_0} \qquad (26.9.3)$$

If the turbulence is isotropic, $\overline{u_1 u_1} = \overline{u_2 u_2} = \overline{u_3 u_3}$ and the turbulence intensity I is equal to the component intensities.

Another quantity of interest, especially in engineering computation methods, is the *turbulent kinetic energy*:

$$k \equiv \tfrac{1}{2}\, \overline{u_i u_i} \tag{26.9.4}$$

Next we take up the kinetic energy of the turbulent fluctuations. The relation governing the turbulent kinetic energy is the trace of Eq. 26.4.4, namely,

$$U_k \partial_k k = -\partial_k(\overline{u_k k}) - \frac{1}{\rho}\, \partial_i(\overline{u_i p}) - \overline{u_i u_k}\partial_k U_i + \nu\overline{u_i \partial_k \partial_k u_i} \tag{26.9.5}$$

The first two terms on the right-hand side of Eq. 26.9.5 are diffusion terms, which redistribute k. The main production term in this equation is the Reynolds stress multiplying the mean shear. On average, the Reynolds stress effect that produces turbulence balances that which destroys mean flow energy. The overall volume-average energy production by Reynolds stresses in Eq. 26.9.5 is equal to the destruction of mean flow kinetic energy by Reynolds stresses in Eq. 26.9.1 in light of the equality in Eq. 26.9.5. Be aware that there is a certain arbitrariness in the way production and diffusion effects are defined in Eq. 26.9.5 (Brodley et al., 1973). When we time-average these effects, we lose information and cannot strictly apply these interpretations to instantaneous motions.

There are several equivalent forms for the viscous term. First introduce the notation for the strain rate of the fluctuations:

$$s_{ij} \equiv \tfrac{1}{2}\, (\partial_i u_j + \partial_j u_i) \tag{26.9.6}$$

Next, note that the viscous dissipation per unit mass from fluctuations is

$$\varepsilon \equiv \frac{\bar{\Phi}}{\rho} = 2\nu\, \overline{s_{ij} s_{ji}} \tag{26.9.7}$$

Introducing these definitions, one can show that

$$\nu\, \overline{u_i \partial_k \partial_k u_i} = 2\nu\partial_k\, (\overline{u_i s_{ki}}) - \varepsilon \tag{26.9.8}$$

Later we will find that dissipation is concentrated in high-frequency eddies that are isotropic and therefore are roughly the same for all component directions. Frequently, the term $2\nu\partial_k(\overline{u_i s_{ki}})$ is neglected (Tennekes and Lumley, 1972, p. 153; Townsend, 1976, p. 42). Another common form is $\nu\overline{u_i\partial_k\partial_k u_i} = \nu\partial_k\partial_k(k) - \nu\overline{\partial_k u_i \partial_k u_i}$. The last term here is sometimes approximated as the dissipation.

Note that the pressure–velocity correlation is a diffusive effect in Eq. 26.9.5. The pressure–strain correlation, which appeared in Eq. 26.4.4 as a production term, does not occur in Eq. 26.9.5, because $\overline{p\,\partial_i u_i} = 0$ (since $\partial_i u_i = 0$). Pressure–velocity correlations only transfer turbulent energy that the Reynolds stress mean shear term produces. To illustrate this, consider the simple shear flow where $U_1(x_2)$, $U_2 = 0$, $U_3 = 0$, and all turbulence properties are uniform in the x_1- and x_3-directions. The turbulent intensities $\tfrac{1}{2}\overline{u_1 u_1}$, $\tfrac{1}{2}\overline{u_2 u_2}$, and $\tfrac{1}{2}\overline{u_3 u_3}$ are controlled by the appropriate equation in 26.4.4. Hence,

$$U_1 \partial_1 (\tfrac{1}{2}\overline{u_1 u_1}) = 0$$

$$= -\partial_2 \left(\overline{u_2 \frac{1}{2} u_1 u_1} \right) - \frac{1}{\rho} \overline{p \partial_1 u_1} - \overline{u_1 u_2} \partial_2 U_1 - \frac{1}{3}\varepsilon$$

$$U_1 \partial_1 (\tfrac{1}{2}\overline{u_2 u_2}) = 0 \qquad\qquad (26.9.9)$$

$$= -\partial_2 \left(\overline{u_2 \frac{1}{2} u_2 u_2} \right) + \frac{1}{\rho} \overline{p \partial_2 u_2} + \frac{1}{\rho} \partial_2 \overline{u_2 p} - \frac{1}{3}\varepsilon$$

$$U_1 \partial_1 (\tfrac{1}{2}\overline{u_3 u_3}) = 0$$

$$= -\partial_2 \left(\overline{u_2 \frac{1}{2} u_3 u_3} \right) + \frac{1}{\rho} \overline{p \partial_3 u_3} - \frac{1}{3}\varepsilon$$

Here, the viscous destruction has been assumed to act equally on all components.

Some interesting physics is implied by Eq. 26.9.9. On the average turbulence production $\overline{u_1 u_2} \partial_2 U_1$ goes entirely into the $\overline{u_1 u_1}$ equation, while pressure–strain production terms $\overline{p \partial_1 u_1}$, $\overline{p \partial_2 u_2}$, and $\overline{p \partial_3 u_3}$ are in all three equations. Since $\overline{p \partial_i u_i} = 0$, these terms redistribute turbulent energy that was originally generated as $\tfrac{1}{2}\overline{u_1 u_1}$ energy into turbulent energy in the other directions. From experiments on wall layers, one finds that $\tfrac{1}{2}\overline{u_1 u_1}$ is much higher than the other components. Net production occurs only in the u_1-direction, but viscous destruction is roughly equal for all components. Pressure–strain is the major intracomponent transfer mechanism.

26.10   ENERGY CASCADE: KOLMOGOROV SCALES AND TAYLOR MICROSCALE

The spectrum of longitudinal turbulent energy was given in Fig. 15.4. These data were taken on a turbulent jet, but they are typical of any turbulent flow. The easiest way to view a spectrum is simply as a function that produces the proper energy when it is integrated over all wavenumbers ($k_1 = 2\pi/$wavelength); that is, $F_1(k_1)$ has the property that

$$\overline{u_1 u_1} = \int_0^\infty F_1(k)\, dk \quad \text{or} \quad \frac{d}{dk}(\overline{u_1 u_1}) = F_1(k_1) \qquad (26.10.1)$$

This equation does not really define $F_1(k_1)$ properly, but it gives one of its major properties. The variable F_1 is a measure of the energy between k_1 and $k_1 + dk_1$ in a Fourier decomposition of $u_1(r_1)$. [Actually, $F_1(k_1)$ and the autocorrelation $R_{11}(r_1)$ are Fourier transforms of each other.] Most of the energy is at low wavenumbers in the larger eddies. The energy decreases at higher wavenumbers because the velocity fluctuations are less intense. Kilmogorov applied dimensional analysis to the energy spectrum to show that it has an overlap region where

$$F_1 \propto k^{-5/3} \tag{26.10.2}$$

This is the special case mentioned at Eq. 15.7.15. The range of k_1 for which Eq. 26.10.2 applies is called the *inertial subrange*.

The arguments that lead to the inertial subrange are important because they reveal some physical aspects of turbulence. Consider first the low-wavenumber (large-eddy) region of the spectrum, where most of the $\overline{u_1 u_1}$ energy exists. These eddies are anisotropic and bear the mark of the way in which they were formed. Jets, wakes, and wall layers have different-shaped spectra in this region. The one common aspect of all these flows is that viscosity does not affect the main energy-carrying eddies. The primary instability- and scale-building processes are inviscid. We let L and u_0 be length and velocity scales that characterize the large eddies. Dimensionally, the energy spectrum at low wavenumber is

$$F_1 = F(k_1, u_0, L)$$

Kolmogorov's argument is that inviscid processes also redistribute turbulent energy into smaller and smaller eddies. This continues until the eddies are so small that viscous forces restrain their growth. We shall see that this *energy cascade* is very long when the Reynolds number is large. The only thing in common between large and small eddies is that the rate at which energy is put into forming the large eddies by the Reynolds stress term must be equal to the viscous dissipation that is occurring at the smaller scales.

The energy of a large eddy is about u_0^2. As the eddy turns over once, we assume that a certain fraction of its energy is lost into smaller scales. Since the turnover time is L/u_0, the rate at which energy is lost is proportional to

$$\varepsilon \approx \frac{u_0^3}{L} \tag{26.10.3}$$

We use the symbol ε because this energy is ultimately dissipated by viscosity. In terms of ε, instead of u_0, the large-scale spectrum is

$$F_1 = F(k_1, \varepsilon, L) \tag{26.10.4}$$

The appropriate nondimensional form is a function of $k_1 L$:

$$\bar{F} \equiv \frac{F_1}{\varepsilon^{2/3} L^{5/3}} = \bar{F}(k_1 L) \tag{26.10.5}$$

This corresponds to Eq. 15.7.13 in the general overlap law analysis.

Consider two flows with the same u_0 and L but with different viscosities, so that the Reynolds numbers are different. These flows have the same large-scale structure, since the main turbulence-building processes are inviscid. The difference occurs in the fine-scale structure. When ν is low, the small eddies can become much smaller before the viscous forces retarding their formation are effective. The range of eddy sizes at high Re is wider, and the smallest eddies are smaller.

As Re $\to \infty$ the small eddies are so far down the cascade that the scale L is no longer important. On the other hand, the viscosity is important. For this special region of high wavenumbers, the spectrum has a form that depends only on ν and ε:

$$F_1 = f(k_1, \varepsilon, \nu) \tag{26.10.6}$$

Kolmogorov's hypothesis was that the small eddies are so much smaller than the large ones that there is no strong relationship between them. In effect the small eddies are isotropic, having no scales other than ε and ν. The energy ε is the only common quantity between the large and small scales. We can nondimensionalize Eq. 26.10.6 into

$$\bar{f} \equiv \frac{F_1}{\varepsilon^{1/4} \nu^{5/4}} = \bar{f}(k_1 \eta) \tag{26.10.7}$$

where η introduces the *Kolmogorov length*. It is defined as

$$\eta \equiv \left(\frac{\nu^3}{\varepsilon} \right)^{1/4} \tag{26.10.8}$$

The Kolmogorov length is a length measure for the smallest eddies in the turbulence. Note that the ratio of the largest eddy size to the smallest is

$$\frac{L}{\eta} = \left(\frac{u_0 L}{\nu} \right)^{3/4} = \mathrm{Re}^{3/4} \tag{26.10.9}$$

As $\mathrm{Re} \to \infty$, the difference in scales becomes very great. A visual example is given by comparing the large- and fine-scale structures in Figs. 26.10 and 26.11, which are at different Reynolds numbers. According to Eq. 15.7.15, the spectrum in the overlap region (the inertial subrange) follows the law

$$\bar{F} = A \cdot (k_1 L)^{-5/3}$$

in outer variables, or

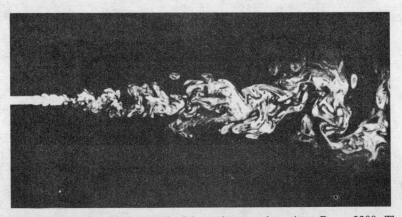

Figure 26.10 Turbulent water jet visualized in a plane on the axis at Re = 2300. The picture resolution exceeds the Kolmogorov scale in the right half. Also note the spiral structure. Reprinted with permission from Dimotakis et al. (1983).

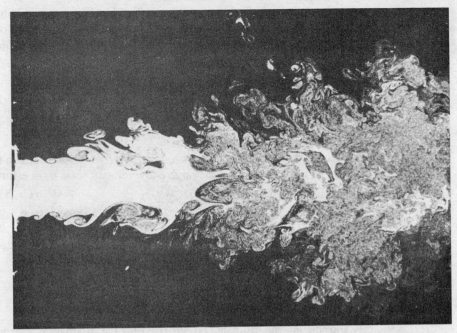

Figure 26.11   Turbulent air jet at a higher Reynolds number (11,000) shows an increase in fine scale structure. Courtesy of J. L. Balint, M. Ayrault, and J. P. Schon, École Centrale de Lyon, France. Work described by Balint et al. (1982).

$$\bar{f} = B \cdot (k_1 \eta)^{-5/3} \qquad (26.10.10)$$

in inner variables. This latter function is, in principle, universally valid for all turbulent flows.

At one time it was thought that the small-scale eddies would be isotropic and also uniformly distributed in space. The experimental evidence is that these eddies occur in patches (a phenomenon called *intermittency of dissipating eddies*) and that they are not completely isotropic. Corrections to Eq. 26.10.10 for these facts turn out to be negligible.

The Kilmogorov length is the smallest turbulent fluctuation that can withstand the damping effect of viscosity. Since η is typically 0.1 to 1 mm, there is no question that the continuum hypothesis applies to common turbulent flows.

The large eddies of size L have velocity fluctuations of intensity u_0. Although there are processes that increase the size of eddies, the net "flow" of energy is to very small size eddies, where viscous dissipation converts the mechanical energy into heat. The size of the eddies where dissipation is important is the Kolmogorov length (Eq. 26.10.8). There is also a Kolmogorov velocity scale that is a measure of the velocity of the small eddies. It is the scale velocity formed from ν and ε:

$$v_{\text{Kol}} \equiv (\nu \varepsilon)^{1/4} \qquad (26.10.11)$$

The fluctuations in the dissipation range have scales η and v_{Kol}.

As a final topic in this section, we consider the proper nondimensional form of the dissipation. Since the small scales are the most important, the Kolmogorov scales will make an order one quantity. From Eq. 26.9.7 we find that the proper form is

$$\varepsilon \equiv \frac{\eta^2}{v_{\text{Kol}}^2} \frac{\varepsilon}{\nu} = 2 \frac{\eta^2}{v_{\text{Kol}}^2} \overline{s_{ij}s_{ji}}$$

$$\varepsilon^* = \frac{\lambda^2}{u_0^2} \frac{\varepsilon}{\nu}$$

(26.10.12)

The second expression introduces λ, the *Taylor microscale*. It is a fictitious length scale defined so that one can use the large eddy velocity scale u_0 in estimating the dissipation; that is,

$$\frac{\eta^2}{v_{\text{Kol}}^2} \sim \frac{\lambda_2}{u_0^2}$$

Hence, using Eqs. 26.10.8 and 26.10.11, we have

$$\lambda^2 \sim u_0^2 \frac{\nu}{\varepsilon}$$

(26.10.13)

By introducing the estimate (Eq. 26.10.3) for the dissipation, $\varepsilon \sim u_0^3/L$, we can see how the Taylor scale compares to L:

$$\frac{\lambda}{L} \sim \left(\frac{u_0 L}{\nu} \right)^{-1/2} = \text{Re}_0^{-1/2}$$

(26.10.14)

Although λ is not as small as η, it still becomes much smaller than L as Re_0 increases.

26.11   WALL TURBULENCE: CHANNEL FLOW ANALYSIS

The presence of a wall modifies turbulence in a fundamental way. To illustrate this class of flows, we consider the flow in a slot formed by plane walls. The essential features of this flow are the same as those for round pipes (curvature effects are not significant) and boundary layers. Assume that the flow is driven by a pressure gradient and is fully developed so that the velocity and Reynolds stress are independent of the flow direction coordinate x (Fig. 26.12). The transverse coordinate y is measured from the lower wall and the half-height h is the centerline where the velocity is U_0. We consider the case where the Reynolds number $\text{Re} = U_0 h/\nu \rightarrow \infty$. The theory developed for this asymptotic case is valid for most Reynolds numbers of practical interest. The presentation is an overly deductive and "rational" approach that yields a minimum of assumptions and provides the simplest theory. Most of the results were actually first produced by intuitive, ad hoc, arguments (often with logical gaps). It is only after a stage of innovation that a process of deduction can be constructed. Even then, since turbulence is not a closed set of equations, critical assumptions based on experiments must be made.

Our experience with incompressible flows tells us that the mean velocity profile is of the form $U = U(y, \nu, (1/\rho)(dP/dx), h)$ (ρ and dp/dx are the only variables with the

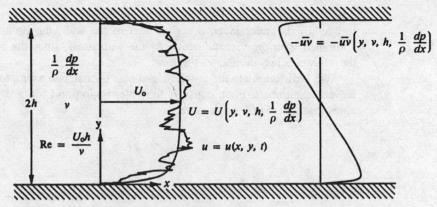

Figure 26.12 Turbulent flow in a plane channel.

dimension of mass and must therefore occur together). Since the centerline velocity $U_0 = U(h, \nu, (1/\rho)(dP/dx), h)$, we may eliminate $(1/\rho)(dP/dx)$ between the two expressions and consider $U = U(y, \nu, U_0, h)$.

With the assumption of a fully developed flow the Reynolds averaged x- and y-momentum equations 26.3.5 reduce to

$$0 = -\frac{1}{\rho}\frac{dP}{dx} - \frac{d\overline{uv}}{dy} + \nu\frac{d^2U}{dy^2} \tag{26.11.1}$$

$$0 = -\frac{1}{\rho}\frac{dP}{dy} - \frac{d\overline{v^2}}{dy} \tag{26.11.2}$$

The second equation can be integrated to yield $P_0 = P + \overline{v^2}$, and since $\overline{v^2}$ is independent of x, we find that $dP/dx = dP_0/dx$. Next, Eq. 26.11.1 is integrated from the wall where the shear stress is τ_0 to an arbitrary position y. The result is

$$0 = -\frac{y}{\rho}\frac{dP_0}{dx} - \overline{uv} + \nu\frac{dU}{dy} - \frac{\tau_0}{\rho} \tag{26.11.3}$$

This equation can be evaluated at the centerline, where all stresses are zero, to relate the wall shear stress and the pressure gradient; $-h\,dP_0/dx = \tau_0$. Thus Eq. 26.11.3 takes on the form

$$-\overline{uv} + \nu\frac{dU}{dy} = \frac{\tau_0}{\rho}\left(1 - \frac{y}{h}\right) \tag{26.11.4}$$

The total stress decreases linearly from the wall according to Eq. 26.11.4.

The no-slip condition requires that the turbulent fluctuations and the Reynolds stresses vanish at the walls. At the wall the stress is entirely viscous, and viscosity must also influence, because of viscous diffusion, at least a thin layer near the wall. As the Reynolds number becomes larger (consider if you like a fixed slot h and a fixed U_0 with ν becoming smaller and smaller) the viscous region becomes smaller compared to h. This gives turbulent wall layers a two-layer structure. In the outer flow the dynamic events that produce the Reynolds stress are inviscid and the direct viscous stress is negligible. In the inner layer, a region next to the wall, the turbulent Reynolds stress is combined with the viscous stress. At the wall itself, since the Reynolds stress is zero, the viscous stress dominates the flow.

We will formulate the problem as a pair of matched asymptotic expansions for high Reynolds numbers. First, consider the outer region and formulate nondimensional variables that are of order one there:

$$Y = \frac{y}{h} \tag{26.11.5}$$

$$\frac{U(y)}{U_0} = F(Y, \text{Re}) \sim F_0(Y) + \Delta_1(\text{Re})F_1(Y) + \cdots \tag{26.11.6}$$

Here $\Delta_1(\text{Re})$ is a gauge function to be determined later.

The first thought would be to scale the Reynolds stresses $\overline{-uv}$ by the velocity U_0; however, doing so does not produce a variable of order one as the Reynolds number becomes large (an experimental fact). The turbulent fluctuations are not a constant fraction of U_0 as the Reynolds number changes. Let us introduce a scale u_* that is a proper measure of the turbulence. Thus, u_* is to be chosen so that as $\text{Re} \to \infty$, an order one variable will be

$$-\frac{\overline{uv}}{u_*^2} = G(Y, \text{Re}) \sim G_0(Y) + \cdots \tag{26.11.7}$$

By arbitrarily introducing another parameter u_* we must eventually define it and determine its variation with Re; that is, we must find that

$$\frac{u_*}{U_0} = \frac{u_*}{U_0}(\text{Re}) \tag{26.11.8}$$

It will be useful to introduce a Reynolds number based on u_*. Let

$$\text{Re*} = \frac{u_* h}{\nu} = \frac{u_*}{U_\infty} \text{Re} \tag{26.11.9}$$

Aside: The critical question here is: What is the variation of $u_*/U_0(\text{Re})$ with Re in the range of interest? The variation in the range of interest is a function that approaches 0 as $\text{Re} \to \infty$. At very high Re some different physics take over (wall roughness) and u_*/U_0 actually becomes constant.

To continue the analysis we write the momentum equation, Eq. 26.11.4, in outer variables and arrange it so that the Reynolds stress term is $O[1]$:

$$G + \left(\frac{U_0}{u_*}\right)^2 \frac{1}{\text{Re}} \frac{dF}{dY} = \frac{\tau_0/\rho}{u_*^2}(1 - Y) \tag{26.11.10}$$

The viscous term on the left side becomes small as $\text{Re} \to \infty$, so to retain the Reynolds stress G, the right-hand side must be of order one. Hence, u_* must be proportional to τ_0/ρ (at least in the first order) and we may set

$$u_*^2 = \frac{\tau_0}{\rho} \qquad (26.11.11)$$

It is useful to note at this point the experimental fact that the shear stress approaches zero as Re $\rightarrow \infty$:

$$C_f = 2\frac{\tau_0}{\rho U_\infty^2} = 2\left(\frac{u_*}{U_\infty}\right)^2 \rightarrow 0 \qquad \text{as} \quad \text{Re} \rightarrow \infty \qquad (26.11.12)$$

This is the experimental evidence that requires us to propose Eq. 26.11.8 in the first place. Furthermore, the rate at which C_f approaches zero is so slow that as Re $\rightarrow \infty$, Re* = u*Re/$U_0 \rightarrow \infty$ and $(U_0/u_*)^2(1/\text{Re}) \rightarrow 0$. This knowledge shows us that the high Reynolds number form of Eq. 26.11.10 is

$$G_0 = 1 - Y \qquad (26.11.13)$$

Note that the viscous stresses are negligible in the outer region; Reynolds stresses are solely responsible for producing the velocity profile. In this respect the outer layer is like a jet or wake.

Next, consider the turbulent kinetic energy equation for the outer layer. Noting that $U_k\partial_k k = 0$, Eq. 26.9.5. is

$$0 = -\overline{uv}\frac{dU}{dy} - \frac{d}{dy}\left[\frac{1}{2}v(uu + vv + ww) + \frac{1}{\rho}\overline{vp'}\right] - \varepsilon \qquad (26.11.14)$$

Expressing Eq. 26.11.14 in outer variables gives

$$0 = -G\frac{dF}{dY} - \frac{u_*}{U_0}\frac{d}{dY}\left[\frac{1}{2}\frac{\overline{v(uu + vv + ww)}}{u_*^3} + \frac{\overline{vp}}{\rho u_*^3}\right]$$

$$- \frac{1}{\text{Re}}\left(\frac{h}{\lambda}\right)^2 \varepsilon_0^* \qquad (26.11.15)$$

Here $\varepsilon^* = \varepsilon(\lambda/u_*)^2/\nu$ and λ/h is the Taylor microscale discussed earlier. From Eq. 26.10.14 one can show that

$$\frac{(h/\lambda)^2}{\text{Re}} \sim \frac{u_*}{U_0} \qquad (26.11.16)$$

Consider how Eq. 26.11.15 must simplify for the case of high Reynolds number. Because $u_*/U_0 \rightarrow 0$ and Re $\rightarrow \infty$, one finds that

$$0 = G_0\frac{dF_0}{dY} \qquad (26.11.17)$$

Since G_0 is not zero, Eq. 26.11.17 means that F_0 = constant. In fact, $F_0 = 1$ from the centerline boundary condition $U(Y = 1) = U_0$.

The first answer is that the mean velocity is approaching a uniform flow ($F_0 = U(Y)/U_0 = 1$). Furthermore, the turbulence in the outer layer, when compared to U_0, is becoming weaker and weaker as the Reynolds number increases ($G_0 = -\overline{uv}/u_*^2$ is finite and $u_*/U_0 \Rightarrow 0$). We may improve on this answer by considering the second term, F_1, in the asymptotic expansion for velocity equation 26.11.6. Reconsidering the kinetic energy equation gives

$$0 = -\Delta_1(\text{Re})G_0 \frac{dF_1}{dY} - \frac{u_*}{U_0} \frac{d}{dY} \left[\frac{1}{2} \frac{\overline{v(uu + vv + ww)}}{u_*^3} + \frac{\overline{vp}}{\rho u_*^3} \right]$$

$$- \frac{u_*}{U_0} \varepsilon^* \tag{26.11.18}$$

If we chose $\Delta_1 = u_*/U_0$, production, diffusion, and dissipation are all possible, giving us a nontrivial form:

$$0 = -G_0 \frac{dF_1}{dY} - \frac{d}{dY} \left[\frac{1}{2} \frac{\overline{v(uu + vv + ww)}}{u_*^3} + \frac{\overline{vp}}{\rho u_*^3} \right] - \varepsilon^* \tag{26.11.19}$$

With $\Delta = u_*/U_0$, outer-layer velocity profile equation 26.11.6 is

$$\frac{U(y)}{U_0} = F(Y, \text{Re}) \sim 1 + \frac{u_*}{U_0} F_1(Y) \tag{26.11.20}$$

Rearranging yields the *defect law*, proposed originally by von Kármán as an empirical correlation:

$$F_1(Y) = \frac{U(y) - U_0}{u_*} \tag{26.11.21}$$

Notice that u_*, introduced as a scale for the turbulence in the outer layer, is now also the scale for the deviation of the outer velocity from centerline value, an effect caused by the Reynolds stress. The centerline velocity U_0 has been demoted to play only the role of a reference. Because of symmetry, $dF_1/dY = 0$ at $Y = 1$.

Next, turn attention to the inner layer next to the wall. Again consider, for the sake of argument, a flow situation with fixed h and U_0. Imagine that the Reynolds number is increased by changing the fluid viscosity ν to smaller and smaller values. There is some distance where the viscous diffusion can destroy the velocity fluctuations. If the viscosity is smaller, the thickness of the wall layer is smaller. In any event, there is an inner layer where viscosity is important and its size depends on the viscosity. Let d be the inner-layer length scale, which is at this stage unknown. Denote the inner-layer distance variable as

$$y^+ = \frac{y}{d} \tag{26.11.22}$$

We expect from the arguments above that $d/h \to 0$ as $\text{Re} \to \infty$. However, the competition between turbulent stresses and viscous forces is not a simple process, and the length scale of the inner layer does not decrease as a simple function of the Reynolds number.

The mean velocity in the inner layer is approaching zero to meet the no-slip condition. Just how much of the mean velocity profile belongs to the inner layer is not known. It could be a constant fraction of U_0 or it might be a smaller and smaller fraction as the Reynolds number increases. To account for both possibilities, let us introduce another unknown scale, which we call u_s. The inner-layer velocity profile is

$$\frac{U(y)}{u_s} = f(y^+, \text{Re}) \sim f_0(y^+) + \cdots \tag{26.11.23}$$

The function $f_0(y^+)$ is called the *law of the wall*.

To complete the definitions of u_s and d, we do some more analysis. The momentum equation is expressed in inner variables and the limit for a high Reynolds number is taken. For physical reasons the final result must contain both Reynolds stresses and viscous stresses:

$$-\frac{\overline{uv}}{u_*^2} + \frac{u_s}{u_*}\frac{h}{d}\frac{1}{\text{Re}_*}\frac{df}{dy^+} = 1 - \frac{d}{h}y^+ \tag{26.11.24}$$

The Reynolds stress term will be of order one if we use the same velocity scale in the inner layer that was used in the outer layer; therefore, we let the inner stress function be $g = \overline{uv}/u_*^2$. Another indication that this is correct is that the outer stress $G_0 = \overline{uv}/u_*^2 = 1$ as $Y \to 0$ (Eq. 26.11.13). The viscous term in Eq. 26.11.24 can be made of order one by setting u_s/u_* and d/h equal to the proper functions of Re_*. To pin down these scales further, reconsider the kinetic energy equation, including the assumption that fluctuations scale with u_*. In the inner variables it is

$$0 = -g\frac{df}{dy^+} - \frac{u_*}{u_s}\frac{d}{dy^+}\left[\frac{1}{2}\frac{\overline{v(uu + vv + ww)}}{u_*^3} + \frac{\overline{vp}}{\rho u_*^3}\right]$$

$$\frac{1}{\text{Re}_*}\frac{u_*}{u_s}\frac{d}{\lambda_i}\frac{h}{\lambda_i}\,\epsilon_i^* \tag{26.11.25}$$

Consider the dissipation term $\varepsilon_i^* - \varepsilon\lambda_i^2/\nu u_*^2$. From Eq. 26.10.4, with $u_0 = u_*$ and $L = d$, we find that $(1/\text{Re}_*)\,d/\lambda\,h/\lambda \sim O[1]$. In the limit of $\text{Re}_* \to \infty$ we want to retain, as physical assumptions, the viscous term in Eq. 26.11.24 and the dissipation term in Eq. 26.11.25. This occurs only if we set

$$u_* - u_s \quad \text{and} \quad \frac{h}{d}\frac{1}{\text{Re}_*} = 1 \quad \text{or equivalently} \quad d - \frac{\nu}{u_*}$$

This completes the definitions of u_s and d, yielding inner variables

$$y^+ = \frac{u_* y}{\nu} \qquad f_0 = \frac{U}{u_*} \qquad g_0 = -\frac{\overline{uv}}{u_*^2} \tag{26.11.26}$$

Note that

$$y^+ = Y\,\text{Re}_* \tag{26.11.27}$$

One can now see that Re_* is physically the ratio of inner-to-outer length scales. At the centerline, $Y = 1$, $y^+ = \text{Re}_*$.

In inner variables, momentum equation 26.11.24 reduces to

$$g_0^+ + \frac{df_0}{dy^+} = 1 \tag{26.11.28}$$

The sum of the viscous and Reynolds stresses is a constant. For this reason the inner layer is sometimes called the *constant stress region*.

There will be a region where the velocity profile functions F and f match. In this region inner and outer functions have common parts. Consider that both the inner and outer representations (Eqs. 26.11.20 and 26.11.23) are valid in the overlap region:

$$F(Y \to 0) = \frac{u_*}{U_0} f(y^+ \to \infty)$$

That is, through first order the common parts are equal:

$$1 + \frac{u_*}{U_0} F_{1-\text{cp}}(Y) = \frac{u_*}{U_0} f_{0-\text{cp}}(y^+) \qquad (26.11.29)$$

The derivatives of the profiles also match, giving us another relation:

$$Y \frac{dF_{1-\text{cp}}}{dY} = y^+ \frac{df_{0-\text{cp}}}{dy^+} = \frac{1}{\kappa} \qquad (26.11.30)$$

Because Y and y^+ ($= Y \, \text{Re}_*$) can vary independently by changing Re_*, each side of Eq. 26.11.30 must be a constant that is denoted as $1/\kappa$.

The solutions to Eq. 26.11.30 are the common parts of F_0 and f_0:

$$f_{0-\text{cp}}(y^+) = \frac{U(y)}{u_*} = \frac{1}{\kappa} \ln y^+ + C_i \qquad \text{as} \quad y^+ \to \infty \qquad (26.11.31)$$

$$F_{1-\text{cp}}(Y) = \frac{U(y) - U_0}{u_*} = \frac{1}{\kappa} \ln Y + C_0 \qquad \text{as} \quad Y \to 0 \qquad (26.11.32)$$

The term *log region* is commonly used to indicate the overlap region between the inner and outer layers. The final and very important result of matching is to fix the relationship between the scaling u_* and the Reynolds number, that is, to determine Eq. 26.11.8. Subtracting Eq. 26.11.31 from Eq. 26.11.32 gives the required scaling law for u_*:

$$\frac{U_0}{u_*} = \frac{1}{\kappa} \ln \frac{u_* \, \text{Re}}{U_0} + C_i - C_0 \qquad (26.11.33)$$

Unfortunately, for computational purposes this scaling law is an implicit function of u_*/U_0. Nevertheless, in principle we have completely determined the scaling of the inner and outer regions. Equation 26.11.33 is called the *logarithmic friction law* because to first order $\frac{1}{2}C_f = (u_*/U_0)^2$ (Eq. 26.11.12). Isakson (1937) and Millikan (1938) were first to derive the log laws using overlap arguments.

In principle, an expression that is uniformly valid for both the inner and outer regions can be formed by constructing a composite expansion. An additive composite is formed by adding the inner and outer expansions and subtracting the common part. For the mean velocity we have

$$\frac{U(y)}{u_*} = f_0(y^+) + \left[F_1(Y) + \frac{U_0}{u_*} \right] - \left[F_1(Y) + \frac{U_0}{u_*} \right]_{\text{cp}}$$

$$= f_0(y^+) + F_1(Y) - [F_1(Y)]_{\text{cp}}$$

or by using Eq. 26.11.33,

$$\frac{U(y)}{u_*} = f_0(y^+) + F_1(Y) - \left(\frac{1}{\kappa} \ln Y + C_0\right)$$

Define the *law of the wake* as

$$W(Y) = F_1(Y) - \left(\frac{1}{\kappa} \ln Y + C_0\right) \qquad (26.11.34)$$

Thus, in the final composite expansion $W(Y)$ is the outer relation that produces a uniformly valid profile:

$$\frac{U(y)}{u_*} = f_0(y^+) + W(Y) \qquad \text{where} \quad Y = y^+/\text{Re}_* \qquad (26.11.35)$$

Together the law of the wall and the law of the wake form a uniformly valid representation for the mean velocity. As is usual with composite expansions, Eq. 26.11.36 contains (the first) effects of Reynolds number on the profiles. Since at $Y = 1$, $y^+ - \text{Re}_*$, $U = U_0$, one can insert Eq. 26.11.31 into Eq. 26.11.35 and compare it with Eq. 26.11.33 to show that

$$W(1) = -C_0 \qquad (26.11.36)$$

Furthermore, because the channel flow is symmetric, from Eq. 26.11.34 we find that

$$\frac{dW}{dY} = -\frac{1}{\kappa} \qquad \text{at} \quad Y = 1 \qquad (26.11.37)$$

The wake law must have a slope $-1/\kappa$ at the centerline.

Using equivalent logic a composite expansion for the Reynolds stress is

$$\frac{\overline{uv}(y)}{u_*^2} = G_0(Y) + g_0(y^+) - G_{0-\text{cp}}(Y) \qquad (26.11.38)$$

The common part is $G_0(Y \to 0) = g_\infty(y^+ \to \infty) = 1$. Hence,

$$\frac{uv(y)}{u_*^2} = 1 - Y + g_0(y^+) - 1$$

$$(26.11.39)$$

$$\frac{\overline{uv}(y)}{u_*^2} = -\frac{y^+}{\text{Re}_*} + g_0(y^+)$$

In principle, g_0^+ is found from Eq. 26.11.28 if f_0 is known. For $y^+ > 30$ (i.e., the log region), $g_0^+ = 1 - 1/\kappa y^+$ and

$$\frac{\overline{uv}(y)}{u_*^2} = 1 - \frac{1}{\kappa y^+} - \frac{y^+}{\text{Re}_*} \qquad (26.11.40)$$

Note that the position of the maximum Reynolds stress is a function of Re_*.

It is of interest to formulate the total stress, Reynolds plus viscous, in the log region. In Eq. 26.11.40 the term $1/\kappa y^+$ is the viscous stress, so the total stress is equal to $1 - y^+/\text{Re}_*$. The total stress is *not* constant in a uniformly valid representation of the log layer; it is constant only in solving for the inner-layer behavior.

Turbulent wall layers have a two-layer structure where a large inviscid layer, molded by Reynolds stress, overlies a thinner region of combined viscous and Reynolds stresses next to the wall. The *friction velocity* u_* is not originally a parameter in the problem statement but is related to the original parameters by Eq. 26.11.33. Several roles are played by u_*:

1. Scale for turbulence intensity in the outer layer

2. Scale for turbulence intensity in the inner layer

3. Scale for size of inner layer, ν/u_*

4. Gauge function for outer expansion (Eq. 26.11.20); equivalently, a scale for the velocity defect in outer layer

5. Scale for velocity in the inner region

6. Slope of velocity profile in the overlap region,

$$\frac{u_*}{\kappa} = \frac{dU}{d\ln y}\bigg|_{\text{overlap}}$$

7. Slope of velocity profile at the wall,

$$u_* = \sqrt{\frac{\tau_0}{\rho}} = v\,\frac{dU}{dy}\bigg|_0$$

The definition of u_* is set (according to tradition) numerically by 7. Both 6 and 7 cannot be satisfied, as higher-order terms in the asymptotic expansions are required.

To summarize: The scales for the outer layer are u_* and h; the inner scales are u_* and ν/u_*. The parameter U_0 is not an outer scale but acts only as a reference for the mean velocity. One should note that in both the inner and outer layers, the turbulent activity has an intensity determined by u_*.

26.12 WALL LAYERS: EXPERIMENTS AND EMPIRICAL CORRELATION

The characteristics of the two-layer structure for flow in a smooth plane channel are also applicable to turbulent boundary layers and flow in round pipes. The obvious modification is $R \to h$ in pipes and for boundary layers $\delta \to h$. In a pipe the inner layer becomes so thin that the transverse curvature is not important. In boundary layers an important fact discovered in the experiments of Ludwieg and Tillmann (1949) was that pressure gradients do not change the law of the wall. Thus, the inner layer for all these situations is exactly the same function $U/u_* = f_0(y^+)$ as shown in Fig. 26.13. These data are actually from a boundary layer without a pressure gradient. Purtell et al. (1981) have shown that the log region exists (with the same slope) to low values of Reynolds numbers. Fernholtz and Findley (1996) evaluate many boundary layer measurements, and a recent set of measurements is given in Österlund (1999) and Österlund et al. (2000). Channel flow measurements are found in Zanoun et al. (2003), and current pipe flow results are discussed by McKeon et al. (2004). Direct numerical simulations continue to higher Reynolds numbers, $\text{Re}_* = 960$, with the calculations to $\text{Re}_* = 590$ analyzed in Moser et al.

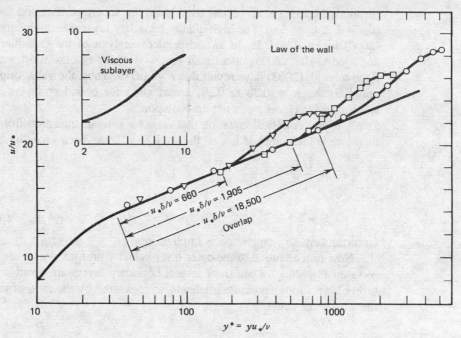

Figure 26.13 Composite velocity profiles for a turbulent boundary layer with zero gradient.

(1999). Interpretation of results using composite expansions is discussed in Panton (2005).

The inner layer consists of several subregions. Closest to the wall, $0 < y^+ < 5$ to 7, is a region called the *viscous sublayer*, where the mean velocity profile is linear. Modest fluctuations occur in this layer, but the profile is as if the flow were determined solely by viscous forces. The region 5 to $7 < y^+ < 30$ to 50 is called the *buffer layer*. It is here that both viscous and Reynolds stresses are important and the velocity profile makes a transition from the linear profile to the log profile. Finally, the overlap region, the region of matching between inner and outer regions, is customarily called the *log region* for the obvious reasons shown in Eqs. 26.11.31 and 26.11.32. Where this region ends is a constant value of $Y = y/\delta$, say 0.15; in terms of y^+, the end depends directly on the Reynolds number $y^+_{log} = 0.15Re_*$. Curves for three different Re_* are shown in Fig. 26.13. (Experimentalists prefer to use Re_θ: roughly, $Re_\delta = 10\ Re_\theta$, $Re_\theta = 3\ Re_*$.)

The value of the von Kármán constant is subject to experimental error and uncertainty. Prandtl (1935) used 0.417 and remarked that von Kármán favored κ between 0.38 and 0.39. Based on Nikuradse's data, Schlichting (1950) determined that $\kappa = 0$-40. East et al. (1979) employed $\kappa = 0.38$ in their boundary layer work, whereas Clauser (1954) favored $\kappa = 0.41$. Coles and Hirst (1968) adopted $\kappa = 0.41$ for the Stanford conference, and $\kappa = 0.41$ had wide use for a long time. Another major change occurred when Zagarola and Smits (1998) found from their superpipe data that $\kappa = 0.436$. However, there are the issues of wall roughness and the proper correction for a Pitot tube in turbulent shear flow. Perry et al. (2001) applied the standard MacMillan correction to the data and found that $\kappa = 0.39$. The proper correction for a Pitot tube is not known with certainty. McKeon et al. (2004) reanalyzed the superpipe data and found that $\kappa = 0.42$, ($C_0 = 1.2$, $C_i = 5.6$). The high-quality boundary layer measurements of Österlund et al. (2000) found $\kappa = 0.38$. In an independent analysis of the Österlund data, Buschmann and Gad-el-Hak (2003) also found that $\kappa = 0.38$. For the most recent channel flows, Zanoun et al. (2003) have found that $\kappa = 0.379$. Thus, the value originally proposed by von Kármán, $\kappa = 0.38$ to 0.39, seems good for boundary layers and channel flows, whereas κ for pipe flow is not agreed upon.

A useful empirical equation that makes a smooth transition from linear to log, and therefore is the complete law of the wall $f_0(y^+)$, has been given by Spalding (1961):

$$u^+ \equiv \frac{U}{u_*}$$

$$y^+ = u^+ + e^{-\kappa C_1}[e^{\kappa u^+} - 1 - \kappa u^+ - \tfrac{1}{2}(\kappa u^+)^2 - \tfrac{1}{6}(\kappa u^+)^3 - \tfrac{1}{24}(\kappa u^+)^4] \quad (26.12.1)$$

Unfortunately, the expression is implicit in u^+.

Now turn attention to the outer-layer velocity profiles, which are given in *defect law* form on Fig. 26.14. Data from several boundary layers are given on this figure. These layers have various pressure gradients, as measured by the ratio of the pressure force to the wall shear stress:

$$\beta \equiv \frac{\delta_*}{\tau_0}\frac{dp}{dx} \quad (26.12.2)$$

Clauser (1954, 1956) defined a boundary layer where $\beta = $ constant for all x as an *equilibrium* boundary layer. They are the turbulent analogue to the Falkner–Skan simi-

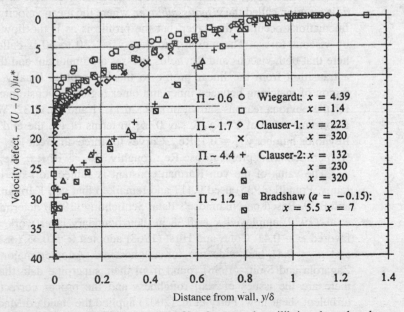

Figure 26.14 Defect velocity profiles for several equilibrium boundary layers.

larity solutions of laminar flow. In fact, when $\beta =$ constant, the external velocity has a power law variation $U_e \sim (x - x_0)^{-a}$. An equilibrium boundary layer has, in principle, a single velocity defect profile for all values of x. This similarity is for the outer layer only. Channel and pipe flow also would show similarity in defect law form, but because each flow has slightly different outer conditions, the profiles would be slightly different.

A second, and more useful, way of representing the outer-layer profiles is in the form of the *law of the wake* (Eq. 26.11.34). In Fig. 26.14 the deviations from the log line [where $f_0(y^+) = (1/\kappa) \ln y^+ + C_i$), which occur at large y^+, actually represent the *law of the wake* because of Eq. 26.11.35. Coles (1956, 1965) introduced the parameter Π to account for different pressure gradients and proposed that all boundary layer that were not too far from equilibrium (i.e., the flow develops "slowly" in the flow direction) could be represented in defect form as

$$W(Y; \Pi) = \frac{\Pi}{\kappa} w(Y) \tag{26.12.3}$$

Hence, Π is a multiplying factor of a universal outer function $w(Y)$. [Actually, Coles originally applied the term *law of the wake* to $w(Y)$.] Of course, $w(0) = 0$ and as part of the definition the $w(1) = 2$ was chosen. Evaluating Eq. 26.11.34 and $Y = 1$ connects Π with the outer log law constant:

$$W(1) = -C_0 = \frac{2\Pi}{\kappa} \tag{26.12.4}$$

One can also replace C_0 in the friction law 26.11.33 to obtain a friction law for equilibrium layers:

$$\frac{U_0}{u_*} = \frac{1}{\kappa} \ln \frac{u_* \, \text{Re}}{U_0} + C_i + \frac{2\Pi}{\kappa} \tag{26.12.5}$$

For boundary layers $\delta \to h$ in $\text{Re} = U_0 \, h / \nu$.

Hinze (1975) proposed the simple approximation $w(Y) = 2 \sin^2(\pi y / 2\delta) = 1 - \cos(\pi Y)$, which works well for most Y but has a *corner defect* in that it does not have slope $1/\kappa$ at $Y - 1$ (see Eq. 26.11.37) To correct the corner defect one must retreat slightly from the form of Eq. 26.12.3. Lewkowicz (1982) has given a good alternative in his formula:

$$w(Y; \Pi) = 2Y^2(3 - 2Y) - \Pi^{-1}Y^2(1 - 3Y + 2Y^2) \tag{26.12.6}$$

Earlier Finley et al. (1966) proposed a simpler correction:

$$w(Y; \Pi) = 2Y^2(3 - 2Y) + \Pi^{-1}Y^2(1 - Y)$$

In these expressions the first group is a very good algebraic approximation to the Coles function and the second group, preceded by Π, corrects the corner defect.

It is not evident on Fig. 26.14, because the Y scale is linear, but all the different curves approach the log law (Eq. 26.11.32) as $Y \to 0$. The constant in Eq. 26.12.3 depends on the type of flow; $C_0 = -2.7$ ($\Pi = 0.55$) for a zero pressure gradient boundary layer (Coles and Hirst, 1968), $C_0 = -0.5$ to -1.25 ($\Pi = 0.1$ to 0.2) for a channel flow

(Panton et al., 1995), and $C_0 = -1$ ($\Pi = 0.2$) (Tennekes and Lumley, 1972, p. 157) for a round pipe.

Boundary layers, even many that are far from equilibrium, can be described by the composite expansion 26.11.31 involving parameters ν, U_0, u_*, δ, Π, C_i, and κ. Coles and Hirst (1968) adopted a procedure by assuming that $\kappa = 0.41$ and $C_i = 5.0$ and then fitting the data (only outer-layer data) with the law of the wake, together with the friction law (Eq. 26.12.5), to find u_*, δ, and Π. This procedure essentially defines δ by the mathematical function used for the law of the wake. As a practical matter, experimentalists have a difficult problem using a definition such as "δ, where $U = 0.99U_{\max}$." An alternative to fitting a wake profile is to integrate data to find δ^* and solve the relation

$$\frac{\delta_*}{\delta} = \frac{1}{\kappa}\frac{u_*}{U_0}\left(\Pi + \frac{59}{60}\right)$$

This formula employs the Lewkowicz equation. Coles's original law produces the same result except that $59/60 \rightarrow 1$.

Next, let us turn our attention to the Reynolds stress. The equation defining g_0, Eq. 26.11.24, implies that g_0 is the behavior of $u\nu(y^+)/u_*^2$ for small y^+ and large Re_*. On Fig. 26.15a experimental Reynolds stress data from a channel flow are plotted in inner variables over a large range of Re_*. Now consider that in Eq. 26.11.39 we have a composite expansion that is uniformly valid in y^+. Solving Eq. 26.11.39 for g_0 yields

$$g_0(y^+) = -\frac{\overline{u\nu}(y)}{u_*^2} + \frac{y^+}{\mathrm{Re}_*} \tag{26.12.7}$$

Experimental data from three different channel flow experiments were processed according to Eq. 26.12.7 and are plotted in Fig. 26.15b–d (Panton, 1990). If there is any trend with Re_*, it is hidden within the scatter of the data. Most recent data by Zanoun et al. (2003) confirms this composite representation.

The line plotted on Fig. 26.15d is a curve fit of the data to the following semiempirical equation:

$$g_0 = \frac{2}{\pi}\arctan\left(\frac{2\kappa}{\pi}y^+\right)\left[1 - \exp\left(-\frac{y^+}{C^+}\right)\right]^2 \tag{26.12.8}$$

This relation satisfies the known Taylor's expansion behavior of g_0 near the wall; $g_0 \sim y^3$ as $y \rightarrow 0$. It also satisfies the requirement needed to match the log layer (see Eqs. 26.11.28 and 26.11.31); $g_0 \sim 1 - \kappa/y^+$ as $y \rightarrow \infty$. Two constants in the relation are κ, the von Kármán constant, and C^+, a scale constant. Typical values of C^+ are 7.7 to 10. Substituting Eq. 26.12.8 into Eq. 26.11.28 and integrating will give the mean velocity profile. When the integration reaches the log layer, one finds that C^+ is related to the additive constant in the log law of the velocity.

26.13   TURBULENT STRUCTURES

It is of interest to examine the details of turbulent fluctuations and see if patterns of motion exist. Knowledge of the motions, their duration, distribution, and occurrence is

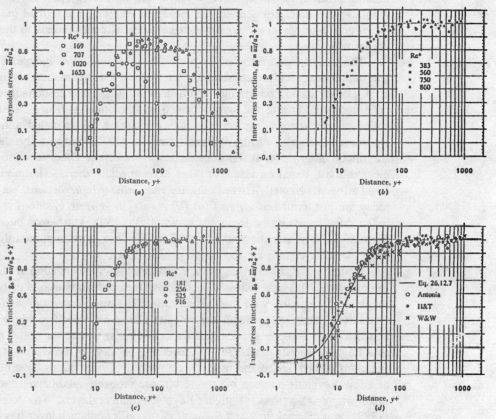

Figure 26.15 Reynolds stress in plane channel flow: (*a*) stress at various Re$_*$, data from Wei and Willmarth (1989); (*b*) stress function computed from data of Harder and Tiederman (1991); (*c*) computed from Antonia et al. (1992); (*d*) computed from Antonia et al. (1992), Harder and Tiederman (1991), and Wei and Willmarth (1989).

useful in formulating mathematical models for prediction. Also, this knowledge is important for devising methods of interrupting or controlling turbulence. The term *coherent structure* is used to mean a spatial flow pattern that remains identifiable for some period of time. The older term *eddy* seems to imply a swirling motion whereas *coherent structure* covers items such as streaks of slowly moving fluid and local shear layers.

Consider the mixing layer shown in Figs. 26.5 and 26.6. There are large strong vortices that grow by entrainment and pairing. They constitute a type of coherent structure. The rolling of the vortices stretches the connecting fluid, called *braids* and longitudinal vortices develop on the braids, which is especially evident in Figs. 26.5 and 26.7. They are important, of course, to mixing on a finer scale than the large vortices. One of the first complete Navier–Sokes calculations of these processes was done by Metcalfe and Riley (1981).

With regard to momentum transport, a nonzero Reynolds stress, $-\rho\overline{uv}$, requires processes with tendencies to have a certain sign u occur with a certain sign of v. A random process with independent u and v will on average produce no Reynolds stress. Although not precisely defined, the incidental motions, are termed *inactive motions* by Townsend. Motions or patterns that make essential contributions to the Reynolds stress are termed *active*.

The study of wall turbulence structure has, because of its industrial and meteorological importance, received considerable attention. In a mathematical classification, Wallace et al. (1972) introduced the idea of quadrant splitting. The instantaneous value of uv is classified according to the sign of u and v. A motion with $u(-)v(+)$, quadrant II, is called an *ejection motion,* and $u(+)v(-)$, quadrant IV, is called a *sweep motion.* To eliminate extraneous events, Willmarth and Lu (1972) placed a threshold value on the magnitude of uv before it was considered as an ejection. Other definitions for sweep and ejection exist, based on visual or other experimental criteria. The motions in quadrants I and III were originally termed *outward* and *wallward interactions,* but more commonly today are just termed *quadrant I* (or *III*) *events.* In general, ejections and sweeps are the major contributors to the Reynolds stress (120 to 140%), whereas interactions substract 20 to 40%. Very near the wall, $y^+ < 12$, sweeps are more important than ejections, and for $y^+ > 12$, ejections are the largest contributors.

In the investigation of coherent structures, flow visualization studies were the first to contribute. This was followed by velocity measurements at one or two points, sometimes in combination with flow visualization, but often based on *conditional sampling.* Conditional sampling averages the velocity after some specified trigger event, say u, is less than u_{rms}. Direct numerical simulations (DNSs), where the entire flow is computed in a time-accurate manner, are very revealing because all flow properties are known as functions of both space and time. Direct numerical simulations have been possible only at a low Reynolds number, but the results are probably qualitative representations, with unknown modifications, of higher-Reynolds-number layers. The work of Kim et al. (1987) on a channel flow and Spalart (1988) on a boundary layer has been a source of much detailed information (Moser et al., 1999). An analysis of turbulent structure from DNS and comparison with previous knowledge was done by Robinson (1991). Reviews of research on mechanisms of wall turbulence are in Panton (1997, 2001).

An important coherent structure is wall streaks. In a research review, Corrsin (1955) discusses unpublished experiments of Beatty, Ferrell, and Richardson. In a tube flow they observed dyed fluid being replaced by a clear fluid. Streaks of dye were observed on the walls. Corrsin states: "The significant property seems to be the strong orientation into streamwise filaments of the residual dye." For the same article, F. Hama supplied Corrsin with a photograph (Fig. 26.16) of a turbulent boundary layer where dye seeped from a flush, cross-stream slit in the wall. The dye collects into streamwise streaks in the flow. Corrsin conjectured: "Presumably this indicates a predominance of axial vorticity near the wall, 'sweeping' the wall fluid into these long narrow stripes." On the other side of the vortex, fluid is being brought closer to the wall from a higher-speed region. Because the fluid originates at greater distances from the wall, the high-speed regions are devoid of dye. Kline et al. (1967) identified and emphasized the importance of streaks.

Figure 26.17 gives flow-visualization photographs taken at various levels in a boundary layer. A thin wire was placed transverse to the flow direction (spanwise) and parallel to the wall. An electric current pulsed through the wire produces tiny hydrogen bubbles that follow the flow. In the viscous sublayer the bubbles congregate into long streaks, as

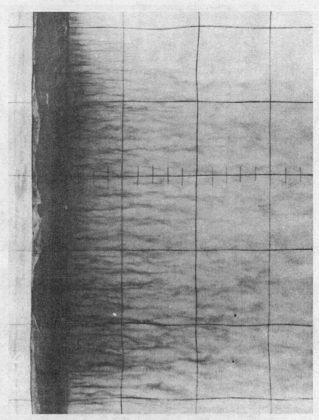

Figure 26.16   First photograph of wall streaks. Taken by and courtesy of F. Hama.

mentioned above. Portions of the low speed streak lift up, sometimes oscillate, and are ejected out into the flow. This is another narrower meaning to the term *ejection*. Several ejections can come from the same streak (Bogard and Tiederman, 1986). The entire process is called the *bursting process* and is described by Blackwelder (1988). In low-Reynolds-number layers the ejection is frequently associated with the passage of a single long-lived streamwise vortex over the streak.

Another coherent structure, the *near-wall shear layer,* separates outer high-speed fluid from sublayer fluid. A peak of high pressure is often noted on the interface of the shear layer as if the slower fluid were decelerating the faster flow. Sweeps of high speed moving toward the wall also occur in the near-wall region but are not made evident by the method of flow visualization in Fig. 26.17.

At $y^+ = 38$, one is in the buffer region and the bubble pattern in Fig. 26.17*b* shows larger-scale activity without long streaks. Because this is a low-Reynolds-number experiment, there is not much difference in the fine scales between the pictures at $y^+ = 38$ and $y^+ = 101$, the log region. Bubble wires in a horizontal position do not give a good impression of the growth in large-scale structures. Recall that the largest scales are on the order of the turbulent layer thickness δ. The final picture at $y^+ = 407$ is in the wake

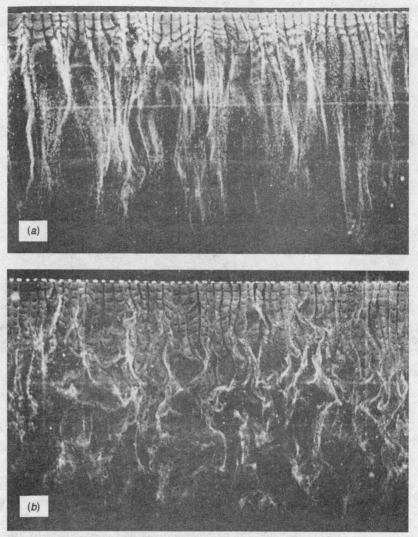

Figure 26.17 Turbulence structure at various heights in a low-Reynolds-number boundary layer is visualized with hydrogen bubbles in water. Flow is from top to bottom; (a) sublayer $y^+ = 2.7$; (b) buffer region $y^+ = 38$; (c) log region $y^+ = 101$; (d) wake region $y^+ = 407$. Reprinted with permission from Kline et al. (1967), Cambridge University Press.

region. The flow here is composed of turbulent fluid ($\omega \neq 0$) and nonturbulent fluid ($\omega = 0$). Wrinkles of a large scale are probably irrotational fluctuations caused by the growth of turbulent bulges. Areas that contain more fine-scale fluctuations, dark areas, are turbulent eddies.

Robinson found that vortices could first be indicated by a vortical core with a low pressure. Vortices oriented in the spanwise direction predominate the log region. Nearest the wall the streamwise vortex predominates, whereas a mixture is found at intermediate heights from the wall. Sometimes vortices form an arch with legs near the wall, a neck

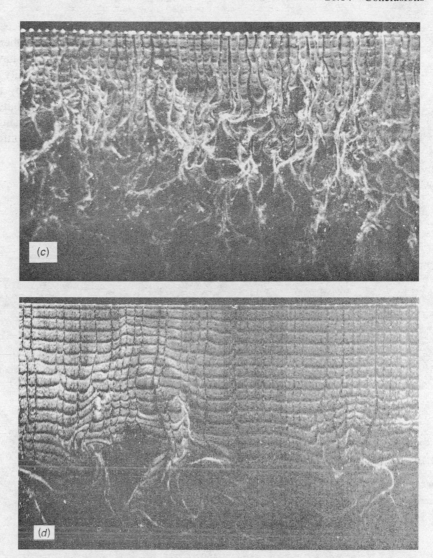

Figure 26.17   (*continued*)

rising away from the wall, and a head with the vortex axis transverse to the wall. A thin structure like this could be called a *hairpin vortex*. The most intense Reynolds-stress-producing events are associated with these vortices. Modification of wall events can lead to a drag reduction [see, for example, Bechart et al. (1997)].

26.14   CONCLUSIONS

Turbulence is a unique phenomenon in the behavior of fields. It is characterized by irregular fluctuations that are self-sustaining. Vorticity exists in the flow before turbulence develops, and a mean vorticity is necessary to sustain it. On the other hand, the large turbulent motions appear to grow by inertia and pressure effects without regard for the viscosity of the fluid. Viscous forces play a subordinate role where they limit the size of the smallest eddies. Two flows at different Reynolds numbers have the same large-scale features, but the range of eddy sizes is larger when the viscosity is lower.

The velocity profiles in free turbulence are determined by the large-scale inviscid eddies (and the initial conditions). On the other hand, wall turbulence always consists of two regions that overlap. The relative size of the regions changes with the Reynolds number, and composite expansions must be used to obtain uniformly valid profiles of the mean velocity and Reynolds stress.

A

Properties of Fluids

	Temperature	Pressure	Density	Kinematic viscosity
Air	15°C	101.3 kPa	1.225 kg/m^3	14.5 × 10^{-6} m^2/s
	59°F	2116 psf	0.07648 lb$_m$/ft^3	156 × 10^{-6} ft^2/sec
Water	15°C	1497 Pa^a	999.2 kg/m^3	1.138 × 10^{-6} m^2/s
	59°F	31.27 psf	62.38 lb$_m$/ft^3	12.25 × 10^{-6} ft^2/sec

	Temperature (°C)	Specific gravity	Kinematic viscosity (m^2/s)
Ethyl alcohol	15	0.79	1.70 × 10^{-6}
Gasoline	15	0.68–0.74	0.46–0.88 × 10^{-6}
Oil (SAE 30)	15	0.88–0.94	5.0 × 10^{-4}
	99		1.0 × 10^{-4}
Glycerine 100%	20	1.26	6.5 × 10^{-4}
50% H$_2$O	20	1.13	5.3 × 10^{-4}
Mercury	15	13.6	12 × 10^{-4}

Conversion Factors and Constants

Standard gravity acceleration: 9.807 m/s^2
32.17 ft/sec^2

Length: 1 m = 3.281 ft
Mass: 1 kg = 2.205 lb$_m$

^{a} Vapor.

Differential Operations in Cylindrical and Spherical Coordinates

Table B.1 Differential Operations in Cylindrical Coordinates (r, θ, z)

$$\nabla \cdot \mathbf{v} = \frac{1}{r}\frac{\partial}{\partial r}(rv_r) + \frac{1}{r}\frac{\partial v_\theta}{\partial \theta} + \frac{\partial v_z}{\partial z}$$

$$\nabla^2 s = \frac{1}{r}\frac{\partial}{\partial r}\left(r\frac{\partial s}{\partial r}\right) + \frac{1}{r^2}\frac{\partial^2 s}{\partial \theta^2} + \frac{\partial^2 s}{\partial z^2}$$

$$\boldsymbol{\tau}:\nabla\mathbf{v} = \tau_{rr}\left(\frac{\partial v_r}{\partial r}\right) + \tau_{r\theta}\left(\frac{1}{r}\frac{\partial v_r}{\partial \theta} - \frac{v_\theta}{r}\right) + \tau_{rz}\left(\frac{\partial v_r}{\partial z}\right) + \tau_{\theta r}\left(\frac{\partial v_\theta}{\partial r}\right) + \tau_{\theta\theta}\left(\frac{1}{r}\frac{\partial v_\theta}{\partial \theta} + \frac{v_r}{r}\right)$$

$$+ \tau_{\theta z}\left(\frac{\partial v_\theta}{\partial z}\right) + \tau_{zr}\left(\frac{\partial v_z}{\partial r}\right) + \tau_{z\theta}\left(\frac{1}{r}\frac{\partial v_z}{\partial \theta}\right) + \tau_{zz}\left(\frac{\partial v_z}{\partial z}\right)$$

$$[\nabla s]_r = \frac{\partial s}{\partial r}, \qquad [\nabla \times \mathbf{v}]_r = \frac{1}{r}\frac{\partial v_z}{\partial \theta} - \frac{\partial v_\theta}{\partial z}$$
$$\underline{}$$
$$W_r$$

$$[\nabla s]_\theta = \frac{1}{r}\frac{\partial s}{\partial \theta}, \qquad [\nabla \times \mathbf{v}]_\theta = \frac{\partial v_r}{\partial z} - \frac{\partial v_z}{\partial r}$$
$$W_\theta$$

$$[\nabla s]_z = \frac{\partial s}{\partial z}, \qquad [\nabla \times \mathbf{v}]_z = \frac{1}{r}\frac{\partial}{\partial r}(rv_\theta) - \frac{1}{r}\frac{\partial v_r}{\partial \theta}$$
$$W_z$$

$$[\nabla \cdot \boldsymbol{\tau}]_r = \frac{1}{r}\frac{\partial}{\partial r}(r\tau_{rr}) + \frac{1}{r}\frac{\partial}{\partial \theta}\tau_{\theta r} + \frac{\partial}{\partial z}\tau_{zr} - \frac{\tau_{\theta\theta}}{r}$$

$$[\nabla \cdot \boldsymbol{\tau}]_\theta = \frac{1}{r^2}\frac{\partial}{\partial r}(r^2\tau_{r\theta}) + \frac{1}{r}\frac{\partial}{\partial \theta}\tau_{\theta\theta} + \frac{\partial}{\partial z}\tau_{z\theta} + \frac{\tau_{\theta r} - \tau_{r\theta}}{r}$$

$$[\nabla \cdot \boldsymbol{\tau}]_z = \frac{1}{r}\frac{\partial}{\partial r}(r\tau_{rz}) + \frac{1}{r}\frac{\partial}{\partial \theta}\tau_{\theta z} + \frac{\partial}{\partial z}\tau_{zz}$$

$$[\nabla^2\mathbf{v}]_r = \frac{\partial}{\partial r}\left[\frac{1}{r}\frac{\partial}{\partial r}(rv_r)\right] + \frac{1}{r^2}\frac{\partial^2 v_r}{\partial \theta^2} + \frac{\partial^2 v_r}{\partial z^2} - \frac{2}{r^2}\frac{\partial v_\theta}{\partial \theta}$$

Table B.1   (*Continued*)

$$[\nabla^2 \mathbf{v}]_\theta = \frac{\partial}{\partial r}\left[\frac{1}{r}\frac{\partial}{\partial r}(rv_\theta)\right] + \frac{1}{r^2}\frac{\partial^2 v_\theta}{\partial \theta^2} + \frac{\partial^2 v_\theta}{\partial z^2} + \frac{2}{r^2}\frac{\partial v_r}{\partial \theta}$$

$$[\nabla^2 \mathbf{v}]_z = \frac{1}{r}\frac{\partial}{\partial r}\left(r\frac{\partial v_z}{\partial r}\right) + \frac{1}{r^2}\frac{\partial^2 v_z}{\partial \theta^2} + \frac{\partial^2 v_z}{\partial z^2}$$

$$[\mathbf{v}\cdot\nabla\mathbf{w}]_r = v_r\left(\frac{\partial w_r}{\partial r}\right) + v_\theta\left(\frac{1}{r}\frac{\partial w_r}{\partial \theta} - \frac{w_\theta}{r}\right) + v_z\left(\frac{\partial w_r}{\partial z}\right)$$

$$[\mathbf{v}\cdot\nabla\mathbf{w}]_\theta = v_r\left(\frac{\partial w_\theta}{\partial r}\right) + v_\theta\left(\frac{1}{r}\frac{\partial w_\theta}{\partial \theta} + \frac{w_r}{r}\right) + v_z\left(\frac{\partial w_\theta}{\partial z}\right)$$

$$[\mathbf{v}\cdot\nabla\mathbf{w}]_z = v_r\left(\frac{\partial w_z}{\partial r}\right) + v_\theta\left(\frac{1}{r}\frac{\partial w_z}{\partial \theta}\right) + v_z\left(\frac{\partial w_z}{\partial z}\right)$$

$$\{\nabla\mathbf{v}\}_{rr} = \frac{\partial v_r}{\partial r}$$

$$\{\nabla\mathbf{v}\}_{r\theta} = \frac{\partial v_\theta}{\partial r}$$

$$\{\nabla\mathbf{v}\}_{rz} = \frac{\partial v_z}{\partial r}$$

$$\{\nabla\mathbf{v}\}_{\theta r} = \frac{1}{r}\frac{\partial v_r}{\partial \theta} - \frac{v_\theta}{r}$$

$$\{\nabla\mathbf{v}\}_{\theta\theta} = \frac{1}{r}\frac{\partial v_\theta}{\partial \theta} + \frac{v_r}{r}$$

$$\{\nabla\mathbf{v}\}_{\theta z} = \frac{1}{r}\frac{\partial v_z}{\partial \theta}$$

$$\{\nabla\mathbf{v}\}_{zr} = \frac{\partial v_r}{\partial z}$$

$$\{\nabla\mathbf{v}\}_{z\theta} = \frac{\partial v_\theta}{\partial z}$$

$$\{\nabla\mathbf{v}\}_{zz} = \frac{\partial v_z}{\partial z}$$

$$\{\mathbf{v}\cdot\nabla\boldsymbol{\tau}\}_{rr} = (\mathbf{v}\cdot\nabla)\tau_{rr} - \frac{v_\theta}{r}(\tau_{r\theta} + \tau_{\theta r})$$

$$\{\mathbf{v}\cdot\nabla\boldsymbol{\tau}\}_{r\theta} = (\mathbf{v}\cdot\nabla)\tau_{r\theta} + \frac{v_\theta}{r}(\tau_{rr} - \tau_{\theta\theta})$$

$$\{\mathbf{v}\cdot\nabla\boldsymbol{\tau}\}_{rz} = (\mathbf{v}\cdot\nabla)\tau_{rz} - \frac{v_\theta}{r}\tau_{\theta z}$$

Table B.1   *(Continued)*

$$\{\mathbf{v} \cdot \nabla \boldsymbol{\tau}\}_{\theta r} = (\mathbf{v} \cdot \nabla)\tau_{\theta r} + \frac{v_\theta}{r}(\tau_{rr} - \tau_{\theta\theta})$$

$$\{\mathbf{v} \cdot \nabla \boldsymbol{\tau}\}_{\theta\theta} = (\mathbf{v} \cdot \nabla)\tau_{\theta\theta} + \frac{v_\theta}{r}(\tau_{r\theta} + \tau_{\theta r})$$

$$\{\mathbf{v} \cdot \nabla \boldsymbol{\tau}\}_{\theta z} = (\mathbf{v} \cdot \nabla)\tau_{\theta z} + \frac{v_\theta}{r}\tau_{rz}$$

$$\{\mathbf{v} \cdot \nabla \boldsymbol{\tau}\}_{zr} = (\mathbf{v} \cdot \nabla)\tau_{zr} - \frac{v_\theta}{r}\tau_{z\theta}$$

$$\{\mathbf{v} \cdot \nabla \boldsymbol{\tau}\}_{z\theta} = (\mathbf{v} \cdot \nabla)\tau_{z\theta} + \frac{v_\theta}{r}\tau_{zr}$$

$$\{\mathbf{v} \cdot \nabla \boldsymbol{\tau}\}_{zz} = (\mathbf{v} \cdot \nabla)\tau_{zz}$$

where the operator $\mathbf{v} \cdot \nabla = v_r \dfrac{\partial}{\partial r} + \dfrac{v_\theta}{r}\dfrac{\partial}{\partial \theta} + v_z \dfrac{\partial}{\partial z}$

Source: Adapted from Bird et al. (1977) by permission of John Wiley & Sons, Inc.

Table B.2   Differential Operations in Spherical Coordinates (r, θ, ϕ)

$$\nabla \cdot \mathbf{v} = \frac{1}{r^2}\frac{\partial}{\partial r}(r^2 v_r) + \frac{1}{r \sin \theta}\frac{\partial}{\partial \theta}(v_\theta \sin \theta) + \frac{1}{r \sin \theta}\frac{\partial v_\phi}{\partial \phi}$$

$$\nabla^2 s = \frac{1}{r^2}\frac{\partial}{\partial r}\left(r^2 \frac{\partial s}{\partial r}\right) + \frac{1}{r^2 \sin \theta}\frac{\partial}{\partial \theta}\left(\sin \theta \frac{\partial s}{\partial \theta}\right) + \frac{1}{r^2 \sin^2 \theta}\frac{\partial^2 s}{\partial \phi^2}$$

$$\boldsymbol{\tau} : \nabla \mathbf{v} = \tau_{rr}\left(\frac{\partial v_r}{\partial r}\right) + \tau_{r\theta}\left(\frac{1}{r}\frac{\partial v_r}{\partial \theta} - \frac{v_\theta}{r}\right) + \tau_{r\phi}\left(\frac{1}{r \sin \theta}\frac{\partial v_r}{\partial \phi} - \frac{v_\phi}{r}\right)$$

$$+ \tau_{\theta r}\left(\frac{\partial v_\theta}{\partial r}\right) + \tau_{\theta\theta}\left(\frac{1}{r}\frac{\partial v_\theta}{\partial \theta} + \frac{v_r}{r}\right) + \tau_{\theta\phi}\left(\frac{1}{r \sin \theta}\frac{\partial v_\theta}{\partial \phi} - \frac{v_\phi}{r}\cot \theta\right)$$

$$+ \tau_{\phi r}\left(\frac{\partial v_\phi}{\partial r}\right) + \tau_{\phi\theta}\left(\frac{1}{r}\frac{\partial v_\phi}{\partial \theta}\right) + \tau_{\phi\phi}\left(\frac{1}{r \sin \theta}\frac{\partial v_\phi}{\partial \phi} + \frac{v_r}{r} + \frac{v_\theta}{r}\cot \theta\right)$$

$$[\nabla s]_r = \frac{\partial s}{\partial r}, \qquad [\nabla \times \mathbf{v}]_r = \frac{1}{r \sin \theta}\frac{\partial}{\partial \theta}(v_\phi \sin \theta) - \frac{1}{r \sin \theta}\frac{\partial v_\theta}{\partial \phi}$$

$$\underset{w_r}{}$$

$$[\nabla s]_\theta = \frac{1}{r}\frac{\partial s}{\partial \theta}, \qquad [\nabla \times \mathbf{v}]_\theta = \frac{1}{r \sin \theta}\frac{\partial v_r}{\partial \phi} - \frac{1}{r}\frac{\partial}{\partial r}(r v_\phi)$$

$$\underset{w_\theta}{}$$

$$[\nabla s]_\phi = \frac{1}{r \sin \theta}\frac{\partial s}{\partial \phi}, \qquad [\nabla \times \mathbf{v}]_\phi = \frac{1}{r}\frac{\partial}{\partial r}(r v_\theta) - \frac{1}{r}\frac{\partial v_r}{\partial \theta}$$

$$\underset{w_\phi}{}$$

$$[\nabla \cdot \boldsymbol{\tau}]_r = \frac{1}{r^2}\frac{\partial}{\partial r}(r^2 \tau_{rr}) + \frac{1}{r \sin \theta}\frac{\partial}{\partial \theta}(\tau_{\theta r}\sin \theta) + \frac{1}{r \sin \theta}\frac{\partial}{\partial \phi}\tau_{\phi r} - \frac{\tau_{\theta\theta} + \tau_{\phi\phi}}{r}$$

Table B.2   (*Continued*)

$$[\nabla \cdot \boldsymbol{\tau}]_\theta = \frac{1}{r^3} \frac{\partial}{\partial r} (r^3 \tau_{r\theta}) + \frac{1}{r \sin \theta} \frac{\partial}{\partial \theta} (\tau_{\theta\theta} \sin \theta) + \frac{1}{r \sin \theta} \frac{\partial}{\partial \phi} \tau_{\phi\theta} + \frac{(\tau_{\theta r} - \tau_{r\theta}) - \tau_{\phi\phi} \cot \theta}{r}$$

$$[\nabla \cdot \boldsymbol{\tau}]_\phi = \frac{1}{r^3} \frac{\partial}{\partial r} (r^3 \tau_{r\phi}) + \frac{1}{r \sin \theta} \frac{\partial}{\partial \theta} (\tau_{\theta\phi} \sin \theta) + \frac{1}{r \sin \theta} \frac{\partial}{\partial \phi} \tau_{\phi\phi} + \frac{(\tau_{\phi r} - \tau_{r\phi}) + \tau_{\phi\theta} \cot \theta}{r}$$

$$[\nabla^2 \mathbf{v}]_r = \frac{\partial}{\partial r} \left(\frac{1}{r^2} \frac{\partial}{\partial r} (r^2 v_r) \right) + \frac{1}{r^2 \sin \theta} \frac{\partial}{\partial \theta} \left(\sin \theta \frac{\partial v_r}{\partial \theta} \right) + \frac{1}{r^2 \sin^2 \theta} \frac{\partial^2 v_r}{\partial \phi^2}$$

$$- \frac{2}{r^2 \sin \theta} \frac{\partial}{\partial \theta} (v_\theta \sin \theta) - \frac{2}{r^2 \sin \theta} \frac{\partial v_\phi}{\partial \phi}$$

$$[\nabla^2 \mathbf{v}]_\theta = \frac{1}{r^2} \frac{\partial}{\partial r} \left(r^2 \frac{\partial v_\theta}{\partial r} \right) + \frac{1}{r^2} \frac{\partial}{\partial \theta} \left(\frac{1}{\sin \theta} \frac{\partial}{\partial \theta} (v_\theta \sin \theta) \right)$$

$$+ \frac{1}{r^2 \sin^2 \theta} \frac{\partial^2 v_\theta}{\partial \phi^2} + \frac{2}{r^2} \frac{\partial v_r}{\partial \theta} - \frac{2 \cot \theta}{r^2 \sin \theta} \frac{\partial v_\phi}{\partial \phi}$$

$$[\nabla^2 \mathbf{v}]_\phi = \frac{1}{r^2} \frac{\partial}{\partial r} \left(r^2 \frac{\partial v_\phi}{\partial r} \right) + \frac{1}{r^2} \frac{\partial}{\partial \theta} \left(\frac{1}{\sin \theta} \frac{\partial}{\partial \theta} (v_\phi \sin \theta) \right)$$

$$+ \frac{1}{r^2 \sin^2 \theta} \frac{\partial^2 v_\phi}{\partial \phi^2} + \frac{2}{r^2 \sin \theta} \frac{\partial v_r}{\partial \phi} + \frac{2 \cot \theta}{r^2 \sin \theta} \frac{\partial v_\theta}{\partial \phi}$$

$$[\mathbf{v} \cdot \nabla \mathbf{w}]_r = v_r \left(\frac{\partial w_r}{\partial r} \right) + v_\theta \left(\frac{1}{r} \frac{\partial w_r}{\partial \theta} - \frac{w_\theta}{r} \right) + v_\phi \left(\frac{1}{r \sin \theta} \frac{\partial w_r}{\partial \phi} - \frac{w_\phi}{r} \right)$$

$$[\mathbf{v} \cdot \nabla \mathbf{w}]_\theta = v_r \left(\frac{\partial w_\theta}{\partial r} \right) + v_\theta \left(\frac{1}{r} \frac{\partial w_\theta}{\partial \theta} + \frac{w_r}{r} \right) + v_\phi \left(\frac{1}{r \sin \theta} \frac{\partial w_\theta}{\partial \phi} - \frac{w_\phi}{r} \cot \theta \right)$$

$$[\mathbf{v} \cdot \nabla \mathbf{w}]_\phi = v_r \left(\frac{\partial w_\phi}{\partial r} \right) + v_\theta \left(\frac{1}{r} \frac{\partial w_\phi}{\partial \theta} \right) + v_\phi \left(\frac{1}{r \sin \theta} \frac{\partial w_\phi}{\partial \phi} + \frac{w_r}{r} + \frac{w_\theta}{r} \cot \theta \right)$$

$$\{\nabla \mathbf{v}\}_{rr} = \frac{\partial v_r}{\partial r}$$

$$\{\nabla \mathbf{v}\}_{r\theta} = \frac{\partial v_\theta}{\partial r}$$

$$\{\nabla \mathbf{v}\}_{r\phi} = \frac{\partial v_\phi}{\partial r}$$

$$\{\nabla \mathbf{v}\}_{\theta r} = \frac{1}{r} \frac{\partial v_r}{\partial \theta} - \frac{v_\theta}{r}$$

$$\{\nabla \mathbf{v}\}_{\theta\theta} = \frac{1}{r} \frac{\partial v_\theta}{\partial \theta} + \frac{v_r}{r}$$

$$\{\nabla\}_{\theta\phi} = \frac{1}{r} \frac{\partial v_\phi}{\partial \theta}$$

Table B.2   (*Continued*)

$$\{\nabla \mathbf{v}\}_{\phi r} = \frac{1}{r \sin \theta} \frac{\partial v_r}{\partial \phi} - \frac{v_\phi}{r}$$

$$\{\nabla \mathbf{v}\}_{\phi \theta} = \frac{1}{r \sin \theta} \frac{\partial v_\theta}{\partial \phi} - \frac{v_\phi}{r} \cot \theta$$

$$\{\nabla \mathbf{v}\}_{\phi \phi} = \frac{1}{r \sin \theta} \frac{\partial v_\phi}{\partial \phi} + \frac{v_r}{r} + \frac{v_\theta}{r} \cot \theta$$

$$\{\mathbf{v} \cdot \nabla \boldsymbol{\tau}\}_{rr} = (\mathbf{v} \cdot \nabla)\tau_{rr} - \frac{v_\theta}{r}(\tau_{r\theta} + \tau_{\theta r}) - \frac{v_\phi}{r}(\tau_{r\phi} + \tau_{\phi r})$$

$$\{\mathbf{v} \cdot \nabla \boldsymbol{\tau}\}_{r\theta} = (\mathbf{v} \cdot \nabla)\tau_{r\theta} + \frac{v_\theta}{r}(\tau_{rr} - \tau_{\theta\theta}) - \frac{v_\phi}{r}(\tau_{\phi\theta} + \tau_{r\phi} \cot \theta)$$

$$\{\mathbf{v} \cdot \nabla \boldsymbol{\tau}\}_{r\phi} = (\mathbf{v} \cdot \nabla)\tau_{r\phi} - \frac{v_\theta}{r}\tau_{\theta\phi} + \frac{v_\phi}{r}[(\tau_{rr} - \tau_{\phi\phi}) + \tau_{r\theta} \cot \theta]$$

$$\{\mathbf{v} \cdot \nabla \boldsymbol{\tau}\}_{\theta r} = (\mathbf{v} \cdot \nabla)\tau_{\theta r} + \frac{v_\theta}{r}(\tau_{rr} - \tau_{\theta\theta}) - \frac{v_\phi}{r}(\tau_{\theta\phi} + \tau_{\phi r} \cot \theta)$$

$$\{\mathbf{v} \cdot \nabla \boldsymbol{\tau}\}_{\theta\theta} = (\mathbf{v} \cdot \nabla)\tau_{\theta\theta} + \frac{v_\theta}{r}(\tau_{r\theta} + \tau_{\theta r}) - \frac{v_\phi}{r}(\tau_{\theta\phi} + \tau_{\phi\theta}) \cot \theta$$

$$\{\mathbf{v} \cdot \nabla \boldsymbol{\tau}\}_{\theta\phi} = (\mathbf{v} \cdot \nabla)\tau_{\theta\phi} + \frac{v_\theta}{r}\tau_{r\phi} + \frac{v_\phi}{r}[\tau_{\theta r} + (\tau_{\theta\theta} - \tau_{\phi\phi}) \cot \theta]$$

$$\{\mathbf{v} \cdot \nabla \boldsymbol{\tau}\}_{\phi r} = (\mathbf{v} \cdot \nabla)\tau_{\phi r} - \frac{v_\theta}{r}\tau_{\phi\theta} + \frac{v_\phi}{r}[(\tau_{rr} - \tau_{\phi\phi}) + \tau_{\theta r} \cot \theta]$$

$$\{\mathbf{v} \cdot \nabla \boldsymbol{\tau}\}_{\phi\theta} = (\mathbf{v} \cdot \nabla)\tau_{\phi\theta} + \frac{v_\theta}{r}\tau_{\phi r} + \frac{v_\phi}{r}[\tau_{r\theta} + (\tau_{\theta\theta} - \tau_{\phi\phi}) \cot \theta]$$

$$\{\mathbf{v} \cdot \nabla \boldsymbol{\tau}\}_{\phi\phi} = (\mathbf{v} \cdot \nabla)\tau_{\phi\phi} + \frac{v_\theta}{r}(\tau_{r\phi} + \tau_{\phi r}) + \frac{v_\phi}{r}(\tau_{\theta\phi} + \tau_{\phi\theta}) \cot \theta$$

where the operator $\mathbf{v} \cdot \nabla = v_r \dfrac{\partial}{\partial r} + \dfrac{v_\theta}{r} \dfrac{\partial}{\partial \theta} + \dfrac{v_\phi}{r \sin \theta} \dfrac{\partial}{\partial \phi}$

Source: Adapted from Bird et al. (1977) by permission of John Wiley & Sons, Inc.

C

Basic Equations in Rectangular, Cylindrical, and Spherical Coordinates

Table C.1 Equation of Continuity

Rectangular coordinates (x, y, z):

$$\frac{\partial \rho}{\partial t} + \frac{\partial}{\partial x}(\rho v_x) + \frac{\partial}{\partial y}(\rho v_y) + \frac{\partial}{\partial z}(\rho v_z) = 0$$

Cylindrical coordinates (r, θ, z):

$$\frac{\partial \rho}{\partial t} + \frac{1}{r}\frac{\partial}{\partial r}(\rho r v_r) + \frac{1}{r}\frac{\partial}{\partial \theta}(\rho v_\theta) + \frac{\partial}{\partial z}(\rho v_z) = 0$$

Spherical coordinates (r, θ, ϕ):

$$\frac{\partial \rho}{\partial t} + \frac{1}{r^2}\frac{\partial}{\partial r}(\rho r^2 v_r) + \frac{1}{r \sin \theta}\frac{\partial}{\partial \theta}(\rho v_\theta \sin \theta) + \frac{1}{r \sin \theta}\frac{\partial}{\partial \phi}(\rho v_\varphi) = 0$$

Source: Adapted from Bird et al. (1960) by permission of John Wiley & Sons, Inc.

Table C.2   Components of the Rate-of-Strain Tensor $S_{ij} = \partial_{(i} v_{j)} = \frac{1}{2}\, \partial_i v_j + \frac{1}{2}\, \partial_j v_i$

Rectangular coordinates (x, y, z):

$$S_{xx} = \frac{\partial v_x}{\partial x} \qquad\qquad S_{yx} = S_{xy} = \frac{1}{2}\left(\frac{\partial v_y}{\partial x} + \frac{\partial v_x}{\partial y}\right)$$

$$S_{yy} = \frac{\partial v_y}{\partial y} \qquad\qquad S_{zy} = S_{yz} = \frac{1}{2}\left(\frac{\partial v_z}{\partial y} + \frac{\partial v_y}{\partial z}\right)$$

$$S_{zz} = \frac{\partial v_z}{\partial z} \qquad\qquad S_{xz} = S_{zx} = \frac{1}{2}\left(\frac{\partial v_x}{\partial z} + \frac{\partial v_z}{\partial x}\right)$$

Cylindrical coordinates (r, θ, z):

$$S_{rr} = \frac{\partial v_r}{\partial r} \qquad\qquad S_{\theta r} = S_{r\theta} = \frac{1}{2}\left[r\frac{\partial}{\partial r}\left(\frac{v_\theta}{r}\right) + \frac{1}{r}\frac{\partial v_r}{\partial \theta}\right]$$

$$S_{\theta\theta} = \frac{1}{r}\frac{\partial v_\theta}{\partial \theta} + \frac{v_r}{r} \qquad\qquad S_{z\theta} = S_{\theta z} = \frac{1}{2}\left(\frac{1}{r}\frac{\partial v_z}{\partial \theta} + \frac{\partial v_\theta}{\partial z}\right)$$

$$S_{zz} = \frac{\partial v_z}{\partial z} \qquad\qquad S_{rz} = S_{zr} = \frac{1}{2}\left(\frac{\partial v_r}{\partial z} + \frac{\partial v_z}{\partial r}\right)$$

Spherical coordinates (r, θ, ϕ):

$$S_{rr} = \frac{\partial v_r}{\partial r} \qquad\qquad S_{\theta r} = S_{r\theta} = \frac{1}{2}\left[r\frac{\partial}{\partial r}\left(\frac{v_\theta}{r}\right) + \frac{1}{r}\frac{\partial v_r}{\partial \theta}\right]$$

$$S_{\theta\theta} = \frac{1}{r}\frac{\partial v_\theta}{\partial \theta} + \frac{v_r}{r} \qquad\qquad S_{\phi\theta} = S_{\theta\phi} = \frac{1}{2}\left[\frac{\sin\theta}{r}\frac{\partial}{\partial \theta}\left(\frac{v_\phi}{\sin\theta}\right) + \frac{1}{r\sin\theta}\frac{\partial v_\theta}{\partial \phi}\right]$$

$$S_{\phi\phi} = \frac{1}{r\sin\theta}\frac{\partial v_\phi}{\partial \phi} + \frac{v_r}{r} + \frac{v_\theta \cot\theta}{r} \qquad S_{r\phi} = S_{\phi r} = \frac{1}{2}\left[\frac{1}{r\sin\theta}\frac{\partial v_r}{\partial \phi} + r\frac{\partial}{\partial r}\left(\frac{v_\phi}{r}\right)\right]$$

Source: Adapted from Bird et al. (1977) by permission of John Wiley & Sons, Inc.

Table C.3 Components of the Stress Tensor for Newtonian Fluids

Rectangular coordinates (x, y, z)

$$\tau_{xx} = \mu\left[2\frac{\partial v_x}{\partial x} - \frac{2}{3}(\nabla\cdot\mathbf{v})\right]$$

$$\tau_{yy} = \mu\left[2\frac{\partial v_y}{\partial y} - \frac{2}{3}(\nabla\cdot\mathbf{v})\right]$$

$$\tau_{zz} = \mu\left[2\frac{\partial v_z}{\partial z} - \frac{2}{3}(\nabla\cdot\mathbf{v})\right]$$

$$\tau_{xy} = \tau_{yx} = \mu\left(\frac{\partial v_x}{\partial y} + \frac{\partial v_y}{\partial x}\right)$$

$$\tau_{yz} = \tau_{zy} = \mu\left(\frac{\partial v_y}{\partial z} + \frac{\partial v_z}{\partial y}\right)$$

$$\tau_{zx} = \tau_{xz} = \mu\left(\frac{\partial v_z}{\partial x} + \frac{\partial v_x}{\partial z}\right)$$

$$\nabla\cdot\mathbf{v} = \frac{\partial v_x}{\partial x} + \frac{\partial v_y}{\partial y} + \frac{\partial v_z}{\partial z}$$

Cylindrical coordinates (r, θ, z)

$$\tau_{rr} = \mu\left[2\frac{\partial v_r}{\partial r} - \frac{2}{3}(\nabla\cdot\mathbf{v})\right]$$

$$\tau_{\theta\theta} = \mu\left[2\left(\frac{1}{r}\frac{\partial v_\theta}{\partial\theta} + \frac{v_r}{r}\right) - \frac{2}{3}(\nabla\cdot\mathbf{v})\right]$$

$$\tau_{zz} = \mu\left[2\frac{\partial v_z}{\partial z} - \frac{2}{3}(\nabla\cdot\mathbf{v})\right]$$

$$\tau_{r\theta} = \tau_{\theta r} = \mu\left[r\frac{\partial}{\partial r}\left(\frac{v_\theta}{r}\right) + \frac{1}{r}\frac{\partial v_r}{\partial\theta}\right]$$

$$\tau_{\theta z} = \tau_{z\theta} = \mu\left(\frac{\partial v_\theta}{\partial z} + \frac{1}{r}\frac{\partial v_z}{\partial\theta}\right)$$

$$\tau_{zr} = \tau_{rz} = \mu\left(\frac{\partial v_z}{\partial r} + \frac{\partial v_r}{\partial z}\right)$$

$$\nabla\cdot\mathbf{v} = \frac{1}{r}\frac{\partial}{\partial r}(rv_r) + \frac{1}{r}\frac{\partial v_\theta}{\partial\theta} + \frac{\partial v_z}{\partial z}$$

Spherical coordinates (r, θ, ϕ)

$$\tau_{rr} = \mu\left[2\frac{\partial v_r}{\partial r} - \frac{2}{3}(\nabla\cdot\mathbf{v})\right]$$

$$\tau_{\theta\theta} = \mu\left[2\left(\frac{1}{r}\frac{\partial v_\theta}{\partial\theta} + \frac{v_r}{r}\right) - \frac{2}{3}(\nabla\cdot\mathbf{v})\right]$$

$$\tau_{\phi\phi} = \mu\left[2\left(\frac{1}{r\sin\theta}\frac{\partial v_\phi}{\partial\phi} + \frac{v_r}{r} + \frac{v_\theta\cot\theta}{r}\right) - \frac{2}{3}(\nabla\cdot\mathbf{v})\right]$$

$$\tau_{r\theta} = \tau_{\theta r} = \mu\left[r\frac{\partial}{\partial r}\left(\frac{v_\theta}{r}\right) + \frac{1}{r}\frac{\partial v_r}{\partial\theta}\right]$$

$$\tau_{\theta\phi} = \tau_{\phi\theta} = \mu\left[\frac{\sin\theta}{r}\frac{\partial}{\partial\theta}\left(\frac{v_\phi}{\sin\theta}\right) + \frac{1}{r\sin\theta}\frac{\partial v_\theta}{\partial\phi}\right]$$

$$\tau_{\phi r} = \tau_{r\phi} = \mu\left[\frac{1}{r\sin\theta}\frac{\partial v_r}{\partial\phi} + r\frac{\partial}{\partial r}\left(\frac{v_\phi}{r}\right)\right]$$

$$\nabla\cdot\mathbf{v} = \frac{1}{r^2}\frac{\partial}{\partial r}(r^2 v_r) + \frac{1}{r\sin\theta}\frac{\partial}{\partial\theta}(v_\theta\sin\theta) + \frac{1}{r\sin\theta}\frac{\partial v_\phi}{\partial\phi}$$

Table C.4 Momentum Equations in Terms of τ^a

Rectangular coordinates (x, y, z):

$$\rho\left(\frac{\partial v_x}{\partial t} + v_x \frac{\partial v_x}{\partial x} + v_y \frac{\partial v_x}{\partial y} + v_z \frac{\partial v_x}{\partial z}\right) = \left(\frac{\partial}{\partial x}\tau_{xx} + \frac{\partial}{\partial y}\tau_{yx} + \frac{\partial}{\partial z}\tau_{zx}\right) - \frac{\partial p}{\partial x} + \rho g_x$$

$$\rho\left(\frac{\partial v_y}{\partial t} + v_x \frac{\partial v_y}{\partial x} + v_y \frac{\partial v_y}{\partial y} + v_z \frac{\partial v_y}{\partial z}\right) = \left(\frac{\partial}{\partial x}\tau_{xy} + \frac{\partial}{\partial y}\tau_{yy} + \frac{\partial}{\partial z}\tau_{zy}\right) - \frac{\partial p}{\partial y} + \rho g_y$$

$$\rho\left(\frac{\partial v_z}{\partial t} + v_x \frac{\partial v_z}{\partial x} + v_y \frac{\partial v_z}{\partial y} + v_z \frac{\partial v_z}{\partial z}\right) = \left(\frac{\partial}{\partial x}\tau_{xz} + \frac{\partial}{\partial y}\tau_{yz} + \frac{\partial}{\partial z}\tau_{zz}\right) - \frac{\partial p}{\partial z} + \rho g_z$$

Cylindrical coordinates (r, θ, z):

$$\rho\left(\frac{\partial v_r}{\partial t} + v_r \frac{\partial v_r}{\partial r} + \frac{v_\theta}{r}\frac{\partial v_r}{\partial \theta} - \frac{v_\theta^2}{r} + v_z\frac{\partial v_r}{\partial z}\right) = \left[\frac{1}{r}\frac{\partial}{\partial r}(r\tau_{rr}) + \frac{1}{r}\frac{\partial}{\partial \theta}\tau_{\theta r} + \frac{\partial}{\partial z}\tau_{zr} - \frac{\tau_{\theta\theta}}{r}\right] - \frac{\partial p}{\partial r} + \rho g_r$$

$$\rho\left(\frac{\partial v_\theta}{\partial t} + v_r \frac{\partial v_\theta}{\partial r} + \frac{v_\theta}{r}\frac{\partial v_\theta}{\partial \theta} + \frac{v_r v_\theta}{r} + v_z\frac{\partial v_\theta}{\partial z}\right) = \left[\frac{1}{r^2}\frac{\partial}{\partial r}(r^2\tau_{r\theta}) + \frac{1}{r}\frac{\partial}{\partial \theta}\tau_{\theta\theta} + \frac{\partial}{\partial z}\tau_{z\theta} + \frac{\tau_{\theta r}-\tau_{r\theta}}{r}\right] - \frac{1}{r}\frac{\partial p}{\partial \theta} + \rho g_\theta$$

$$\rho\left(\frac{\partial v_z}{\partial t} + v_r \frac{\partial v_z}{\partial r} + \frac{v_\theta}{r}\frac{\partial v_z}{\partial \theta} + v_z\frac{\partial v_z}{\partial z}\right) = \left[\frac{1}{r}\frac{\partial}{\partial r}(r\tau_{rz}) + \frac{1}{r}\frac{\partial}{\partial \theta}\tau_{\theta z} + \frac{\partial}{\partial z}\tau_{zz}\right] - \frac{\partial p}{\partial z} + \rho g_z$$

Spherical coordinates (r, θ, φ):

$$\rho\left(\frac{\partial v_r}{\partial t} + v_r \frac{\partial v_r}{\partial r} + \frac{v_\theta}{r}\frac{\partial v_r}{\partial \theta} + \frac{v_\phi}{r\sin\theta}\frac{\partial v_r}{\partial \phi} - \frac{v_\theta^2 + v_\phi^2}{r}\right) = \left[\frac{1}{r^2}\frac{\partial}{\partial r}(r^2\tau_{rr}) + \frac{1}{r\sin\theta}\frac{\partial}{\partial \theta}(\tau_{\theta r}\sin\theta) + \frac{1}{r\sin\theta}\frac{\partial}{\partial \phi}\tau_{\phi r} - \frac{\tau_{\theta\theta}+\tau_{\phi\phi}}{r}\right] - \frac{\partial p}{\partial r} + \rho g_r$$

$$\rho\left(\frac{\partial v_\theta}{\partial t} + v_r \frac{\partial v_\theta}{\partial r} + \frac{v_\theta}{r}\frac{\partial v_\theta}{\partial \theta} + \frac{v_\phi}{r\sin\theta}\frac{\partial v_\theta}{\partial \phi} + \frac{v_r v_\theta}{r} - \frac{v_\phi^2\cot\theta}{r}\right) = \left[\frac{1}{r^3}\frac{\partial}{\partial r}(r^3\tau_{r\theta}) + \frac{1}{r\sin\theta}\frac{\partial}{\partial \theta}(\tau_{\theta\theta}\sin\theta) + \frac{1}{r\sin\theta}\frac{\partial}{\partial \phi}\tau_{\phi\theta} + \frac{(\tau_{\theta r}-\tau_{r\theta}) - \tau_{\phi\phi}\cot\theta}{r}\right] - \frac{1}{r}\frac{\partial p}{\partial \theta} + \rho g_\theta$$

$$\rho\left(\frac{\partial v_\phi}{\partial t} + v_r \frac{\partial v_\phi}{\partial r} + \frac{v_\theta}{r}\frac{\partial v_\phi}{\partial \theta} + \frac{v_\phi}{r\sin\theta}\frac{\partial v_\phi}{\partial \phi} + \frac{v_\phi v_r}{r} + \frac{v_\theta v_\phi}{r}\cot\theta\right) = \left[\frac{1}{r^3}\frac{\partial}{\partial r}(r^3\tau_{r\phi}) + \frac{1}{r\sin\theta}\frac{\partial}{\partial \theta}(\tau_{\theta\phi}\sin\theta) + \frac{1}{r\sin\theta}\frac{\partial}{\partial \phi}\tau_{\phi\phi} + \frac{(\tau_{\phi r}-\tau_{r\phi}) - \tau_{\phi\theta}\cot\theta}{r}\right] - \frac{1}{r\sin\theta}\frac{\partial p}{\partial \phi} + \rho g_\phi$$

Table C.5 Momentum Equations for a Newtonian Fluid with Constant Density (ρ) and Constant Viscosity (μ)

Rectangular coordinates (x, y, z):

$$\rho\left(\frac{\partial v_x}{\partial t} + v_x\frac{\partial v_x}{\partial x} + v_y\frac{\partial v_x}{\partial y} + v_z\frac{\partial v_x}{\partial z}\right) = \mu\left(\frac{\partial^2 v_x}{\partial x^2} + \frac{\partial^2 v_x}{\partial y^2} + \frac{\partial^2 v_x}{\partial z^2}\right) - \frac{\partial p}{\partial x} + \rho g_x$$

$$\rho\left(\frac{\partial v_y}{\partial t} + v_x\frac{\partial v_y}{\partial x} + v_y\frac{\partial v_y}{\partial y} + v_z\frac{\partial v_y}{\partial z}\right) = \mu\left(\frac{\partial^2 v_y}{\partial x^2} + \frac{\partial^2 v_y}{\partial y^2} + \frac{\partial^2 v_y}{\partial z^2}\right) - \frac{\partial p}{\partial y} + \rho g_y$$

$$\rho\left(\frac{\partial v_z}{\partial t} + v_x\frac{\partial v_z}{\partial x} + v_y\frac{\partial v_z}{\partial y} + v_z\frac{\partial v_z}{\partial z}\right) = \mu\left(\frac{\partial^2 v_z}{\partial x^2} + \frac{\partial^2 v_z}{\partial y^2} + \frac{\partial^2 v_z}{\partial z^2}\right) - \frac{\partial p}{\partial z} + \rho g_z$$

Cylindrical coordinates (r, θ, z):

$$\rho\left(\frac{\partial v_r}{\partial t} + v_r\frac{\partial v_r}{\partial r} + \frac{v_\theta}{r}\frac{\partial v_r}{\partial \theta} - \frac{v_\theta^2}{r} + v_z\frac{\partial v_r}{\partial z}\right) = \mu\left[\frac{\partial}{\partial r}\left(\frac{1}{r}\frac{\partial}{\partial r}(rv_r)\right) + \frac{1}{r^2}\frac{\partial^2 v_r}{\partial \theta^2} + \frac{\partial^2 v_r}{\partial z^2} - \frac{2}{r^2}\frac{\partial v_\theta}{\partial \theta}\right] - \frac{\partial p}{\partial r} + \rho g_r$$

$$\rho\left(\frac{\partial v_\theta}{\partial t} + v_r\frac{\partial v_\theta}{\partial r} + \frac{v_\theta}{r}\frac{\partial v_\theta}{\partial \theta} + \frac{v_r v_\theta}{r} + v_z\frac{\partial v_\theta}{\partial z}\right) = \mu\left[\frac{\partial}{\partial r}\left(\frac{1}{r}\frac{\partial}{\partial r}(rv_\theta)\right) + \frac{1}{r^2}\frac{\partial^2 v_\theta}{\partial \theta^2} + \frac{\partial^2 v_\theta}{\partial z^2} + \frac{2}{r^2}\frac{\partial v_r}{\partial \theta}\right] - \frac{1}{r}\frac{\partial p}{\partial \theta} + \rho g_\theta$$

$$\rho\left(\frac{\partial v_z}{\partial t} + v_r\frac{\partial v_z}{\partial r} + \frac{v_\theta}{r}\frac{\partial v_z}{\partial \theta} + v_z\frac{\partial v_z}{\partial z}\right) = \mu\left[\frac{1}{r}\frac{\partial}{\partial r}\left(r\frac{\partial v_z}{\partial r}\right) + \frac{1}{r^2}\frac{\partial^2 v_z}{\partial \theta^2} + \frac{\partial^2 v_z}{\partial z^2}\right] - \frac{\partial p}{\partial z} + \rho g_z$$

Spherical coordinates (r, θ, ϕ):

$$\rho\left(\frac{\partial v_r}{\partial t} + v_r\frac{\partial v_r}{\partial r} + \frac{v_\theta}{r}\frac{\partial v_r}{\partial \theta} + \frac{v_\phi}{r\sin\theta}\frac{\partial v_r}{\partial \phi} - \frac{v_\theta^2 + v_\phi^2}{r}\right)$$
$$= \mu\left[\frac{\partial}{\partial r}\left(\frac{1}{r^2}\frac{\partial}{\partial r}(r^2 v_r)\right) + \frac{1}{r^2\sin\theta}\frac{\partial}{\partial \theta}\left(\sin\theta\frac{\partial v_r}{\partial \theta}\right) + \frac{1}{r^2\sin^2\theta}\frac{\partial^2 v_r}{\partial \phi^2}\right] - \frac{\partial p}{\partial r} + \rho g_r$$

$$\rho\left(\frac{\partial v_\theta}{\partial t} + v_r\frac{\partial v_\theta}{\partial r} + \frac{v_\theta}{r}\frac{\partial v_\theta}{\partial \theta} + \frac{v_\phi}{r\sin\theta}\frac{\partial v_\theta}{\partial \phi} + \frac{v_r v_\theta}{r} - \frac{v_\phi^2\cot\theta}{r}\right)$$
$$= \mu\left[\frac{1}{r^2}\frac{\partial}{\partial r}\left(r^2\frac{\partial v_\theta}{\partial r}\right) + \frac{1}{r^2}\frac{\partial}{\partial \theta}\left(\frac{1}{\sin\theta}\frac{\partial}{\partial \theta}(v_\theta\sin\theta)\right) + \frac{1}{r^2\sin^2\theta}\frac{\partial^2 v_\theta}{\partial \phi^2} + \frac{2}{r^2}\frac{\partial v_r}{\partial \theta} - \frac{2\cot\theta}{r^2\sin\theta}\frac{\partial v_\phi}{\partial \phi}\right] - \frac{1}{r}\frac{\partial p}{\partial \theta} + \rho g_\theta$$

$$\rho\left(\frac{\partial v_\phi}{\partial t} + v_r\frac{\partial v_\phi}{\partial r} + \frac{v_\theta}{r}\frac{\partial v_\phi}{\partial \theta} + \frac{v_\phi}{r\sin\theta}\frac{\partial v_\phi}{\partial \phi} + \frac{v_\phi v_r}{r} + \frac{v_\theta v_\phi\cot\theta}{r}\right)$$
$$= \mu\left[\frac{1}{r^2}\frac{\partial}{\partial r}\left(r^2\frac{\partial v_\phi}{\partial r}\right) + \frac{1}{r^2}\frac{\partial}{\partial \theta}\left(\frac{1}{\sin\theta}\frac{\partial}{\partial \theta}(v_\phi\sin\theta)\right) + \frac{1}{r^2\sin^2\theta}\frac{\partial^2 v_\phi}{\partial \phi^2} + \frac{2}{r^2\sin\theta}\frac{\partial v_r}{\partial \phi} + \frac{2\cot\theta}{r^2\sin\theta}\frac{\partial v_\theta}{\partial \phi}\right] - \frac{1}{r\sin\theta}\frac{\partial p}{\partial \phi} + \rho g_\phi$$

D

Streamfunction Relations in Rectangular, Cylindrical, and Spherical Coordinates

Table D.1 Streamfunction for Plane Two-Dimensional Flow: Rectangular Coordinates

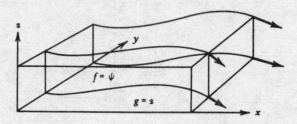

Coordinates: x, y, z

Metric coefficients: $h_x = 1, \quad h_y = 1, \quad h_z = 1$

Velocities: $u(x, y), \quad v(x, y), \quad w = 0$

Streamsurfaces: $f = \psi(x, y), \quad g = z, \quad \nabla g = (0, 0, 1)$

Vector potential: $B_x = 0, \quad B_y = 0, \quad B_z = \psi$

$\mathbf{v} = \nabla f \times \nabla g = \nabla \times \mathbf{B}$: $u = \dfrac{\partial \psi}{\partial y}, \quad v = -\dfrac{\partial \psi}{\partial x}$

$-\boldsymbol{\omega} = \nabla^2 \mathbf{B} = -\nabla \times \nabla \times \mathbf{B}$ $-\omega_z = \dfrac{\partial^2 \psi}{\partial x^2} + \dfrac{\partial^2 \psi}{\partial y^2} = \nabla^2 \psi$

$\quad = \mathbf{i}_z E^2 \psi$: $E^2 \psi = \nabla^2 \psi = \dfrac{\partial^2 \psi}{\partial x^2} + \dfrac{\partial^2 \psi}{\partial y^2}$

Vorticity equation: $\dfrac{\partial \omega_z}{\partial t} + \dfrac{\partial \psi}{\partial y}\dfrac{\partial \omega_z}{\partial x} - \dfrac{\partial \psi}{\partial x}\dfrac{\partial \omega_z}{\partial y} = \nu \nabla^2 \omega_z$

where $-\nabla^2 \omega_z = \psi_{xxxx} + 2\psi_{xxyy} + \psi_{yyyy}$

Flow rate: $Q = (f_2 - f_1)(g_2 - g_1)$
$$g_1 = z_1 = 0, \quad g_2 = z_2 = 1$$
$$Q = \psi_2 - \psi_1$$

Table D.2   Streamfunction for Plane Two-Dimensional Flow: Cylindrical Coordinates

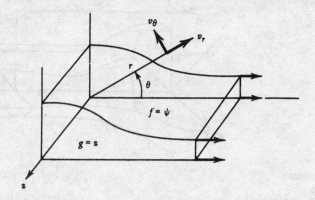

Coordinates:	r, θ, z

Metric coefficients: $h_r = 1, \qquad h_\theta = 1/r, \qquad h_z = 1$

Velocities: $v_r(r, \theta), \qquad v_\theta(r, \theta), \qquad v_z = 0$

Streamsurfaces: $f = \psi(r, \theta), \qquad g = z, \qquad \nabla g = (0, 0, 1)$

Vector potential: $B_r = 0, \qquad B_\theta = 0, \qquad B_z = \psi$

$\mathbf{v} = \nabla f \times \nabla g = \nabla \times \mathbf{B}$:

$$v_r = \frac{1}{r}\frac{\partial \psi}{\partial \theta}, \qquad v_\theta = -\frac{\partial \psi}{\partial x}$$

$-\omega = \nabla^2 \mathbf{B} = -\nabla \times \nabla \times \mathbf{B}$

$$-\omega_z = \frac{\partial^2 \psi}{\partial r^2} + \frac{1}{r}\frac{\partial \psi}{\partial r} + \frac{1}{r^2}\frac{\partial^2 \psi}{\partial \theta^2}$$

$$-\frac{1}{r}\frac{\partial}{\partial r}\left(r\frac{\partial \psi}{\partial r}\right) + \frac{1}{r^2}\frac{\partial^2 \psi}{\partial \theta^2}$$

$= \mathbf{i}_z E^2 \psi$:

$$E^2 \psi = \nabla^2 \psi = \frac{1}{r}\frac{\partial}{\partial r}\left(r\frac{\partial \psi}{\partial r}\right) + \frac{1}{r^2}\frac{\partial^2 \psi}{\partial \theta^2}$$

Vorticity equation:

$$\frac{\partial \omega_z}{\partial t} + v_r\frac{\partial \omega_z}{\partial r} + v_\theta\frac{1}{r}\frac{\partial \omega_z}{\partial \theta} = \nu\frac{1}{r}\frac{\partial}{\partial r}\left(r\frac{\partial \omega_z}{\partial r}\right) + \nu\frac{1}{r^2}\frac{\partial^2 \omega_z}{\partial \theta^2}$$

Flow rate:

$$Q = (f_2 - f_1)(g_2 \quad g_1)$$
$$g_1 = z_1 = 0, \qquad g_2 = z_2 = 1$$
$$Q = \psi_2 - \psi_1$$

Table D.3   Streamfunction for Axisymmetric Flow. Cylindrical Coordinates

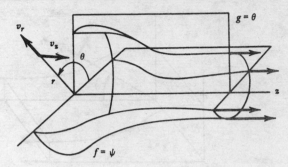

Coordinates:	z, r, θ
Metric coefficients:	$h_z = 1, \qquad h_r = 1, \qquad h_\theta = 1/r$
Velocities:	$v_z(z, r), \qquad v_r(z, r), \qquad v_\theta = 0$
Streamsurfaces:	$f = \psi(z, r), \qquad g = \theta, \qquad \nabla g = (0, 0, r^{-1})$
Vector potential:	$B_z = 0, \qquad B_r = 0, \qquad B_\theta = \dfrac{\psi}{r}$
$\mathbf{v} = \nabla f \times \nabla g = \nabla \times \mathbf{B}$:	$v_z = \dfrac{1}{r}\dfrac{\partial \psi}{\partial r}, \qquad v_r = -\dfrac{1}{r}\dfrac{\partial \psi}{\partial z}$
$-\boldsymbol{\omega} = \nabla^2 \mathbf{B} = -\nabla \times \nabla \times \mathbf{B}$	$-\omega_\theta = \dfrac{\partial}{\partial r}\left(\dfrac{1}{r}\dfrac{\partial \psi}{\partial r}\right) + \dfrac{\partial^2}{\partial z^2}\left(\dfrac{\psi}{r}\right)$
$= \mathbf{i}_\theta h_\theta \mathrm{E}^2 \psi$:	$\mathrm{E}^2 \psi = \dfrac{\partial^2 \psi}{\partial z^2} + r\dfrac{\partial}{\partial r}\left(\dfrac{1}{r}\dfrac{\partial \psi}{\partial r}\right)$
Vorticity equation:	$\dfrac{\partial \omega_\theta}{\partial t} + v_r \dfrac{\partial \omega_\theta}{\partial r} + v_z \dfrac{\partial \omega_\theta}{\partial z} = \dfrac{\omega_\theta v_r}{r} + \nu \dfrac{\partial}{\partial r}\left(\dfrac{1}{r}\dfrac{\partial}{\partial r}(r\omega_\theta)\right)$
	$+ \ \nu \dfrac{\partial^2 \omega_\theta}{\partial z^2}$
Flow rate:	$Q = (f_2 - f_1)(g_2 - g_1)$
	$g_1 = \theta_1 = 0, \qquad g_2 = \theta_2 = 2\pi$
	$Q = 2\pi(\psi_2 - \psi_1)$
	$= 2\pi\psi_2 \qquad \text{if} \quad \psi_1 = 0 \text{ is } z\text{-axis}$

Table D.4 Streamfunction for Axisymmetric Flow: Spherical Coordinates

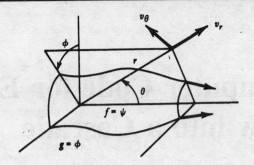

Coordinates: $\qquad\qquad r,\ \theta,\ \phi$

Metric coefficients: $\qquad h_r = 1, \qquad h_\theta = 1/r, \qquad h_\phi = 1/(r\sin\theta)$

Velocities: $\qquad\qquad v(r,\theta), \qquad v_\theta(r,\theta), \qquad v_\phi = 0$

Streamsurfaces: $\qquad f = \psi(r,\theta), \qquad g = \phi, \qquad \nabla g = \left(0,0,\dfrac{1}{r\sin\theta}\right)$

Vector potential: $\qquad B_r = 0, \qquad B_\theta = 0, \qquad B_\phi = \dfrac{\psi}{r\sin\theta}$

$\mathbf{v} = \nabla f \times \nabla g = \nabla \times \mathbf{B}$:
$$v_r = \frac{1}{r^2\sin\theta}\frac{\partial\psi}{\partial\theta}, \qquad v_\theta = \frac{-1}{r\sin\theta}\frac{\partial\psi}{\partial x}$$

$-\boldsymbol{\omega} = \nabla^2\mathbf{B} = \nabla\times\nabla\times\mathbf{B}$
$$-\omega_\phi = \frac{1}{r^2\sin\theta}\frac{\partial}{\partial r}\left[r^2\frac{\partial}{\partial r}\left(\frac{\psi}{r}\right)\right] + \frac{1}{r^3}\frac{\partial}{\partial\theta}\left[\frac{1}{\sin\theta}\frac{\partial\psi}{\partial\theta}\right]$$

$= \mathbf{i}_\phi h_\phi \mathrm{E}^2\psi$
$$\mathrm{E}^2\psi = \frac{\partial^2\psi}{\partial r^2} + \frac{\sin\theta}{r^2}\frac{\partial}{\partial\theta}\left(\frac{1}{\sin\theta}\frac{\partial\psi}{\partial\theta}\right)$$

Vorticity equation:
$$\frac{\partial\omega_\phi}{\partial t} + v_r\frac{\partial\omega_\phi}{\partial r} + \frac{v_\theta}{r}\frac{\partial\omega_\phi}{\partial\theta} = \frac{\omega_\phi}{r}(v_r + v_\theta\cot\theta)$$

$$+ \frac{\nu}{r^2}\frac{\partial}{\partial r}\left(r^2\frac{\partial\omega_\phi}{\partial r}\right) + \frac{\nu}{r^2}\frac{\partial}{\partial\theta}\left[\frac{1}{\sin\theta}\frac{\partial}{\partial\theta}(\sin\theta\omega_\psi)\right]$$

Flow rate:
$$Q = (f_2 - f_1)(g_2 - g_1)$$
$$g_1 - \phi_1 = 0, \qquad g_2 = \phi_2 = 2\pi$$
$$Q = 2\pi(\psi_2 - \psi_1)$$
$$= 2\pi\psi_2 \qquad \text{if} \quad \psi_1 = 0 \text{ on } \theta = 0 \text{ axis}$$

E

Computer Code for Entrance Flow into a Cascade

```
c23456789012345678901234567890
C       Flow in the entrance of a cascade of parallel plates
        IMPLICIT DOUBLE PRECISION(A-H,O-Z)
        DIMENSION U(202,42),V(202,42),VORT(202,42),PSI(202,42)
        DIMENSION VORTN1(202,42),YCORD(42)
        DIMENSIOUM(102),DYVOR(102),AVEDY(102)
        OPEN(6,NAME='ENTRDAT3',TYPE='unknown')
      2 FORMAT(I3,10X,4F15.6)
      1 FORMAT(5(F8.6,1X))
C
C       SET INPUT DATA
C
        II=20
        IO=10
        JJ=10
        AL=4.D0
        RE=1.D0
        EPSI=1.D-4
        EOT1.D-4
C
C       COMPUTE DX , BETA , AND F
C
        AII=DFLOAT(II)
        AJJ=DFLOAT(JJ)
        DX=   AL/AII
        BETA=AL*DFLOAT(JJ)/AII
        BETA2=BETA**2
        PI=DACOS(-1.D0)
        BE2P1=BETA2+1.D0
        DT=.5D0/((1.D0+BETA)/DX+BE2P1*4.D0/RE/DX**2)
        E=(COS(PI/DFLOAT(2*II+1))+BETA2*COS(PI/DFLOAT(JJ)))/BE2P1
        ETA=E**2
        F=2.D0*(1-SQRT(1.D0-ETA))/ETA
C
C       SET INITIAL CONDITIONS AND BOUNDARY VALUES
C
        DO 20 I=1,II+1
        DO 10 J=1,JJ+1
        U(I,J)=1.D0
        V(,J)0.D0
        VORT(I,J)=0.D0
```

```
   10 PSI(I,J)=(DFLOAT(J)-1.D0)/AJJ
   20 CONTINUE
      DO 25 I=IO+1,II+1
      U(I,JJ+1)=0.D0
      V(I,JJ+1)=0.D0
      PSI(I,JJ+1)=1.D0
   25 VORT(I,JJ+1)=3.D0
      DO 27 J=1,JJ+1
      Y=(DFLOAT(J)-1.D)/AJ
      V(II+1,J)=0.D0
      U(II+1,J)=1.5D0*(1.D0-Y**2)
      PSI(II+1,J)=1.5D0*Y-.5D0*Y**3
   27 VORT(II+1,J)=3.D0*Y
C
C      SOLVE FOR VORTICITY AT INTERIOR POINTS
C
   30 ISW2=0
      VORMAX=DABS(VORT(IO+1,JJ+1))
      DO 38 I=2,II
      DO 3 J=2,JJ
      DELSQ=VORT(I+1,J)+VORT(I-1,J)+BETA2*VORT(I,J+1)+BETA2*VORT(I,J-
     11)-2.D0*BE2P1*VORT(I,J)
      IF(U(I,J).GT.0.D0) GO TO 31
      CONU=U(I+1,J)*VORT(I+1,J)-U(I,J)*VORT(I,J)
      GO TO 32
   31 CONU=U(I,J)*VORT(I,J)-(I-1,J*VORT(-1,J)
   32 IF(V(I,J).GT.0.D0) GO TO 35
      CONV=V(I,J+1)*VORT(I,J+1)-V(I,J)*VORT(I,J)
      GO TO 36
   35 CONV=V(I,J)*VORT(I,J)-V(I,J-1)*VORT(I,J-1)
   36 DVORT=DT/DX*(-(CONU+BETA*CONV)+2.D0/RE/DX*DELSQ)
      VORTN1(I,J)=VORT(,J)+DVOT
   37 IF(DABS(DVORT/VORMAX).GT.EVORT) ISW2=1
   38 CONTINUE
C
C      UPDATE VORTICITY MATRIX
C
      DO 40 I=2,II
      DO 39 J=2,JJ
   39 VORT(I,J)=VORTN1(I,J)
   40 CONTINUE
C .
C      SOLVE FOR STREAM FUNCTION
C
   41 SW1=0
      DO 50I=2,II
      DO 49 J=2,JJ
      DSTR=PSI(I+1,J)+PSI(I-1,J)+BETA2*PSI(I,J+1)+BETA2*PSI(I,J-1)-2.D0*
     1BE2P1*PSI(I,J)+VORT(I,J)*DX**2
      PSI(I,J)=PSI(I,J)+F/2.D0/BE2P1*DSTR
   49 IF(DABS(DSTR).GT.EPSI) ISW1=1
   50 CONTINUE
      IF(ISW1GT.0) GO O 41
C
```

```
C         CALCULATE U AND V VELOCITIES AT INTERIOR POINTS
C
      DO 60 I=2,II
      DO 59,J=2,JJ
      U(I,J)=(PSI(I,J+1)-PSI(I,J-1))*BETA/2.D0/DX
   59 V(I,J)=(PSI(I-1,J)-PSI(I+1,J))/2.D0/DX
   60 CONTINUE
C
C         CALCUATE CENTERINE & STAGSTREAMLINE VALUES OF U
C
      DO 75 I=2,II
   75 U(I,1)=PSI(I,2)*BETA/DX
      DO 80 I=2,IO+1
   80 U(I,JJ+1)=(1.D0-PSI(I,JJ))*BETA/DX
C
C         CALCULATE VORT ON THE WALLS
C
     *DO 90 I=IO+2,II
      VORTEMP=VORT(I,JJ+1)
      VORT(I,J+1)=(1.D0-SI(I,JJ))*2*BETA2/DX**2
      DVORT=VORT(I,JJ+1)-VORTEMP
   90 IF(DABS(DVORT/VORMAX).GT.EVORT) ISW2=1
C
C         CRANK-N1COLSON FOR LEADING EDGE VORTICITY
C
      VORT(IO+1,JJ+1)=0.5D0*(VORT(IO+2,JJ+1)+ VORT(IO+2,JJ-1)+
     1VORT(IOJJ-1))-VORT(O+2,JJ)-VORT(IO+1,JJ-1)-
     2VORT(IO,JJ)+2.D0*VORT(IO+1,JJ)
      IF(ISW2.GT.0) GO TO 30
C
C         PRINT OUTPUT
C
      DO 95 I=1,II+1,1
      DO 95 J=1,JJ+1,1
      YCORD(J)=(DFLOAT(J)-1.D0)/AJJ
      WRITE(6,1) YCORD(J),PSI(,J),VORT(I,J)U(I,J),V(I,J)
   95 CONTINUE
      CLOSE(6)
      END
```

F

Computer Code for Boundary Layer Analysis

```
C
C*********** PROGRAM TO SOLVE LAMINAR BOUNDARY LAYER PROBLEMS. *********
C ADAPTED FROM A PROGRAM WRITTEN BY H.A.DWYER,E.D.DOSS,& A.L.GOLDMAN
C               UNIVERSITY OF CALIFORNIA-DAVIS
C
      IMPLICIT DOUBLE PRECISION (A-H,O-Z)
      DIMENSION A(121),B(121),C(121),D(121),E(121),F1(121),F(121),
     2FP(121,2),V(121,2),VBAR(121),UE(500),ALENG(500),BETA(500),
     3BETAM(500)
      REAL NU
      INTEGER SEP,DELPRNT
C
C ******************** FLOW VARIABLES ****************************
C ********** FP(N,M)      VELOCITY RATIO U/UE ******************
C **************** N = POSITION ACROSS BOUNDARY LAYER ***************
C ******M = 1, UPSTREAM VALUES.  M = 2, DOWNSTREAM VALUES. **********
C *****    MM IS THE NUMBER OF STREAMWISE POSITIONS TO BE CALCULATED ***
C ** DN = STEP SIZE IN Y DIRECTION, DX = STEP SIZE IN X DIRECTION ******
C
C     READ IN THE INITIAL PROFILE
C
      OPEN(10, form='formatted', status= 'old',file='BLUin1')
      OPEN(11, form='formatted', status= 'old',file='BLUofX1')
      OPEN(12, form='formatted', status= 'new',file='BLout1')
      READ(10,*) BETAM(1) ,NN
      READ(10,*)(F(N),FP(N,1),N = 1,NN)
      DN = .1D0
C
C     READ IN THE EXTERNAL VELOCITY UE(M) AT THE X-POSITIONS ALENG(M)
C       COMPUTE BETAM(M)=BETA AT M
C
      READ(11,*) MM,DELPRNT
      READ(11,*) (UE(M),ALENG(M),M=1,MM)
      WRITE(12,100)(UE(M),ALENG(M),M=1,MM)
      MPRINT=DELPRNT
      BETAM(2)=DLOG(UE(3)/UE(2))/DLOG(ALENG(3)/ALENG(2))
      DO 20 M=3,MM-1
   20 BETAM(M)=DLOG(UE(M+1)/UE(M-1))/DLOG(ALENG(M+1)/ALENG(M-1))
C
C     EXTRAPOLATE TO GET BETAM(MM)
C
```

```
            DX1=ALENG(MM-1)-ALENG(MM-2)
            DX2=ALENG(MM)-ALENG(MM-1)
            B1=BETAM(MM-1)-BETAM(MM-2)
            BETAM(MM)=BETAM(MM-1)+B1*DX2/DX1
C
C         COMPUTE BETA(M)=BETA AT M+1/2
C
            DO 25 M=1,MM-1
       25 BETA(M)=BETAM(M)
C
C   CALCULATION OF VBAR, THE FIRST STEP IN THE B. L. CALCULATIONS.
C
            DO 3000 N=1,NN
            V(N,1)=-BETAM(1)*F(N)-0.5D0*(BETAM(1)-1.)*(DFLOAT(N-1)*DN*FP(N,1)
          1-F(N))
            VBAR(N)=V(N,1)+0.5D0*(BETAM(1)-1.)*DFLOAT(N-1)*DN*FP(N,1)
     3000 CONTINUE
            I=0
            WRITE(12,350)I,ALENG(1),UE(1),BETAM(1)
            WRITE(12,550)(N,FP(N,1),V(N,1),N=1,NN)
C
C             BEGIN BOUNDARY LAYER CALCULATIONS.
C
            DO 8000 M = 1,MM-1
            X=ALENG(M+1)
            DXI=X-ALENG(M)
            XI=X-0.5D0*DXI
C
C       CALCULATION OF A,B,C,D,E,F,AND NEW VALUES OF VELOCITY
C
            DO 3500 N = 2,NN-1
            A(N) = 1.D0/(2.D0*DN*DN) - VBAR(N)/(4.D0*DN)
            B(N) = -(XI*FP(N,1) /DXI + BETA(M)*FP(N,1) + 1.D0/(DN**2))
            C(N) = 1.D0/(2.D0*DN*DN) + VBAR(N)/(4.D0*DN)
            D(N) = -(FP(N+1,1) - 2.D0*FP(N,1) + FP(N-1,1))/(2.D0*DN*DN) + VBAR(I
          1(FP(N+1,1) - FP(N-1,1))/(4.D0*DN) - BETA(M) -XI*(FP(N,1)**2)/DXI
     3500 CONTINUE
            E(1) = 0.0D0
            F1(1) = 0.0D0
            DO 4000 N = 2,NN-1
            E(N) = -A(N)/( B(N) + C(N)*E(N - 1) )
            F1(N) = (D(N) - C(N)*F1(N - 1) )/( B(N) + C(N)*E(N - 1) )
     4000 CONTINUE
            FP(NN,2) = 1.0D0
            DO 4500 N = 1,NN-1
            NDWN = NN+1 - N
            FP(NDWN-1,2) = E(NDWN-1)*FP(NDWN,2) + F1(NDWN-1)
     4500 CONTINUE
            SEP = 0
            IF( FP(2,2) .LT. 0.0D0 ) SEP = 1
C
C       CONTINUITY EQUATION........NEW VALUES OF VBAR.
C
            V(1,1) = 0.0D0
            V(1,2) = 0.0D0
```

```
       DO 5000 N = 2,NN
       AC =- BETA(M)/4.D0-XI/(2.D0*DXI)-(DFLOAT(N-1)-.5D0)*(BETA(M)-1.D0)/
       BC =-BETA(M)/4.D0-XI/(2.D0*DXI) +(DFLOAT(N-1)-.5D0)*(BETA(M)-1.D0)/
       CC =-BETA(M)/4.D0+XI/(2.D0*DXI) -(DFLOAT(N-1)-.5D0)*(BETA(M)-1.D0)/
       DC =-BETA(M)/4.D0+XI/(2.D0*DXI) +(DFLOAT(N-1)-.5D0)*(BETA(M)-1.D0)/
       V(N,2) = V(N-1,2) + V(N-1,1) - V(N,1) + (AC*FP(N,2) + BC*FP(N-1,2)
      1 + CC*FP(N,1) + DC*FP(N-1,1))*2.D0*DN
 5000 CONTINUE
       DO 5500 N = 2,NN
       VBAR(N) = V(N,2)+FP(N,2)*DFLOAT(N-1)*DN*(BETAM(M+1)-1.D0)/2.D0
C
C      SEND M=2 RESULTS BACK TO M=1
C
       FP(N,1) = FP(N,2)
       V(N,1) = V(N,2)
 5500 CONTINUE
C
C       THE END OF THE PROGRAM.   OUTPUT STATEMENTS.
C
       WRITE(12,350) M+1,ALENG(M+1),UE(M+1),BETAM(M+1)
       IF (SEP.EQ.1) GO TO 7500
       IF(M.LT.MPRINT) GO TO 8000
       MPRINT=MPRINT+DELPRNT
 7500 WRITE(12,550)(N,FP(N,1),V(N,1),N=1,NN)
       IF (SEP.EQ.1) GO TO 8500
 8000 CONTINUE
       WRITE(12,700)
       GO TO 9000
 8500 WRITE(12,701)
       CLOSE(10)
       CLOSE(11)
       CLOSE(12)
  100 FORMAT(2F20.10)
  350 FORMAT( 5X,'M=',I4,5X,'X/L=',F6.4,5X,'UE/UO=',F6.4,5X,'BETAM=',F
      18.4,5X)
  550 FORMAT(4(I3,F8.4,F8.4))
  700 FORMAT(//41H *** THE END ***     THATS ALL SHE WROTE.)
  701 FORMAT(//'FLOW SEPARATED SO CALCULATION WAS STOPPED')
 9000 CONTINUE
       END
```

References

Abbott, I. H., and A. E. Von Doenhoff (1959). *Theory of Wing Sections,* Dover Press, New York.

Abramowitz, M., and I. A. Stegun (1964). *Handbook of Mathematical Functions,* U.S. Government Printing Office, Washington, DC.

Ames, W. F. (1977). *Numerical Methods in Partial Differential Equations,* Academic Press, San Diego, CA.

Andereck, C. D., R. Dickman, and H. L. Swinney (1983). *Phys. Fluids,* **26**, p. 1395.

Andereck, C. D., S. S. Liu, and H. L. Swinney (1986). *J. Fluid Mech.,* **164**, p. 155.

Antar, B. N., and V. S. Nuotio-Antar (1993). *Fundamentals of Low-Gravity Fluid Dynamics and Heat Transfer,* CRC Press, Boca Raton, FL.

Antonia, R. A., M. Teitel, J. Kim, and L. W. B. Browne (1992). *J. Fluid Mech.,* **236**, p. 579.

Aris, R. (1962). *Vector Tensors, and the Basic Equations of Fluid Mechanics,* Prentice Hall, Upper Saddle River, NJ.

Arkilic, E. B., M. A. Schmidt, and K. S. Breuer (1997). *J. Microelectr. Syst.,* **6**, p. 167.

Arkilic, E. B., K. S. Breuer, and M. A. Schmidt (2001). *J. Fluid Mech.,* **437**, p. 29.

Arndt, R. E. A. (1981). In *Annual Review of Fluid Mechanics,* Vol. 13, Annual Reviews, Palo Alto, CA.

Ash, R. L., G. C. Greene, and A. J. Zukerman (1994). *Proc. 12th U.S. National Congress of Applied Mechanics,* Seattle, WA.

Balint, J. L., M. Ayrault, F. Veillon, P. Jeandel, and J. P. Schon (1982). *Proc. International Symposium on Contamination Control.* p. C-1.

Ballal, B. Y., and R. S. Rivlin (1976). *Arch. Rat. Mech. Anal.,* **62**, p. 237.

Banks, W. H. H., P. G. Drazin, and M. B. Zaturska (1988). *J. Fluid Med.* **186**, p. 559.

Basset, A. B. (1888). *Hydrodynamics,* Deighton, Bell and Co., Cambridge, p. 270.

Batchelor, G. K. (1967). *An Introduction to Fluid Dynamics,* Cambridge University Press, New York.

Bayly, B. J., S. A. Orszag, and T. Herbert (1988). In *Annual Review of Fluid Mechanics,* Vol. 20, Annual Reviews, Palo Alto, CA.

Beaudan, P., and P. Main (1994). Report TF-62, Stanford Thermosciences Division.

Bechert, D. W., M. Brose, W. Hage, J. C. T. Vander Hansen and G. Hoppe (1997). *J. Fluid Mech.* **338**, p. 59.

Berger, S. A. (1971). *Laminar Wakes,* Elsevier, New York.

Berker, R. (1963). In *Handbuch der Physik,* Vol. VIII, Pt. 2, Springer-Verlag, New York.

Bernal, L. P., and A. Roshko (1986). *J. Fluid Mech.,* **170**, p. 499.

Bernal, L. P., R. E. Breidenthal, G. L. Brown, J. H. Konrad, and A. Roshko (1980). *Turbulent Shear Flows,* Vol. 2, Springer-Verlag, New York.

Bertin, J. J., and M. L. Smith (1979). *Aerodynamics,* Prentice Hall, Upper Saddle River, NJ.

Betchov, R., and A. B. Szewczyk (1963). *Phys. Fluids,* **6**, p. 1391.

Betz, A. (1915). *Z. Flug. Mot.,* **6**, p. 173.

Betz, A. (1924). *Z. Flug. Mot.,* **15**, p. 100.

Bird, R. B., W. E. Stewart, and E. N. Lightfoot (1960). *Transport Phenomena,* Wiley, New York.

Bird, R. B., R. C. Armstrong, and O. Hassager (1977). *Dynamics of Polymeric Liquids,* Vol. 1, Wiley, New York.

Blackstock, D. T. (1962). *J. Acoust. Soc. Am.,* **34**, p. 9.

Blackstock, D. T. (1966). *J. Acoust. Soc. Am.,* **39**, p. 1019.

Blackwelder, R. F. (1988). In *Transport in Turbulent Flows,* Hemisphere Press, Philadelphia.

Blasius, H. (1908). *Z. Angew. Math. Phys.,* **56**, p. 1 (translation, NACA TM 1256).

Blevins, R. D. (1984). *Applied Fluid Dynamics Handbook,* Van Nostrand Reinhold, New York.

Blottner, F. G. (1970). *AIAA J.,* **8**, p. 193.

Blottner, F. G. (1975). NATO-AGARD Lecture Series 73, Chap. 3.

Bödewadt, U. T. (1940). *Z. Angew. Math. Mech.,* **20**, p. 241.

Bogard, D. G., and W. G. Tiederman (1986). *J. Fluid Mech.,* **162**, p. 380.

Bouard, R., and M. Coutanceau (1980). *J. Fluid Mech.,* **101**, p. 583.

Boussinesq, J. (1877). *Mem. Pres. Acad. Sci., Paris,* **23**, p. 46.

Bradshaw, P. (1966), *J. Fluid Mech.,* **29**, p. 625.

Brand, L. (1957). *Arch. Rat. Mech. Anal.,* **1**, p. 35.

Bridgman, P. W. (1922). *Dimensional Analysis,* Yale University Press, New Haven, CT.

Brodkey, R. S., S. G. Nychas, J. L. Taraba, and J. M. Wallace (1973). *Phys. Fluids,* **16**, p. 2010.

Brown, G. L., and A. Roshko (1974). *J. Fluid Mech.,* **64**, p. 775.

Buckingham, E. (1914). *Phys. Rev. Ser.* 2, **4**, p. 345.

Buschmann, M., and M. Gad-el-Hak (2003). *AIAA J.,* **41**, p. 40.

Butler, K. M., and B. F. Farrell (1992). *Phys. Fluids A,* **4**(8), p. 1637.

Carmichael, B. H. (1981). *Low Reynolds Number Airfoil Survey,* Vol. 1, NASA CR 165803.

Carslaw, H. S., and J. C. Jaeger (1947). *Conduction of Heat in Solids,* Clarendon Press, Oxford.

Catherall, D., and K. W. Mangler (1966). *J. Fluid Mech.,* **26**, p. 163.

Cebeci, T., and P. Bradshaw (1977). *Momentum Transfer in Boundary Layers,* McGraw-Hill, New York.

Cercignani, C. (1990). *Mathematical Methods of Kinetic Theory,* 2nd ed., Plenum Press, New York.

Cercignani, C. (2000). *Rarefied Gas Dynamics,* Cambridge University Press, New York.

Cercignani, C., and A. Daneri (1963). *J. Appl. Phys.,* **9**, p. 3509.

Champagne, F. H. (1978). *J. Fluid Mech.,* **86**, p. 67.

Chan, C. L., M. M. Chen, and J. Mazumder (1988). *J. Heat Transfer,* **110**, p. 140.

Choi, C.-H., K. J. Westin, and K. S. Breuer, (2002). *Proc. IMECE 2002,* New Orleans, LA, ASME IMECE2002-33707.

Chong, M. S., A. E. Perry, and B. J. Cantwell (1990). *Phys. Fluids A,* **2**(5), p. 765.

Cimbala, J., H. Nagib, and A. Roshko (1988). *J. Fluid Mech.,* **190**, p. 265.

Clauser, F. H. (1954). *J. Aerosp. Sci.,* **21**, p. 385.

Clauser, F. H. (1956). *Adv. Appl. Mech.,* **4**, p. 1.

Clift, R., J. R. Grace, and M. E. Weber (1978). *Bubbles, Drops, and Particles,* Academic Press, San Diego, CA.

Cole, J. D., and J. Kevorkian (1981). *Perturbation Methods in Applied Mathematics,* Springer-Verlag, New York.

Coles, D. E. (1956). *J. Fluid Mech.,* **1**, p. 191.

Coles, D. E. (1965). *J. Fluid Mech.,* **21**, p. 385.

Coles, D., and E. A. Hirst (1968). *Proc. Computation of Turbulent Boundary Layers, 1968* AFOSR-IFP-Stanford Conference, Vol. II.

Concus, P. R. (1968). *J. Fluid Mech.,* **34**, p. 481.

Conlisk, A. T. (1989). AIAA Paper 89-0293.

Coon, M. D., and M. Tobak (1995). AIAA Paper 95-0785.

Corrsin, S. (1955). In *Symposium on Naval Hydrodynamics,* F. S. Sherman (ed.), National Research Council Publication 515.

Cousteix, J. (1986). *Annual Review of Fluid Mechanics,* Vol. 18, Annual Reviews, Palo Alto, CA, p. 173.

Craik, A. D. D. (1971). *J. Fluid Mech.,* **50**, p. 393.

Crow, S. D. (1970). *AIAA J.,* **8**, p. 2172.

Dagan, Z., S. Weinbaum, and R. Pfeffer (1982). *J. Fluid Mech.,* **115**, p. 505.

Daube, O. (1992). *J. Comput. Phys.,* **103**, p. 402.

Davey, A. (1961). *J. Fluid Mech.,* **10**, p. 593.

Davis, A. M. J. (1989). *Phys. Fluids A,* **1**(3), p. 475.

Davis, A. M. J. (1991). *Q. Appl. Math.,* **49**(3), p. 507.

Davis, A. M. J. (1993). *Phys. Fluids A,* **5**(4), p. 800.

Davis, A. M. J., and M. E. O'Neil (1977). *J. Fluid Mech.,* **81**, p. 551.

Davis, R. T. (1972). *J. Fluid Mech.,* **51**, p. 417.

Davis, S. H. (2000). In *Perspectives in Fluid Dynamics,* G. K. Batchelor, H. K. Moffatt, and M. G. Worster, (eds.) Cambridge University Press, p. 1.

Dean, W. M. (1998). *Analysis of Transport Phenomena,* Oxford University Press, Oxford, U.K.

Dean, W. R. (1944). *Proc. Cambridge Philos. Soc.,* **40**, p. 214.

Dean, W. R. (1951). *Proc. Cambridge Philos. Soc.,* **47**, p. 127.

Dean, W. R., and P. E. Montagnon (1949). *Proc. Cambridge Philos. Soc.,* **45**, p. 389.

Deiber, J. A., and W. R. Showalter (1979). *AIChE J.,* **25**, p. 640.

Delany, N. K., and N. E. Sorenson (1953). NACA Tech. Note 3038.

de Ruijter, M. J., T. D. Blake, and J. De Coninck (1999). *Langmuir,* **15**, p. 7836.

Dimotakis, P. E., R. C. Miake-Lye, and D. A. Papantoniou (1983). *Phys. Fluids,* **26**, p. 3185.

Donnelly, R. J., and W. Glaberson (1966). *Proc. R. Soc. London Ser. A,* **290**, p. 547.

Dussan, V. E. B. (1977). In *Annual Review of Fluid Mechanics,* Vol. 11, Annual Reviews, Palo Alto, CA, p. 371.

Dussan, V. E. B., and S. H. Davis (1974). *J. Fluid Mech.,* **65**, p. 71.

Dwyer, H. A. (1981). In *Annual Review of Fluid Mechanics,* Annual Reviews, Palo Alto, CA.

East, L. F., W. G. Sawyer, and C. R. Nash (1979). *Roy. Aircraft Establishment, Tech Report* 79040.

Edwards, D. A., H. Brenner, and D. T. Wasan, (1991). *Interfacial Transport Processes and Rheology,* Butterworth-Heinemann, Woburn, MA.

Emmons, H. W. (1949). *Proc. First Symposium on Applied Mathematics,* American Mathematics Society, Providence, RI.

Falkner, V. M., and S. W. Skan (1931). *Philos. Mag.,* **12**, p. 865.

Fehlberg, E. (1969). NASA TR R-315.

Fernholtz, H. H., and J. P. Findley (1996). *Prog. Aerosp. Sci.,* **32**, p. 245.

Finley, P. J., K. C. Phoe, and C. J. Poh, (1966). *La Houille Blanche,* **21**, p. 713.

Finn, R. K. (1953). *J. Appl. Phys.,* **24**, p. 771.

Fornberg, B. (1980). *J. Fluid Mech.,* **98**, p. 819.

Fornberg, B. (1985). *J. Comput. Phys.,* **61**, p. 297.

Fourier, J. B. J. (1822). *Theorie analytic de chaleur,* Paris translation, Dover Press, New York.

Fraenkel, L. E. (1962). *Proc. R. Soc. London, Ser. A,* **267**, p. 119.

Gad-el-Hak, M. (2001). In *MEMS Handbook,* M. Gad-el-Hak (ed.), CRC Press, Boca Raton, FL, Chap. 4.

Gaster, M. (1965). *J. Fluid Mech.,* **22**, p. 433.

Goenka, L. N. (1982). M.S. thesis, The University of Texas, Austin, TX.

Goldstein, S. (1948). *Q. J. Mech. Appl. Math.,* **1**, p. 43.

Goldstein, S. (ed.) (1965). *Modern Developments in Fluid Dynamics,* Dover, New York.

Grabowski, W. J., and S. A. Berger (1976). *J. Fluid Mech.,* **76**, p. 525.

Gradshteyn, I. S., and I. W. Ryzhik (1965). *Tables of Integrals, Series and Products,* Academic Press, San Diego, CA.

Granick, S., Y. Zhu, and H. Lee (2003). *Nat. Mater.,* **2**, p. 221.

Green, G. (1943). *Philos. Mag. (Ser. 7)* **35**, p. 250.

Gresho, P. M. (1991). In *Annual Review of Fluid Mechanics,* Vol. 23, Annual Reviews, Palo Alto, CA, p. 413.

Hadamard, J. S. (1911). *C. R. Acad. Sci.,* **152**, p. 1735.

Hagen, G. (1839). *Poggendorff's Ann. Phys. Chem.* **46**(2), p. 423.

Hamel, G. (1971). *Jahresbericht der Deutschen Mathematiker–Vereinigung,* **25**, p. 34.

Hammache, M., F. K. Broward, and R. F. Blackwelder (2002). *J. Fluid Mech.,* **461**, p. 1.

Happel, J., and H. Brenner (1965). *Low Reynolds Number Hydrodynamics,* Prentice Hall, Upper Saddle River, NJ.

Happel, J., and H. Brenner (1983). *Low Reynolds Number Hydrodynamics,* Martinus Nijhoff, The Hague, The Netherlands.

Harder, K. J., and W. G. Tiederman (1991). *Philos. Trans. R. Soc. Ser. A,* **336**, p. 19.

Hartland, S., and R. W. Hartley (1976). *Axisymmetric Fluid–Liquid Interfaces,* Elsevier, New York.

Hasimoto, H. (1958). *J. Phys. Soc. Jpn.,* **13**, p. 633.

Hasimoto, H., and O. Sano (1980). In *Annual Review of Fluid Mechanics,* Vol. 12, Annual Reviews, Palo Alto, CA.

Hayes, R. A., and J. Ralston (1993). *J. Colloid Interface Sci.,* **159**, p. 429.

Helmholtz, H. (1867). *Philos. Mag.,* **33**(4), p. 485; translated from *Crelle's J.,* 1858, p. 55.

Herbert, T. (1976). *Proc. International Conference on Numerical Methods in Fluid Dynamics,* van de Vooren and Zandbergen (eds.), Springer-Verlag, New York, p. 235.

Herbert, T. (1988). In *Annual Review of Fluid Mechanics,* Vol. 20, p. 187.

Hiemenz, K. (1911). *Dingler's Polytech. J.,* **326**, p. 311.

Hill, M. J. M. (1894). *Philos. Trans. R. Soc. London Ser. A,* **185**, p. 213.

Hill, R., and G. Power (1956). *Q. J. Mech. Appl. Mech.,* **9**, p. 313.

Hinch, E. J. (1991). *Perturbation Methods,* Cambridge University Press, New York.

Hinze, J. O. (1975). *Turbulence,* McGraw-Hill, New York.

Ho, C. M., and P. Huerre (1984). In *Annual Review of Fluid Mechanics,* Vol. 16, p. 365.

Hocking, L. M. (2001). *Eur. J. Appl. Math.,* **12**, p. 195.

Hoerner, S. F. (1965). *Fluid-Dynamic Drag,* Hoerner Fluid Dynamics, Brick Town, NJ.

Homann, F. (1936). *Forsch. Arb. Ing.-Wes.,* **7**, p. 1.

Howarth, L. (1951). *Philos. Mag.,* **42**(7), p. 1433.

Hseih, S.-S., C.-Y. Lin, C.-F. Huang, and H.-H. Tsai (2004). *J. Micromech. Microeng.* **14**, p. 436.

Huerre, P., and P. A. Monkewitz (1990). In *Annual Review of Fluid Mechanics,* Vol. 22, Annual Reviews, Palo Alto, CA, p. 473.

Idelchik, I. E. (1994). *Handbook of Hydraulic Resistance,* 3rd ed., CRC Press, Boca Raton, FL.

Illingworth, C. R. (1950). *Proc. Cambridge Philos. Soc.,* **46**, p. 469.

Isakson, A. (1937). *Zh. Eksper. Teor. Fiz.,* **7**, p. 919.

Jeffery, G. B. (1922). *Proc. R. Soc. London Ser. A,* **101**, p. 169.

Jeffreys, H. (1963). *Cartesian Tensors,* Dover, New York.

Jeong, J., and F. Hussain (1995). *J. Fluid Mech.,* **285**, p. 69.

Jordinson, R. (1970). *J. Fluid Mech.,* **43**, p. 801.

Judy, J., D. Maynes, and B. Web (2002). *Int. J. Heat Mass Transfer,* **45**, p. 3477.

Juvet, P. J., and W. C. Reynolds (1989). AIAA Paper 89-0969.

Kamal, M. M. (1966). *Trans. ASME, J. Basic Eng.,* **88**, p. 717.

Kaplun, S. (1957). *J. Math. Mech.,* **6**, p. 595.

Karamcheti, K. (1966). *Principles of Ideal-Fluid Aerodynamics,* Wiley, New York (now by Krieger Publishing, Malabar, FL).

Karniadakis, E. M., and A. Beskok (2002). *Micro Flows,* Springer-Verlag, New York.

Katz, J., and A. Plotkin (1991). *Low Speed Aerodynamics,* McGraw-Hill, New York.

Keller, H. B. (1978). In *Annual Review of Fluid Mechanics,* Vol. 10, Annual Reviews, Palo Alto, CA.

Keller, H. B., and T. Cebeci (1971). *Lecture Notes in Physics,* Vol. 8, *Proc. 2nd International Conference on Numerical Methods in Fluid Dynamics,* p. 92.

Kelley, R. E. (1967). *J. Fluid Mech.,* **27**, p. 657.

Kennard, E. H. (1938). *Kinetic Theory of Gases,* McGraw-Hill, New York.

Kido, S., and M. Takaoka (1994). In *Annual Review of Fluid Mechanics,* Vol. 26, Annual Reviews, Palo Alto, CA, p. 169.

Kim, J., P. Moin, and R. D. Moser (1987). *J. Fluid Mech.,* **177**, p. 133.

Kirchhoff, R. H. (1985). *Polentin/Flows,* Marcel Dekker, New York.

Klebanoff, P. S., K. O. Tidstrom, and L. M. Sargent (1962). *J. Fluid Mech.,* **12**, p. 1.

Kline, S. J., W. C. Reynolds, F. A. Schraub, and P. W. Runstadler (1967). *J. Fluid Mech.,* **30**, p. 741.

Knapp, R. T., J. W. Daily, and F. G. Hammitt (1970). *Cavitation,* McGraw-Hill, New York.

Kolmogorov, A. N. (1941a). *C. R. Acad. Sci. U.R.S.S.,* **30**, p. 301.

Kolmogorov, A. N. (1941b). *C. R. Acad. Sci. U.R.S.S.,* **32**, p. 16.

Koplik, J., and J. R. Banavar (1995). In *Annual Review of Fluid Mechanics,* Vol. 27, Annual Reviews, Palo Alto, CA, p. 257.

Koplik, J., J. R. Banavar, and J. F. Willemsen (1989). *Phy. Fluids A,* **1**(5), p. 781.

Koschmieder, E. L. (1979). *J. Fluid Mech.*, **93**, p. 515.

Koschmieder, E. L. (1993). *Bénard Cells and Taylor Vortices*, Cambridge University Press, New York.

Koumoutsakos, P., and A. Leonard (1995). *J. Fluid Mech.*, **296**, p. 1.

Kuethe, A. M., and C. Y. Chow (1976). *Foundations of Aerodynamics*, Wiley, New York.

Lagerstrom, P. A. (1988). *Matched Asymptotic Expansions*, Applied Mathematical Sciences, Vol. 76, Springer-Verlag, New York.

Lanchester, L. (1907). *Aerodynamics*, Constable, London.

Landau, L. D., and E. V. Levich (1942). *Acta Physiochim. URSS*, **17**, p. 42.

Landau, L. D., and E. M. Lifshitz (1959). *Fluid Mechanics*, Pergamon Press, New York.

Langhaar, H. L. (1951). *Dimensional Analysis and the Theory of Models*, Wiley, New York.

Langlois, W. E. (1964). *Slow Viscous Flow*, Macmillan, New York.

Lathrop, D. P., J. Fineberg, and H. L. Swinney (1992). *Phys. Rev. Lett.*, **68**, p. 1515.

Lauga, E., and H. A. Stone (2003). *J. Fluid Mech.* **489**, p. 55.

Leal, L. G. (1992). *Laminar Flow and Convective Transport Processes*, Butterworth Heinemann, Woburn, MA.

Leibeck, R. H. (1978). *J. Aircraft*, **15**, p. 547.

Leibovich, S. (1978). In *Annual Review of Fluid Mechanics*, Vol. 10, Annual Reviews, Palo Alto, CA.

Leibovich, S. (1984). *AIAA J.*, **22**, p. 1192.

Lessen, M. (1949). NACA Report 979.

Levich, E. V. (1962). *Physiochemical Hydrodynamics*, Prentice Hall, Upper Saddle River, NJ.

Lewkowicz, A. K. (1982). *Z. Flugwiss. Weltraumforsch.*, **6**(4), p. 261.

Lighthill, M. J. (1958). *J. Fluid Mech.*, **4**, p. 383.

Lighthill, M. J. (1963). In *Laminar Boundary Layer*, L. Rosenhead (ed.), Clarendon Press, Oxford.

Lin, C. C. (1945). *Q. Appl. Math*, **3**, pp. 117, 218, 277.

Lissaman, P. B. S. (1983). In *Annual Review of Fluid Mechanics*, Vol. 15, p. 223.

Lo, L. L. (1983). *J. Fluid Mech.*, **132**, p. 65.

Lock, R. C. (1951). *Q. J. Mech. Appl. Math.*, **4**, p. 42.

Loos, H. G. (1955). *J. Aeronaut. Sci.*, **22**, p. 35.

Lopez, J. M., J. E. Hart, F. Morques, S. Kittelman, and J. Shen (1997). *J. Fluid Mech.,* **338**, p. 59.

Ludwieg, H., and W. Tillmann (1949). *Ing. Arch.,* **17**, p. 288.

Lugt, H. J. (1983). *Vortex Flows in Nature and Technology,* Wiley-Interscience, New York.

Mack, L. M. (1984). AGARD Report 709, March.

Mager, A., and A. G. Hansen (1952). NACA TN. 2658.

Mala, G. M., and D. Li (1999). *Int. J. Heat Fluid Flow,* **20**, p. 142.

Mangler, W. (1945). Ber. Aerodyn. Versuchsanst. Goett. Report 45-A-17.

Maslen, S. H. (1963). *AIAA J.,* **1**, p. 33.

Maxey, M. R., and J. J. Riley (1983). *Phys. Fluids,* **26**, p. 883.

Maxwell, J. C. (1871). *Proc. London Math. Soc.,* **3**, p. 224.

McKeon B. J., J. Li, W. Jaing, J. F. Morrison, and A. J. Smits (2004). *J. Fluid Mech.,* **501**, p. 135.

Messiter, A. F. (1983). *ASME J. Appl. Mech.,* **50**, p. 1104.

Metcalfe, R. W., and J. J. Riley, (1981). In *Lecture Notes in Physics,* Vol. 141, W. C. Reynolds and R. W. MacCormack, (eds.), Springer-Verlag, New York, p. 279.

Michael, D. H., and M. E. O'Neill (1977). *J. Fluid Mech.,* **80**, p. 785.

Michalke, A. (1964). *J. Fluid Mech.,* **23**, p. 521.

Mihaljan, J. M. (1962). *Astrophys. J.,* **136**, p. 1126.

Millikan, C. B. (1938). *Proc. 5th International Conference on Applied Mechanics,* Cambridge, MA, p. 386.

Millikan, R. A. (1923). *Phys. Rev.,* **22**, p. 1.

Milne-Thomson, L. M. (1960). *Theoretical Hydrodynamics,* Macmillan, New York.

Minnaert, M. (1933). *Philos. Mag.,* **16**, p. 235.

Moffatt, H. K. (1964). *J. Fluid Mech.,* **18**, p. 1.

Moore, F. K. (ed.) (1964). *Theory of Laminar Flows,* Princeton University Press, Princeton, NJ.

Morel, T. (1978). *SAE* Paper 780267.

Moser, R. D., J. Kim, and N. N. Mansour (1999). *Phys. Fluids,* **11**, p. 943.

Nahas, N. (1989). Private communication of unpublished work.

Nayfeh, A. H. (1973). *Perturbation Methods,* Wiley, New York.

Neitzel, G. P. (1988). *Phys. Fluids,* **31**, p. 958.

Nikuradse, J. (1942). *Laminare Reibungsschiechten an der lämgsamgeströmten Platte,* Monograph, Zantrale f. Wiss. Berichtswesen, Berlin.

Nishioka, M., and M. Asai (1984). *Turbulence and Chaotic Phenomena in Fluids,* T. Tatsumi (ed.), Elsevier, Amsterdam, p. 87.

Oberbeck. H. A. (1876). *Crelles' J.,* **81**, p. 62.

Obert, E. F. (1960). *Concepts of Thermodynamics,* McGraw-Hill, New York.

O'Brian, V. (1977). *Phys. Fluids,* **20**, p. 1045.

Orr, W. M. F. (1907). *Proc. R. Irish Acad.,* **27**, p. 9.

Oseen, C. W. (1910). *Ark. Mat. Astronom. Fys.,* **6**(29).

Österlund, J. M. (1999). Doctoral dissertation, thesis, Royal Institute of Technology, Stockholm.

Österlund, J. M., A. V. Johansson, H. M. Nagib, and M. H. Hites (2000). *Phys. Fluids,* **12**, p. 2159.

Pan, F., and A. Acrivos (1967). *J. Fluid Mech.,* **28**, p. 643.

Panton, R. L. (1968). *J. Fluid Mech.,* **31**, p. 819.

Panton, R. L. (1990). *J. Fluids Eng.,* **112**, p. 425.

Panton, R. L. (1992). *C. R. Acad. Sci. Paris,* **315**, Ser. II, p. 1467.

Panton, R. L. (2001). *Prog. Aerosp. Sci.,* **37**, p. 341.

Panton, R. L. (2005). *Appl. Mech. Rev.,* **58**, p. 1.

Panton, R. L., and G. Robert (1994). *J. Fluids Eng.,* **116**, p. 477.

Panton, R. L., A. L. Goldman, R. L. Lowery, and M. M. Reischman (1980). *J. Fluid Mech.,* **97**, p. 299.

Panton, R. L., Y. K. Liu, and M. Stanislas (1995). *Proc. IUTAM Symposium on Asymptotic Methods in Turbulent Shear Flows,* Ruhr-University, Bochum, Germany.

Panton, R. L. (ed.) (1997). *Self-Sustaining Mechanisms of Wall Turbulence,* Computational Mechanics Publications, Southampton, Hampshire, England.

Peridier, V. J., F. T. Smith, and J. D. A. Walker (1991). *J. Fluid Mech.,* **232**, p. 99.

Perry, A. E., and C. J. Abell (1975). *J. Fluid Mech.,* **67**, p. 257.

Perry, A. E., and M. S. Chong (1989). In *Annual Review of Fluid Mechanics,* Vol. 19, p. 125.

Perry, A. E., S. Hafez, and M. S. Chong (2001). *J. Fluid Mech.,* **439**, p. 395.

Phillips, H. B. (1933). *Vector Analysis,* Wiley, New York.

Piercy, N. A. V., M. S. Hooper, and H. F. Winny (1933). *Philos. Mag.,* Ser. 7, **15**, p. 647.

Plesset, M. S., and A. Prosperetti (1977). In *Annual Review of Fluid Mechanics,* Vol. 9, p. 145.

Pohlhausen, K. (1921). *Z. Angew. Math. Mech.,* **1**, p. 252.

Poiseuille, J. L. M. (1840). *Comp. Rend.,* **11**, pp. 961, 1041; **12**, p. 112.

Pong, K., C. Ho, J. Liu, and Y. Tai (1994). *Applications of Microfabrication to Fluid Mechanics,* ASME FED-Vol. 197, p. 51.

Pozrikidis, C. (1987). *J. Fluid Mech.,* **180**, p. 495.

Pozrikidis, C. (1992). *Boundary Integral and Singularity Methods for Linearized Viscous Flow,* Cambridge University Press, New York.

Prager, W. (1961). *Introduction to Mechanics of Continua,* Ginn, Boston.

Prandtl, L. (1904). *Verhandlunger IIIrd International Mathematiker Kongresser,* Heidelberg, p. 484 (translation, NASA Memo 452).

Prandtl, L. (1925). *Z. Angew. Math. Mech.,* **5**, p. 136.

Prandtl, L. (1935). In *Aerodynamic Theory,* W. F. Durand (ed.), Vol. III, Art. G (republished by Peter Smith, Gloucester, MA, 1976).

Prandtl, L., and O. G. Tietjens (1934). *Applied Hydro- and Aeromechanics,* McGraw-Hill, New York (Dover, New York, 1957).

Prandtl, L., C. Wieselsberger, and A. Betz (1935). *Ergebnisse der Aerodynamischen Versuchsanstalt zu Gottingen,* Vols. I, III, and IV, Oldenbourg, Munich.

Probstein, R. F. (2003). *Physicochemical Hydrodynamics,* 2ed. Wiley, New York.

Proudman, I., and K. Johnson, (1962). *J. Fluid Mech.,* **12**, p. 161.

Proudman, I., and J. R. A. Pearson (1957). *J. Fluid Mech.,* **2**, p. 237.

Purtell, L. P., P. S. Klebanoff, and F. T. Buckley (1981). *Phys. Fluids,* **24**, p. 802.

Qu, Y. (2004). Private communication.

Ralph, M. E. (1987). *J. Fluids Eng.,* **109**, p. 255.

Rayleigh, Lord (1879). *Proc. R. Soc.,* **29**, p. 71.

Rayleigh, Lord (1911). *Philos. Mag.,* **21**, p. 397.

Rayleigh, Lord (1917). *Philos. Mag.,* **34**(6), p. 94.

Reed, H. L., and W. S. Saric (1989). In *Annual Review of Fluid Mechanics,* Vol. 21, Annual Reviews, Palo Alto, CA, p. 235.

Reshotko, E. (1994). AIAA Paper 94-0001.

Riabouchinsky. D. (1911). *L'Aerophile,* p. 407.

Richardson, E. G., and E. Tyler (1929). *Proc. Phys. Soc. London,* **42**, p. 1.

Roache, P. J. (1972). *Numerical Fluid Dynamics,* Hermosa Press, Albuquerque, NM.

Robinson, S. K. (1991). NASA Tech. Memo 103859.

Rogers, M. H., and G. N. Lance (1960). *J. Fluid Mech.,* **7**, p. 617.

Rosenhead, L. (1940). *Proc. R. Soc. London Ser. A,* **175**, p. 436.

Rosenhead, L. (ed.) (1963). *Laminar Boundary Layers,* Oxford University Press, New York.

Roshko, A. (1961). *J. Fluid Mech.,* **10**, p. 345.

Roshko, A., and K. Koenig (1984). *J. Fluid Mech.,* **156**, p. 167.

Rouse, H., and S. Ince (1957). *History of Hydraulics,* Institute of Hydraulic Research, University of Iowa, Ames, IA.

Ruschak, K. J. (1985). In *Annual Review of Fluid Mechanics,* Vol. 17, Annual Reviews, Palo Alto, CA, p. 65.

Rybczynski, W. (1911). *Bull. Int. Acad. Sci. Cracov,* **1911A**, p. 40.

Saffman, P. G. (1992). *Vortex Dynamics,* Cambridge University Press, New York.

Sampson, R. A. (1891). *Philos. Trans. R. Soc.* **A 182**, p. 449.

Saric, W. S. (1994a). In *Transition: Experiments, Theory, Computations,* T. Corke, G. Erlebacher, and M. Hussaini (eds.), Oxford University Press, New York.

Saric, W. S. (1994b). In *Annual Review of Fluid Mechanics,* Vol. 26, Annual Reviews, Palo Alto, CA, p. 379.

Saric, W. S., and A. H. Nayfeh (1977). *NATO-AGARD Conference Proceedings,* No. 224, Laminar-turbulent transition.

Saric, W. S., and A. S. W. Thomas (1984). In *Turbulence and Chaotic Phenomena in Fluids,* T. Tatsumi, (ed.), North-Holland, Amsterdam, p. 117.

Sarpkaya, T. (1971). *J. Fluid Mech.,* **45**, p. 545.

Schaaf, S. A., and P. L. Chambré (1961). *Flow of Rarefied Gases,* Princeton University Press, Princeton, NJ.

Schatzle, P. R. (1987). Ph.D. dissertation, California Institute of Technology, Pasadena, CA.

Schlichting, H. (1933). *Z. Angew. Math. Mech.,* **13**, p. 260.

Schlichting, H. (1934). *Z. Angew. Math. Mech.,* **14**, p. 368.

Schlichting, H. (1950). *Boundary Layer Theory,* McGraw-Hill, New York (7th ed., 1979).

Schlichting, H., and K. Gersten (2000). *Boundary Layer Theory,* 8th ed., McGraw-Hill, New York.

Schoppa, W., F. Hussain, and R. W. Metcalfe (1995). *J. Fluid Mech.,* **298**, p. 23.

Schubauer, G. G., and H. K. Skramstad (1947). *J. Aeronaut. Sci.,* **14**, p. 69.

Scott, J. C. (1982). *J. Fluid Mech.,* **116**, p. 283.

Sedov, L. I. (1959). In *Similarity and Dimensional Methods in Mechanics,* M. Holt (ed.), Academic Press, San Diego, CA.

Sexl, T. (1930). *Z. Phys.,* **61**, p. 349.

Shapiro, A. H. (1962). *Nature,* **196**, p. 1080.

Sharp, K. V., and R. J. Adrian (2004). *Exp. Fluids,* **36**, p. 4741.

Sharp, K. V., R. J. Adrian, J. G. Santiago, and J. I. Molho (2002). In *The MEMS Handbook,* M. Gad-el-Hak (ed.), CRC Press, Boca Raton, FL, Chap. 6.

Shen, S. F. (1954). *J. Aeronaut. Sci.,* **21**, p. 62.

Sherman, F. S. (1963). In *Rarefied Gas Dynamics,* Vol. II, J. A. Laurmann (ed.), Academic Press, San Diego, CA, p. 228.

Shikhmurzaev, Y. D. (1997). *J. Fluid Mech.,* **334**, p. 211.

Simpson, R. L. (1989). In *Annual Review of Fluid Mechanics,* Vol. 21, Annual Reviews, Palo Alto, CA, p. 205.

Slattery, J. C. (1990). *Interfacial Transport Phenomena,* Springer-Verlag, New York.

Smith, C. R., J. D. A. Walker, A. H. Haidari, and U. Sobrun (1991). *Philos. Trans. R. Soc. London Ser. A,* **336**, p. 131.

Sommerfeld, A. (1904). *Z. Math. Phys.,* **40**. p. 97.

Sommerfeld, A. (1908). *Atti 4th Congr. Int. Math. Rome,* **3**, p. 116.

Sowerby, L. (1954). Report 16832, Aeronautical Research Council, London.

Spalart, P. R. (1988). *J. Fluid Mech.,* **187**, p. 61.

Spalding, D. B. (1961). *J. Appl. Mech.* **28**, p. 455.

Spall, R. E., T. B. Gatski, and R. L. Ash, (1990). *Proc. R. Soc. London Ser. A,* **429**, p. 613.

Spiegel, E. A., and G. Veronis, (1960). *Astrophys. J.,* **131**, p. 442.

Squire, H. B. (1933). *Proc. R. Soc. London Ser. A,* **142**, p. 621.

Squire, H. B. (1951). *Q. J. Mech.,* **4**, p. 321.

Squire, H. B. (1965). *Aeronaut. Q.,* **16**, p. 302.

Stewartson, K. (1954). *Proc. Cambridge Philos. Soc.,* **50**, p. 454.

Stokes, G. G. (1845). *Trans. Cambridge Philos. Soc.,* **8**, p. 287.

Stokes, G. G. (1851). *Trans. Cambridge Philos. Soc.,* **9**, pt. II, p. 8.

Stratford, B. S. (1959). *J. Fluid Mech.* **5**, p. 17.

Stuart, J. T. (1967). *J. Fluid Mech.,* **29**, p. 417.

Stuart, J. T. (1987). *Proc. Symposium on Vortex Control and Breakdown Behavior,* BBC, Baden, Switzerland.

Subramanian, R. S., and R. Balasubramaniam (2001). *The Motion of Bubbles and Drops in Reduced Gravity,* Cambridge University Press, New York.

Sudarshan, E., and N. Mukundew (1974). *Classical Dynamics,* Wiley, New York.

Sullivan, R. D. (1959). *J. Aeronaut. Sci.,* Nov., p. 767.

Swanson, J. C., B. Julian, G. G. Ihas, and R. J. Donnelly (2002). *J. Fluid Mech.,* **461**, p. 51.

Szeri, A. Z. (1980). *Tribology: Friction, Lubrication, and Wear,* Hemisphere Publishing, Philadelphia.

Taneda, S. (1956). *J. Phys. Soc. Jpn.,* **11**, p. 302.

Taneda, S. (1979). *J. Phys. Soc. Jpn.,* **46**, p. 1935.

Tani, I. (1977). In *Annual Review of Fluid Mechanics,* Vol. 9, Annual Reviews, Palo Alto, CA.

Taylor, G. I. (1915). *Philos. Trans. R. Soc. London Ser. A,* **215**, p. 1.

Taylor, G. I. (1921). *Proc. R. Soc. London Ser. A,* **100**, p. 114.

Taylor, G. I. (1923). *Proc. R. Soc. London Ser. A,* **104**, p. 213.

Taylor, G. I. (1950). *Proc. R. Soc. London Ser. A,* **201**, p. 192.

Telionis, D. P. (1981). *Unsteady Viscous Flows,* Springer-Verlag, New York.

Tennekes, H., and J. L. Lumley (1972). *Introduction to Turbulence,* MIT Press, Cambridge, MA.

Thom, A. (1933). *Proc. R. Soc. London Ser. A,* **141**, p. 651.

Thomas, A. S. W. (1983). *J. Fluid Mech.,* **137**, p. 233.

Thompson, P. A., and M. O. Robbins (1990). *Phys. Rev. A,* **41**, p. 6830.

Thompson, P. A., and S. M. Troian (1997). *Nature,* **389**, p. 360.

Thorpe, J. F. (1962). *Am. J. Phys.* **30**, p. 637.

Thwaites, B. (ed.) (1960). *Incompressible Aerodynamics,* Oxford University Press, New York.

Tillmark, N., and H. Alfreddsson (1992). *J. Fluid Mech.,* **235**, p. 89.

Tipei, N. (1962). In *Theory of Lubrication,* W. A. Gross (ed.), Stanford University Press, Stanford, CA.

Tobak, M., and D. J. Peak (1982). In *Annual Review of Fluid Mechanics,* Vol. 14, Annual Reviews, Palo Alto, CA, p. 61.

Tollmien, W. (1929). *Nachr. Ges. Wiss. Goettinger,* p. 21 (translation, NACA Tech. Memo 609).

Tollmien, W. (1931). *Handbuch der Experimentalischen Physik,* Vol. IV, Pt. 1, Leipzig.

Tombach, I. (1974). *Proc. 6th Conference on Aerospace and Aeronautical Meterology,* American Meterological Society, Boston.

Townsend, A. A. (1976). *The Structure of Turbulent Shear Flow,* Cambridge University Press, New York.

Trefethen, L. M., R. W. Bilger, P. T. Fink, R. E. Luxton, and R. I. Tanner (1965). *Nature,* p. 1084.

Trefethen, L. N., A. E. Trefethen, S. C. Reddy, and T. A. Driscoll (1993). *Science,* **261**, July 30, p. 578.

Tritton, D. J. (1959). *J. Fluid Mech.,* **6**, p. 547.

Tritton, D. J. (1977). *Physical Fluid Dynamics,* Van Nostrand Reinhold, New York.

Truesdell, C. A. (1954). *Kinematics of Vorticity,* University of Indiana Press, Bloomington, IN.

Truesdell, C. A. (1968). *Essays in the History of Mechanics,* Springer-Verlag, New York.

Tsien, H. S. (1948). *J. Aeronaut. Sci.,* **13**, p. 653.

Ulmanella, U. (2003). Ph.D. dissertation, Biomedical Engineering Department, UCLA, Los Angeles, CA.

Van Dommelen, L. L., and S. F. Shen (1982). In *Numerical and Physical Aspects of Aerodynamic Flows,* T. Cebeci (ed.), Springer-Verlag, New York.

Van Driest, E. (1946). *J. Appl. Mech. ASME,* **13**, p. Q-34.

Van Dyke, M. (1962). *J. Fluid Mech.,* **44**, p. 813.

Van Dyke, M. (1964). *Perturbation Methods in Fluid Mechanics,* Academic Press, San Diego, CA.

Van Dyke, M. (1970). *Perturbation Methods in Fluid Mechanics,* Parabolic Press, Stanford, CA.

Van Dyke, M. (1982). *An Album of Fluid Motion,* Parabolic Press, Stanford, CA.

Vashy, A. (1892). *Ann. Telegr.,* **19**, p. 25.

Vincenti, W. G. (1982). *Technol. Culture,* **23**(2), p. 145.

Visbal, M. R. (1991). *AIAA J.,* **29**, p. 1273.

Visbal, M. R. (1995). AIAA Paper 95-0585.

Viswanath, D. S., and G. Natarajan (1989). *Data Book on Viscosity of Liquids,* Hemisphere Publishing, Philadelphia.

Von Kármán, T. (1921). *Z. Angew. Math. Mech.,* **1**, p. 233.

Wallace, J. M., H. Eckelmann, and R. S. Brodkey (1972). *J. Fluid Mech.,* **54**, p. 39.

Wang, C. Y. (1994). *J. Fluids Eng.,* **116**, p. 233.

Wang, K. C. (1971). *J. Fluid Mech.,* **44**, p. 813.

Wang, Y. L., and P. A. Longwell (1964). *AIChE J.,* **10**, p. 323.

Weidman, P. D., and N. Riley (1993). *J. Fluid Mech.,* **257**, p. 331.

Weinstein, S. J., and K. J. Ruschak (2004). In *Annual Review of Fluid Mechanics,* Vol. 36, Annual Reviews, Palo Alto, CA, p. 29.

Werlé, H. (1963). *La Houille Blanch,* **28**, p. 330.

Werlé, H. (1980). *Res. Aerosp.,* **5**, p. 35.

Whetham, G. B. (1963). In *Laminar Boundary Layer,* L. Rosenhead (ed.), Oxford University Press, New York, Chap. 3.

Whitehead, L. G., and G. S. Canetti (1950). *Philos. Mag.,* **41**(5), p. 988.

Wieselsberger, C. (1921). *Phys. Z.,* **22**, p. 321.

Williams, J. C. (1977). In *Annual Reviews of Fluid Mechanics,* Vol. 9, Annual Reviews, Palo Alto, CA.

Williamson, C. H. K. (1988). *Phys. Fluids,* **31**, p. 2742.

Willis, D. R. (1962). *Phys. Fluids,* **5**, p. 127.

Willmarth, W. W., and S. S. Lu (1972). *J. Fluid Mech.* **55**, p. 65.

Winant, C. D., and F. K. Browand (1974). *J. Fluid Mech.,* **78**, p. 237.

Xu, J.-J. (1984). *Sci. Sinica A,* **27**, p. 372.

Yih, C. S. (1969). *Fluid Dynamics,* McGraw-Hill, New York (now published by West River Press, Ann Arbor, MI).

Young, N. O., J. S. Goldstein, and M. J. Block (1959). *J. Fluid Mech.,* **6**, p. 350.

Yu, D., R. Warrington, R. Barron, and T. Ameel (1995). *Proc. ASME/JSME Thermal Engineering Conference,* Hawaii, ASME, New York, p. 523.

Zagarola, M. V., and A. J. Smits (1998). *J. Fluid Mech.,* **373**, p. 33.

Zaman, K. B. M., and F. Hussain (1980). *J. Fluid Mech.,* **101**, p. 449.

Zang, H.-Q., U. Fey, B. R. Noack, M. Konig, and H. Eckelmann, (1995). *Phys. Fluids,* **7**, p. 779.

Zanoun, E. S., F. Durst, and H. Nagib (2003). *Phys. Fluids,* **15**, p. 3079.

Zhang, L. H., and H. L. Swinney (1985). *Phys. Rev. A,* **31**, p. 1006.

Zu, Y., and S. Granick (2002). *Phys. Rev. Lett.,* **88**, p. 106102.

Index

A

Acceleration, particle, 52
Accommodation coefficient, 679
Added mass, 491
Adverse pressure gradient, 535
Airfoil, 448
  biconvex, 467, 527
  camber line, 438
  camber ratio, 438
  chord, 437, 443
  lift, 442
  low Reynolds number, 451
  pressure distribution, 446
  thickness ratio, 438
  trailing edge, 444
Algebraic growth, 721
Angle of attack, 442
Angular momentum, 85
Asymptotic expansion, 350
  common part, 359
  composite, 363
  matched, 358

B

Bearing, slipper pad, 620
Bernoulli equation, 126, 381, 406, 469
  unsteady flow, 266
Biharmonic function, 578
Binomial expansion, 348
Biot–Savart law, 398
Blasius flow, 512
Blasius profile, 533
Blasius theorem, 428
Bond number, 638

Boundary condition transfer, 355
Boundary layer, 376, 385, 498
  axisymmetric, 537
  beginning at infinity, 530
  biconvex airfoil, 527
  Blasius, 498
  bridge piling, 527
  channel entrance, 551
  coordinates, 386
  equations, 392, 499, 506
  erupting, 548
  flat plate, 498
  Joukowski airfoil, 524
  kinetic, 679
  plate with transverse pressure gradient, 557
  Pohlhausen, 531
  pressure, 388
  pressure gradient, 392, 535
  scales, 387
  separation, 535
  sweep-independence principle, 559
  thickness, 501
  three-dimensional, 553
  vertical velocity, 521
  wall under sluice gate, 530
Boundary value problem, 501
Boussinesq, 204
Bridgman's equation, 159
Brownian motion, 12
Bubble
  attached to wall, 641
  captive, 641
  flow over, 643
Buffer layer, 765
Bulk expansion coefficient, 21

813